Maternal, Fetal, & Neonatal Physiology

A Clinical Perspective

FIFTH EDITION

Maternal, Fetal, & Neonatal Physiology

A Clinical Perspective

SUSAN TUCKER BLACKBURN, PhD, RN, FAAN

Professor Emerita
Department of Family and Child Nursing
School of Nursing
University of Washington
Seattle, Washington

ELSEVIER

ELSEVIER

3251 Riverport Lane
St. Louis, Missouri 63043

BLACKBURN/MATERNAL, FETAL, & NEONATAL PHYSIOLOGY:
A CLINICAL PERSPECTIVE, FIFTH EDITION

ISBN: 978-0-323-56911-8

Senior Content Strategist: Sandra Clark
Senior Content Development Manager: Laurie Gower
Associate Content Development Specialist: Laurel Shea
Publishing Services Manager: Jeffrey Patterson
Senior Project Manager: Anne Konopka
Design Direction: Paula Catalano

Printed in the United States of America

Last digit is the print number: 9   8   7   6   5   4   3   2   1

Contributors and Reviewers

CONTRIBUTORS

Ilana R. Azulay Chertok, PhD, MSN, IBCLC
Professor, Associate Director of Nursing Research and
   Scholarship
School of Nursing
Ohio University
Athens, Ohio
Postpartum Period and Lactation Physiology

Robin Webb Corbett, PhD, FNP-C, RNC
Associate Professor
Chair, Advanced Nursing Practice and Education
College of Nursing
East Carolina University
Greenville, North Carolina
Physiologic Basis for Reproduction

Georgia R. Ditzenberger, NNP-BC, PhD
Neonatal Nurse Practitioner
School of Medicine
Department of Pediatrics/University of Wisconsin Medical
   Foundation
Meriter Hospital
University of Wisconsin – Madison
Madison, Wisconsin
Clinical Product Surveillance Specialist
GE HealthCare
Madison, Wisconsin
Gastrointestinal and Hepatic Systems and Perinatal Nutrition
Carbohydrate, Fat, and Protein Metabolism
Calcium and Phosphorus Metabolism

Tekoa L. King, CNM, MPH, FACNM
Deputy Editor
Journal of Midwifery & Women's Health
Health Sciences Clinical Professor
School of Nursing
University of California San Francisco
San Francisco, California
Fetal Assessment

Jacqueline H. Wolf, PhD
Professor
Department of Social Medicine
Ohio University
Athens, Ohio
Postpartum Period and Lactation Physiology

REVIEWERS

Cindy Bryant, BSN, RN-BC, CCRN-Neo
Registered Nurse
Texas Children's Hospital
Houston, Texas

Tamara L. Bryant, RN, MSN
Program Chair
Associate of Nursing Program
Southern Regional Technical College
Thomasville, Georgia

Cassie Flock, MSN, RN
Assistant Professor
Department of Nursing
Vincennes University
Vincennes, Indiana

Sara B. Forbus, MSN, RN
Lecturer, Nursing Faculty
School of Nursing
Old Dominion University
Norfolk, Virginia

Carie Linder, APRN, NNP-BS
Neonatal Intensive Care Unit
Integris Baptist Medical Center
Oklahoma City, Oklahoma

Linda Macera-DiClemente, DNP(c), MSN, BA, RN
Lead Faculty
Department of Nursing
Baker College of Auburn Hills
Auburn Hills, Michigan

Christina Mahoney, RN, BSN, CCRN
Staff Nurse II
Neonatal Intensive Care Unit
Boston Children's Hospital
Boston, Massachusetts

Shelora Mangan, DNP, CNS, RNC-OB, EFM-C
Perinatal Clinical Nurse Specialist
Women and Newborn Services
Legacy Health
Portland, Oregon

Kristie K. Marbut, ARNP, MN, NNP-BC, CPNP
Neonatal Nurse Practitioner
Pediatrix Medical Group
Tacoma, Auburn, Puyallup, Washington
Lecturer
University of Washington
Seattle, Washington
University of Utah
Salt Lake City, Utah

Andrea C. Morris, DNP, RNC-NIC, CCRN, CNS
Neonatal Clinical Nurse Specialist
Neonatal Intensive Care Unit
Queen of the Valley Hospital, Citrus Valley Medical Center
West Covina, California

Christina M. Rutledge, RN, MN, CNE
Module Leader
Practical Nurse Course
AMEDD Center and School, Madigan Army Medical Center
Tacoma, Washington

Patricia Scheans, DNP, NNP-BC
Neonatal Nurse Practitioner, Clinical Support for Neonatal
   Care
Women and Newborn Services
Legacy Health
Portland, Oregon

Kathy Sheppard, PhD, MA, MSN, RN
Interim Dean and Professor of Nursing
Department of Nursing
University of Mobile
Mobile, Alabama

Julie Marie Anderson Symes, EdD, RN, IBCLC
Nurse Faculty, Lecturer
School of Health Sciences
Department of Nursing
University of South Dakota
Rapid City, South Dakota

Valerie Wright, DNP, RN, CNE
Associate Dean of Nursing
Department of Nursing
Lincoln Land Community College
Springfield, Illinois

Preface

Accurate assessment and clinical care appropriate to the developmental and maturational stage of the mother, fetus, and neonate depend on a thorough understanding of normal physiologic processes and the ability of the caregiver to understand the effects of these processes on pathologic alterations. Information on normal pregnancy and perinatal physiology and its clinical implications can be found in various sources. These sources are often either fragmented, too basic in level, too focused on one phase of the perinatal period (and thus lacking integration within the maternal-fetal-neonatal unit), or lacking in the clinical applications relevant to patient care. Thus they do not adequately meet the needs of nurses in specialty and advanced clinical nursing practice.

Therefore the goal of the first and subsequent editions of this book was to create a single text that brought together detailed information on the physiologic changes that occur throughout pregnancy and the perinatal period, with emphasis on the mother, fetus, and neonate and the interrelationships among them. Maturational changes during infancy, childhood, and adolescence are also discussed. The purpose of this book is not to provide a manual of specific assessment and intervention strategies or to focus on pathophysiology—it is to present current information on the normal physiologic adaptations and developmental physiology that provides the scientific basis and rationale underlying assessment and management of the low-risk and high-risk pregnant woman, fetus, and neonate. Because the focus of this book is on physiologic adaptations, the psychological aspects of perinatal and neonatal nursing are not addressed. These aspects are certainly equally as important but are not within the realm of this text.

This book provides detailed descriptions of the physiologic processes associated with pregnancy and with the fetus and neonate. The major focus is on the normal physiologic adaptations of the pregnant woman during the antepartum, intrapartum, and postpartum periods; anatomic and functional development of the fetus; transition and adaptation of the infant at birth; developmental physiology of the neonate (term and preterm); and a summary of the maturation of each body system from infancy to adolescence. Clinical implications of these physiologic adaptations as they relate to the pregnant woman, maternal-fetal unit, and neonate are also examined. Each chapter describes the effects of normal physiologic adaptations on clinical assessment and interventions with low-risk and high-risk women and neonates with selected health problems. Of special interest to those seeking quick access to clinical information are boxes with recommendations for clinical practice that are included in each chapter, referencing pages with relevant content that provides the rationale underlying each recommendation. New to this edition is an appendix with definitions of abbreviations frequently used in the text.

Advanced practice nursing must be based on a sound physiologic base. Thus I hope that this book will be a useful foundation reference for specialty and advanced practice nurses in both primary and acute care settings, as well as for graduate programs in maternal, perinatal, and neonatal nursing and nurse midwifery. This book may also hold appeal for other health care professionals including physicians; physical, occupational, speech, and respiratory therapists; and nutritionists involved in obstetrics and neonatology.

ACKNOWLEDGMENTS

The help and support of many individuals were critical in making this book a reality. These include former and current students, nursing staff, and colleagues who stimulated me to continue to expand my knowledge of perinatal and neonatal physiology and examine the scientific basis for nursing interventions with pregnant women and neonates. The women, neonates, and their families for whom I have cared and from whom I have learned a great deal also stimulated development of this book. Thank you to Ilana Azulay Chertok, Robin Webb Corbett, Georgia Ditzenberger, Tekoa King, and Jacqueline Wolf for sharing their expertise in the chapters they contributed to this edition. Special thanks to Susan Skinner and Elizabeth Posey for their assistance with manuscript preparation. I am grateful for the efforts of the reviewers, whose constructive comments and suggestions helped in refining the content and in making this book more useful for the intended audience. My appreciation and thanks also goes to the staff at Elsevier, particularly Laurel Shea, Associate Content Development Specialist, and Anne Konopka, Senior Project Manager, for their assistance in the development and production of this book. Finally I would like to thank my family for their support, guidance, and encouragement in all of my endeavors.

Susan Tucker Blackburn

Contents

UNIT II
Adaptations in Major Body Systems in the Pregnant Woman, Fetus, and Neonate

8   Hematologic and Hemostatic Systems, 215

9   Cardiovascular System, 251

10 Respiratory System, 297

Biologic Basis for Reproduction

The biologic basis for reproduction includes genetic mechanisms and principles, gametogenesis, and embryonic development of the reproductive system. The process of reproduction is influenced by chromosomal and gene structure and function and many mediating and signaling factors, including transcription factors, growth factors, and signaling molecules. Reproduction is also influenced by physiologic processes such as hormonal control mechanisms and the hypothalamic-pituitary-ovarian axis, which are described in Chapter 2.

Knowledge of genetics continues to expand at a remarkable rate. The Human Genome Project (HGP), an international collaborative effort begun in 1990 and completed in 2003, within days of the 50th anniversary of Watson and Crick's description of the deoxyribonucleic acid (DNA) double helix, accomplished its goal of identifying the human DNA sequence, developing an international database, and developing new investigative tools and methods of analysis.[55,56] An integral part of the HGP was the identification and analysis of the ethical, legal, and social issues generated by this new knowledge. Since the completion of the HGP, work has focused on further analysis and interpretation of DNA structure with development of a catalog of human genome components including protein coding genes, nonprotein coding genes, and elements that regulate transcription and chromosome function, along with increasing knowledge of the human genome, epigenetics, and chromatin organization.[15,53] This knowledge continues to expand our understanding of both human development and the pathogenesis, diagnosis, and treatment of diseases.[53,55] Much is still to be understood about gene regulation; noncoding DNA sequences; coordination between gene expression, protein synthesis and conservation, and posttranslational events; complex interaction of proteins; gene therapies; developmental genetics; genes involved in complex traits; and multigene disorders.[15,53,55,56]

CHROMOSOMES AND GENES

The human genome is the totality of the DNA sequences, containing all of an individual's genetic information. Only about 2% to 3% of the human genome is directly involved in protein synthesis; the remainder has regulatory functions via the noncoding or cis-regulatory sequences. "The main purpose of cis-regulatory sequences is to receive, translate and relay information, in the form of activated signal transduction cascades, to the core transcriptional apparatus that is directly responsible for gene transcription . . . changes in the cis-regulatory genome also define individual differences within species including disease susceptibility and drug response."[15]

Chromosomes

Each human cell, except for the gametes (ovum and sperm), normally contains 46 chromosomes (diploid number) consisting of 22 pairs of autosomes and 1 pair of sex chromosomes. Autosomal genes are located on the autosomes (chromosomes common to both sexes) and are homologous (a pair of chromosomes with identical gene arrangements). Males have a pair of nonhomologous chromosomes, the X and Y sex chromosomes, although there are homologous segments on the tips of the short ends of the X and Y chromosomes.[52] In the female, the sex chromosomes (XX) are homologous. One of each chromosome pair comes from the mother and one from the father. The ovum and sperm have only 23 chromosomes (haploid number). This reduction in the number of chromosomes occurs during meiosis. With fertilization and union of the nuclei of the ovum and sperm, the diploid number of 46 chromosomes is restored in the zygote.

Chromosomes are classified by structure and banding pattern, which varies depending on the stain used or by color if spectral analysis is used. Structural characteristics include the location of the centromere (metacentric, submetacentric, or acrocentric) and the length or size of the chromosomes (Figure 1-1). The upper arm of each chromosome is referred to as the p arm; the lower arm is the q arm. Sections of the p and q arm are numbered according to the banding patterns of mitotic chromosomes, so specific loci along each chromosome can be identified. Each band contains many genes. Gismo-trypsin banding (G-banding) has been a widely used banding technique. More recent spectral methods of karyotyping and fluorescent in situ hybridization (FISH) techniques such as chromosome painting, locus-specific mutations FISH, and interphase FISH allow for greater resolution and specificity of chromosome segments and genes. The karyotype is a pictorial display of chromosomes.

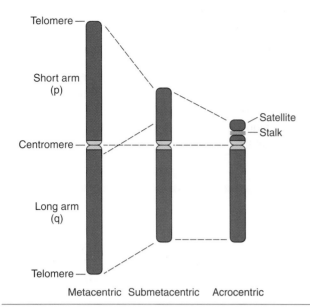

FIGURE 1-1   Schematic diagram of human chromosomes demonstrating metacentric, submetacentric, and acrocentric chromosomes. The location of the centromere, telomere, and short (p) and long (q) arms are indicated. (From Morton, C.C. & Miron, P.M. [2004]. Cytogenetics in reproduction. In J.F. Strauss & R. Barbieri [Eds.]. *Yen and Jaffe's reproductive endocrinology: Physiology, pathophysiology, and clinical management* [5th ed.]. Philadelphia: Saunders.)

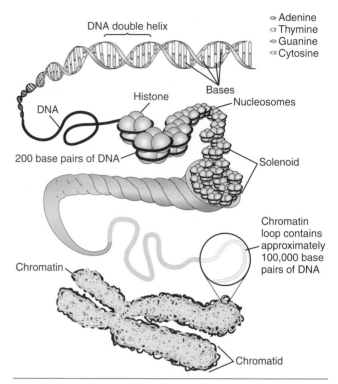

FIGURE 1-2   Structure of DNA and patterns of DNA coiling. DNA is wound around histones to form nucleosomes. These are organized into solenoids that in turn compose chromatin loops. (From Jorde, L.B., Carey, J.C., & M.J. Bamshad. [2016]. *Medical genetics* [5th ed.]. Philadelphia: Elsevier.)

Chromosomes are composed of the DNA double helix complexed with histone and nonhistone chromosomal proteins that form coils known as *chromatin*.[43] The histones help condense and compact the DNA and also help regulate gene expression.[43] In each chromosome the continuous DNA strand is wound around histone (protein) spools (DNA plus histone is referred to as a *nucleosome*) that are coiled around each other to form solenoids. The solenoids are coiled into chromatin threads (Figure 1-2).[24,32] Within the chromatin, nucleosomes are joined to other nucleosomes by linked DNA strands.[64] DNA in nucleosomes is tightly coiled and must be unwound for DNA transcription to occur. The DNA double helix is similar to a flexible ladder, with the sides composed of deoxyribose and phosphate and each rung composed of two nitrogen bases connected by hydrogen bonds (see Figure 1-2).

X Chromosomes

In all of a woman's somatic cells (but not in her germ cells), one of the two X chromosomes is inactivated (lyonization) and remains condensed. The inactive X is seen in interphase as the Barr body. The number of Barr bodies is one less than the number of X chromosomes. Therefore a normal male has no Barr bodies and neither does a woman with Turner syndrome (XO); a normal female (XX) has 1 Barr body, as does a male with Klinefelter syndrome (XXY). In the female, both X chromosomes are reactivated during gametogenesis. Thus the woman produces ova with two active X chromosomes, which undergo recombination (exchange of genetic material) with each other. In the female blastocyst, inactivation occurs in all cells 7 to 10 days after fertilization.[62] The inactivated X is random in each cell—it

could be the X chromosome received from its mother or the X chromosome received from its father—and the same X is inactive in all descendants of that cell. However, in the trophoblast tissue (which is extraembryonic tissue that will become the placenta and chorion) of the preembryonic blastocyst, all the paternally derived X chromosomes are inactivated, whereas all the maternal X chromosomes are active.[32,38,64] The inactive X is reactivated in the oogonium so with gametogenesis the woman produces ova with two active X chromosomes.

In the inactive X, the *XIST* gene on the long arm (q13) is transcribed to produce a noncoding ribonucleic acid (RNA) that coats the inactive X to prevent transcription of its genes.[32] Inactivation also involves methylation of critical segments of DNA (binding of methyl groups to DNA cytosine, especially in the promoter area of the gene, which also prevents the gene from being transcribed) and histone deacetylation.[38,64] These processes help maintain long-term X inactivation in women.[32] Not all genes on the inactive X are inactive; 10% to 15% of the genes on the inactive X remain active.[24,32] The active genes on the inactive X are generally located on the tip of the short arm and are homologous with genes on the distal end of the Y chromosome.[32] Thus males and females receive an equal dose of these genes.[32]

Genes

Genes are the functional units of heredity consisting of DNA sequences that code for specific amino acids and thus for formation of specific proteins and noncoding areas. Each human is believed to have approximately 20,000 to 23,000 genes; however, these genes can synthesize up to five times as many proteins through formation of splicing isoforms.[43,64] Genes are constantly changing in interaction with the environment (see Genomics and Epigenetics).[5,15,51] Genes are distributed in clusters along the chromosome, so some areas have many genes, and others have few.[32] The protein-coding sequences of DNA are called *exons* (expression sequences). Exons have a consistent identifying sequence of nucleotides at each end. Interspersed between these are noncoding sequences, called *introns* (intervening sequences) (Figure 1-3).[43] Noncoding DNA

segments regulate gene transcription and other processes, although many of their functions are still unknown.[53] Some of these sequences are needed for formation of DNA transcription factors, RNA translation, chromosome pairing, and other regulatory functions that regulate transcription and translation; others have no known function.[32,43] Noncoding sequences include promoters (initiation of transcription), enhancers (up-regulation of promoter activity), silencers (downregulation of promoter activity), and insulators (insulate promoters from enhancers and silencers), as well as termination sequences.[15,43,64] Within the noncoding area are sections of repeated sequences; the exact function of these sequences is unknown.[43]

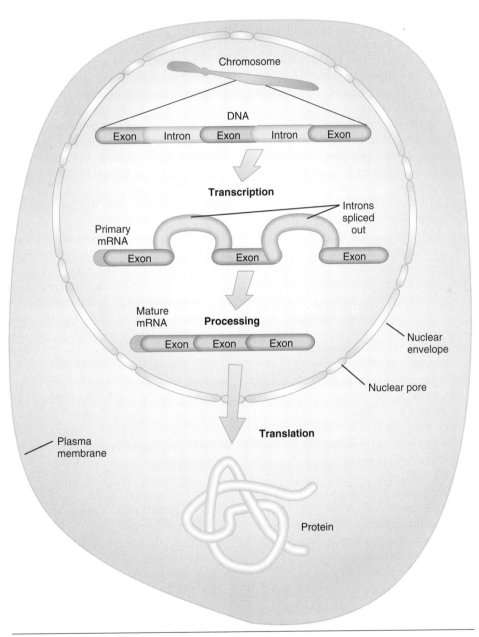

FIGURE 1-3 Summary of the steps leading from DNA to proteins. Replication and transcription occur in the cell nucleus. The messenger RNA (mRNA) is then transported to the cytoplasm, where translation of the mRNA into amino acid sequences composing a protein occurs. (From Jorde, L.B., Carey, J.C., & M.J. Bamshad. [2016]. *Medical genetics* [5th ed.]. Philadelphia: Elsevier.)

Genes are essential in determining and maintaining cell structural integrity and cell function and in regulating biochemical and immunologic processes.[24] Some genes control the function of other genes; others regulate the process of embryonic and fetal development. Genes direct protein synthesis and regulate the rate at which proteins are synthesized. The specific proteins synthesized vary depending on the type of cell. For example, a muscle cell synthesizes myosin for muscle contraction, the pancreatic islet cells synthesize insulin, and the liver cells produce γ-globulin. Although the full complement of genes is present in all cells, genes are selectively switched on and off via methylation and similar processes. Therefore all genes are not active at the same time. This activation process is important during development (see Regulation of Development in Chapter 3) and is influenced by age, cell type, and function. In addition, each gene can produce multiple splicing isoforms (also called *splice variants*), each isoform producing a different product. The different isoforms are produced by the splicing and reorganization of exons within a given gene.[42,53] As a result, a single gene can guide the production of many different forms of messenger RNA (mRNA) and thus proteins with individual biologic functions.[9,13,64] For example, a *WT1* gene isoform is critical for gonad development, whereas another isoform of this gene is involved in renal development in the embryo.[64]

Genes are arranged in linear order and in pairs on homologous chromosomes, one chromosome and its genes coming from an individual's mother, the other from the father. Each gene has a specific location, called a *locus,* on the chromosome. One copy of a gene normally occupies any given locus. In somatic cells, the chromosomes are paired so that there are two copies of each gene (alleles). The corresponding genes at a given locus on homologous chromosomes govern the same trait, but not necessarily in the same way. If gene pairs are identical, they are homozygous; if they are different, they are heterozygous. In the heterozygous state, one of the alleles may be expressed over the other. This allele is considered dominant, meaning that the trait is expressed if the dominant allele is present on at least one of the pair of chromosomes. Recessive traits can be expressed only when the allele responsible for that trait is present on both chromosomes or when the dominant allele is not present (as with X-linked genes in the XY male, who is hemizygous for that trait). *Genotype* refers to the genetic makeup of an individual or a particular gene pair. The observable expression of a specific trait is referred to as the *phenotype.* A trait may be a biochemical property, an anatomic structure, a cell or organ function, or a mental characteristic. Thus traits are derived from the action of the gene and not from the gene itself.[24,41,80]

DNA and RNA

The transmission of hereditary information from one cell to another is a function of DNA. DNA also contains the instructions for the synthesis of proteins that determine the structure and function of that cell. The nucleus contains DNA; protein assembly occurs within the cytoplasm in the ribosomes. The transfer of information from the nucleus to the site of synthesis is the role of mRNA, which is synthesized on the surface of DNA and regulated by other RNA forms.[5,53]

Both DNA and RNA are nucleic acids made up of a nitrogenous purine (adenine and guanine) or pyrimidine (cytosine and thymine or uracil) base, a sugar (deoxyribose for DNA and ribose for RNA), and a phosphate group (see Figure 1-2). Together these substrates form a structure that is linked in a linear sequence by phosphodiester bonds. DNA is composed of two antiparallel complementary chains of opposite polarity. These strands form a double helix in which the sides are the phosphate and sugar groups and the crossbars are complementary bases joined by hydrogen bonds. Only complementary bases form stable bonds; thus adenine (A) always pairs with thymine (T), and guanine (G) always pairs with cytosine (C). Therefore the sequence of the bases on one strand determines the sequence of bases on the other.

RNA is a single strand rather than a double helix and contains adenine, cytosine, guanine, and uracil (U), which pairs with adenine, because thymine is not present. RNA folds on itself, and these folding patterns (motifs) are important for RNA-RNA and RNA-protein recognition and interaction.[7] Types of RNA include: (1) mRNA, (2) ribosomal RNA (rRNA), (3) transfer RNA (tRNA), and (4) nuclear RNA (nRNA) including micro RNA (miRNA).[5,19,53,54] mRNA receives information from the DNA and serves as the template for protein synthesis. tRNA brings the amino acids to mRNA and positions them correctly during protein synthesis. One of the structural components at the protein assemblage site (ribosome) is rRNA. The passage of information from DNA to RNA is called *transcription;* the assemblage of the proper sequence on amino acids is *translation.*

DNA transcription takes place in the nucleus as the DNA strands separate in the region of the gene to be transcribed. RNA polymerase enzymes bind on one DNA strand just ahead of the gene and synthesize a copy of the DNA until the termination sequence (poly A tail) is reached and the copied sequence (pre-mRNA or RNA transcript) is released and the DNA strand rewinds. The transcript is processed before leaving the nucleus as mRNA. Introns (noncoding areas of DNA) are removed and promoter and terminator structures are added to promote stability and efficiency of translation (Figure 1-4). Various other proteins are involved in transcription in specific tissues and at specific developmental stages.[32] The RNA transcript may also be spliced in various ways (alternate splicing) to produce different proteins from the same gene. The remaining exons form the mature mRNA, which moves to the cytoplasm for translation.[32,80]

The processed mRNA acts as a template (recipe) for polypeptide and protein synthesis in the cytoplasmic ribosome, where mRNA codons are read and translated into amino acids. The ribosome is formed from rRNA and proteins. Free amino acids combine with the corresponding tRNA in the presence of specific enzymes. Amino acid–tRNA complexes bind to sites on the ribosome in the order specified by mRNA. The amino acid is attached to the growing peptide chain, and the tRNA, freed of its amino acid, is released.

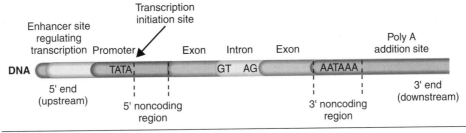

FIGURE 1-4 Overview of gene structure, showing initiation site, promoter and upstream regulation (enhancer) sequences, noncoding region, and a poly A addition site. (From Jorde, L.B., Carey, J.C., & M.J. Bamshad. [2016]. *Medical genetics* [5th ed.]. Philadelphia: Elsevier.)

A new amino acid–tRNA complex is attached to the vacated site on the ribosome. These steps are repeated until all the codons have been read. The completed protein chain is released from the ribosome when the mRNA termination codon is reached.[80] Before release the polypeptide may be modified.[32]

nRNA is a form of pre-mRNA that makes the initial transcript of the gene that after processing will be moved from the nucleus to cytoplasm by mRNA.[64] MiRNAs are small RNA molecules that bind to specific mRNA sequences to upregulate or downregulate them.[24,32] The nRNAs and miRNAs have important regulatory functions.[19,53] The miRNA are involved in most cellular processes and have a role in modulating regulatory processes that control development, cell differentiation, and organ function.[19,53,54] For example, miRNA may bind to mRNA transcripts, thus preventing gene expression.[24] Many miRNAs have been identified; many are being investigated as biomarkers of health and disease and have been implicated in the pathophysiology of diseases such as cystic fibrosis (CF), cardiac disorders, neurologic diseases, and many forms of cancer.[5,19,53,54] In the placenta, miRNAs are believed to play a role in trophoblast regulation and function and perhaps in the pathogenesis of placental and related disorders such as preeclampsia, fetal growth restriction, and preterm labor.[54] The potential of miRNAs as biomarkers of placental health are being investigated.[54]

The sequence of bases along the DNA makes up the genetic code that specifies the sequence of amino acids in each protein. Each of the 20 amino acids is designated by a specific sequence of three bases (codon). A gene codes for a single protein, which is a series of amino acids. The four bases (A, T or U, C, and G) can be arranged in 64 triplet combinations, of which 61 are used to specify the 20 amino acids. Most amino acids are represented by several codons. For example, AUG codes for methionine, and CAU and CAC both code for histidine. The other three codons are termination codes, which designate the end of a gene.'

GENOMICS AND EPIGENETICS

Genetics involves examination of individual genes and their effects. Genomics is "the study of the functions and the interactions of all the genes in the genome."[25] This focus includes gene-environment interactions and will increase our understanding

of complex disorders such as diabetes, Alzheimer disease, hypertension, and cancer.[25] Genomics includes a focus on genetic variations that may alter the risks of disease and on how genes interact with chemical, infectious, environmental, physical, and pharmacologic agents, with an increased emphasis on risk assessment and prevention; development of new diagnostic, treatment, and prognostic techniques; and new fields of study such as pharmacogenetics.[36] Genomics continues to generate ethical, legal, and social issues.[55]

Epigenetics is "the study of heritable traits that are not caused by changes in DNA sequences."[66] Epigenetics is another way that genes are regulated; epigenetic mechanisms alter gene transcription, modify the genome, and "can be inherited during cell division, but do not imply changes to DNA sequence and mutations."[53] Epigenetic transcriptional regulatory mechanisms include DNA methylation, histone modification, acetylation, chromatin compaction, and miRNAs (see Genes).[5,24,51] These changes are influenced by environmental stimuli and, once they occur, remain within an individual's genome for their life span.[51,65] Epigenetic mechanisms may have a role in fetal programming and in the effects of early exposure to stress and later predisposition to certain disorders in adulthood (see Chapters 16 and 19).[32,66]

Recent animal evidence suggests epigenetic changes may persist through meiosis and gametogenesis to somatic cells.[51,65,68] This concept is controversial, and more research is needed. However, if this occurs, an environmental agent might not only affect the developing fetus but also the fetal germ cells, so the effect could be passed on to the next generation, leading to transgenerational effects that are mediated by heritable RNAs.[65,68]

Genetic polymorphisms are variations in the genome sequence that occur throughout the genome with a frequency of about 1 in 100 base pairs.[69] Polymorphisms may involve the substitution of a single nucleotide base (single nucleotide polymorphisms [SNPs]) or a group of alleles or alternate gene forms that are inherited together (haplotypes). SNPs are the simplest form of DNA variation among individuals.[69] The human genome contains more than 10 million SNPs.[25] Polymorphisms may be nonfunctional and have no effect on the individual or alter expression of a protein that increases the risk of disease, especially with exposure to specific environmental agents or drugs.[35] SNPs associated with diseases have been found primarily in noncoding areas of DNA, especially those that have regulatory functions.[15,53] These variations may be important in altering the effects of exposures to environmental health hazards such as mercury, alcohol, tobacco smoke, air pollutants, and other toxins, leading to different levels of risk and susceptibility to disease and to adverse environmental influences within the population.[16,35] Because SNPs can result in individual differences in responses to drugs, understanding these variations can individualize pharmacologic management.

Research in this area has also identified polymorphic genes and environmental influences that can alter susceptibility to birth defects.[16,82] For example, genetic differences in folate metabolism may increase the risk of neural tube defects and pregnancy loss; a rare transforming growth factor-α polymorphism has been linked with orofacial clefts with exposure to cigarette smoke; differences in enzymes needed for metabolizing anticonvulsant drugs may increase the risk of congenital anomalies in women taking these drugs; polymorphisms in alcohol metabolism may increase the risk of fetal alcohol syndrome; and polymorphisms in drug metabolizing enzymes may result in impaired pregnancy maintenance with exposure to cigarette smoke or male infertility with exposure to organophosphate pesticides.[16,82] Study of polymorphisms and gene-environment interactions are leading to better understanding of complex reproductive disorders such as preeclampsia, infertility, and preterm labor as well as disorders such as diabetes, hypertension, infection, coronary artery disease, obesity, and psychiatric disorders.[24,69,82]

CELL DIVISION

Genetic material is passed to daughter cells in two ways: via mitosis in somatic cells, and in germ cells via mitosis (during the initial development of germ cells) or meiosis (during gametogenesis). Before the onset of either mitosis or meiosis, DNA replication must occur. Before a cell divides, the accurate replication of the genetic material stored within the DNA of the parent cell is essential. During DNA replication, the strands of the double helix uncoil, relax, and separate. The exposed nucleotide bases pair with complementary free nucleotides. DNA polymerase links the nucleotides together, resulting in two identical molecules of DNA to pass on to daughter cells. DNA replication involves several enzymes, including DNA polymerase, which add new nucleotides to the DNA strand, proofread the replicated DNA, and repair any errors.[32] DNA replication occurs simultaneously at multiple points along the chromosome, which speeds up the process.[32] DNA replication is illustrated in Figure 1-5. Mitosis and meiosis are illustrated in Figure 1-6.

Mitosis

Mitosis is the process by which growth of an organism occurs and cells repair and replace themselves. This process maintains the diploid number of 46 chromosomes, forming two daughter cells, each with a single strand of DNA, that are exact replicas of the parent (unless a mutation occurs). The cell cycle consists of four stages: gap 1 (G1), synthesis (S), gap 2 (G2),

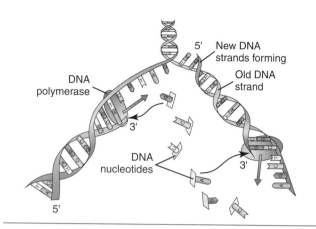

FIGURE 1-5 DNA replication. The hydrogen bonds between the two original strands are broken, allowing the bases in each strand to undergo complementary base pairing with free bases. The process forms two new double strands of DNA. (From Jorde, L.B., Carey, J.C., & M.J. Bamshad. [2016]. *Medical genetics* [5th ed.]. Philadelphia: Elsevier.)

and mitosis (M). G1, S, and G2 comprise interphase. During G1, the longest stage, proteins needed by the cell are synthesized and substances needed for DNA replication are amassed; DNA replication occurs in the S stage. After completion of DNA replication, each chromosome consists of two identical strands of DNA, called *sister chromatids*. G2 is a resting stage, during which errors in DNA are corrected and the cell prepares for the final M stage, in which the cell divides.[43] The length of time for a cell to complete the entire cycle varies with the type of cell and may last hours (epithelial tissues) to weeks (liver cells).[9] The cell cycle is regulated by enzymes such as cyclin-dependent kinases (CDKS), which are control switches for the cycle (i.e., switching from G1 to S or from S to G2); maturation promoting factor, which triggers progression through the cell cycle; protein 63, which blocks the cycle if the DNA is damaged to allow time for DNA repair; and protein 27, which can also block the cycle by binding to cyclins and blocking entry into S.[32] Alterations in these substances can lead to production of mutations and cancerous cells.[9,32]

Thus before initiation of cell division, DNA replication has already occurred (see Figure 1-6). At this point each cell still has 46 chromosomes, but each chromosome has two strands of DNA, which is twice the usual amount of DNA. Just before cell division, the duplicated DNA threads (chromatin) change from a loose, relaxed mass and become condensed and tightly coiled, forming the rod-shaped chromosomes. This condensing process facilitates the transfer of DNA to the daughter cells. This change is the first sign of cell division.

As the cell enters prophase, the chromosomes each consist of two DNA threads (sister chromatids). The two chromatids are joined at a single point called the *centromere*. Late in prophase the nuclear membrane begins to disintegrate. The centrioles (two small cylindrical bodies) separate and move to opposite sides of the cell. A number of microtubules are observable at this stage. These are spindle fibers that extend from one side of the cell to the other, between the centrioles.

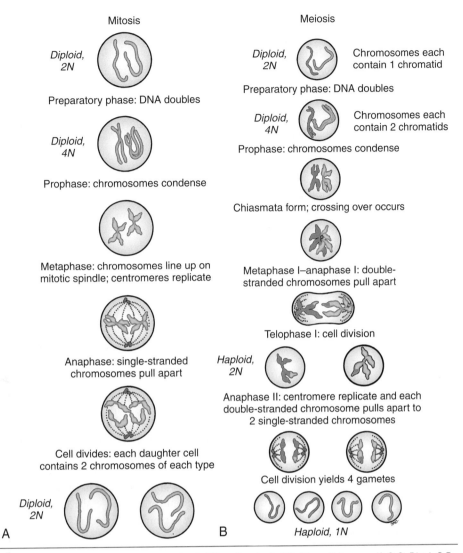

FIGURE 1-6   Summary of stages in mitosis **(A)** and meiosis **(B).** (From Schoenwolf, G.C.,Bleyl, S.B., Brauer, P.R., & Francis-West, P.H. [2009]. *Larsen's human embryology* [4th ed.]. Philadelphia: Churchill Livingstone.)

During metaphase the chromatids line up on the metaphase plate in the center of the cell. Other spindle fibers now extend from the centrioles and are attached to the centromere region of the chromosome. In anaphase, the chromosomes divide at the centromere into sister chromatids that are pulled to opposite poles. As the chromosomes reach their respective poles, they begin to uncoil and elongate. A ring of protein appears around the center of the cell and the cell begins to constrict along a plane perpendicular to the spindle apparatus, creating a division in the cell membrane and cytoplasm (cytokinesis). This constriction continues, creating two cells. At the end of this phase (telophase), the nucleus and nuclear membrane reform and the spindle fibers disappear. Division is complete, and the two daughter cells move into interphase.

Meiosis

Meiosis is the process of germ cell division that is designed to reduce the number of chromosomes from the diploid (46) to haploid (23) number. In this process there are two sequential divisions. The first meiotic division is a reduction division; the second is an equational one (see Figure 1-6). Meiosis results in daughter cells that have 23 chromosomes: one chromosome from each pair of autosomes and one sex chromosome. Each of the 23 chromosomes consists of a single strand of DNA. Fusion of sperm and ovum through fertilization restores the diploid number (46) of chromosomes. Oogonia and spermatogonia arise from the primordial germ cells (see Embryonic and Fetal Development of the Reproductive System). Before initiation of meiosis, the primary oocyte or spermatocyte form as DNA replicates so that each chromosome consists of two chromatids (identical strands of DNA) joined at the centromere.

The first meiotic division consists of four phases (prophase, metaphase, anaphase, and telophase) and results in four haploid (23 chromosome) daughter cells, each chromosome having two strands of DNA, or twice the usual amount (see Figure 1-6). Prophase is the longest, accounting for 90% of meiosis I, and most complex phase. Prophase is divided into five stages. In the first stage (leptotene) the chromosomes are threadlike but already duplicated. Although consisting of two chromatids, the chromosome appears as a single strand. The nuclear membrane is intact. The sister chromatids maintain close contact because of the formation of a meiosis-specific cohesion complex formed in this stage. Also, a complex forms that tethers the homologous chromosomes to each other.[45] As the cell moves into the zygotene stage, homologous chromosomes pair up (synapse).

The chromosomes shorten and condense during the pachytene stage. The two chromatids in each chromosome are distinct and can now be seen clearly. Crossover and exchange of segments of genetic material (recombination) occurs at this time between the maternally derived chromatids of one of the chromosome pairs and the paternally derived chromatids of the other homologous chromosome (Figure 1-7). Approximately 30 to 40 crossovers occur (one to two per chromosome).[64] The sites of exchange are called *chiasmata*. Crossing over allows an individual to inherit a mixture of genetic material from maternal and paternal sides, increasing genetic diversity. The pairs of chromatids separate from each other during the diplotene stage. Once this separation is completed, the nuclear membrane dissolves (diakinesis stage). The chromosomes are maximally condensed, chiasmata are terminated, and normal disjunction (separation of chromosomes) occurs.[9,80] This mechanism is regulated by meiotic-specific genes and involves multiple steps. All 23 chromosome pairs are involved in recombination, except that in males the XY pair only does so at the distal ends.[32,64] Some areas of chromosome pairs have greater frequency of recombination, others less. Recombination is more common in genes that are farther apart on chromosomes.[64]

Between diakinesis and metaphase I, the nucleus disappears and spindle fibers form. In metaphase the chromosomes line up on the metaphase plate. Homologous chromosomes are paired and attached to spindle fibers at the centromere. The centrioles are at opposite poles. In anaphase I, the centromeres are not divided and the chromatids are not pulled to opposite poles as occurs with mitosis. Instead, each pair of chromosomes separates, with one of each chromosome pair going to each pole (see Figure 1-6). In telophase I, the nuclear membranes reform and the cell divides to form a secondary oocyte or spermatocyte.[9,80] Each has 23 chromosomes, one member of

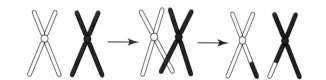

FIGURE 1-7 Illustration of chiasma formation and crossing over during meiosis. Genetic material is exchanged between homologous chromosomes. (From Levine, F. [2012]. Basic genetic principles. In R.A. Polin, W.W. Fox, & S.H. Abman [Eds.]. *Fetal and neonatal physiology* [4th ed.]. Philadelphia: Saunders.)

each original chromosome pair; each chromosome has two chromatids attached at the centromere (i.e., each chromosome has twice the usual amount of DNA). In the female, cell division is unequal, with one daughter cell receiving 23 chromosomes and most of the cytoplasm; the other cell receives 23 chromosomes and minimal cytoplasm (Figure 1-8). This cell is called the *first polar body* and eventually disintegrates.

In the second meiotic division, no DNA replication occurs. Prophase II is similar to mitosis. During metaphase the chromosomes (only one of each pair is present, each with twice the usual DNA) align along the equator of the cell. Centrioles again appear at the cell poles, and spindle fibers form. As the cell moves from metaphase II to anaphase II, the centromeres divide and the two chromatids from each chromosome separate and move to opposite poles. In telophase II, the nuclear membrane reforms and cell division occurs, forming the spermatid or ovum.[9,80] The end result is haploid (23 chromosome) cells, with one of each chromosome pair in each cell (see Figure 1-8); each chromosome now has the normal amount of DNA. Again cell division in the females is unequal, resulting in the formation of one ovum and the second polar body (see Oogenesis).

GAMETOGENESIS

Gametogenesis is the process by which the primordial germ cells develop into mature gametes (ova or sperm). These processes are known as *oogenesis* (female) and *spermatogenesis* (male). Oogenesis and spermatogenesis are illustrated in Figure 1-8. Primordial germ cells are discussed further under Embryonic and Fetal Development of the Reproductive System.

Oogenesis

Oogenesis is the process of ovum development, which, unlike spermatogenesis, begins in fetal life. In the female embryo, germ cell mitosis begins during migration of the germ cells to the gonadal ridge and continues after the primordial germ cells arrive in the ovary from the yolk sac. During early fetal life (from 2 to 7 months), mitotic proliferation of the oogonia is rapid.[16,24] The oogonia continue to enlarge, their DNA replicates, and they become primary oocytes. The primary oocytes enter meiosis I, then arrest in the diplotene stage of prophase I (see Figure 1-6) and remain dormant until puberty or later.[14,67] The nucleus of the arrested primary oocyte swells and becomes the germinal vesicle, which is believed to protect the DNA.[67] Meiosis begins by around 12 weeks' gestation, and all oogonia have begun meiosis by the 5th month.[67] Retinoic acid produced by surrounding tissues stimulates the primordial germ cell in females to enter meiosis.[9] By birth, a layer of follicular epithelial cells surrounds the primary oocytes, forming the primordial follicles. The follicular cells are important in controlling meiosis, including the meiotic arrest and resumption of meiosis with development of luteinizing hormone (LH) receptors.

The meiotic arrest is a result of factors produced by the oocyte and surrounding follicular cells. Increased cyclic

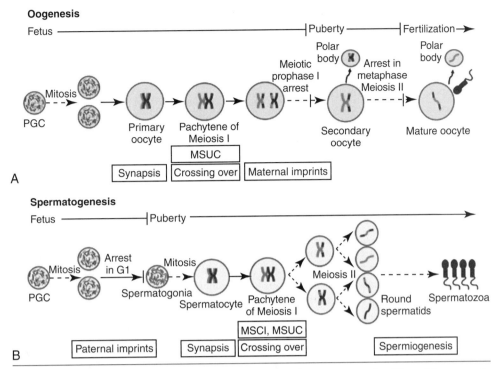

FIGURE 1-8 Developmental transitions in female and male gametogenesis. Primordial germ cells (PGCs) form during embryonic development. **(A)** In the developing ovaries, they undergo mitotic divisions before entering meiosis I, after which primary oocytes arrest in prophase I until ovulation. Upon onset of sexual maturation, oocytes complete meiosis I and arrest in metaphase of meiosis II, until fertilization occurs. **(B)** Male PGCs defer meiosis and undergo mitotic proliferation in the developing male gonad until arresting in G1. From sexual maturity onward, spermatogonia resume mitotic proliferation to form spermatocytes, which then activate meiotic differentiation and form four haploid spermatids each, which in turn develop into spermatozoa. For simplicity, meiosis is shown for one pair of homologous chromosomes (in light gray and dark gray). The timing of meiotic recombination, maternal and paternal imprint acquisition, meiotic silencing of unpaired chromatin (MSUC), meiotic sex chromosome inactivation (MSCI), and spermiogenesis are indicated. (From Kota, S.K. & Feil, R. [2010]. Epigenetic transitions in germ cell development and meiosis. *Dev Cell, 19,* 676.)

adenosine monophosphate (cAMP) inactivates a maturation-promoting factor (MPF) that normally stimulates meiosis; cyclic guanosine monophosphate (cGMP) inactivates the enzyme phosphodiesterase 3A (PDE3A). As a result cAMP is not broken down and remains at a high level, inhibiting completion of meiosis. In addition, LH closes gap junctions (areas of cell-to-cell communication) so that an oocyte maturation–inhibiting peptide produced by the surrounding follicular cells cannot enter the oocyte.[9,21,52,64] The primary oocytes will remain dormant in this arrested state until sometime after puberty. At this time cAMP levels decrease, MPF is activated, and meiosis resumes in follicles selected to mature in a given cycle (see Chapters 2 and 3).[9]

By 20 weeks' gestation, there are 6 to 7 million primary oocytes. This peak is followed by a gradual degeneration of oogonia, which continues until menopause.[9,32,64] By birth, less than 1 to 2 million, and perhaps as few as 600,000 to 800,000, remain; of these approximately 40,000 are still remaining by puberty.[9,24,52,64] Only about 400 of these oogonia will become secondary follicles.[9,52] During oogenesis, arrest, and later oocyte maturation, the oocyte must undergo various changes to become "fertilization competent."[21,27,48] These changes include accumulation of mRNA, proteins, and lipids; development of Golgi, mitochondria, and rRNA to meet cell needs immediately after fertilization; formation of sperm-specific receptors; and development of mechanisms to block entry of more than one sperm if the cell is fertilized.[9,21,48] These changes are critical, because the oocyte supplies the mitochondria and most of the cytoplasm, including most of the organelles and nonchromosomal molecules, to the fertilized ovum.[21]

During each ovarian cycle after puberty, a small number of primary oocytes develop further. Generally only one will mature and be ovulated.[27] Follicle-stimulating hormone (FSH) and LH from the pituitary gland cause an increase in the size of the oocyte and formation of the zona pellucida (see Chapters 2 and 3) around the oocyte. Before ovulation, the first meiotic division is completed, with an unequal division of the cytoplasm, yielding one secondary oocyte and the first polar body, which degenerates. Although the polar body is nonfunctional, it may divide during the second meiotic division.[9] Once the first meiotic division is completed, the secondary oocyte begins the second meiotic division. Ovulation occurs when the secondary oocyte enters metaphase II, where it again arrests, approximately 3 hours before ovulation.[64] After ovulation, the oocyte moves into the fallopian tube ampulla, the usual site of fertilization. The longer the oocyte remains unfertilized after ovulation, the greater the risk of alterations in intracellular calcium regulation, oxidative stress, and mitochondria damage that can impair oocyte quality and embryo development.[44,73] Meiosis II is completed only if the sperm penetrates the ovum. Meiosis II is also characterized by unequal division of the cytoplasm in the female, resulting in formation of a mature oocyte and the second polar body, which disintegrates. The remaining primary oocytes remain arrested in meiosis I. These processes are controlled by paracrine factors such as KIT ligand (a granulose cell regulator of oocyte development and its receptor), growth-differentiating factor-9, and bone morphogenic protein-15; activation of cell receptors; and sharing of factors via gap junctions between cells.[37] Reproductive endocrinology and follicle maturation are discussed in Chapter 2. Ovulation is discussed further in Chapters 2 and 3; fertilization is described in Chapter 3.

Spermatogenesis

Sperm development in the seminiferous tubules involves three stages: (1) mitosis (spermatogonial multiplication), (2) meiosis (production of haploid cells), and (3) spermiogenesis (maturation of spermatids to mature spermatozoa). In the male embryo, germ cell mitotic proliferation begins during migration of the germ cells to the gonadal ridge.[38,67] Once these cells reach the ridge, mitosis arrests in the G1 phase of the cell cycle. Meiotic arrest in sperm occurs as a result of a cytochrome P45 enzyme, which inactivates retinoic acid (which normally stimulates entry into meiosis) and other factors.[9,23] The Sertoli cells secrete substances to nourish the germ cells (see Development of the Testes). Spermatogenesis begins at puberty with the release of androgens. Once begun, the process is continuous for the remainder of the life span, because the spermatogonial stem cell population continues to replenish itself.

The androgens and proteins produced locally modulate spermatogenesis within the tubule. Spermatogenesis is regulated by FSH and LH from the pituitary gland. FSH stimulates development of androgen receptor proteins by the Sertoli cells. Spermatogenesis is also regulated by LH, which binds to the Leydig cells and stimulates testosterone production, which then stimulates the Sertoli cells.[63] Transcription factors act on Sertoli cells to regulate germ cell development during mitosis and meiosis and on spermatids to regulate postmeiotic differentiation into mature sperm.[7,81] Spermatogenesis is mediated via gap junctions between adjacent Leydig cells, adjacent Sertoli cells, and between Sertoli and germ cells, as well as by paracrine and autocrine pathways.[59]

The spermatogonia are located inside the seminiferous tubules. The seminiferous tubule is divided into two zones: (1) the basal compartment, or outer layer (zone 1), of the tubule, and (2) the luminal compartment, or inner layer (zone 2). The basal compartment is composed of type A spermatogonia that are renewed through mitosis. Some of these

continue to proliferate and serve as stem cells, whereas others separate from the basal membrane and begin to migrate toward the lumen. These cells are known as *type B spermatogonia*. As migration progresses, the cells undergo further morphologic changes, becoming primary spermatocytes. The first and second meiotic divisions occur with further differentiation in the luminal zone, resulting in formation of secondary spermatocytes and spermatids.

During the first meiotic division, the primary spermatocytes reduce their chromosome count to half (haploid)—each chromosome having two chromatids joined at the centromere—and become two secondary spermatocytes; each chromatid has two strands of DNA, or twice the usual amount. The second meiotic division involves separation of the two chromatids of each chromosome (with one going to each daughter cell), forming four spermatids, each with 23 chromosomes and a single strand of DNA (see Figure 1-8). The luminal spermatids undergo spermiogenesis, which is the transformation process from ordinary cell structure to sperm cell with head, acrosome (apical enzyme-filled vesicle), midpiece (containing mitochondria to generate energy for movement), and tail with microtubules for propulsion and removal of most of the cytoplasm. The cytoplasm is transferred from the maturing spermatids to the Sertoli cells via complexes that connect the developing gamete to the Sertoli cells.[67] Changes in chromatin organization within the sperm nucleus occur during postmeiotic spermatogenesis and by imprinting, a process important in differentiation of male versus female germ cells and in the control of fetal growth and development (Box 1-1).[7,10,77] From the initial growth phase of the spermatogonia to the final product takes approximately 74 days.[23,52] Once completed, the sperm are set free in the seminiferous tubules and transported via the fluid to the epididymis and ductus deferens, where they are stored until ejaculation (see Chapter 3). At the time of their release from the tubules, the spermatozoa are still morphologically immature and lack motility. While traversing the epididymis, and after ejaculation, they continue to differentiate. The final maturational process in sperm development is capacitation, which involves changes to the acrosome for release of enzymes necessary for ovum penetration (see Chapter 3).

Abnormal Gamete Development

Abnormal gamete development is the result of either chromosomal or morphologic abnormalities. The effects of maternal or paternal age at the time of conception can be seen in fresh gene mutations. The older the parents are, the greater the likelihood that they will generate germ cells that contain gene mutations that can be passed on to the embryo. DNA damage and replication errors are more likely to occur in males, because spermatogenesis involves continual cell division and DNA replication, whereas nondisjunction is more common in females.[52] Oocyte fertility begins to decrease after 30 years.[21] The likelihood of chromosomal abnormalities increases after 35 years of age in females, and this may be because of nondisjunction from prolongation of meiosis over many years

BOX 1-1   Imprinting

Imprinting involves heritable changes in gene expression that result in a change in gene activity so the imprinted gene remains in a silent state.[8] For most genes, both the maternally inherited and paternally inherited alleles (gene forms) are expressed. With imprinted genes, only one of the two alleles is expressed and that allele is essential for normal development. Genomic imprinting is a "phenomenon that sets a parental signature on a specific deoxyribonucleic acid (DNA) segment during gametogenesis or before fertilization so that it is modified and functions differently depending on the parental origin of the DNA segment."[34]

Imprinted gene expression differs depending on the parent from which the chromosome originated. Genomic imprinting involves four mechanisms: methylation, acetylation, RNA interference, and chromatin remodeling.[8,78] Methylation is the most studied of these mechanisms. All cells contain two homologous chromosomes: one inherited from one's mother (with female imprints) and another from one's father (with male imprints). During development of germ cells, these imprints are erased in the first meiotic division and new sex-specific imprints established in the gametes. For example, in a male the paternally derived chromosomes have a male imprint and the maternally derived chromosomes have a female imprint. During spermatogenesis the germ cell chromosomes are reprogrammed to have only male imprints. During oogenesis similar types of changes occur during oocyte maturation (see Figure 1-8). As a result the gametes are reprogrammed so that sperm carry only paternal imprints and ova carry only maternal imprints. This reprogramming occurs in two phases.[8,78] Phase 1 occurs in the female during oocyte maturation and in males during spermatogenesis. In this phase the existing imprinting is removed and a new sex-specific imprinting occurs. Phase 2 ". . . occurs after fertilization and involves global demethylation in the embryo prior to implantation. Global remethylation then occurs post-implantation. Most imprinted genes, however, escape the second phase of reprogramming and remain intact throughout embryonic development."[8] About 100 imprinted genes have been identified, and these are found in clusters containing both maternal and paternal genes and a gene that controls the imprinting of the surrounding genes.[8,33,78]

Imprinted genes are inactive in all cells within the body. Loss of imprinting in these genes can lead to disorders such as Prader-Willi and Angelman syndromes (see Nontraditional Patterns of Inheritance).

(see Alterations in Chromosome Number). Gametes may also experience alterations in morphology. This is much less common in oocytes than in sperm. Although some oocytes may have two or more nuclei, they probably never mature. In each ejaculate, up to 20% of the sperm are grossly abnormal, having either two heads or two tails. Their ability to fertilize the ovum is probably limited because of decreased or abnormal motility and inability to pass through the cervical mucus, thereby terminating their access to the ovum. An increase in the percentage of abnormal sperm can reduce fertility.[52]

GENETIC AND CHROMOSOMAL DISORDERS

Genetic diseases are the result of detrimental changes in the structure of individual genes (gene disorders) or in the entire chromosome (cytogenetic or chromosomal disorders). These disorders can be inherited (see Modes of Inheritance) or arise as new mutations or from alterations in chromosomal number or structure during cell division. Mutations are not always deleterious, but rather may introduce genetic variation into the species. Cytogenetic or chromosomal disorders result when a large number of genes are damaged.[43] Individuals born with chromosomal defects often demonstrate both physical and mental alterations.[41] Most gene disorders are mutations in a single or small number of genes, whereas major chromosome errors involve a change in chromosome number or structure. Chromosomal alterations are seen in up to 60% of spontaneous abortions, approximately 6% of stillborn infants, and 0.5% to 0.7% of live born infants.[9,64] Chromosomal abnormalities can also be a cause of infertility. Most chromosomal abnormalities arise during gametogenesis, although errors can also occur during fertilization or after fertilization.

Alterations in Chromosome Number

Deviations from euploidy (the correct number of chromosomes) are of two types. *Polyploidy* refers to an exact multiple of the haploid (23) set of chromosomes. For example, *triploidy* refers to a zygote with 69 chromosomes (three of each). Triploidy may arise from fertilization of an ovum (23 chromosomes) with two sperm (each carrying 23 chromosomes) or from fusion of the ovum (23 chromosomes) and polar body (23 chromosomes), which is then fertilized by a sperm (23 chromosomes). *Aneuploidy* is the term used for cases in which there is not an exact multiple. Monosomy is a subset of aneuploidy in which one member of a pair of chromosomes is missing. Monosomies are rarely viable. The most common monosomy seen in live born infants is a female with Turner syndrome who has only one X chromosome. Trisomy refers to the presence of an extra chromosome. Aneuploidy is seen in 1% to 2% of sperm, about 20% of oocytes and blastocysts, 35% of spontaneous abortions, 4% of stillborn infants, and 0.3% of live born infants.[27] The most common alterations seen in spontaneous abortions are Turner syndrome (XO) and trisomies 16, 21, and 22.[32,52] The most common trisomies seen in live born infants are trisomies 21 (Down syndrome), 13 (Patau syndrome), and 18 (Edward syndrome). Individuals with Klinefelter syndrome—another example of an alteration in numbers of sex chromosomes—are XXY males. Alterations in chromosome numbers often result from nondisjunction during cell division.

Nondisjunction is an error in cell division and can occur during mitosis or meiosis. Nondisjunction is failure of a pair of chromosomes to separate and move to opposite poles during anaphase. If this occurs during meiosis, alterations in chromosome number will occur in the gametes that are produced. For example, in the case of formation of gametes with a trisomy or monosomy, one gamete will have 24 chromosomes and the other will have only 22 (Figure 1-9). Once fertilization occurs, the gamete with 24 chromosomes forms a zygote with 47 chromosomes (trisomy with an extra copy of one chromosome, such as an extra 21 in trisomy 21). About 95% of Down syndrome cases are a result of trisomy 21. In

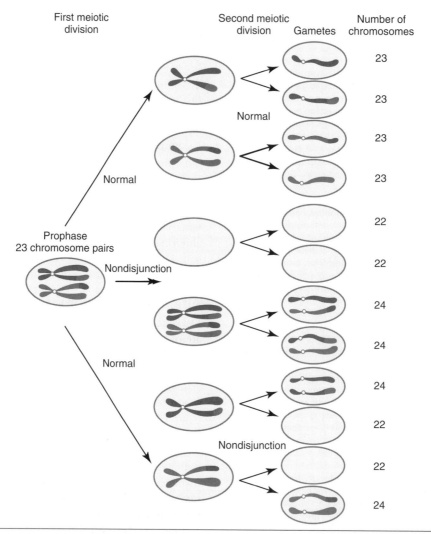

FIGURE 1-9   Possibilities of nondisjunction. *Top arrow,* Normal meiotic division; *middle arrow,* nondisjunction during the first meiotic division; *bottom arrow,* nondisjunction during the second meiotic division. (From Carlson, B.M. [2013]. *Human embryology and developmental biology* [5th ed.]. Philadelphia: Saunders.)

the alternative situation, a 45-chromosome zygote (monosomy for a specific chromosome with one chromosome missing) is formed from the joining of 22- and 23-chromosome gametes. Most autosomal trisomies and all autosomal monosomies are nonviable.

Nondisjunction is more likely to occur during the recombination that takes place during the first meiotic division. In meiosis I errors, the homologous chromosomes may travel together to the same pole or fail to pair and thus end up at the same pole, or the sister chromatids may separate prematurely. Nondisjunction during the second meiotic division is caused by failure of sister chromatids to separate.[27] One model (the limited oocyte pool hypothesis) suggests that a relative scarcity of oocytes at optimal stages of maturation increases the risk of abnormal gametes. Most trisomies that occur in the first meiotic division have a maternal age effect. However, it is unclear whether the precipitating event occurs prenatally, during oocyte meiotic arrest, or preovulatorily when meiosis

resumes, nor is it known what environmental factors may mediate these errors.[27]

Nondisjunction in the autosomes during meiosis is more common in females than in males. Maternal nondisjunction in the first meiotic division accounts for approximately 33% of trisomy 18 and up to 65% of trisomy 21, whereas maternal nondisjunction in the second meiotic division accounts for approximately 56% of trisomy 18 and 23% of trisomy 21.[27] Paternal nondisjunction accounts for 80% of Turner syndrome (XO females) in which the paternal X is lost during meiosis or early after fertilization. Nondisjunction leading to Klinefelter syndrome (XXY male) occurs equally in the mother and father, usually in meiosis I, especially in the father.[27] Chromosomal abnormalities are described further in the next section.

Nondisjunction can also occur during mitosis after formation of the zygote. If nondisjunction occurs in the first cell division after fertilization, one daughter cell receives 45 chromosomes and the other 47 chromosomes. The cell with 45 chromosomes usually does not survive; the zygote continues to develop from the 47-chromosome cell and is a trisomy. If mitotic nondisjunction occurs later in development, some cell lines have the normal number of cells and some have an abnormal number. This is called *mosaicism.* Approximately 2% to 4% of individuals with Down syndrome are mosaics; that is, they have some cells with the normal 46 chromosomes and some cells with 47 chromosomes as a result of an extra chromosome 21. Mosaicism can result from anaphase lag during cell division, where one of the pair of chromosomes moves slowly toward the pole during anaphase and is lost.[24]

Alterations in Chromosome Structure

Variations in chromosome structure are more common than alterations in chromosomal number. Some have minimal effect, whereas others are devastating. Alterations in chromosome structure include (1) deletions, (2) duplications, (3) inversions, (4) isochromosomes, (5) instability syndromes, (6) unstable triplet nucleotide repeats, and (7) translocations (Figure 1-10).

Deletions, the loss of part of a chromosome, can occur anywhere on the chromosome. Loss of a very small section of

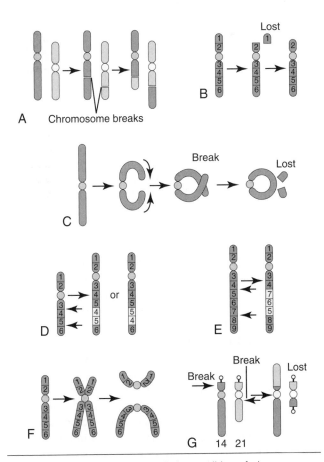

FIGURE 1-10 Various structural abnormalities of chromosomes. **A,** Reciprocal translocation. **B,** Terminal deletion. **C,** Ring chromosomes. **D,** Duplication. **E,** Paracentric inversion. **F,** Isochromosome. **G,** Robertsonian translocation. (From Moore, K.L., Persaud, T.V.N. & Torchia, M.G. [2015]. *The developing human: Clinically oriented embryology* [10th ed.]. Philadelphia: Saunders.)

the gene is referred to as a *microdeletion.* Terminal deletions (see Figure 1-10, *B*) are those occurring on the ends. For example, persons with cri du chat syndrome have a terminal deletion of part of the short (p) arm of chromosome 5. Interstitial deletions occur along the body of the chromosome, with the ends reattaching. If the broken piece is missing a centromere, the piece is lost during cell division. Occasionally, broken fragments may be incorporated into another chromosome. Other examples of deletion syndromes are Wilms tumor (deletion of part of the short arm of chromosome 11), retinoblastoma (deletion of part of the long arm of chromosome 13), Prader-Willi syndrome (deletion of part of the long arm of the paternally derived chromosome 15), Angelman syndrome (deletion of part of the long arm of the maternally derived chromosome 15), Duchenne muscular dystrophy (deletion of part of the short arm of the X chromosome), and DiGeorge syndrome (deletion of part of the long arm of chromosome 22).[24,32] A variation of deletion defects are ring chromosomes (see Figure 1-10, *C*), in which part of each end of the chromosomes are broken off and the ends attach to each other.

Duplications (see Figure 10, *D*) occur when extra copies of genes are created or obtained during crossing over. This duplication may or may not result in phenotypic changes. Inversions (e.g., a paracentric inversion) (see Figure 1-10, *E*) result from two breaks and the subsequent 180-degree rotation of the broken segment. This results in a sequence change and rearrangement of genes in reverse order. Chromosome pairing cannot occur normally during meiosis, resulting in an increased incidence of spontaneous abortions. This may also explain some cases of infertility. Isochromosomes occur when the chromosome, with its replicated DNA, divides across the centromere (instead of dividing into two sister chromatids), resulting in one chromosome with just upper arms and one with just the lower arms (see Figure 1-10, *F*). Instability syndromes such as Fanconi anemia and xeroderma pigmentosum involve alterations in DNA repair.[32]

Unstable nucleotide repeats are multiple repetitions of a series of three bases (codon) at a certain point along the chromosome. These disorders usually demonstrate anticipation, which can be manifest in different ways and the disorder becomes more severe with subsequent generations. Some individuals carry the permutation, such as expanded nucleotides, but not enough to cause the disorder. Examples of disorders caused by nucleotide repeats are myotonic dystrophy, Huntington disease (chromosome 4), and fragile X syndrome (X chromosome). For example, in fragile X syndrome, the unstable CGG nucleotide repeat occurs at the end of the X chromosome. Instead of the usual number of CGG repeats (fewer than 50), there are many more, with severity of the disorder associated with the number of repeats. Expansion of the number of repeats occurs during meiosis in females. Fragile X syndrome is characterized by a mutation in the fragile X mental retardation gene *(FXMR1)* that normally encodes an RNA-binding protein important for normal neuron morphology and neurologic development.[11] Fragile X syndrome is the most common cause of inherited developmental delay and mental retardation and is more common in males than in females. In Huntington disease, the expansion on chromosome 4 occurs primarily in sperm cells; thus the disorder is more likely to occur when passed through males. Age of onset is usually between 40 and 60 years of age. Increased numbers of repeats are associated with a younger age of onset.[32]

Translocations occur after breaks in one or more chromosomes (usually nonhomologous) so genetic material is transferred from one chromosome to another. A balanced translocation occurs when chromosomes exchange pieces and no genetic material is lost. If material is gained or lost, it is considered an unbalanced translocation. Individuals with balanced translocations appear normal; those with unbalanced translocations may have multiple anomalies. Reciprocal translocations (see Figure 1-10, *A*) involve breaks in two chromosomes, with exchange of genetic material. Translocations are also seen with some forms of leukemia and solid tumors.[32,64]

Robertsonian translocations (see Figure 1-10, *G*) involve acentric chromosome pairs 13 through 15 and 21 and 22, which tend to cluster during meiosis.[64] The translocation occurs when the short arms of two chromosomes break off and are lost, and the long arms fuse together at the centromere to form a single chromosome. For example, an individual with normal 14 and 21 chromosomes and a 14/21 translocation has an abnormal karyotype and number of chromosomes (i.e., only 45 chromosomes) but a normal phenotype (normal amount of genetic material). However, depending on which combination of 21 and 14 chromosomes are transferred to the gametes, this individual can produce normal, carrier, monosomic (for 21 or 14), or trisomic (for 21 or 14) offspring. Approximately 3% to 4% of Down syndrome is caused by translocations, most commonly between chromosomes 14 and 21, but also seen between 21 and 13, 14, 15, or 22.[64] These individuals have 46 chromosomes, because the abnormal extra chromosome 21 is attached to a chromosome 14.

Gene Disorders

Mutations are permanent changes in DNA. Mutations can involve changes in the sequence of bases, involving large amounts of DNA, as occurs with chromosomal abnormalities; alterations in one or a few bases that result in production of a deficient (common in recessive disorders), defective, or novel protein; or, in someone who is heterozygous, an abnormal protein that interferes with the protein produced by the normal gene.[24,32] Mutations can be spontaneous or inherited. If the mutation occurs in a somatic cell, it is transmitted only within that cell line; all other cell lines are free of that mutation. However, if a mutation occurs in a germ cell or gamete, it is transmitted to all somatic and germ cells of the offspring, and thus can be passed to that individual's offspring and future generations.

Gene mutations are alterations in the nucleotide sequences that result in biochemical or structural disorders characterized by defective or deficient cellular functioning or altered production of structural components (e.g., skin, muscles,

hemoglobin, and connective tissue). The consequences of these alterations depend on the type of molecule affected, defect, metabolic reaction, site of action, remaining residual activity, gene interactions, environment, and degree of adaptation.[41] Examples of types of mutations include missense (changes in a single amino acid), nonsense (altered placement of a stop codon, producing a shortened or expanded amino acid chain), frameshift (insertion of nucleotides that alter the pattern of subsequent codons and thus the amino acids added to the chain), promoter (alters RNA polymerase affinity, reducing the amount of mRNA and thus protein produced), and splice-site (alteration at the borders of the introns that can lead to expanded nucleotide repeats).[24,32]

There are hundreds of known gene disorders. General categories of gene disorders include (1) hemoglobinopathies, (2) disorders of carbohydrate metabolism (enzyme defects such as galactosemia or excess glycogen accumulation such as glycogen storage disorders), (3) disorders of lipid metabolism (altered transport such as hyperlipidemia or enzyme defects such as medium chain acyl-CoA dehydrogenase deficiency), (4) disorders of amino acid metabolism (enzyme defects such as phenylketonuria or congenital adrenal hyperplasia or deficient intestinal or renal absorption such as Hartnup disease), (5) altered degradative pathways (lysosomal storage and uric acid cycle disorder), (6) deficient or abnormal circulating proteins (clotting factors leading to hemophilia or globulins leading to immunologic disorders), (7) alterations in membrane receptors or transport molecules (such as hypercholesterolemia or CF), (8) immunologic disorders (such as immunodeficiency disorders), and (9) cancer genetics. Several examples are described further in this section.

Hemoglobinopathies may arise from qualitative or quantitative changes in hemoglobin. For example, both sickle cell anemia and β-thalassemia involve mutations in the gene on chromosome 11 for production of hemoglobin β chains. The most common mutation in sickle cell anemia involves a single point mutation (change in just one amino acid, with a valine instead of a glutamic acid inserted into the 146 amino acid sequence that makes up β chains). This mutation results in formation of qualitatively different β globulin chains (HbS). With β-thalassemia, fewer β chains of normal length are produced because of a reduced production rate or absence of synthesis. The α chains have fewer β chains to pair with and accumulate and precipitate. More than 300 different mutations in the β chain gene have been identified in individuals with various forms of β-thalassemia.[32] With α-thalassemia, two pairs of genes (for a total of four genes) control synthesis of α chains for hemoglobin on chromosome 16, with two α globulin genes on each chromosome 16. The clinical status of individuals depends on the number of genes in the two gene pairs that are deleted or abnormal. If just one of the four genes is deleted, the individual is a "silent" carrier. If two genes are absent or inactivated, the individual will have minimal anemia and hemoglobin H disease; three deleted or inactivated genes lead to mild to moderate anemia. Two inactivated genes and one abnormal gene leads to moderate to severe anemia. If all four genes are absent or inactive, these infants develop severe fetal hydrops (edema) and congestive heart failure and are usually stillborn or die soon after birth.[32] However, a few infants have survived with bone marrow transplants.[32]

Metabolic defects result in blocked metabolic pathways, accumulation of toxic precursors, lack of end-product production, and loss of feedback inhibition. Metabolic defects are referred to as *inborn errors of metabolism (IEM);* more than 500 IEMs have been identified, of which approximately 25% manifest in the neonate.[20] Newborn screening targets some of these disorders (see Genetic Screening). For example, phenylalanine is a precursor for tyrosine formation. Tyrosine is then broken down (mediated by tyrosinase), to produce substances such as melanin and byproducts used in synthesis of neurotransmitters. Phenylalanine catabolism is mediated by the enzyme *phenylalanine hydroxylase (PAH).* Individuals with phenylketonuria (PKU) have a mutation of the gene required for production of this enzyme. As a result, these individuals have altered enzyme production and have difficulty converting phenylalanine to tyrosine. Phenylalanine and byproducts of alternative metabolic pathways accumulate with a deficiency of tyrosine. The accumulated phenylalanine and alternative pathway byproducts are excreted in the urine (leading to a musky odor), interfere with tyrosinase function, and are toxic to the central nervous system. The decreased tyrosine leads to a lack of melanin (resulting in the light skin and eye color observed in these individuals), altered neurotransmitters, and neurologic abnormalities.

MODES OF INHERITANCE

The way in which a particular trait is transmitted to offspring is referred to as the *mode of inheritance.* The major modes of inheritance are those that follow traditional mendelian patterns (autosomal and sex-linked inheritance), multifactorial inheritance, and nontraditional patterns. Mendelian patterns follow the principles identified by Mendel (Table 1-1) and influence inheritance of both normal traits and mutated genes. Autosomal dominant traits are the result of a dominant allele at a particular locus on an autosome. When a characteristic is the result of a recessive allele, the mode of inheritance is known as *autosomal recessive.* Genetic diseases resulting from

the mutation of a single allele are called *dominant;* those that result from mutation of both alleles are called *recessive.* The traits or disorders expressed by autosomal genes usually occur with the same frequency in males as in females. The latter is not true of sex-linked traits and disorders, which occur with higher frequency in males than in females. This is because the genes located on the X chromosome are present in only one copy in males. Therefore the genes that are on that chromosome are expressed and are considered hemizygous in males.[41] Polygenic traits are governed by the additive effect of two or more alleles at different loci.[41]

Several types of dominance (simple, or complete; partial, or incomplete) and codominance affect the phenotype.[32,41] In simple, or complete, dominance, the heterozygous genotype (dominant allele present on one of the chromosome pair) produces a phenotype similar to that produced by the homozygous genotype (dominant allele present on both of the chromosome pair) for dominant traits. With partial, or incomplete, dominance, the heterozygous genotype (one copy of the recessive gene and one copy of the dominant gene) produces a phenotype that is intermediate between the recessive homozygous (i.e., two copies of a recessive gene) and dominant homozygous (i.e., two copies of a dominant gene) phenotypes. For example, an individual who is a heterozygote (carrier) for familial hypercholesterolemia will have fewer low density lipoprotein receptors and higher blood cholesterol levels than a healthy individual but will have more receptors and lower cholesterol levels than someone with two recessive genes.[32]

Codominance occurs when both alleles are expressed, so that in the heterozygous state, both the dominant and recessive gene products are produced. The gene producing normal β chains for adult hemoglobin (HbA) and the gene producing abnormal β chains (HbS) seen with sickle cell anemia are examples of codominance. If both chromosomes in the pair have the normal β chain gene, HbA is produced; if both chromosomes have the abnormal genes, HbS is produced and the individual has sickle cell anemia. However, if one of the chromosomes has the normal gene and one has the abnormal gene (heterozygote), both HbA and HbS are produced. This individual has the sickle cell trait.

For some traits, such as the ABO blood type (encoded by a gene on chromosome 9), multiple alleles are present. Although any given individual has only two genes for blood type (one on each chromosome in the pair), there are more than two forms of the gene present in the population. For example, although there are genes for types A, B, and O present in humans, an individual has only two alleles. That person may have two identical alleles (AA, BB, or OO), or may have two different alleles (AO, BO, or AB). In the ABO system, A and B are codominant and O is recessive to both A and B. Thus someone who has the AO genotype has the A blood type phenotype. Similarly, a BO individual has the B phenotype. However, someone with the AB genotype has AB blood, because A and B are codominant and thus are both expressed.[32,41]

Other factors that influence whether or not an individual with a certain genotype actually manifests the trait are penetrance and

TABLE 1-1 Mendelian Principles of Inheritance

PRINCIPLE	DESCRIPTION
Dominance	In the competition of two genes at the same locus on paired chromosomes, one gene may mask or conceal the other. The individual manifests the dominant gene's characteristic. The concealed trait is termed *recessive.*
Segregation	During meiosis, paired chromosomes are separated to form two gametes. Therefore the genes remain unchanged and are transferred from one generation to the next.
Independent assortment	When displayed traits have alleles at two or more loci, each is distributed within the gametes randomly, independent of each other.

variable expression. With differences in penetrance, not everyone with the abnormal genes actually manifests the trait or disorder. This is an "all-or-nothing" type of phenomenon. Reduced penetrance (approximately 10% of known carriers of the abnormal gene do not have the disorder) is often seen with autosomal dominant conditions such as retinoblastoma. Other disorders, such as Huntington disease, demonstrate age-dependent penetrance (the disorder may not appear until later in life); however, the earlier signs appear, the more severe the disorder.[32] *Variable expression* refers to the different manifestations of the phenotype that can be observed in individuals with the same genotype. This leads to wide variations in the clinical severity of individuals with some disorders.[24,32] Examples of disorders with variable expression include neurofibromatosis and osteogenesis imperfecta. As mentioned previously, some disorders also exhibit anticipation, a tendency for the disorder to become more severe with each subsequent generation. This is common with disorders characterized by unstable nucleotide repeats, such as myotonic dystrophy, Huntington disease, and fragile X syndrome.[32]

Autosomal Inheritance

The inheritance of these traits is dependent on the differences between alleles of a particular locus on an autosomal pair. In this type of inheritance, it makes no difference which parent carries the genotype, because the autosomes are the same in both sexes.

Autosomal Recessive Inheritance

A trait governed by a recessive allele is expressed only when the homozygous condition exists.[41] For an individual to demonstrate the trait or disorder, both parents must carry the recessive allele. If an affected person reproduces with a homozygous unaffected person, their children will be heterozygous for the trait and will not manifest the disease, but they will be carriers. If two carriers reproduce, then the probability (for each pregnancy) is about 25% that the child will manifest the disease, 50% that the child will be a carrier, and 25% that the child will neither have the disease nor be a carrier. When an affected person reproduces with a carrier, the probability is about 50% that a child will have the disease and 50% that the child will be a carrier. Usually an affected child is the offspring of two heterozygotes who are themselves clinically normal. However, heterozygotes may have a decreased level of the affected enzyme or protein.[24,32]

Disorders transmitted by recessive inheritance often involve altered enzymes. Typically only about 50% of the normal amount of these enzymes is sufficient for normal function.[43] Examples of autosomal recessive disorders include CF, PKU, hypothyroidism, Tay-Sachs disease, congenital adrenal hyperplasia, and galactosemia. Hemoglobinopathies such as sickle cell disease are also transmitted by autosomal recessive inheritance. Characteristics of disorders inherited by autosomal recessive inheritance are listed in Box 1-2.

Autosomal Dominant Inheritance

In autosomal dominant inheritance, traits and disorders are expressed in the heterozygote state, and the probability of

BOX 1-2   Major Characteristics of Autosomal Recessive and Dominant Inheritance and Disorders

Autosomal Recessive Inheritance	Autosomal Dominant Inheritance
The mutant gene is located on an autosome.	The mutant gene is located on an autosome.
Two copies of the mutant gene are needed for phenotypic manifestations.	Only one copy of the mutant gene is needed for effects to be evident.
Males and females are affected in equal numbers, on average.	Males and females are affected in equal numbers, on average.
There is usually no sex difference in clinical manifestations.	There is usually no sex difference in clinical manifestations.
Affected individual receives one mutant gene from each parent.	Vertical family history through several generations may be seen.
Family history is usually negative, especially for vertical transmission (in more than one generation).	There is wide variability of expression.
Other affected individuals in the family in the same generation (horizontal transmission) may be seen.	Penetrance may be incomplete, so the gene may appear to "skip" a generation.
Consanguinity is present more often than in other modes of inheritance.	There is an increased paternal age effect.
Fresh gene mutation is rare.	Fresh gene mutation is common.
Age of disease onset is early newborn, infancy, and early childhood.	Later age of onset is common.
Often involves an enzyme defect or deficiency.	Normal offspring of an affected person have normal children.
Disease course is usually severe.	A structural protein defect is often involved.

Adapted from Lashley, F.R. (1998). *Clinical genetics in nursing practice* (2nd ed.). New York: Springer.

transmission to the offspring is 50% with each pregnancy. Most autosomal dominant disorders are more severe if the individual is homozygous rather than heterozygous for the disorder.[32] Autosomal dominant disorders often involve mutations in genes that regulate complex metabolic pathways or produce structural proteins. Examples of autosomal dominant disorders include Huntington disease (triplet nucleotide repeats), osteogenesis imperfecta (mutations in the collagen gene), and familial hypercholesterolemia (mutations in the receptor for very-low-density lipoproteins).[43] When the gene is present, it is expressed in the phenotype and can be traced through a number of generations. Expression of these genes rarely skips a generation, and a person not affected will not transmit the gene. Therefore the affected individual will have an affected parent, unless the condition is the result of fresh mutation, which is a common finding in most autosomal dominant conditions. An exception to this is Huntington disease, in which new mutations are extremely rare.[32]

Some autosomal dominant disorders (e.g., achondroplasia) are apparent at birth, whereas others (e.g., Huntington disease, adult-onset polycystic kidney disease) have a variable and usually adult onset. Other characteristics of autosomal dominant inheritance include a wide variation in expression in those individuals affected and altered penetrance. Penetrance may also not be complete. *Penetrance* refers to whether there is phenotypic recognition of the mutant gene. If a gene is fully penetrant, the trait it controls is always manifested in the individual. If it is not fully penetrant, the disease may appear to skip a generation; that is, a particular genotype produces a particular trait in some individuals but not in others. A parent may be diagnosed with a particular disorder only after having several affected offspring.[43] A paternal age effect is seen with some autosomal dominant disorders.[41] Box 1-2 summarizes characteristics of autosomal dominant inheritance.

Sex-Linked Inheritance

Genes on the X chromosome are identified as X-linked, whereas those on the Y chromosome are Y-linked. There are many X-linked genes; however, there is limited evidence for Y-linked genes except for some associated with the male phenotype. Males can transmit X-linked genes to their daughters but not to their sons, and sons can receive X-linked genes only from their mothers. Female offspring can be either homozygous or heterozygous for X-linked genes because of their dual X chromosomes. Males are hemizygous for X-linked genes, because they have only one X chromosome. X-linked inheritance in females is influenced by X-chromosome inactivation (see earlier discussion on X chromosomes). Exceptions to the random inactivation are seen in some single-gene disorders such as Duchenne muscular dystrophy, in which the normal X tends to be the active one.[46] Box 1-3 summarizes characteristics of X-linked recessive and dominant inheritance.

X-Linked Recessive Inheritance

In males, an X-linked recessive gene is always expressed, because there is no corresponding gene on the Y chromosome. In females, recessive genes of this nature are usually expressed only when the recessive allele is present in the homozygous form (i.e., on both of the woman's X chromosomes). Occasionally a female may demonstrate the trait secondary to the random inactivation of one of the X chromosomes in each cell. The degree to which this individual expresses the trait depends on the proportion of cells in which the X with the dominant gene has been inactivated. The larger the proportion is, the greater the likelihood that the X-linked trait will be visible. Examples of X-linked recessive inheritance include hemophilia, color blindness, and Duchenne muscular dystrophy.

X-Linked Dominant Inheritance

In X-linked dominant inheritance, the trait will be demonstrated in both males and females. Who will be affected and to what degree depend on the genotype of the parents. All the daughters of an affected father will receive the X chromosome

---

BOX 1-3   Major Characteristics of X-Linked Recessive and Dominant Inheritance and Disorders

X-Linked Recessive Inheritance	X-Linked Dominant Inheritance
The mutant gene is located on the X chromosome.	The mutant gene is located on the X chromosome.
One copy of the mutant gene is needed for phenotypic effect in males.	One copy of the mutant gene is needed for phenotypic manifestation.
Two copies of the mutant gene are usually needed for phenotypic effect in females.	X inactivation modifies the gene effect in females.
Males are more commonly affected than females.	Often lethal in males and so may see transmission only in female line.
Unequal X inactivation can lead to manifesting heterozygote female carriers.	Affected families show excess of female offspring.
Transmission is often through heterozygous (carrier) females.	Affected male transmits gene to all his daughters and none of his sons.
All daughters of affected males are carriers.	Affected males have affected mothers (unless it is a new mutation).
All sons of affected males are normal.	There is no male-to-male transmission.
There is no male-to-male transmission.	There is no carrier state.
There may be fresh gene mutations.	Disorders are relatively uncommon.

Adapted from Lashley, F.R. (1998). *Clinical genetics in nursing practice* (2nd ed.). New York: Springer.

---

with the dominant gene and will express the disease. However, none of the sons of this father will be affected. When the mother is heterozygous and the father is not affected, the probability is 50% that offspring will be affected. If the mother is homozygous, the probability is 100% that children of either gender will be affected. If the father is also affected, the daughters will be homozygous for the disease. X-linked dominant disorders are rare; examples are X-linked hypophosphatemia and vitamin D–resistant rickets.

Y-Linked Inheritance

Because only males have Y chromosomes and there is no corresponding allele on the X chromosome, these traits occur only in males. If a Y-linked trait is present, it will be expressed. There is no dominance or recessiveness. When a father with a Y-linked chromosome transfers genetic material, all the sons will be affected and none of the daughters will. The Y chromosome also contains multiple testes-determining genes that control gonad development and spermatogenesis (see Development of the Gonads).

Multifactorial Inheritance

Multifactorial inheritance results from the interaction of multiple genetic and environmental factors. Multifactorial inheritance includes traits such as height and blood pressure. Multifactorial disorders include birth defects (e.g., neural tube defects, some congenital heart defects, congenital dislocated hips, cleft lip and palate, pyloric stenosis, Hirschsprung disease) and adult-onset disorders (e.g., some forms of breast and other cancers, bipolar affective disorders, coronary heart disease, types 1 and 2 diabetes). Some disorders can also arise from purely environmental causes as well as via multifactorial inheritance. For example, although some congenital heart defects have a multifactorial inheritance, these defects may also arise as the result of teratogen exposure (see Chapter 7). Multifactorial disorders are often polygenic and may be additive. The threshold model proposes that a certain threshold or liability must be present for the disorder to occur; the additive polygenic model suggests that multiple genes have an accumulative effect to determine phenotype.[32] Although multifactorial disorders are often polygenic, not all polygenic disorders or traits are multifactorial (i.e., involve an interaction among genetic and environmental factors).[32] The risk of a multifactorial disorder increases with the number of individuals in the family who are affected, closeness of the relationship (highest in first-degree relatives—parents, siblings, offspring), and severity of the disorder. Thus the greater the severity of a birth defect, the greater the risk of recurrence in first-degree relatives.[32,41]

Nontraditional Modes of Inheritance

Nontraditional modes of inheritance involve patterns that do not follow traditional mendelian principles. Examples of these patterns include alterations in genomic imprinting, uniparental disomy, gonadal (germline) mosaicism, and mitochondrial inheritance.

Genomic imprinting (see Box 1-1) involves modifications in a specific DNA segment before fertilization so that it functions differently depending on the parental origin of the DNA. Thus with genomic imprinting, gene expression differs depending on the parent from which the chromosome originated. Imprinting is a part of normal development; however, disorders can arise from alterations in imprinting. For example, with triploidy (severe growth failure and mental retardation, with most spontaneously aborted), if the extra set of chromosomes comes from the father (i.e., the zygote has 46 paternal chromosomes and 23 maternal), there is marked growth failure in the embryo, with overgrowth of placental tissue. Conversely, if there are two sets of maternal and one set of paternal chromosomes, early embryo growth is normal, with poor placental and chorion development. Complete hydatidiform moles (see Chapter 3) have two sets of paternal chromosomes and none of maternal origin. Loss of imprinting of growth factors may play a role in childhood cancers such as Wilms tumor.

Another example of genomic imprinting is seen with deletions on the long arm of chromosome 15 (q11–13). Some genes in this area are only active in the gene inherited from the father; others are only active in the maternal gene. If the deletion comes from the father (loss of genes that are only active in the father), the offspring has Prader-Willi syndrome; if the deletion is on the maternal chromosome (loss of genes that are only active in the mother), the offspring has Angelman syndrome. These syndromes have completely different phenotypes. Angelman syndrome is characterized by mental retardation, seizures, absence of speech, frequent smiling, and paroxysmal laughing; Prader-Willi syndrome is characterized by overeating and obesity, behavior problems, and mild to moderate mental retardation. This process is not completely understood but involves epigenetic modifications of the histones by methylation and acetylation that leads to inactivation of certain sites on the chromosome. The initial modifications occur during gametogenesis, wherein the previous imprints (i.e., from one's mother or father) are erased and new ones established based on the respective parental pattern.[33] More than 100 imprinted genes, which often occur in clusters, have been identified.[33] The pattern of methylation is unique to the maternal versus paternal genes and the pattern is replicated when the cell divides.[8,78]

Uniparental disomy occurs when the offspring gets both copies of a chromosome from the same parent. For example, Prader-Willi and Angelman syndromes can also arise with uniparental disomy. With Prader-Willi syndrome both number 15 chromosomes come from the mother; with Angelman syndrome, both arise from the father. Other disorders associated with uniparental disomy are Beckwith-Wiedemann syndrome (two paternal number 11 chromosomes), Silver-Russell syndrome (two maternal number 7 chromosomes), and transient neonatal diabetes mellitus (two paternal number 6 chromosomes).[32]

Gonadal (or *germline*) *mosaicism* refers to mutations that occur in some germ cells. All germ cells (oogonia or spermatogonia) initially undergo mitosis before meiosis and gametogenesis begin. If the mutation occurs at some point during these cell divisions, some cell lines entering meiosis and forming gametes will have the mutation, whereas others will not. This can produce pedigrees that are inconsistent with either dominant or recessive inheritance. For example, a dominant disorder may appear in two offspring of normal parents, or an unaffected parent may have affected children by two different partners. The parents do not have the mutation in their somatic cells, but in their germ cells. Their offspring have the mutation in both somatic and germ cells and can pass it on to subsequent generations.[32] Examples of disorders that have been transmitted by this mechanism are achondroplasia and some forms of osteogenesis imperfecta.[32]

Mitochondrial inheritance is unique in that the mitochondria, which are cytoplasmic organelles involved in cellular respiration and production of energy, have their own unique circular mitochondrial DNA (mtDNA) and genes, which encode proteins needed for oxidative phosphorylation as well as tRNA and rRNA.[32] Mitochondrial genes code for different amino acids than does nuclear DNA. Mitochondria are present in the cytoplasm of the ovum; the sperm does not have any cytoplasm and thus mtDNA to pass on to the offspring. Thus each person, whether male or female, inherits mtDNA only from the mother. Mitochondrial disorders are rare and generally involve disorders of the central nervous system, skeletal muscles, eyes, or heart. When they occur, all of the woman's offspring are affected.[32]

EMBRYONIC AND FETAL DEVELOPMENT OF THE REPRODUCTIVE SYSTEM

Embryonic and fetal development of the reproductive system involves the formation of the gonads, genital ducts, and external genitalia from undifferentiated primordial structures (indifferent stage) within the embryo that are adapted to meet the functional needs of the two sexes (Figure 1-11). For the male, the gonads differentiate into the testes and the duct system becomes the efferent ductules of the testes, the duct of the epididymis, the ductus deferens, the seminal vesicles, and most of the urethra. The external genitalia become specialized to form the penis and scrotum. For the female, the gonads differentiate into the ovaries; the duct system becomes the uterine (fallopian) tubes, uterus, and vagina; and the external genitalia develop into the vulva.

This developmental process begins at fertilization with the determination of genetic sex, passing through three other stages before birth. These include differentiation of gonadal sex, somatic sex, and neuroendocrine sex. After birth, sexual

differentiation continues with the development of social, psychological, and secondary sex characteristics. These stages determine the final sexual characteristics and behavior of the individual.

Genetic sex is determined by the genes at the time of fertilization and is defined by the sex chromosome complement. Gonadal sex is defined by the structure and function of the gonads; somatic sex involves all other genital organs; and neuroendocrine sex is established by the cyclic or continuous production of gonadotropin-releasing hormones (GnRHs).

Prenatally the reproductive system develops from analogous undifferentiated structures in both sexes. Table 1-2 illustrates the indifferent structures and their male and female derivatives. The basic pattern is the female phenotype; the male reproductive system develops only when the Y chromosome, testosterone, and other organizing substances are present. Prenatal reproductive system development involves three areas: the gonads, the genital ducts, and the external genitalia.

Genetic control of sex determination involves multiple genes and factors in male and female embryos. Key genes controlling development of the gonadal ridge into the bipotential gonad include *SRY* (sex region on the Y chromosome) and *Wnt4*.[61] These genes produce transcription factors that influence other genes to produce signaling molecules and other proteins that lead to changes characteristic of the male

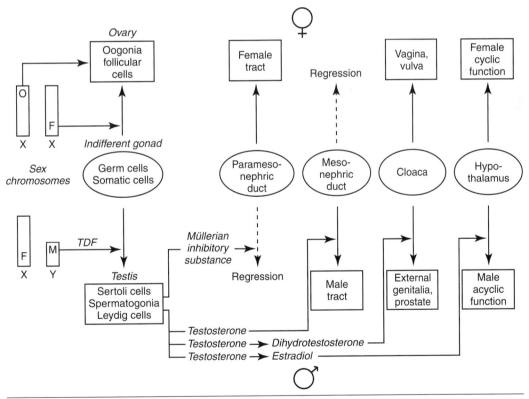

FIGURE 1-11   Proposed regulatory mechanisms in prenatal sexual differentiation. The indifferent stages are in the middle oval blocks. Female structures differentiate upward and male structures downward *(solid vertical arrows)*. Regulatory factors and their source and target are indicated by *solid horizontal arrows*. Regression is indicated by *dashed arrows*. *F,* gene for ovarian differentiation; *M,* gene for testicular differentiation; *O,* gene for further ovarian development; *TDF,* testis-determining gene. (From Pelliniemi, L. & Dym, M. [1994]. The fetal gonad and sexual differentiation. In D. Tulchinsky & A.B. Little [Eds.]. *Maternal-fetal endocrinology* [2nd ed.]. Philadelphia: Saunders.)

TABLE 1-2   Comparison of Male and Female Derivatives of Indifferent Structures in Reproductive System Development

INDIFFERENT STRUCTURE	MALE DERIVATIVE	FEMALE DERIVATIVE
Genital ridge	Testes	Ovary
Primordial germ cells	Spermatozoa	Ova
Sex cords	Seminiferous tubules (Sertoli cells)	Follicular cells
Mesonephric tubules	Efferent ductules	Epoöphoron
	Paradidymis	Paroöphoron
Mesonephric (wolffian) ducts	Appendix of epididymis	Appendix of ovary
	Epididimal duct	Gartner duct
	Ductus deferens	
	Ejaculatory duct	
Paramesonephric (müllerian) ducts	Appendix of testes	Uterine (fallopian) tubes
	Prostate utricle	Uterus
		Upper vagina
Definitive urogenital sinus (lower part)	Penile urethra	Lower vagina
		Vaginal vestibule
Early urogenital sinus (upper part)	Urinary bladder	Urinary bladder
	Prostatic urethra	Urethra
Genital tubercle	Penis	Clitoris
Genital folds	Floor of penile urethra	Labia minora
Genital swellings	Scrotum	Labia majora

From Carlson, B.M. (2013). *Human embryology and developmental biology* (5th ed.). Philadelphia: Elsevier Saunders.

or female phenotype.[64] In males, *SRY* (located at Yp11) and *SOX9* complemented by *DAX1* are important for testicular development.[61] *SRY* is considered the master gene for testes development, producing a transcription factor that initiates events leading to male development.[52,64] Other genes involved in development of the male reproductive system control development and activity of androgen receptors for wolffian duct stabilization and external genitalia development; production of müllerian-inhibiting substance (MIS) and its receptor and genes for formation of testosterone.[61] Chromosomal translocations, microdeletions, and androgen receptor gene mutations are examples of defects that can lead to male infertility. For example, *DAX-1* and *DAX-2* are needed for sperm production, and mutations in these genes can result in azoospermia. *SF1* and *SOX9* increase concentrations of MIS from Sertoli cells and induce the testes to secrete FGF9, which causes tubules from the mesonephric duct to enter the gonadal ridge and increase production of steroidogenesis factor-1 (SF1), which leads to differentiation of Sertoli and Leydig cells; upregulation of testosterone-producing genes; and production of MIS, leading to regression of the paramesonephric duct.[9,64]

Female gonadal differentiation occurs in the absence of the testes-organizing genes on the Y chromosome and under the influence of estrogens.[39] *Wnt4* is believed to be the ovarian-determining gene, upregulating *DAX1* and regulating other genes needed for ovarian development.[9,64] *Wnt4* is also important in conversion of the müllerian duct into the uterus and fallopian tubes. *Wnt4* upregulates *DAX1* to inhibit *SOX9* (involved in testicular development).[64] Genes involved in ovarian induction and organization appear to act only if the testes-organizing gene (*SRY*) on the Y chromosome is not active.

Development of the Primordial Germ Cells

Primordial germ cells (PGCs) are first seen at 24 days after fertilization.[9,52] These cells originate in the epiblast near the origin of the allantois and migrate through the primitive streak into the yolk sac, following signaling from surrounding tissues.[38,64,71] PGCs proliferate in the yolk sac and in the 4th week begin to migrate by amoeboid movements along the dorsal mesentery of the hindgut to the gonadal ridge, where they colonize the primitive gonads.[38,52,64,67] PGC induction, proliferation, and differentiation is under the control of several sequentially activated genes and multiple gene factors, as is the attraction between the gonadal tissue and the PGCs.[9,52,71] If migration is altered and PGCs enter nongonadal tissues, they usually die, but if not, the germ cells might develop into extragonadal teratomas.[9,67] Mitotic cell proliferation continues during this migration. The PGCs also undergo changes in chromatin organization during migration and on entering the gonad. These changes include imprinting with loss of methylation and changes in DNA histone proteins. The DNA demethylation and chromatin modulation ensures pluripotential receptiveness to induction signals that result in the formation of oocytes and spermatocytes.[71] DNA methylation and imprinting will be reestablished (see Box 1-1) after fertilization. By 42 to 48 days, the PGCs, which have increased from approximately 100 to up to 5000 cells, arrive in the gonadal ridge, where they are incorporated into the mesenchyme.[16,64]

Development of the Gonads

The human gonads consist of the ovaries in the female and the testes in the male. These structures are derived from three cellular sources: (1) PGCs, (2) underlying mesenchyme, and (3) coelomic epithelium.[9]

Indifferent Stage

During the 5th week of gestation, a thickening of the coelomic epithelium on the medial side of the mesonephros (see Chapter 11) can be seen; this becomes the genital or gonadal ridge.[52,64] Development of the gonadal ridge is controlled by a group of genes that produce proteins critical for development of this ridge. The surface cells proliferate to form a solid cord of cells that grow downward with fingerlike projections into the mesenchyme, forming the primary sex cords.[52] PGCs enter the gonadal ridge late in the 5th week and migrate into the developing sex chords during the 6th week.[9] At the end of 6 weeks, the gonads remain sexually indistinguishable. Two layers can be identified within the gonads: the cortex (coelomic epithelium) and the medulla (mesenchyme). In the XX embryo, the cortex differentiates into the ovary and the medulla regresses. In the XY embryo, the medulla differentiates into the testes and the cortex regresses. Retinoic acid in the gonad and adjacent tissues stimulates expression of key meiotic genes.[64,71]

Development of the Testes

Development of the testes begins at 7 to 8 weeks' gestation. Timing is critical. If Sertoli cell precursors for testicular differentiation do not receive *SOX9* gene signals by a set time, PGCs enter meiosis and the gonad becomes an ovary.[9,52] The primary sex cords condense and extend into the medulla. Here they branch, canalize, and anastomose to form a network of tubules, the rete testis. These cords are separated from the surface epithelium by a dense layer of connective tissue, the tunica albuginea. Septa grow from the tunica into the medulla to divide the testis into wedge-shaped lobules. Each lobule contains approximately one to three seminiferous tubules, interstitial cells, and supporting cells.

The cords remain solid until puberty when the lumen is canalized and seminiferous tubules are formed. Canalization of the seminiferous cords results in formation of the walls of the tubules by Sertoli (supporting) cells and spermatogenic (germinal) epithelium, which is derived from the primary germ cells.[52,64,72] The Sertoli cells multiply during growth of the cords until they constitute the majority of the epithelium during fetal life and provide nutrients for the maturing spermatids in adult life.[52,72] The Sertoli cells produce MIS (also called *antimüllerian hormone*), a glycoprotein of the transforming growth factor-β family, by 6 to 7 weeks. MIS stimulates involution of the müllerian (paramesonephric) ducts. Males produce MIS until puberty.[52] As the Sertoli cells grow, they engulf the germ cells and secrete hormones and factors such as inhibin, activin, cytokines, MIS, and insulin-like growth factor-1 to nourish and sustain the germ cells.[16,72] These cells may also secrete a meiosis-inhibiting factor to inhibit spermatogonia meiosis until puberty.[9]

The mesenchyme contributes masses of interstitial cells (Leydig cells), which proliferate between the tubules. These cells differentiate by 7 to 8 weeks and are functional almost immediately, producing testosterone and other androgens.[64] Testicular testosterone peaks at 12 to 14 weeks, decreases, then peaks again at 28 to 32 weeks' gestation, followed by a decrease to term. Fetal androgens are thought to be important in priming the brain for the male pattern of hormonal release after puberty.[16] The Leydig cells are highly active in the 3rd through 5th gestational months. The rise in testosterone parallels the increase in Leydig cells; after 18 weeks Leydig cells begin to involute and decrease in number so that testosterone levels decrease until puberty.[9] Testosterone and other androgens induce formation of the male genital ducts and masculinization of the external genitalia. In addition, the Leydig cells suppress the development of the müllerian ducts.[52] The testicles start to descend into the inguinal canal during the 6th month, entering the scrotal swellings by 8 to 9 months' gestation. The inguinal canal closes after testes descent.[61]

Development of the Ovaries

In XX embryos, gonadal development begins around 7 weeks' gestation but occurs more slowly; the ovary is not clearly identifiable until 10 weeks.[52] The primary sex cords do develop and extend into the medulla of the developing ovary but are not prominent and later degenerate. By the 12th week, the medulla is mainly connective tissue, with scattered groups of cells that represent the prospective rete ovarii. The rete ovarii appears to be derived from migrating mesonephric cells, which may later give rise to the follicular cells.

During the 4th month, secondary sex cords (cortical cords) grow into the gonad from the germinal epithelium (surface epithelium).[52] As the cortical cords enlarge, the primordial germ cells are incorporated into them. At around 16 weeks the cords begin to break up into clusters, surrounding the primitive ova (oogonia) with a single layer of flattened supportive follicular cells derived from the cortical cords.[52] After meiotic arrest of the oocyte, the follicular cells become surrounded by a layer of granulosa cells. This complex is the primordial follicle, which will later become the primary follicle (see Chapter 3).[52] Cells of the primordial follicle secrete substances to nurture the oocytes. The surface epithelium becomes separated from the follicles, which lay in the cortex, by a thin fibrous capsule, the tunica albuginea. The ovary, like the testis, separates from the regressing mesonephros, becoming suspended by its own mesentery (mesovarium).[52] The ovary seems to have no significant role in the development of the genital ducts and external genitalia.[16]

For primary ovarian differentiation, only one X chromosome need be present, so this stage proceeds in 45, X (Turner syndrome) fetuses. Later development of the female genital system (from about 15 weeks on) requires the presence of two X chromosomes, so most 45, X individuals have abnormal follicular development with oocyte degeneration (gonadal dysgenesis).[52] Locally produced estrogen is present by 10 to 14 weeks, peaks at 20 weeks, and may begin to program the hypothalamus for cyclic release of gonadotropins after puberty.[16]

Development of the Genital Ducts

Both male and female embryos have two pairs of genital ducts, the mesonephric (wolffian) duct, which forms at 28 to 39 days, and the paramesonephric (müllerian) duct, which forms laterally to the wolffian ducts and gonad at 40 to 42 days.[16] The mesonephric duct originates as part of the urinary system and is incorporated into the developing gonad during the 6th week of gestation. The müllerian ducts initially develop alongside the wolffian ducts in both sexes but reach complete development only in females. The female ducts differentiate autonomously without external regulatory factors, whereas the male system is regulated by testicular androgens and MIS.

Indifferent Stage

The wolffian ducts drain the mesonephric kidneys and develop into the ductus deferens, the epididymis, and the ejaculatory ducts in the male when the mesonephric tubules degenerate. In the female the wolffian ducts almost completely degenerate. The müllerian ducts develop bilaterally alongside the wolffian ducts. The müllerian ducts run caudally parallel to the wolffian ducts, then cross in front of them, fusing to form a Y- or funnel-shaped canal.[52] The müllerian ducts are retained in the female and regress in the male.

Development of the Male Genital Ducts

MIS stimulates involution of the müllerian ducts in the male during the 8th week. Under the influence of testosterone and other androgens, the wolffian ducts are retained and incorporated into the genital system. Most of the mesonephric tubules disappear, except those that are in the region of the testes. These 5 to 12 mesonephric tubules lose their glomeruli and join with the rete testis. This creates a communication between the gonads and the wolffian duct. At this point the tubules are called the *efferent ductules;* these greatly elongate and become convoluted, making up the majority of the caput epididymis. The wolffian duct becomes the ductus epididymis in this region. Below this area, the wolffian duct incorporates muscle tissue and becomes the ductus deferens (vas deferens). The urethra makes up the remainder of the male genital duct system. Development of the male genital ducts is completed by 12 weeks. Local secretion of testosterone from the testes causes differentiation of the ipsilateral wolffian duct; systemic secretion of testosterone influences differentiation of the external genitalia. Thus a female with excess systemic testosterone (such as occurs with congenital adrenal hyperplasia) will not develop structures that arise from the wolffian duct (because these structures arise from production of local testosterone from the testes) but will have ambiguous genitalia (influenced by systemic testosterone from the adrenals).[61] MIS is produced bilaterally and acts on the side produced. Thus if only one testis develops, MIS will not be produced and act on that side of the body where the testis is missing, so the müllerian duct will not regress on that side.[61]

Development of the Female Genital Ducts

In the female embryo, the wolffian ducts regress at 11 weeks because of a lack of testosterone and other androgens, whereas the müllerian ducts are retained because of a lack of MIS and the presence of estrogens.[64] It has been suggested that the caudal portions of the wolffian ducts may be involved in formation of the vagina either directly or by actions on müllerian tissue.[9] Female sexual development, which is under control of the *Wnt* and *HOX* gene families and estrogens, is not dependent on the presence of ovaries.[49,52] The müllerian ducts become the fallopian tubes, uterus, and proximal vagina in the female. The cranial unfused portions of the müllerian ducts develop into the fallopian tubes; the caudal portion fuses to form the uterovaginal primordium. The latter gives rise to the epithelium and glands of the uterus and to the vaginal wall. The endometrial lining and the myometrium are derived from the surrounding mesenchymal tissue. The vaginal epithelium is derived from the endoderm of the urogenital sinus, and the fibromuscular wall of the vagina develops from the uterovaginal primordium. Initially the vagina is a solid cord (the vaginal plate); the vaginal lumen is formed as the central cells of the plate break down.

The broad ligaments are formed from the peritoneal folds that occur during fusion of the müllerian ducts. The broad, winglike folds extend from the lateral portions of the uterus to the pelvic wall. The folds of the broad ligaments are continuous with the peritoneum and divide the pelvis into anterior and posterior portions. Between the layers of the broad ligament, the mesenchyme proliferates to form loose connective tissue and smooth muscle. This complex of tissue provides support and attachment for the uterus, fallopian tubes, and ovaries.

Development of the External Genitalia

The early development of the external genitalia is similar in male and female embryos. Distinguishing characteristics can be seen during the ninth week of gestation, with definitive characteristics being fully formed by the twelfth week.[52] Development of the external genitalia is summarized in Figure 1-12.

Indifferent Stage

The external genitalia initially appear similar. Early in the 4th week, a swelling can be identified at the cranial end of the cloacal membrane; this is the genital tubercle. Genital (labioscrotal) swellings and genital folds soon develop alongside the cloacal membrane. The genital tubercle elongates at this time and is the same length in both sexes. The urorectal septum fuses with the cloacal membrane, dividing the membrane into a dorsal anal membrane and a ventral urogenital membrane. These membranes rupture around the 8th week, forming the anus and urogenital orifice. The urethral sinus, which is continuous with the urogenital orifice, forms on the ventral surface of the genital tubercle at this time (see Figure 1-12).[52] The ovaries gradually descend from the lumbar region to the pelvis.[52,64]

Development of the Male External Genitalia

The androgens produced by the fetal testes, especially dihydrotestosterone, induce the masculinization of the external genitalia of the male embryo.[52] The genital tubercle continues to elongate, forming the penis and pulling the genital folds forward. This results in the development of the lateral walls of the urethral groove by the genital folds (see Figure 1-12, A). The posterior-to-anterior fusion of the genital folds as they come in contact results in the development of the spongy urethra and the progressive movement of the urethral orifice toward the glans of the penis. The opening, however, remains on the undersurface of the phallus.[52] Backward growth of a plate of ectodermal tissue from the tip of the phallus to the urethra forms the terminal part of the urethra. Once canalized, the urinary and reproductive systems will have achieved an open system. This, along with the descent of the testes into the genital swellings (scrotum), completes the development of the external genitalia (see Figure 1-12, A).

After the penile urethra has formed, the connective tissue surrounding the urethra becomes condensed to form the corpus cavernosum urethrae, in which numerous wide and convoluted blood vessels having many arteriovenous anastomoses develop. The genital swellings also grow toward each other and fuse to form the scrotum. External genitalia development in the male is complete by 14 weeks except for continued phallic growth and testicular descent. Tissue swelling

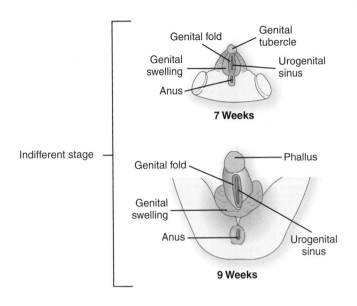

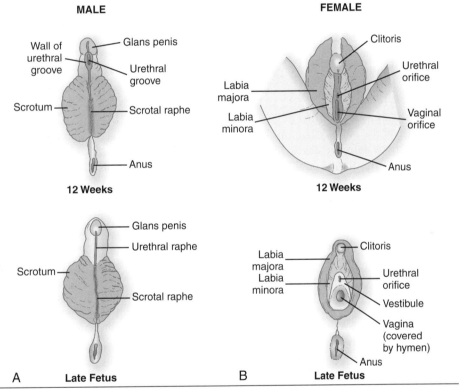

FIGURE 1-12 Differentiation of the external genitalia in males **(A)** and females **(B)**. (From Carlson, B.M. [2013]. *Human embryology and developmental biology* [5th ed.]. Philadelphia: Saunders.)

occurs to dilate the inguinal canal and scrotum in preparation for the descent of the testes, which is usually complete by the 8th month of gestation.

Descent of the testes occurs in two phases: transabdominal descent and inguinoscrotal descent. Descent is moderated by many forces, including the enlargement of the pelvis, trunk growth, and the testes' remaining relatively stationary, as well as the influence of gonadotropins, MIS and androgens.[29,52,64] The testis is released from the urogenital ridge and moves toward the scrotum. Descent through the inguinal canals begins

around 26 weeks.[52] At about 32 to 33 weeks, the testes reach the scrotum. Once passage is complete, the inguinal canal contracts around the spermatic cord. The spermatic cord consists of the vas deferens, blood vessels, and nerves. In 97% of term infants, the testes have descended bilaterally before delivery. During the first 3 months after delivery, most undescended testes will descend without intervention.[29,52,64] Failure of testicular descent results in cryptorchidism with decreased testosterone production and is associated with failure of spermatozoa production and increased risk of renal anomalies.[52,64]

Development of the Female External Genitalia

Without androgens, feminization of the indifferent external genitalia occurs and is complete by 11 weeks. Initially, the genital tubercle grows rapidly; however, it gradually slows, becoming the relatively small clitoris. The clitoris develops like the penis, except that the urogenital folds do not fuse. Both the urethra and the vagina open into the common vestibule, which is widely open after the disappearance of the urogenital membrane. The opening is flanked by the urethral folds and the genital swellings, which become the labia minora and majora, respectively (see Figure 1-12, *B*).

Anomalies of the Genital Tract

Anomalies encountered in the reproductive system may be secondary to any of three major factors occurring individually or in combination: (1) genetic makeup, (2) endocrine and hormonal environment, and (3) mechanical events. Each may lead to alterations in development and reproductive ability. Because the embryo is genitally bipotential, when genetic or hormonal factors alter development, the embryo may develop various disorders of sex development.[4,30,39] Mechanical congenital anomalies are related to developmental arrests, interference, or failures that result in changes in normal morphologic patterns.

Disorders of Sex Development

Absence of one or both gonads is a rare disorder. If gonadal agenesis is unilateral, absence of the renal system on the affected side is common. Failure or defective development of nephrogenic mesenchyme is probably the cause, although the etiology of such failure is not known.

Turner syndrome is one of the more common sex chromosome abnormalities. This syndrome is seen in an estimated 0.8% to 1% of spontaneously aborted fetuses and in 1 in 2500 females at birth.[24] The absence or deletion of an X chromosome usually results in an individual with a 45, XO karyotype, with 80% resulting from paternal nondisjunction.[3] Mosaics (46,XX/45,XO) often have functioning ovaries. In most other cases, however, there is ovarian dysgenesis associated with other somatic abnormalities.[3] Although women with Turner syndrome rarely have a spontaneous pregnancy, they can conceive with assisted reproductive technologies, although they have higher rates of maternal complications and maternal mortality.[12] Klinefelter syndrome (47,XXY) is seen in 1 out of 700 to 1000 live births and is characterized by a small testis and impaired spermatogenesis.[24]

Ovotesticular disorders of sex development are extremely rare.[30,52] Individuals may be 46,XX; 46,XY; or mosaic XX/XY. They have both ovarian and testicular tissue, either as separate organs or as a single ovotestis. Usually the gonadal tissue is not functional, but in some individuals oogenesis and spermiogenesis may occur simultaneously. The external genitalia are ambiguous, but the rest of the physical appearance may be either male or female. This abnormality seems to be the result of an error in sexual determination and lack of dominance of the cortex or medulla of the genital ridge.[52] Possible causes include translocation of testicular differentiation genes to the X chromosome, a mutant gene, or undetected XY cells in the gonad.

The presence of a uterus and fallopian tubes indicates defective functioning of MIS. In those individuals who are mosaic 46,XX/XY, the cause involves the union of two zygotes of different genetic sex. The two cell lines develop normally, with limits being set by their topographic distribution during ontogeny.

XY disorders of sex development involve alterations in androgen synthesis or action. Infants have more or less dysgenetic testes with an XY constitution. There is incomplete differentiation of the external genitalia secondary to testicular dysgenesis and insufficient testosterone production.[3] This abnormality may be associated with altered development of the internal genitalia because of inadequate production of MIS and thus the müllerian ducts fail to completely regress.[3] Causes may include a deficiency in the 5α-reductase enzyme necessary to convert testosterone to dihydrotestosterone so that external virilization can occur. In testicular feminization syndrome, there is an inability to bind androgens in target tissues; in other situations, transmission of androgens from the receptor to the nucleus is blocked.[3,52] Externally, the genitalia may be either ambiguous or feminine. Internal structures may also vary. These male infants have varying degrees of phallic and müllerian duct development, even though their karyotype is 46,XY. When differentiation occurs, males with 5α-reductase deficiencies have testosterone and its derivatives in the external genitalia tissue but not in the developing wolffian duct. Testosterone may appear in the wolffian ducts after the period of tissue sensitivity has passed.[3,52] Males with the X-linked gene for testicular feminization (46,XY) have normally differentiated testes; however, these children look like normal females. The vagina ends in a blind pouch, and the uterus and fallopian tubes are nonexistent or rudimentary.[52] The testes are usually intraabdominal or inguinal, or they may descend into the labia majora. There are high levels of circulating testosterone with elevated levels of gonadotropins. Unfortunately, testosterone receptor sites will not bind or incorporate testosterone into the cells in the genital swellings and genital folds.[52] These individuals have female genitalia, and at puberty there is development of female secondary sex characteristics; however, menstruation does not occur. The psychosexual orientation of these children is usually female.[3,52]

XX disorders of sex development involve androgen excess in 46,XX female infants who have a congenital virilization of the external genitalia. This is usually termed *adrenogenital syndrome* or *congenital adrenal hyperplasia (CAH)*, meaning hyperfunction of the adrenal cortices associated with ambiguous genitalia. The most common cause is an excessive production of androgens, which may be a result of maternal disease (e.g., adrenal tumor) but is more likely to be of fetal origin. Lack of 21-hydroxylase (an enzyme involved in steroid metabolism) is usually the cause of CAH. Most often these cases involve clitoral hypertrophy, partial fusion of the labia majora, and a persistent urogenital sinus. Infants with this syndrome do have functioning ovaries, fallopian tubes, uterus, and cervix. The wolffian duct does not develop. Often there are other metabolic disorders (seen also in males with CAH) that require complex care.[3] (CAH is described in Chapter 19.)

Hypospadias and Epispadias

Hypospadias (in which the urethral orifice is on the ventral surface of the penis) may be an isolated abnormality or associated with a disorder of sex development, especially if the penis is very abnormal. The more severe the degree of hypospadias is, the higher the possibility of testicular dysgenesis and of cryptorchidism. This defect occurs in 3 to 5 out of 1000 live births and is probably caused by inadequate androgen production, resulting in failure of urogenital fold fusion and incomplete spongy urethra formation.[52,64] The incidence of hypospadias has increased in the past 15 to 20 years for unknown reasons, but possibly because of increased environmental estrogens from industrial chemicals and pesticides.[64] There are four types of hypospadias, with 80% being either glandular or penile. The other 20% are penoscrotal or perineal. Variations in this defect are related to the timing and degree of hormonal failure.[9,52] Epispadias is a relatively rare congenital anomaly, occurring once in every 30,000 live births. The dorsal surface urethral opening is often associated with exstrophy of the bladder. Epispadias may be glandular or penile and is probably caused by caudal development of the genital tubercle, resulting in the urogenital sinus being on the dorsal surface once the membrane has ruptured.[9,52]

Uterovaginal Malformation

Fusion defects of the müllerian ducts result in varying degrees of structural duplication. Complete fusion failure leads to the development of two complete genital tracts, in which the vagina is divided in two by a septum, with a separate cervix and uterine body associated with each half (didelphia). If one of the müllerian ducts fails to develop entirely, the result will be a unicornate uterus. Various other anomalies may also result, including a single vagina with double cervices, a single vagina and cervix associated with a uterus subdivided into halves, or a single uterus that is incompletely separated by a septum (bicornate, unicornate, vagina simplex). Any of these anomalies may result in infertility.[52]

CLINICAL IMPLICATIONS
Genetic Screening

Carrier screening of adults is done for selected disorders. Usually a population at increased risk for a specific disorder is targeted. An example of population screening is screening of individuals of Ashkenazi Jewish descent for Tay-Sachs disease. Another example is carrier screening for CF, which is recommended for couples planning pregnancy or seeking prenatal care.[76] Couples may also be screened for other disorders, depending on risk factors.[60] Issues with genetic screening and diagnosis include interpretation or misinterpretation of data and risks, discrimination (employment, education, insurance), psychological and social concerns, and issues of the right to know versus the right not to know if one carries a specific gene mutation, because genetic disorders are family disorders.

A genetic history should be a routine part of prenatal care to identify women with an increased risk of genetic disorders and birth defects. The family history is a valuable tool in evaluating gene-environment interactions, risk identification, and preventive care.[26] Components of genetic history include family and obstetric history (including a history of pregnancy loss or early infant death, mental retardation or learning disabilities, known genetic disorders, or having infants with anomalies in either of the parents or their families), ethnic background (some recessive disorders occur with markedly increased frequency in specific ethnic groups), maternal and paternal age, and potential teratogen exposures.[76] Genetic screening and the use of diagnostic techniques such as amniocentesis and chorionic villus sampling (CVS) allow for prenatal identification of increasing numbers of chromosomal, genetic, and other congenital anomalies. Maternal serum screening is used to screen for selected chromosomal anomalies, neural tube defects, and other disorders.[18] Routine ultrasounds provide an opportunity to observe for major anomalies in the fetus. Ultrasound markers that may allow noninvasive diagnosis have also been identified for infants with Down syndrome and other disorders.[31,70] These techniques and others are described in Chapter 3.

Newborn screening for genetic and other disorders was begun in the 1960s with screening for PKU; additional disorders were added in subsequent years. Newborn screening is the only mandated genetic screening. In the United States each state determines the disorders that will be screened. A uniform screening panel has been developed with 32 primary disorders and 26 secondary conditions.[74] Individual states screen for most or all of the primary disorders and many of the secondary disorders.[57] The March of Dimes recommends that all infants be screened for at least 34 disorders, including selected fatty acid, amino acid, and organic acid disorders; hemoglobin disorders; lysosomal storage disorders; congenital hypothyroidism; adrenal disorders such as congenital adrenal hyperplasia; and other disorders such as galactosemia, CF, hearing loss, severe combined immunodeficiency, biotinidase deficiency, and critical congenital heart disease.[47]

Introduction of techniques such as tandem mass spectrometry (MS/MS) significantly expand the numbers of disorders that can be readily screened. MS/MS can be used to rapidly screen newborns for multiple metabolic disorders in a single analytic run using the dried filter paper blood spot that has been the mainstay of newborn screening since its inception.[6,40,58] MS/MS is effective in identifying infants with various disorders of fatty acid oxidation, amino acid disorders, and organic acidopathies. MS/MS has also raised questions in that disorders can now be identified for which effective therapies have not yet been developed. In addition, more infants are being identified with variations that are not clinically significant.[40,58] In addition, although the number of infants diagnosed with metabolic disorders has increased, it is not clear whether all of these individuals would have eventually become symptomatic.[28] Other concerns about newborn screening include the role of written informed parental consent (not currently required in most states) for testing and storage of blood spots for epidemiologic research.[28,40,58] There are also continuing concerns about the effects of false-positive screens on parental stress and parent-infant interaction. Availability of newer techniques such as DNA microarray technology and other techniques will continue to alter newborn screening.[55,58]

Genetic Disorders and Pregnancy

Genetic disorders can influence the course of pregnancy and have implications for both the mother and the fetus/newborn. In addition, the anatomic and physiologic changes of pregnancy can influence the course of the disorder. Women with severe genetic disorders may have difficulty conceiving. However, with earlier diagnosis after birth and improved therapies, many individuals with genetic disorders are surviving to adulthood and having children. This section focuses on women with two genetic disorders, CF and PKU, as examples.

CF is an autosomal recessive multisystem disorder that is most common in women of European descent (1 out of 3000 to 3300 live births) and Ashkenazi Jewish (1 out of 3970 live births) populations.[76] CF is caused by an abnormal gene on chromosome 7. This gene codes for a protein (CF transmembrane conductance regulator, or CFTR) needed for regulating chloride transport across cell membranes. There are more than 1000 CFTR mutations; 70% of CF patients have one of the eight most common mutations.[32] Differences in mutations leads to variations in phenotype and severity. With decreasing mortality, more women with CF are surviving to childbearing age. Although men with CF are often infertile without assisted reproductive technologies, women with CF are able to conceive, although they may have altered fertility, possibly because of impaired ovulation as a result of the effects of the altered CFTR on the hypothalamus, on uterine secretions and cervical mucus, and in the endometrium and fallopian tubes.[1,50] If the partner of a woman with CF is not a carrier, all of their children will be carriers. If the partner is a carrier, there is a 50% risk with each pregnancy of having a child with CF; all nonaffected offspring will be carriers.

CF involves alterations in the exocrine glands and mucus-secreting glands, especially the pancreas and sweat glands, affecting the respiratory, digestive, and reproductive systems. Prepregnancy pulmonary function is a predictor of pregnancy outcome. The normal changes in the respiratory system during pregnancy (see Chapter 10) may stress already-compromised pulmonary function, resulting in decompensation and increased maternal and fetal mortality and morbidity.[27] Women with mild CF generally do well during pregnancy.[50,79] However, women with moderate to severe CF, especially those with hypoxemia, cor pulmonale, and poor nutritional status, often do not do well.[12,79] Particularly ominous is preexisting pulmonary hypertension. In these women, the usual pregnancy increase in cardiac output cannot be accommodated within the pulmonary vasculature. This leads to further desaturation, myocardial hypoxia, decreased cardiac output, and increased hypoxia.[79] Weight loss or poor weight gain during pregnancy is associated with a poor outcome.[12,79] McArdle reviewed as series of nine studies published since 2000 of pregnancy outcomes in women with CF.[50] Most studies reported an increased prematurity rate with a further increase in preterm births in women with lower pregnancy lung function or diabetes.[12,50] Forced expiratory volume in 1 sec (FEV_1) of less than 50% to 60% was associated with an increased risk of poorer outcomes, including increased risk of pregnancy loss, prematurity, and low birthweight, and, in some studies, with increased maternal mortality and pregnancy complications. Overall there was no evidence that long-term survival was different in women with CF who became pregnant versus those who did not (mean survival in all individuals with CF was 37.4 years in 2008).[17,50]

As mentioned previously, PKU is an amino acid autosomal recessive disorder caused by mutations in a gene on chromosome 12 for the production of the enzyme PAH. Severity depends on the mutations; 600 mutations have been identified.[2,32] The deficiency of PAH results in elevated levels of phenylalanine, which can damage the central nervous system. Outcomes have improved in individuals with PKU because of newborn screening and early initiation of a phenylalanine-restricted diet. "Lifelong dietary restriction and therapy improves quality of life in women with PKU and should be encouraged."[2] Women with PKU have normal fertility. However, their fetuses are at risk if the woman's phenylalanine levels are elevated during pregnancy. Phenylalanine readily crosses the placenta with a 1.5 fetal-to-maternal plasma ratio.[2] The teratogenic effects of high levels of maternal serum phenylalanine include mental retardation, congenital heart defects, intrauterine growth restriction, spontaneous abortion, altered facies, and microcephaly.[2,12,32] Exposure to high levels of phenylalanine in the first 8 weeks of gestation increases the risk of structural defects; high levels from 8 to 12 weeks increases the risk of altered growth of the brain and body; and high levels after 12 weeks increases the risk of altered neurologic development.[12] Dietary control and treatment for 3 months before conception and during pregnancy can reduce sequelae. The American College of Obstetricians and Gynecologists recommends that phenylalanine levels be below 6 mg/dL (363.2 μmol/L) for at least 3 months before conception and below 2 to 6 mg/dL (121.1 to 363.3 μmol/L) during pregnancy.[2] However, many women of childbearing age with PKU may not adhere to the unpalatable phenylalanine-free diet.[2]

Up to 50% of women with PKU have a PAH gene variant in which tetrahydrobiopterin (BH4) or sapropterin supplements may improve PAH activity and thus the ability to tolerate phenylalanine.[75] These supplements are cofactors in the breakdown of phenylalanine and biosynthesis of serotonin and other neurotransmitters and have been a useful adjunct to dietary therapy in nonpregnant individuals with PKU. Study of the use of these supplements for pregnant women is limited to date.[2,22]

SUMMARY

The biologic basis for reproduction includes an understanding of basic genetic mechanisms and principles, including cell division, gametogenesis, chromosomal and genetic alterations, and modes of inheritance. Our knowledge in these areas remains limited but is increasing rapidly. The current revolution in genetic knowledge has markedly altered and challenged our understanding of health and disease and provision of health care, and it will continue to do so. The more nurses and other health care providers understand about these areas and the reproductive processes described in Chapter 2, the more they can work toward ways to improve perinatal outcome. Clinical implications for mothers and neonates can be found in Box 1-4.

BOX 1-4   Recommendations for Clinical Practice Related to Chromosomes and Reproductive Biology

Understand the biologic basis for genetic and chromosomal disorders (pp. 1-6, 11-15).
Understand modes of inheritance (pp. 15-19; see also Boxes 1-2 and 1-3).
Provide counseling and health teaching to parents regarding genetic disorders and modes of inheritance (pp. 15-19).
Perform a genetic and family history as part of routine care (p. 25 and see Chapter 3).
Counsel parents about prenatal screening and assist them in interpreting results (p. 25 and see Chapter 3).
Teach parents with a familial history of chromosomal or genetic abnormalities about the basis for the disorder (pp. 15-19).

Refer parents with a familial history of chromosomal or genetic abnormalities for genetic counseling (p. 25 and see Chapter 3).
Refer neonates born with abnormal genitalia for complete endocrine evaluation, ultrasonography of internal structures, and chromosomal assessment (pp. 24-25).
Teach parents about newborn screening (p. 25).
Understand the effects of genetic disorders on the woman and her fetus during pregnancy (p. 26).
Provide counseling and health teaching to women with genetic disorders before and during pregnancy (p. 26).

References

1. Ahmad, A., Ahmed, A., & Patrizio, P. (2013). Cystic fibrosis and fertility. *Curr Opin Obstet Gynecol, 25,* 167.
2. American College of Obstetricians and Gynecologists Committee on Genetics. (2015). ACOG Committee Opinion No. 636: maternal phenylketonuria. http://www.acog.org/Resources-And-Publications/Committee-Opinions/Committee-on-Genetics/Management-of-Women-With-Phenylketonuria. Accessed 05.05.16.
3. Arbolito, V. A., & Vilain, E. (2013). Disorders of sexual development. In J. F. Strauss & R. Barbieri (Eds.), *Yen and Jaffe's reproductive endocrinology: Physiology, pathophysiology, and clinical management* (7th ed.). Philadelphia: Elsevier Saunders.
4. Barbaro, M., Wedell, A., & Nordenström, A. (2011). Disorders of sex development. *Semin Fetal Neonatal Med, 16,* 119.
5. Bernat, V., & Disney, M. D. (2015). RNA Structures as Mediators of Neurological Diseases and as Drug Targets. *Neuron, 87,* 28.
6. Berry, S. A. (2015). Newborn screening. *Clin Perinatol, 42,* 441.
7. Bettegowda, A., & Wilkinson, M. F. (2010). Transcription and post-transcriptional regulation of spermatogenesis. *Philos Trans R Soc Lond B Biol Sci, 365,* 1637.
8. Biliya, S., & Bulla, L. A., Jr. (2010). Genomic imprinting: The influence of differential methylation in the two sexes. *Exp Biol Med (Maywood), 235,* 139.
9. Carlson, B. M. (2013). *Human embryology and developmental biology* (5th ed.). Philadelphia: Elsevier Saunders.
10. Carrell, D. T., & Hammoud, S. S. (2010). The human sperm epigenome and its potential role in embryonic development. *Mol Hum Reprod, 16,* 37.
11. Chen, E., & Joseph, S. (2015). Fragile X mental retardation protein: A paradigm for translational control by RNA-binding proteins. *Biochimie, 114,* 147.
12. Chetty, S. P., Shaffer, B. L., & Norton, M. E. (2011). Management of pregnancy in women with genetic disorders: Part 2: Inborn errors of metabolism, cystic fibrosis, neurofibromatosis type 1, and Turner syndrome in pregnancy. *Obstet Gynecol Surv, 66,* 765.
13. Collins, P. (2008). Cellular mechanisms in development. In C. R. Rodeck & M. J. Whittle (Eds.), *Fetal medicine: Basic science and clinical practice* (2nd ed.). London: Churchill Livingstone.
14. Coticchio, G., et al. (2015). Oocyte maturation: gamete-somatic cells interactions, meiotic resumption, cytoskeletal dynamics and cytoplasmic reorganization. *Hum Reprod Update, 21,* 427.
15. Cowie, P., Hay, E. A., & MacKenzie, A. (2015). The noncoding human genome and the future of personalized medicine. *Expert Rev Mol Med, 17,* e4.
16. Cummings, A. M., & Kavlock, R. J. (2004). Gene-environment interactions: A review of effects on reproduction and development. *Crit Rev Toxicol, 34,* 461.
17. Cystic Fibrosis Foundation. (2009). Patient registry: Annual data report 2009. http://www.cff.org. Accessed 22.04.11.
18. Dugoff, L.; Society for Maternal-Fetal Medicine. (2010). First- and second-trimester maternal serum markers for aneuploidy and adverse obstetric outcomes. *Obstet Gynecol, 115,* 1052.
19. Dunham, A., et al. & ENCODE Project Consortium. (2012). An integrated encyclopedia of DNA elements in the human genome. *Nature, 489,* 57.
20. El-Hattab, A. W. (2015). Inborn errors of metabolism. *Clin Perinatol, 42,* 413.
21. Gosden, R., & Lee, B. (2010). Portrait of an oocyte: our obscure origin. *J Clin Invest, 120,* 973.
22. Grange, D. K., et al. (2014). Sapropterin dihydrochloride use in pregnant women with phenylketonuria: an interim report of the PKU MOMS sub-registry. Phenylketonuria Demographics Outcomes and Safety (PKUDOS) registry; Maternal Phenylketonuria Observational Program (PKU MOMS) sub-registry. *Mol Genet Metab, 112,* 9.
23. Griswold, M. D. (2016). Spermatogenesis: the commitment to meiosis. *Physiol Rev, 96,* 1.
24. Groden, J., et al. (2014). Human basic genetics and patterns of inheritance. In R. K. Creasy, et al. (Eds.), *Creasy & Resnik's Maternal-fetal medicine: Principles and practice* (7th ed.). Philadelphia: Elsevier Saunders.
25. Guttmacher, A. E., & Collins, F. S. (2002). Genomic medicine: A primer. *N Engl J Med, 347,* 1512.
26. Guttmacher, A. E., Collins, F. S., & Carmona, R. H. (2004). The family history—more important than ever. *N Engl J Med, 351,* 2333.
27. Hassold, T., & Hunt, P. (2001). To err (meiotically) is human: The genesis of human aneuploidy. *Nat Rev Genet, 2,* 280.
28. Hiraki, S., & Green, N.S. (2010). Newborn screening for treatable genetic conditions: Past, present and future. *Obstet Gynecol Clin North Am, 37,* 11.
29. Hughes, I. A., & Acerini, C. L. (2008). Factors controlling testis descent. *Eur J Endocrinol, 159,* S75.
30. Hughes, I. A. (2010). The quiet revolution: Disorders of sex development. *Best Pract Res Clin Endocrinol Metab, 24,* 159.
31. Hyett, J., Mogra, R., & Sonek, J. (2014). First trimester ultrasound assessment for fetal aneuploidy. *Clin Obstet Gynecol, 57,* 142.
32. Jorde, L. B., et al. (2016). *Medical genetics* (5th ed.). Philadelphia: Elsevier.
33. Kacem, S., & Feil, R. (2009). Chromatin mechanisms in genomic imprinting. *Mamm Genome, 20,* 544.
34. Kalousek, D. K., & Vekemons, M. (2000). Confirmed placental mosaicism and genomic imprinting. *Baillieres Best Pract Res Clin Obstet Gynecol, 14,* 723.
35. Kelada, S. N., et al. (2003). The role of genetic polymorphisms in environmental health. *Environ Health Perspect, 111,* 1055.
36. Khoury, M. J. (2003). Genetics and genomics in practice: The continuum from genetic disease to genetic information in health and disease. *Genet Med, 5,* 261.
37. Kidder, G. M., & Vanderhyden, B. C. (2010). Bidirectional communication between oocytes and follicle cells: Ensuring oocyte developmental competence. *Can J Physiol Pharmacol, 88,* 399.
38. Kota, S. K., & Feil, R. (2010). Epigenetic transitions in germ cell development and meiosis. *Dev Cell, 19,* 675.
39. Kousta, E., Papathanasiou, A., & Skordis, N. (2010). Sex determination and disorders of sex development according to the revised

nomenclature and classification in 46, XX individuals. *Hormones (Athens)*, 9, 218.

40. la Marca, G. (2014). Mass spectrometry in clinical chemistry: the case of newborn screening. *J Pharm Biomed Anal*, 101, 174.
41. Lashley, F. R. (2005). *Essentials of clinical genetics in nursing practice*. New York: Springer.
42. Lee, M. K., et al. (2017). Regulation of embryogenesis. In R. A. Polin, et al. (Eds.), *Fetal and neonatal physiology* (5th ed.). Philadelphia: Elsevier Saunders.
43. Levine, F. (2017). Basic genetic principles. In R. A. Polin, et al. (Eds.), *Fetal and neonatal physiology* (5th ed.). Philadelphia: Elsevier Saunders.
44. Lord, T., & Aitken, R. J. (2013). Oxidative stress and ageing of the post-ovulatory oocyte. *Reproduction*, 146, R217.
45. Lynn, A., Ashley, T., & Hassold, T. (2004). Variation in human meiotic recombination. *Annu Rev Genomics Hum Genet*, 5, 317.
46. Lyon, M. K. (1999). X-chromosome inactivation. *Curr Biol*, 9, R235.
47. March of Dimes. (2016). Newborn screening tests for your baby. http://www.marchofdimes.org/baby/newborn-screening-tests-for-your-baby.aspx. Accessed 30.04.16.
48. Marteil, G., Richard-Parpaillon, L., & Kubiak, J. Z. (2009). Role of oocyte quality in meiotic maturation and embryonic development. *Reprod Biol*, 9, 203.
49. Massé, J., et al. (2009). The developing female genital tract: From genetics to epigenetics. *Int J Dev Biol*, 53, 411.
50. McArdle, J. R. (2011). Pregnancy in cystic fibrosis. *Clin Chest Med*, 32, 111.
51. Montirosso, R., & Provenzi, L. (2015). Implications of epigenetics and stress regulation on research and developmental care of preterm infants. *J Obstet Gynecol Neonatal Nurs*, 44, 174.
52. Moore, K. L., Persaud, T. V. N., & Torchia, M. G. (2015). *The developing human: Clinically oriented embryology* (10th ed.). Philadelphia: Elsevier Saunders.
53. Moraes, F., & Góes, A. (2016). A decade of human genomic project conclusion: Scientific diffusion about our genome knowledge. *Biochem Mol Biol Educ*, 44, 215.
54. Mouillet, J. F., et al. (2015). MicroRNAs in placental health and disease. *Am J Obstet Gynecol*, 213, S163.
55. Murray, J. C. (2012). Impact of the Human Genome Project on neonatal care.

In C. A. Gleason & S. Devaskar (Eds.), *Avery's diseases of the newborn* (9th ed.). Philadelphia: Saunders.

56. National Human Genome Research Institute. (n.d.). Human Genome Project. https://www.genome.gov. Accessed 05.05.16.
57. National Newborn Screening and Global Resource Center. (n.d.). http://genes-r-us.uthscsa.edu/. Accessed 05.05.16.
58. Ombrone, D., et al. (2016). Expanded newborn screening by mass spectrometry: New tests, future perspectives. *Mass spectrometry review*, 35, 71.
59. Pointis, G., et al. (2010). Physiological and physiopathological aspects of connexins and communicating gap junctions in spermatogenesis. *Philos Trans R Soc Lond B Biol Sci*, 365, 1607.
60. Ram, K. T., & Klugman, S. D. (2010). Best practices: Antenatal screening for common genetic conditions other than aneuploidy. *Curr Opin Obstet Gynecol*, 22, 139.
61. Remeithi, S. A. L., & Wherrett, D. K. (2015). Disorders of sex development. In R. J. Martin, A. A. Fanaroff, & M. C. Walsh (Eds.), *Fanaroff and Martin's neonatal-perinatal medicine: Diseases of the fetus and infant* (10th ed.). Philadelphia: Elsevier Saunders.
62. Ross, M. T. (2005). The DNA sequence of the human X chromosome. *Nature*, 434, 325.
63. Ruwanpura, S. M., McLachlan, R. I., & Meachem, S. J. (2010). Hormonal regulation of male germ cell development. *J Endocrinol*, 205, 117.
64. Sadler, T. W. (2015). *Langman's medical embryology* (13th ed.). Philadelphia: Wolters Kluwer.
65. Schaefer, S., & Nadeau, J. H. (2015). The genetics of epigenetic inheritance: modes, molecules, and mechanisms. *Q Rev Biol*, 90, 381.
66. Schierding, W., et al. (2017). Epigenetics. In R. A. Polin, et al. (Eds.), *Fetal and neonatal physiology* (5th ed.). Philadelphia: Elsevier Saunders.
67. Schoenwolf, G. C., et al. (2015). *Larsen's human embryology* (5th ed.) Philadelphia: Elsevier Saunders.
68. Sharma, A. (2015). Transgenerational epigenetic inheritance: resolving uncertainty and evolving biology. *Biomol Concepts*, 6, 87.
69. Shastry, B. S. (2009). SNPs: Impact on gene function and phenotype. *Methods Mol Biol*, 578, 3.
70. Sonek, J., & Croom, C. (2014). Second trimester ultrasound markers of fetal aneuploidy. *Clin Obstet Gynecol*, 57, 159.

71. Spiller, C. M., & Bowles, J. (2015). Sex determination in mammalian germ cells. *Asian J Androl*, 17, 427.
72. Stukenborg, J. B., Colón, E., & Söder, O. (2010). Ontogenesis of testis development and function in humans. *Sex Dev*, 4, 199.
73. Takahashi, T., et al. (2013). Molecular mechanism of poor embryo development in postovulatory aged oocytes: mini review. *J Obstet Gynaecol Res*, 39, 1431.
74. US Department of Health and Human Services. (2015). Advisory Committee on Heritable Disorders in Newborns and Children. Recommended uniform screening panel: core conditions. http://www.hrsa.gov/advisorycommittees/mchbadvisory/heritabledisorders/recommendedpanel/. Accessed 03.05.16.
75. Vockley, J., et al. & American College of Medical Genetics and Genomics Therapeutics Committee. (2014). Phenylalanine hydroxylase deficiency: diagnosis and management guideline. *Genet Med*, 16, 188.
76. Wapner, R. J. (2014). Prenatal diagnosis of congenital disorders. In R. K. Creasy, et al. (Eds.), *Creasy & Resnik's Maternal-fetal medicine: Principles and practice* (7th ed.). Philadelphia: Elsevier Saunders.
77. Ward, W. S. (2010). Function of sperm chromatin structural elements in fertilization and development. *Mol Hum Reprod*, 16, 30.
78. Weaver, J. R., Susiarjo, M., & Bartolomei, M. S. (2009). Imprinting and epigenetic changes in the early embryo. *Mamm Genome*, 20, 532.
79. Whitty, J. E., & Dombrowski, M. P. (2014). Respiratory diseases in pregnancy. In R. K. Creasy, et al. (Eds.), *Creasy & Resnik's Maternal-fetal medicine: Principles and practice* (7th ed.). Philadelphia: Elsevier Saunders.
80. Widmaier, E., et al. (2016). *Vander's Human physiology: The mechanism of body function* (14th ed.). New York: McGraw-Hill Education.
81. Wolgemuth, D. J., & Roberts, S. S. (2010). Regulating mitosis and meiosis in the male germ line: Critical functions for cyclins. *Philos Trans R Soc Lond B Biol Sci*, 365, 1653.
82. Zhu, H., Kartiko, S., & Finnell, R. H. (2009). Importance of gene-environment interactions in the etiology of selected birth defects. *Clin Genet*, 75, 409.

Physiologic Basis for Reproduction

Robin Webb Corbett

The body has eight endocrine glands that secrete hormones that control growth, glucose metabolism, metabolic functions, potassium, calcium and sodium metabolism, and reproduction. These hormones travel via the circulatory system to bind with receptors and initiate cell reactions to regulate myriad body functions. However, the hormones work synergistically with the nervous system for regulation and maintenance of homeostasis in the body.

Hormones regulate differentiation of the reproductive and central nervous systems in the developing fetus; stimulation of sequential growth and development during childhood and adolescence; and coordination of male and female reproductive systems.

Hormones facilitate sexual reproduction, maintenance of an optimal internal environment, and initiation of corrective and adaptive responses with emergencies. These important physiologic processes are regulated by two major systems: the nervous system and the hormonal system. Hormonal regulation of reproductive processes is via the hypothalamic-pituitary-ovarian (HPO) system in the female and the hypothalamic-pituitary-testes system in the male (Figure 2-1).

This chapter reviews and discusses the hormonal regulation of reproductive processes for both the male and female. It addresses reproductive hormones, oogenesis, spermagenesis, puberty, the ovarian and menstrual cycle, and changes in the aging female and male specific to reproduction.

HYPOTHALAMIC-PITUITARY-OVARIAN/ TESTICULAR AXIS

During reproductive life, reproductive function is regulated by cyclic reproductive neuroendocrinology, which is dependent on the complex interplay of a feedback system involving the ovary or testes, hypothalamus, and anterior pituitary. Expression of hypothalamic-pituitary hormones stimulates ovarian steroid secretion and folliculogenesis (Figure 2-2); the testes produce testosterone, which stimulates spermatogenesis. The gonadotropins (follicle-stimulating hormone [FSH] and luteinizing hormone [LH]) and gonadal steroids (estrogen, progesterone, and testosterone) evoke follicular maturation, ovulation, and pregnancy in the female and

spermatogenesis and steroidogenesis in the male. Thus a woman's and man's reproductive status is entrained to their cyclic neuroendocrine environment.

Hormones

A hormone is a chemical substance secreted into body fluids by a cell or a group of cells that exerts a physiologic effect on other cells of the body, its target cells. Hormones are released into the bloodstream by endocrine glands. The blood carries the hormones to specific cells or organs, hormonal target sites.

Hormone Activators, Receptors, and Messenger Systems

Hormones are chemical messengers that have specific rates and patterns of secretion (e.g., diurnal patterns). These patterns—which are pulsatile and have circadian or ultradian rhythmicity—depend on the levels of circulating substrates, calcium, sodium, or the hormones.[48] Various factors affect the circulating level of hormones. Receptor affinity and concentration are regulated by the intracellular and extracellular environment, such as body temperature, calcium and sodium concentrations, and serum pH. Other physiochemical factors affecting hormone release include urea concentration and the lipid matrix of the plasma membrane. Circulating hormone levels are also regulated by growth and development, diet, drugs, sleep-wake cycle, seasonal environmental cues (photoperiod [dark-light cycle]), and exercise.[37,51] Most hormone secretion is episodic (ultradian rhythm) and circadian.[51]

Hormones are constantly excreted by kidneys or deactivated by the liver. Hormones are classified by structure, target gland or origin, effects, or chemical classes. Structural categories of hormones include proteins (prolactin), glycoproteins (FSH and LH), polypeptides (oxytocin), steroids (estrogens, progestins, and testosterone), and fatty acids (prostaglandins and thromboxanes).[2,73] For each hormone, there is a specific cellular receptor, located on the cell surface or within the cell. The majority of hormonal receptors are very large proteins. Hormones bind with appropriate cell receptors, forming a hormone receptor complex, and act on the cell to initiate specific cell functions or activities.

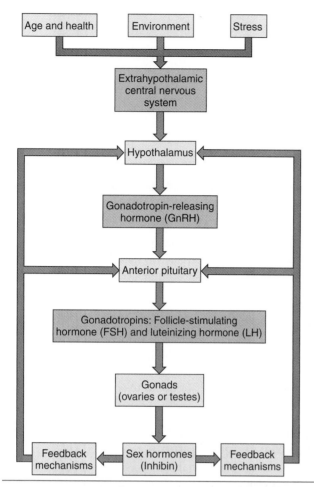

FIGURE 2-1   Hormonal stimulation of the gonads: the hypothalamic-pituitary-gonadal axis. (Adapted from McCance, K.L. & Huether, S.E. [2006]. *Pathophysiology: The biologic basis for disease in adults and children* [5th ed.]. St. Louis: Mosby.)

Receptor locations vary with the type of hormones. For example, protein or peptide hormone receptors are located in or on the cell membrane, whereas steroid hormones such as estrogen diffuse freely across the plasma membrane and have their receptors in the cell cytoplasm. Thyroid hormone receptors are located in the nucleus. Hormone binding with the target cell receptor causes the number of receptors to decrease, a process known as *down-regulation* (Figure 2-3). In contrast, with up-regulation, low concentrations of hormones increase the number of receptors per cell. As the receptors decrease with down-regulation, responsiveness of the target tissue decreases. In the unbound state, receptors are inert.

Receptor activation on the target cell may be initiated by a variety of mechanisms such as a first messenger system, a second messenger system, and genetic sequencing. In the first messenger system, the hormone recognizes and binds with its specific receptor. Formation of the hormone receptor complex activates enzymes within the cell with subsequent phosphorylation. The second messenger system may act synergistically or antagonistically

to regulate cell activities. Second messengers include cyclic adenosine monophosphate (cAMP), inositol triphosphate, calcium ions, phospholipids, and the calcium-calmodulin complex.

Cellular responses are initiated by transmission of an intracellular signal via a second messenger (Table 2-1) that signals the effect of the hormone on the target cell as membrane transport. Hormone receptor binding increases the intracellular level of second messengers. For example, the cAMP second messenger system (Box 2-1) binds with a G protein and converts adenosine triphosphate into cAMP, which then activates a protein kinase A (PKA) pathway, leading to phosphorylation and enzyme activation (Figure 2-4). FSH, LH, and human chorionic gonadotropin (hCG) are hormones that respond to the cAMP second messenger system.[2,84] FSH and LH act on the ovary via the cAMP intracellular signaling pathway.[84] Cyclic adenosine monophosphate is a common intracellular messenger during both follicular and luteal phases.[84] Gonadotropin-releasing hormone (GnRH) is activated via the phospholipase C second messenger system (Box 2-2).

Hormones bind with the receptor at the cell membrane, catabolizing phosphatidyl-inositol biphosphate into inositol triphosphate and the second messenger diacylglycerol. Similar to cAMP, diacylglycerol activates a protein kinase, phosphorylates, and initiates the cellular response (Figure 2-5). Diacylglycerol activity may result in the synthesis of prostaglandins or combine with calcium, activating cellular metabolic action. Calcium is accessed from the intracellular endoplasmic reticulum and mitochondria by inositol triphosphate, which activates cell functions. Calcium is also mobilized in the calcium-calmodulin second messenger system by binding intracellularly with calmodulin. This binding mediates the use of calcium in the activation, inhibition, or phosphorylation of protein kinases, with subsequent cellular response.[48] After binding with specific receptors, steroid hormones synthesize proteins, which in the nucleus bind with chromosomal deoxyribonucleic acid (DNA) to facilitate the formation of messenger ribonucleic acid (mRNA) and subsequent proteins via genetic instructions.[30]

Hormone Storage

There is no single way in which endocrine glands store and secrete hormones. The amount of hormone stored in the glandular cells is minuscule, but large amounts of precursor molecules, such as cholesterol and its intermediaries, are present within the cell. With specific stimulation, enzymes initiate conversion of these precursors to the final hormone followed by hormone expression. For example, the protein hormone prolactin is initially formed by the endoplasmic reticulum. Known as a preprohormone, this protein is larger than the active hormone and is cleaved (split) while still in the endoplasmic reticulum, yielding a smaller protein molecule—prohormone. The prohormone is transported in vesicles to the Golgi apparatus, where the protein is further processed to form the final active protein hormone. The Golgi apparatus compacts the hormone

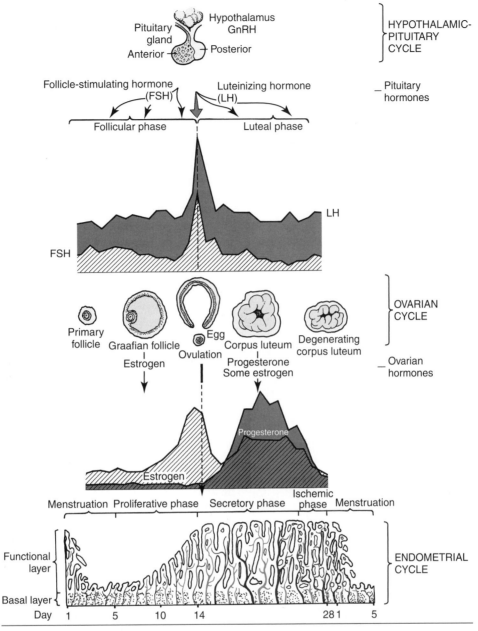

FIGURE 2-2 Menstrual cycle: hypothalamic-pituitary, ovarian, and endometrial. *GnRH,* Gonadotropin-releasing hormone. (From Lowdermilk, D.L. & Perry, S.E. [2007]. *Maternity & women's health care* [9th ed.]. St. Louis: Mosby.)

molecules into small membrane-encapsulated vesicles known as *secretory vesicles.* There the final hormone is stored in the cytoplasmic compartment of the endocrine cell, awaiting its specific signal (nerve, hormonal, or chemical) for hormone secretion.

Hypothalamic and Pituitary Glands

The pituitary gland, also known as the hypophysis, is composed of two segments: the anterior and posterior lobes (Figure 2-6). The hypophysis is pea-sized and approximately 15 mm long, sitting in a protected saddle-shaped sphenoid bone cavity (the sella turcica) at the base of the brain, directly behind the nasal base. The pituitary gland is slightly heavier in women and increases in size during pregnancy. The pars tuberalis, pars distalis, and intermediate lobe comprise the anterior lobe, the adenohypophysis.[57] The neurohypophysis (i.e., posterior lobe) is composed of the median eminence, infundibular stem, and neural lobe.[48,57] Most hormones are secreted by the anterior pituitary, including growth hormone, adrenocorticotropin, thyroid-stimulating hormone, FSH, LH, and prolactin. Specific to reproductive physiology, anterior pituitary gland cells known as *gonadotrophs* secrete FSH and LH.[36] About 60% of gonadotrophs (10% to 15% of pituitary cells) are multihormonal, secreting both FSH and LH.[47]

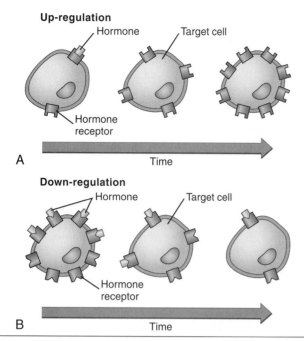

FIGURE 2-3   Regulation of target cell sensitivity. If synthesis of new receptors occurs faster than degradation of old receptors, then the target cell will have more receptors and thus be more sensitive to the hormone. This phenomenon **(A)** is called *up-regulation,* because the number of receptors goes up. If the rate of receptor degradation exceeds the rate of receptor synthesis, then the target cell's number of receptors will decrease **(B).** Because the number of receptors and thus the sensitivity of the target cells goes down, this phenomenon is called *down-regulation. Shading* represents hormone concentration. (From Thibodeau, G.A. & Patton, K.T. [2007]. *Anatomy and physiology* [6th ed.]. St. Louis: Mosby.)

TABLE 2-1   Second Messengers Identified for Specific Hormones

SECOND MESSENGER	ASSOCIATED HORMONES
Cyclic AMP	Adrenocorticotropic hormone (ACTH)
	Luteinizing hormone (LH)
	Human chorionic gonadotropin (hCG)
	Follicle-stimulating hormone (FSH)
	Thyroid-stimulating hormone (TSH)
	Antidiuretic hormone (ADH)
	Thyrotropin-releasing hormone (TRH)
	Parathyroid hormone (PTH)
	Glucagon
Cyclic GMP	Atrial natriuretic hormone
Calcium	Angiotensin II
	Gonadotropin-releasing hormone (GnRH)
	Antidiuretic hormone (ADH)
IP$_3$ and DAG	Angiotensin II
	Luteinizing hormone–releasing hormone (LHRH)

AMP, Adenosine monophosphate; *DAG,* diacylglycerol; *GMP,* guanosine monophosphate; *IP$_3$,* inositol triphosphate.
From McCance, K.L. & Huether, S.E. (2006). *Pathophysiology: The biologic basis for disease in adults and children* (5th ed.). St. Louis: Mosby.

BOX 2-1   Hormones That Use the Adenyl Cyclase–cAMP Second Messenger System

Adrenocorticotropic hormone (ACTH)
Angiotensin II (epithelial cells)
Calcitonin
Catecholamines (β-receptors)
Corticotropin-releasing hormones (CRH)
Follicle-stimulating hormone (FSH)

Glucagon
Human chorionic gonadotropin (hCG)
Luteinizing hormone (LH)
Parathyroid hormone (PTH)
Secretin
Thyroid-stimulating hormone (TSH)
Vasopressin (V$_2$ receptor, epithelial cells)

From Guyton, A.C. & Hall, J.E. (2016). *Textbook of medical physiology* (13th ed.). Philadelphia: Saunders.

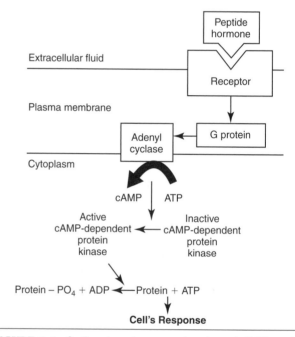

FIGURE 2-4   Cyclic adenosine monophosphate *(cAMP)* mechanism, by which many hormones exert their control of cell function. ADP, Adenosine diphosphate; ATP, adenosine triphosphate. (From Guyton, A.C. & Hall, J.E. [2006]. *Textbook of medical physiology* [11th ed.]. Philadelphia: Saunders.)

BOX 2-2   Hormones That Use the Phospholipase C Second Messenger System

Angiotensin II (vascular smooth muscle)
Catecholamines (α-receptors)
Gonadotropin-releasing hormone (GnRH)
Growth hormone–releasing factor (GHRF)

Oxytocin
Thyroid-releasing hormone (TRH)
Vasopressin (V$_1$ receptor, vascular smooth muscle)

From Guyton, A.C. & Hall, J.E. (2016). *Textbook of medical physiology* (13th ed.). Philadelphia: Elsevier.

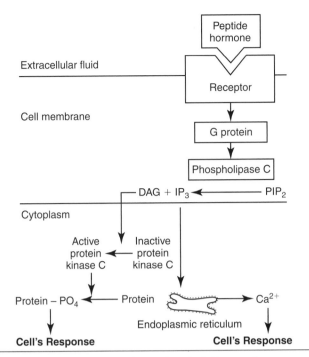

FIGURE 2-5 The cell membrane phospholipid second messenger system, by which some hormones exert their control of cell function. *DAG,* Diacylglycerol; *IP3,* inositol triphosphate; *PIP2,* phosphatidyl-inositol biphosphate. (From Guyton, A.C. & Hall, J.E. [2016]. *Textbook of medical physiology* [17th ed.]. Philadelphia: Saunders.)

Only two hormones are secreted by the posterior pituitary: antidiuretic hormone (arginine vasopressin) and oxytocin.

To regulate physiologic processes, communication must occur between the pituitary gland, the hypothalamus, and the target glands and cells. The pituitary gland connects to the hypothalamus directly above the pituitary stalk. The anterior pituitary gland is linked to the hypothalamus via blood vessels known as the *hypothalamic-hypophyseal portal system* (Figure 2-6). The pituitary receives blood from the paired superior hypophyseal arteries, which arise from the internal hypophyseal artery, a branch of the internal carotid arteries, and merge at the upper pituitary stalk.[48,51] The inferior hypophyseal and trabecular arteries supply the neural lobe. The anterior pituitary sinusoids receive blood from the hypophyseal portal vessels, long and short portal veins that arise in the median hypothalamic eminence.[51]

Hypothalamic hormones, which are either releasing hormones (RHs) or inhibiting hormones (IHs), control expression of the anterior pituitary hormones. RHs and IHs are discharged into the blood vessels of the hypothalamic-hypophyseal portal system. The vascular system permits transport of GnRHs from the hypothalamus down the pituitary stalk to the anterior pituitary lobe, where they trigger the release of anterior pituitary gonadotropins (FSH and LH). Blood vessels end in capillaries at both ends, allowing movement of RHs that moderate pituitary secretion from the hypothalamus (see Figure 2-6). When hypothalamic neurons (neurosecretory neurons) are stimulated, these neurosecretory cells respond by releasing RHs into the portal circulation and then to the anterior pituitary.[82] Hypothalamic RHs travel via nerve fibers to the infundibulum of the neurohypophysis and enter the peripheral circulation by the hypothalamic-hypophysial portal vessels.[26] Long and short portal vessels travel parallel to the pituitary stalk and terminate in the anterior pituitary capillaries.[26]

The posterior pituitary lobe receives nerve fibers from the supraoptic and paraventricular nuclei of the anterior hypothalamus through the pituitary stalk, known as the *neurohypophysis.* The posterior pituitary, an extension of the hypothalamus, is composed of glial-like cells (i.e., pituicytes), the supporting structure for terminal nerve fibers and terminal nerve endings. Axon terminals comprise the major part of the neural lobe. Axon terminals are derived from the magnocellular secretory neurons (one type of hypothalamic neurosecretory cell) of the paraventricular and supraoptic nuclei of the hypothalamus (see Figure 2-6). A cell body located in the supraoptic or paraventricular hypothalamic nucleus projects its neuronal process into the neural lobe and the neurohormone (posterior pituitary hormones) is released from the nerve endings. The axon terminals traverse the internal zone median eminence and in association with the capillary plexus secrete posterior pituitary hormones into the hypophyseal veins and subsequently the general circulation.[48] Posterior pituitary hormones travel from the hypothalamus to the neurohypophysis via neurosecretory neurons.[51] Neurohypophyseal hormones travel to the neurohypophyseal tract through the pituitary stalk for storage in the posterior pituitary capillary nerve endings via neurophysins (protein binders).[30] Nerve endings, which are shaped like bulbous knobs, lie on the surfaces of the capillaries, onto which are secreted vasopressin and oxytocin.

REPRODUCTIVE HORMONES IN FEMALES AND MALES

The HPO/hypothalamic-pituitary-testicular axis is regulated by hormones synthesized and expressed by the hypothalamus, pituitary, ovaries, testicles, and adrenals (Figure 2-7). Some of these hormones and their physiology are well known. These hormones include LH, FSH, activin, inhibin, follistatin, estrogens, progesterone, dehydroepiandrosterone sulfate (DHEAS), dehydroepiandrosterone (DHEA), 5xdihydrotestosterone (DHT), androsterone, and testosterone (Table 2-2). Other hormones are less well known. These include oocyte maturation inhibitor, luteinization inhibitor, and gonadotropin surge–inhibiting factor. Hormonal innervation is independent but also interdependent with other hormones, specifically dose response and receptor proliferation and sensitivity.

Hormones synthesized by the hypothalamus include GnRHs, which mediate anterior pituitary hormone secretion. Kisspeptins, neuropeptides, are synthesized by the neuronal pathway in the hypothalamic arcuate and the anteroventral

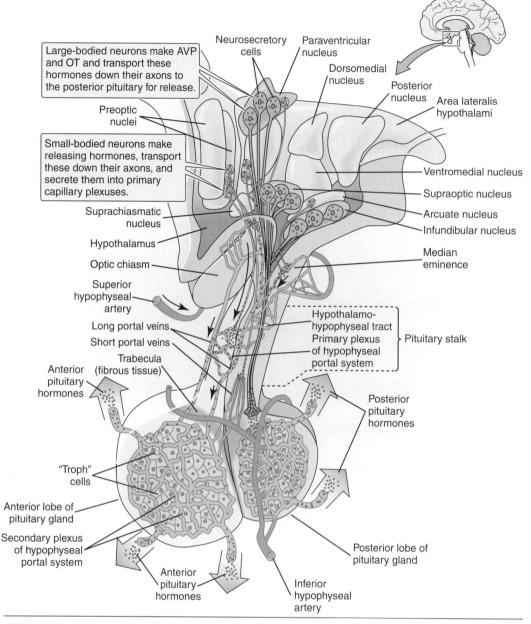

Large-bodied neurons make AVP and OT and transport these hormones down their axons to the posterior pituitary for release.

Small-bodied neurons make releasing hormones, transport these down their axons, and secrete them into primary capillary plexuses.

Neurosecretory cells

Paraventricular nucleus

Dorsomedial nucleus

Posterior nucleus

Area lateralis hypothalami

Preoptic nuclei

Ventromedial nucleus

Supraoptic nucleus

Arcuate nucleus

Infundibular nucleus

Suprachiasmatic nucleus

Hypothalamus

Optic chiasm

Median eminence

Superior hypophyseal artery

Long portal veins

Short portal veins

Trabecula (fibrous tissue)

Hypothalamo-hypophyseal tract

Primary plexus of hypophyseal portal system

Pituitary stalk

Anterior pituitary hormones

Posterior pituitary hormones

"Troph" cells

Anterior lobe of pituitary gland

Secondary plexus of hypophyseal portal system

Anterior pituitary hormones

Inferior hypophyseal artery

Posterior lobe of pituitary gland

FIGURE 2-6   The hypothalamic-pituitary portal system. *AVP,* arginine vasopressin; *OT,* oxytocin. (From Boron, W.F. & Boulpaep, E.L. [2005]. *Medical physiology.* Philadelphia: Saunders.)

periventricular regions (Figure 2-8). Signaling via a G-protein coupled receptor (KISS1R), kisspeptins stimulate the release of GnRH. A positive feedback mechanism exists between estradiol and the anteroventral periventricular neurons in the hypothalamus and is necessary for the preovulatory LH surge. Conversely, estradiol negatively affects kisspeptin release in the arcuate neurons, which regulates gonadotropin tonic release.[14] In addition, kisspeptin neurons in the arcuate express two neurotransmitters, neurokinin B and dynorphin, known as *KNDy neurons.* Neurokinin B activates KNDy neurons, stimulating GnRH release, and dynorphins inhibit GnRH expression after neurokinin B stimulation.[10,58] In response to stimulation by GnRH, the anterior pituitary expresses the

hormones known collectively as *gonadotropins* (i.e., FSH, LH) that enhance follicular proliferation and maturation and subsequent ovulation in females. The ovaries and adrenal cortices synthesize DHEA, the precursor hormone for the steroidal hormones estrogen, progesterone, and testosterone. Steroidal hormones (i.e., estrogen, progesterone) and gonadotropins enhance follicular proliferation and maturation of the dominant follicle in preparation for the midcycle LH surge and ovulation.

In males, the gonadotropins regulate steroidogenesis and gametogenesis in the testes. The FSH/LH ratio is lower in males than in females. Leydig cells, in response to LH, synthesize and secrete testosterone. FSH acts on the seminiferous

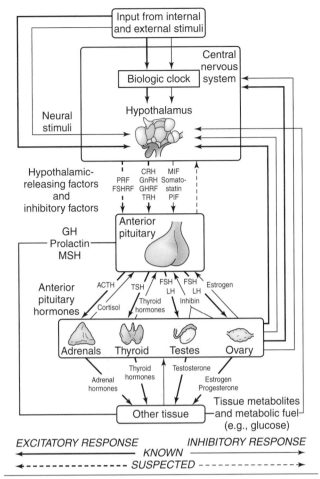

EXCITATORY RESPONSE ◀──────── KNOWN ────────▶ INHIBITORY RESPONSE

◀- - - - - - - - - - - - - SUSPECTED - - - - - - - - - - - - - -▶

FIGURE 2-7 The relationships and feedback mechanisms of the hypothalamus and pituitary glands. Hypothalamic releasing and inhibitory factors include corticotropin-releasing hormone *(CRH)*, gonadotropin-releasing hormone *(GnRH)*, growth hormone–releasing factor *(GHRF)*, thyrotropin-releasing hormone *(TRH)*, dopamine, somatostatin, prolactin-inhibiting factor *(PIF)*, and prolactin-releasing factor *(PRF)*. Anterior pituitary hormones include growth hormone *(GH)*, prolactin, adreno-corticotropic hormone *(ACTH)*; thyrotropin, or thyroid-stimulating hormone *(TSH)*; follicle-stimulating hormone *(FSH)*; and luteinizing hormone *(LH)*. Posterior pituitary hormones include arginine vasopressin and oxytocin. FSHRF, Follicle-stimulating hormone–releasing factor; MIF, melanocyte-stimulating hormone–inhibiting factor; MSH, melanocyte-stimulating hormone. (From Frohman, L.A. [1980]. In D.T. Krieger and J.C. Hughes [Eds.]. *Neuroendocrinology. A hospital practice book.* Sunderland, MA: Sinauer Associates. Illustration by Nancy Lou Gahan and Albert Miller. Copyright by The McGraw-Hill Companies, Inc.)

tubules, where stimulation by FSH enhances germ cell maturation. Receptors for testosterone and FSH are located on the Sertoli cell's germinal epithelium. Sertoli cells are responsible for sperm production, with daily production of approximately 1.54 sperm per Sertoli cell.[55]

Luteinizing Hormone

LH is a glycoprotein that is secreted by the anterior pituitary. LH is the primary hormone involved in ovulation. This hormone promotes theca interstitial cell androgen biosynthesis

with the eventual conversion to estradiol in the presence of FSH.[2,27] Small but sustained increments of LH enhance the development and growth of small antral follicles to the preovulatory stage. Receptors for LH are located in the ovarian thecal and luteal cells and testicular Leydig cells.[2]

Under the influence of FSH and LH, granulosa cells acquire LH receptors in the mid- to late follicular phase. These gonadotropins synergistically promote follicular development, increase granulosa cells, and produce inhibin.[43] In the preovulatory phase, LH levels rise dramatically, a process known as the *LH surge*. Within 10 to 12 hours of the LH peak levels (or 28 to 32 hours of the onset of the LH surge), ovulation occurs.

Nicotine (tobacco use) inhibits pulsatile LH secretion in males but not in females.[21] LH stimulates the synthesis and secretion of testosterone by the Leydig cells in the testis.[55]

Follicle-Stimulating Hormone

FSH is a glycoprotein gonadotropin secreted by the anterior pituitary. FSH promotes follicular growth and differentiation, initiates expression of FSH and LH receptors, inhibin and activin activities, and estrogen synthesis. Receptors for FSH are located on the ovarian granulosa and testicular Sertoli cells.[2] FSH is instrumental in estrogen formation, pubertal development, and follicular maturation.[7] FSH is instrumental in the induction of aromatase in granulosa cells for estrogen production.[81] Although not mandatory for early follicular development, FSH is necessary for follicular development beyond the small antral follicle size.[7] Antral formation is enhanced in response to FSH expression.[57] In concert with estradiol, FSH increases FSH receptors and LH receptors located on the granulose.[81] Testosterone suppresses the secretion of GnRH and FSH and LH; inhibin and follistatin inhibit FSH secretion. In contrast, activin stimulates the secretion of FSH.[55] FSH receptors are located on the germinal epithelium of the Sertoli cells. Proliferation of the Sertoli cells is correlated with FSH and LH exposure. FSH acts specifically on the seminiferous tubules.

Activin

Activin is a glycoprotein that activates the release of FSH.[33,44] Composed of dimers of the β-inhibin subunits, activin A is synthesized in gonadal tissue but may also be synthesized in nongonadal organs, such as bone marrow.[9] Activin A has been isolated in the placenta and fetal membranes during pregnancy.[34] Higher activin concentrations overcome the effect of inhibin, with a resulting increase in FSH expression. Activin levels are independent of FSH stimulation.[9] Activin levels are highest midcycle and in the late luteal–early follicular phase. Levels are even higher in pregnancy, peaking at term.[34,81] Jenkin and colleagues[34] suggest that elevated activin A concentrations are associated with fetal distress. Activin in the granulosa promotes FSH-induced growth of LH receptors on granulosa cells and inhibits synthesis of thecal cell LH, progesterone, and estrogen. In addition, activin may

TABLE 2-2   Blood Production Rates, Secretion Rates, Metabolic Clearance Rates and Normal Serum Concentration of Sex Steroid Hormones

STEROID HORMONE	REPRODUCTIVE PHASE	MCR (L/day)	PR (mg/day)	SR (mg/day)	REFERENCE VALUES
MEN				**Testes**	
Androstenedione		2200	2.8	1.6	80.2–209.7 ng/dL (2.8–7.3 nmol/L)
Testosterone		950	6.5	6.2	198.8–1000 ng/dL (6.9–34.7 nmol/L)
Estrone		2050	0.15	0.11	10–67.56 ng/dL (37–250 pmol/L)
Estradiol		1600	0.06	0.05	<10.1–57.2 pg/mL (<37–210 pmol/L)
Estrone sulfate		167	0.08	Insignificant	600–2500 pmol/L
WOMEN				**Ovary**	
Androstenedione		2000	3.2	2.8	88.8–349.6 ng/dL (3.1–12.2 nmol/L)
Testosterone		500	0.19	0.06	20.2–80.7 ng/dL (0.7–2.8 nmol/L)
Estrone	Follicular	2200	0.11	0.08	2.9–10.8 ng/dL (110–400 pmol/L)
	Luteal	2200	0.26	0.15	310–660 pmol/L
	Postmenopausal	1610	0.04	Insignificant	22–230 pmol/L
Estradiol	Follicular	1200	0.09	0.08	<10.1–98.1 pg/mL (<37–360 pmol/L)
	Luteal	1200	0.25	0.24	190.1–340.5 pg/mL (699–1250 pmol/L)
	Postmenopausal	910	0.006	Insignificant	<10.1–38.1 pg/mL (<37–140 pmol/L)
Estrone sulfate	Follicular	146	0.10	Insignificant	700–3600 pmol/L
	Luteal	146	0.18	Insignificant	1100–7300 pmol/L
Progesterone	Follicular	2100	2.0	1.7	0.3–3.0 nmol/L
	Luteal	2100	25.0	24.0	19.0–45.0 nmol/L

MCR, Metabolic clearance rate; *PR,* production rate; *SR,* secretion rate.
From Strauss, J.F. (2014). The synthesis and metabolism of steroid hormones. In J.F. Strauss & R.L. Barbieri (Eds.). Yen and Jaffe's reproductive endocrinology (7th ed.). Philadelphia: Elsevier.

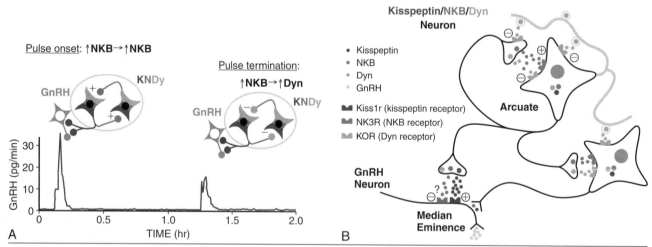

FIGURE 2-8   Model of how kisspeptin/neurokinin B/dynorphin (KNDy) neurons may participate in the generation of gonadotrophin-releasing hormone (GnRH) pulses as proposed by Lehman and colleagues **(A)** and Wakabayashi and colleagues **(B). A,** By this model neurokinin B *(NKB, magenta)* stimulates and dynorphin *(DYN, red)* suppresses kisspeptin release, with kisspeptin stimulating GnRH neuronal firing. The onset of a GnRH pulse is triggered by an initial increase of NKB, which stimulates further NKB (positive feedback loop) and increases kisspeptin output. NKB stimulation of KNDy neurons also stimulates DYN release, and after a short time, the increase of DYN suppresses kisspeptin (and NKB) release. This withdrawal of kisspeptin stimulation terminates the GnRH pulse. **B,** By this model KNDy neurons in the arcuate nucleus form a neural circuit, within which NKB (magenta)accelerates and DYN (red) reduces KNDy neuron activation. These reciprocal effects produce episodic activation of KNDy neurons, increasing kisspeptin release at the median eminence. Kisspeptin in turn stimulates GnRH release into the hypophyseal portal system. KOR, kappa opiate receptor. *KOR,* kappa opioid receptor; *NK3R,* neurokinin 3 receptor. *(A,* Adapted from Lehman, M.M., Coolen, L.M., & Goodman R.L. [2010]. Minireview: kisspeptin/neurokinin B/dynorphin [KNDy] cells of the arcuate nucleus: a central node in the control of gonadotrophin-releasing hormone secretion. *Endocrinol, 151,* 3479; *B,* From Strauss, J.F. & Barbieri, R. L. [2014]. *Yen & Jaffe's reproductive endocrinology* [7th ed.] Philadelphia: Saunders; and Wakabayashi, Y., et al. [2010]. Neurokinin B and dynorphin A in kisspeptin neurons of the arcuate nucleus participate in generation of periodic oscillation of neural activity driving pulsatile gonadotrophin-releasing hormone secretion in the goat. *J Neurosci, 30,* 3124.)

promote maturation of oocytes.[81] Activin A concentrations during the menstrual cycle range from 100 to 200 pg/mL, whereas postmenopausal levels may be five times higher than those levels. Activin levels do not vary according to age or gender.[26]

Inhibin

Inhibin, another glycoprotein, suppresses FSH secretion from the hypophysis.[33,44] Inhibin is synthesized primarily by the granulosa cells and is secreted into the follicular fluid.[24] Synthesis of inhibin is regulated in response to gonadotropins or factors that increase intracellular cAMP. There are two different forms of inhibin: inhibin A and inhibin B. Both have similar biologic characteristics; the primary difference is that hormonal synthesis is regulated differently during the follicular and luteal phases (Figure 2-9). FSH regulates inhibin production by the ovarian granulosa cells. LH augments inhibin production in the granulosa cells with the acquisition of its LH receptors. In addition, ovarian insulin-like growth factor 1 (IGF-1) and vasoactive intestinal peptide stimulate inhibin synthesis. Levels of inhibin vary in the menstrual cycle from 100 IU/L to 1500 IU/L. In the follicular phase,

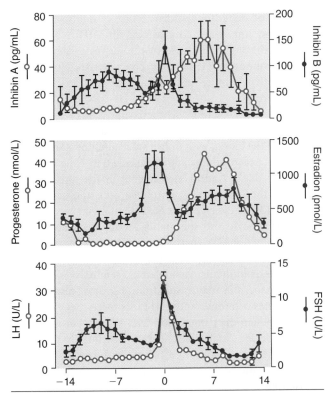

FIGURE 2-9 Plasma concentrations of inhibins A and B *(top)*, progesterone and estradiol *(middle)*, and luteinizing hormone *(LH)* and follicle-stimulating hormone *(FSH) (bottom)* during ovulatory cycles in women. Data are aligned to the day of the midcycle LH peak (day 0). Mean ± standard error is shown. (From Jameson, L. & DeGroot, L. [2010]. *Endocrinology: Adult and pediatric, vol II* [6th ed.]. Philadelphia: Elsevier Saunders.)

inhibin concentrations are low; levels increase in the luteal phase. In response to rising FSH levels in the luteal-follicular phase, inhibin levels drop dramatically. With menopause, inhibin concentrations are reduced, with decreases in inhibin B noted initially.[33]

Inhibin A is produced by the luteinized granulosa cells and expressed by the dominant follicle or corpus luteum.[33] Inhibin A slowly increases during the late follicular phase, stimulated by incremental LH expression, and is present in high levels during the early follicular and midfollicular phases, peaking in the midluteal phase. This is followed by a decreasing inhibin A in the late follicular phase.[33] The initial late follicular reduction in inhibin A is followed by a decreased but consistent level thereafter. During the second half of the menstrual cycle, concentrations of inhibin A increase markedly parallel to increasing concentrations of estradiol. FSH and LH stimulate expression of inhibin A by the dominant follicle.[33] Levels of inhibin A are positively correlated with follicular size.[81] Levels increase in midpuberty.[26]

Inhibin B is produced by the ovarian granulosa cells and Sertoli cells of the testis.[33] Inhibin B decreases FSH synthesis and obscures the effects of low activin levels.[44,55] In the early follicular phase, there are increased levels of FSH and estradiol. These hormones stimulate inhibin B expression from the luteinized granulosa cells. Thus inhibin B levels increase during the early follicular phase and reach their highest point at the early to midfollicular phase of the menstrual cycle.[33] Levels are highest in the granulosa cells of small luteal antral follicles. Then inhibin B levels continuously decrease, becoming undetectable after the LH surge.[81] No association has been noted with inhibin B levels and follicular size.[81] Levels of inhibin B increase during childhood, peaking in midpuberty and decreasing thereafter.[26]

Follistatin

Follistatin is derived from the granulosa cells of the small antral and preovulatory follicles. It is a polypeptide that, like inhibin, also suppresses FSH expression and may modulate the effects of activin on FSH.[26,33,81] However, follistatin is only about one third as active as inhibin. Other physiologic roles of follistatin include the protein binding of activin (which restricts the bioavailability of activin) and the synthesis of progesterone.[70,81] Concentrations of follistatin remain relatively constant throughout the menstrual cycle.[81] Levels of follistatin do not vary during puberty, although increases occur with normal menses.[26] Follistatin levels increase in pregnancy with peak levels at term.[34]

Steroid Hormones

The steroidal hormones—androgens, estrogens, and progestogens—are primarily produced by the gonads and adrenals (see Table 2-2). Steroid hormones are not stored but are produced as needed.[73] Cholesterol is the precursor for steroid hormones (Figure 2-10). Steroidogenic cells

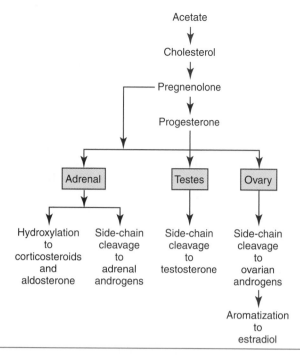

FIGURE 2-10   The unified concept of steroid hormone synthesis. Characteristic steroid secretory functions of the ovary, testes, and adrenal gland are shown. The pathway from acetate to progesterone is common to all. (From Ryan, K.J. [1972]. Steroid hormones and prostaglandins. In D.E. Reid, K.J. Ryan & K. Benirschke [Eds.]. *Principles and management of human reproduction.* Philadelphia: Saunders.)

express low-density lipoprotein (LDL) receptors, in particular, and high-density lipoprotein (HDL) receptors to uptake cholesterol. Steroidogenesis commences with LH stimulating the conversion of cholesterol to pregnenolone within the mitochondria of the theca interna cells (Figure 2-11). Transfer of the cholesterol within the mitochondria is enhanced by a steroidogenic acute regulatory protein (StAR).[73] Steroid synthesis requires a number of enzymes, including hydroxylases, dehydrogenases, reductase, transferases, steroid sulfatase, sulfotransferases, and an aromatase (Table 2-3).[73] The hydroxylases and aromatase descend from the P450 family and act as a catalyst to steroidogenesis.[73] Aromatase transcription for hormonal synthesis is evoked with follicular development at the 7-mm stage.[67]

The gonads (i.e., ovaries, testes) produce most of the steroidal hormones; the adrenal cortex produces minimal amounts of estrogens and dihydrotestosterone. Progesterone and pregnenolone are also synthesized by the placenta from cholesterol precursors. Synthesis of steroidal hormones may follow one of two pathways: the pregnenolone pathway or the progesterone pathway (Figure 2-12). From the pregnenolone pathway the hormones DHE and androstenediol are produced. DHE and androstenediol may enter the progesterone pathway in the synthesis of the prohormones androstenedione and testosterone, respectively, with final conversion to the hormone dihydrotestosterone. Also from this pathway, androstenedione is converted to estrone (E_1) and testosterone is converted to estradiol. In women, approximately 60% of

circulating testosterone is derived from the peripheral conversion of androstenedione. Steroidal hormonal levels vary in the reproductive cycle and in the reproductive life of women and men (Box 2-3).[74]

Dehydroepiandrosterone Sulfate, Dehydroepiandrosterone, 5xdihydrotestosterone, and Androstenedione

The major androgen precursors are DHEAS, DHT, DHEA, and androstenedione. These androgen precursors precede steroidal synthesis. Secreted by the ovaries and adrenals, the androgen precursors begin to increase in early adolescence and decline in the 5th and 6th decades. DHEA increases during adrenarche, around 7 to 9 years of age, peaking in the early 20s and then declining.[71] Thereafter, follicular maturation, increased estradiol levels, and LH stimulation are necessary for ovarian androgen synthesis. Androgens are the precursors of estrogen and progesterone synthesis.

During the menstrual cycle, particularly the follicular phase, two thirds of testosterone is derived from peripheral conversion of androstenedione. During pregnancy, the fetal adrenal produces DHEA, the precursor of placental estrogen synthesis. DHEA is a hormone produced primarily by the adrenals and less so by the ovaries. The physiologic role of dehydroepiandrosterone is unknown.[18] Age is the most important determinant in DHEA hormonal variance, although the cause of the decreased levels with aging is unknown.[77] Hormonal concentrations of DHEA decline with age more so than do estrogen, progesterone, or testosterone.[77]

In males, testosterone synthesis into DHT takes place principally in the target glands. Testosterone is primarily secreted in the blood, with only a small amount stored in the testis. The testis produces approximately 6 to 7 mg of testosterone per day.[55] Androgen receptors in the testis are expressed in the Sertoli cells, peritubular cells, and Leydig cells (Figure 2-13). These receptors are essential for spermatogenesis, spermatocyte and spermatid development, and testosterone production. The spermatic vein is the primary route of transport to the general circulation. DHT from testosterone acts on the epididymis, vas deferens, seminal vesicles, and prostate. Aspermia may result from a lack of testosterone. Estradiol, testosterone, and DHT are necessary for these effects. Wolffian duct expression with subsequent masculinization of fetal sexual differentiation is primarily related to testosterone (see Chapter 1). Changes in the external genitalia, prostate, and urethra are caused by DHT. Both DHT and testosterone are necessary for growth of the penis. Testosterone production is greatest during the time of differentiation of the external genitalia, between 9 and 14 weeks' gestation, and subsequently decreases.[55]

Estrogens

Estrogens include estrone (E_1), estradiol, and estriol (E_3) (Figure 2-14). In nonpregnant women, the ovaries are the

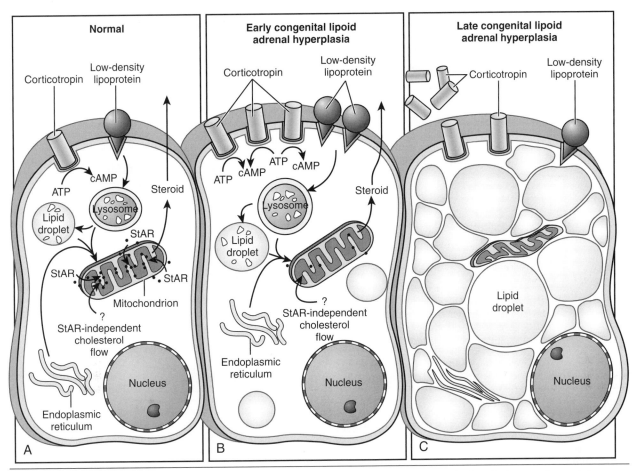

FIGURE 2-11 Steroidogenic acute regulatory protein *(StAR)*. In the healthy steroidogenic cell, binding of adrenocorticotropic hormone *(ACTH)* stimulates transport of low-density lipoprotein (LDL) cholesterol into the cell by endocytosis. LDL is processed by lysosomes and either stored in lipid droplets or transferred to the mitochondria. Meanwhile, cholesterol is also synthesized independently by the endoplasmic reticulum mechanisms that may be StAR-dependent or independent. *ATP*, Adenosine triphosphate; *cAMP*, cyclic adenosine monophosphate. (From Bose, H.S., Sugawara, T., Strauss, J.F. 3rd, Miller, W.L., & International Congenital Lipoid Adrenal Hyperplasia Consortium. [1996]. The pathophysiology and genetics of congenital lipoid adrenal hyperplasia, *N Engl J Med 335*, 1870. In Jameson, L. & DeGroot, L. [2010]. *Encocrincology: Adult and pediatric, vol II* [6th ed.]. Philadelphia: Saunders.

TABLE 2-3 Enzymes Used in Steroidogenesis

ENZYME	DESIGNATION
Cholesterol side-chain cleavage	CYP11A
17α-Hydroxylase	CYP17
17,21-Lyase	CYP17
21-Hydroxylase	CYP21
11β-Hydroxylase	CYP11B1
Aldosterone synthetase	CYP11B2
Aromatase	CYP19
3β-Hydroxysteroid dehydrogenase	3βHSD
17β-Hydroxysteroid dehydrogenase	17βHSD
5β-Reductase	5αRed

From Busilo, J., Rhen, T., & Cidlowski, J. (2014). The synthesis and metabolism of steroid hormones. In S.C. Yen, R.B. Jaffe, & R.L. Barbieri (Eds.). Reproductive endocrinology: Physiology, pathophysiology, and clinical management (7th ed.). Philadelphia: Elsevier.

primary source of estrogens; the adrenal cortices also produce small amounts. Before ovulation, the follicles secrete estradiol, which is dependent on the thecal cell androgen production. During pregnancy, the placenta produces significant quantities of estrogens. The principal estrogen of

the reproductive years is estradiol produced by the ovaries. Estriol, a weak estrogen, is derived from the conversion of either estradiol or estrone. Estrone is derived from androgens of the adrenals and ovaries. Estradiol has 12 times the estrogenic potency of estrone and 80 times that of estriol.[30] During the reproductive years, estrone concentrations are greater than those of estradiol, with levels ranging from 1000 pg/mL (3699 pmol/L) in the follicular phase to luteal levels of 1800 pg/mL (6658.2 pmol/L). The greater biologic potency of estradiol establishes it as the dominant estrogen at this time. Conversely, estradiol levels dramatically decrease with menopause and there is a higher estrone-estradiol ratio, with estrone becoming the dominant estrogen of the menopausal period. The "two-cell, two-gonadotropin" theory proposes that two cells (i.e., thecal and granulosa cells) and the two gonadotropins (i.e., FSH and LH) stimulate estrogen synthesis (Figure 2-15).[27,49,81]

Androgen formation from cholesterol occurs in the theca interna with LH stimulation. Androgen is then converted to estrogens. In addition, antral follicles produce estradiol, and these follicles ovulate in response to gonadotropin

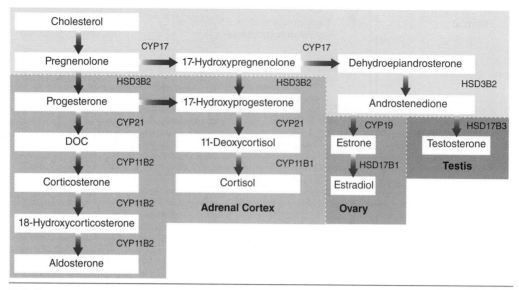

FIGURE 2-12 The pathways of adrenal, ovarian, and testicular steroidogenesis. *Dark solid lines* indicate predominant pathways for adrenal steroidogenesis. *Dashed lines* indicate predominant pathways for gonadal steroidogenesis. *DOC,* deoxycorticosterone. (From Witchel, S.F. & Lee, P.A. [2002]. Ambiguous genitalia. In M.A. Sperling [Ed.]. *Pediatric endocrinology.* [2nd ed.]. Philadelphia: Saunders.)

BOX 2-3 Postulated Ontogeny of the Hypothalamic-Pituitary-Gonadal Circuit

FETUS

Medial basal hypothalamic LHRH neurosecretory neurons (pulse generator) operative by 80 days' gestation

Pulsatile secretion of FSH and LH by 80 days' gestation

Initially unrestrained secretion of LHRH (100 to 150 days of gestation)

Maturation of negative gonadal steroid feedback mechanism by 150 days' gestation—sex difference

Low level of LHRH secretion at term

EARLY INFANCY

Hypothalamic LHRH pulse generator highly functional after 12 days of age

Prominent FSH and LH episodic discharges until approximately 6 months of age in males and 12 months of age in females, with transient increase in plasma levels of testosterone and estradiol in males and females, respectively

LATE INFANCY AND CHILDHOOD

Intrinsic CNS inhibition of hypothalamic LHRH pulse generator operative; predominant mechanism in childhood; maximal sensitivity by approximately 4 years of age

Negative feedback control of FSH and LH secretion highly sensitive to gonadal steroids (low set point)

LHRH pulse generator inhibited; low amplitude and frequency of LHRH discharges

Low secretion of FSH, LH, and gonadal steroids

LATE PREPUBERTAL PERIOD

Decreasing effectiveness of intrinsic CNS inhibitory influences and decreasing sensitivity of hypothalamic-pituitary unit to gonadal steroids (increased set point)

Increased amplitude and frequency of LHRH pulses, initially most prominent with sleep (nocturnal)

Increased sensitivity of gonadotrophs to LHRH

Increased secretion of FSH and LH

Increased responsiveness of gonad to FSH and LH

Increased secretion of gonadal hormones

PUBERTY

Further decrease in CNS restraint of hypothalamic LHRH pulse generator and of the sensitivity of negative feedback mechanism to gonadal steroids

Prominent sleep-associated increase in episodic secretion of LHRH gradually changes to adult pattern of pulses about every 90 minutes

Pulsatile secretion of LH follows pattern of LHRH pulses

Progressive development of secondary sexual characteristics

Spermatogenesis in males

Middle to late puberty—operative positive feedback mechanism and capacity to exhibit an estrogen-induced LH surge

Ovulation in females

CNS, Central nervous system; *FSH,* follicle stimulating hormone; *LH,* luteinizing hormone; *LHRH,* LH-releasing hormone.

Adapted from Grumbach, M. M., Roth, J. C., Kaplan, S. L., & Kelch, R. P. (1974). Hypothalamic-pituitary regulation of puberty in man: Evidence and concepts derived from clinical research. In M.M. Grumbach, G.D. Grave, & F.E. Mayer (Eds.). Control of the onset of puberty. New York, John Wiley & Sons; P.R. Larsen, et al. (Eds.). (2003). Williams textbook of endocrinology (10th ed.). Philadelphia: Saunders.

---

stimulation (Figure 2-16).[19,62] Stress is known to negatively affect hormonal stimulation. Estradiol blood levels are significantly lower in women diagnosed with depression.[51]

Estradiol stimulates follicular maturation. Increased levels of estrogen by day 5 in the ovarian cycle act to inhibit FSH and LH release. Estrogen priming facilitates FSH development of granulosa LH receptors. Increasing estrogen levels stimulate LH secretion during the follicular phase. During this phase, estrogen facilitates the endometrial changes of the proliferative phase. Endometrial tissue depth increases from

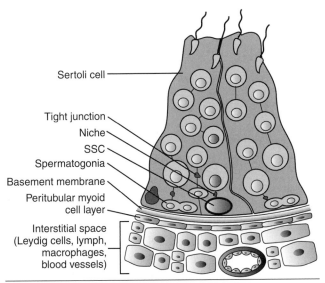

Sertoli cell

Tight junction
Niche
SSC
Spermatogonia
Basement membrane
Peritubular myoid
cell layer
Interstitial space
(Leydig cells, lymph,
macrophages,
blood vessels)

FIGURE 2-13   The site of the spermatogonial stem-cell (SSC) niche in the seminiferous epithelium. SSCs are in contact with the basal lamina and are found in the basal compartment of the seminiferous epithelium, below the Sertoli cell tight junctions and surrounded by Sertoli cell cytoplasm. In addition to factors produced by Sertoli cells that regulate SSCs, the nearby peritubular cells and Leydig cells are possible additional sources of molecules that influence SSC functions. (From Johnston, D.S., Wright, W.W., DiCandeloro P., Wilson, E., Kopf, G.S., & Jelinsky, S.A. [2008]. Stage-specific gene expression is fundamental characteristic of rat spermatogenic cells and Sertoli cells. *Proc Natl Acad So USA 105,* 8315. In Jameson, L. & DeGroot, L. (Eds.). [2010]. *Endocrinology: Adult and pediatric, vol II* [6th ed.]. Philadelphia: Elsevier Saunders.

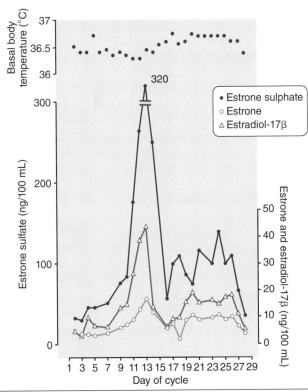

FIGURE 2-14   Circulating levels of estrone, estradiol-17β, and estrone sulfate during the menstrual cycle. (From Fraser, I.S., Tworoger, S.S., Hecht, J.L., Rosner, B.A., Colditz, G.A., & Hankinson, S.E. [1998]. *Estrogens and progestogens in clinical practice.* Philadelphia: Churchill Livingstone.)

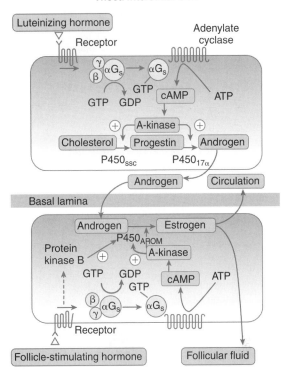

FIGURE 2-15   The two-cell, two-gonadotropin system for estradiol synthesis in the follicle. Luteinizing hormone (LH) and follicle-stimulating hormone (FSH) are shown to stimulate adenylate cyclase via G-protein–coupled receptors. The cAMP generated from ATP activates protein kinase A to stimulate expression of the respective steroidogenic enzymes in thecal and granulose cells. In addition, in granulosa cells, FSH binding to the FSH receptor leads to activation of protein kinase B, probably via a phosphatidyl inositol second message, which augments aromatase expression. *ATP,* Adenosine triphosphate; *cAMP,* cyclic adenosine monophosphate; *GDP,* guanosine diphosphate; *GTP* guanosine triphosphate. (Adapted from Erickson, G.F. & Shimasaki, S. [2001]. The physiology of folliculogenesis: the role of novel growth factors. *Fertil Steril, 76,* 943.)

1 to 2 mm to 3.5 to 5 mm, with tortuous gland development, increased mitotic activity, and expansion of the spiral arteries. In response to estrogen, the cervical mucus becomes more watery and clear, with increased stretchability before ovulation (spinnbarkeit). During the follicular phase, the cervical os opens; it closes during the luteal phase. Uterine and fallopian tube changes in response to rising estrogen levels include rhythmic contractions to facilitate sperm motility and ovum retention, respectively.

Increased breast sensitivity during the luteal phase is believed to be related to estrogen levels. After ovulation, the corpus luteum produces estrogen and progesterone. Increased levels of estrogen, in concert with progesterone, during the luteal phase inhibit FSH and LH secretion. As the corpus luteum degenerates, estrogen levels decrease. GnRH levels rise in response, with a subsequent increase in FSH and LH to initiate folliculogenesis.

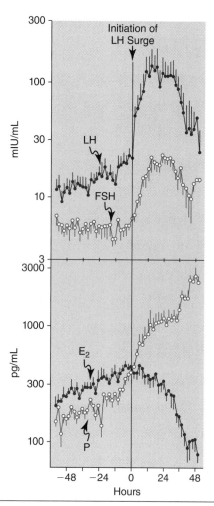

FIGURE 2-16   Mean (± standard error) luteinizing hormone *(LH)*, follicle-stimulating hormone *(FSH)*, estradiol *(E₂)*, and progesterone *(P)* levels measured every 2 hours for 5 days at midcycle in seven studies. Data were centered at the initiation of the gonadotropin surge. The data are plotted on a logarithmic scale. (From Hoff, J.D., Quigley, M.E., & Yen, S.S.C. [1983]. Hormonal dynamics at midcycle: A reevaluation. *Endocrinol Metab, 57,* 792.)

In males, testosterone is converted to DHT by testicular 5x-reductase and then to estradiol by testicular aromatase. Estrogen receptor-B and aromatase activity are located in the germ cells and Sertoli cells. Estrogens in concert with androgens are necessary for the changes in prostate development and proliferation.[55] The role of estrogens in regard to testicular function is not clear.[55]

Progestogens

Progesterone is the only naturally occurring steroidal progestogen. The ovaries produce progesterone primarily early in the follicular phase, but large amounts of progesterone are converted by the granulosa cells to estrogens. With the LH surge, there is a subsequent increase in progesterone. In concert with estrogen, progesterone stimulates significant FSH secretion and a subsequent increase in granulosa LH receptors (see Figure 2-16). Follicular wall elasticity is secondary to increased progesterone levels.

Progesterone production in the follicular phase is 2.5 mg/day, whereas luteal phase production is 25 mg/day.[44] For the first 6 to 10 weeks after conception, the primary site of progesterone production is the corpus luteum.[50,52] Progesterone levels rise significantly, peaking at approximately day 8 of the luteal phase. Increased levels of progesterone—along with estrogen via negative feedback—limit the expression of FSH and LH. With involution of the corpus luteum, progesterone levels drop dramatically. In contrast with fertilization of the oocyte, the placenta becomes the primary producer of progesterone after approximately 10 gestational weeks.[44] Progesterone modulates the effects on the reproductive organs, including the "quieting" of the fallopian tubes during the luteal phase to assist the fertilized ovum in its transport to the uterus. This quieting also extends to the uterus to facilitate trophoblast implantation (see Chapter 3).[44] In addition, progesterone suppresses T cell processes, inhibiting fetal tissue rejection (see Chapter 13).[44] Progesterone levels are negatively correlated with body mass index.[77] Ethnicity also contributes significantly to variances in progesterone levels.[77]

The role of progesterone in the testis is not clear, although progesterone receptors have been identified on spermatozoa and in peritubular cells.[55]

Testosterone

Testosterone is an androgen derived from the androgenal precursors DHEA and DHEAS.[61] Between 30% and 50% of androgens originate in the adrenals and ovaries, with the remainder deriving from peripheral tissue conversion in liver and adipose tissue.[61]

At birth, male newborns have a comparable testosterone level to that of normal adults, which decreases within 7 days, increases again in the 2nd month, and then falls significantly in the 6th month of life. At approximately 7 years, androgens are produced in response to DHE by the adrenal gland. Gonadotropin secretion, beginning around 10 years, leads to nocturnal pulsatile LH secretion with increased testosterone levels. With maturity, testosterone has a circadian pattern with 25% lower levels at night in comparison with the early morning levels. As with females, testosterone concentrations decrease with aging.[55]

Secretion of androgens commences at approximately 6 to 8 years of age, influenced primarily by elevated DHEAS and less so by androstenedione levels.[61] Levels begin to reach adult levels during adolescence and begin to decline in the 50s. Mean testosterone production rates decrease from 200 mcg/day premenopausally to 150 mcg/day perimenopausally. Synthesis of testosterone occurs early in the follicular cycle by the ovaries. Most testosterone is converted into estrogens by the granulosa cells. Testosterone levels decline with age. Body mass index is the most important predictor of testosterone levels.[77]

In males, the maximal levels of DHEA and DHEAS are from the ages of 20 to 25 years, with a subsequent decrease over the years. At 60 years of age, DHEA and DHEAS levels are only a third of their previous levels.[55] Testosterone and DHT decrease the GnRH pulsatile frequency at the hypothalamus.[55]

Oocyte Maturation Inhibitor

The factor leading to oocyte meiotic arrest in the prophase stage is believed to be oocyte maturation inhibitor.[30,49] It is postulated that meiosis resumes with the complex interplay of oocyte maturation inhibitor and granulosa cumulus cells (see Chapter 3).

Luteinization Inhibitor

The existence of another chemical factor, luteinization inhibitor, is suggested by the ability of granulosa cells from large preovulatory follicles to initiate spontaneous luteinization.[81]

Gonadotropin Surge–Inhibiting Factor

Gonadotropin surge–inhibiting factor is believed to be a nonsteroidal substance that inhibits the LH surge and FSH expression as normally occurs by either estradiol or GnRH. In contrast to inhibin, which inhibits only FSH expression,

gonadotropin surge–inhibiting factor suppresses both FSH and LH. The ovaries are the source of this short-acting factor.[81]

Relaxin

Produced by the luteal cells of the corpus luteum, relaxin is believed to facilitate decidualization of the endometrium and suppress contractions of the uterine myometrium. Relaxin is associated with collagen remodeling and cervical softening.[44] Levels are highest in the first trimester, peaking at 1.2 ng/mL between 8 and 12 weeks' gestation and decreasing approximately 20% for the remainder of the pregnancy.[81]

Feedback Systems

Hormone secretion is regulated by feedback systems, which can be negative or positive (Figure 2-17). The negative feedback system is the most common. As the level of a hormone rises, it inhibits the initiation of further release of that hormone. Secretion of the pituitary hormone to a level above the set point causes a decrease in secretion of that same pituitary

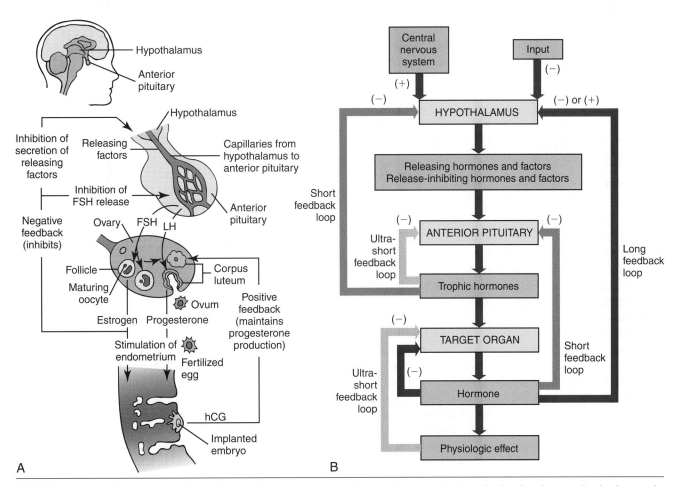

FIGURE 2-17   Feedback loops. **A,** Endocrine feedback loops involving the hypothalamus-pituitary gland and end organs (endocrine regulation). **B,** General model for control and negative feedback regulation. This regulation is possible at three levels: target organ (ultrashort feedback), anterior pituitary (short feedback), and hypothalamus (long feedback). (From McCance, K.L. & Huether, S.E. [2006]. *Pathophysiology: The biologic basis for disease in adults and children* [5th ed.]. St. Louis: Mosby.)

hormone into the blood. For example, the administration of moderate amounts of estrogen will lower the secretion of FSH and LH into the blood. In the normal menstrual cycle, high levels of progesterone and moderate levels of estrogen during the luteal phase will lower gonadotropin secretion by a long-loop negative feedback. With positive feedback, a rising hormone level will increase secretion of the same hormone. High levels of estrogen in blood increase the secretion of LH and FSH from the adenohypophysis, resulting in a surge of these gonadotropins.[33]

Physiologic effects are produced by peripheral target tissues (gonads) and travel via the bloodstream to the brain and pituitary gland. In addition to the negative and positive feedback loops, there are long, short, and ultrashort loops. In the long-loop feedback, the gonadotropins (FSH and LH) increase the gonadal secretion of steroidal hormones. These steroidal hormones (i.e., estrogen, progesterone) influence the secretion of LH and FSH by their feedback effects on the systems controlling gonadotropin secretion. In the short-loop feedback system, LH or FSH circulates in the vascular system, returns to the median eminence of the hypothalamus, and subsequently decreases the secretion of GnRH from the neurosecretory axons.[7,30] This is a more direct negative feedback system that does not involve gonadal steroid hormones. In the ultrashort-loop feedback, the GnRH may directly stop GnRH secretion from the neurosecretory axons in the median eminence. At present, only the short and ultrashort feedback loops have been demonstrated to be negative. On the other hand, the long-loop feedback system may be either positive or negative. High serum levels of estrogen increase the secretion of LH and FSH from the adenohypophysis, resulting in an LH surge with ovarian release of the ovum.

Gonadotropin-Releasing Hormone

Gonadotropin-releasing neurons are located in the arcuate nucleus of the medial basal hypothalamus and in the preoptic area of the anterior hypothalamus.[7,27] The GnRH pulse generator exhibits pulsatile secretion at 60- to 90-minute intervals from the medial basal hypothalamus with ultradian rhythm. Pulsation frequency and amplitude vary depending on hormonal stimulation or inhibition, substrates, and other hormones.[7,26] Continuous exposure to GnRH decreases the responsiveness of the receptors, leading to increased down-regulation.[3] For example, during the luteal phase, there is a significant decrease in the GnRH pulse generator.[27] In response to GnRH, the anterior pituitary gland secretes FSH and LH. GnRH pulse frequency during the luteal follicular phase modulates FSH secretion to initiate folliculogenesis.[80] Both hormones are small glycoproteins that stimulate the ovary by combining with specific FSH and LH receptor cells located in the cell membranes (Figure 2-18). cAMP, the second messenger system in the cell cytoplasm, promotes mobilization and expression of FSH and LH from storage granules in the gonadotropes.[27]

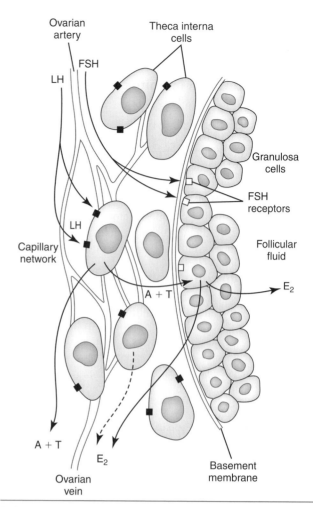

FIGURE 2-18   Diagram of action of gonadotropins on the follicle and the synthesis of estrogens. Luteinizing hormone *(LH)* interacts with receptors on the thecal cells to stimulate production of androgens and small amounts of estradiol *(E₂)*. Follicle-stimulating hormone *(FSH)* activates the aromatase enzyme system in the granulosa cells by interacting with receptors. A, Androstenedione; T, testosterone. (From Band, D.T. [1984]. The ovary. In C.R. Austin & R.V. Short [Eds.]. *Hormonal control of reproduction,* vol. 3. Cambridge: Cambridge University Press.)

REPRODUCTIVE PROCESSES IN THE FEMALE AND MALE
Oogenesis

In utero, the ovaries function in response to placental secretion of chorionic gonadotropin. In utero, oogenesis commences as early as week 3.[24,49,81] There are two pools of follicles within the ovary: the resting follicle pool made up of primordial follicles and the growing follicle pool. Within the primordial follicles are the oocytes, which originate from the primordial germ cells.[63,65] Germ cells form oogonia via mitosis. Oogonia enter meiosis and arrest in the diplotene stage of meiosis maintained by the maturation-promoting factor complex.[63] The oogonia are now known as *primary oocytes.* Formation of the primordial germ cells begins in the ovarian medulla and then moves toward the outer ovary. Folliculogenesis during the fetal period is a time of epigenetic change.[12] Fetal pituitary FSH secretion has been detected as early as 12 to 14 gestational weeks.[3] Serum FSH levels at 20 to 28 gestational weeks are comparable to levels postmenopausally. Whereas the adult pulse generator frequency is from 60 to 120 minutes, the fetal GnRH frequency pulsates every 60 minutes. By 6 to 7 gestational weeks, there are approximately 10,000 germ cells. At approximately 20 gestational weeks, the maximal number (6 to 7 million) of primordial follicles are present; this number decreases throughout the reproductive life of the woman, until depletion at the climacteric.[7,81] Atresia of the follicles begins at 24 weeks' gestation with oogenesic cessation at approximately 28 weeks' gestation, at which time there is no further ova production.[81] At birth, the newborn ovaries contain approximately 200,000 to 400,000 follicles arrested in the prophase stage of meiosis.[49,81] (Oogenesis is described further in Chapter 1.)

Spermatogenesis

Sperm production takes place within the complex endocrine environment, and environmental factors may negatively affect sperm parameters.[32] The development of mature germ cells in the seminiferous tubules involves three stages: (1) mitosis (spermatogonial multiplication), (2) meiosis (production of haploid cells), and (3) spermiogenesis (maturation of spermatids to mature spermatozoa). The androgens and proteins produced locally modulate spermatogenesis seen within the seminiferous tubule (see Chapter 1).

The seminiferous tubule is divided into basal and luminal compartments. The basal compartment is the outer layer (zone 1) of the tubule, whereas the luminal compartment is the inner layer. The basal compartment is composed of stem cells (type A spermatogonia) that are renewed through mitosis. Some of these continue to proliferate and serve as stem cells, whereas others (preleptotene spermatocytes or type B spermatogonia) separate from the basal membrane and begin to migrate toward the lumen. As migration progresses, the cells undergo further morphologic changes, becoming primary spermatocytes. The first and second meiotic divisions occur with further differentiation in the adluminal zone, resulting in the formation of secondary spermatocytes and spermatids. The luminal spermatids undergo a complex sequence of changes within the cell organelles (spermiogenesis). (Spermatogenesis and spermiogenesis are discussed further in Chapter 1.)

Spermatogenesis is the differentiation and proliferation of diploid germ cells, via a six-stage system.[55] There are two type of spermatogonia, type A and type B. Type A can be classified as Ap or Ad; Ap differentiate to type B, the spermatogonium. Over 1 to 3 weeks the spermatocytes, via first meiotic division, become secondary spermatocytes. With the second meiotic division, lasting only 1 to 2 days, there is a reduction in the chromosome number for the development of the spermatids. Spermiogenesis is the process by which the spermatids undergo shaping of the cell nucleus and formation of the flagellum. During spermiogenesis there are four phases: Golgi, cap, acrosomal, and maturation phases. In the Golgi phase, craniocaudal symmetry occurs. During the cap phase, the acrosome develops and the spermatids become elongated. During the acrosomal phase, the cell nucleus chromatin becomes greatly condensed and the spermatids further elongate. The expulsion of the remaining cytoplasm, known as the *residual body,* occurs during the maturation phase. Sperm are then released into the tubular lumen, passing into the epididymis. Sperm development from an Ap spermatogonium into a mature sperm requires minimally four spermatogenic cycles, with each cycle lasting approximately 16 days. Because sperm are present in the epididymis at varied stages, a spermatogenesis cycle ranges from 64 to 74 days.[55]

The sperm move down the tubules by contraction and fluid secretion by the Sertoli cells. The evolution process takes approximately 74 days. Of these 74 days, about 50 days are spent in the seminiferous tubule. Each stage of spermatogenesis has a specific time frame, 16 to 18 days for spermatogonia, 23 days for primary spermatocytes, 1 day for secondary spermatocytes, and about 23 days for spermatids.[35] At the time of their release into the seminiferous tubules, the spermatozoa are still morphologically immature and lack motility. While traversing the epididymis (which takes 14 to 21 days), they continue to differentiate. Forward motility is achieved in the proximal epididymis. (Ejaculation, sperm transport, and fertilization are described in Chapter 3.)

Puberty

The age of puberty varies across ethnicities. Although not completely understood, it is posited that puberty is controlled via the central nervous system, genetic, and environmental factors.[17,76] GnRH is released from the hypothalamic GnRH neurons. Neurotransmitters, as catecholamines, prostaglandins, and serotonin, act to either inhibit or stimulate the process. Other contributing factors include body mass index, nutritional status, steroid hormones, and ethnicity.[12,42]

During pregnancy, fetal FSH and LH are detectable at approximately 10 gestational weeks, increasing until 25-29 gestational weeks. Fetal serum levels peak at midgestation and then decrease by term. Fetal FSH levels are higher in female fetuses while levels of LH are higher in male fetuses. After birth, there is an increase in infant LH and FSH, which then decrease over subsequent days. In the first 6 to 12 weeks after birth, these levels peak as a result of increased hypothalamic-pituitary-gonadal (HPG) axis activity. Levels then decrease over the following months,[42] with serum FSH levels higher in female infants than male infants.[39] During childhood, HPG activity is suppressed by the central nervous system. Although quiescent during this juvenile pause, by the age of 5 to 7 years there is increased LH and FSH secretion, even before the physiologic changes accompanying puberty.[42]

The GnRH neurons, located in the arcuate nucleus of the hypothalamus, release episodic pulses of GnRH into the hypothalamic hypophyseal portal plexus. Receptors in the anterior pituitary gland, gonadotropes, then release FSH and specifically LH in the portal system with subsequent stimulation of the gonads.[42] Increased serum LH levels are

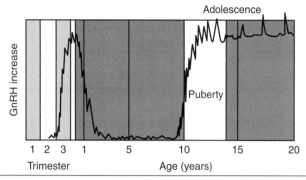

FIGURE 2-19 The ontogeny of gonadotropin-releasing hormone (GnRH) secretion from fetal life to adolescence. Note the prepubertal nadir and upswing of GnRH secretory activity at the onset of puberty. This is followed by irregular luteinizing hormone surges during adolescence. (From Yen, S.S.C. [1987]. Reproductive strategy in women: neuroendocrine basis of endogenous contraception. In R. Rolland [Ed.]. *Neuroendocrinology of reproduction.* Amsterdam: Excerpta Medica.)

sleep dependent and are accompanied during puberty by a rise in amplitude of nocturnal gonadotropin pulses.[39] Ovarian response requires episodic secretion of GnRH at 70- to 90-minute intervals. In response to FSH, ovarian granulosa cells secrete androstenedione, a primary component for estradiol production. In contrast, in the male, the Leydig cells produce testosterone in response to LH.[42]

GnRH episodic pulses increase in frequency at about 10 years of age (Figure 2-19), increasing at night during sleep (Figure 2-20).[39,42,79] With puberty, estradiol stimulus via positive feedback initiates the hypothalamic pulse generator. This hormonal stimulus is dependent on an adequate LH pool for the LH surge, ovarian follicles responsive to FSH, and a pituitary gland responsive to GnRH. LH pulses have been detected as early as midchildhood. With the onset of puberty, there is a greater increase in LH pulse amplitude compared with pulse frequency.[39] There is a progressive increase in FSH and LH daytime pulsatility, with a subsequent decrease in sleep-entrained pulse amplification (Figure 2-21).[39] Prepubertal girls have high FSH concentrations. FSH is necessary for pubertal development, and rising FSH levels accompany follicular development.[40] Ovary activation occurs in response to increasing LH pulses.[45]

There is increased gonadotropin sensitivity to GnRH with the cessation of the gonadostat.[23] Control of GnRH release is mediated via a neuroendocrine cascade composed of neuropeptides, neurotransmitters, and neurosteroids. These neuropeptides include opioids, neuropeptide Y, galanin, and corticotropin-releasing factor (CRF). Neurotransmitters include dopamine, melatonin, serotonin, γ-aminobutyric acid (GABA), and noradrenaline. The neurotransmitters dopamine, norepinephrine, and epinephrine stimulate GnRH secretion. Serotonin is norepinephrine mediated. DHEA (an antagonistic neurosteroid) and allopregnanolone (an agonistic neurosteroid) are also important factors in initiating puberty.[23]

Puberty, secondary to gonadal hormone stimulation, is the initiation of physical changes in both the male and female. Physical changes manifest between 8 and 13 years of age.

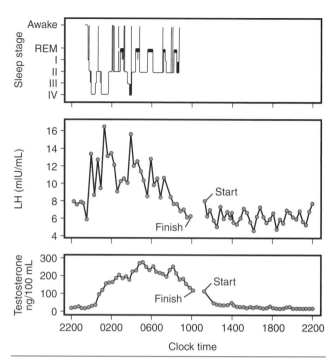

FIGURE 2-20 Plasma luteinizing hormone (LH) and testosterone sampled every 20 minutes in a 14-year-old boy in pubertal stage 2. The histogram displaying sleep stage sequence is depicted above the period of nocturnal sleep. Sleep stages are rapid eye movement *(REM)* with stages I to IV shown by depth of line graph. Plasma LH is expressed as mIU/mL. Plasma testosterone is expressed as nanograms per 100 mL. To convert LH values to international units per liter, multiply by 1.0. To convert testosterone values to nanomoles per liter, multiply by 0.03467. (From Boyar, R.M., Rosenfeld, R.S., Kapen, S., Finkelstein, J.W., Roffwarg, H. P., Weitzman, E. D., & Hellman, L. [1974]. Human puberty: Simultaneous augmented secretion of luteinizing hormone and testosterone during sleep. *J Clin Invest, 54,* 609. Copyright of the American Society for Clinical Investigation; Kronenberg, H., Melmed, S., Polonsky, K., & Larsen, R. (2008). *Williams textbook of endocrinology* (11th ed.). Philadelphia: Elsevier.)

Tanner criteria are used to stage the usual sequence of attainment of pubertal milestones in males and females. The staging criteria evaluate breast, pubic hair, and male genital development, with stage 1 as prepubertal and stage 5 as adult.

Male Puberty

During the neonatal period, the hypothalamic-pituitary-testicular axis is functioning with increased levels of reproductive hormones and gonadotropins. This time is known as "minipuberty," lasting approximately 12 months in females with mammary development and 6 months in males with enlargement of Leydig and Sertoli cells and the external genitalia.[63] After this increased activity is a period of quiescence, known as the "juvenile pause," until puberty.[63,76] Male puberty markers include Tanner staging but should also include an estimation of testicular volume (a volume of 3 mL or more indicates puberty has begun); early morning testosterone levels are the best marker of impending male puberty.[76]

Adrenarche, the increased production of adrenal sex steroids (DHEA, DHEAS, and androstenedione), occurs before the

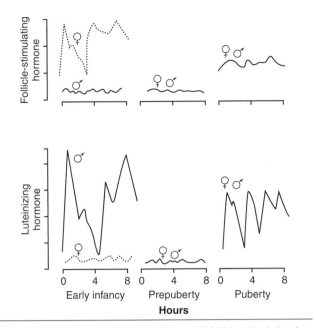

FIGURE 2-21 Changes in the patterns of follicle-stimulating hormone and luteinizing hormone secretion at puberty. (From Oerter-Klein K and Cutler GB Jr (1996). Changes in the patterns of follicle-stimulating hormone and luteinizing hormone secretion at puberty. In S.G. Hillier, H.C. Kitchener, & J.P. Neilson [Eds.]. *Scientific essentials of reproductive medicine*. Philadelphia: Saunders.)

TABLE 2-4 Stages of Pubertal Development (Tanner)

	Girls	
STAGE	**BREAST**	**PUBIC HAIR**
1	Prepubertal	No pigmented hair
2	Budding with larger areolae	Small amount of coarse, pigmented hair mostly along labia majora
3	Enlargement of breast and areolae	Spread of coarse, pigmented hair over mons pubis
4	Secondary mound of areolae	Almost adult pattern
5	Mature contour	Adult pattern

	Boys		
STAGE	**GENITALIA**	**PUBIC HAIR**	**TESTICULAR VOLUME**
1	Prepubertal	No pigmented hair	<3 mL
2	Thinning and darkening of scrotum, increased size of penis	Small amount of coarse, pigmented hair at base of penis	3–8 mL
3	Increased diameter of penis	Coarse, pigmented hair extends above penis	10–15 mL
4	Increased diameter and length of penis	Almost adult pattern	15–20 mL
5	Adult size and shape	Adult pattern	≥25 mL

From Witchel, S.F. & Plant, T.M. (2014). Puberty: gonadarche and adrenarche. In J Strauss & R. Barbieri (Eds.). Yen and Jaffe's reproductive endocrinology (7th ed.). Philadelphia: Elsevier.

production of gonadal steroids.[59] After adrenarche, the gonadal sex steroids, testosterone and estradiol, are secreted. Testosterone secretion marks the gonadarche, occurring before physiologic changes of puberty. Secreted diurnally, levels of testosterone are higher earlier in the day. Estradiol levels vary considerably, increasing later at night than testosterone and peaking by midmorning.[39] In puberty, gonadal steroids rise gradually, increasing with successive Tanner stages.[42] Other sex steroids of adrenal and gonadal origin—DHEA, estrone, androstenedione, and 17α-hydroxyprogesterone (17-OHP)—are also secreted. In response, sex steroid–binding protein levels increase.[42]

Reproductive capability in men begins with spermarche. Unlike menarche, which occurs toward the end of puberty, spermarche begins early in puberty, preceding the peak growth spurt and beginning at an average of 13.5 years of age. Puberty generally takes about 4 years to complete, beginning somewhere between 11 and 16 years of age. During this time there are growth and development of the reproductive organs, rapid physical growth, and development of secondary sex characteristics (Table 2-4).

The specific stimulus or mechanism for initiating puberty is unclear. There is an increase in the release of pituitary gonadotropins, which stimulates the production of androgens, particularly testosterone. Testosterone levels increase after nocturnal pulsatile LH secretion, peaking in the early morning.[39] Spontaneous morning erections are secondary to these increased testosterone levels. Synthesis of testosterone and other androgens results in the changes in the reproductive system and somatic tissue.

The major changes include the enlargement of the testes and penis; development of pubic, axillary, facial, and body hair; rapid skeletal growth; hypertrophy of the larynx, with subsequent deepening of the voice; increased activity of the sweat and sebaceous glands; and muscular hypertrophy. Along with these changes, the seminiferous tubules begin sperm production. Before this point, a meiosis-inhibiting factor may be secreted by the Sertoli cells to inhibit spermatogonia meiosis. For males, testicular enlargement from the growth of the seminiferous tubules is the best indicator of pubertal activation of the HPO axis and occurs before other physical changes. Increased testicular volume usually occurs between 9 and 14 years.[59] Pubertal development before 9.5 years of age in males is considered precocious puberty.[42,59] At midpuberty in males, gynecomastia, sperm production with ejaculation, and increasing height and weight occur. Sperm production with ejaculation may occur at midpuberty, but mature sperm is not present until about a year after the growth of the penis.

Other physiologic changes accompanying later adolescence include development of facial and chest hair and extension of pubic hair.[42] The mean age of Tanner stage 2 pubic hair development is 12 years (11.2 years for African American males).[42] Tanner stage 5 pubic hair development also varies by ethnicity, with median ages of 16 years for European-American, 15 years for African American, and 15.8 years for Mexican American males.[42] In contrast to females, in males pubertal linear growth begins in Tanner stage 3 and may continue after stage 5. Therefore males are taller at the time of peak height velocity.[42]

Female Puberty

In females, the mean age of menarche, defined as the initial menses, is 12 to 12.7 years of age and has been for the previous 30 years. Although the age of menarche has decreased by 2 to 3 months per decade since the mid-1800s, present research does not document a continuation of this trend. Earlier menarche is posited to be the result of better nutrition, increased body mass, increased light exposure, and decreased disease. Median pubertal stages among females vary by ethnicity. Later menarche (15 years of age or older) is associated with subfecundity and infertility.[29]

Breast development, termed *thelarche* is the best indicator of pubertal activation of the HPO axis.[17,42] The National Health and Nutrition Examination Survey (NHANES) III survey found the onset of breast development for European Americans is 10.4 years, for African Americans is 9.5 years, and for Mexican American girls is 9.8 years.[42] Even though the onset of development may vary, the survey found the median age for complete adult breast development is 14 years for the population as a whole.[42] Breast development before 8 years of age is considered precocious puberty.[59] Pubertal growth is the result of increasing estradiol levels, beginning before stage 2 breast development. Thelarche precedes pubarche by approximately 1 to 1.5 years, with menarche occurring approximately 2.5 years after thelarche.[6] Peak height growth occurs before menarche, during breast stage 3.[42] After menarche, female pubertal growth decelerates. Therefore even though girls have an earlier onset of puberty within the normal range, both girls and boys complete puberty at approximately the same age. Attainment of physical parameters is not earlier for girls despite a longer "growing season."[46]

After birth, the ovaries are dormant until puberty, although some primordial follicles partially respond to the FSH of childhood.[5] At puberty, 300,000 to 600,000 follicles await activation; however, only approximately 400 to 500 oogonia mature as secondary follicles for ovulation.[5,11,54,81] Oocytes are arrested in the prophase stage of the first meiotic division, converting oogonia to primary oocytes until ovulation. With ovulation, meiosis commences and the first polar body is formed.[7,81] Atresia of the remaining ovarian follicles occurs in response to apoptosis. Apoptosis is the programmed cell self-destruction without an accompanying inflammatory response. (Meiosis is discussed further in Chapter 1.)

After puberty, with increased FSH and LH expression, the ovaries and follicles are stimulated. Oocytes are surrounded by a single layer of granulosa cells that are believed to nourish the ovum and secrete oocyte maturation–inhibiting factor. Oocyte maturation–inhibiting hormone maintains the ova as primordial follicles in the first stage of meiotic division as in fetal development.[49,81]

Ovarian Cycle

The ovarian cycle consists of the follicular phase and the luteal phase (Figure 2-22). During the follicular phase there is ovarian follicular maturation and ovulation. The luteal phase includes the development of the corpus luteum from luteinization of the granulosa and theca interna cells. With involution of the corpus luteum, a new ovarian cycle begins.

The follicular phase commences with follicular growth in response to gonadotropin stimulation. A primordial follicle contains an oocyte with a single layer of granulosa cells. Developing into preantral follicles or primary follicles, the oocyte is covered with multiple layers of granulosa cells. FSH expression by the granulosa cells parallels formation of the antral cavity. Follicles mature from primordial to preantral follicles even without LH and FSH stimulation, but subsequent maturation does not occur without FSH stimulation.[40]

Follicular maturation to the antral stage is believed to require a 3-month trajectory (85 days).[7,27,49] The "trajectory of follicle growth"—from follicle recruitment to follicle selection to dominant follicle—is interdependent on gonadotropins (Figure 2-23).[7,25,27] Gonadal steroids act to "guide" the process from primordial follicle to the secondary follicular stage.[25,27]

The GnRH pulse generator has a frequency of approximately one discharge per hour (60 to 90 minutes), resulting in a GnRH pituitary portal circulation bolus. Research suggests that there is a corresponding LH pulse for each GnRH pulsation.[27] Hormone priming (i.e., small doses over a period of time) induces an increased LH pulse amplitude, which over 4 hours enhances GnRH receptors. Activation of the system initiates a sequence of reproductive endocrinology events (Figure 2-24). Specialized neurons in the hypothalamus synthesize and secrete GnRH in response to hormonal and neural stimuli. The GnRH pulse generator varies dependent on cycle timing. In the early follicular phase, the LH generator pulses approximately every 94 minutes (compared with late follicular phase pulsations every 60 to 70 minutes, 100 minutes during the early luteal phase, and late luteal phase pulsations every 200 minutes).[7] More rapid pulses are associated with increased LH secretion and slower pulses are associated with FSH secretion.[7] Both ovaries have an equal opportunity for stimulation and alternate ovulation.

The neurosecretory cells integrate neuronal input from the feedback signals of the developing ovarian follicle. GnRH is secreted into the capillary venous network, bathing the anterior pituitary gland through the portal circulation. GnRH binds to membrane receptors located in the pituitary gonadotropes via cAMP and calcium mobilization, stimulating gonadotropin release.[83] Then pituitary gonadotropes secrete LH and FSH in pulses into the peripheral circulation. During the follicular phase of the ovarian cycle, the GnRH pulse generator operates at the same frequency as in its unmodulated state (i.e., independent of HPO stimulation), releasing GnRH from secretory packets.

Differentiation of follicles is believed to be multifactorial. Endocrine, paracrine, and autocrine factors modulate the effect of FSH on the growing follicles.[66] Rising FSH levels are noted in the early follicular phase, stimulating increased

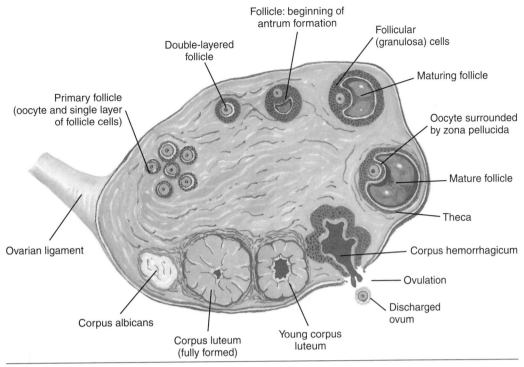

FIGURE 2-22   Cross-section of the ovary during reproductive years. (From Thibodeau, G.A. & Patton, K.T. [2007]. *Anatomy and physiology* [6th ed.]. St. Louis: Mosby.)

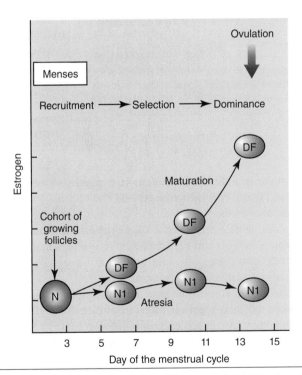

FIGURE 2-23   Time course for recruitment, selection, and ovulation of the dominant ovarian follicle *(DF)* with onset of atresia among other follicles *(N₁)* of the cohort. (From Hidgen, G.D. (1986). Time course for recruitment, selection, and ovulation of the dominant ovarian follicle (DF) with onset of atresia among other follicles (N1) of the cohort. (From Hidgen, G.D. [1986]. Physiology of follicular maturation. In H.W. Jones, Jr., G.S. Jones, G.D. Hodgen, & Z. Rosenwaks. [Eds.]. In vitro fertilization. Baltimore: Williams & Wilkins.)

inhibin B secretion (Figure 2-25; see also Figure 2-9).[79,80] FSH and LH secretion increases significantly. The increase in FSH precedes that of LH by several days. With FSH stimulation, follicular development progresses. Follicular recruitment consists of follicular maturation from a primordial follicle to a secondary follicle. A primordial follicle (30 to 60 μm in diameter) is a primary oocyte in the late diplotene phase that is surrounded by a single layer of approximately 15 pregranulosa cells.[81] Primordial follicles have been detected as early as 16 weeks' gestation, with formation ceasing by 6 months postpartum. Follicular growth is accelerated when the germinal vesicle reaches approximately 20 μm in diameter.

Primary follicles (greater than 60 μm in diameter) are primary oocytes surrounded by a single layer of granulosa cells.[81] Spindle cells of the ovarian stroma develop into granulosa cells, which rapidly proliferate. Granulosa cells give rise to the theca follicular cells, which are composed of two sublayers: the theca interna and theca externa (see Figure 2-22). The theca interna (the inner sublayer) develops the follicular blood supply and secretes steroidal hormones, androgens which aromatize to estradiol.[5] The theca externa (the external layer) becomes the capsule of the maturing follicle as it comes in contact with the surrounding stroma. The theca externa is believed to produce an angiogenic factor. Differentiation of the thecal cells concludes the primary follicle stage. Development of the zona pellucida is characteristic of a preantral primary follicle.[81] Mucopolysaccharides secreted by the granulosa cells comprise the zona pellucida.[13]

Secondary follicles (less than 120 μm) are primary oocytes surrounded by approximately 600 granulosa cells, arranged in

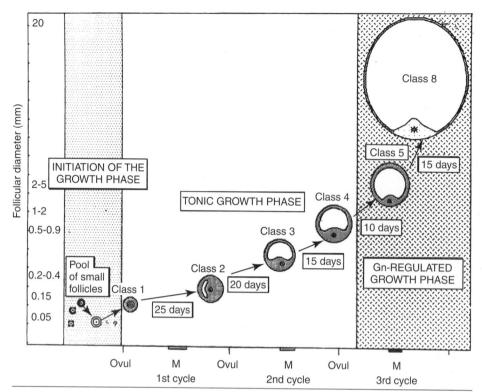

FIGURE 2-24   Complete follicular growth trajectory. Class 1 follicle is a secondary follicle with thecal cells and is presumed to become responsive to gonadotropins. Although the tonic (early) stage of follicle development (class 1 to 4) is likely to be gonadotropin dependent (albeit to a lesser extent), the final stages of follicular development (class 5 to 8) are the ones heavily dependent on gonadotropins. According to this view, late luteal phase, class 5 follicles constitute the cohort from which the follicle destined to ovulate in the following cycle is recruited. The exponential gonadotropin-dependent growth phase (class 5 to 8) takes place during the follicular phase of the cycle following the third menses from initiation of the growth phase. During this time, follicular selection and dominance are accomplished. The total duration of the process wherein a class 1 follicle is converted into a preovulatory class 8 follicle is estimated to be 85 days and spans three ovulatory cycles. *Gn*, Gonadotropin; *M*, menses; *Ovul*, ovulation. (From Larsen, P.R., Kronenberg, H.M, Melmed, S. & Polonsky, K. [2003]. *Williams textbook of endocrinology* [10th ed.]. Philadelphia: Saunders.)

several layers.[81] Follicular enlargement is secondary to oocyte growth, proliferation of granulosa cells, and thecal cell differentiation. Accompanying the proliferation of granulosa cells and secondary follicles is the development of FSH, estrogen, and androgen receptors that become coupled as gap junctions.[81]

Ovarian activin promotes FSH expression. Rising FSH levels in turn promote accelerated growth of 6 to 12 primordial follicles each cycle.[30] Follicular recruitment of secondary follicles follows FSH and LH expression and occurs in the first 4 to 5 days of the cycle, leading to a selected follicle cohort from days 5 to 7. Until day 7 of the early follicular phase, all maturing follicles possess gametogenic potential for follicular selection.[27]

As follicles develop (ranging from 200 to 400 µm in diameter) in response to increased FSH, antral formation follows.[81] Follicular fluid that is high in estrogen is expressed by the granulosa cells (see Figure 2-24). Antral development heralds follicle maturation as a vesicular follicle and graafian follicle. With antral formation, the follicle is called a *vesicular follicle;* rapid proliferation of the granulosa and thecal cells continues with estradiol expression.[8,69] Continued follicular maturation

as a vesicular follicle is dependent on activation of the granulosa and thecal cells by increased FSH and follicular estrogen. In response to the rising follicular estrogen levels, the granulosa cells develop increased FSH receptors and sensitivity.[27] Receptors for FSH and LH are present on the follicular granulosa cells and thecal cells (antral follicles), respectively.[3] Vesicular follicular enlargement results.

The follicle dominance attained during the midfollicular and late follicular phases is determined by rising serum FSH levels and by specific follicular sensitivity to FSH.[66,81] Initially, there is an intercycle rise in FSH that promotes follicular development. Dominant follicles have a greater sensitivity to FSH than the remaining growing follicles. Granulosa cells secrete inhibin and follistatin, both peptides that suppress FSH secretion during the midfollicular phase. Also, with increasing ovarian levels of follistatin and inhibin B in the midfollicular to late follicular phase (the time of follicle selection), there is a corresponding decrease in FSH secretion. During the midfollicular and late follicular phases, the number of developing dominant follicles decreases in response to lower serum FSH

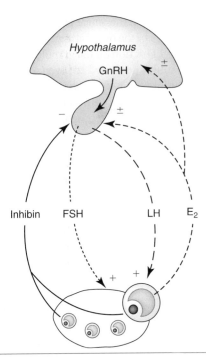

FIGURE 2-25   The hypothalamic-pituitary-ovarian axis in women during the follicular phase. Estradiol *(E₂)* feeds back at both the hypothalamus and anterior pituitary to inhibit the secretion of follicle-stimulating hormone *(FSH)* and luteinizing hormone *(LH)* (negative feedback). Under certain conditions, it can provoke the discharge of LH (positive feedback). Inhibin arising from both dominant and small antral follicles suppresses the synthesis and release of FSH by the anterior pituitary. GnRH, Gonadotropin-releasing hormone. (From Hillier, S.G. [1998]. Biosynthesis and secretion of ovarian and adrenal steroids. In I.S. Fraser, Jansen, R. P. S. Lobo, R.A., Whitehead, M. I. [Eds.]. *Estrogens and progestogens in clinical practice*. Philadelphia: Churchill Livingstone.)

levels and sensitivity.[66] With follicle selection, secondary to gonadotropic stimulus, one single follicle matures and is dominant (days 8 to 12). Follicle dominance is determined by the late follicular phase (approximately 7 days before ovulation) and is established when the follicle is 3 to 8 mm.[67,81] When follicular cells are 10 mm, LH receptors are located on the granulosa cells.[5] In contrast to follicular recruitment that transcends ovarian cycles, the follicular selection and dominant phase is completed within one cycle.

Factors contributing to follicle dominance include the ability of the follicle to aromatize androgens from the midfollicular phase on, specifically estradiol and a high granulosa cell mitotic index.[27,57,81] As the dominant follicle matures, it expresses increased estradiol, with a subsequent rise in serum estradiol levels.[81] About 90% of circulating estradiol is secreted by the dominant follicle.[3,27] In addition, the dominant follicle contains FSH and estrogen intrafollicularly. Late follicular phase estradiol levels are at their highest levels within the follicle and blood. During follicular maturation when plasma estradiol levels exceed a threshold level of approximately 250 pg/mL (917.8 pmol/L) for 36 hours, the negative feedback system is overridden by a positive feedback result. Estrogen's positive system feedback relationship with the hypothalamus stimulates increased secretion of GnRH and follows the

"priming" of the adenohypophysis by high-frequency GnRH.[3] Estrogen modulates the release of FSH and LH by the gonadotropin pulse generator when "read" by the pituitary gland. Hormonal patterns are illustrated in Figure 2-26.

Higher levels of interleukin-8 (IL-8) and interleukin-11 (IL-11), both chemotaxic cytokines, are found in more dominant follicles.[64] IL-8 activates neutrophils and promotes cell proliferation and angiogenesis.[64] In addition, genes are involved in ovarian development and function. Many of these genes are yet to be identified but include transcription factors, extracellular growth factors, and RNA-binding proteins.[81]

Follicular growth may also be categorized by class or phase (see Figure 2-24).[81] The tonic growth phase involves the conversion of a preantral follicle (class 1) to an antral follicle up to 2 mm in diameter (class 4). Follicular development during the tonic growth phase is gonadotropin-dependent. With development of the theca interna, class 1 follicles are activated by gonadotropin stimulation. Tonic follicular growth occurs over three menstrual cycles. During the first menstrual cycle, secondary follicles mature as class 1 follicles in the early luteal phase (days 15 to 19). In the following menstrual cycle, which is designated the second cycle, class 1 follicles are converted into class 2 follicles (days 11

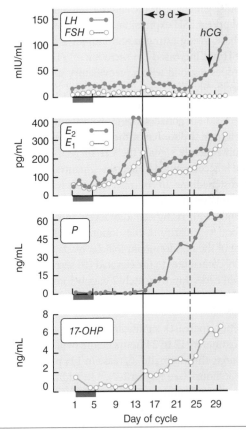

FIGURE 2-26   Hormonal patterns of human chorionic gonadotropin *(hCG)*, luteinizing hormone *(LH)*, follicle-stimulating hormone *(FSH)*, estradiol *(E2)*, estrone *(E1)*, progesterone *(P)*, and 17α-hydroxyprogesterone *(17-OHP)* during a menstrual cycle. Note the rise in hCG, which is detectable on cycle days 26 and 27. (From Creasy, R.K., Resnik, R., & Iams, J.D. [Eds.]. [2004]. *Maternal-fetal medicine: Principles and practice* [5th ed.]. Philadelphia: Saunders.)

to 15 of the second cycle). Early antral development is noted in class 2 follicles. Also during the second cycle, approximately 20 days later, class 2 follicles mature to class 3 follicles (end of the luteal phase). In the late follicular phase of the third menstrual cycle, class 3 follicles become class 4 follicles.

Conversion of class 4 follicles to class 5 is gonadotropin-dependent and occurs in the late luteal phase of cycle 3. All follicular maturation beyond class 4 is strongly dependent on FSH and LH.[81] Follicular recruitment during the late luteal phase for the succeeding cycle will occur from class 5 follicles. During this phase, which is even more gonadotropin-dependent, follicles mature from class 5 to class 8 before ovulation, averaging 5 days per class. Follicular selection and dominance occurs during this gonadotropin growth phase. Maturation of the follicle is accompanied by follicular growth, with an increase from 5 to 20 mm in diameter.

The hypothalamus responds via negative feedback to the moderately increased estrogen levels by inhibiting the secretion of gonadotropins. Decreasing FSH concentration and FSH sensitivity initiate follicle atresia of the nondominant follicles.[27] Higher follicular fluid levels of IL-11 have been noted in atretic follicles.

Over 2 to 3 days, the rising ovarian estradiol levels sensitize the LH pulse generator in the anterior pituitary gland to secrete LH but suppress FSH expression. In the midfollicular to late follicular phase, rising estrogen and inhibin B levels result in reduced FSH but increased LH secretion.[80,81] The pituitary gland gonadotropes respond with a preovulatory surge of gonadotropins (specifically LH) into the peripheral circulation.[27] Thus estrogen levels signal the hypothalamus, which regulates the pulsatile expression of gonadotropin.[24] Follicles greater than 18 mm in diameter are the source of the increased estradiol secretion, which subsequently signals the LH surge.[3,9] The LH surge of ovulation is accompanied by decreases in intrafollicular estradiol and androstenedione. In contrast, increases in progesterone and 17-OHP are noted intrafollicularly. Inhibin A levels increase concurrently with rising estradiol levels and follicular maturation. Thecal vascularity of the dominant follicle is more than twice that of the nondominant follicles by day 9. This increased vascularity contributes to the elevated LH secretion on day 12 in the ovarian cycle, approximately 2 days before ovulation.[81]

Ovulation

LH secretion increases significantly (i.e., 6- to 10-fold), peaking approximately 12 to 24 hours before ovulation.[54] Known as the *LH surge,* this dramatic increase in LH precedes ovulation by up to 36 hours (see Figure 2-2).[81] In addition, the LH surge stimulates resumption of the first meiotic division, so the mature follicle contains secondary oocytes.[24,27,81] FSH also increases, but to a lesser degree (approximately twofold).

The ovum surrounded by loosely packed follicular cells is known as the *cumulus oophorus* and is located to one side of the follicle. Follicular swelling results from the synergistic effect of the increased FSH and LH levels before ovulation. Follicular hyperemia and prostaglandins secreted in the follicular tissues contribute to plasma transudation and subsequent follicular swelling. With proliferation of the granulosa

cells and accumulation of the antral fluid, the follicle enlarges, moving to the surface of the ovary at approximately 5 to 6 days before ovulation.[81] LH action on the granulosa cells 2 to 3 days before ovulation causes decreased estrogen secretion but, conversely, increased inhibin and progesterone levels.[5] Therefore 1 day before ovulation, estrogen levels are decreasing with increasing incremental levels of progesterone.

The LH surge lasts, on average, 48 hours, with a rapid ascension for approximately 14 hours before the peak and with a descending limb of approximately 20 hours. In response to the ovulation-inducing LH surge, the dominant follicle ruptures (days 13 to 15), with subsequent formation of the corpus luteum. Although this is accompanied by drastic decreases in estradiol and inhibin B, there are rising levels of inhibin A and the second increase in progesterone at approximately 36 hours after initiation of the LH surge. Ovulation occurs approximately 35 to 44 hours after the LH surge.

As the follicle enlarges, a small cystlike protrusion (i.e., the stigma) develops in the outer follicular wall. Proteolytic enzyme digestion of the mature follicle capsule wall, prostaglandin contraction of the theca externa smooth muscle, and possibly plasminogen activators and matrix metalloproteinase together promote stigma rupture. Initially, fluid oozes from the follicle. Then the oocyte, surrounded by the zona pellucida, extrudes and is carried out by the viscous follicular fluid.

Luteal Phase

Progesterone dominates during the luteal phase of the ovarian cycle. The remaining granulosa cells of the ruptured follicle are changed into lutein cells via stimulation by LH remaining from the LH surge.[27] With luteinization, granulosa cells fill with lipids and become yellowish.[81] Thecal cells of the corpus luteum produce androgens. Androgens are progressively converted to androgenic steroids and then to estrogens and progesterone.[81] The luteinization process is enhanced by rising LH levels accompanying the LH surge and is dependent on the degree of exposure. The process continues with only the initial LH surge, although with decreased secretion of androgens and a shortened corpus luteum life span. The corpus luteum, along with lutein cells, secretes increasing amounts of estrogen and progesterone, particularly progesterone, producing approximately 25 to 50 mg per day (Figure 2-27).[81] The corpus luteum has a lifespan of approximately 11 to 17 days with a mean of 14.2 days and is dependent on trophoblastic hCG for progesterone secretion, glandular growth, and prevention of involution.[52,81]

During the luteal phase of the ovarian cycle, FSH and LH levels drop drastically in response to high levels of estrogen and, to a lesser extent, progesterone as secreted by the corpus luteum. Gonadotropin concentrations, especially FSH, further decrease secondary to the increased hormone concentration of inhibin A secreted by the luteal cells as signaled by the anterior pituitary gland.[3] Secretion of the hypothalamic pulsatile GnRHs declines, leading in turn to decreased LH pulses in response to increased progesterone levels and hypothalamic signaling.[3] In contrast to the early follicular phase, secretion of the LH pulse generator declines from pulses every 60 to 90 minutes to one pulse every 7 to 8 hours with an increase in the pulse amplitude.

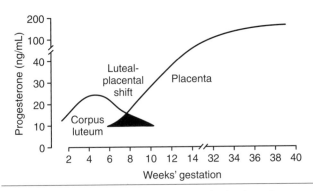

FIGURE 2-27   The shift in progesterone production from the corpus luteum to the placenta between the 7th and 9th week of gestation. (From Creasy, R.K., Resnik, R., & Iams, J.D. [Eds.]. [2004]. *Maternal-fetal medicine: Principles and practice* [5th ed.]. Philadelphia: Saunders.)

Luteal cells of the corpus luteum constitute the principal source of progesterone (the hormone of pregnancy) and, to a lesser degree, estrogen during the first 10 weeks of gestation. Progesterone levels during the luteal phase suppress FSH levels. Decreased FSH levels (lowest of the cycle) prevent folliculogenesis. LH levels after ovulation differ little from those of the follicular phase secondary to the increased amplitude of the LH pulse generator.[27] LH provision is necessary to maintain the corpus luteum.

Midluteally, peak levels of progesterone and estrogen are noted. These peak ovarian steroid levels are coupled with an endometrium favorable to trophoblastic implantation. During the luteal phase, uterine contractility decreases, becoming nearly quiescent at the time of blastocyst implantation.[19]

The placental hormone hCG (see Chapter 3) "rescues" or enhances corpus luteum development and continuation during its first 3 to 4 months.[27,44,81] Luteinization-inhibiting hormone prevents corpus luteum formation and the subsequent luteinization process until ovulation has occurred.

Corpus Luteum Demise

The corpus luteum involutes in approximately 9 to 11 days unless the oocyte is fertilized.[15] Decreased LH levels signal the corpus luteum (approximately 1.5 cm) to begin the involution process at day 21. By day 26, the corpus luteum has progressively involuted to become the corpus albicans, which over the following weeks is replaced by connective tissue. As the corpus luteum involutes, estrogen, progesterone, and inhibin levels fall, removing the feedback inhibition of the anterior pituitary gland. As a result, the anterior pituitary begins to secrete progressively more FSH and, in a few days, LH.

With involution, progesterone continues to decrease to a level similar to that of the follicular phase. The declining inhibin A levels 48 hours before menstruation (in concert with rising FSH levels) contribute to follicular recruitment. One day before menstruation, the LH pulse generator frequency increases and amplitude decreases, with a subsequent increase in inhibin B and follicular development. Increased GnRHs are secreted in response to the lower progesterone and estrogen levels, initiating a new ovarian cycle. Menstruation begins. The new ovarian cycle commences with follicular recruitment, selection, and dominance.

Menstruation

Menarche is the first menstrual cycle; the mean age of menarche ranges from 12 to 12.7 years of age in the United States.[42,53,59] As mentioned previously, declines in age of menarche are believed to be associated with improved nutrition, increased body mass, increased light exposure, and decreased disease. According to Tanner's staging, menarche commonly occurs at stage 4.[42] Menarche usually occurs 2 to 3 years after the initiation of breast development.[59]

With early menstrual cycles, the developing follicles secrete only estrogens. Estrogen secretion is variable and is unopposed by progesterone.[45] As a result, early cycles are anovulatory and irregular for 1 to 2 years, with variable menstrual flow.[45,59] Generally within 1 to 2 years, menstrual frequency stabilizes at 28 days, ranging from 26 to 34 days, with pattern variations noted at the extremes of reproductive ages.[27] The interval between menstrual cycles averages 28.1 days for women reporting cycle lengths ranging from 15 to 45 days.[15] Cycle length variations primarily occur in the follicular-proliferative phase.[27] Menses usually lasts 4 to 6 days with most menstrual discharge occurring within the first 24 hours, with the maximal flow occurring on day 2.[4,27] The duration of the is very individualistic but is normally consistent each cycle. Menses of less than 2 days or greater than 7 days are considered abnormal.[45]

Over 3 to 7 days, uterine blood loss averages approximately 35 mL (ranging from 25 to 60 mL), with an equal amount of serous fluid loss per menstrual cycle.[4,15,19] Intersubject menstrual blood loss variations are also noted.[4,31] Iron loss accompanying menstruation is believed to be approximately 0.4 to 1 mg/day of the cycle up to 12 mg/cycle.[4,15,68] Menstrual blood loss of greater than 60 mL per menses is positively correlated with iron deficiency anemia.[45] Menstrual discharge has a distinctive fleshy odor secondary to tissue necrosis and endometrial ischemia and anoxia.

Endometrial Cycle

The endometrial cycle of the uterus is composed of proliferative and secretory phases and menstruation. During the proliferative phase there is development of vascular, endothelial, and stromal cells with thickening of the endometrium, whereas during the secretory phase there is ongoing growth and changes in the spiral arteries and endometrial cells to facilitate implantation. With menstruation, there is regression of the endometrium and spiral artery coiling with subsequent endometrial hypoxia, ischemia, and endometrial degeneration.[15]

Whereas the ovary is sensitive to FSH and LH, the uterus is more sensitive to estrogen and progesterone (Figure 2-28). The uterine endometrium comprises three layers: the functionalis, containing the stroma (mesenchymal connective tissue); the spongy zone; and the germinal basalis layer, which is adjacent to the myometrium (Figure 2-29).[22,27,45] Whereas the functionalis layer is denuded each menstrual cycle, the germinal basalis remains constant throughout.[27,45] During the proliferative phase there is reepithelialization of the functionalis endometrium and angiogenesis in the basilis layer. Also, in the basilis layer, the stroma become more dense

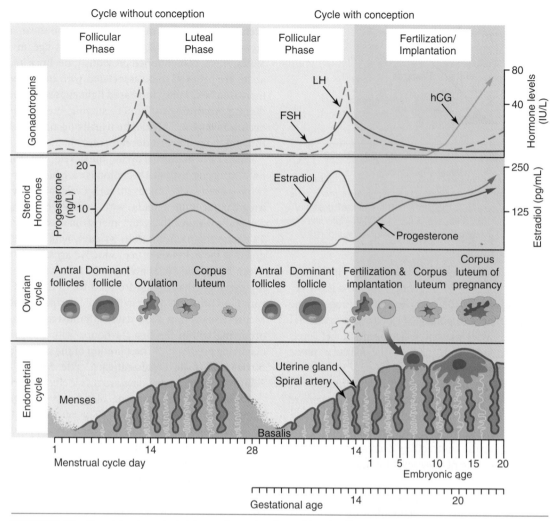

FIGURE 2-28 Gonadotropin control of the ovarian and endometrial cycles. The ovarian-endometrial cycle has been structured as a 28-day cycle. The follicular phase (days 1 to 14) is characterized by rising estrogen levels, endometrial thickening, and selection of the dominant "ovulatory" follicle. During the luteal phase (days 14 to 21), the corpus luteum (CL) produces estrogen and progesterone, which prepare the endometrium for implantation. If implantation occurs, the developing blastocyst begins to produce human chorionic gonadotropin (hCG) and rescues the corpus luteum, thus maintaining progesterone production. *FSH,* follicle-stimulating hormone; *LH,* luteinizing hormone. From Cunningham, F., Leveno, K.J., Bloom, S.L., et al. (2013). *Williams Obstetrics* (24th ed.). New York: McGraw-Hill.

and there is glandular hyperplasia, whereas in the functionalis the stroma is looser and the glands more separated.[15]

With fertilization, the endometrial tissue changes from secretory tissue to decidual tissue in preparation for implantation.[15] Under the influence of progesterone, the endometrial stroma is transformed to decidual cells.[15] The decidual tissue contains bone marrow cells and immunologic substances such as cytokines, relaxin, inhibin, growth factors, and prorenin to facilitate "acceptance" of the implanting trophoblast.[15] Immunologically to facilitate implantation and protect the fetus and the woman from ascending organisms during pregnancy and menstruation, a number of leukocytes and lymphocytes are found in the reproductive tract, specifically in the endometrium in varying levels. This natural immunity includes an increase in neutrophils during the perimenstrual phase, with macrophages increasing from the proliferative to the menstrual phases and CD8 cells increasing in the proliferative

phase. Natural killer (NK) cells, present in the perimenstrual endometrium, increasing in the secretory phase and with pregnancy, are found in the decidua during the first trimester.[45] Uterine blood is supplied by the uterine and ovarian arteries, which branch to form the arcuate arteries. These arcuate arteries further branch to form the spiral (coiled) arteries and the basal (straight) arteries (see Figure 2-29). Spiral arteries supply primarily the endometrial basal layer and are responsive to vasoconstrictive factors; basal vessels are not responsive to vasoconstrictive factors.[15] Spiral arteries underlying the placenta undergo marked changes with pregnancy (see Chapter 3).

Menstrual Phase

Menstrual bleeding is initiated with arterial vasoconstriction, subsequent hematoma formation, and relaxation of the endometrial arteries, followed by bleeding, with resultant anoxia.[15]

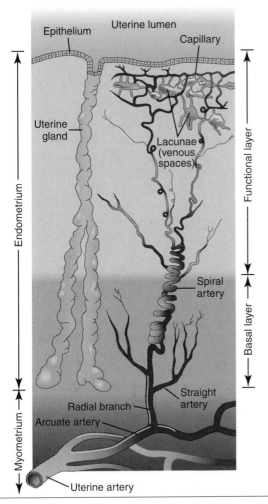

FIGURE 2-29 The glands and vasculature of the endometrium. (From Moore, K.L. & Persaud, T.V.N. [2003]. *The developing human: Clinically oriented embryology* [7th ed.]. Philadelphia: Saunders.)

Proliferative Phase

The proliferative phase (the first 11 days of the cycle) is also known as the estrogen phase, corresponding to the follicular phase of the ovarian cycle. Proliferative phase variations account for most of the menstrual cycle irregularities.[27] After menstruation, a thin layer of endometrial stroma is left, with few epithelial cells in the endometrial glands and crypts. In the early proliferative phase, the endometrial glands are simple and straight.[27] With increasing ovarian estrogen the endometrium spongy layer, stromal and epithelial cells, and glandular and stromal mitoses proliferate.[15,62] Neutrophils adherent to the endometrium may be the source of vascular endothelial growth factor, promoting endometrial angiogenesis.[22] During the late proliferative phase there is continued growth of the stroma and glands, with corkscrew convolutions, edema, lymphocytes, and macrophages. Cervical mucus significantly increases. From days 12 to 14 of the cycle, there is maximized endometrial growth and proliferation. Growth of the endometrial tissue ranges from 0.5 mm to 5 mm (Figure 2-30).[15,27]

Secretory Phase

The secretory phase, or the following 12 days, corresponds to the luteal phase of the ovarian cycle, with increased secretion of estrogen and progesterone. At ovulation, the endometrium is 3 to 4 mm thick and the endometrial glands secrete a thin, stringy mucus. These mucus strings line the cervical canal, providing channels to guide the sperm. There are increased endometrial lipid and glycogen deposits, along with stromal cytoplasm and tortuosity of blood vessels.[27] In response to progesterone, vacuoles are formed approximately 36 to 48 hours after ovulation.[15] Stromal edema contributes to enlargement of the endometrium. Increased endoplasmic reticulum and mitochondria are noted in the endometrial epithelial cells.

Apoptotic changes occur in the endometrial tissue throughout the endometrial cycle.[69] Fissures form in the functionalis layer, and necrotic outer endometrial fragments of the functionalis detach at the hemorrhagic sites for approximately 48 hours after the initiation of menstruation. This results in desquamation of the superficial endometrial layers down to the basalis layer within 48 to 72 hours, leaving a thin endometrium that cyclically regenerates from the spongy layer. Two-thirds of the functionalis layer of the endometrium may be shed during menstruation.[15] Endometrial tissue and seeping blood evoke uterine contractions.

Menstrual blood clotting and fibrinolysis are orchestrated by hormonal endometrial stimulation.[15] Progesterone facilitates production of tissue factor and plasminogen activator inhibitor–1 for blood coagulation. In contrast, plasminogen activator is released with the necrotic endometrium and enhances the nonclotting properties of the menstrual fluid.[15] In addition, leukocytes and prostaglandins are released with the desquamated tissue and blood.[15] Uterine leukocytes are thought to protect the uterus from infection, although the endometrium is completely desquamated.

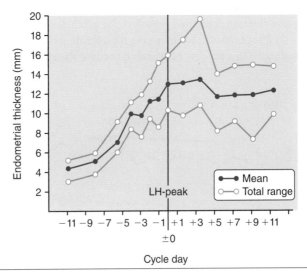

FIGURE 2-30 The endometrial thickness (in mm) measured by transvaginal ultrasound, presented as mean and total range, in 16 women during an ovulatory cycle. Each point on the curve represents a minimum of six observations. *LH,* Luteinizing hormone. (From Bakos, O., Lundkvist, O., & Bergh, T. [1993]. Transvaginal sonographic evaluation of endometrial growth and texture in spontaneous ovulatory cycles: A descriptive study. *Hum Reprod, 8,* 799.)

Midsecretory and Late Secretory Phases

Spotting or breakthrough bleeding may result from decreased estradiol levels at ovulation. Midcycle pain, also referred to as *mittelschmerz*, occurs on the side of the dominant follicle.[54] Accompanying the LH surge is a basal temperature nadir.[28] The basal temperature increases 0.5° to 1° F (0.3° to 0.6°C) on day 16 of the cycle (after the LH surge) and remains elevated for approximately 11 to 14 days (Figure 2-31).[28] The endometrium responds to the increased progesterone with edema and further secretory development. Endometrial venules and sinusoidal spaces fill with blood and stromal cells accumulate cytoplasm, forming the predecidual endometrial layer. Decidualization is facilitated by transforming growth factor-β and progesterone.[15]

Endometrial spiral arteries coil and lengthen, and the endometrial glands become increasingly tortuous. Endometrial secretory activity is greatest 6 days after ovulation.[27] Increased estradiol and progesterone contribute to maximal stroma edema on day 22.[27] The highly vascularized endometrium is then 5 to 6 mm thick and is secreting tissue factors, coagulation factor, plasminogen activator inhibitor–1, and other factors.[15] Coiled arteries lengthen rapidly in the thickening endometrium. Endometrial secretions increase, preparing for implantation of the fertilized ovum.

If fertilization of the oocyte does not occur, the corpus luteum degenerates secondary to decreased estrogen and progesterone levels. Blood vessels of the secretory endometrium undergo vasoconstriction, with arterial relaxation and subsequent bleeding followed by ischemia and endometrial tissue necrosis. Menstruation occurs.

With fertilization, the secretory endometrium is further transformed to decidual tissue (see Chapter 3). In response to increased estrogen and progesterone, the endometrial stromal cells become decidual cells surrounded by a membrane.[15] Growth of the decidua ranges from 5 to 10 mm in depth in preparation for implantation.[15] Embryonic expression of the heparin-binding epidermal growth factor promotes implantation and trophoblast invasion through paracrine and autocrine signaling.[41] This process helps cells penetrate the stroma and displace the arteriole endothelium. hCG produced by the syncytiotrophoblast (outer layer of the trophoblast) rescues the corpus luteum, thereby increasing estrogen and progesterone levels. The blastocyst implants and pregnancy occurs. (Implantation is discussed further in Chapter 3.)

Premenstrual and Ischemic Phase

The uterus responds to the declining gonadal steroids by stimulating the uterine endometrial cells, followed by involution on days 26 to 28. Without support from the corpus luteum, vasospasm occurs in the arterioles and coiled arteries and blood vessels in the endometrial mucosa from 4 to 24 hours before menstruation.[15,30] Endothelin 1 of the endometrium epithelium or stroma promotes vasospasm and vasoconstriction of the endometrial arteries. With vasospasm and decreased estrogen and progesterone, necrosis of the basal layer of the endometrium and stratum vascular blood vessels results and blood pools beneath the endometrium.[27] About 1 to 2 days before menstruation, stroma and epithelial cells of the endometrium produce IL-8 and monocyte chemotactic protein–1, which are chemotactic factors for neutrophils and monocytes.[15] As the corpus luteum ceases to function, there is resorption of the endometrial edema, with subsequent endometrial shrinking.

Gestational Follicular Development

During pregnancy, limited follicular maturation continues in response to gonadotropin stimulation. Although follicular growth may continue until delivery, atresia soon follows. Atresia of the follicles occurs before the follicles can grow to ovulatory size.

Male Reproductive Endocrinology

The hormones of the male reproductive system are released by the hypothalamus, anterior pituitary, and testes. Release is both systemic and local, being continuous or acyclic after puberty. Slight diurnal changes in plasma testosterone levels occur. The release of male reproductive hormones is controlled by a negative feedback loop along the hypothalamic-pituitary-testicular axis (see Figure 2-7).

Testosterone is an androgen produced by the Leydig cells of the testes. Initial production of testosterone early in embryonic development is responsible for development of the male reproductive organs and external genitalia. Production becomes active again at puberty. Testosterone is necessary for spermatogenesis, development of male secondary sex characteristics, bone growth, growth and development of male reproductive organs, sexual drive, and potency. The testes also produce small amounts of other androgens.

The hypothalamus regulates the testicular environment by secreting GnRH, which is moderated further by norepinephrine, serotonin, endorphin, melatonin, and dopamine. GnRH secretion occurs once every 70 to 90 minutes.[75] The pulsatile pattern is required for the production and release of LH and FSH by the anterior pituitary.

Both LH and FSH act directly on the testes, stimulating spermatogenesis and testosterone production. Both hormones have a high affinity for their respective receptors. Once bound, they activate the protein kinase cascade via cAMP. LH stimulates

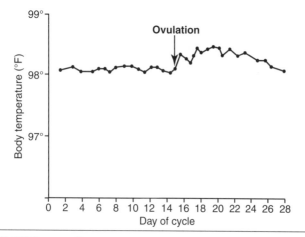

FIGURE 2-31 Elevation of body temperature shortly after ovulation. (From Guyton, A.C. & Hall, J.E. [2016]. *Textbook of medical physiology* [17th ed.]. Philadelphia: Elsevier.)

the Leydig cells to initiate steroidogenesis by synthesizing androgens from cholesterol precursors. Along with androgen production, LH is responsible for triggering spermatogenesis.

The effects of FSH complement those of LH. FSH binds to receptor sites in the Sertoli cells, stimulating the production of proteins that in turn affect spermatogenesis. FSH is also responsible for facilitating mitosis in the spermatogonia and initiating meiosis in the spermatocyte. Lastly, FSH seems to be necessary for the maturation of the spermatid. Normal levels of FSH are necessary to maintain normal sperm quality. Note that sperm quality can be affected by a number of external factors including mobile phone use and other environmental exposures.[16,72]

Testicular testosterone is believed to act directly on the germ cells and Sertoli cells. Through diffusion and active transport, testosterone supports the germinal epithelium and regulates spermatogenesis.

Climacteric

Menopause and the *climacteric* are both terms referring to a woman's transition from a reproductive to a nonfertile state. This transition encompasses myriad physiologic and psychosocial changes. Although they are sometimes used interchangeably, the terms *climacteric* and *menopause* have different meanings. The climacteric is the transitional period encompassing the perimenopausal, menopausal, and postmenopausal years. From 37.5 years of age onward, there is increased follicular atresia and the ovaries are less responsive, resulting in decreased female fertility.[11] Decreased female fertility precedes menopause. The climacteric continues for approximately 2 to 5 years after menopause and includes the physiologic and psychosocial changes accompanying estrogen deprivation.

The term *menopause* (from the Greek word for "to stop") means cessation of menses and is confirmed by amenorrhea for 12 months. The mean age of menopause is 51.4 years of age, with a range of 42 to 58 years.[11] By their early 50s, most women (90%) experience menopause.[11] Premature menopause (menopause at age younger than 40 years of age) occurs in approximately 1% of women.[11] Other factors may also contribute to menopausal changes. For example, tobacco use may accelerate ovarian aging. Women who smoke may experience menopause as much as 2 years earlier than nonsmokers.[81] In addition, a strong association has been noted between maternal and daughters' ages at menopause, suggesting a genetic component.[11]

The 2 years preceding and following menopause are referred to as *perimenopause*. Women who are perimenopausal experience menstrual cycles that are irregular and have greater variation in length and intensity.[1] Figure 2-32 shows reproductive staging as defined by the Stages of Reproductive Aging Workshop.[11] The reproductive interval is stages −5 to −3, with stages −2 to −1 called the menopausal transition and stages −1 to −2 as postmenopausal.[11] Postmenopausal is further categorized as *early*, which is the first 5 years after the final menstrual period (FMP), and *late*, defined as beginning 5 years after the FMP and continuing until the woman's death.[11]

With reproductive aging, the primary changes occur in the ovary and follicles (particularly the oocytes).[11] Oocytes in women of advanced reproductive age (40 to 45 years) have been found to have abnormal chromosomal alignment at metaphase and increased meiotic nondisjunction.[81] Although ovarian follicles may form more rapidly, they are the same size as in earlier years. At menopause, the ovaries are atrophic and weigh less than 10 g. The ovarian medulla is large and

Stages:	−5	−4	−3	−2	−1	0	+1	+2
Terminology:	**Reproductive**			**Menopausal Transition**			**Postmenopause**	
	Early	Peak	Late	Early	Late*		Early*	Late
				Perimenopause				
Duration of stage:	Variable			Variable		ⓐ 1 yr	ⓑ 4 yrs	Until demise
Menstrual cycles:	Variable to regular	Regular		Variable cycle length (>7 days different from normal)	≥2 skipped cycles and an interval of amenorrhea (≥60 days)	Amen ∝ 12 mos	None	
Endocrine:	Normal FSH	↑FSH		↑FSH			↑FSH	

*Stages most likely to be characterized by vasomotor symptoms   ↑ = elevated

FIGURE 2-32   The Stages of Reproductive Aging Workshop (STRAW) staging system. Amen, Amenorrhea; *FSH,* follicle-stimulating hormone. (From Soules, M.R., Sherman, S., Parrott, E., Rebar, R., Santoro, N., Utian, W., & Woods, N. [2001]. Executive summary: Stages of Reproductive Aging Workshop (STRAW). *Fertil Steril, 76,* 874.)

contains sclerosed blood vessels. With aging, there is a decrease in the total follicular population and in each type of follicle, although no difference has been noted in the total number of follicles of the right and left ovaries. The ovaries secrete primarily androstenedione at levels four times the premenopausal levels, contributing to increased ovarian vein testosterone levels (15 times higher).

During perimenopause, minimal follicles are present at various stages (i.e., primordial to atretic) of development. It is believed that in the decade before menopause there is a significant increase in follicular atresia, which accounts for the minimal ovarian follicles. For 1 to 5 years perimenopausally, menstrual cycles lengthen, and ovulation frequency and reproductive hormone levels vary (see Figure 2-32 and Table 2-2).[56] In a woman's mid-30s and 40s, the hormone inhibin B begins to progressively decline.[20] Subsequently, FSH levels increase as a compensatory mechanism.[11,20,78] Initially, LH levels stabilize at approximately premenopausal levels, although they begin to rise after amenorrhea of 12 months and then plateau.[38] Changes in inhibin and FSH concentration may precede decreased levels of estrogen and progesterone.

During menopause, estrone becomes the major estrogen; it is derived primarily from peripheral aromatization of adrenal androstenedione, mainly in adipose tissue.[11] Thus the daily production of estrone is significantly related to the woman's body mass index.

With ovarian aging, there is a decrease in estradiol synthesis.. After menopause, androstenedione expression decreases by approximately 50%. Postmenopausally, estradiol production declines to about 12 mcg/day, compared with up to 500 mcg/day during the reproductive years. In contrast, estrone levels increase to 80 mcg/day during menopause compared with premenopausal levels of 40 mcg/day.[11] The hypothalamic-pituitary-estrogen positive-feedback mechanism no longer initiates LH secretion.[78] As ovulation frequency decreases, anovulatory cycles increase, with a subsequent decrease in progesterone.

Reproductive hormone levels change with menopause (see Table 2-2). Hormonal confirmation of menopause includes a 10% to 20% increase in FSH levels and LH levels three to five times greater than those in earlier menstrual cycles. FSH levels increase gradually but do so significantly. LH levels greater than 40 IU/L and early follicular FSH levels greater than 30 IU/L are common clinical markers for ovarian reserve.[49] FSH levels maximize approximately 1 to 3 years after menopause. Postmenopausally, testosterone levels decrease from 200 mcg/day to 150 mcg/day. Therefore an androgen excess state exists.

Menopausal declines in the sex steroids and estradiol particularly have numerous physiologic and psychological effects (Figure 2-33), including vasomotor instability, breast tissue reduction, sleep difficulties, depression, atrophy of urogenital epithelium, atrophy of vaginal tissue and dermis, osteoporosis, coronary heart disease, lethargy, headaches, and concentration difficulties. Vasomotor symptoms (hot flashes or night sweats) are reported by 65% to 76% of perimenopausal women. The prevalence of vasomotor symptoms is positively correlated with serum FSH levels.[11,60]

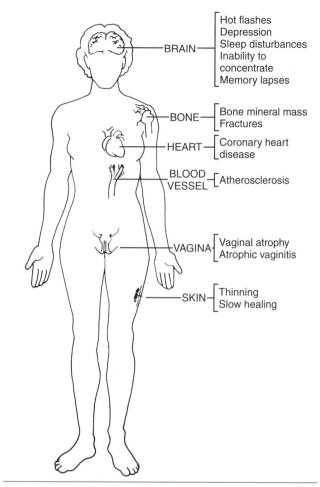

FIGURE 2-33 Effect of estrogen deprivation or reduced estrogen on different organ and tissue systems at or after menopause. (From Dawood, M.Y. [2000]. Menopause. In L.J. Copeland [Ed.]. Textbook of gynecology [2nd ed.]. Philadelphia: Saunders.)

Aging Male

Males do not experience a cessation in reproductive ability in the same manner that females experience menopause. There is a gradual decline in testosterone production and in spermatogenesis with aging, but this finding varies.[55] Reproductive ability is usually not compromised, however. The production rate of sperm for a 20-year-old male is approximately 6.5 million sperm per gram per day. By the age of 50 to 90 years of age, a decline is noted and averages 3.8 million sperm per gram per day.[35] With advancing age, it is purported there is incompetence in the hypothalamic-pituitary-testicular feedback system with resulting inadequate LH levels.[55] In addition, there is a decrease in normal morphologic and motile sperm. In later life, atrophy of the external genitalia may occur.[55] Concomitantly there are involution of the testes and degenerative changes in the Leydig cells, thereby diminishing the production of testosterone. With declining health or exacerbation of chronic diseases, there is a decrease in sperm production and ejaculate volume.[55] The age at which these events occur is variable among individual men, and some do not experience them at all.

BOX 2-4 Recommendations for Clinical Practice Related to the Physiologic Basis for Reproduction

Understand the basic processes involved in the hypothalamic-pituitary-ovarian/testicular axis (pp. 29-44; Figures 2-5, 2-7, 2-17; Box 2-3).

Understand the basic processes involved in steroidogenesis (pp. 37-43; Figures 2-10, 2-11, 2-12, and 2-15).

Counsel women and men regarding physical and physiologic changes during puberty; reproduction; and premenopause, menopause, and postmenopause for women and reproductive functions in aging for men (pp. 44-59; Figure 2-33; Tables 2-2 and 2-4; Box 2-3).

Provide teaching to families regarding physical and physiologic changes during puberty, reproduction, the climacteric for females and reproductive functions for the older male (pp. 44-58; Figures 2-2, 2-7, 2-13. 2-14, and 2-16 to 2-33; Tables 2-2 and 2-4).

Counsel families regarding follicular growth and development (pp. 48-53; Figures 2-2, 2-15, 2-22, and 2-23).

Understand the usual patterns of reproductive hormone production and counsel men, women, and families regarding the changes during the woman's life span (pp. 33-48, 53, 56-58; Figures 2-2, 2-14, 2-16, 2-17, 2-19, 2-26, 2-28, and 2-30; Table 2-2).

Provide health teaching regarding the ovarian cycle and changes during the woman's life span (pp. 44-53, 56-58; Figures 2-1, 2-2, 2-7, 2-9, 2-14, 2-16, 2-23 to 2-26, 2-30, and 2-31).

Provide health teaching regarding the endometrial cycles and changes during the woman's life span (pp. 48-56; Figures 2-2, 2-17, 2-22, and 2-27 to 2-29).

Provide health teaching regarding spermatogenesis and changes during the man's life span (pp. 45-48, 56, 58; Figures 2-1, 2-7, and 2-10 to 2-13).

Educate and provide support to families undergoing reproductive alterations (pp. 45-48, 57-58).

Teach families who have experienced reproductive problems the basic principles of neuroendocrinology in the process (pp. 29-44, 57-58; Figures 2-1, 2-2, 2-6, 2-7, 2-17, 2-28, and 2-32).

SUMMARY

The hormone pathway is critical to human reproduction and development. These physiologic processes provide the foundation for the reproductive life cycle; embryology, pregnancy, puberty, aging, and infertility. Reproductive endocrinology is an orchestrated cascade of events initiated in utero and mediated by hormonal control. Episodic pulses of gonadotropin-releasing factors and hormones modulate the secretion of gonadal steroids, estrogen, progesterone, and testosterone. Cyclical follicular development and maturation, in concert with endometrial changes, prepare for the fertilized oocyte. Hormonal regulation of testicular function and spermatogenesis are necessary for fertilization of the oocyte. Knowledge of the HPO/hypothalamic-pituitary-testicular axis undergirds reproductive health and obstetric, infertility, gynecologic, and andrologic nursing. Recommendations for clinical practice related to the physiologic basis for reproduction are summarized in Box 2-4.

References

1. Astrup, K. (2004). Menstrual bleeding patterns in pre- and perimenopausal women. A population-based prospective diary study. *Acta Obstet Gynecol Scand*, *83*, 197.

2. Auchus, R. J. (2014). The glycoprotein hormones and their receptors. In J. F. Strauss & R. L. Barbieri (Eds.), *Yen and Jaffe's reproductive endocrinology: Physiology, pathophysiology, and clinical management* (7th ed.). Philadelphia: Elsevier Saunders.

3. Baird, D. T. (1999). Feedback mechanisms. In I. S. Fraser (Ed.), *Estrogens and progestogens in clinical practice*. Philadelphia: Churchill Livingstone. UPDATE

4. Baldwin, R. M., Whalley, P. J., & Pritchard, J. A. (1961). Measurements of menstrual blood loss. *Am J Obstet Gynecol*, *81*, 739.

5. Beckman, C., et al. (2013). *Obstetrics and gynecology* (7th ed.). Philadelphia: Wolters Kluwar.

6. Bordini, B., & Rosenfield, R. L. (2011). Normal pubertal development: Part II: Clinical aspects of puberty. *Pediatrics in Review*, *32*, 281.

7. Bulun, S. E., & Adashi, E. Y. (2016). The physiology and pathology of the female reproductive axis. In H. K. Kronenberg, et al. (Eds.), *Williams textbook of endocrinology* (13th ed.). Philadelphia: Elsevier Saunders.

8. Carr, B. (2005). The ovary and the normal menstrual cycle. In B. Carr, R. Blackwell, & R. Azziz (Eds.), *Essential reproductive medicine*. New York: McGraw-Hill.

9. Casper, F. W., et al. (2001). Concentrations of inhibins and activin in women undergoing stimulation with recombinant follicle-stimulating hormone for in vitro fertilization treatment. *Fertil Steril*, *75*, 32.

10. Catteau, A., et al. (2016). Leptin and its potential interest in assisted reproduction cycles. *Hum Reprod Update*, *22*, 320.

11. Cedars, M., & Evans, M. (2008). Menopause. In J. R. Scott, et al. (Eds.), *Danforth's obstetrics and gynecology* (9th ed.). Philadelphia: Lippincott Williams & Wilkins.

12. Chan, K. A., Tsoulis, M. W., & Sloboda, D. M. (2015). Early life nutritional effects on the female reproductive system. *J Endocrinol*, *224*, R45.

13. Chiquoine, A. D. (1960). The development of the zona pellucida of the mammalian ovum. *Am J Anat*, *106*, 149.

14. Colledge, W. H. (2013). The neuroendocrine regulation of the mammalian reproductive axis. *Exp Physiol*, *98*, 1519.

15. Cunningham, F. G., et al. (2014). *Williams obstetrics* (24th ed.). New York: McGraw-Hill.

16. Dama, M. D., & Bhat, M. N. (2013). Mobile phones affect multiple sperm quality traits: a meta-analysis. *F1000 Research*, *2*, 40.

17. Dwyer, A., et al. (2015). Hypogonadism in adolescence. *Eur J Endocrinol*, *173*, R15.

18. Ebeling, P., & Koivisto, V. A. (1994). Physiological importance of dehydroepiandrosterone. *Lancet*, *343*, 1479.

19. Fanchin, R., et al. (2001). Uterine contractility decreases at the time of blastocyst transfers. *Hum Reprod*, *16*, 1115.

20. Freeman, E. W., et al. (2001). Hot flashes in the late reproductive years: Risk factors for African-American and Caucasian women. *J Women's Health Gender-Based Med*, *10*, 67.

21. Funabashi, T., et al. (2005). Nicotine inhibits pulsatile luteinizing hormone secretion in human males but not in human females, and tolerance to this nicotine effect is lost within one week of quitting smoking. *J Clin Endocrinol Metab*, *90*, 3908.

22. Gargett, C. E., et al. (2001). Focal vascular endothelial growth factor correlates with angiogenesis in human endometrium. Role of intravascular neutrophils. *Hum Reprod*, *16*, 1065.

23. Genazzani, A. R., et al. (2000). Neuropeptides, neurotransmitters, neurosteroids, and the onset of puberty. *Ann N Y Acad Sci*, *900*, 1.

24. Gill, S., & Hall, J. (2005). Neuroendocrinology. In B. Carr, R. Blackwell, & R. Azziz (Eds.), *Essential reproductive medicine*. New York: McGraw-Hill.

25. Goodman, A. L., & Hodgen, G. D. (1983). The ovarian triad of the primate menstrual cycle. *Recent Prog Horm Res*, *39*, 1.

26. Gordon, C., & Laufer, M. (2005). The physiology of puberty. In S. J. Emans, M. R. Laufer, & D. P. Goldstein (Eds.), *Pediatric & adolescent gynecology* (5th ed.). Philadelphia: Lippincott Williams & Wilkins.

27. Gordon, K., & Oehninger, S. (2000). Reproductive physiology. In L. J. Copeland (Ed.), *Textbook of gynecology* (2nd ed.). Philadelphia: Saunders.

28. Greene, C. A., & O' Keane, J. A. (2000). Investigation of the infertile couple. In L. J. Copeland (Ed.), *Textbook of gynecology* (2nd ed.). Philadelphia: Saunders.

29. Guldbrandsen, K., et al. (2014). Age of menarche and time to pregnancy. *Hum Reprod, 29,* 20158.

30. Hall, J. E. (2016). *Guyton & Hall's textbook of medical physiology* (13th ed.). Philadelphia: Saunders.

31. Hallberg, L., et al. (1966). Menstrual blood loss—a population study. Variation at different ages and attempts to define normality. *Acta Obstet Gynecol Scand, 45,* 320.

32. Harlev, A., et al. (2015). Smoking and male infertility: An Evidence-Based Review. *World J Mens Health, 33,* 143.

33. Helm, K. D. (2014). Neuroendocrine control of the menstrual cycle. In J. F. Strauss & R. L. Barbieri (Eds.), *Yen and Jaffe's reproductive endocrinology: Physiology, pathophysiology, and clinical management* (7th ed.). Philadelphia: Elsevier Saunders.

34. Jenkin, G., et al. (2001). Physiological and regulatory roles of activin A in late pregnancy. *Mol Cell Endocrinol, 180,* 131.

35. Jones, E., & DeCherney, A. (2003). The male reproductive system. In W. Boron & E. Boulpaep (Eds.), *Medical physiology.* Philadelphia: Saunders.

36. Kaiser, U., & Ho, K. K. (2016). Pituitary physiology and diagnostic evaluation. In S. Melmed, et al. (Eds.), *Williams textbook of endocrinology* (13th ed.). Philadelphia: Elsevier.

37. Kronenberg, H. M. K., et al. (2016). Principles of endocrinology. In S. Melmed, et al. (Eds.), *Williams textbook of endocrinology* (13th ed.). Philadelphia: Saunders.

38. Kwekkeboom, D. J., et al. (1990). Serum gonadotropins and a subunit decline in aging normal postmenopausal women. *J Clin Endocrinol Metab, 70,* 944.

39. La Rosa, C., Traggiai, C., & Stanhope, R. (2004). Normal childhood, puberty and adolescence. In S. Creighton, et al. (Eds.), *Paediatric and adolescent gynaecology: A multidisciplinary approach.* New York: Cambridge University Press.

40. Layman, L. C., & McDonough, P. G. (2000). Mutations of follicle stimulating hormone-β and its receptor in human and mouse: Genotype/phenotype. *Mol Cell Endocrinol, 161,* 9.

41. Leach, R. E., et al. (1999). Multiple roles for heparin-binding epidermal growth factor-like growth factor are suggested by its cell-specific expression during the human endometrial cycle and early placentation. *J Clin Endocrinol Metab, 84,* 3355.

42. Lee, P. (2005). Early pubertal development. In T. Moshang (Ed.), *Pediatric endocrinology: The requisites in pediatrics.* St. Louis: Mosby.

43. Levy, D. P., et al. (2000). The role of LH in ovarian stimulation-exogenous LH: Let's design the future. *Hum Reprod, 15,* 2258.

44. Liu, J. H. (2014). Endocrinology of pregnancy. In R. K. Creasy, et al. (Eds.), *Creasy & Resnik's maternal-fetal medicine: Principles and practice* (7th ed.). Philadelphia: Elsevier Saunders.

45. Liu, P. Y. (2014). The structure, function, and evaluation of the female reproductive tract. In J. F. Strauss & R. L. Barbieri (Eds.), *Yen and Jaffe's reproductive endocrinology: Physiology, pathophysiology, and clinical management* (7th ed.). Philadelphia: Elsevier.

46. Llop-Vinolas, D., et al. (2004). Onset of puberty at eight years of age in girls determines a specific tempo of puberty but does not affect adult height. *Acta Paediatr, 93,* 874.

47. Longcope, C. (1998). Metabolism of estrogens and progestogens. In I. S. Fraser, et al. (Eds.), *Estrogens and progestogens in clinical practice.* Philadelphia: Churchill Livingstone.

48. Low, M. (2016). Neuroendocrinology. In S. Melmed, et al. (Eds.), *Williams textbook of endocrinology* (13th ed.). Philadelphia: Elsevier Saunders.

49. Macklon, N. S., & Fauser, B. C. J. M. (1999). Aspects of ovarian follicle development throughout life. *Horm Res, 52,* 161.

50. Marshall, J. C. (2014). Menopause and aging. In J. F. Strauss & R. L. Barbieri (Eds.), *Yen and Jaffe's reproductive endocrinology: Physiology, pathophysiology, and clinical management* (7th ed.). Philadelphia: Elsevier. Saunders.

51. Matzuk, M. M., & Mesiano, S. (2014). Neuroendocrinology of reproduction. In J. F. Strauss & R. L. Barbieri (Eds.), *Yen and Jaffe's reproductive endocrinology: Physiology, pathophysiology, and clinical management* (7th ed.). Philadelphia: Elsevier Saunders.

52. Mesen, T., & Young, S. (2015). Progesterone and the luteal phase: a requisite to reproduction. *Obstet Gynecol Clin N Am, 42,* 135.

53. Mitan, L. A. P., & Slap, G. B. (2000). Adolescent menstrual disorders. *Adolesc Med, 84,* 851.

54. Moore, K. L., & Persaud, T. V. N. (2015). *The developing human: Clinically oriented embryology* (10th ed.). Philadelphia: Elsevier Saunders.

55. Nieschlag, E., Behre, H., & Nieschlag, S. (2010). *Male reproductive health and dysfunction* (3rd ed.). NY: Springer.

56. O'Connor, K. A., Holman, D. J., & Wood, J. W. (2001). Menstrual cycle variability and the perimenopause. *Am J Hum Biol, 13,* 465.

57. Palter, S. F., et al. (2001). Are estrogens of import to primate/human ovarian folliculogenesis? *Endocr Rev, 22,* 389.

58. Plant, T. (2015). The hypothalamo-pituitary-gonadal axis. *J Endocrinol, 226,* T41.

59. Polotsky, A. J., & Woodruff, T. J. (2014). Puberty: Gonadarche and adrenarche. In J. F. Strauss & R. L. Barbieri (Eds.), *Yen and Jaffe's reproductive endocrinology: Physiology, pathophysiology, and clinical management* (7th ed.). Philadelphia: Elsevier Saunders.

60. Randolph, J., et al. (2005). The relationship of longitudinal change in reproductive hormones and vasomotor symptoms during the menopausal transition. *J Clin Endocrinol Metab, 90,* 6106.

61. Rittmaster, R. S. (2000). Hyperandrogenism. In L. J. Copeland (Ed.), *Textbook of gynecology* (2nd ed.). Philadelphia: Saunders.

62. Rogers, R. J., et al. (2001). Dynamics of the membrana granulosa during expansion of the ovarian follicular antrum. *Mol Cell Endocrinol, 171,* 41.

63. Rojas, J., et al. (2015). Physiologic course of female reproductive function: A molecular look into the prologue of life. *J Pregnancy, 2015,* 715735.

64. Runesson, E., et al. (2000). Gonadotropin- and cytokine-regulated expression of the chemokine interleukin 8 in the human pre-ovulatory follicle of the menstrual cycle. *J Clin Endocrinol Metab, 85,* 4387.

65. Sanchez, F., & Smitz, J. (2012). Molecular control of oogenesis. *Biochim Biophys Acta, 1822,* 1896.

66. Scheele, F., & Schoemaker, J. (1996). The role of follicle-stimulating hormone in the selection of follicles in human ovaries: A survey of the literature and a proposed model. *Gynecol Endocrinol, 10,* 55.

67. Schneyer, A. L., et al. (2000). Dynamic changes in the intrafollicular inhibin/activin/follistatin axis during human follicular development: Relationship to circulating hormone concentrations. *J Clin Endocrinol Metab, 85,* 3319.

68. Scott, D. E., & Pritchard, J. A. (1967). Iron deficiency in healthy young college women. *JAMA, 199,* 147.

69. Shikone, T., et al. (1997). Apoptosis of human ovary and uterine endometrium during the menstrual cycle. *Horm Res, 48,* 27.

70. Sidis, Y., et al. (2001). Follistatin: Essential role for the N-terminal domain in activin binding and neutralization. *J Biol Chem, 276,* 17718.

71. Siiteri, P. (2005). The continuing saga of dehydroepiandro-sterone (DHEA). *J Clin Endocrinol Metab, 90,* 3795.

72. Skakkebaek, N., et al. (2016). Male reproductive disorders and fertility trends: Influences of environment and genetic susceptibility. *Physiol Rev, 96,* 55.

73. Streuli, I. (2014). The synthesis and metabolism of steroid hormones. In J. F. Strauss & R. L. Barbieri (Eds.), *Yen and Jaffe's reproductive endocrinology: Physiology, pathophysiology, and clinical management* (7th ed.). Philadelphia: Elsevier Saunders.

74. Styne, D. M., & Grumbach, M. M. (2016). Physiology and disorders of puberty. In S. Melmed, et al. (Eds.), *Williams textbook of endocrinology* (13th ed.). Philadelphia: Elsevier Saunders.

75. Tena-Sempere, M., Levallet, J., & Huhtaniemi, I. (2004). Gonadotrophin receptors. In S. Creighton, et al. (Eds.), *Pediatric and adolescent gynecology: A multidisciplinary approach.* New York: Cambridge University Press.

76. Tinggaard, J., et al. (2012). The physiology and timing of male puberty. *Curr Opin Endocrinol Diabetes Obes, 19,* 197.

77. Ukkola, O., et al. (2001). Age, body mass index, race and other determinants of steroid hormone variability: The HERITAGE Family Study. *Eur J Endocrinol, 145,* 1.

78. Weiss, G. (2001). Menstrual irregularities and the perimenopause. *J Soc Gynecol Invest, 8,* S65.

79. Welt, C. K., et al. (1997). Frequency modulation of follicle-stimulating hormone (FSH) during the luteal-follicular transition: Evidence for FSH control of inhibin B in normal women. *J Clin Endocrinol Metab, 82,* 2645.

80. Welt, C. K., et al. (2001). Differential regulation of inhibin A and inhibin B by luteinizing hormone, follicle-stimulating hormone, and stage of follicle development. *J Clin Endocrinol Metab, 86,* 2531.

81. Witchel, S. F., & Steuli, I. (2014). The ovarian life cycle. In J. F. Strauss & R. L. Barbieri (Eds.), *Yen and Jaffe's reproductive endocrinology: Physiology, pathophysiology, and clinical management* (7th ed.). Philadelphia: Elsevier Saunders.

82. Woodruff, T. K., & Mather, J. P. (1995). Inhibin, activin and the female reproductive axis. *Annu Rev Physiol, 57,* 219.

83. Young, E. A., et al. (2000). Alteration in the hypothalamic-pituitary-ovarian axis in depressed women. *Arch Gen Psychiatry, 57,* 1157.

84. Zeleznik, A. J. (2001). Modifications in gonadotropin signaling: A key to understanding cyclic ovarian function. *J Soc Gynecol Invest, 8,* S24.

Prenatal Period and Placental Physiology

The prenatal period encompasses the period from conception to birth. During this period the pregnant woman experiences major physiologic and psychological changes that support maternal adaptations, support fetal growth and development, and prepare the mother for the birth process and transition to parenthood. Simultaneously the embryo and fetus are developing from a single cell to a complex organism. Supporting this development are the placenta, fetal membranes (amnion and chorion), and amniotic fluid. These structures protect and nourish the embryo and fetus and are essential for the infant's survival, growth, and development.

Alterations in maternal physiology, endocrine function, embryonic and fetal development, or placental function and structure can lead to maternal disorders and fetal death, malformations, poor growth, or preterm birth. Prenatal screening and diagnosis can be used to evaluate the fetus. Assessment of placental size and function and amniotic fluid volume and composition is useful in evaluating fetal growth and health status during gestation. This chapter describes events that result in conception and provides an overview of pregnancy; related endocrinology; and development of the embryo, fetus, and placenta. Specific clinical implications related to normal and abnormal development are discussed.

OVERVIEW OF PREGNANCY

The duration of pregnancy averages 266 days (38 weeks) after ovulation, or 280 days (40 weeks) after the first day of the last menstrual period (Figure 3-1). This equals 10 lunar months, or just over 9 calendar months. During these months, the almost-solid uterus, with a cavity of 10 mL or less, develops into a large, thin-walled organ. The total volume of the contents of the uterus is 5 L or more at term, 500 to 1000 times the original capacity.[37]

Most of the changes encountered during pregnancy are progressive and can be attributed to either hormonal responses or physical alterations secondary to fetal size. The preimplantation endocrine system controls the reproductive cycle. In the woman, this involves the cyclic release of pituitary gonadotropins and secretion of estrogen and progesterone by the ovary (see Chapter 2).

The postimplantation endocrine systems of the mother, placenta, and fetus control the integrity and duration of gestation. These processes include (1) maintenance of the corpus luteum by human chorionic gonadotropin (hCG); (2) production of estrogen, progesterone, human chorionic somatomammotropin (hCS), and other hormones and growth factors by the placenta; and (3) release of oxytocin (by the posterior pituitary), prolactin (by the anterior pituitary), and relaxin (by the ovary, uterus, and placenta).

Changes in specific organ systems and metabolic processes during pregnancy and their clinical implications are described in detail in Units II and III. This section presents an overview of physiologic changes during each trimester of pregnancy based on the time from the start of the last menstrual period. Concomitant with these adaptations and equally significant are psychological adaptations; these adaptations are not discussed because the focus of this text is on physiologic changes.

First Trimester

During the first trimester, the woman experiences the first signs and symptoms of pregnancy. The first sign of pregnancy is usually cessation of menses. The average cycle length is 28 days, with a range of 15 to 45 days. The first missed period is suggestive of pregnancy; by the time the second period is missed, pregnancy becomes probable. Brief or scant bleeding may occur during pregnancy, most commonly in the first trimester around the time of implantation.

Breast tenderness and tingling, especially around the nipple area, often occurs beginning at 4 to 6 weeks. Increased breast size and vascularity are usually evident by the end of the 2nd month and are caused by growth of the secretory duct system. Colostrum leakage may occur by 3 months. Enlargement of the sebaceous glands around the nipple (Montgomery's glands) may also be apparent.

Nausea with or without vomiting may occur any time of the day or night. This symptom usually begins about 4 to 6 weeks after the onset of the last menstrual period and usually resolves by 10 to 12 weeks, but may last longer in some women. An increase in frequency of urination is seen during the first trimester. Excessive fatigue is often experienced and may last throughout the first 12 weeks. The cause of this

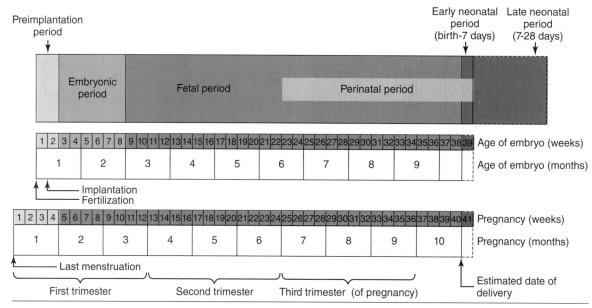

FIGURE 3-1 The two time scales used to depict human development. Embryonic development, in the upper scale, is counted from fertilization (or from ovulation [i.e., postovulatory days]). The clinical estimation of pregnancy is counted from the last menstrual period and is shown on the lower scale. Note that there is a 2-week discrepancy between these scales. The perinatal period is very long because it includes all of the preterm deliveries. (From Standring, S. [2005]. *Gray's anatomy: The anatomical basis of clinical practice* [39th ed.]. Edinburgh: Churchill Livingstone.)

fatigue is unknown, but it may be a response to hormonal shifts. Hormonal changes are also believed to be responsible for the dyspnea experienced during this period.

Physical signs associated with pregnancy include the Goodell sign (softening of the cervix and vagina with increased leukorrheal discharge), Hegar sign (softening and increased compressibility of the lower uterine segment), and Chadwick sign (bluish-purple discoloration of the vaginal mucosa, cervix, and vulva) by 8 weeks. Although a presumptive sign of pregnancy, the Chadwick sign is only useful in primiparous women. By 8 to 10 weeks, fetal heart tones can be auscultated by Doppler ultrasonography. Real-time ultrasound can pick up fetal heart movements earlier. Maternal cardiovascular changes are also occurring, with stroke volume and cardiac output increasing and systemic vascular resistance decreasing. These changes contribute to increased renal plasma flow and glomerular filtration.[37] Weight gain during the first trimester is usually small.

Second Trimester

The second trimester is characterized by marked maternal changes as the fetus's presence becomes more evident. The uterus, which starts as a pear-shaped organ, becomes ovoid, as length increases over width. With this growth, the uterus moves into the abdominal cavity and begins to displace the intestines. The tension and stretching of the broad ligament may lead to painful sensations. Normally contractions during the second trimester are irregular and usually painless.

The increasing vascularity of the vagina and pelvic viscera may result in increased sensitivity and heightened arousal and sexual interest. Mucorrhea is not uncommon as a result of the hyperactivity of the vaginal glandular tissues. This change may increase the pleasure experienced during sexual intercourse. Spontaneous orgasm and multiple orgasms may occur as a result of the increased congestion. Leukorrhea often occurs, with thick, white, acidotic (pH of 3.5 to 6.0) discharge that may contribute to inhibition of pathogenic colonization of the vagina.[37] Perineal structures also enlarge as a result of the vasocongestion, increased vascularity, hypertrophy of the perineal body, and fat deposition that began during the first trimester.

The breasts become increasingly more nodular. Colostrum can be easily expressed at this stage. The nipples become larger and more deeply pigmented. The areolae have also broadened. Increased skin pigmentation occurs elsewhere as well. The line from the umbilicus to the symphysis pubis (linea alba) may darken very distinctly and is referred to as the *linea nigra*. Darkening of the skin over the forehead and cheeks (melasma or chloasma gravidarum) can also result from hormonal changes. Most pigmentation changes fade by a year after delivery, but some may persist.

Other cutaneous changes include the appearance of spider nevi and capillary hemangiomas. The former usually resolve; the latter may shrink but often do not completely disappear after delivery. The breakdown of underlying connective tissue may result in reddish, irregular stretch marks on the abdomen, buttocks, thighs, or breasts. Little can be done to prevent the formation of stretch marks, which may fade with time.

Increased estrogen levels may result in hyperemic, soft, swollen gums that bleed easily. Increased salivation also may occur. Good oral and dental care is important. Elevated progesterone levels decrease the motility of the gastrointestinal tract. By the end of the second trimester, esophageal regurgitation may lead to heartburn. Fluid retention and constipation also may occur as pregnancy progresses.

Maternal blood volume rises significantly during these months, and hematocrit and hemoglobin levels begin to fall due to hemodilution. Blood pressure decreases slightly, whereas the heart rate increases by 10 to 20 beats per minute. Hemodynamic changes continue. Most women develop a systolic murmur during the second or third trimesters. Glomerular filtration rate increases. Bladder and ureter tone is decreased, and the ureters become more tortuous, increasing the risk of urinary tract infection.

Protein and carbohydrate needs increase markedly, contributing to the weight gain during this phase. The mother first perceives fetal movement (quickening) at 16 to 20 weeks' gestation (earlier in successive pregnancies). These movements become perceptible to a hand on the mother's abdomen toward the end of this period. By 20 weeks, the uterus will be at the level of the umbilicus.

Third Trimester

In the third trimester fatigue, dyspnea, and increased urinary frequency are experienced. Fatigue and dyspnea are related to the increased weight and pressure exerted by the greatly enlarged uterus. Thoracic breathing predominates. Increased urinary frequency results from pressure of the presenting part against the bladder.

The uterine wall thins to 5 to 10 mm by term. The fetus can be easily palpated through the uterine wall, and fetal movements are quite visible. The uterus reaches almost to the liver, and broad ligament pain may become more intense as tension is increased. Uterine contractions become more regular and uncomfortable and are easily detected and palpable near term.

The heart is displaced slightly to the left as a result of the increased pressure from the enlarged uterus. Blood pressure rises slightly, and cardiac output remains unchanged. Total blood volume peaks at 32 to 34 weeks' gestation. Dependent edema is common because blood return from the lower extremities is reduced. Increasing pelvic congestion, relaxation of the smooth muscle in the veins, and the increased pressure of the growing fetus may result in varicosities of the perineum and rectum. Constipation and obesity may lead to development of engorged blood vessels.[37]

The growing uterus displaces the intestines and stomach. A hiatal hernia may develop along with increasing heartburn and a decreased stomach capacity. The bladder is pulled up and out of the true pelvis by the growing uterus. This stretches the urethra and increases the susceptibility to urinary tract infection.

The increased elasticity of connective and collagen tissue leads to relaxation and hypermobility of the pelvic joints.

Separation of the symphysis pubis results in instability of the sacroiliac joint. The center of gravity shifts lower with development of a progressive lordosis to compensate for the anterior shift of the uterus. Balance is maintained by an enhanced cervicodorsal curvature, leading to difficulty in walking and the characteristic waddling gait. Stress on the ligaments and muscles of the middle and lower back and spine may lead to discomfort and back pain.[37]

The process of conception and the changes related to pregnancy are truly remarkable events. The coming together of all factors brings about the appropriate and necessary environment for the nurturance and development of the next generation.

CONCEPTION

For conception to occur, a precise set of sequential events must take place. The probability of a viable conception per menstrual cycle is less than 40% to 50%.[27,104] The process of conception and fetal survival is selective, as evidenced by implantation failures and the approximately 50% anomaly rate encountered in spontaneously aborted fetuses.[104,133] Gametogenesis is described in Chapter 1. The ovarian and endometrial cycles necessary for conception and early support of the fertilized ovum, as well as follicle maturation, are described in Chapter 2. This section examines ovulation, sperm transport, fertilization, cleavage, and zygote transport.

Ovulation

The ovary is responsible for gametogenesis and steroid hormone synthesis. Integration of ovarian steroid synthesis, follicle maturation, ovulation, and corpus luteum function is essential for fertilization and implantation. Estrogen and progesterone have significant effects on tubal and uterine motility, endometrial proliferation, and the properties of the cervical mucus.[37] For fertilization to take place, the oocyte must become "fertilization competent" (see Chapter 1). The close proximity of the oocytes and follicular cells in the ovary allows bidirectional communication by the follicle and oocyte via gap junctions (intracellular membrane channels) to work together to control meiotic arrest and resumption; follicle maturation; ovulation; and corpus luteum formation, function, and regression. The hypothalamus and anterior pituitary regulate these latter morphologic changes through secretion of gonadotropin-releasing hormone (GnRH) and gonadotropins. Follicle-stimulating hormone (FSH) and luteinizing hormone (LH) act synergistically (see Chapter 2). Follicle maturation is illustrated in Figure 3-2 (see also Figure 2-22).

Bidirectional cross-talk between oocytes and their surrounding cumulus cells (follicular cells in direct contact with the oocyte), via thin axonlike projection from the cumulus cells that extend through the zona pellucida membrane around the oocyte forming gap junctions, begins with the primordial follicle.[36,113] LH and FSH influence opening and

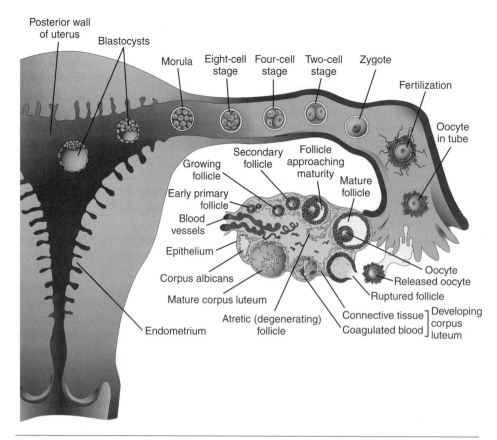

FIGURE 3-2   Summary of the ovarian cycle, fertilization, and human development during the first week. (From Moore, K.L., Persaud, T.V.N., & Torchia, M.G. [2015]. *The developing human: Clinically oriented embryology* [10th ed.]. Philadelphia: Saunders.)

closing of the gap junctions.[45,113] Cumulus cells support oocyte metabolism, meiotic arrest and resumption, and cytoplasmic changes.[36]

Usually only one follicle matures and is ovulated, although the exact mechanism for this is unknown. At the beginning of the menstrual cycle, up to 15 to 20 primary (preantral) follicles are stimulated by FSH, but only 6 to 12 enlarge, with a 100-fold increase in cell size and change in diameter from approximately 40 μm to 120 μm.[36] This is a time of intense cellular activity, with production of macromolecules and organelles. Many of the gene products generated are not used until after fertilization when they are needed for early survival of the fertilized ovum.[36] During maturation the oocyte also undergoes changes in chromatin configuration, mitochondrial distribution, and endoplasmic reticulum. Meiotic spindles develop at the periphery rather than the center as with other cells. This enhances extrusion of the polar body with cell division.[36]

Of these growing follicles, several develop into antral follicles. Eventually one follicle becomes dominant and begins to function independent of FSH. This follicle secretes inhibin, which inhibits pituitary FSH. Because the other maturing follicles are still dependent on FSH, which is now decreased, they begin to regress and degenerate.[27] The process of follicular

development and maturation is described in the section on the Ovarian Cycle in Chapter 2.

In the fully developed follicle (Graafian or tertiary follicle), multiple layers of granulosa cells line the antral side of the basement membrane (membrane granulosa), and a cumulus of granulosa cells surrounds the oocyte. Proliferation and maturation of these cells are stimulated by many paracrine factors, especially growth differentiation factor 9 (GDF9) and bone morphogenetic factor 15 (BMP15), which are members of the transforming growth factor-β (TGF-β) family.[36,113,133] GDF9 is also important for oocyte maturation and differentiation. The *Kit* gene and KIT ligand (KITL) are also important in oocyte development, activating a cascade of substances that stimulate oocyte proliferation and differentiation and prevent apoptosis.[113] Androids promote follicular growth by FSH and insulin-like growth factors (IGFs) and their receptors.[45] MicroRNA (miRNA) is also involved, via gene regulation, in oocyte maturation, folliculogenesis, corpus luteum function, and early embryonic development.[73]

Oxygen and nutrients diffuse across the granulosa cells to the oocyte. Antral fluid contains proteins, enzymes, proteoglycans, and hormones such as FSH and steroids.[27] The oocyte is surrounded by the zona pellucida, which contains sperm receptors. The external theca layers around the follicle consist of the outer theca externa (capsular-like covering) and vascularized, glandular inner theca interna. Under the stimulation of FSH, the theca and granulosa cells produce large amounts of estrogen (primarily estradiol), which peak about 24 hours before ovulation. Production of estrogen stimulates proliferation of the endometrium, thinning of cervical mucus, and LH secretion.[133]

LH levels rise, which increases production of progesterone and inhibin A by the dominant follicle through interaction of LH with LH receptors on granulosa cells. The rise in progesterone occurs 12 to 24 hours before ovulation and elicits a rapid and marked surge in LH secretion, paralleling the midcycle FSH peak (see Chapter 2). The LH peak is essential for ovulation, which occurs 28 to 36 hours later.[27,37] The midcycle surge of LH initiates ovulation by stimulating prostaglandin (PG) synthesis (PGE and PGF), leading to formation of collagenase and other proteolytic enzymes with disruption of the gap junctions between the oocyte and follicular cells.[27,113] The LH surge also increases concentration of maturation-promoting factors, which disrupts meiotic inhibition and initiates completion of the first meiotic division.[36,113,133]

The principle factor in meiotic arrest is cyclic adenosine monophosphate (cAMP), which in combination with other factors prevents activation of oocyte maturation–promoting factors and thus maintains meiotic arrest. Cyclic guanosine monophosphate (cGMP) inactivates the enzyme phosphodiesterase 3A (PDE3A) so cAMP levels remain high. The increased LH along with GDF9 and BMP15 stimulate the granulosa cells to stimulate the cumulus cells to produce epidermal growth factor (EGF). EGF decreases oocyte cGMP so PDE3A levels and thus cAMP increases and meiosis resumes.[50,113]

The oocyte completes its first meiotic division 10 to 12 hours before ovulation, forming the secondary oocyte (23 chromosomes plus most of the cell cytoplasm) and first polar body (23 chromosomes and minimal cytoplasm). The small polar body is nonfunctional and degenerates (see Chapter 1). The LH surge also causes a decrease in estradiol production. Progesterone and PG activity results in expression of proteases and growth factor transcription factors, especially ADAMTS1 (a matrix metalloproteinase that cleaves collagen to separate the cumulus layer with its enclosed ovum from the rest of the follicle for release with ovulation).[113]

Ovulation begins with a protrusion or bulge on the ovarian wall. A small avascular spot (stigma) develops, forms a vesicle, and ruptures, extruding the secondary oocyte, follicular fluid, and surrounding cells. Rupture is believed to be caused by enzymatic digestion of the follicular wall via the action of proteases (e.g., collagenase, plasmin, and hyaluronic acid), which dissolve connective tissues.[60,104] The oocyte is surrounded by the zona pellucida and corona radiata (radially arranged granulosa cells). The second meiotic division begins with ovulation, then arrests in metaphase.[133] The second meiotic division is not completed until fertilization. The

oocyte is swept by the fimbriae into the fallopian tube. Muscular contraction of the tube and, primarily, beating of the cilia move the ovum along the tube to the ampulla (the usual site of fertilization). If unfertilized, the ovum usually dies within 24 hours.[104]

Corpus Luteum

After ovulation, the follicular walls and theca collapse inward and become vascularized (see Figure 3-2). The granulosa cells undergo a luteinizing process to form the corpus luteum. The corpus luteum secretes progesterone, beginning within 30 to 40 hours of the LH surge. A small amount of estrogen is secreted by the theca cells.[27] If fertilization has taken place, implantation occurs during the latter part of this week. Around the time of implantation, the trophoblast tissue secretes hCG, a luteotropin that stimulates the corpus luteum to continue to function. hCG may alter the metabolism of the uterus to prevent the release of substances that result in luteal regression. The corpus luteum can only produce progesterone for about 10 days without hCG stimulation.[27] If implantation does not occur, hCG is not produced, the corpus luteum begins to regress, undergoing apoptosis (mediated by uterine luteolytic factors such as PG), and involution begins.[27] The decline in steroid hormones results in menstruation.

The corpus luteum is essential for continuation of the pregnancy until the placenta has developed the capacity to secrete estrogens and progesterone. Removal of the corpus luteum before this time usually leads to a miscarriage.[133] From 6 to 10 weeks, there is a transition period in which both the placenta and corpus luteum are producing hormones; by 7 weeks the placenta is capable of producing sufficient progesterone to maintain pregnancy if needed. At 6 to 8 weeks, there is a dip in progesterone levels, indicating a decline in corpus luteum functioning. This is followed by a secondary rise in progesterone (presumably as a result of placental takeover) without a rise in the metabolite 17α-hydroxyprogesterone (secreted by the corpus luteum). Around 32 weeks there is a more gradual rise in this metabolite, indicating increased placental utilization of fetal precursors.

Sperm Transport

Spermatozoa have not completely differentiated when they are released into the lumen of the seminiferous tubules (see Chapter 1). They are nonmotile and incapable of fertilization. Mature sperm have a condensed and genetically inactive nucleus. Reactivation of the nucleus occurs once the sperm enters the cytoplasm of the ovum.[161] Sperm are moved down the seminiferous tubules and through the epididymis and vas deferens by (1) the pressure of additional sperm forming behind them, (2) seminal fluid, and (3) peristaltic action. Biochemical and morphologic maturation of the sperm occurs during their 1- to 21-day passage through the epididymis, activating various signaling pathways and surface proteins such as those of the ADAM protein family.[38] Further modifications occur after ejaculation so that the sperm can bind to the zona pellucida of the ovum. Sperm are stored in the vas deferens and epididymis before ejaculation. Ejaculation occurs through the urethra with contraction of the ampulla and the ejaculatory duct upon orgasm.

The volume of ejaculate ranges from 2 to 6 (mean 3.5) mL and usually contains 100 million sperm per milliliter.[104] Men with less than 10 million sperm per milliliter are likely to be sterile.[104] Some spermatozoa are immature, senescent, or abnormal, and generally only the normal and strongest sperm are able to complete the journey within the female reproductive tract to the upper end of the fallopian tube. As sperm move along the epididymis, they begin to gain motility. Sperm become fully motile in the semen after entering the female reproductive tract.[161] Semen provides fructose for energy, an alkaline pH for protection against the acid environment of the vagina, micronutrients, amino acids, and oxidative and nonoxidative agents.[21] Semen also dilutes the sperm to improve motility. Sperm move at 2 to 3 mm per minute. Motility is slower in the acidic vaginal environment and faster in the alkaline uterine environment.[104] Failure of sperm to achieve motility is a cause of male infertility; for potential fertility, at least 40% should be motile by 2 hours after ejaculation.[104]

The neck and midpiece of the spermatozoa contain a pair of centrioles, the base of the tail apparatus, and the mitochondrial sheath. The mitochondria are arranged in a tight helical spiral around the anterior portion of the flagellum (tail). Mitochondria supply the adenosine triphosphate (ATP) required for independent motility. Sperm must reach the ovum within an allotted time or they exhaust their energy supply and die. Sperm survival in the uterus is relatively short because phagocytosis by leukocytes begins within a few hours. Sperm retain their ability to fertilize the ovum for 1 to 3 days.[134] However, most sperm do not survive for more than 48 hours.[27,104]

Once deposited at the external cervical os, some ejaculated sperm cross the cervical mucus facilitated by a decrease in mucus viscosity at midcycle (9 to 16 days), allowing for more rapid migration. Within minutes, these sperm enter the uterine cavity, although some get caught in cervical crypts and endometrial glands. The cervical crypts provide a short-term reservoir or storage site from which sperm are gradually released; this may increase the chance of fertilization.[104] Uterine motility, stimulated by PGs in seminal fluid that cause smooth muscle contraction, facilitates initial sperm transport.[74] Other sperm move more slowly (2 to 3 mm/hr) or are stored in cervical crypts and slowly released.[27]

Sperm chemotaxis (organized movement of the sperm toward the ovum) is stimulated by chemoattractants in follicular fluid, and possibly the cumulus oorphus and ovum as well as PGs produced by the oocyte and cumulus cells.[113] Other components of follicular fluid that may also act as chemoattractants include heparin, progesterone, atrial natriuretic peptide, epinephrine, oxytocin, calcitonin, and acetylcholine.[47] Capacitated sperm appear to be responsive to a sperm chemotrophic factor and other chemicals released by the follicle ovum and use these substances to "find" the ovum.[134]

Sperm have a role in modulation of maternal immune responses to pregnancy (see Chapter 13). Sperm entry into the female tract generates a transient inflammatory response. Seminal fluid factors contribute to expression of growth factors such as TGF-β and proinflammatory and other cytokines that enhance embryo development.[21] It has been proposed that the female reproductive tract may select sperm for fertilization via genetic molecular recognition mechanisms to reduce the risk of more than one sperm penetrating the ovum and possible genetic and immune matching.[68]

Fertilization

The process of fertilization has been defined in three different ways: (1) the instant of sperm and ovum fusion, (2) time from sperm-ovum fusion to development of the male and female pronuclei, and (3) time from sperm-ovum fusion to the first mitotic division (about 24 hours). Fertilization begins with contact between the sperm and secondary oocyte, arrested in the metaphase of the second meiotic division (see Chapter 1). Fertilization usually occurs in the upper third of the fallopian tube, usually in the ampulla. Before fertilization, the sperm must undergo two final maturational changes: capacitation and the acrosome reaction.

Capacitation involves physiologic and biologic changes, including removal of the glycoprotein coat and seminal plasma proteins from the plasma membrane over the acrosome (head of the sperm), which allows the acrosome reaction to occur.[138] Capacitation usually occurs in the fallopian tubes while the sperm are attached to the tubal epithelial lining but may begin while the sperm is still in the uterus.[27] This process is stimulated by substances in the female genital tract and follicular fluid.[1,60,104,138]

Capacitated sperm are chemiotaxically active.[47] Approximately 2% to 14% of sperm are capacitated at any time, with continuous replacement of sperm that lose their capacitation with newly capacitated sperm. Each sperm can only become capacitated once in its lifespan.[47] This constant replacement of capacitated sperm extends the time when fertilization is possible by continuous production of "ripe" sperm.[47] Thus, after ejaculation, precapacitated, capacitated, and postcapacitated sperm, as well as sperm that have undergone the acrosomal reaction, can be found within the female genital tract.

Of the millions of sperm in the ejaculate, only up to 300 to 500 sperm are found in the fallopian tubes at any given time.[27,133] The ampulla of the ovulatory tube has more sperm than the ampulla of the nonovulatory tube. Although it takes only one sperm to penetrate the ovum, it appears that many more are necessary to effect passage of the spermatozoa through the corona radiata to the ovum. The number of spermatozoa that are ejaculated does not appear to influence the number of sperm that enter the fallopian tubes unless very low counts occur.

The acrosome reaction with release of enzymes through small holes in the acrosomal membrane must occur for successful penetration of the corona radiata and zona pellucida by the sperm. The acrosome is a saclike structure on the head of the sperm containing many enzymes, including acid glycohydrases, proteases (such as acrosin), phosphatases, esterases, and hyaluronidase.[27,104,138] The capacitated sperm binds to the zona pellucida of the ovum, initiating the acrosome reaction (sperm activation). The sperm penetrates the zona pellucida and binds to the outer membrane of the oocyte (Figure 3-3).

The zona pellucida is an ovum-specific extracellular membrane composed of three glycoproteins (ZP1, ZP2, and ZP3) that act as ligands (molecules that bind to receptors) for sperm receptors. ZP3 mediates sperm binding and the acrosomal reaction.[133] Roles of the zona pellucida include sperm activation (acrosome reaction), preventing fertilization by more than one sperm, protecting the ovum before fertilization, and protecting the fertilized ovum until shortly before implantation.[27,134] Binding of the sperm to ZP3 is mediated by a sperm surface protein.[134] Once a sperm has bound to ZP3, a zonal reaction occurs with release of lysosomal enzymes. This reaction causes physicochemical alterations in the zona pellucida that make it impenetrable to other sperm.

The sperm head traverses the perivillous space between the plasma membranes and zona pellucida and attaches to the surface of the oocyte, and their plasma membranes fuse. This process is mediated by integrins (adhesion molecules) on the ovum surface along with zona binding proteins and other substances produced by the sperm.[1,134] The head and tail of the sperm enter the oocyte, leaving the outer plasma membrane of the sperm attached to the outer membrane of the oocyte. The ovum has a layer of cortical secretory granules along the inside of its plasma membrane. After sperm entry, the sperm-ovum interaction releases a wave of calcium along the zona pellucida, resulting in fusion of the cortical granules with the plasma membrane of the ovum and release of hydrolytic enzymes, proteases, and polysaccharides into the perivillous space.[27] This modifies the zona pellucida glycoproteins, preventing activation and entry of other sperm.[113]

After entering the cytoplasm of the oocyte, the sperm undergoes rapid morphologic changes. The tail of the sperm degenerates and the head enlarges to form the male pronucleus. Each pronucleus has 23 chromosomes (22 autosomes and 1 sex chromosome). Sex of the offspring is determined by the male and depends on whether the sperm that enters the ovum contains an X or Y chromosome. The sperm nucleus becomes reactivated so that it can again synthesize DNA and RNA.[161] This processing involves removal of the nuclear membrane with exposure of the sperm chromatin to the cytoplasm of the ovum. The nuclear protein is remodeled and

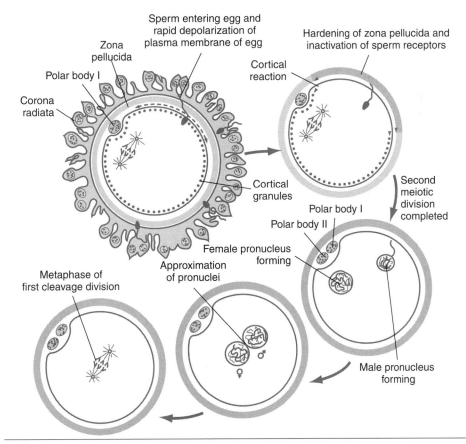

FIGURE 3-3 Summary of the main events involved in fertilization. (From Carlson, B.M. [2013]. *Human embryology and developmental biology* [5th ed.]. Philadelphia: Saunders.)

the nucleus decondenses, becoming larger and more spherical. A new nuclear envelope develops, forming the male pronucleus and activating DNA transcription and replication. This is believed to be mediated by factors in the cytoplasm of the ovum. This process takes about 3 to 4 hours, during which the developing male pronucleus gradually approaches the female pronucleus.[161]

The ovum must be metabolically activated. Entry of the sperm into the ovum triggers two events: (1) the cortical and zonal reactions described earlier, which blocks entry of other sperm, and (2) a transient increase in intracellular calcium accompanied by an increase in oxidative metabolism.[27,113] The increased calcium stimulates the oocyte to complete its second meiotic division with extrusion of the second polar body into the perivitelline space. The nucleus enlarges and is called the female pronucleus. The oocyte is now mature and metabolically active.[113] Failure of calcium signaling can lead to complete failure (triploidy) or partial failure (abnormalities of chromosomal number of the second meiotic division, cleavage arrest, and alterations in development of the inner cell mass and trophectoderm [trophoblast]). These alterations can result in implantation failure and miscarriage.[148]

The female and male pronuclei approach each other, their membranes disintegrate, and the nuclei fuse (see Figure 3-3). Chromatin strands intermingle, and the diploid number (46) of chromosomes is restored. The *zygote* (from the Greek, meaning "yoked together") is formed, and mitotic division (cleavage) begins. The zygote measures 0.2 mm in diameter and carries the genetic material necessary to create a unique human being. Fertilization results in species variation, with half of the chromosomes coming from the mother and half from the father, mixing the genes each parent originally received from their parents.[104]

Cleavage and Zygote Transport

Cleavage involves a series of rapid mitotic cell divisions that begins with the first mitotic division of the zygote and ends with formation of the blastocyst. Cleavage is under the control of mitosis-promoting or maturation-promoting factor (MPF).[27] The zygote divides into two daughter cells (blastomeres) about 30 hours after fertilization; each of these cells divides into two smaller cells, which also divide, and so forth (see Figure 3-2). The dividing cells are contained by the zona pellucida and become progressively smaller with each subsequent division, with no change in the total mass of the zygote. The trophoblast secretes an immunosuppressant protein called *early pregnancy factor (EPF)* by 24 to 48 hours after fertilization. Pregnancy tests within the first 10 days after fertilization use EPF in maternal serum.[104]

During this time developmental control is transferred from the mother to the zygote. Maternal-to-zygote transition (MZT) is the process by which the sperm and oocyte are reprogrammed after fertilization into the totipotential embryo.[86,89] Immediately after fertilization the maternal genome controls development. By the 4- to 8-cell stage the embryonic genome has been activated (although there may be some

activity before this point).[89] Within hours after fertilization the paternal genome undergoes DNA demethylation, followed by imprinting (see Box 1-1 on p. 11) of the entire embryonic genome (however imprinted regions that are uniquely male or females remain constant).[89] This reprogramming involves two main processes: (1) maternal clearance or removal of maternal messenger ribonucleic acid (mRNA) and proteins that were needed for oocyte maturation and early embryo development via mechanisms such as deadenylation and other processes regulated by miRNA and RNA binding protein and (2) activation of the zygotic genome which involves changes in the zygote's cell cycle, chromatin structure, histone modifications, epigenetic prepatterning, and transcription factors.[10,86,89,143]

Cell division occurs every 12 to 24 hours. By 3 to 4 days, the zygote has divided into 8 to 16 blastomeres. Around the eight- to nine-cell stage, the blastomeres realign and form a tight ball of cells mediated by cell surface adhesion glycoproteins. This process, called *compaction,* allows increased interaction between cells needed for formation of the inner cell mass. This occurs via gap and tight junctions.[27]

The zygote remains in the ampulla for the first 24 hours, then is propelled down the fallopian tube by ciliary action over the next few days. At the 12- to 16-cell stage (about 3 days after fertilization), the zygote becomes a solid cluster of cells called the *morula* (from the Latin word for "mulberry," which it resembles).[27] The zygote reaches the uterine cavity 3 to 4 days after fertilization (about 90 hours or 5 days after follicle rupture). Development is now under control of the embryonic genome. Fluid (which provides nutrients) from the uterine cavity enters the morula as the blastocyst is formed.

The blastocyst consists of four distinct components: (1) zona pellucida, a thick glycoprotein membrane that is beginning to stretch and thin; (2) trophectoderm (trophoblast), a one-cell-thick outer layer of flattened cells that will form the placenta and chorion; (3) inner cell mass (embryoblast), a one- or two-cell-thick, crescent-shaped cluster of cells that will form the embryo; and (4) fluid-filled blastocyst cavity.[104] The zona pellucida protects the zygote from adhering to the mucosa of the fallopian tube and from rejection by the maternal immune system (see Chapter 13). Position of individual cells and gene transcription factors influence which cells become trophoblast and which become inner cell mass. For example, *Oct4* and *Nanog* are transcription factors found in all blastomeres in the morula. In the cells that become the inner cell mass, these transcription factors continue to be expressed but are turned off in the cells of the future trophoblast.[134] If these gene transcription factors are deficient, all or most of the cells in the blastocyst become part of the trophectoderm, resulting in a molar pregnancy (see Gestational Trophoblast Disease). The blastocyst floats free in the uterine cavity from 90 to 150 hours after ovulation, then begins to implant 6 to 7 days after fertilization (Figure 3-4).

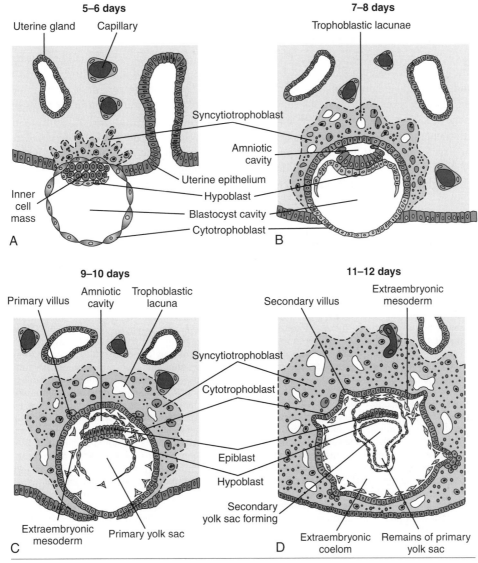

FIGURE 3-4 Implantation and early development of the embryo. **A,** Syncytiotrophoblast invades the endometrium. **B,** Most of the embryo is embedded in the endometrium with early formation of trophoblastic lacunae. The amniotic cavity and primary yolk sac are beginning to form. **C,** Implantation is almost complete; primary villi are forming and the embryonic mesoderm is appearing. **D,** Implantation is complete; secondary villi and the secondary yolk sac are forming. (From Carlson, B.M. [2004]. *Human embryology and developmental biology* [3rd ed.]. St. Louis: Mosby.)

EMBRYONIC AND FETAL DEVELOPMENT

The infant develops progressively from the single-cell fertilized egg to a highly complex multicellular organism. The genetic constitution of the individual is established at the time of fertilization. During development of the embryo and fetus, genetic information is unfolded to control morphologic development. Alterations in genetic information or morphologic development can modify the structure and function of cells and organs and result in congenital defects. Principles of genetic regulation of development and morphogenesis are described in this section, followed by an overview of embryonic and fetal development. Development of specific body systems is described in Units II and III.

REGULATION OF DEVELOPMENT

Embryonic development combines growth, differentiation, and organization of cellular components at all levels. As development progresses, differential synthesis is established, resulting in cellular differentiation. Growth is the process of creating more of a substance that is already present through increase in cell size and number. In contrast, differentiation is the creation of new types of substances, cells, tissues, and organs that were not previously present. Organization is the process by which these elements are coordinated into functional integrated units. Morphogenesis is the production of a special form, shape, or structure of a cell or group of cells and occurs by the precise organization of cell populations into distinct organs.[77]

The mechanisms controlling morphogenesis are complex and incompletely understood.[27] Factors involved in control of development in the embryo are summarized in the following text and are described further in Box 3-1. Development is controlled by specific genes and receptors mediated by secreted molecules and intercellular communications.[27,35,85,86] Much of the current knowledge of control of development comes from animal models. Often the names of these genes or their products reflect characteristics of the animals or situations in which they were first identified. Developmental genes control the definition of body axes (ventral/dorsal, anterior/posterior, left/right, medial/dorsal) and patterning (arrangement of different cells to form tissues and organogenesis).[78] Pattern formation within different regions, such as the neural tube, somites (that form bones and muscles), and limbs involves cell determination, development of signaling centers, and cell differentiation.[78] All of these processes involve the coordination of signaling molecules and other proteins, DNA transcription factors, extracellular matrix components, enzymes, and transport systems.[78]

Development genes are involved in cell differentiation and proliferation into adulthood and if later altered can lead to malignancies. Imprinted genes (see Box 1-1 on p. 11) are also important in prenatal and placental development as well as in

---

BOX 3-1 Factors Involved in Regulation of Embryogenesis

Embryogenesis is regulated by developmental genes and receptors, signaling molecules, transcription factors, and other molecules. Transcription factors are proteins that turn other genes on and off, thus controlling gene expression. Transcription factors remain within the cell and bind to DNA at the promoter or enhancer regions of specific genes or regulate mRNA production.[27] Often a cascade is set up, wherein the transcription factor turns on various genes which in turn can regulate other genes. Initially these regulatory genes send out signals that induce expression of other genes, which in turn induce expression of still other genes and so forth until genes that encode development of specific structures or functions of cells or tissues within the embryo are expressed.[134] The molecules produced regulate cell activities, such as causing a cell to differentiate in a specific way, and are modulated by positive and negative feedback loops (see Chapter 1). Examples of developmental gene families include *homeobox (HOX), PAX* and high mobility group *(HMG)*.[78,86] (Homeobox is a DNA sequence within a given gene that codes for specific transcription factors that regulate development of various tissues and organs.) For example, the *HOX* genes are involved with craniocaudal organization; the *PAX* gene family is involved with development of the urogenital system, central nervous system (CNS), thyroid gland, and eye, among other sites.[27] HMG genes such as the *SOX* family include genes needed for development of the genital system (see Chapter 1).[78]

Changes in cells within the embryo are influenced by combinations of intracellular and extracellular signals.[86] Intercellular signaling molecules (first messengers), many of which are growth factors, influence other cells by binding to receptor molecules (Figure 3-5). Signaling molecules act in a paracrine fashion; that is, they are secreted into the spaces surrounding the cell where the molecules are produced and diffuse between cells in that area.[78,133] These molecules bind to receptor molecules on cell membranes. After a series of protein interactions, a transcription factor is activated and a signal is sent to the cell nucleus and a gene is expressed resulting in production of specific proteins needed to guide development.[27,133]

Receptor molecules can be intracellular or on the cell surface. Extracellular receptors are binding sites for ligands (hormones, growth factor, or cytokine). Binding to the receptor alters the receptor and stimulates an intercellular response (signal transduction) either directly via a protein kinase or indirectly via a second messenger such as cyclic adenosine monophosphate (cAMP). Signaling molecules may also act by inhibiting other signaling molecules.[27] Juxtacrine signaling also occurs via three mechanisms: (1) interaction of a protein on one cell membrane with a receptor on the surface of another cell; (2) via gap junctions (see Chapter 4 for further discussion of gap junctions), or (3) interaction of extracellular matrix ligands (collagen, proteoglycans, fibronectin, and laminin) with receptors on neighboring cells.[133]

Major paracrine receptor families and signaling pathways include *Wnt, Hedgehog, transforming growth factor-β (TGF-β)*, and *tyrosine kinase* families as well as *Notch, Integrin,* and retinoic acid signaling.[78,133,134] The *Wnt* family is involved in the dorsal/ventral axis and formation of the midbrain, muscles, gonads, and kidneys. Alterations are associated with tumors and possibly congenital anomalies.[78] The hedgehog family, such as the sonic hedgehog *(Shh)* gene, is involved in patterning of many tissues and organs, including axis formation, motor neuron induction, somite differentiation, neural tube induction and patterning, and limb patterning.[27,133,134] Mutations are associated with central nervous system (e.g., holoprosencephaly), axial skeletal, and limb abnormalities as well as with some basal cell carcinomas.[27,78] The TGF-β family includes TGF-β, which is important in mesoderm induction and myoblast proliferation, activin (granulose cell proliferation, mesoderm induction), inhibin (inhibition of gonadotropin secretion by the pituitary), müllerian inhibitory substance (regression of the paramesonephric duct; see Chapter 1), bone morphogenetic proteins, and decapentaplegic (limb development).[27,35,133,134] The TGF-β family is also involved in angiogenesis, axon growth, mesoderm differentiation, and epithelial branching in the lung and kidneys.[133] Defects in TGF-β signaling can lead to vascular and skeletal disorders as well as pulmonary hypertension and cancer.[134]

Tyrosine kinase signaling involves growth factors (GFs) such as fibroblast growth factor (FGF), epidermal growth factor (EGF), insulin-like growth factors (IGFs), platelet-derived GFs, and vascular endothelial GF (VEGF).[133,134] FGFs are involved in cell migration, growth, and differentiation needed for brain patterning and limb formation. FGFs are found in bone, so mutations in FGF receptor genes can lead to skeletal dysplasia and disorders such as achondroplasia, Crouzon syndrome, Apert syndrome, and some forms of craniosyntosis.[78] Defects in Notch signaling can lead to skeletal disorders such as Alagille syndrome and spondylocostal dysostosis as well as cancers such as T-cell acute lymphoblastic leukemia.[134] Integrins are receptors that are involved in linking the extracellular matrix and cell cytoskeleton and in signal transduction that can lead to changes in cell size, shape, and position.[134] Defective integrin signaling can lead to alterations in extracellular proteins such as collagens, fibrillins, and proteoglycans. Developmental failure can lead to skin and connective tissue disorders such as epidermolysis bullosa; Marfan syndrome; and cancers of the breast, intestine, and reproductive organs.[78,134] Retinoic acid (derived from vitamin A) acts as a morphogen, which is "a diffusible substance that determines cell fate during development in a concentration-dependent manner."[134]

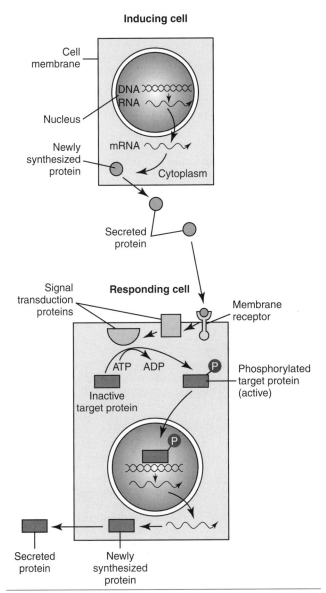

Inducing cell

Cell membrane

DNA

RNA

Nucleus

mRNA

Newly synthesized protein

Cytoplasm

Secreted protein

Responding cell

Signal transduction proteins

Membrane receptor

ATP   ADP

P

Phosphorylated target protein (active)

Inactive target protein

P

Secreted protein

Newly synthesized protein

FIGURE 3-5 Example of signal transduction. Inducing cells influence their neighbors by secreting small proteins (growth factors) that diffuse to adjacent cells (responding cells) and bind to their membrane receptors. This initiates an intracellular signaling cascade through a series of signal transduction proteins and phosphorylation events. Phosphorylated proteins enter the nucleus, where they alter gene expression, leading to the synthesis of new proteins. *ADP,* Adenosine diphosphate; *ATP,* adenosine triphosphate; *P,* phosphorus. (From Schoenwolf, G.C., Bleyl, S.B., Brauer, B.S., & Francis-West, P.H. (2009). *Larsen's human embryology* (4th ed.). Philadelphia: Churchill Livingstone Elsevier.)

development and function of metabolic processes. Developmental gene expression is modified by a variety of factors during development.[104] Although the first cell divisions after fertilization are under maternal genetic control, by the two- to four-cell stage, the embryonic genome is activated and is producing many intercellular signaling proteins and transcription factors.

Transcription factors are proteins that turn other genes on and off, thus controlling expression of these genes. Some of these transcription factors act as master switches regulating groups of genes.[86] Positive feedback induces further production of regulatory proteins and gene transcription factors that influence that cell or other target cells. Negative feedback results in the production of inhibitors. This process is controlled by interactions of genes with environmental factors that turn the gene on and off at precise intervals.

Each gene can produce multiple isotypes, each isotype producing a different product. The different isotypes are produced by the splicing and reorganization of exons within a given gene (see Figure 1-3).[85] As a result, a single gene can guide the production of many different forms of mRNA and formation of proteins with unique biologic functions. Thus individual genes may have different functions at different stages of development and with development of specific organs.[27,35]

Alterations in developmental genes and their products can result in congenital anomalies through various mechanisms. Mechanical failures involve defects in structural genes such as collagen resulting in qualitative or quantitative differences. For example, collagen mutations are seen in osteogenesis imperfecta, Apert syndrome, and epidermolysis bullosa; a fibrillin defect is seen in Marfan syndrome. Alterations in cell numbers caused by regulatory failures can lead to overgrowth, such as occurs in Beckwith-Wiedemann syndrome, or undergrowth, such as occurs with some forms of microcephaly. Failure of cell migration during development leads to anomalies such as lissencephaly (failure of neuronal migration) or Hirschsprung disease (failure of neural crest cells to migrate and form ganglia). Failure of the developmental switch to turn genes on and off can upset the development timetable and also lead to defects. Additional information on regulation of development is in Box 3-1 on p. 70.

Mechanisms of Morphogenesis

The human embryo's progression through stages of development is shared by many other creatures (phylogenetic recapitulation). As a result, animal models can be useful in understanding developmental processes and deviations in humans. Development and maturation generally proceed in a cephalocaudal direction. Morphogenesis is accomplished by a variety of genetically controlled mechanisms. Various tissues and organs are at different stages of maturity throughout development. For example, the gut and bladder are essentially structurally complete at birth, whereas the long bones and lung alveoli do not reach maturity for years after birth. Therefore various organs are more or less vulnerable to insults and toxic agents at different stages of development. Morphogenic mechanisms are induced by the signaling pathway and transcription factors described in the previous section and Box 3-1.

Cell Differentiation

Initially all cells are similar and unspecialized, but each must eventually become 1 of 350 different cell types found in the human body.[145] Cells pass through two phases to become specialized. In the first phase (determination), the cell becomes restricted in its developmental capabilities and loses the ability to develop in alternative ways. Cell determination occurs for the first time in the blastocyst, with formation of the inner cell mass (which forms the embryo) and trophoblast (which becomes the placenta). In the second phase (differentiation), cells develop distinctive morphologic and functional characteristics. Initially, cell position determines the fate of the cell. Specific differentiation is regulated by interactions between cell populations and is controlled by *HOX* and other gene families that are switched on to produce specific signaling molecules in a sequential manner.[145] Cell differentiation often involves induction (discussed in the next section), in which one tissue signals (induces) a second tissue (responder) to differentiate into a specific structure. Signals are sent between cells in both directions (cross-talk) to complete the differentiation.[133]

Induction

Induction is the process by which cells in one part of the embryo influence cells around them to develop in a specific way. Induction requires inductors, or cells that stimulate reactions in surrounding cells via signal transduction and induced tissue, which is made up of cells that have the capacity or competence to respond to these protein signals via cell membrane receptor molecules (see Figure 3-5). At some point, inductors and inducers lose their ability to perform these actions.[35]

Secondary induction is a cascade of developmental events and is a common way many parts of the embryo are formed. For example, in the nervous system, the notochord is a primary inductor or organizer for brain development. The forebrain reacts to secondary inductors in the mesoderm to form the optic cup, which then induces adjacent ectoderm to form the eye lens. The eye lens then induces epidermis around it to form the corneal epithelium. Other examples of induction are in the formation of the gastrointestinal system, where the gut endoderm induces the surrounding mesenchyme to differentiate into organs such as the liver or pancreas (see Chapter 12) or in the renal system where the ureteric bud causes the surrounding mesenchyme to become nephrons (see Chapter 11).[133]

If any of these steps is interfered with, the next stage in development may not occur, or it may occur abnormally. If these alterations occur early in the developmental sequence, complete organ agenesis may result.[104] An example of chemical pathway activity during secondary induction is the interaction of activin and TGF-β, which influences branching of epithelial tubes in the kidney, pancreas, and salivary glands.[85,133]

Differential Cell Proliferation

Differential cell proliferation results from localized differences in rates of cell division. Proliferation is controlled by cell signaling mechanisms and growth factors. These differences may lead to a buildup of cells in certain areas or may result in a phenomenon called *invagination,* in which cells growing more slowly than surrounding cells appear to be "sinking" into tissues. In fact, one set of cells is overtaking the other cells in growth. This phenomenon can be seen during the development of the neural groove, the oral cavity, and the nostrils. The rate of cell proliferation is modulated by interactions of receptor molecules on the surface of the cells with systemic and local growth factors that stimulate proliferation during organogenesis. A period of rapid cell proliferation often precedes differentiation. Proliferation inhibition by teratogenic agents may cause defects. Growth inhibition can also be caused by lack of space (when space runs out, tissues stop proliferating). For example, with a diaphragmatic hernia, the intestinal contents are in the thoracic cavity and may inhibit lung development.

Programmed Cell Death

Programmed cell death or apoptosis is a precisely timed event—under genetic control and cell feedback mechanisms—that occurs in many of the embryonic tissues as part of normal development. The process involves the release of lysosomal hydrolytic enzymes that dissolve cells, thereby altering the tissues. This mechanism is responsible for lumen formation in solid tubes (trachea and parts of the gut) and the disappearance of the webbing between the fingers and toes. If enzyme release is inhibited, syndactyly, some forms of bowel atresia, or imperforate anus may result. If enzyme activity is increased, micromelia (shortened limbs) may result.[145]

Cell Size and Shape Changes

Cell size and shape changes occur with elongation or narrowing and swelling or shrinkage. Elongation or narrowing is accomplished by the coordinated activities of cell microfilaments and microtubules. Microtubules are long cylinders containing tubulin, a substance that alters its length when polymerized (i.e., joined together to form a molecule of higher molecular weight [MW]). Certain chemicals (including some found in microorganisms) inhibit tubulin polymerization and normal microfilament action. Changes in osmotic balance or interference in transport of elements across the membranes results in swelling or shrinkage of cells.

Cell Migration

During development some cells move around in a fashion similar to that of an amoeba. This process is dependent on microtubular and microfilament elongation and contraction. Migration involves the elongation of the leading edge of the cell, followed by adhesion of the cell to a new contact point. Contraction of the cell toward the new adhesion site results in movement of the cell. Alterations or interference may limit cell migration and result in a defect. Hirschsprung disease (absence of intestinal ganglion cells) results from failure of neural crest cells to migrate. From 3 to 6 months' gestation, millions of neurons and glial cells within the central nervous system migrate from their point of origin in the periventricular germinal matrix to their eventual loci in the cerebrum.

Alterations in this migration can result in alterations in central nervous system (CNS) organization and function (see Chapter 15).[133,145]

Cell Recognition and Adhesion

Cell recognition and adhesion is a mechanism that involves the adhesion of certain cells, such as the neural folds, which meet and fuse to form the neural tube. The recognition and adhesion process involves interaction of specific substrates (e.g., integrins, glycoproteins, cell surface enzymes) on one cell with complementary substrates, enzymes, or adhesion molecules on the membrane of another cell. A similar mechanism is seen with adhesion during cell migration. Interference with cellular membrane substrates may prevent adhesion. Alterations in this mechanism may be responsible for cleft palate or neural tube defects.

Folding of the Embryo

The embryo begins as a relatively straight line of cells. As new cells form, the embryo is forced to conform to available space. To adapt to the confined space, the embryo folds (curves) in both transverse and longitudinal planes. Folding in the transverse plane causes the embryo to become cylindrical in shape; longitudinal folding results in the head and tail folds. Structures within the embryo (e.g., heart, intestines) also undergo folding to conform to the space available to them. Folding is mediated by signaling and other proteins.

Overview of Embryonic Development

Preembryonic development occurs from the time of conception and zygote formation until 2 weeks' gestation. By the time of implantation, the inner cell mass consists of 12 to 15 cells. At about 7 days, the first of three germ cell layers that give rise to the embryo—the hypoblast, or primitive endoderm—appears.[27] During the second week the bilaminar embryo develops as the inner cell mass differentiates to form the epiblast along the inner part of the amniotic cavity.

The developing organism appears as a flat disk with a connecting stalk that will become part of the umbilical cord. Cytotrophoblast cells around the inner wall of the blastocyst cavity form the primitive yolk sac (see Figure 3-4, C) and extraembryonic coelom, which serves as a transfer interface and nutrient reservoir.[75] Connective tissue (extraembryonic mesoderm) fills in the space between the cytotrophoblast cells and the extraembryonic coelomic membrane. Near the end of the second week, cavities appear in the extraembryonic mesoderm and fuse to form the extraembryonic coelom. A secondary yolk sac (see Figure 3-4, D) develops from the primary sac (which gradually disintegrates) and provides for early nutrition of the embryo. Part of it is eventually incorporated into the primitive gut. The fluid in this cavity is an ultrafiltrate of maternal serum with placental and secondary yolk sac products.[75] An endodermal cell thickening (prochordal plate) appears at one end of the disk and is the future site of the mouth and cranial region.

The embryonic period lasts from 2 weeks after fertilization until the end of the 8th week. This period is the time of organogenesis. Figure 3-6 summarizes the major stages in development of specific organ systems. Development of specific organ systems is described in detail in Chapters 8 to 20. This section provides an overview of major events during embryogenesis.

The 3rd week of development coincides with the first missed menstrual period (see Figure 3-1). During the 3rd week, growth becomes more rapid, with development of the mesoderm and establishment of the trilaminar embryo; formation of the neural tube (CNS), somites (bones and other supporting structures), and coelom (body cavities); and development of a primitive cardiovascular system.

The primitive streak (thick band of epiblast cells) appears at 15 days in the midline of the dorsal aspect of the embryonic disk.[104] Cells in the primitive streak migrate between the endoderm and ectoderm to form the mesoderm; the epiblast layer becomes the ectoderm, establishing the trilaminar embryo. Cells from the mesoderm later migrate out into the embryonic body to become mesenchyme and form supporting tissues.

The ectoderm layer eventually forms the central and peripheral nervous systems, epidermis, hair, nails, inner ear, epithelium of the sensory organs, nasal cavity and mouth, salivary glands, and mucous membranes. The middle mesoderm layer develops into the dermis; muscle; connective tissue; skeleton (tendon, bones, cartilage); circulatory and lymphatic systems; kidneys; gonads; and the lining of the pericardial, pleural, and peritoneal cavities. The endoderm forms the epithelium of the digestive, respiratory, and urinary tracts as well as the thyroid and parathyroid glands.[27,104]

Development is in a cranial-to-caudal direction, with the embryo initially being a pear-shaped disk with a broad cephalic end and a narrow caudal end. The primitive streak elongates cranially to form a midline rod of cells, or notochord. The notochord extends to the prochordal plate, where the endoderm and ectoderm fuse into the oropharyngeal membrane. Other cells from the primitive streak migrate around the notochord and prochordal plate to form a cardiogenic area where the heart will develop. At the caudal end the endoderm and ectoderm fuse into the cloacal membrane.[27,104]

The ectoderm over the notochord thickens to form the neural plate, which will eventually form the neural tube, which gives rise to the brain and spinal cord. The mesoderm on either side of the notochord thickens to form two long columns that divide into paired cuboidal bodies (somites). Somites give rise to the skeleton and its associated musculature and much of the dermis. Somite development can be used to distinguish the stage of embryonic development. The foregut and body cavities begin to develop. Mesoderm cells aggregate in the cardiogenic area at 18 to 19 days to form two endocardial tubes, which fuse by 19 to 20 days.[27,104] Primitive blood cells and vessels develop in the yolk sac, chorion, and embryo, and by 21 days' gestation they link with heart tubes to form a primitive cardiovascular system.

EMBRYONIC DEVELOPMENT

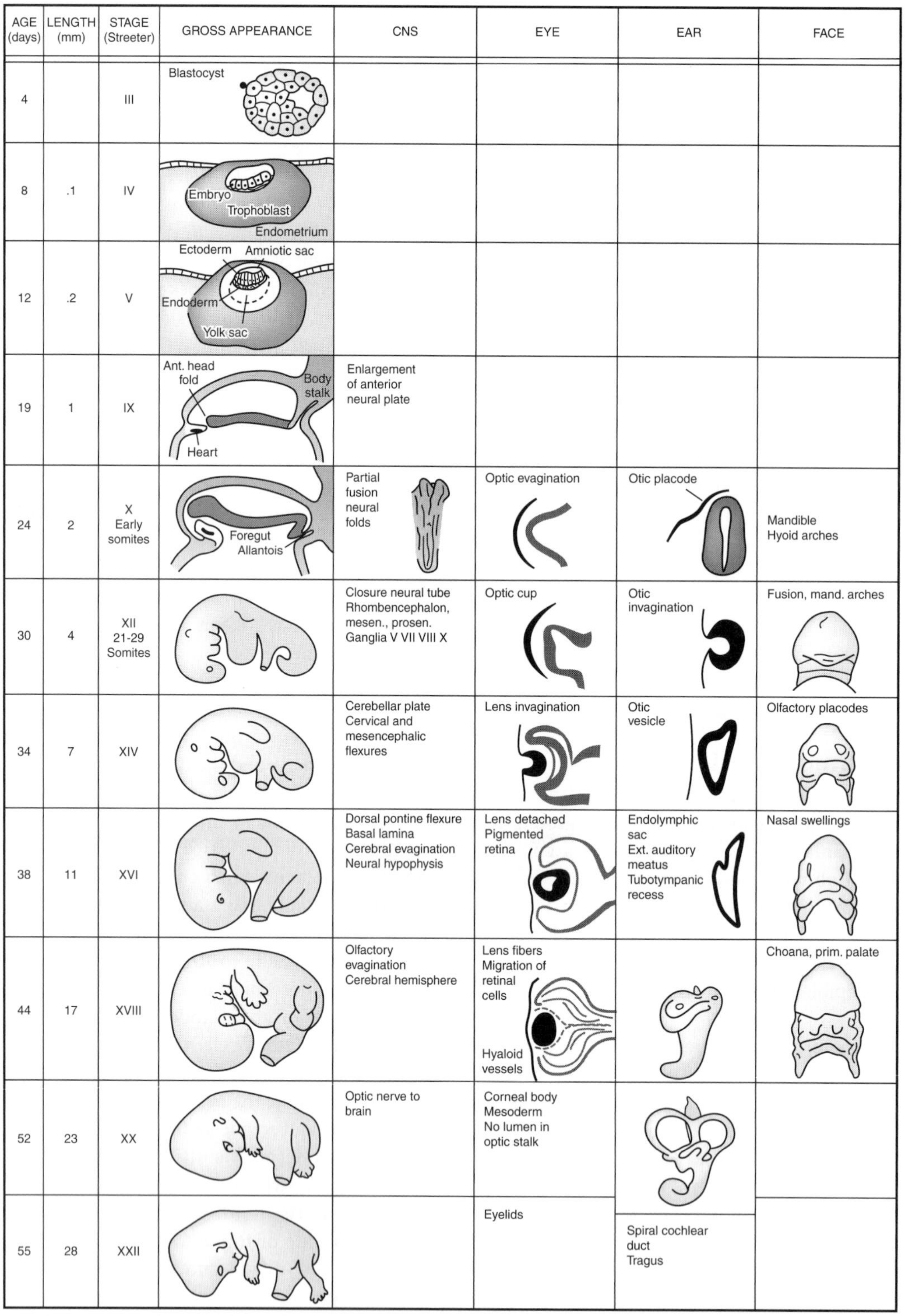

AGE (days)	LENGTH (mm)	STAGE (Streeter)	GROSS APPEARANCE	CNS	EYE	EAR	FACE
4		III	Blastocyst				
8	.1	IV	Embryo Trophoblast Endometrium				
12	.2	V	Ectoderm Amniotic sac Endoderm Yolk sac				
19	1	IX	Ant. head fold Body stalk Heart	Enlargement of anterior neural plate			
24	2	X Early somites	Foregut Allantois	Partial fusion neural folds	Optic evagination	Otic placode	Mandible Hyoid arches
30	4	XII 21-29 Somites		Closure neural tube Rhombencephalon, mesen., prosen. Ganglia V VII VIII X	Optic cup	Otic invagination	Fusion, mand. arches
34	7	XIV		Cerebellar plate Cervical and mesencephalic flexures	Lens invagination	Otic vesicle	Olfactory placodes
38	11	XVI		Dorsal pontine flexure Basal lamina Cerebral evagination Neural hypophysis	Lens detached Pigmented retina	Endolymphic sac Ext. auditory meatus Tubotympanic recess	Nasal swellings
44	17	XVIII		Olfactory evagination Cerebral hemisphere	Lens fibers Migration of retinal cells Hyaloid vessels		Choana, prim. palate
52	23	XX		Optic nerve to brain	Corneal body Mesoderm No lumen in optic stalk		
55	28	XXII			Eyelids	Spiral cochlear duct Tragus	

A

FIGURE 3-6   **A–D,** Timetable of human embryonic and fetal development. *asc,* Ascending; *cartil,* cartilage; *cereb,* cerebral; *CNS,* central nervous system; *desc,* descending; *epith,* epithelial; *evag,* evagination; *ext,* external; *intest,* intestinal; *lat,* lateral; *mand,* mandibular; *masc,* masculinization; *mesen,* mesencephalon; mesench, mesenchyme; *ossif,* ossification; *prim,* primary; *prosen,* prosencephalon; *RBCs,* red blood cells; *sept,* septum; *urogen memb,* urogenital membrane; *urorect,* urorectal; *ventric,* ventricular. The embryonic ages for Streeter's stages XII-XXII have been altered in accordance with the human data from Iffy, L. Shepard, T.H., Jakobovits, A., Lemire, R.J., & Kerner, P. (1967). The rate of growth in young human embryos of Streeter's horizons. 13 to 23. Acta Anat (Basel), 66, 178-186. (From Jones, K.L. [1996]. *Smith's recognizable patterns of human malformation* [5th ed.]. Philadelphia: Saunders.)

The embryonic ages for Streeter's stages XII-XXII have been altered
in accordance with the human data from Iffy, L., et al.: Acta Anat., 66:178, 1967.

EXTREMITIES	HEART	GUT, ABDOMEN	LUNG	UROGENITAL	OTHER
					Early blastocyst with inner cell mass and cavitation (58 cells) lying free within the uterine cavity
					Implantation Trophoblast invasion Embryonic disk with endoblast and ectoblast
		Yolk sac			Early amnion sac Extraembryonic mesoblast, angioblast Chorionic gonadotropin
	Merging mesoblast anterior to prechordal plate	Stomodeum Cloaca		Allantois	Primitive streak Hensen's node Notochord Prechordal plate Blood cells in yolk sac
	Single heart tube Propulsion	Foregut		Mesonephric ridge	Yolk sac larger than amnion sac
Arm bud	Ventric. outpouching Gelatinous reticulum	Rupture stomato-deum Evagination of thyroid, liver, and dorsal pancreas	Lung bud	Mesonephric duct enters cloaca	Rathke's pouch Migration of myotomes from somites
Leg bud	Auric. outpouching Septum primum	Pharyngeal pouches yield parathyroids, lat. thyroid, thymus Stomach broadens	Bronchi	Ureteral evag. Urorect. sept. Germ cells Gonadal ridge Coelom, Epithelium	
Hand plate, Mesench. condens. Innervation	Fusion mid. A-V canal Muscular vent. sept.	Intestinal loop into yolk stalk Cecum Gallbladder Hepatic ducts Spleen	Main lobes	Paramesonephric duct Gonad ingrowth of coelomic epith.	Adrenal cortex (from coelomic epithelium) invaded by sympathetic cells = medulla Jugular lymph sacs
Finger rays, Elbow	Aorta Pulmonary artery Valves Membrane ventricular septum	Duodenal lumen obliterated Cecum rotates right Appendix	Tracheal cartil.	Fusion urorect. sept. Open urogen. memb., anus Epith. cords in testicle	Early muscle
Clearing, central cartil.	Septum secundum			S-shaped vesicles in nephron blastema connect with collecting tubules from calyces	Superficial vascular plexus low on cranium
Shell, Tubular bone				A few large glomeruli Short secretory tubules Tunica albuginea Testicle, interstitial cells	Superficial vascular plexus at vertex

B

FIGURE 3-6, cont'd

Continued

FETAL DEVELOPMENT

AGE (weeks)	LENGTH (cm)		WT (g)	GROSS APPEARANCE	CNS	EYE, EAR	FACE, MOUTH	CARDIO-VASCULAR	LUNG
	C-R	Tot.							
7½	2.8				Cerebral hemisphere Infundibulum, Rathke's	Lens nearing final shape	Palatal swellings Dental lamina, Epithel.	Pulmonary vein into left atrium	
8	3.7				Primitive cereb. cortex Olfactory lobes Dura and pia mater	Eyelid Ear canals	Nares plugged Rathke's pouch detach. Sublingual gland	A-V bundle Sinus venosus absorbed into right auricle	Pleuroperitoneal canals close Bronchioles
10	6.0				Spinal cord histology Cerebellum	Iris Ciliary body Eyelids fuse Lacrimal glands Spiral gland different	Lips, Nasal cartilage Palate		Laryngeal cavity reopened
12	8.8				Cord-cervical and lumbar enlarged, Cauda equina	Retina layered Eye axis forward Scala tympani	Tonsillar crypts Cheeks Dental papilla	Accessory coats, blood vessels	Elastic fibers
16	14				Corpora quadrigemina Cerebellum prominent Myelination begins	Scala vestibuli Cochlear duct	Palate complete Enamel and dentine	Cardiac muscle condensed	Segmentation of bronchi complete
20						Inner ear ossified	Ossification of nose		Decrease in mesenchyme Capillaries penetrate linings of tubules
24	32		800		Typical layers in cerebral cortex Cauda equina at first sacral level		Nares reopen Calcification of tooth primordia		Change from cuboidal to flattened epithelium Alveoli
28	38.5		1100		Cerebral fissures and convolutions	Eyelids reopen Retinal layers complete Perceive light			Vascular components adequate for respiration
32	43.5		1600	Accumulation of fat		Auricular cartilage	Taste sense		Number of alveoli still incomplete
36	47.5		2600						
38	50		3200		Cauda equina, at L-3 Myelination within brain	Lacrimal duct canalized	Rudimentary frontal maxillary sinuses	Closure of: foramen ovale, ductus arteriosus, umbilical vessels, ductus venosus	
First postnatal year +					Continuing organization of axonal networks Cerebrocortical function, motor coordination Myelination continues until 2-3 years	Iris pigmented, 5 months Mastoid air cells Coordinate vision, 3-5 months Maximal vision by 5 years	Salivary gland ducts become canalized 5-7 months Relatively rapid growth of mandible and nose Teeth begin to erupt 5-7 months	Relative hypertrophy left ventricle	Continue adding new alveoli

C

FIGURE 3-6, cont'd

GUT	UROGENITAL	SKELETAL MUSCLE	SKELETON	SKIN	BLOOD, THYMUS LYMPH	ENDOCRINE
Pancreas, dorsal and ventral fusion	Renal vesicles	Differentiation toward final shape	Cartilaginous models of bones Chondrocranium Tail regression	Mammary gland		Parathyroid associated with thyroid Sympathetic neuroblasts invade adrenal
Liver relatively large Intestinal villi	Müllerian ducts fusing Ovary distinguishable	Muscles well represented Movement	Ossification center Sternum	Basal layer	Bone marrow Thymus halves unite Lymphoblasts around the lymph sacs	Thyroid follicles
Gut withdrawal from cord Pancreatic alveoli Anal canal	Testosterone Renal excretion Bladder sac Müllerian tube into urogenital sinus Vaginal sacs, prostate	Perineal muscles	Joints	Hair follicles Melanocytes	Enucleated RBCs Thymus yields reticulum and corpuscles Thoracic duct Lymph nodes; axillary iliac	Adrenalin Noradrenalin
Gut muscle layers Pancreatic islets Bile	Seminal vesicle Regression, genital ducts		Tail degenerated Notochord degenerated	Corium, 3 layers Scalp, body hair Sebaceous glands Nails beginning	Blood principally from bone marrow Thymus—medullary and lymphoid	Testicle— Leydig cells Thyroid— colloid in follicle Anterior pituitary acidophilic granules Ovary—prim. follicles
Omentum fusing with transverse colon Mesoduodenum, asc. and desc. colon attach to body wall Meconium Gastric, intest. glands	Typical kidney Mesonephros involuting Uterus and vagina Primary follicles	In-utero movement can be detected	Distinct bones	Dermal ridges hands Sweat glands Keratinization		Anterior pituitary—basophilic granules
	No further collecting tubules			Venix caseosa Nail plates Mammary budding	Blood formation decreasing in liver	
						Testes—decrease in Leydig cells
						Testes descend
	Urine osmolarity continues to be relatively low			Eccrine sweat Lanugo hair prominent Nails to fingertips		
			Only a few secondary epiphyseal centers ossified in knee		Hemoglobin 17-18 g Leukocytosis	
			Ossification of 2nd epiph. centers—hamate, capitate, proximal humerus, femur. New ossif. 2nd epiph. centers till 10-12 yrs. Ossif. of epiphyses till 16-18 yrs.	New hair, gradual loss of lanugo hair	Transient (6 wk) erythroid hypoplasia Hemoglobin 11-12 g 7S gamma globulin produced by 6 wks. Lymph nodes develop cortex, medulla	Transient estrinization Adrenal—regression of fetal zone. Gonadotropin with feminization of ♀ 9-12 yr. (onset); masc. of ♂ 10-14 yr. (onset)

D

FIGURE 3-6, cont'd

The 4th week is a time of body building. The embryo becomes cylindrical and begins to assume a C-shape as a result of transverse and longitudinal folding. The neural tube fuses during days 21 to 28. The cranial area enlarges and develops cephalic and cervical flexure, with the head oriented in the characteristic flexed position. The heart is prominent and begins beating at 20 to 22 days. Small swellings become visible on the lateral body walls at 26 (arm buds) and 28 (leg buds) days. The branchial arches (from which the face, mandible, and pharynx will develop) become visible; however, facial structures are not distinct and human likeness is not clear yet. The embryo is 2 to 5 cm long.[27,104]

As the embryo enters the 5th week, the form develops a humanlike appearance.[104] Head growth is rapid as a result of brain development. The embryo further flexes into the characteristic C-shape and the facial area comes into close approximation with the heart prominence. The forelimbs begin to develop, and paddle-shaped hand plates with digital ridges are visible. The heart chambers are forming, and five distinct areas in the brain are visible. The cranial nerves are present. Retinal pigment and the external ear begin to appear.

Limb differentiation continues in the 6th week, short webbed fingers develop, and toe rays form. The face is much more distinct, the jaws are visible, and the nares and upper lip are present. Heart development is almost complete, and circulation is well established. The liver is prominent and producing blood cells. The intestines enter the proximal portion of the umbilical cord.

The last 2 weeks of the embryonic period are a time of facial, organ system, and neuromuscular development. The head is rounded and more erect although still disproportionately large. The eyes are open, and the eyelids are developing. The eyelids fuse by the end of the 8th week and do not open again until about the 25th week. The mouth, tongue, and palate are complete. The external ear is distinct, although it is still low on the head. The regions of the limbs are distinct, and elbow and wrist flexion are possible. Fingers are longer and the toes are differentiated. The feet have moved to the midline. The forearms gradually rise above the shoulder level, and the hands often cover the lower face. The abdomen is less protuberant, and the body is covered by thin skin.[27,104]

Neuromuscular development leads to movement, which can be seen on ultrasound although not felt. The gastrointestinal and genitourinary systems have separated, and the kidneys have achieved their basic structure, although nephron development will continue until 34 to 36 weeks' gestation. Although the internal genitalia have differentiated, the external genitalia have not. The rectal passage is complete, and the anal membrane is perforated, resulting in an open digestive system.[27,104]

Overview of Fetal Development

The fetal period extends from the end of the 8th week of gestation until term. All major systems and external features are established or have begun to develop by the beginning of this period. During the early fetal period (9 to 20 weeks), there is further differentiation of body structures, with a gradual increase in functional ability. By 6 months, the fetus has achieved 60% of its eventual length and 20% of its weight.[104] During the late fetal period (20 weeks to term), further maturation of organ and body systems occurs, along with a marked increase in weight. Organization is a prominent feature of this period.

During weeks 9 through 12, the embryo is 5 to 8 cm long and weighs 8 to 14 g. The head is half the body length. The body length doubles during these weeks. Head growth slows down, the neck lengthens, and the chin is lifted off the chest. The face is broad with widely set eyes, fused lids, and low-set ears. Teeth begin forming under the gums, and the palate fuses. Fingernails become apparent, and the arms reach their final relative length.[27,104]

Micturition and swallowing of amniotic fluid begin. The esophageal lumen forms, and the intestines reenter the abdominal cavity and assume their fixed positions. The bone marrow begins blood formation. The external genitalia differentiate, and by 12 weeks' gestation sexual determination is possible visually.

From 13 to 16 weeks, rapid growth continues. The length of the embryo almost doubles during these weeks. The embryo weighs 20 g by the end of the 16th week.[104] The eyes and ears have achieved more normal positions, giving the face a distinctively human look. Fetal skin is extremely thin, and lanugo is present. There is increased muscle and bone development, which along with establishment of initial neuromuscular connections results in increased fetal movements. Skeletal ossification continues during this period. Brown fat deposition and meconium formation begin.[27,104]

Growth slows slightly during the next month (17 to 20 weeks), and the legs reach their final relative positions. During this period, fetal movement is felt by first-time mothers (earlier with successive pregnancies). Fetal heart tones are now audible with a stethoscope. Myelination of the spinal cord begins. Head hair, eyelashes, and eyebrows can be seen. The sebaceous glands are active, resulting in vernix caseosa deposition. Lung development continues as bronchial branching is completed and terminal air sacs begin to develop. The pulmonary capillary bed is forming in preparation for gas exchange. By 20 weeks' gestation, the fetus weighs about 300 g and is 25 cm long.[104]

After 20 weeks, weight increases substantially. By 24 to 25 weeks, the fetus weighs 650 to 780 g and is 30 cm long.[104] The body is better proportioned. The skin is translucent, and subcutaneous fat has yet to be laid down. Fingerprint and footprint ridges are formed, and the eye is structurally complete.

During weeks 25 to 28, the gas exchange ability of the lungs improves so that extrauterine life can be sustained. Subcutaneous fat begins to form, and head hair and lanugo are well developed. The eyes open as the lids unfuse. CNS development allows initiation of rhythmic breathing movements and partial temperature control. The testes begin to descend into the scrotum.

From 29 weeks to term, fat and muscle tissue are laid down and skin thickness increases. Although the bones are fully formed, ossification is not complete. Vernix caseosa and lanugo begin to disappear as term gestation is approached and growth slows. The testes descend into the scrotum. The infant fills the uterine cavity, and the extremities are flexed against the body. Myelination and skeletal ossification progresses, and sleep-wake cycles are established. By 38 to 40 weeks, fetal size averages 3000 to 3800 g and 45 to 50 cm.[104]

Intrauterine Environment

The uterine environment normally provides the ideal stimulation for the development and refining of organ systems for transition to and interaction with the extrauterine environment. The amniotic fluid provides the space for the developing fetus to grow and protection from the external environment. Amniotic fluid cushions against external pressure, allowing pressure to the uterus to be transmitted from one side to the other with minimal exertion on the fetus. The weightless space allows for the symmetric development of the face and body. Adequate volume facilitates normal lung development and, until late gestation, exercise and neuromuscular development. The amniotic sac and uterine wall give the fetus something to push against during "practice" activities.

The maternal body provides the fetus with a darkened environment, which may become grayer as the uterus grows and stretches. Auditory stimuli are rich and include the sound of blood flow through the umbilical cord. Most of these sounds are patterned and rhythmic. Extrauterine sounds, such as voices and music, are transmitted in a muted form to the fetus. The maternal system maintains a warm thermal environment. Kinesthetic and vestibular stimulation are provided by maternal movement and changes in position. Other stimuli that influence the activity and responses of the fetus and neonate include maternal biorhythms and diurnal, circadian, and sleep-wake cycles. Exposure of the fetus to these stimuli and events provides appropriate experiences that enhance neurologic organization and establishment of synaptic connections (see Chapter 15). These activities are critical for successful transition to extrauterine life and for establishing physiologic and social relationships necessary to ensure survival.

THE PLACENTA AND PLACENTAL PHYSIOLOGY

The human placenta is a hemochorial villous organ that is essential for transfer of nutrients and gases from the mother to the fetus and for removal of fetal waste products. Thus the placenta performs functions similar to the lungs, gastrointestinal system, liver, kidneys, and endocrine organ.[30] Alterations in placental development and function markedly influence fetal growth and development and the ability of the infant to survive in intrauterine and extrauterine environments. The placenta also influences maternal health and later outcomes of the infant. Much is still unknown about the placenta and its functions. As a result the National Institute of Child Health and Human Development has established the Human Placental Project to better understand placental development, structure, and function; identify markers of placental dysfunction and related therapeutic interventions; and examine the long-term role of the placenta in health and disease.[59]

Placental Development

Implantation

Implantation is mediated by a coordinated sequence of interactions between maternal and embryonic cells.[43] Implantation involves (1) loss of the zona pellucida ("hatching" of the blastocyst) 5 days after fertilization, followed by rapid proliferation of the trophectoderm to form the trophoblast cell mass; (2) alignment and adherence of the blastocyst to the endometrial luminal surface between the openings of uterine glands, which stimulates the decidual reaction; (3) erosion of the epithelium of the endometrial surface, with burrowing of the blastocyst beneath the surface as uterine stromal cells encapsulate it; (4) migration of placental trophoblast into the endometrium with disruption of capillary beds; and (5) remodeling of maternal capillary beds to form blood-filled trophoblastic lacunae.[30,134] With hatching, the blastocyst acquires the ability to attach to the uterus. Both implantation and placentation require many signaling pathways and substances and ongoing communication (cross-talk) between the developing blastocyst and maternal endometrium via hormones, cytokines, growth factors, and other immunoregulatory substances.[43,90]

The endometrium must undergo physiologic changes for implantation to occur (see Endometrium and Decidua), with a narrow period of maximal uterine receptivity ("window of implantation") for implantation.[43] The ideal window for synchronization between the uterus and blastocyst and thus normal implantation is believed to occur around 8 days after ovulation.[30,90,112,133] Specific receptors (integrin αVβ3) appear on endometrial cells on day 19 of the menstrual cycle, opening the implantation window; this window is closed several days later.[43,74,90,133] Implantation can also occur in other tissues, resulting in ectopic pregnancy, without this restricted time interval. The endometrium prepares for implantation by the cyclic secretion of 17β-estradiol and progesterone. These hormones regulate the expression of growth factors and cytokines in the uterus, which in turn alter the endometrial surface.[43]

Uterine receptivity is characterized by increased vascularity and edema of the endometrium, increased secretory activity of the endometrial glands, decrease in the polysaccharide matrix surface coating of the epithelial cells, and development of pinopods (microprotrusions, also called uterodomes) on the epithelial surface.[30,111,134] The pinopods interact with microvilli on the trophoblast during initial attachment of the blastocyst. Markers of endometrial receptivity are the appearance of pinopods (that last only 1 to 2 days), cell adhesion molecules such as integrins, cytokines (especially the interleukin family), homeobox genes and their transcription factors (see Regulation of Development), growth factors (especially the TGF-β family), proteases and their inhibitors, and endocrine mediators including estrogens, progesterone, calcitonin, hCG, prolactin, and corticotropin-releasing hormone (CRH).[90,112]

Uterine receptivity must be synchronized with preimplantation, implantation, and placentation signaling by the zygote and blastocyst. Many signaling pathways and substances are involved in this process, including (1) EPF; (2) preimplantation factor (PIF); (3) growth factors such as EGF, TGF-α, platelet-derived growth factor, IGFs, tumor necrosis factor-α (TNF-α), and colony stimulating factor 1; (4) immunoregulatory cytokines such as interleukin-1 (IL-1), interleukin-6 (IL-6), and TGF-β; (5) cyclooxygenase-2 and PGs; (6) platelet activity factor (PAF); (7) vascular endothelial growth factor (VEGF); (8) L-selectin ligands (sLE) and sLE receptors; and (9) hCG.[30,43,72,112] Before implantation the trophoblast is activated. This process occurs 5 to 6 days after fertilization and lasts about 24 hours. The initial signaling between the trophoblast and luminal epithelium is closely linked with immunologic mechanisms (see Chapter 13).[58,112]

By 5 to 6 days after fertilization, the blastocyst rests on and adheres to the endometrium.[72] Metabolism increases, with localized changes seen at the eventual site of the implantation. The place of attachment is usually on the upper posterior wall of the uterus, near the side where the ovary with the corpus luteum is located, but it can occur at various other intrauterine and extrauterine sites.[90]

Ligands (molecules that bind to receptors) such as cytokines, growth factors, and hormones on the trophectoderm of the hatched blastocyst bind to cell surface adhesion molecules on the surface of the luminal endometrium. Further attachment and invasion is mediated by integrins (transmembrane glycoproteins with α and β subunits that can be up-regulated via interaction with other substances), IL-10, metalloproteinases, VEGF, and L-selectin.[74,90,124] Integrins serve as cell surface receptors for fibrinogen, fibronectin, collagen, and laminin.[90] Laminin promotes attachment; fibronectin promotes invasion of the blastocyst into the uterine epithelium.[133] Adhesion (apposition) is initially unstable, relying on interaction between uterine epithelial pinopods and trophoblast microvilli, then stabilizes and is followed by trophoblast invasion of the endometrium.[112] The blastocyst orients itself so that the embryonic pole containing the embryo-forming inner cell mass contacts the endometrial surface first.[30]

The trophectoderm (trophoblast) attaches to endometrial extracellular matrix proteins, secretes proteases to degrade these proteins, and begins to invade the endometrium.[144] Fingerlike projections of trophoblast cells protrude between the cells of the endometrial epithelium into the endometrial stroma.[54] The trophoblast cells then migrate between the cells of the endometrial extracellular matrix until they reach maternal blood vessels. Regulatory substances on both trophoblast and endometrial tissue enhance interaction, invasion, and trophoblast proliferation. These substances include (1) metalloproteinases (e.g., collagenases, gelatinases, stromelysins); (2) plasminogen activation; (3) plasmin-regulating factors; (4) cytokines such as IL-1β (stimulates trophoblast invasion); and (5) growth factors such as EGF and TGF-β (limits invasion and induces syncytium formation).[43,63,90,150] Other factors limit trophoblast invasion and develop as part of the decidual reaction. For example, the decidua (i.e., the altered endometrium during pregnancy) secretes protease inhibitors such as TGF-β and tissue inhibitor of metalloproteinase (TIMP). The trophoblast may also autoregulate its invasion via secretion of TGF-β, TIMP, and hCG.[43] If trophoblast invasion is too extensive, placenta accreta can result; if invasion is too little, the risk of miscarriage or placental abruption is increased.

By the 7th day after fertilization, the trophoblast begins to differentiate into two layers: the inner cytotrophoblast and the outer syncytiotrophoblast layer.[54,144] The mononuclear cytotrophoblast is a mitotically active layer that forms new syncytial cells, the chorionic villi, and the amnion. The cytotrophoblast serves as a stem cell population to generate new trophoblast cells and cooperates with the maternal decidua to allow immunotolerance (see Chapter 13).[50] The syncytiotrophoblast is a thick multinuclear mass, without distinct cell boundaries, that puts out fingerlike projections that invade the endometrial epithelium, engulfing uterine cells (see Figure 3-4). Slight bleeding may occur during this process, which may be mistaken for a scanty, short menstrual period. The trophoblast, primarily the syncytiotrophoblast, produces hCG (which maintains the corpus luteum during early pregnancy) as well as estrogens, progesterone, hCS, and other substances (see Placental Endocrinology). The functions of the trophoblast are summarized in Table 3-1.

Several forms of extravillous trophoblast are derived from the cytotrophoblast. Interstitial trophoblast migrates into the

TABLE 3-1 Functions of the Trophoblast

FUNCTION	EFFECTORS
Erosion of maternal tissue to make space for implantation and growth	Proteases (e.g., plasminogen system, matrix metalloproteinases)
Hormone secretion	hCG, hCS, estrogen, progesterone, and others
Transport nutrients and waste products	Substrate specific transporters, trophoblast, endothelial plasma membranes
Placental attachment	Adhesion molecules in the extracellular matrix and at the cell surface
Migration and arterial transformation	Adhesion molecules, proteases, extracellularw matrix components

hCG, Human chorionic gonadotropin; hCS, chorionic somatomammotropin.
Adapted from Aplin, J. (2000). Maternal influences on placental development. *Semin Cell Dev Biol, 17,* 116.

uterine tissue and attaches the anchoring villi of the placenta to the decidua. Human leukocyte antigen-G (HLA-G) is expressed on the anchoring trophoblast and helps protect fetal tissue from the maternal immune system (see Chapter 13).[50,58] Other extravillous trophoblast migrates out from the placenta into the endometrium and spiral arteries. This type of trophoblast has two roles: (1) conversion of the maternal spiral arteries into low-resistance, high-capacity vessels and (2) formation of plugs at the top of the spiral arteries to limit maternal blood flow into the placenta during the first trimester (see Placental Circulation).[58,74,90] Implantation is complete by 10 days after fertilization.[54] At this point, the blastocyst lies beneath the endometrial surface and is covered by a blood clot and cellular debris. By 10 to 12 days, the endometrial epithelium has regenerated in this area.[112]

Many ova that are fertilized never implant. One-third to one-half of all zygotes never become blastocysts; 70% to 75% of blastocysts implant and 51% of these survive to the 2nd week.[104] Implantation can be selectively inhibited by administration of low-dose estrogen for several days after sexual intercourse ("morning-after" pill). Estrogen preparations such as diethylstilbestrol act by altering the normal balance of estrogen and progesterone during the secretory phase of the endometrial cycle, making the endometrial lining unsuitable for implantation. Estrogen may also accelerate passage of the zygote along the fallopian tube so that it arrives in the uterus before the secretory phase of the endometrial cycle is established.[104]

Ectopic Pregnancy. Extrauterine implantation results in an ectopic pregnancy in 1 in every 80 to 250 pregnancies.[104] The incidence of ectopic pregnancy has increased fourfold since 1972 and accounts for 10% to 11% of maternal mortality in the United States.[37] Ectopic pregnancy is the most common cause of maternal death in the first 20 weeks of pregnancy. Much of the increased incidence in recent years is believed to be a result of the prevalence of sexually transmitted infections (STIs) and pelvic inflammatory disease (PID). The most common site for an ectopic pregnancy is the isthmus and ampulla of the fallopian tubes.[104] This probably results from delay in transport of the zygote from the site of fertilization to the uterine cavity. If transport is delayed, the blastocyst emerges from the zona pellucida while in the fallopian tube and adheres to and implants in tubal mucosa. The delay may be caused by tubal adhesions or mucosal damage from PID.[104] PID and salpingitis disrupt and damage the tubal mucosa, decreasing the number of cilia, which are essential for timely movement of the zygote along the tube. Alterations in the concentrations of progesterone, estrogen, and PGs may also delay ovum transport.

Endometrium and Decidua

The uterine endometrial lining consists of an epithelial layer that contains ciliated and mucus-secreting cells. These cells penetrate into the endometrial stroma and may enter the underlying myometrium. The endometrium is divided into two functional zones (see Figure 2-29). The deepest basalis layer lies adjacent to the myometrium. This layer responds to progesterone stimulus with secretory activity and provides the base for endometrial regeneration after menstrual sloughing.[98,144] The superficial (functionalis) layer of endometrium includes the outer compacta and the middle spongiosa, which contains glands and blood. During the secretory phase of the menstrual cycle, the endometrium undergoes physical changes in preparation for implantation (see Chapter 2).

With conception these changes become more extensive. Under stimulation of progesterone and estrogen, the epithelium and stromal cells become progressively hypertrophic and develop subnuclear vacuoles rich in glycogen and lipids.[30,54,123,150] Early nutrition of the blastocyst comes from digestion of substances in endometrial tissue and surrounding capillaries. The endometrial changes during pregnancy are known as the decidual reaction, and the altered endometrial lining is known as the decidua. The decidual reaction involves remodeling of the extracellular matrix with changes in collagen, proteoglycans, and glycoproteins. Estrogen and progesterone pathways that control epithelial and stromal function during implantation and decidualization include (1) CCATT, enhancer-binding protein-β (transcription factor); (2) homeobox-10 (transcription factor); (3) bone morphogenetic protein 2 (morphogen); (4) Wnt4 (morphogen); (5) Indian hedgehog (morphogen); and (6) gap junctions.[123] A poor decidual reaction is associated with placenta accreta and ectopic pregnancy.[43] In addition these pathways are altered in endometriosis, leading to impaired implantation.[123] Decidualization also involves alterations in local immune cells and processes and changes in maternal spiral arteries (see Placental Circulation). As decidualization increases, the window of receptivity for implantation is closed. Defective decidualization can lead to altered placentation and fetal growth restriction and may increase the risk of preterm labor and preeclampsia.[30]

In addition to its role in early nutrition of the embryo, the decidua may protect the endometrium and myometrium from uncontrolled invasion by the trophoblast cell mass.[54] The decidua also acts as a physical barrier and—via production of cytokines that promote trophoblast attachment, not invasion—to protect the endometrium during the period when trophoblast cells migrate out of the placenta to the maternal spiral arteries (see Maternal Uteroplacental Circulation). A somewhat hypoxic environment appears to be needed in early pregnancy for trophoblast invasion and differentiation; high oxygen levels may alter morphogenesis.[74,157]

The decidua is divided into three sections (Figure 3-7). The *decidua capsularis,* just above the area of trophoblast proliferation, initially covers the growing embryo. With development of the chorion, the decidua capsularis gradually regresses. The portion of the decidua on which the blastocyst rests forms a soft, spongy vascular bed known as the *decidua basalis,* site of the future placenta.[7] Large numbers of maternal macrophages, especially maternal natural killer cells, migrate into the decidua basalis (see Chapter 13).[110,150] Decidual macrophages are important in maternal tolerance of the implanting blastocyst and cooperate with fetal trophoblast cells in remodeling maternal spiral arteries during

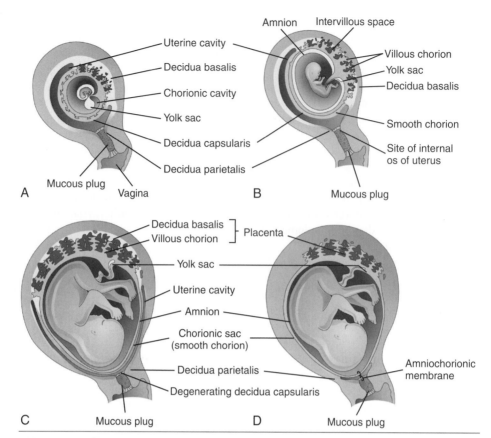

FIGURE 3-7   Changes in the decidual layers with growth of the embryo and fetus and development of the amniotic cavity. **A–D,** Sagittal sections of the gravid uterus from the 5th to 22nd weeks show the changing relations of the fetal membranes to the decidua. In **D,** the amnion and chorion are fused with each other and the decidua parietalis, thereby obliterating the uterine cavity. Note also in **D** that the chorionic villi persist only where the chorion is associated with the decidua basalis; here they form the villous chorion (fetal portion of the placenta). (From Moore, K.L., Persaud, T.V.N., & Torchia, M.G. [2015]. *The developing human: Clinically oriented embryology* [10th ed.]. Philadelphia: Elsevier Saunders.)

pregnancy (see Placental Circulation).[110] At the interface between the trophoblast and decidua basalis is a specialized extracellular matrix rich in fibrin and fibronectin that supports trophoblast adhesion and migration.[7] The remaining portion is known as the *decidua parietalis* (or decidua vera).

The decidua basalis forms the maternal portion of the placenta and the stratum in which separation of the placenta will occur at delivery.[37,104] With embryonic growth, the decidua basalis is progressively compressed. The glands and blood vessels become distorted and assume oblique and horizontal courses. As the embryo fills the lumen of the uterus, the decidua capsularis disappears. By 18 to 20 weeks after conception, the chorion laeve and decidua parietalis meet and fuse, obliterating the uterine cavity (see Figure 3-7).[54,55,124]

Development of the Amniotic Cavity

The amniotic cavity appears during the second week after fertilization as the blastocyst is burrowing into the endometrium. Small spaces appear between the inner cell mass and cytotrophoblast. These spaces coalesce to form a narrow amniotic cavity that gradually enlarges to completely surround the fetus (see Figure 3-7).

The amniotic cavity develops a thin epithelial roof or lining. This lining is the amnion, which arises from amnioblasts (amniogenic cells) from the cytotrophoblast. The floor of the amniotic cavity is formed from the embryonic epiblast germ layer. Initially a small amount of fluid may be secreted by the amniotic epithelial cells, but the major early source of amniotic fluid is probably maternal serum. With advancing gestation, the epithelial cells of the amnion become more cuboidal or columnar and are covered with microvilli.[104]

Placentation

As the syncytiotrophoblast proliferates and invades the endometrial stroma, the blastocyst slowly sinks into the endometrium. By 7 to 8 days after fertilization, intersyncytial spaces or lacunae are seen in the syncytiotrophoblast (see Figure 3-4).[55] Growth factors such as leukemia inhibition factors (LIF) and fibroblast growth factor (FGF) are important for trophoblast proliferation and differentiation needed for placental development.[144]

Considerable interaction and signaling occurs between maternal and placental tissue during pregnancy.[25] This crosstalk may be mediated by exosomes (extracellular vesicles containing signaling molecules, such as proteins, miRNA, and mRNA), which regulate target cell activity and mediate intercellular communication. During pregnancy the placenta releases exosomes into the maternal circulation from about 6 weeks' gestation, with numbers increasing as pregnancy progresses.[99,106,144] Although the exact roles of exosomes are not completely understood, they are believed to have a role in maternal immune tolerance and placental development.[99] Exosomes and miRNA are being investigated as possible biomarkers of placental health.[99,106]

Capillaries in the endometrium grow and surround the syncytiotrophoblast, forming a capillary plexus connected to the early lacunae.[165] The lacunae fill with a nutritive substance or filtrate containing primarily glandular fluid derived from maternal blood that diffuses through the trophoblast to the embryo. Individual lacunae fuse into lacunar networks that will later develop into the intervillous spaces (IVS) and become filled with maternal blood. Endometrial capillaries around the implanted embryo become congested and dilated, forming sinusoids.

Blood flow into the IVS is limited in the first trimester, and the IVS is filled primarily with a filtrate of maternal serum and secretions from the endometrial glands.[23,24,74,76,118] Thus during the first trimester histotrophic nutrition from the uterine glands supports the developing embryo.[144] Uterine gland secretions include amino acids, glycoproteins, glucose, ions, cytokines, hormones, enzymes, growth factors, and proteases and their inhibitors.[144] In animal models, and probably humans, the placenta can upregulate uterine gland activity, perhaps via exosomes, to meet embryo needs.[25]

The highly oxygenated maternal blood does not fill the IVS until fetal vessels are established in the villi and mechanisms to protect the fetus against oxidative stress are established.[24,25,74,76] This begins at 8 to 9 weeks and increases after 10 to 12 weeks.[24] Before that time, trophoblast plugs fill the tops of the spiral arteries, controlling arterial pressure and limiting blood flow into the IVS.[81,124] Oxygen concentration in the IVS at 8 weeks is 20 mm Hg or less (3% to 5% O_2) versus 60 mm Hg (8% to 10% O_2) in the surrounding decidua.[118] Thus initial placental and embryonic development occurs in a relatively hypoxic environment. This environment may stimulate production of VEGF and stimulate chorionic vascularization.[24,28,74,76] Low O_2 levels may be essential for control of angiogenesis and early cardiovascular development by hypoxia-inducible factors (HIF).[157,163]

HIFs are oxygen-sensitive transcription factors that act as mediators to allow cells to adjust to low O_2 conditions and facilitate placental vascularization and signaling for trophoblast differentiation.[118,163] HIFs are activated by both hypoxia and nonhypoxic factors such as the renin-angiotensin system, GFs, and cytokines.[118,120] For example, HIF-1 regulation via angiotensin II increases extravillous trophoblast growth, cellular proliferation, and soluble Fms-like tyrosinekinase–1 (s-FLT-1). Alterations are seen in the pathophysiology of preeclampsia (see Chapter 9). HIF-1 and TGF-β inhibit trophoblast invasion, whereas HIF-1 and

insulin-like growth factor-2 (ILGF-2) increase trophoblast growth.[118,120]

Early flow of maternal blood into the IVS has been reported to be primarily in the periphery of the developing placenta.[76] Jauniaux and colleagues postulate that higher oxygen flow in the periphery may induce regression of villi and formation of the chorion laeve (chorion).[25,76] Increased flow in the central area of the developing placenta may increase the risk of early pregnancy loss because of oxidative damage to the trophoblast.[76] By 11 to 12 weeks the spiral arteries become patent and maternal blood flow into the IVS and fetal oxygen levels increase. Vascular changes in the uteroplacental vessels are described further in Placental Circulation.

Development of the Villi

The placenta consists of the outer epithelial layer, derived from trophoblast cells, and an inner vascular network and connective tissue stroma, derived from embryonic mesoderm. Initially the lacunae are separated by trabecular columns of syncytiotrophoblast (primary villous stems), which provide the framework for development of the placental chorionic villi. The cytotrophoblast differentiates into vascular cytotrophoblast, which fuses to form chorionic villi, and the extravascular invasive trophoblast, which is involved in remodeling of the spiral arteries (see Placental Circulation).[83] Placental villi mediate passage of nutrients, gases, waste products, and other substances between mother and fetus.[50] Chorionic villi begin to appear toward the end of the second week of gestation as proliferation of the cytotrophoblast layer produces columns of cells or fingerlike processes known as *primary chorionic villi*.[83] A mesenchymal core grows within these primary villi, forming secondary villi. Blood vessels within the villi arise from this mesenchymal core within a few days, forming tertiary villi.[54,83]

As the columns of cytotrophoblast cells proliferate, they extend through the syncytiotrophoblast, expanding laterally to meet and fuse with adjoining cytotrophoblast columns. This forms the cytotrophoblastic shell and divides the syncytiotrophoblast into an inner layer and a peripheral layer. The peripheral layer degenerates and is replaced by fibrinoid material.[50,54] Villous development is stimulated by growth factors such as VEGF and placental-like growth factor and by the relatively hypoxic environment. VEGF is found in maternal plasma by 6 weeks' gestation and peaks at the end of the first trimester, similar to the pattern seen with hCG. During the third trimester, placental growth factors enhance formation of terminal villi.[83] The low-oxygen environment stimulates angiogenesis, trophoblast formation, and increased numbers of highly vascularized terminal villi.[83]

The cytotrophoblastic shell is the point of contact between the fetal tissue and maternal tissue; it attaches the chorionic sac to the basal plate. The basal plate is formed by the compact and spongy zones of the maternal decidua basalis, remnants of the trophoblast, and fibrinoid material. By the end of the fourth month, the shell has regressed, with replacement of the cytotrophoblast cell columns by fibrinoid material (Rohr layer) and formation of clumps (islands) of cytotrophoblast cells.[54] A layer of fibrinoid material (Nitabuch layer) also develops within the spongy zone of the decidua basalis. This is the level of placental separation at delivery (Figure 3-8).

Villi containing blood vessels (tertiary villi) arise around 20 days postconception.[55,165] By 21 to 22 days, a primitive fetoplacental circulation is established between blood in the vessels of the villi, vessels forming in the embryo, the primitive heart, and blood islands in the yolk sac (see Chapters 8 and 9). The villi that arise from the chorionic plate and attach to the maternal decidua basalis are known as *anchoring* (or *stem*) *villi.* Initially embryonic and fetal blood vessels develop within stem villi by branching angiogenesis.[81,83] Stem villi, which contain arteries and veins as well as some arterioles and venules, make up about one-third of the villi in the mature placenta.[55] Mature intermediate villi grow from the sides of stem villi and project into the IVS (see Figure 3-8). These intermediate villi, which constitute approximately 25% of the villi in the mature placenta, contain primarily fetal capillaries, with a few small arterioles and venules.[54,55] Intermediate villi and their branches (terminal villi), constitute the major area of exchange between maternal and fetal circulations. Terminal villi contain multiple dilated capillaries or sinusoids and account for 30% to 40% of the mature villous tree.[55] Terminal villi bulge into the villous cytotrophoblast so that maternal and fetal blood are separated only by a thin syncytiotrophoblast layer.[83]

Alterations in development of the villous system may lead to miscarriage or fetal growth restriction.[165]

Initially there are two divisions within the chorionic villi. The chorion laeve forms the chorion; the chorion frondosum forms the fetal portion of the placenta. At first, villi cover the entire surface of the chorionic sac. Beginning around 8 weeks' gestation, villi near the decidua capsularis become compressed, blood flow decreases, and the villi degenerate, leaving a bare avascular area (smooth chorion, or chorion laeve). Simultaneously, villi near the decidua basalis (villous chorion, or chorion frondosum) rapidly enlarge, increase in number, and develop a mesenchymal core and blood vessels.

Anchoring villi grow more slowly than other portions of the placenta. As a result, during the 3rd month, folds of the basal plate are pulled up into the IVS (see Figure 3-8). These folds (known as the *placental septa*) do not extend to the chorionic plate and have no known morphologic or physiologic function.[54]

By 40 to 50 days after ovulation, the trophoblast has invaded far enough into the endometrium to reach and begin to erode maternal spiral arterioles. Trophoblast plugs fill the tops of the spiral arteries until around 10 to 12 weeks' gestation, when the arteries open up and begin to supply blood to the IVS.[7] This is the time when the mature placenta is established. The chorion laeve fuses onto the decidua vera, forming the chorion or outer fetal membrane. The inner membrane, the amnion, is derived from the amniogenic cells (amnioblasts) of the cytotrophoblast (see Development of the Amniotic Cavity).

Placental Growth

By 4 months, the placenta has achieved its full thickness, with no new lobules or stem villi added after 10 to 12 weeks. Circumferential placental growth continues with further ramification of stem villi (via growth and extension of new trophoblast sprouts, followed by growth of the mesenchymal core and development of blood vessels), lengthening of existing villi, and increases in the size and number of placental capillaries.[37,104] Much of the expansion of villi after 20 weeks is in the terminal villi. Mature intermediate villi elongate in the third trimester, which assists in generation of new terminal villi branches. As a result of the proliferation of terminal villi, the surface area for placental exchange continues to increase until late in gestation. In addition, the thickness of the tissue layers separating maternal and fetal blood thins, thus enhancing diffusion. Trophoblast sprouts not used to form new villi break off, enter the maternal circulation, lodge in the mother's lung capillaries, and are cleared by proteolysis.

After 30 weeks' gestation, syncytial knots develop, pulling the syncytium and its nuclei into "piles" several layers thick and leaving a thin, attenuated, anuclear membrane in the intervening areas.[104] These areas (known as the *vasculosyncytial membrane*) appear to, but do not actually, fuse with dilated fetal capillaries and are believed to be specialized regions that facilitate placental gas exchange.[54]

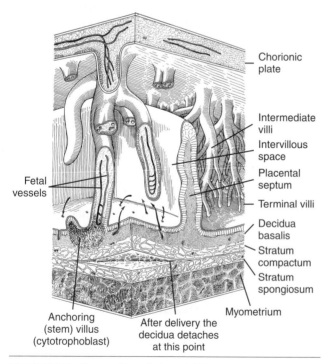

Fetal vessels

Chorionic plate

Intermediate villi

Intervillous space

Placental septum

Terminal villi

Decidua basalis

Stratum compactum

Stratum spongiosum

Myometrium

Anchoring (stem) villus (cytotrophoblast)

After delivery the decidua detaches at this point

FIGURE 3-8 Composition of placental tissues near term. *Arrows* indicate the blood flow from uteroplacental arteries to the intervillous space and back to the uteroplacental veins. (From Duplessis, G.D.T. & Haegel, P. [1971]. *Embryologie.* New York: Masson. English edition by Springer-Verlag; Chapman and Hall; and Masson, 1972.)

of chromosomal abnormalities with ICSI, although it is unclear whether there are increased risks of congenital anomalies from the procedure or if the increase reported in some studies is caused by the reason for the infertility (usually male-factor infertility) or the increase in multiples, who have higher rates.[52,66] An association between IVF and a minor increase in the incidence of birth defects has also been reported in some studies.[52] The rate of ectopic pregnancy is higher with ART.[20]

Assessment of the Embryo and Fetus

Prenatal Screening

Prenatal screening begins in the preconception period with evaluation of risks and discussion of potential risks and approaches to decrease risk. These approaches include folic acid supplementation in all women of childbearing age (see Chapter 15), identification of women at risk for preterm birth (see Chapter 4), and genetic screening (see Chapter 1) or strategies to decrease risk in women with chronic disorders such as diabetes mellitus (see Chapter 16), cardiovascular problems (see Chapter 9), or genetic disorders.

Techniques available for prenatal screening include history, risk assessment, carrier testing, first trimester genetic screening, second trimester genetic screening, and ultrasound (which is done as part of both first and second trimester screening). A genetic history should be a routine part of preconceptional and prenatal care to identify women with an increased risk of genetic disorders and birth defects. Components of genetic history include family and obstetric history (including a history of pregnancy loss or early infant death, mental retardation or learning disabilities, known genetic disorders, or previous anomalies in either the parents or their families), ethnic background (some recessive disorders occur with markedly increased frequency in specific ethnic groups), maternal and paternal age, and potential teratogen exposures.[155] Based on family and ethnic background, carrier screening may be offered for specific autosomal recessive disorders such as Tay-Sachs disease (in Ashkenazi Jewish heritage), sickle cell disease (African and Mediterranean background), or thalassemias (Mediterranean and Asian background).[78] The American College of Obstetricians and Gynecologists (ACOG) and American College of Medical Genetics recommend cystic fibrosis screening in the preconception or prenatal periods.[4] Cystic fibrosis screening does not test for all of the hundreds of mutations that have been identified in the cystic fibrosis gene, but only for those with a frequency in the U.S. population of greater than or equal to 0.1%.[3,4]

Fetal aneuploidy risk can be evaluated prenatally "on the basis of a combination of maternal age, prior family history, maternal serum biochemical tests and fetal ultrasound markers."[16] Ultrasound markers for both first and second trimester screening have been identified for infants with Down syndrome.[95,111,155] The genetic sonogram involves examination for markers found on second trimester ultrasounds that are observed more frequently in infants with chromosomal abnormalities.[143] This assessment is usually done between 18

and 22 weeks, although it can be done earlier (after 14 weeks). Evaluation before 18 weeks is reported to provide better screening of minor markers, whereas use at 18 weeks and later provides a more complete evaluation of fetal anatomy because the fetal heart, corpus callosum, and cerebellar vermis are more complete.[143] These findings include shortened femur or humerus, increased nuchal fold, intracardiac echogenic foci, echogenic bowel, renal pyelectasis.[142] Doppler flow studies are used to assess fetal status (see First Trimester Screening and Second Trimester Screening below) and risk of maternal complications. Abnormal ductus venosus (DV) wave forms at 11 to 13 weeks are associated with an increased risk of aneuploidy, congenital heart defects, and twin-to-twin transfusion syndrome (TTTS) in monochorionic twins.[95] DV wave forms can be used for fetal surveillance later in pregnancy with fetal growth restriction, monochorionic twins with TTTS, fetal hydrops, and fetal supraventricular tachycardia.[13] Alterations in cardiac preload or afterload can produce changes in pressure gradients and DV wave forms.[13,95] Uterine artery Doppler has been used in the first trimester for screening for early-onset preeclampsia and fetal growth restriction in at-risk women.[9]

First Trimester Screening. First trimester screening methods include maternal serum screening and ultrasound and Doppler flow studies for increased nuchal translucency (NT), echogenicity of the nasal bone, abnormal DV blood flow, tricuspid valve regurgitation, and increased hepatic artery flow.[71,95,111,155] NT is a result of a subcutaneous accumulation of fluid behind the fetal neck, possibly because of delayed development of the lymphatic system to drain fluid that flows into the nuchal area. Infants with trisomies tend to have more collagen and elastic connective tissue, allowing for accumulation.[71] NT is associated with an increased risk of spontaneous abortion, other aneuploidies, and fetal anomalies. NT may also be useful in early diagnosis of some congenital heart defects (because of the excess extravascular fluid).[71] The optimal time to assess NT and DV and tricuspid flow alterations is at 11 to 13 weeks.[13,71]

Maternal serum is screened for the free beta subunit of hCG and PAPP-A between 10 and 13 weeks. Fetal cell-free DNA (cfDNA) in maternal serum has been used with increased frequency (see Fetal Cell-Free DNA Analysis).[17,57] The free beta subunit of hCG (see Placental Endocrinology), which is detectable 10 days after ovulation, initially doubles every 1.5 to 2 days, peaking at 8 to 10 weeks.[80] PAPP-A is a large MW glycoprotein synthesized by the placental syncytiotrophoblast and released directly into maternal serum. PAPP-A is detectable at approximately 6 weeks of pregnancy and doubles every 6 days, plateauing at 14 weeks. Maternal smoking decreases PAPP-A; multiple gestation increases both hCG and PAPP-A.[111]

Levels of the free beta subunit of hCG are increased in infants with trisomy 21 and decreased in infants with trisomy 13 and 18.[111] Decreased levels of PAPP-A are seen with trisomy 21, 13, and 18, impending death, and impaired fetal well-being. A Cochrane review of 56 studies of first trimester screening found maternal age, PAPP-A, and serum free beta–hCG most accurately detected trisomy 21 with a false positive rate of 5%.[2] First trimester screening does not screen for neural tube defects, although these and other defects may be detected on first trimester ultrasound.[9]

Second Trimester Screening. Second trimester screening is done less commonly with the advent of first trimester screening. Second trimester screening is called *maternal serum multiple marker screening (MMS),* enhanced or expanded maternal serum α-fetoprotein (AFP) screening, triple screen, or quad screen (depending on the components used). Screening is done on maternal serum at 15 to 20 weeks (optimum is 16 to 18.5 weeks). Different combinations of components are used. The screen initially involved three components: AFP, unconjugated estriol (uE3), and the free beta subunit of hCG with the later addition of inhibin A (for the quad screen).

AFP is an oncofetal glycoprotein that moves from fetal to maternal blood via diffusion across the fetal membranes. AFP is initially synthesized in the yolk sac and from the 3rd month in the fetal gastrointestinal system and liver.[44,155] AFP normally increases until 10 to 14 weeks, then decreases.[61,155] AFP levels are elevated in infants with neural tube defects and low with fetal loss, some trisomies, and growth restriction.[100] AFP may also be elevated in infants with ventral wall defects such as omphalocele and gastroschisis, esophageal atresia, some skin defects (such as epidermolysis bullosa and aplasia cutis), and renal nephrosis.[155] An elevated AFP has also been associated with placenta previa, abnormal placental adherence (placenta accreta), gestational hypertension, preeclampsia, fetal growth restriction, and abruption; low AFP has been associated with preterm birth and macrosomia.[44]

uE3 is a reflection of fetal functional maturity, because precursors for placental production must be produced by the fetus. Levels are decreased in infants with trisomies, Turner syndrome, anencephaly, congenital adrenal hyperplasia, fetal growth restriction, and fetal loss.[44] Inhibin A is a glycoprotein from the placenta and provides negative feedback to the pituitary to prevent FSH release and has a role in cell differentiation and immune function.[44] Inhibin A normally increases until 10 weeks, then plateaus until 25 weeks, followed by a rise until term. Levels are decreased in infants with trisomy 21. Increased levels of AFP and hCG in women with normal fetuses have been associated with an increased risk of stillbirth, abruption, preterm labor, pregnancy-induced hypertension, miscarriage, and low birth weight.[44,61] Similarly, decreased uE3 has been associated with increased risk of preeclampsia, fetal growth restriction, miscarriage, and intrauterine fetal death. Increased second trimester free beta hCG is associated with placental dysfunction with preeclampsia, fetal loss, preterm birth, and fetal growth restriction.[44]

Maternal serum second trimester screening is used to screen for Down syndrome, trisomy 18, and neural tube defects (spina bifida and anencephaly). Some infants with Turner syndrome may also be identified. AFP and hCG are most useful in screening for Down syndrome, whereas AFP is most useful for screening for neural tube defects (see Chapter 15). Each laboratory has its own cut-off for positive

screen, so results are usually reported in multiples of the median (MoM). Abnormal values for AFP are generally less than 0.5 and greater than 2.5 MoM.[154] Factors that can influence screening results include maternal age, race, and weight; gestational age; and maternal diabetes.

If a woman has a positive screen, follow-up ultrasound and sometimes amniocentesis are indicated. Second trimester ultrasound markers for trisomy 21 and other aneuploidy include a nuchal fold of 5 mm or larger, cystic hydroma, hypoplastic or absent nasal bone, shortened humerus and femur, echogenic intracranial foci, hyperechogenic bowel (also seen with cystic fibrosis, cytomegalovirus, and severe fetal growth restriction), facial alterations, and other findings.[143,155] Reported detection rates (and false positive rates) for trisomy 21 using maternal age MA and second trimester screening parameters are 65% to 70% (5%) for MA plus triple screen parameters; and 65% to 70% (5%) for MA plus quad screen parameters.[111] Stepwise screening, combining first and second trimester screening results, (i.e., MA, NT, PAPP-A [11 to 13 weeks] and quadruple screen) has a detection rate of 90% to 94% with a 5% false positive rate.[111]

Fetal Cell-Free DNA Analysis. Developing technology for analysis of DNA from fetal nucleated red blood cells, mesenchymal stem cells, and trophoblast cells in maternal circulation or free fetal DNA in maternal plasma reduces the need for invasive testing.[17,57,84] Fetal cfDNA increases progressively, accounting for 3% to 6% of the DNA in maternal plasma; levels increase with fetal aneuploidy.[84] Evaluation of fetal cfDNA in maternal serum has been used with increased frequency as an alternative noninvasive prenatal screening test. cfDNA consists of approximately 150 base pairs and represents the entire fetal genome.[17] Fetal cfDNA, probably primarily from the placenta rather than the fetus, is found in maternal plasma as early as 4 weeks and currently is primarily used for detection of fetal aneuploidies, with other uses under investigation.[17,57] Trisomy 21 screening of singleton pregnancies using cfDNA from maternal blood is reported to have higher detection rates (99%) and lower false positives (less than 0.1%) than other screening methods currently used.[57] However, detection rates for trisomy 13, trisomy 18, and sex chromosome disorders were found to be lower than those for trisomy 21.[57]

Other Techniques. At least six biomarker algorithms have been developed for first trimester prediction of preeclampsia using placental biomarkers such as PAPP-A, GH-V, and s-FLT-1. Reported detection rates for early-onset preeclampsia range from 44% to 92% with 5% false positive rates.[6] Early prediction of women at high risk allows use of preventive therapies such as low-dose aspirin.[6,117] Other strategies being evaluated for predicting preeclampsia include maternal risk factors, mean maternal arterial pressure, ultrasound, fetal cfDNA, and placenta-specific miRNA.[117]

Prenatal Diagnosis

Assessment of fetal status and placental function and analysis of the constituents of amniotic fluid are useful in evaluating the growth and health of the fetus, the ability of the fetus to withstand the stresses of labor and delivery, and timing of delivery. Newer techniques have improved monitoring of fetal and placental status with high-risk pregnancies. Techniques for evaluation of placental function consist of biochemical monitoring of the fetoplacental unit, antepartum fetal heart rate surveillance, fetal blood gas monitoring, and the biophysical profile. These are discussed in Chapter 6. Chorionic villus sampling (CVS) and amniocentesis allow for prenatal diagnosis of increasing numbers of chromosomal, genetic, and other congenital anomalies. Percutaneous umbilical blood sampling can be used for both prenatal diagnosis and therapy. Routine ultrasound studies provide an opportunity to observe for major and minor anomalies in the fetus. Ultrasound can also be used to monitor fetal growth and well-being. In addition, newer imaging techniques, such as fetal magnetic resonance imaging and three-dimensional ultrasonography, enhance diagnosis of fetal anomalies.[84,143]

Genetic screening and use of diagnostic techniques such as CVS, amniocentesis, and the genetic ultrasound allow for prenatal identification of increasing numbers of chromosomal, genetic, and other congenital anomalies. Timing for these techniques is illustrated in Figure 3-15. Because a complete chromosomal analysis takes time, all of these techniques are associated with increased parental anxiety and concern. The goal of prenatal diagnosis is to provide parents with the assurance that they will have a child who is unaffected by the specific disorders being evaluated. Most women participate in prenatal testing for reassurance; 90% to 95% will have a normal fetus. If an abnormality is identified, prenatal diagnosis provides parents with an opportunity to prepare for the birth of an affected infant; plan for delivery, care, and management of the infant; or elect to terminate the pregnancy. In some cases, early diagnosis provides options for fetal therapy, such as intervention for urinary tract obstructions to reduce prenatal renal damage (see Chapter 11), some forms of neural tube defects (see Chapter 15), some forms of congenital heart defects (see Chapter 9), transfusions for hematologic conditions (see Chapter 8), or pharmacologic interventions (see Chapter 7). Indications for prenatal diagnosis include maternal age greater than 35 years; paternal age greater than 50 or 55 years; history of two or more miscarriages; previous pregnancy or family history of genetic or chromosomal disorder; parents who are known or suspected carriers of a specific genetic disorder; previous child with or family history of a neural tube or other birth defect, especially defects known to have a multifactorial inheritance pattern; exposure to known teratogens; and women with positive first or second trimester screening results.[155]

Preimplantation Genetic Diagnosis. Genetic analysis of the oocyte or polar body is sometimes done as part of IVF, usually because of a family history of a specific genetic disorder or to detect aneuploidy. Preimplantation genetic diagnosis, also with IVF, is done at the eight-cell stage, usually around

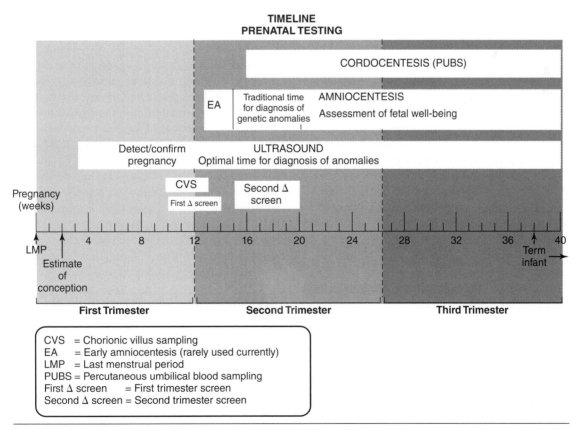

FIGURE 3-15   Usual timeline for prenatal testing. (Modified from a figure originally developed by Brock, K.A. [1990]. Seattle: University of Washington.)

3 days after fertilization removing one or two blastomeres at 3 days or 5 to 12 cells from trophectoderm in the 5 to 7 day blastocyst.[155] The cells are evaluated using fluorescent in situ hybridization (FISH), polymerase chain reaction (PCR), or multiplex ligation-dependent amplification (MLPA) techniques, often followed by confirmatory conventional cytogenetic analysis.[17,132] Molecular approaches such as microarray methods are useful for genetic disorders. These have a more rapid turnaround time than previous methods and include array-comparative genome hybridization (aCGH) and single nucleotide polymorphism (SNP) array to identify microdeletions, microduplications, and regions of homozygosity.[17]

Chorionic Villus Sampling. CVS is an alternative to genetic amniocentesis. CVS is generally performed 10 to 13 weeks after the last menstrual period (see Figure 3-15). Earlier than this, chorionic villi may not be sufficiently developed for adequate tissue sampling and risk of limb anomalies is increased; later, the chorion laeve is disappearing and the chorion frondosum is forming the definitive placenta. Both transabdominal and transcervical (because the uterus is still in the pelvis) approaches can be used after the gestational sac and implantation site are located by ultrasound. However, transabdominal approaches are preferred because of a lower miscarriage rate.[116]

Trophoblast tissue is aspirated from several sites on the chorion. This tissue can be analyzed for chromosome anomalies or with enzyme assay (for inborn errors of metabolism) or DNA analysis (hemoglobinopathies and other disorders).[155] Advantages of CVS include early diagnosis before the pregnancy is obvious to others and, for some assays, a decreased waiting period for results. Disadvantages include a risk of spontaneous abortion, infection, bleeding, and amniotic fluid leakage; uncertainty about long-term effects on the infant; and inability to do AFP assays for diagnosis of neural tube defects at this stage of gestation.[155,159] The error rate for CVS is higher than with amniocentesis.[17] CVS before 10 weeks' gestation has been associated with an increased risk of limb defects and is not recommended.[159] CVS between 10 and 13 weeks is a safer alternative for first trimester prenatal diagnosis than early amniocentesis.[159] Transabdominal CVS can also be done in the second and third trimesters.[116,155]

Amniocentesis. Genetic amniocentesis has traditionally been performed in most centers at 15 to 16 weeks (range, 15 to 20 weeks) (see Figure 3-15), because at this time amniotic fluid volume has reached 150 to 250 mL (so approximately 20 to 30 mL can easily and safely be removed), the uterus has reached the pelvic brim (so a transabdominal approach can be used), adequate fetal cells are available, and diagnostic studies can be completed in time for a second trimester abortion (if this option is chosen by the parents).[159] Error rates are less than 0.01% to 0.02%.[17] The overall incidence of miscarriage is 0.5% to 1%; the risk is higher with advanced maternal age.[146] The incidence of other maternal and fetal complications (spotting, fluid leak, bleeding, and infection) is low.[159] Early amniocentesis before 14 to 15 weeks has also been used in some centers, although it is currently uncommon. An increased risk of fetal loss, amniotic fluid leakage, and 10-fold increase in talipes equinovarus has been reported with early amniocentesis.[116,155,159]

Cellular and biochemical components of amniotic fluid change with gestational age and are useful indicators of fetal maturity and well-being. Amniotic fluid contains cells from the amnion, fetal skin, buccal and bladder mucosa, and tracheal lining. Amniotic fluid cells can be examined to determine fetal sex (important with sex-linked disorders) and to diagnose genetic and chromosomal disorders using DNA and enzymatic analysis. PCR techniques can be used to identify in utero infection such as cytomegalovirus, toxoplasmosis, or parvovirus B19.[116] Rapid detection of trisomies 21, 13, and 18 and alterations in sex chromosome numbers can be obtained within 24 hours using FISH, PCR, or MLPA techniques, often followed by confirmatory conventional cytogenetic analysis.[17] Amniotic fluid can be cultured for karyotype (to identify other chromosomal abnormalities) or for biochemical assay (to identify specific inherited metabolic disorders), analyzed using DNA hybridization and restriction enzyme techniques (for detecting gene deletions that occur with disorders such as hemoglobinopathies), and analyzed for quantification of AFP (screening for neural tube defects and other anomalies). Newer microarray technology (also called *molecular karyotyping*) such as aCGH and SNP has been used when multiple congenital anomalies are seen on ultrasound and conventional karyotyping is normal to detect microdeletions, duplications, and other alterations.[164] Cellular and biochemical components of amniotic fluid can be used to evaluate fetal health and maturity, including fetal lung maturity (see Chapter 10).

Umbilical Blood Sampling. Percutaneous umbilical blood sampling (PUBS), also called *cordocentesis* and *fetal blood sampling,* involves use of the umbilical cord to obtain fetal blood samples. Umbilical blood sampling has been used in the prenatal diagnosis of inherited blood disorders (hemoglobinopathies and coagulopathies), in detection of congenital infection, to assess fetal anemia (in Rh isoimmunization and in thrombocytopenia), and in fetal therapy such as blood transfusions. The most common genetic use is evaluation of mosaic findings from CVS or amniocentesis.[155] This technique is performed using real-time ultrasound as early as 16 weeks after the last menstrual period (see Figure 3-15). Complications include infection, preterm labor, bleeding, thrombosis, transient fetal arrhythmia, and fetal loss.[19,155]

Alterations in Placenta, Umbilical Cord, and Amniotic Fluid

An intact and adequately functioning placenta and amniotic fluid are critical for fetal survival and well-being. Without the placenta the fetus could not survive, because it would have no alternatives for essential processes such as respiratory gas exchange and nutrition. This section discusses alterations in the placenta and amniotic fluid in low- and high-risk pregnancies, the implications for the fetus and neonate from placental dysfunction and alterations in amniotic fluid volume, and the basis for common cord and placental abnormalities. Alterations in placental structure and function may lead to alterations in fetal programming (see Chapters 12, 16, and 19) and increase the risk of later disease.[91,149] Longtine and Nelson note that "placental structure and function are affected by developmental plasticity, epigenetic effects, as well as by exogenous or endogenous stressors, nutrient limitation, or metabolic imbalances. The resulting placental dysfunction can affect fetal development in utero and predispose the adult to a variety of diseases."[92]

Alterations in the Appearance of the Placenta and Membranes

The appearance of the placenta (color, size, consistency) often provides clues to maternal or placental dysfunction or pathologic processes in the fetus. The color of the placenta is determined by fetal hemoglobin. Pale placentas suggest fetal anemia. The placenta is paler in immature infants and congested in infants of diabetic mothers. Edematous, pale, and bulky placentas are seen with immune and nonimmune hydrops fetalis, TTTS (in the donor twin), fetal congestive heart failure, and infection.[124] These placentas may also contain more Hofbauer cells, an immature trophoblast layer, and other changes similar to those seen with hypoxia. Placentas less than 2 to 2.5 cm thick are may occur with IUGR; those more than 4 cm thick may be a result of diabetes mellitus and fetal hydrops.

The placenta responds to hypoxia and ischemia with formation of excessive syncytial knots, proliferation of villous cytotrophoblast (Langhans) cells, nucleated erythrocytes, fibrinoid necrosis of the villi, increased perivillous fibrin, and thickening of the trophoblast basement membrane.[54,124] The placentas from women with preeclampsia often have infarcts, hematomas, and characteristic histologic changes such as excessive proliferation of cytotrophoblast tissue within the villi and fibrin deposits.[54] Infarctions are also seen in placentas of infants with IUGR whose placentas are also small and in placentas from women with elevated hemoglobin levels (more than 13 g/dL [130 g/L]) in the second half of pregnancy. In this latter group, the infarctions may be a result of increased blood viscosity and thrombosis. Placentas of women who smoke may demonstrate increased thickness of the villous membrane that may reduce efficiency of diffusion. Pathologic changes in placentas of infants with fetal growth restriction are linked to reductions in placental blood flow and include thickening of villous trophoblastic basal membrane, villous infarction, thrombi, hematomas, villitis, and decreased mean placental weight and fetal-placental weight ratios.[153]

Thrombi in the veins along the chorionic plate appear as yellow streaks on the surface of the placenta. These thrombi are associated with velamentous insertion of the cord and may embolize. Infarctions are often seen near the margins of the placenta; central infarctions are less common and more serious, in that they may disrupt IVS circulation. Infarctions are areas of ischemic necrosis of primary villi resulting from obstruction of IVS blood flow because of thrombi or marked impairment of blood flow in the spiral arteries.[37,54] Initially these infarcted areas are red, later turning brown, gray, and then white with fibrin deposition; they may be covered with necrotic decidua. Hematomas and thrombi may be seen in the IVS. Infarctions may be a way the fetus responds to villi that have inadequate maternal perfusion; that is, the flow of blood to the affected villus is reduced so blood normally flowing to that villus can be redistributed to areas where maternal circulation is adequate.

Multiple plaques or nodules on the fetal surface of the placenta are found with amnion nodosum (associated with oligohydramnios and renal agenesis), squamous metaplasia (benign disorder), and infection.[37] With chorioamnionitis, the placenta often has an opaque surface and may be foul smelling or edematous.[124] Infection with *Candida albicans* is associated with white or yellow nodules on the placental surface.[37] Chronic inflammatory lesions include villitis, chronic chorioamnionitis, and chronic deciduitis of the decidua basalis.[82]

Meconium staining of the membranes may also occur. Because meconium is not discharged until after fetal gastrointestinal peptides (e.g., motilin) have reached critical levels, meconium passage is uncommon in preterm infants and more common in postterm infants. Green membranes are not necessarily a result of meconium; accumulations of hemosiderin (as may occur with hemolysis and circumvallation) also stain the membranes green.[124] Green pigment can be found in amniotic macrophages an hour after meconium is discharged and in chorionic macrophages by 2 to 3 hours. With extended exposure to meconium, extraplacental membranes become edematous and the membranes and placenta become tan-green or brown.

Alterations in Amniotic Fluid Volume

An understanding of the processes involved in the production of amniotic fluid and the pattern of fluid accumulation during pregnancy is necessary for assessing uterine growth and identifying women who need further evaluation (see Amniotic Fluid). Alterations in production and removal of amniotic fluid can lead to polyhydramnios (hydramnios) or oligohydramnios.

Polyhydramnios. Polyhydramnios (also called *hydramnios*), has traditionally been defined as accumulation of more than 2000 mL of fluid in a single amniotic sac at term.[46] More recently the amniotic fluid index (AFI), based on the largest amniotic fluid pocket seen on ultrasound, has been used (25 cm or larger at any gestational age or a maximum vertical pocket [MVP] more than 8 cm in depth).[88,102] Polyhydramnios has an overall incidence of 1% to 2%.[132] It can occur gradually during pregnancy or rapidly over a few days or weeks. Polyhydramnios is idiopathic in 60% of women but is also associated with maternal disease; multiple gestation; immune and nonimmune hydrops fetalis; Down syndrome and other chromosomal anomalies; and fetal gastrointestinal, cardiac, and neural tube anomalies. However, women with any of these complications can also have normal amniotic fluid volume. Idiopathic or essential polyhydramnios (i.e., with no known cause) is believed to arise from an unexplained imbalance in water exchange between the fetus, mother, and amniotic fluid. Increased AQP water channel expression has been described in pregnancies complicated by idiopathic polyhydramnios.[39,132,162] Second trimester polyhydramnios resolves spontaneously 40% to 50% of the time with good fetal outcomes.

Although multiple gestation often results in increased accumulation of amniotic fluid, in most cases this is not true polyhydramnios, because the fluid is distributed among several sacs, each sac containing usual amounts of fluid. An increased incidence of polyhydramnios has been reported in MZ monochorionic twins with arteriovenous anastomoses within their shared placenta and TTTS (see Placental Abnormalities in Multiple Gestation). Development of polyhydramnios in these pregnancies may be the result of excessive urination, polycythemia, and transudation of fluids. The elevated venous pressure and altered fluid dynamics seen with hydrops fetalis and some cardiovascular disorders may lead to excessive accumulation of amniotic fluid. Polyhydramnios is more common in diabetic women, perhaps because of fetal polyuria caused by fetal hyperglycemia or because of alterations in osmotic gradients as a result of increased amniotic fluid glucose.

Congenital anomalies are more common in pregnancies complicated by polyhydramnios. Neural tube defects, particularly anencephaly, may result in polyhydramnios as a result of decreased fetal swallowing or transudation of fluid from the exposed meninges. Polyhydramnios associated with chromosomal anomalies may be related to reduced fetal swallowing and, in some infants with Down syndrome, duodenal atresia. Although polyhydramnios is seen in many infants with esophageal or duodenal atresia (presumably because of decreased fetal swallowing and decreased gut absorption), these pregnancies may also have normal amniotic fluid volume. The basis for this finding is unclear but suggests that amniotic fluid homeostasis is a very complex mechanism involving the interaction of many variables.

Treatment options include fetal therapy (e.g., if the cause is fetal hydrops or arrhythmias); serial amniocenteses; and administration of PG synthetase inhibitors such as indomethacin. Indomethacin is believed to work by increasing fluid reabsorption by the fetal lungs, decreasing fetal urine production, and increasing fluid movement across the membranes to the mother. Indomethacin has potential serious maternal and fetal side effects.

Oligohydramnios. Oligohydramnios is an AFI of 5 cm or less or MVP of 2 cm or less.[88,102] Oligohydramnios can occur at any time during gestation and is seen in 1% to 2% of pregnancies.[46] Oligohydramnios is rarer than polyhydramnios and is associated with amnion abnormalities, placental insufficiency, and fetal urinary anomalies.[145] Any alterations in formation or excretion of urine by the fetus in the second half of gestation can result in oligohydramnios. Oligohydramnios

may lead to umbilical cord compression in labor and fetal distress.

Inadequate amniotic fluid during labor can be caused by premature rupture of the membranes, oligohydramnios, or early amniotomy. A lack of adequate fluid removes the natural protective cushioning effect of this fluid and increases the risk of cord compression and fetal heart rate decelerations during contractions. Interventions for alterations in fetal heart rate patterns are discussed in Chapter 6. Decreased fetal urine output and reduced amniotic fluid also occur with use of PG synthetase inhibitors such as indomethacin, ibuprofen, and sulindac.[46]

Severe fetal renal anomalies (agenesis, dysplasia, or obstructive disorders) may lead to oligohydramnios because of decreased or no urine output. Bilateral renal agenesis in conjunction with pulmonary hypoplasia, musculoskeletal abnormalities, and a characteristic facies is known as *Potter syndrome* and is associated with oligohydramnios. Several of the findings in Potter syndrome may be deformation defects arising from lack of amniotic fluid.[77]

Movement produced by fetal muscular activity is an integral component of normal morphologic development. Mechanical forces can lead to defects either from intrinsic forces (e.g., fetal myoneuropathy, development of an organ in an abnormal and excessively small site, or alterations in the normal flow or volume of body fluids) or from external forces (e.g., a bicornate uterus, fibromas, or oligohydramnios) that interfere with fetal mobility.[101]

The constraints on fetal movement imposed by oligohydramnios can result in a cascade of developmental events resulting in fetal anomalies. These anomalies include congenital contractures (because of relative or complete immobilization of the joints in a confined space); lung hypoplasia (lack of room for development of the thorax and for the subsequent stretch or distention of lung tissue required for normal lung growth); shortened umbilical cord (length is related to stretching from fetal activity); dysmorphic facies including micrognathia, low-set ears, small alae nasi, and hypertelorism (molding of the face by compressive forces); growth restriction (fetal motor activity seems important for normal development of muscle mass and weight gain); perhaps microgastria (lack of stretching and distention because the volume of amniotic fluid available for swallowing is reduced); and "loose" skin (stretched by the attempts of the constrained fetus to move).[101] This sequence has been termed the *fetal akinesia/hypokinesia deformation sequence.*[101]

Oligohydramnios is also associated with amnion nodosum. In this disorder, yellow-gray nodules or plaques consisting of desquamated fetal epidermal cells, hair, and vernix are found in and on the amnion and on the placental surface (fetal side). This debris is probably pressed into the amnion by close approximation of the fetal skin and amnion in the presence of oligohydramnios. Oligohydramnios may also occur with IUGR (as a result of decreased urine flow rates) or with prolonged pregnancy.

Abnormalities of the Cord and Placenta

Abnormalities of the cord and placenta arise from alterations in implantation and placentation or from disorders of the trophoblast. Occasionally these abnormalities may have minimal effect on the fetus and the outcome of the pregnancy; more often, serious and sometimes fatal conditions develop so that the pregnancy cannot be maintained or fetal development and survival are threatened. At times, maternal survival and reproductive function may also be compromised.

Abnormalities of Implantation and Separation. The major abnormalities of implantation and separation of the placenta are placenta previa, abruptio placentae, and placenta accreta. Placenta previa is implantation of the placenta over the internal cervical os so that it encroaches on a portion of the dilated cervix. A low-lying placenta is one that is near the os but does not overlie it. The incidence of placenta previa worldwide is 1 in 200 pregnancies; risk factors include previous cesarean section, spontaneous or elective pregnancy termination, and uterine surgery.[139] Various theories have been proposed to explain the pathogenesis of placenta previa, including defective vascularization of or damage to the endometrium, alteration of the normal ovum transport mechanism, and development of the placenta in the decidua capsularis.[37,54,158]

If the blastocyst implants in endometrium that is poorly vascularized because of atrophic or inflammatory changes, the placenta may develop a larger decidual surface area to compensate for an inadequate blood supply and grow downward into the lower uterine segment.[37] If vascularization of the endometrium in the upper uterine segment is poor, the blastocyst may continue to descend, implanting by chance in healthier endometrium in the lower uterine segment. Altered transport of the blastocyst because of abnormal uterine motility, deviations in the size or shape of the uterine cavity, scars, or fluid in the cavity can also result in displacement of the blastocyst to the lower uterus.[37]

Normally the chorionic villi initially surround the entire embryo but later degenerate beneath the decidua capsularis, forming the chorion laeve. By 4 months, the growing fetus fills the uterine cavity and the decidua capsularis fuses with the decidua vera (see Figure 3-7). If chorionic villi near the lower uterus fail to degenerate as the decidua capsularis fuses with the decidua vera, these villi can become incorporated into the placenta and impinge on the lower uterine segment.[37,54] The incidence of a low-lying placenta is higher in early gestation than at term because of the growth of the lower uterine segment.[97]

A placental abruption is separation of a normally implanted placenta before the delivery of the fetus. Abruptio placentae is initiated by hemorrhage into the decidua basalis with formation of a hematoma that leads to separation and compression of the adjacent portion of the placenta. Hemorrhage may develop secondary to degenerative changes in the arteries supplying the IVS and with thrombosis, degeneration of the decidua, and vessel rupture with formation of a retroplacental hemorrhage.[54] Possible causes include maternal hypertension (secondary to essential hypertension, preeclampsia, chronic renal disease, cocaine or nicotine use, or alterations in the transformation of the spiral arteries), compression or occlusion of the inferior vena cava, circumvallate placenta, or trauma.[37,54,97,125,128] The incidence of abruptio placentae is increased with maternal cocaine use, because these drugs induce vasoconstriction of placental blood vessels and a sudden elevation in maternal blood pressure.

Placenta accreta is a general term used to describe any placental implantation in which there is abnormally firm adherence of all or part of the placenta to the myometrium. As a result, there is partial or total absence of the decidua basalis and attachment of the chorionic villi to the fibrinoid (Nitabuch) layer or myometrium. Occasionally the villi invade the myometrium (placenta increta) or penetrate through the myometrial wall (placenta percreta) and into surrounding structures such as the bladder. Placenta accreta often occurs when decidual formation is defective, such as with implantation over uterine scars or in the lower uterine segment. A 13-fold increase in the prevalence of placenta accreta in recent decades has been correlated to increased cesarean sections.[121,160] Placenta accreta is associated with placenta previa, particularly in the presence of a uterine scar such as from a previous cesarean birth, and with significant morbidity including severe hemorrhage, uterine perforation, infection, and hysterectomy.[37,54,121,139,158,160]

Abnormalities of Placentation. The size and configuration of the placenta are influenced by the degree of vascularization of the decidua and the number and arrangement of the primitive villi that later compose the fetal portion of the placenta.[37] The major clinically significant abnormalities of placental configuration result in circumvallate, marginate, or succenturiate placentas.

With circumvallate placenta, the area of the chorionic plate is reduced. As chorionic villi invade the decidua, the fetal membranes fold back upon themselves, creating a dense, grayish-white raised ring encircling the central portion of the fetal surface. The fetal vessels forming the cord stop at this ring rather than covering the entire fetal surface of the placenta. The risk of abruptio placenta is increased with circumvallate placentas. Marginate (or circummarginate) placentas also arises from a chorionic plate that is smaller than the basal plate. In these placentas the white ring composed of the fetal membranes coincides with the margin of the placenta, without the folding back of the membranes seen in circumvallate placentas.[54]

The cause of circumvallate and marginate placentas is uncertain, although partial or complete forms are seen in up to 25% of gestations.[136] Possible causes include subchorial infarcts, formation of insufficient chorion frondosum, and an abnormally deep implantation of the blastocyst causing part of the fetal surface to be covered by the decidua vera. These placentas are often asymptomatic, but circumvallate placentas have been linked to threatened abortion, preterm labor, painless vaginal bleeding after 20 weeks, placental insufficiency, and intrapartum and postpartum hemorrhage.[37,54]

Succenturiate placenta involves development of one or more smaller accessory lobes in the membranes that are attached to the main placenta by fetal vessels. This abnormality arises when a group of villi distant to the main placenta fail to degenerate, implantation is superficial, or implantation occurs in a confined site (e.g., a bicornate uterus) so that attachment of the trophoblast also occurs on the opposing wall.[37,54] The accessory lobes may be retained, leading to postpartum hemorrhage or infection. These placentas are often associated with malrotation of the implanting blastocyst with velamentous insertion of the cord.[37]

Abnormalities of the Umbilical Cord. The umbilical cord may develop knots, loops, torsion, or strictures. These alterations are associated with increased fetal mortality and morbidity.[54] Excessively long cords (greater than 75 to 100 cm) are more likely to develop knots, torsion, or prolapse. These long cords are associated with increased fetal activity. Abnormally short cords (less than 30 to 32 cm) are associated with asphyxia at birth as a result of traction on the cord with fetal descent.[37,136] Abnormally short cords are also associated with decreased fetal activity because tension on the cord normally promotes growth. The decreased fetal activity that occurs with Down syndrome, neuromuscular disorders, and fetal malformations may result in a short cord.

A single umbilical artery occurs in about 1% of newborns and probably arises from agenesis or degeneration of the missing vessel early in gestation.[127] This anomaly is associated with an increased incidence of fetal cardiovascular, gastrointestinal (esophageal and anal atresia), and urinary tract anomalies.[127]

Battledore placenta, or insertion of the cord at or within 1.5 cm of the margin of the placenta (seen in 5% to 7% of placentas), may be clinically benign but has been linked to preterm labor, fetal distress, and bleeding in labor because of cord compression or vessel rupture.[97,136] With velamentous insertion (1% to 2% of placentas), the cord inserts into the membranes so that the vessels run between the amnion and chorion before entering into the placenta.[97] These variations in insertion of the cord probably arise at the time of implantation. Velamentous insertion is more common in multiple births.

Normally the blastocyst implants with the inner cell mass adjacent to the endometrium and the trophoblast that will form the placenta. The body stalk, which will become the cord, aligns with the center of the placenta. Rotation of the inner cell mass (and body stalk) gives rise to eccentric insertions of the cord. The degree of rotation will influence how far the umbilical cord will be from the center of the placenta (i.e., eccentric, marginal, velamentous). Velamentous insertion may lead to rupture and fetal hemorrhage associated with a high fetal mortality, particularly with vasa previa (when the fetal vessels are located along the lower uterine segment, crossing the internal cervical os, and presenting ahead of the fetus).[37,56,97,158]

Gestational Trophoblast Disease

Gestational trophoblast disease includes hydatidiform mole and gestational trophoblast tumors (derived from neoplastic hyperplastic changes). Both forms of trophoblast disease are associated with markedly elevated levels of hCG.[37] Hydatidiform moles result from deterioration of the chorionic villi into a mass of clear vesicles. Histologically, hydatidiform mole is characterized by hyperplasia of the syncytiotrophoblast and the cytotrophoblast, edema of the avascular villous stroma, and cystic cavitations within the villous stroma. The villi become converted into molar cysts connected to each other by fibrous strands. There may be no fetus (complete mole) or the remains of a degenerating fetus or amniotic sac (partial or incomplete mole). The fetus in an incomplete molar pregnancy rarely survives to delivery.[37]

The karyotype of a complete mole is usually 46,XX (90%) and is derived from duplication of a haploid X-carrying (23,X) sperm. The remainder are 46,XY and arise from fertilization of the ovum by two sperm with failure of the maternal genome to participate in development.[18] Thus the mole is usually androgenic in origin; that is, the ovum develops under the influence of a spermatozoon nucleus. The nucleus of the ovum is inactivated or lost before fertilization. A complete mole is associated with increased risk of later choriocarcinoma.

In an incomplete or partial mole, the hydatidiform changes are focal; that is, there is slowly progressive swelling of some villi (which are usually avascular), whereas other vascular villi develop with a functioning fetoplacental circulation.[37] The karyotype of this type of mole is usually triploid (69,XXX; 69,XXY; or 69,XYY). An incomplete mole results from fertilization of a normal haploid ovum (23,X) by two haploid sperm (dispermy) or a single diploid sperm.[18,54] A third type involves heterozygous diploid fertilization of an empty ovum with two haploid sperm (46,XX or 46,XY). This form of mole is associated with an increased risk of gestational trophoblast tumors.

Multiple Gestation

The incidence of multiple gestation in the United States is 1 in 30 live births and has doubled in recent years.[15,156] This increase is attributed to delayed childbearing and increased use of ART and is predominantly an increase in DZ twins, although MZ twinning is also increased.[15,69] The arrangement of membranes and placentas in twin gestations is determined by the type of twin and the stage of gestation at which twinning occurs. The incidence of twin conceptions is greater than that of twin births. Ultrasound studies indicate that up to 12% of pregnancies begin as twins but are converted to singleton pregnancies by the asymptomatic loss of one embryo.[54] Spontaneous reduction in the number of embryos is seen in 36% of pregnancies that begin as twins, 53% of triplet pregnancies, and 63% of quadruplet pregnancies.[42]

The basic types of twins are MZ (arising from division of a single ovum after fertilization) and DZ (simultaneous fertilization of two ova enclosed within a single follicle or theca, or ovulation of two ova from one or both ovaries that are then fertilized independently). Most (70%) twins are DZ. A third type of twinning has been proposed to result from simultaneous fertilization of an ovum and the first polar body by two sperm, although supporting evidence is scanty and controversial.[15] This section focuses on twins, because higher-order multiples (e.g., triplets, quadruplets) can be MZ, DZ, or multizygotic, with attributes that are variations of findings characteristic of twins.

Twin zygosity cannot be determined solely by the number of placentas. Two types of placentas are seen: monochorionic, which occurs with MZ twins, and dichorionic, which may occur with either MZ or DZ twins. Dichorionic placentas may be separate or fused (with a ridge in the central fusion plane). Examinations to determine zygosity often involve morphologic examination of the chorion, amnion, and yolk sac as well as DNA analysis, which can be done quickly and reliably by restriction fragment length polymorphism (RFLP) analysis.[15,69] Noninvasive determination of zygosity prenatally assessing fetal cfDNA in maternal plasma has been reported.[69] Placentas and membranes of twins and other multiple births should always be saved and sent for pathologic examination for morphologic and DNA analysis.

MZ twins may have one or two placentas (which may be separate or fused). The placentas and membranes of MZ twins may be monochorionic-monoamniotic, monochorionic-diamniotic, or dichorionic-diamniotic (fused or separate). About 70% of MZ twins are monochorionic and 30% are dichorionic.[15,41] With higher-order multiple births, placentas and membranes may be monochorionic-monoamniotic, monochorionic-multiamniotic, or multichorionic-multiamniotic

(Figure 3-16). Although DZ twins always have two dichorionic-diamniotic placentas, the placentas may be fused and appear to be single. Fused placentas increase the risk of growth restriction in one or both infants as a result of competition for space and abnormal cord insertions. About 80% of twins can be differentiated according to zygosity (i.e., as MZ or DZ) at or shortly after birth as follows (percentages are approximate): (1) 23% are monochorionic and therefore the infants are MZ; (2) 30% are dichorionic with a male and female twin and are almost always DZ; and (3) 27% are same-sex twins but with different blood types and thus usually DZ. The remaining 20% are same-sex twins with similar blood types who are either MZ twins with dichorionic placentas (either separate or fused) or DZ twins of the same sex (with separate or fused placentas).[15,41] Monochorionic twins of opposite sexes occur occasionally, possibly because of reciprocal chimerism or embryo fusion followed by later separation. Determination of the zygosity of these twins requires further investigation and DNA analysis.

Perinatal mortality is 3 to 11 times higher in twins than singletons.[5,15,69] This risk is affected by zygosity and placental and membrane characteristics. For example, mortality is two to three times higher in monochorionic twins than in dichorionic (either DZ or MZ) twins. Monochorionic twins tend to weigh less and are more commonly growth restricted in utero than are dichorionic twins. The incidence of congenital anomalies is higher in MZ twins than in DZ twins.[5,41,147] Structural defects in MZ twins may also arise from deformations caused

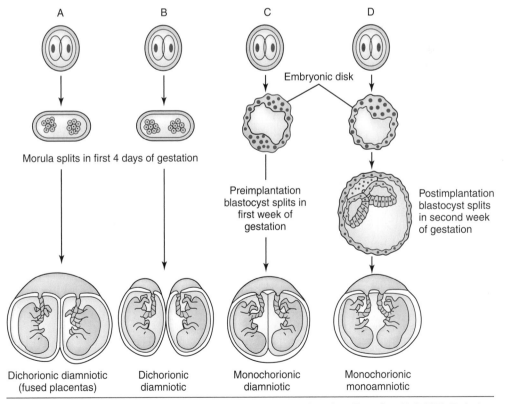

FIGURE 3-16   The development and placentation of monozygotic twins. (From Fox, H. [1997]. *Pathology of the placenta* [2nd ed.]. Philadelphia: Saunders.)

by limited intrauterine space, disruption of blood flow because of placental vascular anastomoses, or localized defects in early morphogenesis. Discordant growth with birthweight differences of more than 25% occurs in 10% to 15% of monochorionic and dichorionic twins.[69] This may be a result of unequal sharing of the placenta (in MZ twins), genetic factors, or a less favorable implantation site and maternal spiral artery conversion in dichorionic twins.[69]

Monozygotic Twins

Spontaneous MZ twins occur in 3.5 to 4 in 1000 births.[15] The rate of MZ twinning is relatively constant worldwide and in most cases is probably a random event that is an accident in embryonic development. However, though not common, familial MZ twinning with an autosomal dominant inheritance pattern has been described.[93] The exact mechanism for monozygotic twinning is unclear, but there are two main theories: splitting theory (splitting of a single inner cell mass) and codominance theory (development of more than one organizing axis).[156] MZ twinning may also involve a teratogenic exposure.[15] Evidence for a teratogenic basis include an increased frequency with increased maternal age, discordant malformations in twin pairs, and susceptibility for development of codominant axes.[93] MZ embryos may arise from a delay in implantation secondary to adverse environmental conditions such as inadequate nutrition or oxygen deprivation or to formation of two cell lines from early mosaicism (see Chapter 1) that triggers separation. The increased frequency of MZ twins reported in ART and after ovulation induction may be a result of damage to the blastocyst or breaks in the zona pellucida that normally keeps the blastocyst

intact.[62,93] MZ twins are not completely "identical" but often have subtle differences in DNA, minor to major differences in birth weight, or the presence of congenital defects in one twin caused by unequal allocation of blastomeres. Postzygotic genetic events that can lead to MZ pair differences include postzygotic crossing-over or nondisjunction, imprinting differences, discordant cytoplasmic segregation, chromosomal mosaicism, altered patterns of X-chromosome inactivation in female MZ twins, or late gene mutations (see Chapter 1).[93,156] Separation may interrupt left-right axial orientation, resulting in "mirror-image" twins. This is seen in 10% to 15% of MZ twins and involves mirror imaging of physical characteristics, but not situs inversus.[62] MZ twinning can occur at three different stages of development: (1) during the early blastomere stage, (2) during formation of the inner cell mass, and (3) with development of the embryonic disk (see Figure 3-16). The stage of development determines the number of placentas and arrangement of membranes (Figure 3-17).

Separation of the ovum during the early blastomere stage, accounting for 20% to 30% of MZ twins, usually occurs about 2 days after fertilization while the blastomere is in the two- to four-cell stage (see Figure 3-16, *A* and *B*).[15] Because this is before differentiation of any cells, the two blastomeres will develop independently into morulae, blastocysts, and embryos, each with separate placentas, chorions, and amnions (dichorionic-diamniotic). These blastocysts will implant at separate sites. If these sites are close together, the placentas may fuse (see Figure 3-16, *A*). Membranes separating the embryos will contain the amnion-chorion of infant 1 and the chorion-amnion of infant 2 separated by their fused placentas. This arrangement of infants, placentas, and membranes,

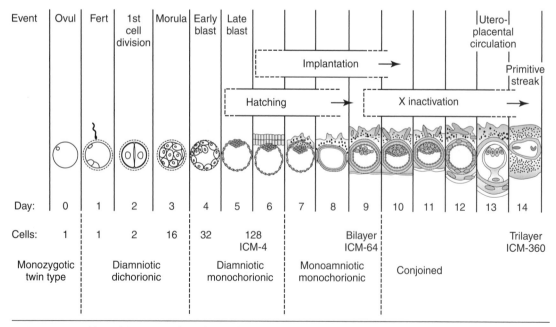

FIGURE 3-17 Normal human embryonic development with timing of monozygotic twinning superimposed. *ICM,* Inner cell mass. (From Hall, J.G. [2001]. Twins and twinning. In D.L. Rimoin, J.M. Connor, & R.E. Pyeritz. [Eds.]. *Emery and Rimoins's principles and practice of medical genetics,* vol 1 [4th ed.]. New York: Churchill Livingstone.)

pathogenesis, and clinical significance. *Am J Obstet Gynecol, 213,* S53.

83. Kingdom, J. (2000). Development of the placental villous tree and its consequences for fetal growth. *Eur J Obstet Gynecol Reprod Biol, 92,* 35.

84. Kumar, S., & O'Brien, A. (2005). Recent developments in fetal medicine. *BMJ, 328,* 1002.

85. Lee, M. K., et al. (2017). Regulation of embryogenesis. In R. A. Polin, et al. (Eds.), *Fetal and neonatal physiology* (5th ed.). Philadelphia: Saunders.

86. Lee, M. T., Bonneau, A. R., & Giraldez, A. J. (2014). Zygotic genome activation during the maternal-to-zygotic transition. *Annu Rev Cell Dev Biol, 30,* 581.

87. Lewi, L., & Verh, K. (2010). Monochorionic diamniotic twin pregnancies pregnancy outcome, risk stratification and lessons learnt from placental examination. *Acad Geneeskd Belg, 72,* 5.

88. Lewi, L., Deprest, J., & Hecher, K. (2013). The vascular anastomoses in monochorionic twin pregnancies and their clinical consequences. *Am J Obstet Gynecol, 208,* 19.

89. Li, L., Lu, X., & Dean J. (2013). The maternal to zygotic transition in mammals. *Mol Aspects Med, 34,* 919.

90. Liu, J. H. (2014). Endocrinology of pregnancy. In R. K. Creasy, et al. (Eds.), *Creasy & Resnik's Maternal-fetal medicine: Principles and practice* (7th ed.). Philadelphia: Saunders.

91. Longtine, M. S., & Nelson, D. M. (2011). Placental dysfunction and fetal programming: The importance of placental size, shape, histopathology, and molecular composition. *Semin Reprod Med, 29,* 187.

92. Lopriore, E., et al. (2009). Risk factors for neurodevelopment impairment in twin-twin transfusion syndrome treated with fetoscopic laser surgery. *Obstet Gynecol, 113,* 361.

93. Machin, G. (2009). Non-identical monozygotic twins, intermediate twin types, zygosity testing, and the non-random nature of monozygotic twinning: A review. *Am J Med Genet Part C Semin Med Genet, 151C,* 110.

94. Macias, R. I., Marin, J. J., & Serrano, M. A. (2009). Excretion of biliary compounds during intrauterine life. *World J Gastroenterol, 15,* 817.

95. Maiz, N., & Nicolaides, K. H. (2010). Ductus venosus in the first trimester: Contribution to screening of chromosomal, cardiac defects and monochorionic twin complications. *Fetal Diagn Ther, 28,* 65.

96. Mamede, A. C., et al. (2012). Amniotic membrane: from structure and functions to clinical applications. *Cell Tissue Res, 349,* 447.

97. Marino, T. (2004). Ultrasound abnormalities of the amniotic fluid, membranes, umbilical cord, and placenta. *Obstet Gynecol Clin North Am, 31,* 177.

98. Maruyama, T., et al. (2010). Human uterine stem/progenitor cells: Their possible role in uterine physiology and pathology. *Reproduction, 140,* 11.

99. Mitchell, M. D., et al. (2015). Placental exosomes in normal and complicated pregnancy. *Am J Obstet Gynecol, 213,* S173.

100. Mizejewski, G. J. (2003). Levels of alpha-fetoprotein during pregnancy and early infancy in normal and disease states. *Obstet Gynecol Surv, 58,* 804.

101. Moessinger, A. C. (1989). Morphological consequences of depressed or impaired fetal activity. In W. P. Smotherman & S. R. Robinson (Eds.), *Behavior of the fetus.* Caldwell, NJ: Telford Press.

102. Moise, K. J. (2013). Toward consistent terminology: assessment and reporting of amniotic fluid volume. *J Semin Perinatol, 37,* 370.

103. Monga, M., & Mastrobattista, J. M. (2014). Maternal cardiovascular, respiratory and renal adaptation to pregnancy. In R. K. Creasy, et al. (Eds.), *Creasy & Resnik's Maternal-fetal medicine: Principles and practice* (7th ed.). Philadelphia: Saunders.

104. Moore, K. L., Persaud, T. V. N., & Torchia, M. G. (2015). *The developing human: Clinically oriented embryology* (10th ed.). Philadelphia: Saunders.

105. Moore, T. R. (2011). The role of amniotic fluid assessment in evaluating fetal well-being. *Clin Perinatol, 38,* 33.

106. Mouillet, J. F., et al. (2015). MicroRNAs in placental health and disease. *Am J Obstet Gynecol, 213,* S163.

107. Myatt, L., & Webster, R. P. (2009). Vascular biology of preeclampsia. *J Thromb Haemost, 7,* 375.

108. Myatt, L. (2010). Review: Reactive oxygen and nitrogen species and functional adaptation of the placenta. *Placenta, 31,* S66.

109. Myatt, L., & Sun, K. (2010). Role of fetal membranes in signaling of fetal maturation and parturition. *Int J Dev Biol, 54,* 545.

110. Nagamatsu, T., & Schust, D. J. (2010). The immunomodulatory roles of macrophages at the maternal-fetal interface. *Reprod Sci, 17,* 209.

111. Nicolaides, K. H. (2011). Screening for fetal aneuploidies at 11 to 13 weeks. *Prenat Diagn, 31,* 7.

112. Norwitz, E. R., Schust, D. J., & Fisher, S. J. (2001). Implantation and the survival of early pregnancy. *N Engl J Med, 345,* 1400.

113. Nunes, C., et al. (2015). Signaling pathways involved in oocyte growth, acquisition of competence and activation. *Hum Fertil (Camb), 18,* 149.

114. Osol, G., & Mandala, M. (2009). Maternal uterine vascular remodeling during pregnancy. *Physiology (Bethesda), 24,* 58.

115. Palermo, G. D., Neri, Q. V., & Rosenwaks, Z. (2015). To ICSI or not to ICSI. *Semin Reprod Med, 33,* 92.

116. Papp, C., & Papp, Z. (2003). Chorionic villus sampling and amniocentesis: What are the risks in current practice? *Curr Opin Obstet Gynecol, 15,* 159.

117. Park, H. J., Shim, S. S., & Cha, D. H. (2015). Combined screening for early detection of pre-eclampsia. *Int J Mol Sci, 16,* 17952.

118. Patel, J., et al. (2010). Regulation of hypoxia inducible factors (HIF) in hypoxia and normoxia during placental development. *Placenta, 31,* 951.

119. Penn, A. A. (2017). Endocrine and paracrine function of the human placenta. In R. A. Polin, et al. (Eds.), *Fetal and neonatal physiology* (5th ed.). Philadelphia: Saunders.

120. Pringle, K. G., et al. (2010). Beyond oxygen: Complex regulation and activity of hypoxia inducible factors in pregnancy. *Hum Reprod Update, 16,* 415.

121. Publications Committee, Society for Maternal-Fetal Medicine, & Belfort, M. A. (2010). Placenta accreta. *Am J Obstet Gynecol, 203,* 430.

122. Qin, J., et al. (2016). Assisted reproductive technology and the risk of pregnancy-related complications and adverse pregnancy outcomes in singleton pregnancies: a meta-analysis of cohort studies. *Fertil Steril, 105,* 73.

123. Ramathal, C. Y., et al. (2010). Endometrial decidualization: Of mice and men. *Semin Reprod Med, 28,* 17.

124. Redline, R. (2015). Placental pathology. In R. J. Martin, A. A. Fanaroff, & M. C. Walsh (Eds.), *Fanaroff and Martin's neonatal-perinatal medicine: Diseases of the fetus and infant* (10th ed.). Philadelphia: Saunders.

125. Redline, R. W. (2015). Classification of placental lesions. *Am J Obstet Gynecol, 213,* S21.

126. Redman, C. W., & Staff, A. C. (2015). Preeclampsia, biomarkers, syncytiotrophoblast stress, and placental capacity. *Am J Obstet Gynecol, 213,* S9.

127. Rittler, M., et al. (2010). Single umbilical artery and associated malformations in over 5500 autopsies: Relevance for perinatal management. *Pediatr Dev Pathol, 13,* 465.

128. Romero, R., et al. (2011). Placental bed disorders in preterm labor, preterm PROM, spontaneous abortion and abruptio placentae. *Best Pract Res Clin Obstet Gynaecol, 25,* 313.

129. Romero, R., Dey, S. K., & Fisher, S. J. (2014). Preterm labor: one syndrome, many causes. *Science, 345,* 760.

130. Rosenfeld, C. R. (2017). Regulation of the placental circulation. In R. A. Polin, et al. (Eds.), *Fetal and neonatal physiology* (5th ed.). Philadelphia: Saunders.

131. Ross, M. G., & Brace, R. A. (2001). National Institutes of Child Health and Human Development conference summary: Amniotic fluid biology—basic and clinical aspects. *J Matern Fetal Med, 10,* 2.

132. Ross, M. G., & Beall, M. H. (2014). Amniotic fluid dynamics. In R. K. Creasy, et al. (Eds.), *Creasy & Resnik's Maternal-fetal medicine: Principles and practice* (7th ed.). Philadelphia: Saunders.

133. Sadler, T. W. (2015). *Langman's medical embryology* (13th ed.). Philadelphia: Wolters Kluwer.

134. Schoenwolf, G. C., et al. (2015). *Larsen's human embryology* (5th ed.). Philadelphia: Saunders.

135. Schroder, H. J., & Power, G. G. (1997). Engine and radiator: Fetal and placental interactions for heat dissipation. *Exp Physiol, 82,* 403.

136. Schuler-Maloney, D. (2000). Placental triage of the singleton placenta. *J Midwifery Womens Health, 45,* 104.

137. Sha, X. Y., et al. (2011). Maternal-fetal fluid balance and aquaporins: From molecule to physiology. *Acta Pharmacol Sin, 32,* 716.

138. Signorelli, J., Diaz, E. S., & Morales, P. (2012). Kinases, phosphatases and proteases during

sperm capacitation. *Cell Tissue Res, 349,* 765.

139. Silver, R. M. (2015). Abnormal placentation: Placenta previa, vasa previa, and placenta accreta. *Obstet Gynecol, 126,* 654.
140. Slaghekke, F., et al. (2009). TAPS and TOPS: Two distinct forms of fetal-fetal transfusion in monochorionic twins. *Z Geburtshilfe Neonatol, 213,* 248.
141. Slaghekke, F., et al. (2010). Twin anemia-polycythemia sequence: Diagnostic criteria, classification, perinatal management and outcome. *Fetal Diagn Ther, 27,* 181.
142. Sonek, J., & Nicolaides, K. (2010). Additional first-trimester ultrasound markers. *Clin Lab Med, 30,* 573.
143. Sonek, J., & Croom, C. (2014). Second trimester ultrasound markers of fetal aneuploidy. *Clin Obstet Gynecol, 57,* 159.
144. Spencer, T. E. (2014). Biological roles of uterine glands in pregnancy. *Semin Reprod Med, 32,* 346.
145. Staples, D., & Rankin, J. (2010). *Physiology in childbearing with anatomy and related biosciences* (3rd ed.). Edinburgh: Bailliere Tindall.
146. Tabor, A., & Alfirevic, Z. (2010). Update on procedure-related risks for prenatal diagnosis techniques. *Fetal Diagn Ther, 27,* 1.
147. Taylor, M. J., & Fisk, N. M. (2000). Prenatal diagnosis in multiple pregnancy. *Baillieres Best Pract Res Clin Obstet Gynaecol, 14,* 663.

148. Tesarik, J. (1999). Calcium: Signaling in human preimplantation development: A review. *J Assist Reprod Genet, 16,* 216.
149. Thompson, J. A., & Regnault, T. R. (2011). In utero origins of adult insulin resistance and vascular dysfunction. *Semin Reprod Med, 29,* 21.
150. Trundley, A., & Moffett, A. (2004). Human uterine leukocytes and pregnancy. *Tissue Antigens, 63,* 1.
151. Vähäkangas, K., & Myllynen, P. (2009). Drug transporters in the human blood-placental barrier. *Br J Pharmacol, 158,* 665.
152. Valsky, D. V., et al. (2010). Selective intra-uterine growth restriction in monochorionic twins: Pathophysiology, diagnostic approach and management dilemmas. *Semin Fetal Neonatal Med, 15,* 342.
153. Vedmedovska, N., et al. (2011). Placental pathology in fetal growth restriction. *Eur J Obstet Gynecol Reprod Biol, 155,* 36.
154. Wald, N. J., et al. (2000). Assay precision of serum alpha fetoprotein in antenatal screening for neural tube defects and Down's syndrome. *J Med Screen, 7,* 74.
155. Wapner, R. J. (2014). Prenatal diagnosis of congenital disorders. In R. K. Creasy, et al. (Eds.), *Creasy & Resnik's Maternal-fetal medicine: Principles and practice* (7th ed.). Philadelphia: Saunders.
156. Weber, M. A., & Sebire, N. J. (2010). Genetics and developmental pathology of twinning. *Semin Fetal Neonatal Med, 15,* 313.

157. Webster, W. S., & Abela, D. (2007). The effect of hypoxia in development. *Birth Defects Res C Embryo Today, 81,* 215.
158. Wiedaseck, S., & Monchek, R. (2014). Placental and cord insertion pathologies: screening, diagnosis, and management. *J Midwifery Womens Health, 59,* 328.
159. Wilson, R. D. (2000). Amniocentesis and chorionic villus sampling. *Curr Opin Obstet Gynecol, 12,* 81.
160. Wortman, A. C., & Alexander, J. M. (2013). Placenta accreta, increta, and percreta. *Obstet Gynecol Clin North Am, 40,* 137.
161. Wright, S. J. (1999). Sperm nuclear activation during fertilization. *Curr Top Dev Biol, 46,* 133.
162. Zhu, X., et al. (2010). The expression of aquaporin 8 and aquaporin 9 in fetal membranes and placenta in term pregnancies complicated by idiopathic polyhydramnios. *Early Hum Dev, 86,* 657.
163. Zimna, A., & Kurpisz, M. (2015). Hypoxia-Inducible Factor-1 in Physiological and Pathophysiological Angiogenesis: Applications and Therapies. *Biomed Res Int, 2015,* 549412.
164. Zuffardi, O., et al. (2011). Array technology in prenatal diagnosis. *Semin Fetal Neonatal Med, 16,* 94.
165. Zygmunt, M., et al. (2003). Angiogenesis and vasculogenesis in pregnancy. *Eur J Obstet Gynecol Reprod Biol, 110,* S10.

Parturition and Uterine Physiology

During parturition the actions of the myometrium, decidua, fetus, placenta, and membranes must be integrated to achieve birth of the fetus without compromising fetal or placental perfusion. This process requires synchronization between myometrial activity and changes in cervical structure and is mediated by a cascade of events and signals that convert the uterus from the quiescent phase seen throughout much of pregnancy to the activated structure needed for birth. Although our understanding of these factors has increased markedly in recent years, many aspects remain unknown.

This chapter reviews the structure of the uterus and individual myometrial cells; changes during pregnancy; physiology of parturition with respect to cervical dilation, initiation of labor, and myometrial contractions; and clinical implications related to preterm and postterm labor onset, labor induction, and dystocia. Maternal pain during labor is discussed in Chapter 15.

UTERUS

The uterus is a major site of physiologic activity during the childbearing years. Alterations in the endometrium occur with the monthly menstrual cycle (see Chapter 2) and during pregnancy (see Chapter 3). Myometrial activity is associated with menstruation, sperm transport, zygote transport, implantation, pregnancy, and parturition.[3] During pregnancy the uterus supports growth and development of the embryo and fetus. At the end of pregnancy, the uterine myometrium must move from a relatively inactive state to produce the strong, synchronous, coordinated contractile forces needed to expel the fetus and placenta. Knowledge of the physiologic changes that bring about this transition in uterine function is incomplete at present but is the focus of much interest and research.

Uterine Structure

The uterine wall consists of three layers: (1) internal endometrium, (2) myometrium, and (3) external serous epithelial layer (perimetrium), with an area known as the *junctional zone* between the first two layers.[34,76,164] The thin serosa protects the uterus and provides a relatively inelastic base upon which the myometrium develops tension to increase intrauterine pressure. During early pregnancy the endometrial cells enlarge and a hypersecretory state develops with changes in cellular composition as the endometrium is remodeled into the decidua to support implantation, placental development, and fetal nutrition (see Chapter 3).[82]

The myometrium consists of four muscle layers separated by a vascular zone. The muscle layers form a web that supports and protects the developing fetus. The inner layer, below the decidua, is circular and perpendicular to the long axis of the uterus. This layer runs clockwise and counterclockwise in a spiral. The middle layer consists of interlacing fibers in a figure-eight shape interspersed with blood vessels. The outer two layers run parallel to the longitudinal axis of the uterus.[82,123,131] These muscle layers are composed of smooth muscle cells arranged in interconnected bundles of 10 to 50 partially overlapping cells set in a matrix of collagenous connective tissue and ground substance.[21,47] The ground substance transmits the contractile forces from individual myometrial cells along the muscle bundle.[21] Around the bundles of smooth muscle cells are fibroblasts, blood and lymphatic vessels, and nerve cells. The subendothelial myometrium forms the junctional zone where myometrial contractions arise in the nonpregnant uterus.[76,82] Myocytes in the junctional zone have a greater nuclear area, decreased extracellular matrix, less water content, and greater blood perfusion than those in the outer myometrium.[76] Because the uterine muscle layers have different embryonic origins, they have distinct endocrine responses and thus may respond differentially to uterotonic agonists and antagonists.[76]

The uterus is innervated primarily by the sympathetic nervous system along with some fibers from the cerebrospinal tract and the parasympathetic nervous system.[34] These include adrenergic neurons (postganglionic sympathetic fibers from lumbar and mesenteric ganglia), cholinergic neurons (sparse, primarily innervating the cervix), and peptidergic neurons.[82,131] Adrenergic fibers are most dense in the fallopian tubes, cervix, and vagina and are relatively sparse in the uterine corpus and fundus. Compared with other smooth muscle cells, which tend to be richly innervated, the uterus has a relatively low density of nerves to smooth muscles cells.[47] The myometrium normally contracts spontaneously unless this ability is altered by endocrine, paracrine, or apocrine factors. This intrinsic ability is suppressed during pregnancy, then enhanced during labor.[3]

The role of the nervous system in myometrial activity is poorly understood. The adrenergic and peptidergic nerves may play a role in suppressing myometrial contractility during pregnancy.[21,47] Adrenergic fibers in the uterine wall disappear near term, leaving only those in the cervix and uterine horns. Peptidergic and sympathetic nerves also decrease markedly during pregnancy.[152] Thus control of contractility during pregnancy changes to local control, particularly prostaglandins (PGs) in the decidua and chorion and oxytocin in the myometrium. Communication between myometrial cells during labor occurs primarily via gap junctions (see Gap Junction Formation).

Uterine Growth

The uterus increases in weight, length, width, depth, volume, and overall capacity during pregnancy. The nonpregnant uterus weighs 40 g to 70 g, increasing to 1100 g to 1200 g by term; uterine volume increases from 10 mL to 5 L.[111] The increased volume is primarily a result of increases in myocyte size.[131] The elastic properties of the uterus support its growth during pregnancy. Uterine growth begins after implantation. Initially, growth primarily involves hyperplasia and is influenced by estrogen and growth factors (e.g., insulin-like growth factor 1 [IGF-1], epidermal growth factor, transforming growth factors, fibroblast growth factor-β), and is independent of the effects of stretching from the growing embryo.[23,82,96] This early uterine growth occurs regardless of whether the embryo is implanted in the uterus or at an extrauterine site.[114,123] Blood vessels, lymphatic vessels, fibrous tissue, and connective tissue also increase, as does blood flow (see Chapter 9).

Later uterine growth involves primarily hypertrophy of the myocytes, stimulated by estrogens, and remodeling of the extracellular matrix, mediated by distention of the uterus by the enlarging fetus.[82,96,111] As the uterus grows, the ratio of ribonucleic acid (RNA) to deoxyribonucleic acid (DNA) increases because of increased RNA synthesis and total protein. By 3 to 4 months, the uterine wall has thickened from 10 to 25 mm. With further distention the wall thins to 5 to 10 mm at term. Myometrial smooth muscle fibers increase in length from 50 to 500 μm and width from 5 to 15 μm because of a progressive increase in actin and myosin content.[96,114,123] The isthmus becomes thinner and more distensible, forming the lower uterine segment.[111] Smooth muscle cell creatinine phosphatase, adenosine triphosphate (ATP), and adenosine diphosphate (ADP) also increase to term.[114] The isthmus does not undergo hypertrophy and becomes thin and distensible to allow passage of the fetus.[96]

The height of the uterine fundus reaches the maternal umbilicus by about 20 weeks' gestation and the xiphoid process of the sternum by 8 months. As the fetal head descends into the pelvis ("lightening") late in gestation, the fundal height becomes slightly lower.

After 12 to 16 weeks' gestation, as the fundus changes from a spherical shape to become more dome shaped, distention occurs primarily in a cephalic direction.[96] The shape of the fundus influences intrauterine pressure. In a sphere, tension is a geometric function of the radius of curvature; in a cylinder, tension is a linear function (and thus is lower).[114] In the absence of contractions, intrauterine pressure peaks at midpregnancy, then decreases as the shape of the fundus changes. The pressure remains low until term despite the increasing intrauterine volume.

Uterine smooth muscle undergoes phasic contractile activity. At midgestation, contractions of the circular muscles of the uterus are weaker than those of the longitudinal muscles. Contractile strength increases in the circular muscles so that by term these muscles are similar to longitudinal muscles in their contractile ability. The basis for this change is believed to be differences in membranous electrical events, cell-to-cell coupling via gap junctions, and intracellular calcium release.[47]

MYOMETRIUM

The myometrium has two basic properties: contractility and elasticity. Contractility is the ability to lengthen and shorten. Elasticity is the ability to grow and stretch to accommodate the enlarging uterine contents, maintain uterine tonus, and permit involution after delivery.

Myometrial Cell Structure

The contractile units of the uterus are the smooth muscle cells in a connective tissue matrix. Movement of contractile forces along the uterus occurs from transmission of tension generated by individual smooth muscle cells to other smooth muscle cells and the connective tissue matrix.[47] Uterine smooth muscles are unique in that active, synchronous contraction of these muscles occurs only during the birth process.

Myometrial cells contain three types of protein myofilaments (actin, myosin, and intermediate), microtubules, and protein structures called *dense bodies*. Myosin is a hexamer approximately 160 nm long. Myosin is the principal contractile protein. Myosin is laid down in thick (15 to 18 nm) myofilaments that optimize interaction with actin and generation of force.[21,82] Myosin filaments consist of two heavy chains with a molecular weight of 200 kDa, arranged in a head-and-tail structure, and two light chains. The helical heavy chains unite at one end of the filament to form two globular heads that protrude from the myosin at regular intervals (Figure 4-1).[2,96] The two light chains (molecular weights of 20 and 17 kDa) are bound to the head in the neck region (see Figure 4-1). The longer light chain (molecular weight 20 kDa) has a regulator role in muscle contraction and can bind to calcium and magnesium and become phosphorylated.[2,21,82,96] In addition to the two light chains, the myosin head also contains sites for magnesium adenosine triphosphatase (Mg-ATPase) (an enzyme necessary for the interaction of actin and myosin and subsequent generation of force) and an actin binding site where the actin and myosin interact.[21,82] The helical tail, formed by the heavy chains, transmits the force (tension) generated by the interaction of myosin and actin. Myosin filaments are unidirectional and longer in smooth muscle than in striated muscle. This allows actin to interact with the myosin heads throughout the length of the myosin, increasing the

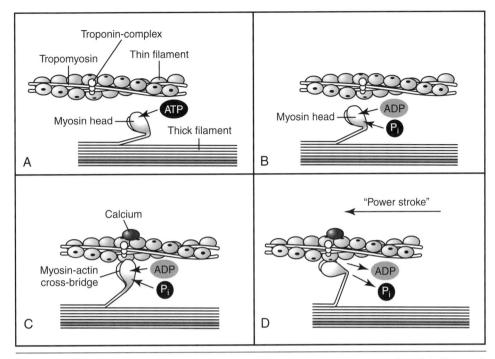

FIGURE 4-1 Mechanics of muscle contraction. **A,** The appearance of the contractile unit is illustrated. The thick filament refers to myosin; the thin filament is actin. Myosin binding sites on the actin filaments are covered by a thin filament known as tropomyosin that obscures the myosin-binding sites, therefore preventing the myosin heads from attaching to actin and forming cross-bridges. Adenosine triphosphate (ATP) binds to the myosin head. The troponin complex is attached to the tropomyosin filament. **B,** The hydrolysis of ATP into adenosine diphosphate (ADP) and inorganic phosphate (Pi) allows the myosin head to assume its resting position. **C,** The binding of calcium to the troponin complex results in a conformational change that allows binding site between actin and myosin to be exposed with the formation of actin-myosin cross-bridges. **D,** The formation of actin-myosin cross-bridges results in release of ADP and Pi, causing the myosin heads to bed and slide past the myosin fibers. This "power stroke" results in a shortening of the contractile unit and the generation of force within the muscle. At the end of the power stroke, the myosin head releases the actin-binding site, is cocked back to its furthest position, and binds to a new molecule of ATP in preparation for another contraction. The binding of myosin heads occurs asynchronously (i.e., some myosin heads are binding actin filaments while other heads are releasing them), which allows the muscle to generate a continuous smooth force. Cross-bridge formations must therefore form repeatedly during a single muscle contraction. (From Norwitz, E.R. & Lye, S.J. [2009]. Biology of parturition. In R.K. Creasy, R. Resnik, J.D. Iams, C.J. Lockwood, & T.R. Moore. [Eds.]. *Creasy & Resnik's Maternal-fetal medicine: Principles and practice* [6th ed.]. Philadelphia: Saunders Elsevier, p. 78.)

maximum degree of shortening to 5 to 10 times greater than that of skeletal muscle.[21,82]

Actin is a globular protein monomer (molecular weight 45 kDa) with six isoforms. The α-actin and γ-actin isoforms are the ones primarily involved in contraction; β-actin forms part of the cytoskeleton.[2] Actin polymerizes into long, thin (6 to 9 nm) filaments. These filaments originate in and are distributed between dense bodies.[96] Adenosine triphosphatase (ATPase) activity on the myosin head initiates formation of cross-links or bonds between actin and myosin. The myosin head rotates and pulls on the actin filament, creating tension (force) with a relative spatial displacement (shortening).[82] Interaction of myosin and actin is illustrated in Figure 4-1.

The intermediate fibers form a structural network. These fibers may be involved in signal transduction, contractile activity, and secretion of collagen and extracellular matrix components.[2,23] Interstitial-like cells located on the borders of

myometrial smooth muscle bundles may also have a role in cell signaling.[59,73] The microtubules, formed by tubulin, are involved in myometrial hyperplasia and hypertrophy during pregnancy. Tubulin is a substrate for G-protein receptor kinase, a substance involved in myosin phosphorylation and downregulation of β2-adrenoreceptors.[23] The dense protein bodies are scattered throughout the cytoplasm and on the inner surface of the cell membrane and are attached to the poles of the smooth muscle cell by intermediate (10-nm thick) filaments and actin thin filaments. The dense bodies and their filaments form a supportive structure for the contractile filaments and a network of actin attachment sites (adhesion plaques).[21,23,82] These structures enable the uterus to enlarge and generate forces sufficient for expulsion of most fetuses regardless of their weight or position.

Compared with striated muscle cells, smooth muscle cells are smaller, have a higher ratio of surface area–to–cell volume, and have less myosin. Actin filaments predominate, with approximately 11 to 15 actin filaments per myosin filament versus a 6:1 ratio in skeletal muscle.[21,82] Filaments in smooth muscle occur in random rather than regular bundles throughout the cell, so these muscles do not have the striated appearance seen in skeletal muscle. The myofilaments in smooth muscle are oriented obliquely to the long axis of the muscle fibers, which allows the muscle to exert a large force along a short distance at low velocity. This may account for the ability of the myometrium to sustain strong contractions over many hours. The maximal force per area is similar to or greater than that of skeletal muscle. In smooth muscle the pulling force can be exerted in any direction, whereas in skeletal muscle the force generated and the resultant contraction are aligned with the axis of the muscle fibers.[21]

Changes During Pregnancy

During pregnancy the myometrium is believed to undergo changes in cellular phenotype. These proposed phases include (1) early proliferative phase with myocyte hyperplasia (see Uterine Growth); (2) synthetic phase with myocyte hypertrophy, interstitial matrix (ground substance) synthesis, and remodeling of local adhesions (see Uterine Growth); (3) contractile phase with upregulation of contractile proteins and downregulation of inhibitory pathways; (4) labor phase with expression of contraction-associated proteins (CAPs), synthesis of uterotonic agents, and development of intense contractions (this phase also involves upregulation of proinflammatory cytokines, which activate cellular adhesion molecules with leukocyte infiltration inducing localized inflammation in the decidua and myometrium); and (5) postpartum involution with apoptosis, wound repair, and tissue regenerations (see Chapter 5).[134] Postpartum repair may be mediated by myometrial stem cells.[87,134]

Myometrial quiescence during pregnancy is mediated by increases in progesterone, relaxin, nitric oxide (NO), and prostacyclin (PGI_2).[82] The decreased myometrial excitability during most of pregnancy is also related to a high K+ conductance and decreased connectivity between myocytes and muscle bundles.[12] Uterine blood flow increases during pregnancy from 2% of cardiac output before pregnancy to 10% to 20% by term.[111] Uterine blood flow is redistributed from similar amounts flowing to endometrium and myometrium in the nonpregnant uterus to 80% to 90% flowing to the placenta during pregnancy, with the remainder divided equally between the endometrium and myometrium.[111] Changes in uterine blood flow are caused by decreased placental vascular resistance as a result of remodeling of the spiral arteries (see Chapter 3), which results in increased vessel diameter and decreased resistance, estrogens, vascular endothelial growth factor, angiotensin II, NO, and PGI_2.[111]

The uterus is never completely quiescent; low-frequency, low-amplitude activity occurs even in the nonpregnant state.[2,21,82,95,119] The frequency of contractions increases during pregnancy with an increase of approximately 5% per week.[98] Diurnal periodicity has been reported with increased frequency at night (five to six

per hour) and lowered frequency in the early afternoon (two to three per hour) near term.[98] Initially these contractions tend to be mild, irregular, nonsynchronized, and focal in origin and are generally not felt by the pregnant woman. As pregnancy progresses, contractions become more intense and frequent and more are felt by the woman. During the third trimester, spontaneous contractions progressively increase in frequency with decreased negative membrane potential and an increase in action potentials.[12,164] With the onset of labor, contractions become regular, coordinated, and intense as individual myometrial cells contract in harmony. The contractile force is about five times greater in the pregnant than in the nonpregnant myometrium. Synchronous contraction of the uterus is dependent on formation of gap junctions (see Gap Junction Formation).[47,95,96]

Alterations in the character of uterine contractions result from structural and functional changes in the myometrium as a result of the estrogen-progesterone environment of pregnancy. These changes include the following:

1. Change in the velocity and timing of action potentials. In the nonpregnant uterus, action potentials occur at the peak of a contraction at a velocity of about 6 cm/sec. In pregnancy the action potential occurs much closer to the beginning of the contraction wave and at 1 to 2 cm/sec.
2. Changes in membrane potentials. The resting membrane potential depolarized during pregnancy from −70 mV before pregnancy to −55 mV in late pregnancy.
3. Hypertrophy and hyperplasia of the myometrial cells, with increased contractile proteins, under the influence of estrogen.
4. Increased sensitivity of the myometrium to the effects of myosin light-chain kinase phosphorylation.
5. Alteration in the arrangement of muscle bundles. In pregnancy these bundles are arranged in closer contact, enhancing gap junction formation.
6. Development of the sarcoplasmic reticulum. This enhances calcium movement.
7. Increased number of mitochondria and cellular adenosine triphosphate (ATP). This enhances energy production by the myometrial cell.[2,12,47,95,96,111,164]

Near labor onset the myometrial contractile capacity increases as the myometrium undergoes activation (see Parturition). There is enhanced communication among the cells of the uterus at term, so that the action potential covers the entire uterus in 2 to 3 seconds, resulting in nearly simultaneous contraction of the myometrium. This phenomenon may result from the increased velocity of the action potentials, the closer arrangement of muscle bundles with gap junction formation, and the increased number of muscle cells.[47,98]

CERVIX

The cervix is important in keeping the fetus in utero against active and passive forces such as the weight of the fetus and amniotic sac and passive pressure of the uterine wall.[103] During pregnancy the cervix increases in mass, water content, and vascularization. The connective tissue of the uterus (particularly the cervix) undergoes changes in its viscoelastic plasticity so that, by term, "it combines the properties of a rubber band with those of saltwater taffy."[114] For the fetus to be expelled, the cervix must first change from a relatively rigid to a soft, distensible structure. Myometrial contractions exert a slow, steady pull on the cervix, resulting in cervical stretching but with little rebound between contractions. This leads to progressive cervical dilation. After delivery the cervix returns to its nonpregnant shape and consistency.[103]

Structure of the Cervix

The cervix is composed of an extracellular tissue matrix (composed primarily of collagen, elastin, glycosaminoglycans, and proteoglycans) covered by a thin cellular layer of smooth muscle and fibroblasts that penetrate into the connective tissue matrix.[81,96,111] Approximately 85% to 90% of the cervix is composed of collagen, and 10% to 15% is smooth muscle.[66,132] The amount of smooth muscle varies between the upper (25%), middle (16%), and lower (6%) portions of the cervix. The extracellular matrix consists of a dense network of interlacing collagen and elastin fibers embedded in viscous ground.[103,165] The extracellular matrix imparts tensile mechanical stiffness to the cervical tissue.[165]

The collagen fibers form a relatively rigid rod-shaped structure and impart tensile strength to the cervix, important during pregnancy to retain the fetus.[21] Collagen in the cervix is primarily types I and III (both types found mainly in the connective tissue stroma) and type IV (associated with smooth muscle and vascular components).[66,103] About 80% of the collagen in the stroma is type I and 20% is type III.[132] The collagen fibers are arranged in cross-linked triple helices. The cross-linking protects the collagen fibers from being broken down by collagenase and proteases.[81,103] Elastin is haphazardly arranged parallel to and between collagen fibers, imparting elasticity to the cervical tissue and contributing to the integrity of the tissue.[47,81] The elastin-to-collagen ratio is greatest at the internal os. Elastin can stretch in any direction to twice its length and thus may be important in the ability of the cervix to distend in labor and then return to its normal shape after parturition.[81,95]

The ground substance is composed of proteoglycans with glycosaminoglycans attached to a glycoprotein core. The major glycosaminoglycans in the cervix are dermatan sulfate (70%), heparan sulfate (15%), and hyaluronan or hyaluronic acid (15%).[21] These substances are large charged molecules that bind together, attract water, and coil around and lock the collagen fibrils in place.[21]

Changes During Pregnancy

Cervical load increases with fetal growth altering cervical length, volume, and uterocervical angle during pregnancy.[103] During pregnancy the cervix is softer with higher hydraulic permeability and tensile strength.[103] Cervical remodeling occurs throughout pregnancy and includes softening, ripening, dilation, and subsequent repair.[18,111,151] Softening begins in the first trimester and is a slow process mediated by progesterone. Increased tissue compliance, increased epithelia and fibroblast proliferation, and protective factors are characteristics of cervical softening.[103,111,151]

In the nonpregnant cervix, collagen fibers are in bundles forming cablelike structures. As pregnancy progresses the bundles become less dense with thinner and more loosely packed fibers with reduced mechanical strength.[81,111] Hyaluronic acid (which has a high affinity for water) and cervical water content increases.[81] The total collagen increases and is remodeled to maintain cervical integrity. However, the relative amount of collagen decreases 30% to 50% as a result of increases in other proteins and in the water content of the extracellular matrix.[157] Decorin, a dermatan sulfate proteoglycan that coats the collagen fibers, increases during later pregnancy and labor.[81,96] Decorin and hyaluronic acid separate the collagen fibrils, increasing fibril dispersion and disorganization.[157] Smooth muscle cells in the cervix enlarge, then later undergo programmed cell death at term.[81]

Fibroblasts, leukocytes, macrophages, and eosinophils proliferate in the cervix during pregnancy. These changes may be important in altering vasopermeability to increase cervical water content and in secretion of proteases for cervical ripening. The fibroblasts are also involved in the metabolism of collagen and glycosaminoglycans.

Cervical Ripening and Dilation

The rigid cervix of pregnancy must become distensible to expel the fetus.[21] Cervical ripening and distention begins several weeks before delivery and involves biochemical changes in the cervix that are mediated by both hormonal (estrogens, progesterone, oxytocin, relaxin, and PGs) and mechanical factors (cervical stretch and the pressure from the descending fetal head).[111] This process is accompanied by localized decreases in progesterone and increases in estrogen levels, increased tissue water content, increased high-molecular-weight hyaluronic acid, increased tissue monocytes and vascularization, disorganization of collagen fibers, decrease in tensile strength, and increased viscoelasticity.[111,151,165] After delivery, postpartum repair is mediated by synthesis of extracellular matrix molecules, metabolism of high-molecular-weight hyaluronic acid to the low molecular weight form, proinflammatory gene expression, increased neutrophils, and macrophage activation.[151]

Ripening and dilation are inflammatory processes that involve changes in collagen, extracellular matrix proteins, glucosaminoglycans, and smooth muscle with enzymatic degradation of collagen, loss of collagen elasticity, and reduction of tensile strength.[18,114,127,145] Factors responsible for the maintenance of cervical integrity during pregnancy and cervical ripening at the end of pregnancy include remodeling of the extracellular matrix and apoptosis mediated by increases in degradative enzymes such as matrix metalloproteinases (MMPs), synthesis of extracellular matrix proteins, increased collagen turnover, disruption of collagen fibrils, increase in the decorin-to-collagen ratio, increased hyaluronic acid and thus cervical water content, and infiltration of the cervix by neutrophils and macrophages.[18,27,111,122,157] These processes are mediated by cytokines such as interleukin-1 (IL-1), interleukin-6 (IL-6), interleukin-8 (IL-8), and tumor necrosis factor-α (TNF-α). IL-1 and TNF-α alter the adhesiveness of vascular epithelium. IL-6 increases prostaglandin (PG) and leukotriene (LT) production. This dilates cervical blood vessels and enhances movement of neutrophils into the cervix. IL-8 is a proinflammatory chemokine (chemokines are a type of cytokine that mediates chemoattraction) that stimulates MMP-8 and increases neutrophil chemotaxis.[66,145,157] IL-8 and similar substances attract inflammatory cells that release proinflammatory cytokines such as IL-1β and IL-1α. These cytokines activate the nuclear factor-κ-B (NF-κB) signaling pathway, which can block progesterone receptor mediated actions.[18] NF-κB is a transcription factor–signaling gene involved in immune and inflammatory responses that regulates gene expression of many factors involved in parturition.[158]

Collagen is degraded by MMPs such as collagenase, elastase, and other nonspecific proteolytic enzymes, resulting in a loss of collagen fibrils. The MMP system is a series of proteins that, with zinc as a cofactor, act in a cascade to degrade collagen. Both MMPs and MMP inhibitors increase during pregnancy. During most of pregnancy these are in balance, but in late pregnancy there is a net increase in MMPs, leading to collagen degradation and disorganization. Hyaluronic acid (which loosely binds collagen fibrils) stimulates MMP production in the cervix and neutrophil chemotaxis.[81] Neutrophils and macrophages also secrete MMP and are a major source of MMP-8 (neutrophil collagenase).[66] MMP activity is enhanced by IL-1 and IL-8. Hyaluronic acid increases by 50%

with labor onset, then decreases rapidly after delivery, accompanied by a decrease in dermatan sulfates, especially decorin (which tightly binds collagen fibrils thus resulting in loosening and dispersal of collagen bundles), and an increase in the water content of the cervix.[81,96] This weakens the structure of the cervix by decreasing the cross-bridges between collagen fibers and decreases the collagen content.

A proposed mechanism for the process of cervical ripening and dilation is illustrated in Figure 4-2. In summary, cervical ripening involves an inflammatory cascade with release of proinflammatory cytokines (e.g., IL-1, IL-6, and especially IL-8 and TNF-α), leading to infiltration of the cervix by leukocytes and macrophages, which in turn release and activate MMPs. MMPs alter the synthesis of extracellular matrix proteins and increase collagen turnover and retention of water.[28] As a result, collagen is degraded and collagen fibers are disrupted and dispersed.

Endocrine control of cervical ripening is a complex process that involves a cascade of changes in estradiol, progesterone, and relaxin mediated by PGI_2, prostaglandin E2 (PGE_2), prostaglandin $F2_\alpha$ ($PGF_{2\alpha}$), NO, and cytokines.[21,27,28,94,104] Progesterone inhibits collagen breakdown. Alterations in the estrogen-to-progesterone ratio correlate with increased procollagenase activity, collagen degradation, and apoptosis (programmed cell death). Increased cervical relaxin may activate collagen peptidase and mediate changes in water and mucopolysaccharide content of the cervix.[21] Uterine activity is enhanced by mechanical stretching of the cervix (Ferguson reflex). This response may be a result of the effects of $PGF_{2\alpha}$ and oxytocin release stimulated by cervical stretching.

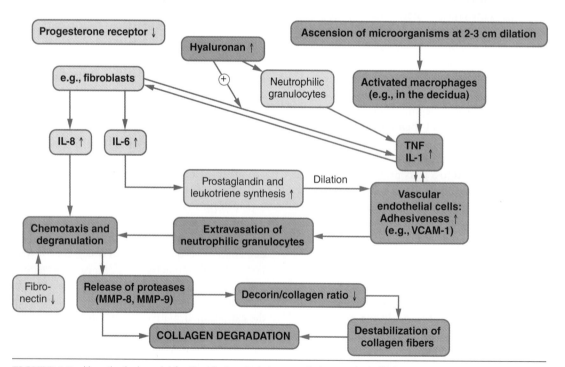

FIGURE 4-2 Hypothetical model for the biochemical changes during cervical dilation at term. *IL,* Interleukin; *MMP,* matrix metalloproteinase; *TNF,* tumor necrosis factor; *VCAM,* vascular cell adhesion molecule. (From Winkler, M. & Rath, W. [1999]. Changes in the cervical extracellular matrix during pregnancy and parturition. *J Perinatol Med, 27,* 58.)

PGE$_2$ and PGF$_{2\alpha}$ have a localized influence on cervical softening. PGE$_2$ action on the cervix is independent of uterine contractile activity and is used to improve cervical inductability (i.e., responsiveness of the cervical tissue) before induction of labor (e.g., when delivery is indicated because of risk factors). PGE$_2$ also dilates small blood vessels in the cervix—increasing leukocyte extravasation—and stimulates neutrophil chemotaxis.[82] PGs also enhance collagenase activity, increase production of proteoglycans that bind water, and decrease decorin, which is needed for collagen stability. Increased cortisol near term increases placental and fetal membrane PG production by upregulating prostaglandin-H synthetase-2 (PGHS-2) in the membranes and downregulating 15-hydroxyprostaglandin dehydrogenase (PGDH) in the trophoblast.[111]

NO in the cervix increases near term and may act with PGE$_2$ to induce cervical vasodilation and neutrophil infiltration and may regulate MMP activation.[27,28,104] Inductable NO synthetase (iNOS) is present in macrophages and regulates NO in response to inflammatory stimuli. NO stimulates release of PGE$_2$ and regulates cyclooxygenase-2 (COX-2, an enzyme needed to convert arachidonic acid to PGs) to locally increase PGE$_2$.[145,156]

RUPTURE OF FETAL MEMBRANES

The fetal membranes are a major site of PG synthesis and metabolism. The fetal membranes also contain abundant 11-βhydroxysteroid dehydrogenase 1 (11β-HSD1), which converts inactive cortisone to active cortisol, and thus plays a role in regulating metabolism and transport of cortisol between fetal and maternal circulations (see Chapter 19).[102] A possible feedback loop within the fetal membranes has been postulated involving glucocorticoids, proinflammatory cytokines, surfactant protein-A, 11β-HSD1, PGs, and cortisol to enhance fetal organ maturation and labor onset (see Initiation of Labor).[102]

The amnion and chorion are connected by an extracellular matrix (fibrous proteins embedded in polysaccharide gelatinous matter). The chorion adheres to the decidua. With delivery, the decidua and chorion must separate to allow expulsion of the membranes.[93,127] This process involves dissolution of fetal fibronectin, an extracellular matrix protein found at the decidua-chorion interface.[102,127]

The exact mechanism for rupture of the membranes is unknown, but it is believed to be caused by "a programmed biochemical set of events leading to collagen remodeling and superimposed physical stretch forces leading directly to tissue damage" and thus rupture.[71] The fetal membranes are distended 40% at 25 to 27 weeks' gestation, 60% at 30 to 34 weeks and 70% at term.[18] Membrane rupture is associated with disruption of the extracellular matrix and basement membrane by MMPs that alter collagen (a major component of the amnion and chorion) and degrade components of these structures.[43,49,93,155]

The tensile strength of the membranes, which is greater in the amnion, is imparted by type I, III, and IV collagenous fibers that maintain the noncollagenous components (elastin, proteoglycans, microfibrils, decorin, plasminogen, and integrins) of the extracellular matrix.[92,113] The extracellular matrix and the membranes themselves undergo continual remodeling by MMPs during pregnancy to adapt to changes in uterine pressure and volume.[92] This process is regulated by a balance between MMPs and tissue inhibitors of MMPs (TIMPs) mediated by prostaglandins (PGs), cytokines (including IL-1 and TNF-α), and chemokines.[49,92,127,93] Labor is associated with an increase in MMPs and poly (ADP-ribose) polymerase and a decrease in TIMPs.[93] Increases in neutrophils, macrophages, and monocytes and in the decidual-chorionic interface right before labor onset, coinciding with increases in proinflammatory cytokines and chemokines, enhances this process.[43,49,104,105,155] IL-1 and TNF-α, which increase during labor, may in turn mediate upregulation of MMPs, induce apoptosis, and increase PGE$_2$.[71] Regional induction of MMPs in the membranes over the internal cervical os before labor may target this area for later rupture.[87,93] This area is reported to have increased MMP-9, decreased TIMP, and increased apoptosis with labor.[18,41,49,97,113]

Hyperdistention with pressure of the presenting part along with increased hydrophobicity results in loss of phospholipids that normally lubricate the chorion-amnion interface, leading to increased shear force with cellular fracturing and rupture. Sweeping or stripping of the fetal membranes results in mechanical disruption and increased phospholipase A$_2$ release, both of which increase PGF$_{2\alpha}$.[56,147,148]

Premature rupture of the membranes (PROM), or rupture before onset of uterine contractions, may be related to factors such as mechanical stress (polyhydramnios, multiple gestation), alterations in membranous collagen, or chorioamnionitis.[92] These events may result in increases in extracellular matrix degrading enzymes and inappropriate MMP activation.[92] Women with PROM may have alterations in membranes such as decreased collagen fibers, disruption of collagen fiber patterns, and deposition of amorphous material between the fibers.[18] With chorioamnionitis a variety of vaginal and cervical microorganisms have been demonstrated to produce bacterial collagenases and proteases that alter membrane integrity and reduce the pressure needed for rupture.[93] Bacterial colonization increases cytokines and leads to an imbalance of MMPs and TIMPs.[93] PROM may be mediated by collagenolytic enzymes from the placenta and amniotic fluid that increase in activity with increasing gestational age. Deficiency of protease inhibitors and abnormal expression of certain MMPs have been reported with PROM.[155] Other physical factors associated with PROM include higher pressures from uterine contractions or polyhydramnios and prolapsing membranes with cervical dilation.[93] The risk of PROM is increased with factors such as multiple pregnancy, maternal bleeding, poor maternal nutrition, lean body mass, and maternal smoking.[93]

PARTURITION

"Parturition is a multifactorial physiologic process that involves multiple interconnected positive feed forward and negative feedback loops. Each of these loops is connected to others in a carefully time-regulated fashion. When parturition occurs normally, both maternal and fetal processes are involved."[107] Parturition is an inflammatory event modulated by environmental, endocrine, and physical factors.[127] At term this inflammatory process is a response to endocrine signals from the fetus and mechanical stretch; in preterm labor it may be caused by infection or other processes that alter tissue integrity.[90] Initiation of labor is associated with migration of leukocytes and macrophages into the myometrium, cervix and fetal membranes, release of chemotaxic factors leading to increased expression of proinflammatory cytokines and increased NF-κB (transcription factor that regulates gene expression).[18,48,90] Mendelson proposed that this inflammatory response and NF-κB activation "promote uterine contractility via (1) direct activation of contractile genes (e.g., COX-2 [cyclooxygenase-2], oxytocin receptor, and connexin 43) and (2) impairment of the capacity of PR [progesterone receptor] to mediate uterine quiescence."[90] Parturition involves anatomic, biochemical, immunologic, endocrinologic, and clinical events.[18] The major events in parturition are fetal membrane rupture, cervical dilation, myometrial contractility, placental separation, and uterine involution. These events are mediated by increases in MiRNA expression, which promotes progressive contractions and removes repression of contractile genes that contributed to uterine quiescence during pregnancy.[127]

Initiation of Labor

Initiation of labor involves a complex interplay of maternal and fetal physiologic and genetic factors and endocrine signaling whose specific interrelationships and significance are still not completely understood.[24] Labor initiation is regulated by the fetal genome via two integrated pathways: endocrine (fetal hypothalamic-pituitary-placental axis) and mechanical (fetal growth places tension of the uterine wall), which leads to myometrial biochemical and molecular changes that increase contraction-associated proteins (CAPs) involved in myometrial excitability.[134] Prostaglandins are the final common pathway in mechanisms of labor onset. Uterine stretch stimulates the myometrium to produce proinflammatory cytokine and chemokines that are believed to result in an inflammatory response in the myometrium and decidua that contributes to labor onset.[73,134] Uterine stretch also increases oxytocin receptors and gap junctions and alters calcium and potassium channels.[164]

Challis and Lye proposed that parturition is divided into four phases: (1) phase 0, quiescence; (2) phase 1, activation; (3) phase 2, stimulation; and (4) phase 3, involution.[23] Phase 0 occurs for 95% of pregnancy. During this phase, progesterone and other uterotonic inhibitors—including PGI_2, relaxin, NO, and parathyroid hormone–related peptide (PTHrP)—maintain myometrial quiescence.[90]

During phase 1, activation, which accounts for about 5% of the duration of pregnancy, levels of uterotonic inhibitors decrease, whereas estrogen increases, mediated by transcription factors that up-regulate expression of CAPs.[48,134] CAPs include gap junction proteins (particularly connexin 43 [Cx43]),

myometrial oxytocin receptors, PGE_2 receptors (known as EP_1 to EP_4), $PGF_{2\alpha}$ receptors (known as FP), and calcium channels.[23,82] Activation involves an increase in expression of genes that encode CAPs. A major transcription factor that regulates CAP expression is NF-κB and its mediators, TNFα, IL-1β, IL-8, and COX-2.[32,90] NF-κB activity is decreased during pregnancy because of progesterone/progesterone-receptor blocking and upregulation of NF-κB inhibitors. At term signals from the fetus increase with macrophage activation and migration, release of cytokines and chemokines, and NF-κB activation.[90] These fetal signals include augmented placental corticotropin-releasing hormone (CRH) production, increased uterine stretch by the growing fetus, and secretion of surfactant lipids and surfactant protein A (SP-A).[90] SP-A synthesis begins only after 80% of gestation has been completed.[90] Surfactant phospholipids and SP-A contain arachidonic acids that serve as a precursor for PG production (Box 4-1) by the amnion. With maturation of the fetal hypothalamic-pituitary-adrenal system (see Chapter 19), fetal and placental CRH are increased, stimulating production of estrogens, locally altering the estrogen-to-progesterone ratio with functional withdrawal of progesterone (see Progesterone) and thus altering the hormonal milieu.[23,82,88,111] These changes increase myometrial excitability, responsiveness to uterotonics (e.g., PGs, oxytocin), and electrical coupling.[21,23,27,28,88]

Stretching of the uterus may regulate myometrial contractility by increasing CAP gene expression and myometrial activation.[23,57] During much of gestation this expression is blocked by progesterone. The functional progesterone withdrawal at term results in activation and CAP expression. In multiple gestations, one of the reasons that the risk of preterm labor is increased is that stretch-attenuating pathways are overwhelmed by the greatly increased myometrial tensile stress, shifting the balance regulating myometrial contractility toward activation.[23,80]

Myometrial activation is part of a conditioning or preparatory stage during which there is activation of uterine contractility, cervical ripening, and activation of fetal membranes (Figure 4-3).[27] The activation stage involves interaction of the uterus, cervix, and fetal membranes and involves endocrine, immune, and neural control mechanisms.[27,28] Once myometrial activation has occurred, current tocolytics may be less effective in suppressing contractions.[82] During phase 1, myometrial contractions become more regular, with higher frequency and amplitude.[23] Transition from phase 0 to phase 1 is a normally gradual process over the last few weeks of pregnancy.[23]

Phase 2, which accounts for about 0.2% of pregnancy duration, involves stimulation of the myometrium by uterotonics, primarily PGs and oxytocin, and initiation of coordinated forceful contractions.[23] Once labor is initiated, myometrial contraction and relaxation proceed via the enzymatic phosphorylation and dephosphorylation of myosin and subsequent promotion and inhibition of myosin-actin interaction. Phase 3, involution (see Chapter 5), is primarily mediated by oxytocin.[23,82]

Labor depends on complicated interactions and genetic influences between the fetus and mother.[111] Labor onset is

BOX 4-1   Prostaglandins

Prostaglandins (PGs) are "bioactive lipids and members of the eicosanoids family derived from arachidonic acid, which act in a paracrine or autocrine manner and function via binding to specific G-protein-coupled receptors, activating intracellular signaling and gene transcription."[68] PGs act as intermediaries, exerting their major effect at the subcellular level at or near the site of production. PGs are usually metabolized locally but may enter the blood to be rapidly inactivated by pulmonary and hepatic enzymes. PGs are classified into subgroups based on the configuration of their 5-carbon ring. PGE_2, $PGF_{2\alpha}$, and prostacyclin (PGI_2) are the most important in reproductive processes. During pregnancy, PGs are needed for maternal cardiovascular changes, including preventing hypertension and increasing uteroplacental blood flow, and in cervical ripening and the initiation of labor. Surfactant secreted into the amniotic fluid by the fetal lung also provides another source of arachidonic acid for PG synthesis by the amnion.[90,134] Surfactant protein A (SP-A) from the fetal lung and the decidua may play a role in regulating PG production during pregnancy.[90,134,143] PGs are synthesized rapidly, are relatively unstable, and have a short half-life. PGs are formed by enzymatic oxidation of arachidonic acid, a polyunsaturated fatty acid precursor found in an esterified form (glycophospholipid). Formation of PG requires that arachidonic acid be changed to a nonesterified form either directly by cellular phospholipase A_2 or indirectly by phospholipase C. Nonesterified arachidonic acid can be further metabolized by specific microsomal or cytosolic enzymes via several pathways (including cyclooxygenases and lipoxygenases). There are two forms of cyclooxygenase: COX-1 and COX-2. COX-1 is normally produced to maintain physiologic homeostasis; COX-2 is inductable by exogenous signals such as myometrial activation or infection. PGs and thromboxane A_2 (TXA_2) are formed via the cyclooxygenase pathway under the influence of prostaglandin synthetase and thromboxane synthetase. TXA_2 is a platelet aggregation factor and vasoconstrictor whose actions are balanced by the opposing actions of PGI_2. Nonsteroidal antiinflammatory agents such as aspirin and indomethacin inhibit formation of PGs and TXA_2, by blocking cyclooxygenase activity. Because PGs mediate the action of the hypothalamus in responding to pyrogens released during an infection, aspirin effectively reduces fever. Arachidonic acid metabolism via the lipoxygenase pathway leads to the production of various acids followed by the formation of leukotrienes. Leukotrienes are chemotaxic and chemokinetic for leukocytes. PGs act on G-protein–coupled receptors tied to different effector systems. There are eight subtypes of PG receptors found in different tissues: TXA_2, PGI_2, PGF, PGD, and four types of PGE receptors. Eicosanoids are signaling molecules synthesized primarily from arachidonic acid. The four major groups are prostaglandins, prostacyclins, thromboxanes, and leukotrienes.[11] Thromboxanes are platelet aggregation factors and potent vasoconstrictors that oppose the action of PGI_2.

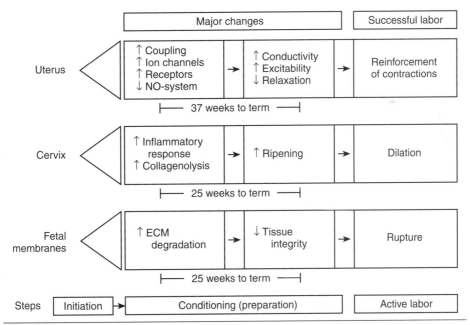

FIGURE 4-3   Model of changes in the uterus, cervix, and fetal membranes for initiation of labor. *ECM,* Extracellular matrix; *NO,* nitric oxide. (From Maul, H., Maner, W.L., Saade, G.R., & Garfield, R.E. [2003]. The physiology of uterine contractions. *Clin Perinatol, 30,* 668.)

believed to be controlled by the fetal genome via several interrelated pathways involving endocrine and mechanical signaling.[24] Gestational age upregulation of genes within and maturation of the fetal HPA axis is critical for timing and control of labor. Timing of the maturation of the fetal HPA axis is probably set soon after implantation; however, stress or other factors may alter the clock.[111]

The endocrine pathway operates primarily between the fetus and placenta. Increased expression of fetal genes and increased placental CRH leads to increased fetal cortisol and dehydroepiandrosterone sulfate (DHEAS). Cortisol stimulates further placental CRH; DHEAS increases placental estriol production. Thus the concomitant functional withdrawal of progesterone results from local alterations in the estrogen-to-progesterone ratio. Estrogen acts on PG synthesis to promote further placental CRH secretion, upregulate CAPs to enhance gap junction (Cx43) formation, increase activity of $PGF_{2\alpha}$ and possibly oxytocin receptors, and enhance expression of myosin light-chain kinase and calmodulin needed for myometrial smooth muscle contraction.[111] The increase in cortisol also upregulates prostaglandin H_2 synthetase enzymes, which increase synthesis and release of PGE_2 and $PGF_{2\alpha}$ from the cells of the amnion, chorion, and decidua.[24] PGs promote further CRH secretion by the placenta. The mechanical pathway is stimulated by uterine growth. Uterine stretch stimulates expression of CAP genes and CAP activation, which increase the contractility of the myometrium and its responsiveness to prostaglandins.[24,164] Along with these changes are a decrease in cyclic adenosine monophosphate (cAMP) pathways that promote uterine relaxation during pregnancy, resulting in decreased protein kinase A (PKA) and increased actin fiber formation.[141] A proposed mechanism for the initiation of labor at term is illustrated in Figure 4-4. This interaction can be altered by stress, infection, hemorrhage, excess stretch, and other factors leading to preterm labor.[24]

Endocrine and Other Factors

Endocrine, paracrine, and other factors believed to influence uterine quiescence, activation, contractility, and the onset of labor are described in this section. The fetal hypothalamic-pituitary-adrenal (HPA) axis plays a critical role in the timing and onset of labor onset.

Corticotropin-Releasing Hormone and the Fetal Hypothalamic-Pituitary-Adrenal Axis

CRH is a neuropeptide produced primarily in the hypothalamus and, during pregnancy, by the placenta and myometrium. Placental CRH is the major source of CRH during pregnancy, with increased levels found in maternal and fetal circulations before labor onset.[14,158] Placental CRH concentrations increase up to 50- to 100-fold in the last 6 to 8 weeks of gestation, paralleling the increase in fetal cortisol.[79,88] CRH is also produced by the decidua, chorion, and amnion. CRH receptors found in the myometrium, placenta, decidua, fetal membranes, adrenal gland, and other organs are upregulated near term.[14,22,57,157] CRH actions are mediated by a network of G-protein–coupled membrane-bound receptors.[50] High- and low-affinity CRH receptor isoforms are found in the myometrium, fetal membranes, and placenta.[111] The high-affinity isoforms predominate during pregnancy when CRH inhibits production and increases degradation of prostaglandins, with increased activity of cAMP and nitric oxide synthetase promoting myometrial quiescence.[111] Low-affinity isoforms predominate near term with enhanced prostaglandin production, along with myometrial contractility and responsivity to prostaglandins and oxytocin.[111]

During pregnancy, CRH affects the myometrium by inhibiting PGE_2, increasing cAMP, and upregulating nitric oxide (NO) synthetase.[57,111,116] CRH has a role in trophoblast growth, tissue remodeling via MMPs, immune function, and control of placental vasomotor tone.[116] Placental CRH influences the onset of labor by inducing fetal cortisol production via positive feedback to the placenta to further increase CRH, which increases myoactivity.[14] Increased cortisol stimulates production of PG by the fetal membranes and increases DHEAS and thus estrogen production. Estrogens induce CAP formation and release of oxytocin and MMP-9 needed for membrane rupture and placental separation.[14] Thus CRH has "a protective role for the myometrium by preventing uterine contractions [during pregnancy], whereas at term CRH enhances the myometrial contractile response to $PGF_{2\alpha}$, PGE_2 and oxytocin."[23]

In the mother, serum CRH (primarily from the placenta) increases steadily to 35 weeks, then increases markedly with the onset of labor.[116,139] Before 35 weeks, most of the CRH is neutralized by binding to CRH-binding protein (CRH-BP) produced in the maternal liver, placenta, decidua, amnion, and chorion.[14,57,157] Levels of this binding protein decrease 50% in the last 6 weeks of gestation.[157] Several weeks before labor onset, CRH concentrations begin to exceed concentrations of CDH-BP, with an increase in circulating free (physiologically active) CRH to term.[48,79,88,116,157] The increased CRH stimulates an increase in myometrial PG receptors, PG release, and fetal cortisol.[14,24,79,116] Increased fetal cortisol stimulates PG synthesis by increasing PGHS-2 and decreasing PG catabolism by decreasing PGDH expression.[24,79,116] PGDH activity in pregnancy may be maintained by activation of glucocorticoid receptors (GRs), which respond to both progesterone and cortisol. Near labor onset, the increased cortisol displaces progesterone from the GRs. This inhibits PGDH activity and production.

CRH levels are maximal at the end of labor, decreasing rapidly immediately after birth and reaching prepregnancy levels by 24 hours postpartum.[48,139] Elevated levels of CRH in the second trimester have been associated with an increased risk of spontaneous preterm delivery.[48,116,157] CRH levels are lower with a slower rise with postterm labor.[157]

As noted previously, CRH is involved in increasing placental estriol and fetal glucocorticoid production.[14,79,142] Placental CRH is believed to stimulate fetal adrenocorticotropic hormone (ACTH), which in turn stimulates the fetal adrenal cortex to produce glucocorticoids such as cortisol and DHEAS.[79,142] DHEAS is needed by the placenta to produce estrogens, particularly estriol. Cortisol stimulates fetal lung maturation (see Chapter 10) and further placental CRH production. This is in contrast to the effect of increased cortisol on the hypothalamus, where it has an inhibitory effect. In the placenta, glucocorticoids stimulate CRH receptors and increase CRH production.[79,116,142]

Progesterone

Progesterone, acting via progesterone receptors (PR), is thought to have a major role in controlling uterine and cervical function and suppressing uterine excitement throughout gestation. Progesterone interacts with cell membrane receptors to stimulate cAMP, which, along with cyclic guanosine monophosphate (cGMP), sequesters intracellular calcium in the sarcoplasmic reticulum (SR), thus decreasing contractility. Progesterone also enhances uterine quiescence by downregulating genes needed

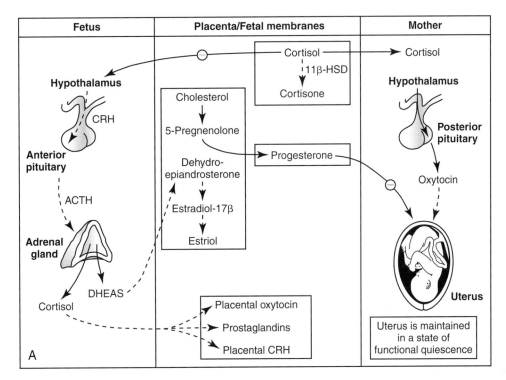

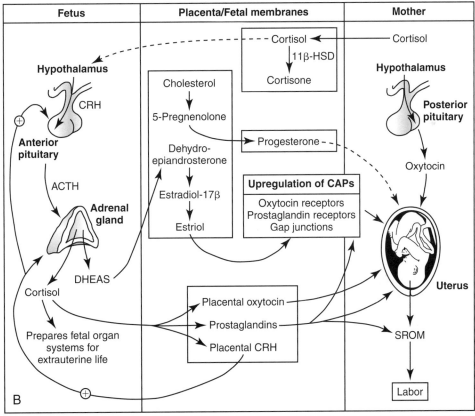

FIGURE 4-4 Proposed parturition cascade for labor induction at term. The spontaneous induction of labor at term in the human is regulated by a series of paracrine and autocrine hormones acting in an integrated parturition cascade. **A,** The factors responsible for maintaining uterine quiescence throughout pregnancy. **B,** The factors responsible for the onset of spontaneous labor. They include the withdrawal of the inhibitory effects of progesterone on uterine contractility and the recruitment of cascades that promote estrogen (estriol) production and lead to upregulation of the contraction-associated protein in the uterus. *ACTH,* Adrenocorticotropic hormone (corticotropin); *CAPs,* contraction-associated proteins; *CRH,* corticotropin-releasing hormone; *DHEAS,* dehydroepiandrostenedione; *11 β-HSD,* 11β-hydroxysteroid dehydrogenase; *SROM,* spontaneous rupture of membranes. (From Norwitz, E.R., Mahendroo, M., & Lye, S.J. [2014]. Biology of parturition. In R.K. Creasy, R. Resnik, J.D. Iams, C.J. Lockwood, T.R. Moore, & M.F. Greene [Eds.]. *Creasy & Resnik's maternal-fetal medicine: Principles and practice* [7th ed.]. Philadelphia: Saunders.)

to produce the CAPs needed for labor, limiting production of stimulatory PGs, suppressing release of proinflammatory cytokines that increase PG formation, suppressing NF-κB activity, and upregulating the NO system and other relaxants.[23,48,90,127,131,142] Progesterone metabolites may inhibit oxytocin binding and signaling as well as proinflammatory cytokines to help keep the uterus in a relatively quiescent state during pregnancy.[111] Supplementation with 17-α-hydroxyprogesterone caproate (17-OHPC) decreases the incidence of preterm birth in some high-risk women (see Preterm Labor and Birth).[38,128]

Systemic progesterone levels do not fall in humans, and regional differences in progesterone levels are seen. A functional withdrawal of progesterone action is seen in the myometrium in late pregnancy that is mediated by transcription factors. Near labor onset, the NF-κB transcription factor is activated and induces a proinflammatory cascade.[18,90] This is associated with increased expression of oxytocin receptors, contractile genes, and PGHS-2, which along with activation of NF-κB impairs PR function by downregulating PR activation, increasing metabolism of progesterone, and upregulating inhibitory PR isoforms such as progesterone receptor A (PR-A) and progesterone receptor C (PR-C).[23,48,90,101,111]

Progesterone interacts with both nuclear (transcriptional) and extramembrane PRs in myometrial cells. The nuclear PRs modulate gene expression and protein activation; the membrane PRs act via direct coupling that induces intracellular signaling cascades.[94] Both of these effects influence myometrial contractility. The functional progesterone withdrawal also involves changes in the expression of progesterone receptor isoforms PR-A and PR-B.[48,94,157,158] PR-A inhibits PR-B mediated by NF-κB. PR-B activates progesterone responsiveness in tissues.[22,32,48,94,157] The PR-A/PR-B ratio increases in late pregnancy; thus the inhibitory effect of PR-A becomes more dominant, reducing the progesterone responsiveness of PR-B.[22,157,158] As a result, PR-B activation is decreased, leading to a functional progesterone withdrawal; decreasing progesterone enhances further activation of NF-κB.[48] PR-C may inhibit upregulation of progesterone-PR signaling in the myometrium.[94,111,157]

The local functional withdrawal of progesterone removes the progesterone-induced suppression of estrogen receptors, thus increasing myometrial contractility.[111] In addition, the cortisol-dominant estrogen effects from the fetal-placental unit near term may override the effects of progesterone.[111] Progesterone and cortisol have antagonistic effects, so the functional decrease in progesterone in late pregnancy when cortisol levels are increased enhances contractility.[142] Cortisol may also compete with progesterone for progesterone-receptor binding.

Estrogen

Estrogen levels increase beginning at 34 to 35 weeks. Estrogens promote formation of gap junctions; upregulate oxytocin receptors in the myometrium; enhance lipase activity and release of arachidonic acid, thus stimulating PG production; increase binding of intracellular calcium; and increase myosin phosphorylation.[21,47,48,79,131] Estrogen (particularly estriol) production by the placenta (see Chapter 3) is dependent on fetal adrenal

precursors. The placenta produces more than 90% of the estriol in pregnancy. DHEAS from the fetal adrenal is hydroxylated to 25-OH-DHEAS in the fetal liver. 25-OH-DHEAS is used by the placenta to produce estriol. Increased CRH stimulates ACTH to increase DHEAS output by the fetal adrenal, which leads to increased estrogen in late gestation.

Late pregnancy is characterized by a marked increase in estriol with a slower increase in estradiol. This change in the estriol/estradiol ratio increases prostaglandin formation and decreases formation of transcription factors that inhibit gap junction formation.[141] Concentrations of estradiol and estrone in amniotic fluid increase 15 to 20 days before onset of either term or preterm labor. Estrone produced locally in the chorion and decidua may influence the intrauterine progesterone-to-estrogen ratio, promote production of stimulatory PGs (PGF$_{2\alpha}$, PGE$_2$), and decrease production of inhibitory PGs (PGI$_2$). Increased stimulatory PGs and estrogens increase expression of oxytocin and PG receptors, L-type calcium channels, myosin light-chain kinase, calmodulin, PGHS, and gap junctions (Cx43).[142]

Prostaglandins

PGs (see Box 4-1) are produced in the decidua and fetal membranes and have a central role in the initiation of labor. PGs bind to the cell membrane, increase the frequency of action potentials, and stimulate actual muscle contraction. PGs are the final common pathway in mechanisms of labor onset.[18,68] PGF$_{2\alpha}$, thromboxane, PGE$_1$, and PGE$_2$ promote myometrial contractility by increasing gap junction permeability and calcium influx into the myometrium; PGE$_2$, PGD$_2$, and PGI$_2$ inhibit contractions.[111] PGF$_{2\alpha}$, PGE$_1$, and PGE$_2$ also modify oxytocin release, inhibit progesterone synthesis, and increase expression of gap junction proteins.[131]

During most of pregnancy, PG synthesis is low and PG receptors in the myometrium are downregulated.[79,111] PGDH expression, which is stimulated by progesterone, is high in the chorion, reducing transfer of PGs from the fetal-placental unit to the decidua and myometrium during much of pregnancy.[111] Upregulation and increased PG production near the end of pregnancy are stimulated by CRH, cortisol, and uterine stretch and mediated by increased PGHS and decreased PGDH.[18,157] Levels of PGE$_2$ and PGF$_{2\alpha}$ increase before and during labor in maternal plasma and amniotic fluid.[18,79] PGs mediate labor onset and enhance contractility through increasing expression of gap junction proteins (Cx43), oxytocin receptors, and PG receptors (EP and FP), inducing MMP synthesis in the fetal membranes and cervix to enhance membrane rupture and cervical ripening, increasing expression of PR-A and PR-B, and increasing sarcoplasmic calcium levels in the cytoplasm and extracellular calcium entry into myometrial smooth muscle cells.[18,79,96] PGs are needed for changes in the extracellular matrix and increased MMP synthesis during cervical ripening and for decidual and fetal membrane changes leading to membrane rupture and placental delivery at birth.[18,145,156]

The amnion is a major site of PG synthesis with high levels of PGHS and minimal PGDH activity at the time of labor onset.[101] In the amnion, the major PG is PGE_2. The decidua also has high levels of PGHS and minimal PGDH. PGDH predominates in the chorion, located between the amnion and decidua.[23,122] The decidua produces $PGF_{2\alpha}$, PGE_2, and PGD_2; the myometrium produces mainly PGI_2.[111] PGHS is found in two forms. One form (PGHS-1) is always present for normal homeostasis; the other form (PGHS-2 or COX-2) is upregulated by cytokines, growth factors, and glucocorticoids.[23] Expression of COX-2, produced in the fetal membranes and myometrium, is regulated by NF-κB and induced by proinflammatory cytokines.[32,111] COX-2 activity increases to term with further marked increase in labor. COX-2 activity in the amnion is the rate-limiting step in production of PGs. Increased COX-2 activation is associated with a decrease in PGDH in the chorion, which allows PGs produced in the amnion to cross the chorion and enter the myometrium to stimulate contractions.[18] Increases in cortisol increase COX-2 expression in the fetal membranes and downregulate PGDH in the chorion. This promotes cervical ripening and myometrial contractions.[111]

PGs act by interacting with specific PG cell membrane receptors that are coupled with G-proteins and tied to different effector substances.[11] Activation of $PGF_{2\alpha}$, thromboxane A_2 (TXA_2), EP_1 receptors (increases intracellular calcium), and EP_3 receptors (inhibits adenyl cyclase) stimulates contractions. Activation of PGD_2, EP_2 receptors (stimulates adenyl cyclase), and PGI_2 receptors inhibits contractions.[11] Uterine quiescence may be enhanced by this coupling and by increases in relaxant PGs, such as PGI_2.[101] Coupling near term increases with upregulation of PGE_2 contractile receptors (EP_1 and EP_3) and the $PGF_{2\alpha}$ receptor (FP) and loss of relaxatory PGE_2 receptors (EP_2 and EP_4).[101] By increasing the PRA/PRB ration, PGE_2 and $PGF_{2\alpha}$ induce a functional progesterone withdrawal.[18] Contractile receptors are most abundant in the fundus, the forces of which are needed for propulsion of the fetus, whereas relaxatory receptors are more abundant in the lower uterine segment and may enhance passage of the fetal head and shoulders.

The placenta produces PGE_2, PGD_2, PGI_2, and TXA_2. After delivery, placental TXA_2 may be important in enhancing hemostasis after placental separation. PGI_2 is produced by the pregnant and the nonpregnant myometrium as well as by the placental vasculature; it helps maintain uterine quiescence.[82] PGI_2 increases in late pregnancy and with uterine distention by the fetus.[82] PGI_2 is a potent vasodilator that inhibits platelet aggregation and protects the vascular epithelium. PGI_2 is important in maintaining blood flow to the placenta and in ensuring adequate uterine blood flow during labor.[21] Suppression of PGI_2 formation leads to vasoconstriction and is believed to have a role in preeclampsia (see Chapter 9).

Oxytocin

Oxytocin is synthesized in the hypothalamus and released from the posterior lobe of maternal and fetal pituitary glands. Oxytocin is also produced in the myometrium, decidua, placenta, and fetal membranes. Concentration in the maternal circulation is stable during pregnancy but increases during the second stage of labor.[111] The rate of fetal oxytocin secretion increases after spontaneous initiation of labor.[111] Under the influence of estrogen, the sensitivity of the myometrium to the effects of oxytocin changes markedly during pregnancy. Alterations in myometrial sensitivity to oxytocin are mediated by changes in the density and affinity of oxytocin receptors.[96] Upregulation of oxytocin receptors before labor may also be regulated by mechanical stretch.[164]

Oxytocin receptors (OTRs) in the myometrium increase 50- to 100-fold in early pregnancy and up to 200 to 300-fold by term.[96,111,116] The greatest concentration of OTRs is found in the fundus, with few in the lower uterine segment and cervix.[111] OTRs are G-protein–coupled receptors whose effects are mediated by phospholipase C, which mediates production of nonesterified arachidonic acid and thus PGs. This increases inositol 1,4,5-triphosphate (InsP3), which increases intracellular calcium and thus myometrial contractility.[11,131] Binding of oxytocin to OTRs on the cell membrane increases the frequency of pacemaker potentials and lowers the threshold for initiation of action potentials, thus lengthening the duration and increasing the frequency of action potentials in the uterus.[12] Failed induction and postterm pregnancies are associated with a decreased concentration of oxytocin receptors. Oxytocin is a stimulant that is used to induce or augment labor. Oxytocin does not work as well as a labor stimulant for induction of labor before term, possibly because of the lack of adequate oxytocin receptors.

Relaxin

Relaxin is an insulin-like ovarian hormone produced initially by the corpus luteum and then by the myometrium and placenta. Relaxin levels are greatest during the first trimester but remain detectable in maternal circulation throughout gestation, falling rapidly after delivery.[21,116] Relaxin is involved in decidualization and implantation (see Chapter 3), modulation of MMP activity, and myometrial quiescence.[131] Relaxin also induces vasodilation and plays a role in maternal hemodynamic, renal, and musculoskeletal changes during pregnancy (see Chapters 9, 11 and 15).[31] Relaxin increases cAMP, inhibits calcium increases in the myocyte, decreases affinity of myosin light-chain kinase for calmodulin and myosin, and activates potassium channels.[96,131] Activation of these channels hyperpolarizes the membrane with uterine relaxation.[82] Relaxin acts synergistically with progesterone in blocking uterine activity and maintaining myometrial quiescence during pregnancy and may suppress oxytocin release.[133] Relaxin enhances cervical ripening and may help regulate gap junction permeability.

Nitric Oxide

NO is produced by the decidua, fetal membranes, placental syncytiotrophoblast, and fetal and placental vascular epithelium. NO regulates vascular tone via release of PGI_2 from endothelial cells. NO and its substrate, L-arginine, help maintain myometrial quiescence, cervical rigidity, and maternal systemic vasodilation during pregnancy and in regulating fetal and uteroplacental blood flow.[96] NO and progesterone are believed to work together to downregulate genes needed for CAP production for parturition.[27] Levels of NO are elevated in the myometrium but not in the cervix during pregnancy. NO relaxes the myometrium and maintains cervical rigidity.[28] Near term, levels of NO decrease in the uterus and increase in the cervix. In the myometrium, NO activates the cGMP pathway, which results in decreased intracellular calcium concentrations and interferes with myosin light-chain kinase activity.[111] Thus a fall in NO is involved in initiation of labor, whereas an increase in NO is believed to help cervical ripening.[28]

NO synthesis is mediated by nitric oxide synthetase (NOS). NOS isoforms found in the fetal membranes and decidua may have different roles during pregnancy: neuronal NOS (nNOS or NOS-1) enhances uterine quiescence, endothelial NOC (eNOS or NOS-III) is important in uteroplacental and fetal circulation, and inducible NOS (iNOS or NOS-II) from macrophages plays a role in cervical ripening.[144] Levels of NOS in the uterus decrease near term and disappear during labor.

Cytokines and Other Factors

Inflammatory processes and mediators are a major component in enhancing uterine contractility and cervical ripening.[48] Cytokines such as IL-1, IL-6, IL-8 (especially), TNF-α, interferon, and transforming growth factor-β (TGF-β) play important roles in mediating the events of parturition.[18,48,90] IL-1 stimulates PG production by the amnion, decidua, and myometrium; IL-1β induces calcium stores and calcium entry into the myocyte; IL-1β and TNF-α stimulate arachidonic acid release and COX-2 expression to increase PG production via NF-κB; IL-6 stimulates PGHS for PG production by the amnion, chorion, and decidua; and IL-8, produced by the chorion, decidua, placenta, myometrium, and endometrium, induces neutrophil chemotaxis and activation, production of MMPs, and cervical ripening and may play a role in formation of the lower uterine segment.[24] TNF-α also stimulates PG production by the amnion and decidua. TGF-β is involved in regulating the effects of progesterone on PTHrP, Cx43, and gap junction formation. Epidermal growth factor promotes uterine contractions by increasing intracellular calcium and increasing PG synthesis in the decidua and fetal membranes.[111] PTHrP, adrenomedullin, and calcitonin gene–related protein (CGRP) have a relaxant effect on myometrium that is removed near labor onset, with a decrease in amniotic fluid PTHrP near term labor onset.[111] PTHrP is a vasorelaxant and also has a role in placental calcium transport (see Chapter 17).[116] Magnesium competes with calcium for calmodulin binding, reducing myosin light-chain kinase and prompting uterine relaxation.[116] Endothelin levels and receptors also increase during pregnancy. Endothelin is a peptide that modulates fetoplacental circulation and enhances myometrial contractility by increasing intracellular calcium and PG production.[96,111]

Myometrial Contraction

Myometrial contraction is mediated via interaction of actin and myosin. In smooth muscle such as myometrium, contraction and relaxation are regulated primarily via enzymatic phosphorylation

and dephosphorylation of myosin. The key enzyme is MLCK, the principal control mechanism for smooth muscle contractility.[80] Activity of MLCK is regulated by calcium, calmodulin, and cAMP-mediated phosphorylation, which are in turn influenced by hormones and pharmacologic agents. The mechanisms for myometrial smooth muscle contraction are described here and summarized in Figure 4-5.

Initiation of action potentials in uterine smooth muscle is primarily dependent on the influx of Ca^{2+} across the cell membrane, although ions such as Na^+ and K channels are also involved. Intracellular calcium is essential for activation of MLCK, and calcium levels increase significantly with contractions. MLCK is associated with the long light chain of myosin and is activated by changes in intracellular calcium. Excitation of the myometrial cell increases concentrations of free calcium in the cytoplasm.[21,47] The calcium may be released from intracellular stores in the sarcoplasmic reticulum mediated by InsP3. Because calcium stores in the sarcoplasmic reticulum are relatively sparse, calcium from other sources (i.e., intracellular membrane-bound calcium vesicles, mitochondrial stores, or extracellular calcium) is also required.[47,82]

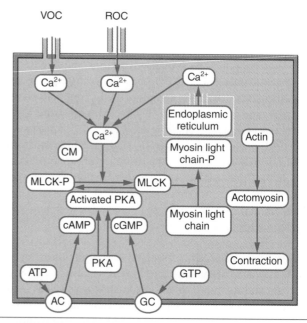

FIGURE 4-5 Biochemistry of myometrial contraction and relaxation. Myosin light-chain kinase *(MLCK)* is the central molecule regulating uterine contractility. It is activated by calcium *(Ca²⁺)* bound to calmodulin *(CM)*. Cytoplasmic calcium concentration is the result of calcium released from deposits in the endoplasmic reticulum plus the influx of extracellular calcium through channels that are voltage-operated or receptor-operated. MLCK is deactivated by protein kinase A *(PKA)*, which in turn is activated by cyclic adenosine monophosphate *(cAMP)* and cyclic guanine monophosphate *(cGMP)*. β-agonists inhibit uterine contractions by activating adenyl cyclase *(AC)* with formation of cAMP, whereas nitric oxide has the same effect by activating guanylate cyclase *(GC)* and increasing production of cGMP. Calcium channel blockers relax muscle by inhibiting calcium influx through voltage-operated channels *(VOCs)*. *P,* Phosphorus; *ROC,* receptor-operated channel. (From Arias, F. [2000]. Pharmacology of oxytocin and prostaglandins. *Clin Obstet Gynecol, 43,* 457.)

The main mechanisms for transport of extracellular calcium across the cell membrane into myometrial cells are as follows: L-type voltage-dependent Ca^{2+} channels activated by the action potential, adenosine triphosphate (ATP)–dependent pumps (via Ca, Mg-ATPase), and Ca^{2+}-activated K^+ channels (which set the threshold for activation of the cell membrane).[2,80,164] Potassium channels are the main outward current flow, decreasing the likelihood that L-type voltage-dependent Ca^{2+} channels will open, and are believed to be downregulated in late gestation, increasing calcium flow and thus contractility.[164] The myometrial cell resting membrane potential has decreased by term to near the level at which the L-type voltage-dependent Ca^{2+} channels open.[12] Magnesium may trigger further intracellular calcium release. Voltage-dependent channels are the major channels and allow passage of calcium when the potential across the cell membrane falls to a critical level. In smooth muscles, the action potential is carried by calcium rather than by sodium as in nerve cells. Repolarization involves movement of K^+ into the myocyte and inactivation of the calcium channels.[2] These channels are G-protein–coupled. Movement of calcium across these channels can be blocked by calcium antagonists or slow channel blockers such as nifedipine.

Intracellular free calcium levels must be 10^{-6} to 10^{-7} M for MLCK activation.[82] Although the amount of free calcium is critical in determining whether the muscle contracts or relaxes, calcium does not act independently. Calcium must first bind with calmodulin, forming a calcium-calmodulin complex, which in turn activates MLCK.[2,21] Calmodulin is a cytoplasmic regulatory calcium-binding protein that is activated by increases in unbound intracellular calcium.[2,21] Calcium binding to calmodulin changes its configuration so calmodulin can modulate the activities of enzymes and protein such as MLCK. Activated MLCK catalyzes phosphorylation (addition of a phosphate group) of the myosin light chain. Phosphorylation activates the ATPase on the myosin head with the release of chemical energy needed for the subsequent binding of myosin and actin (actomyosin). The result is release of adenosine diphosphate (ADP) and a phosphorus molecule, which changes the configuration of the myosin with flexion of the head on the tail. This flexion pulls on the actin filament and the muscle contracts (see Figure 4-1).[21,80,82,141] Other proteins involved in regulation of actin-myosin interaction include tropomyosin, caldesmon (CaD), and calponin.[96] For example, CaD acts as a "brake" on myosin by opposing biochemical and stretch forces on the uterine wall.[99] Stretch can also activate contractility by activating myosin and actin filaments via receptor-mediated signaling (such as agonist activated pathways or via oxytocin) or via focal adhesion signaling.[99,141]

Myometrial relaxation occurs when calcium is removed. As soon as intracellular Ca^{2+} levels increase, mechanisms to remove calcium are stimulated. These mechanisms include uptake by the SR, extrusion across the cell membrane mediated by Ca^{2+} extruding proteins, and decreased MLCK sensitivity to calcium.[106] Relaxation involves the action of the enzyme–myosin light-chain phosphatase. With removal of the phosphate group from the myosin head, the actin no longer recognizes the myosin. Actin-myosin interaction is inhibited, and the muscle cell relaxes. Reduction in MLCK activity because of decreased calcium-calmodulin levels also leads to muscle relaxation, as does inhibition of phosphorylation by increased levels of cAMP and cGMP.[2,21] cAMP and cGMP are second messengers (i.e., they carry the message of a hormone to the site where the hormonal effect is realized) that lower the affinity of myosin for calcium-calmodulin or reduce intracellular calcium by stimulating calcium return to intracellular stores or extrusion across the cell membrane.[47]

The relative activity of adenyl cyclase (mediates cAMP synthesis) and phosphodiesterase (mediates cAMP breakdown) influences myometrial contractility by altering cAMP levels within the cell. Adenyl cyclase increases intracellular cAMP, which reduces calcium-calmodulin complexes and intracellular calcium levels and thus MLCK (see Figure 4-5). Hormones and pharmacologic agents influence activity of MLCK and cAMP. For example, adenyl cyclase is activated by β-adrenergic agonists, resulting in increased cAMP and reduced contractility. Substances such as α-adrenergic agonists that inhibit phosphodiesterase, which normally mediates cAMP breakdown, also result in elevated levels of intracellular cAMP.[23,80,141]

Oxytocin and $PGF_{2\alpha}$ enhance contractility by increasing intracellular calcium levels and the rate of MLCK phosphorylation. Oxytocin also releases calcium from intracellular stores and inhibits calcium uptake by the sarcoplasmic reticulum, extending actin-myosin interaction and thus muscle contraction. Relaxin increases cAMP, which inhibits MLCK phosphorylation and induces muscle relaxation.

The myosin head contains magnesium adenosine triphosphatase (Mg-ATPase) sites where ATP is hydrolyzed, converting chemical energy to mechanical force. Energy (released from ATP by myosin ATPase) is critical for myometrial contraction. ATP is used for both actin-myosin interaction and ion transport. If adequate oxygen and glucose are not available for ATP formation, as may occur with prolonged labor, the contractile process will be inhibited.

PGs and oxytocin promote release of calcium from intracellular pools or prevent uptake of calcium into these pools. This promotes contractility. On the other hand, agents that inhibit myometrial activity (e.g., progesterone, relaxin, PGI_2, and β-agonists) promote calcium sequestration or extrusion (via cAMP-dependent enzymes) and thus myometrial relaxation.[21,23,80]

In summary, control of myometrial activity is dependent on enzymatic phosphorylation of myosin by MLCK to allow interaction of actin and myosin. Endocrine, biochemical, and physical factors mediate MLCK activity, uterine activity, and myometrial structural and functional alterations. Before onset of labor, the myometrium undergoes activation, with decreases in substances that maintain uterine quiescence and increases in CAPs that enhance uterine contractility (see Figure 4-3).

Coordination of Uterine Contractions

Electrical and contractile activity in smooth muscle cells is controlled by myogenic, neurogenic, and endocrine control systems.[21,46] Myogenic activity, the spontaneous activity of the myometrium that occurs in the absence of any neural or hormonal input, includes the intrinsic excitability of the muscle cell, the ability of the muscle to contract spontaneously, and the mechanisms that produce rhythmic contractions. Neurogenic and endocrine control systems are superimposed on the muscle's inherent myogenic properties to initiate, augment, and suppress myometrial activity.[21,46] Myogenic control is dominated by hormonal influences, especially those of estrogen and progesterone, which influence myogenic characteristics through their generally opposing actions, as well as the mechanical forces from uterine stretching.[57,99,131] Uterine contractility is reduced during most of pregnancy, primarily because of influences of progesterone and to a lesser extent relaxin and human chorionic gonadotropin, so even if the myocyte depolarizes, the electrical signals are not transmitted to surrounding cells.[141] Neurogenic control is not critical, because labor can occur in women with spinal injury (see Chapter 15), although the length of labor may be altered.

Coordination of contractions occurs by coupling of myometrial cells via electrical (e.g., gap junctions) and chemical (e.g., PGs, oxytocin) mechanisms. Polarization and depolarization of the cell membranes moves the electrical signals across the myometrium.[3] These electrical signals are generated by movement of calcium through ion channels into the myometrial cell. Action potentials propagate rapidly throughout the uterus, initiating movement of calcium into the cells via voltage-dependent channels, which activate myofilaments, resulting in a contraction. Thus "muscle cells of the uterus act as independent oscillators that become increasingly coupled by gap junctions toward the end of pregnancy."[141] Propagation of uterine electrical activity is characterized by patterns of individual electrical spikes that spread out in multiple directions; these are more rapid in the longitudinal than transverse or circumferential directions.[119]

Spontaneous cycles of activity in myometrial cells are characterized by (1) slow, rhythmic fluctuations in the magnitude of electrical potential across the cell membrane and (2) spikes of electrical activity that occur in bursts at the crests of slow waves (action potentials) and become synchronous at parturition (a single spike can initiate a contraction; multiple spikes are needed to maintain forceful contractions).[96] Action potentials occur in bursts; with progression of labor, electrical activity becomes more organized with an increase in amplitude and duration.[111] The more frequent the action potential, the more frequent the contraction; the duration of the action potential is the duration of the contraction; and the number of spikes is reflected in the force of the contraction.[96,111]

"Labor occurs as a consequence of the combination of increased myocyte to myocyte connectivity, increased depolarizations that last longer, and activated intracellular contractile machinery."[141] Cell depolarization triggers a change in the Na^+, Ca^{2+}, and K^+ conductance (action potential). The elevated K^+ gradient during pregnancy makes it more difficult for the myocyte to depolarize. However, by late pregnancy potassium channels decrease, prolonging the action potential and further altering the resting membrane potential.[141] The action potential increases membrane permeability to calcium and release of intracellular calcium stores.[47] As long as extracellular K^+ concentrations are high, action potentials increase in frequency. When maximum ion concentrations are reached within the cell, ionic stability is restored by active outward transport of Na^+ and Ca^{2+}, intracellular uptake of calcium, and recapturing of intracellular K^+. The muscle cell returns to a resting state.

As action potentials are conducted to neighboring myometrial cells, groups of cells contract, leading to what is perceived by the woman as a uterine contraction. Coordination of uterine contractions occurs when all myometrial cells contract nearly simultaneously. Coordination and synchronization of contractions is mediated by the low-resistance gap junctions between myometrial cells. These junctions allow propagation of the action potential between cells and thus throughout the uterus and are critical for the effectiveness of myometrial contractility during labor.[18]

Gap Junction Formation

Smooth muscle bundles normally separated from each other within connective tissue may come into closer approximation to form intercellular gap junctions (low-resistance bridges or intercellular communication channels). Gap junctions allow transfer of current-carrying ions and exchange of second messengers between the cytoplasm of adjacent cells.[82] Thus gap junctions are the site where the action potential is propagated from cell to cell. Increased gap junction interaction is associated with improved propagation of electrical impulses, increased conduction velocity, and coordinated contractility of the myometrium.[46,47]

Gap junction resister-like proteins are called connexins (Cx). The major connexin in uterine gap junctions is Cx43.[96,131] Cx43 increases to term and is maximal during labor. Increased Cx43 is associated with decreased electrical resistance and thus myometrial contractility.[82] Connexins within the cell membranes of adjacent smooth muscle cells align to create symmetric openings (gap junctions) between their cytoplasm. Each opening or pore contains multiple channels; each channel consists of six connexins aligned symmetrically in a hexametric structure with six connexins in the adjacent cell.[96,131] These pores are separated by a narrow gap and provide a pathway for transport of ions, metabolites, and second messengers.[21] Gap junctions can be open or closed, thus controlling intercellular communication. Increased permeability across the junctions increases synchrony of electrical conduction and muscular contraction and subsequently more effective labor.[18]

The number and size of gap junctions increase markedly during gestation, reaching approximately 1000 per cell in late pregnancy or during labor with an increase in diameter to about 250 nanometers.[47,96,131] Gap junctions are absent or infrequent in nonpregnant myometrium and decline markedly within 24 hours of delivery.[21,47,131] An increase in gap junctions is seen in women in preterm labor; delay in the formation of gap junctions is associated with prolonged pregnancy.[21,47,86] Myometrial stretch may also increase gap junctions.[57]

Estrogen stimulates gap junction formation by stimulating synthesis of connexins. One way progesterone may function to inhibit labor and maintain the pregnancy is by inhibition of estrogen-enhanced connexin synthesis.[47] Some PGs stimulate whereas others inhibit gap junction formation, either directly or indirectly via estrogen and progesterone activities.[47] Gap junction formation is also inhibited or decreased by indomethacin, relaxin, isoxsuprine, isoproterenol, and transcription factors stimulated by progesterone; oxytocin has little effect.[131,141] Lack of adequate concentrations of gap junctions decreases the effectiveness of oxytocin; as a result, oxytocin may not be effective with women experiencing preterm or postterm labor. Increased intracellular calcium reduces coupling, and increased cAMP in the uterus decreases gap junction permeability.[46,47] One mechanism by which relaxin, PGI_2, and β-agonists are believed to inhibit myometrial contractility is by increasing intracellular cAMP, which uncouples gap junctions, thus preventing synchronous uterine activity.[46,96]

Physiologic Events During a Uterine Contraction

A normal uterine contraction spreads downward from the cornus within about 15 seconds. Although the actual contractile phase begins slightly later in the lower portion of the uterus, functional coordination of the uterus is such that the contraction peak is attained simultaneously in all portions. The intensity of the contraction decreases from the cornus downward and is essentially absent in the cervix.

Resting baseline tonus in labor is at an intrauterine pressure of approximately 10 to 12 mm Hg (1.33 to 1.59 kPa), which may increase to 30 mm Hg (3.99 kPa) with hypertonia.[114] Uterine contractions can be palpated abdominally with intrauterine pressure greater than 10 to 20 mm Hg (1.33 to 2.66 kPa) and perceived by the woman at 15 to 20 mm Hg (1.99 to 2.66 kPa).[95] During early first stage, intrauterine pressure increases 20 to 30 mm Hg (2.66 to 3.99 kPa) above resting values, increasing to greater than 50 mm Hg (6.65 kPa) in the active phase and to 100 to 150 mm Hg (13.3 to 19.95 kPa) during a Valsalva maneuver with maximal expulsive efforts.[95] A laboring woman generally perceives pain at pressures greater than 25 mm Hg (3.32 kPa) or more, although this varies with individual thresholds. Thus the duration of a contraction assessed from palpation or patient perception will be shorter than the actual contraction, and the duration between contractions will seem longer.[95] Women exhibit marked individual variation in the intensity, frequency, and duration of contractions. Positioning and the use of oxytocin, analgesics, and anesthesia also influence contractions.

CLINICAL IMPLICATIONS FOR THE PREGNANT WOMAN AND HER FETUS

Labor and delivery place additional stressors on the maternal-fetal unit, which may be further increased in high-risk situations. Alterations in the physiologic processes of parturition can have a significant effect on the well-being of the mother,

fetus, and neonate. Knowledge of these processes is critical in understanding the basis for nursing care and therapies to initiate or inhibit labor and the etiologic factors in dystocia and preterm or postterm labor onset.

Maternal Position During Labor

Positioning during labor is influenced by cultural factors, obstetric practices, place of delivery, technology, and the preferences of the mother and health care providers.[78,91] Maternal position during labor influences the characteristics and effectiveness of uterine contractions, fetal well-being, maternal comfort, and course of labor.[37,51,91,125,126] Genetic factors also play a role in how quickly a woman transitions to active labor and the length of labor.[162]

Historically a variety of positions have been used for labor and delivery. Delivery positions currently used in many U.S. institutions include lithotomy, lateral (Sims), semisitting, dorsal (or modified lithotomy), squatting, and occasionally kneeling.[126] Although lithotomy has often been used routinely in the past, primarily for the comfort and convenience of the person delivering the infant, this position has no physiologic advantages and may interfere with expulsive efforts.[70] Therefore alternative positions are currently being used in most settings.

Several positions have advantages or disadvantages from an anatomic and physiologic standpoint. During the first stage of labor, upright positions, such as sitting, standing, squatting, and kneeling, allow the abdominal wall to relax, and the influence of gravity causes the uterine fundus to fall forward. This directs the fetal head into the pelvic inlet in an anterior position and applies direct pressure to the cervix, which helps stimulate and stretch the cervix.[168] A Cochrane review found that walking or upright positions during the first stage of labor reduced the labor duration, risk of cesarean birth, and the need for epidural; use of these positions was not associated with adverse maternal or fetal effects.[74]

An upright position during the second stage has been associated with a decrease in cesarean birth and instrumental delivery and a reduction in labor duration.[124] Feedback from the cervix to the myometrium may stimulate more intense contractions and shorten labor.[78] The lateral recumbent position reduces pressure on maternal blood vessels and promotes venous return and cardiac output, thus increasing uterine perfusion and fetal oxygenation.[91] Side-lying may be effective during labor with a posterior fetus, by allowing the weight of the uterus and fetus to tip away from the back and permitting application of counterpressure over the lumbosacral area.

Position at delivery should optimize alignment for fetal descent and maximize the capacity of the pelvis and efficiency of maternal expulsive efforts.[126] Squatting enhances engagement and descent of the fetal head and increases maternal pelvic diameters. In this position the upper portion of the symphysis pubis is compressed and the bottom part separated slightly. This results in an outward movement and separation of the innominate bones and backward movement of the lower sacrum. The pelvic outlet increases 28% with increased transverse (1 cm) and anteroposterior (0.5 to 2 cm) diameters. Thigh pressure against the abdomen during squatting may also promote fetal descent and correction of unfavorable fetal positions. Sitting or semisitting (30-degree angle) may have similar advantages.[42,78,140]

Dorsal and supine positions have been associated with adverse effects on maternal hemodynamics and fetal status and with the supine hypotension syndrome.[42,112,126,140] A supine position is a disadvantage during engagement and descent of the fetal head because this position does not optimize fetal alignment, maximize pelvic diameter, or maximize efficiency of maternal expulsive efforts.[78] Supine positions have also been associated with an increase in instrumental deliveries and episiotomies and with a statistically but not clinically significant decrease in estimated blood loss at delivery.[37] Side-lying and hands-knees positions have been associated with less perineal trauma.[70] In addition, a systematic review of interventions to prevent perineal trauma recommended use of warm perineal compresses.[1]

Most studies of maternal positioning during labor have compared the effects of two positions, so findings vary with the positions used. A Cochrane Review of 22 studies (n = 7280) of maternal positioning during second-stage labor in women without epidurals concluded that any upright or lateral position compared with a supine or lithotomy position decreased the length of the second stage, need for forceps, episiotomy, severe pain, and abnormal fetal heart rate patterns; increased the risk of blood loss (particularly with use of birthing chairs or stools); and slightly increased the risk of perineal tears. A nonsignificant trend toward shorter second stage labor in the upright position was also found.[51] In the supine position, contractions were more frequent but less intense than in the side-lying position. The use of the supine position during the first stage of labor compromised effective uterine activity, prolonged labor, and increased use of drugs to augment labor.[125] Placing a woman in the side-lying position increased the intensity and decreased the frequency of contractions and promoted greater uterine efficiency.[21,23,39,140] Frequency and intensity of contractions and uterine activity increased with sitting or standing. Upright positions (e.g., standing, sitting, squatting, kneeling), as opposed to supine positions, were associated with more regular and intense contractions, less likelihood of an epidural, and shorter duration of first and second stages and total labor.[74,78] The lateral recumbent position (compared with sitting) led to more intense, less frequent contractions and greater uterine efficiency during the first stage.[37,125] In women who had epidurals during the second stage of labor, the reviewers did not find clear evidence of differences between upright and recumbent positions.[67]

Positional effects appear as soon as the maternal position is changed and last as long as the position is maintained.[125] Changes are more marked with spontaneous than with induced labor and do not seem to be affected by parity or fetal position. Alternating positions after the woman has maintained one position for a period can enhance the effectiveness of contractions. If the woman prefers a supine position, alternating this position with standing or side-lying can increase the efficiency of contractions.[125] Although many studies have not found specific alterations in fetal status associated with maternal position, positions that increase the efficiency of contractions and decrease the duration of labor may reduce fetal stress.[51,125]

Maternal comfort is an important consideration. Many women prefer lateral or standing positions over supine.[91] Position preferences may change during labor. A woman may prefer sitting or walking during early labor and later may prefer semirecumbent or side-lying with pillow support as labor progresses. Roberts summarizes factors to consider in selecting a position conducive to labor progress and maternal comfort: "potential mechanical advantage of the position; the associated hemodynamic alterations and subsequent uteroplacental perfusion; the position of the fetus; the woman's perception of her contractions, discomfort, and fatigue; and obstetric indications for confinement to bed for continuous fetal monitoring, medication, or care."[125]

Maternal Pushing Efforts During the Second Stage

The second stage of labor is biphasic, with a latent phase (from complete dilation until a strong urge to push, during which the fetus passively descends into the vagina) and active phase with strong bearing down efforts as the fetal head nears the perineum.[54] The physiologic approach (laboring down or passive descent) focuses on spontaneous pushing as the mother feels the need versus the directed (closed glottis or Valsalva) approach. Laboring down increases spontaneous vaginal births and deceases the amount of time spent in active pushing.[72,112,136] Laboring down in women with epidurals usually involves no bearing down until the fetal head is visible or the woman has an urge to push. Laboring down in women with epidurals increased the likelihood of vaginal delivery and unassisted vaginal births.[65,67,70,153] No studies have determined how long is "delayed pushing"; most sources recommend 1 to 3 hours depending on parity, use of anesthetics, and amount of progress.[70]

There have been concerns regarding the effects of bearing down (i.e., prolonged Valsalva maneuver) and the Valsalva maneuver on maternal hemodynamics and fetal status.[54,78,126] A long Valsalva push increases maternal intrathoracic and intraabdominal pressure and decreases cardiac output, uterine blood flow, and blood in the intervillous space and thus fetal oxygenation.[54] Maternal hypotension and fetal hypoxia may develop more rapidly with supine position or epidural anesthesia. Maternal hemodynamic changes with bearing down and the Valsalva maneuver are mediated by sympathetic discharge and catecholamine release, which also increase maternal discomfort and, in combination with maternal acidosis, may decrease uterine activity.[126]

Investigations have compared the effects of open-glottis pushing (based on involuntary maternal urges to push) with those of the Valsalva maneuver accompanying directed bearing down.[46,163] Bearing down that lasts more than 5 to 6 seconds was associated with decreased maternal blood pressure and placental blood flow, alterations in maternal and fetal oxygenation, decreased fetal pH and Po_2, increased fetal Pco_2, an increased incidence of fetal heart rate pattern changes, and delayed recovery of the fetal heart rate with asphyxia; others have found shorter duration second stage with closed-glottis pushing.[163] Open-glottis pushing was not associated with changes in maternal blood pressure (probably because intrathoracic pressure elevations were not sustained) or fetal pH.[3] Spontaneous involuntary pushing with minimal straining has been associated with fewer episiotomies, forceps deliveries, and second-degree to third-degree perineal tears and a shorter second stage.[78,126] A recent review of 20 studies (n = 3691) of immediate versus delayed pushing or pushing using the Valsalva maneuver versus other pushing techniques found that with "epidural use, delayed pushing resulted in longer second stages but a shorter time pushing and increases spontaneous vaginal delivery. No other maternal or neonatal variables differed between delayed and immediate pushing. In addition the data for the type of pushing, with or without epidural, evidence did not conclusively support either method."[75] This review concluded that women should be encouraged to bear down based on their preferences and comfort.

Preterm Labor and Birth

Infants born prematurely are at high risk for health alterations during the neonatal period and for later neurodevelopmental problems. As a result, much effort has been directed toward eliciting the causes for preterm labor and developing intervention strategies to prevent the onset of labor and to terminate uterine contractions that begin before term. Preterm labor is defined as the onset of regular contractions with progressive cervical effacement and dilation before 37 weeks.[18] "In 2014, 1 in 10 babies (9.6% of live births) was born preterm in the United States."[108] The reduction in preterm birth rates over time is believed to be primarily a result of the reduction in nonmedically indicated cesarean births, decreases in adolescent and multiple pregnancy, and use of progesterone supplementation for women at risk for preterm labor.[61,103,129] Preterm labor involves a group of factors that individually or in combination influence the various pathways involved in control of labor onset (see Figure 4-4). Preterm delivery may be caused by maternal or fetal factors such as fetal growth restriction, placenta previa, preeclampsia, or placental abruption that results in early termination of the pregnancy (approximately 20% of all preterm labors); PROM (approximately 30%); intraamniotic and other infection (20% to 25%); or spontaneous, unexplained reasons (25% to 30%).[155] The etiology of spontaneous preterm birth is multifactorial including anatomic, physiologic, pathologic, genetic, demographic, and ethnic factors.[13,103] Major risk factors for preterm birth are a history of previous preterm birth and a cervical length of 20 mm or less at 18 to 24 weeks gestation.[20,61,158] Women who have had a previous spontaneous preterm birth have a 15% to 50% recurrence risk; the risk is inversely related to gestational age of the previous preterm birth.[158] These women may be candidates for progesterone supplementation. Cervical cerclage in women with a short cervical length may decrease risk of preterm birth.[61]

Preterm birth also has a heritable basis in some women.[111,135] Labor onset is believed to be controlled by the fetal genome via several interrelated pathways involving endocrine and mechanical signaling.[24,111] Genetic factors may include individual genes, genes-environment interactions, and gene-gene interaction.[115] Currently there are many ongoing studies examining the genetic basis of preterm birth.[85,100,115,154] For example, polymorphisms in the TNF-α gene promoter region are associated with shorter gestation length and increased risk of spontaneous preterm birth in the presence of bacterial vaginosis (BV).[55,111,135] Other work has focused on areas such as genetic variations in proinflammatory and antiinflammatory cytokine genes and their receptors, single nucleotide polymorphisms, and gene patterns in families.[85,115,154,166]

Four major mechanisms have been proposed for preterm labor (Figure 4-6): (1) infection and inflammation (decidual, chorioamniotic, or systemic); (2) decidual hemorrhage or abruption; (3) maternal and fetal stress (activation of the maternal or fetal hypothalamic-pituitary-adrenal axis); and (4) uterine overdistention or stretch.[18,64,69,111] Genetics and environment may have roles in all of these factors.[127] Inflammation activates a cytokine response, leading to increased MMPs and uterotonics. Initiation of preterm labor by infection or inflammation is a result of release of proinflammatory chemokines and cytokines such as IL-1β, IL-8, TNF-α, platelet-activating factor, and other mediators that increase production of prostaglandins by the fetal membranes and decidua resulting in myometrial contractions and membrane rupture.[18,127,159,167]

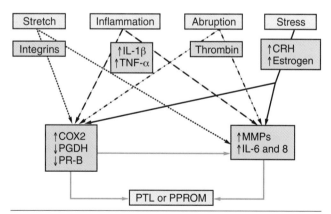

FIGURE 4-6   Principle biochemical mechanisms responsible for the main pathways of premature parturition. *COX2*, Cyclooxygenase-2; *CRH*, corticotropin-releasing hormone; *IL-1β*, interleukin-1β; *MMPs*, matrix metalloproteinases; *PGDH*, prostaglandin dehydrogenase; *PPROM*, preterm premature rupture of membranes; *PR-B*, progesterone receptor-B; *PTL*, preterm labor; *TNF-α*, tumor necrosis factor-α. (From Buhimschi, C.S. & Norman J.E. [2014]. Pathogenesis of spontaneous preterm labor. In R.K. Creasy, R. Resnik, J.D. Iams, C.J. Lockwood, T.R. Moore, & M.F. Greene. [Eds.]. *Creasy & Resnik's maternal-fetal medicine: Principles and practice* [7th ed.]. Philadelphia: Saunders.)

Intrauterine (both clinical and subclinical) infections, including chorioamnionitis, BV, and extrauterine infections (including malaria, pyelonephritis, tuberculosis, pneumonia, and periodontal disease [see Chapter 12]) have been implicated.[60,135,158,159,160,167] BV is "a pathologic state characterized by the loss of normal vaginal flora, particularly *Lactobacillus* species, and overgrowth of other microbes, including *G vaginalis, Bacteroides* sp, *Mobiluncus* sp, and *Mycoplasma hominis*."[120] Data regarding whether screening and prophylactic treatment with antibiotics for women at risk for spontaneous preterm birth are conflicting, with reports of increased risks in some studies.[16,60,120,142,149,158] A recent Cochrane review found that antibiotic prophylaxis did not reduce the risk of premature rupture of membranes or delivery (except in women with a previous preterm birth who also had BV).[149]

Both preterm labor and PROM may be adaptive events that occur when the intrauterine environment is "hostile." If the response to intrauterine infection is secretion of uterotonic agents, preterm labor results; if the response is protease (MMPs) production, PROM results.[142] A fetal inflammatory response syndrome (FIRS) has been described.[18,24,120] FIRS involves funisitis (umbilical cord inflammation) and chorionic vascularitis and is characterized by "systemic activation of the fetal immune system and defined by elevated IL-6 concentrations in neonatal cord blood."[120] Other biomarkers of FIRS include IL-β1, IL-8, and possibly C-reactive protein.[120]

These infants have been reported to be at increased risk of cerebral palsy and chronic lung disease.[127]

Decidual hemorrhage, usually from placental abruption, with thrombin formation can activate phosphatidylinositol-signaling pathways that stimulate uterine contractions, release of plasminogen activators, and enhance activation of MMPs, neutrophil chemoattractants, and neutrophil activating chemokines.[17,41,127] Maternal or fetal stress may activate labor via increases in CRH leading to increased estriol production and increased PGs and other substances via immune and inflammatory pathways (Figure 4-7).[15,127,158] Uterine overdistention (polyhydramnios or multifetal gestation) or reduction in expansive capacity (uterine anomalies) activates cytokines (Figure 4-8).[18,142] The underlying mechanism may be myometrial stretch, which induces activation of integrin receptors and stretch-activated calcium channels, and phosphorylation of platelet-derived growth factors and G-proteins in the myometrium. These changes lead to increased MMPs, expression of inflammatory cytokines (IL-8 ,TNF-α, IL-1β), PGs, and NO in the cervix with cervical ripening and further stretching and rupture of the fetal membranes.[18,118,141,158] Stretch can also induce myometrial contractions by PG release, expression of gap junctions, and increased oxytocin receptors.[73,77,158]

An intervention to prevent preterm birth is use of 17-OHPC for women with a risk for preterm labor or history of

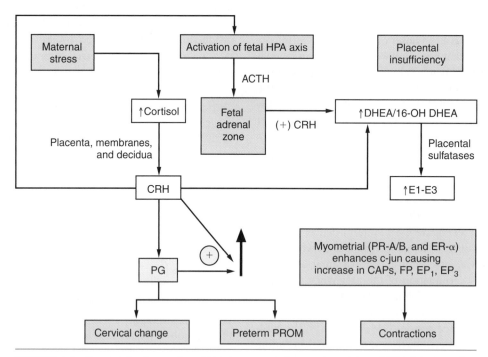

FIGURE 4-7   Proposed pathways by which stress can induce preterm labor. *ACTH*, Adrenocorticotropic hormone (corticotropin); *CAPs*, contraction-associated proteins; *c-jun*, a transcription factor; *CRH*, corticotropin-releasing hormone; *DHEA*, dehydroepiandrosterone; *E1-E3*, estrone, estradiol, estriol; *EP₁* and *EP₃*, prostaglandin E receptors types 1 and 3; *ER-α*, estrogen receptor-α; *FP*, prostaglandin f receptor; *HPA*, hypothalamic-pituitary-adrenal; *PG*, prostaglandins; *PR*, prostaglandin receptor; *PROM*, premature rupture of membranes. (From Romero, R. & Lockwood, C.J. [2009]. Pathogenesis of spontaneous preterm labor. In R.K. Creasy, R. Resnik, J.D. Iams, C.J. Lockwood, & T.R. Moore. [Eds.]. *Creasy & Resnik's maternal-fetal medicine: Principles and practice* [6th ed.]. Philadelphia: Saunders Elsevier.)

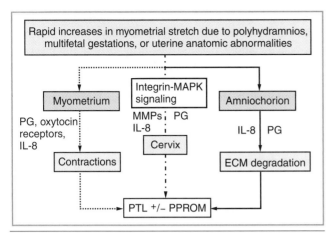

FIGURE 4-8 Proposed mechanism by which stretch can induce preterm labor. *ECM,* Extracellular matrix; *IL-8,* interleukin-8; *MAPK,* mitogen-activated protein kinase; *MMPs,* metalloproteinases; *PG,* prostaglandins; *PTL,* preterm labor; *PPROM,* preterm premature rupture of membranes. (From Buhimschi, C.S. & Norman J.E. [2014]. Pathogenesis of spontaneous preterm labor. In R.K. Creasy, R. Resnik, J.D. Iams, C.J. Lockwood, T.R. Moore, & M.F. Greene [Eds.]. *Creasy & Resnik's maternal-fetal medicine: Principles and practice* [7th ed.]. Philadelphia: Saunders.)

a previous preterm birth.[38,62,89,128] Progesterone has an antiin-flammatory role (inhibits NF-κB, COX-2, and PG synthesis and decreases cytokine production) and promotes uterine quiescence (inhibits ion channels and OTR, gap junction, and PG receptor formation).[158] Metaanalyses found that use of 17-OHPC in singleton pregnancies decreased both preterm births by 33% or more and the incidence of infants weighing less than 2500 g.[20,38] Petrini and colleagues estimated that if all eligible women in the United States were treated, the prematurity rate would be reduced by 2% or by about 10,000 preterm births per year.[117] Neurodevelopmental follow-up at 48 months of offspring exposed to 17-OHPC in utero showed no difference with control group children.[110] The American College of Obstetricians and Gynecologists has recommended use of 17-OHPC for women with a history of previous spontaneous preterm birth.[7] 17-OHPC has been found to be ineffective in multifetal pregnancies and in women with a short cervical length.[84,130,161] Use of vaginal progesterone in women with cervical length of 20 mm or less was found to decrease the rate of preterm birth before 34 weeks, but 17-OHPC was not effective.[38,77,130,161]

Altering Uterine Motility and Cervical Ripening

Uterine activity can be controlled directly by blocking or stimulating specific hormonal receptors or altering electromechanical coupling and indirectly via agents that interfere with the synthesis of enzymes and other mediators of myometrial contraction and relaxation. Use of these agents must take into consideration the physiologic properties of, as well as the pharmacologic actions on, both the cervix and the myometrium. A postterm woman with altered myometrial contractility and an unripe (resistant) cervix needs an agent that increases and coordinates myometrial activity and decreases cervical resistance. On the other hand, agents used for women in preterm labor lead to myometrial relaxation and increase cervical resistance. This section examines pharmacology of labor related to control of cervical ripening, labor induction, and labor inhibition.

Control of Cervical Ripening

Cervical ripening is not dependent on myometrial contractions and occurs in the absence of regular uterine contractions. PGE_2 (dinoprostone) and misoprostol (synthetic PGE_1) are used for preinduction cervical ripening.[66,144,148,162] Physiologic ripening is under the control of local mediators, in particular PGE_2, whose action is influenced by local mediators. Exogenous PGE_2 induces cervical ripening by relaxing cervical smooth muscle, enhancing enzymatic collagen degradation, and increasing hyaluronic acid and MMP.[144,148] Misoprostol binds to EP_3 and EP_4 receptors and may have a greater effect on the cervix than PGE_2.[58,144] Antiprogesterone agents (RU-486, or mifepristone) have also been evaluated as alternative cervical ripening agents. RU-486 stimulates IL-8 release.[27,144,148,162] Foley catheters have also been used to mechanically dilate the cervix with release of PGs from fetal membranes. Misoprostol has also been used for labor induction, although there have been concerns regarding the risks of uterine hyperstimulation in women with a previous cesarean birth.[11,144,148] Misoprostol has been reported to be less effective for third-stage labor than oxytocin and other uterotonics.[63]

PGE_2 tablets, gels, and pessaries all increase the chance of vaginal delivery within 24 hours and increase the risk of uterine hyperstimulation with fetal heart changes, but do not alter cesarean birth rate.[150] Another metaanalysis reported a similar effectiveness of oral misoprostol versus oral dinoprostone in labor induction, with less frequent cesarean birth with oral misoprostol; fewer cesarean births were reported with misoprostol than oxytocin use.[4] Misoprostol (intravaginally, orally, or sublingual) and dinoprostone (vaginal insert or gel) compared to oxytocin or placebo both increase the likelihood of delivery within 24 hours with no change in cesarean birth rates but an increase in tachsystole.[147,162] A metaanalysis of these interventions found that vaginal misoprostol "was the most effective cervical ripening method to achieve vaginal delivery within 24 hours, but had the highest incidence of uterine hyperstimulation" and fetal heart rate changes.[25] The lowest rate of uterine hyperstimulation occurred with use of Foley catheter; cesarean birth rates were lowest with oral misoprostol use.[25]

Induction and Augmentation of Uterine Activity

Oxytocin (and synthetic forms such as Pitocin and Syntocinon) is usually the drug of choice to initiate uterine activity if the condition of the cervix is favorable.[34,162] Oxytocin is used for labor augmentation and induction and to promote uterine contraction after parturition.[137,162] Because oxytocin has little effect on the cervix, an unripe cervix may resist even forceful oxytocin-induced myometrial contractions.

Oxytocin increases myometrial cell membrane spike activity, possibly by altering calcium flux through voltage-dependent calcium channels. Effects of oxytocin on uterine activity depend on the concentration of oxytocin receptors on the myometrial cells, number of available receptors, receptor affinity for oxytocin, and metabolic state of the myometrium. Oxytocin is a potent octapeptide synthesized in the hypothalamus and then transported along the neurons to the posterior pituitary gland via carrier proteins and released episodically. Oxytocin release can also be stimulated by nipple stimulation (similar to the mechanism with suckling described in Chapter 5).[140] Side effects include excessive uterine activity and uterine hyperstimulation with fetal hypoxia.[137,162] Use of misoprostol for labor induction is discussed in Control of Cervical Ripening. A systematic review of interventions for labor induction found that oxytocin with amniotomy and vaginal misoprostol was most likely to result tin vaginal delivery within 24 hours.[5] Nonpharmacologic interventions include use of Foley or other catheters (see previous section), amniotomy, and sweeping of the membranes to induce phospholipase A_2 and $PGF_{2\alpha}$ release.[5] Membrane sweeping increases the likelihood of spontaneous labor, decreases the length of gestation, and has not been shown to increase risk in women who are group B streptococcus positive.[56,147]

Inhibition of Labor

Inhibition of uterine smooth muscle contractions is used in the management of preterm labor. Uterine activity–inhibiting drugs (tocolytics) are most effective in stopping labor for 2 to 7 days and thus delay labor so glucocorticoids can be given to enhance fetal lung maturity (see Chapter 10). However, tocolytics do not decrease the overall rate of preterm delivery and there is little evidence that long-term prophylactic or maintenance use is effective.[19,36,60,111] Maternal responses to tocolytics are influenced by gene polymorphisms, which can influence the effectiveness of a given tocolytic in an individual woman.[84] For example, CYP3A5 polymorphisms correlate with nifedipine level.[84] Many tocolytic drugs have been investigated, including calcium channel blockers, oxytocin receptor antagonists, β-adrenergic agonists, magnesium sulfate, and prostaglandin synthetase inhibitors.[12,52,60,111,158] Because each group of drugs has a different action, combinations of drugs may enhance their effectiveness because they act synergistically. The actions of tocolytics focus on factors that regulate MLCK, such as calcium and cAMP, thus preventing myosin light-chain phosphorylation and muscle contraction.[135]

Calcium antagonists (calcium channel blockers) are organic compounds such as nifedipine that act on the cell membrane to inhibit the influx of extracellular calcium through voltage-dependent channels, decreasing intracellular calcium and reducing release of stored calcium from intracellular sites.[12,19,52,106,135] These agents are less effective in blocking influx through receptor-operated channels that are less specific for calcium. Calcium antagonists may also act by altering calcium-calmodulin binding and thus inhibiting

actin-myosin interaction. A Cochrane Review concluded that nifedipine can delay delivery for 2 to 7 days with a favorable risk-benefit ratio.[44] Because this drug crosses the placenta, there have been concerns regarding the potential for adverse fetal or neonatal effects, although no significant issues have been reported to date.[36,44] Nifedipine has been found to be superior to magnesium sulfate. Nifedipine may be associated with better neonatal outcomes and fewer maternal and fetal side effects.[135] Calcium channel blockers are not recommended in combination with magnesium sulfate or β-agonists or for women with intrauterine infection, maternal hypertension, or cardiac disease.[135]

Magnesium affects smooth muscle excitation, excitation-contraction coupling, and the contractile apparatus by modulating calcium uptake, binding, and distribution in the cell; competitive blocking of Ca^{2+} influx across the cell membrane; and activation of adenyl cyclase and cAMP.[19,135] Magnesium regulates the voltage-gated calcium channels to prevent them from opening in response to the action potential. Thus magnesium sulfate acts on the myometrium, primarily by competitive antagonism to control calcium entry into the cell, reducing intracellular Ca^{2+} levels and thus contractility. Magnesium sulfate has low tocolytic efficacy with little data to support its effectiveness as a tocolytic, and concerns have been raised about fetal and neonatal bone density with use for more than 5 to 7 days.[10,53] However, short-term use (usually less than 48 hours) of magnesium sulfate before 32 weeks' gestation has neuroprotective benefits with a decrease in moderate to severe cerebral palsy in offspring reported in several metaanalyses.[8,9,29,33,40,86,135]

β-Adrenergic agonists (β-sympathomimetics) are effective in postponing delivery for 24 to 48 hours but do not significantly reduce the rate of preterm birth or alter neonatal mortality or morbidity. Drugs in this class that have been used for inhibition of preterm labor include ritodrine, terbutaline, fenoterol, isoxsuprine, salbutamol, hexoprenaline, and orciprenaline. Because significant side effects are common, these agents have been replaced by other agents.[35,135,158] β-Adrenergic agonists act to relax myometrial cells by triggering intracellular formation of cAMP. These effects are mediated by β_2-receptors on the outer membrane of the myometrial cell.

Oxytocin receptor agonists such as atosiban are synthetic oxytocin analogs that competitively bind to myometrial oxytocin receptors, decreasing release of intracellular calcium and closing calcium voltage channels to prevent entry of extracellular calcium.[12] These agents act directly by blocking oxytocin receptors and indirectly by altering PG synthesis in the decidua. Atosiban has been used primarily in Europe and New Zealand. A metaanalysis of oxytocin receptor agonists found these agents, compared with a placebo, β-adrenergic agonists, or nifedipine, were not superior in terms of pregnancy prolongation or neonatal outcomes but did have fewer maternal adverse effects than the other tocolytics.[45] Another metaanalysis found that neither atosiban nor β-agonists were as effective as nifedipine.[30]

Prostaglandin synthetase (cyclooxygenase) inhibitors reduce PG synthesis and include nonsteroidal antiinflammatory agents such as indomethacin, ketorolac, meloxicam, and sulindac. These agents block PG synthesis by interfering with cyclooxygenase, the enzyme that regulates the production of PGs from arachidonic acid.[121] Because PGs are important in both initiation of myometrial activity and cervical ripening, the potential of this group of agents has generated considerable interest. Although their effectiveness has been documented, concerns remain over the potential risk for premature closure of the fetal ductus arteriosus and other side effects such as pulmonary hypertension and alterations in renal function.[12,158] The concern about ductal closure is that PG synthetase inhibitors act on both COX-1 (found primarily in fetal cardiovascular tissues) and COX-2 (found in the myometrium and fetal membranes). The risk for premature ductal closure is dose dependent and seems greatest in fetuses past 35 weeks' gestation and with long-term therapy. Generally indomethacin is used only for brief courses at 32 weeks' gestation or earlier.[135]

Dystocia

Dysfunctional labor can result from problems in the powers (alteration in myometrial function, expulsive forces, and contraction patterns), passage (obstruction of fetal descent by the maternal bony pelvis or soft tissues), or passenger (altered fetal size, position, or presentation). Functional dystocia caused by alterations in the physiologic function (powers) results in inadequate contractility and failure of the cervix to dilate. The cellular and molecular basis for weak or ineffective myometrial contractions includes lack of adequate stimulation, depression or the presence of some form of strong inhibitory control, or a combination of these events.[46] Dystocia may have a genetic basis in some women.[6]

An understanding of the usual duration and progression of labor is important in defining and identifying dystocia.[138] Cheng et al. found that with the use of epidurals, nulliparous women had longer first and second stage labors.[26] Neal et al. concluded in their metaanalysis that in nulliparous women with spontaneous active labor, cervical dilation occurred at a mean of 1.2 cm/hour and lasted a mean of 6 hours.[109] They also calculated that "at the statistical limits, the weighted "active labor" duration was 13.4 hours (mean + 2 standard deviations) and the dilation rate was 0.6 cm per hour (mean − 2 standard deviations)."[109]

Stimulation or inhibition of myometrial activity is influenced by myogenic, neurogenic, and endocrine control systems.[46] Dystocia secondary to alterations in myogenic properties arises from factors such as modifications in intracellular ion concentration (as a result of an inadequate supply of energy or calcium) with depression or absence of myometrial contractility, closure or inadequate function of gap junctions with modifications in the propagation of electrical events, and poor synchronization of contractions across the uterus. Abnormalities in gap junction structure or function may arise from alterations in regulatory hormones or their receptors. Dystocia can also arise secondary to alterations in neurogenic control (overstimulation by inhibitory neurons or understimulation by excitatory neurons) or in endocrine control systems. These latter alterations arise directly from inadequate levels of hormones or their receptors or indirectly from alterations in gap junction function or structure.[46]

Supportive interventions for women experiencing dystocia are directed toward preventing or reducing maternal fatigue, providing calories for energy, maintaining hydration, monitoring fluid and electrolyte status, appropriate positioning, assessing maternal-fetal status at least every 15 minutes during induction and augmentation, and maintaining fetal homeostasis.[138] Energy (ATP) is essential for labor progression. If adequate calories and ATP are not available, ketoacidosis may develop. With inadequate ATP, the effectiveness of uterine contractions is further impeded. Women with dystocia whose labor is not progressing and who are exhausted may be provided with a period of medicated therapeutic rest.[46]

Postterm Labor

Postterm labor is the onset of labor more than 10 days beyond the established due date.[12] Fetal and neonatal morbidity increases after 42 weeks, often as a result of the effects of prolonged gestation on placental morphology and functional ability. Postterm pregnancies are associated with an increased frequency of both intrauterine growth restriction (in 10% to 20% of postterm pregnancies) and macrosomia (in most), fetal distress, meconium aspiration, congenital anomalies, and intrauterine death.[122]

Factors that may result in failure of initiation of spontaneous labor and postterm gestation include (1) lack of the normal increase in estrogen near term, perhaps because of anencephaly and associated adrenal hypoplasia, deficiency in placental sulfatase (necessary for production of estrogen), or fetal adrenal hypoplasia; (2) altered adrenocortical function, leading to reduction in cortisol levels (cortisol promotes hydroxylation of progesterone, reduction in progesterone levels, and increases in estrogen precursors); (3) alterations in local bioregulators of cervical ripening; and (4) decreased fetal adrenocorticotropic factors such as CRH and ACTH, which stimulate fetal cortisol and estrogen precursor production, perhaps related to delayed maturation of the fetal brain.[122,156] There may also be a genetic risk.[156] The result is delay in myometrial activation with failure of oxytocin receptor, PG receptor, or gap junction development or delay in cervical ripening.[122]

SUMMARY

An understanding of physiologic processes during the intrapartum period is essential for recognition of the effects of parturition on the pregnant woman and the fetus and in optimizing maternal, fetal, and neonatal outcome. This knowledge provides the basis for assessment of functional and dysfunctional labor patterns and maternal responses to pharmacologic agents used to alter or control uterine activity, for recognition of preterm labor, and for interventions such as positioning during the first and second stages of labor. Recommendations for clinical practice related to parturition and uterine physiology during parturition are summarized in Box 4-2.

BOX 4-2   Recommendations for Clinical Practice Related to Parturition and Uterine Physiology

Recognize usual changes in the uterine size and shape during pregnancy (pp. 115-116).

Know the usual changes in the myometrium during pregnancy and their bases (p. 118).

Recognize factors involved in the initiation of labor and know how these may be altered (pp. 122-128 and Figure 4-4).

Understand the physiologic basis for myometrial contraction and factors that may alter muscular contraction (pp. 128-129).

Assess contractions and document their characteristics (p. 131).

Monitor energy and oxygen needs of the laboring woman (pp. 128-129).

Understand the basis for cervical ripening and dilation and factors that may alter this process (pp. 119-121).

Avoid use of the supine position for prolonged periods during the first stage of labor (pp. 131-132).

Promote use of upright positions in first-stage (especially early) labor (pp. 131-132).

Assist the woman in selecting a position conducive to labor progress and maternal comfort (pp. 131-132).

Assist the woman in selecting a position at delivery to optimize alignment for fetal descent and maximize capacity of the pelvis and efficiency of maternal expulsive efforts (pp. 131-133).

Teach the woman to use open-glottis pushing (pp. 132-133).

Avoid supine positions during the second stage (pp. 131-132 and Chapter 9).

Recognize factors that increase the risk of preterm labor and intervention strategies (pp. 133-135 and Figures 4-6, 4-7, and 4-8).

Understand the basis for pharmacologic agents used to control cervical ripening (p. 135).

Understand the basis for pharmacologic agents used for induction or augmentation of labor (pp. 135-136).

Monitor the woman for side effects of agents used to induce or augment labor (pp. 135-136).

Understand the basis for pharmacologic agents used to inhibit labor (pp. 136-137).

Monitor the woman for side effects of agents used to inhibit labor (pp. 136-137).

Recognize and monitor for factors that can lead to dystocia (p. 137).

Monitor the woman with postterm labor for fetal distress (p. 137 and Chapter 6).

References

1. Aasheim, V., et al. (2011). Perineal techniques during the second stage of labour for reducing perineal trauma. *Cochrane Database Syst Rev, 2011*(12), CD006672.

2. Aguilar, H. N., & Mitchell, B. F. (2010). Physiological pathways and molecular mechanisms regulating uterine contractility. *Hum Reprod Update, 16,* 725.

3. Akerlund, M. (1997). Contractility in the nonpregnant uterus. *Ann N Y Acad Med, 828,* 213.

4. Alfirevic, Z., Aflaifel, N., & Weeks, A. (2014). Oral misoprostol for induction of labour. *Cochrane Database of Syst Rev, 2014*(6), CD001338.

5. Alfirevic, Z., et al. (2016). Methods to induce labour: a systematic review, network meta-analysis and cost-effectiveness analysis. *BJO, 123,* 1462.

6. Algovik, M., et al. (2010). Genetic evidence of multiple loci in dystocia-difficult labor. *BMC Med Genet, 11,* 105.

7. American College of Obstetricians and Gynecologists. (2012). ACOG Practice Bulletin no 130. Prediction and prevention of preterm birth. *Obstet Gynecol, 120,* 694.

8. American College of Obstetricians and Gynecologists. (2016). Practice Bulletin No. 159: Management of Preterm Labor. *Obstet Gynecol, 127,* e29.

9. American College of Obstetricians and Gynecologists and Society for Maternal-Fetal Medicine. (2010). Magnesium sulfate before anticipated preterm birth for neuroprotection. Committee Opinion No. 455. *Obstet Gynecol, 115,* 669.

10. American College of Obstetricians and Gynecologists and Society for Maternal-Fetal Medicine. (2016). Committee Opinion No. 652: Magnesium Sulfate Use in Obstetrics. *Obstet Gynecol, 127,* e52.

11. Arias, F. (2000). Pharmacology of oxytocin and prostaglandins. *Clin Obstet Gynecol, 43,* 453.

12. Arrowsmith, S., et al. (2014). Myometrial physiology—time to translate? *Exp Physiol, 99,* 495.

13. Barros, F. C., et al. (2015). The distribution of clinical phenotypes of preterm birth syndrome: implications for prevention. *JAMA Pediatr, 169,* 220.

14. Beshay, V. E., Carr, B. R., & Rainey, W. E. (2007). The human fetal adrenal gland, corticotropin-releasing hormone, and parturition. *Semin Reprod Med, 25,* 14.

15. Boggess, K. A. (2005). Pathophysiology of preterm birth: Emerging concepts of maternal infection. *Clin Perinatol, 32,* 561.

16. Brocklehurst, P. H., et al. (2013). Antibiotics for treating bacterial vaginosis in pregnancy. *Cochrane Database Syst Rev, 2013*(1), CD000262.

17. Buhimschi, C. S., et al. (2010). Novel insights into molecular mechanisms of abruption-induced preterm birth. *Expert Rev Mol Med, 12,* e35.

18. Buhimschi, C. S., & Norman J. E. (2014). Pathogenesis of spontaneous preterm labor. In R. K. Creasy, et al. (Eds.), *Creasy & Resnik's Maternal-fetal medicine: Principles and practice* (7th ed.). Philadelphia: Saunders.

19. Caritis, S. N. (2011). Metaanalysis and labor inhibition therapy. *Am J Obstet Gynecol, 204,* 95.

20. Caritis, S. N., et al. (2016). What we have learned about the role of 17 alpha-hydroxyprogesterone caproate in the prevention of preterm birth. *Semin Perinatol, 40,* 273.

21. Challis, J. R., & Lye, S. J. (1994). Parturition. In E. Knobil & J. Neill (Eds.), *The physiology of reproduction* (2nd ed.). New York: Raven.

22. Challis, J. R., et al. (2002). Prostaglandins and mechanisms of preterm birth. *Reproduction, 124,* 1.

23. Challis, J. R., & Lye, S. J. (2004). Characteristics of parturition. In R. K. Creasy, R. Resnik, & J. D. Iams (Eds.), *Maternal-fetal medicine: Principles and practice* (5th ed.). Philadelphia: Saunders.

24. Challis, J. R., Lye, S. J., & Dong, X. S. (2005). Transcriptional regulation of human myometrium and the onset of labor. *J Soc Gynecol Invest, 12,* 65.

25. Chen, W., et al. (2016). A systematic review and network meta-analysis comparing the use of Foley catheters, misoprostol, and dinoprostone for cervical ripening in the induction of labour. *BJOG, 123,* 346.

26. Cheng, Y., et al. (2009). The second stage of labor and epidural use: A larger effect than previously suggested. *Am J Obstet Gynecol, 201,* S46.

27. Chwalisz, K., & Garfield, R. E. (1997). Regulation of the uterus and cervix during pregnancy and labor: Role of progesterone and nitric oxide. *Ann N Y Acad Sci, 828,* 238.

28. Chwalisz, K., & Garfield, R. E. (1998). Role of nitric oxide in the uterus and cervix: Implications for the management of labor. *J Perinat Med, 26,* 448.

29. Conde-Agudelo, A., & Romero, R. (2009). Antenatal magnesium sulfate for the prevention of cerebral palsy in preterm infants less than 34 weeks' gestation: a systematic review and metaanalysis. *Am J Obstet Gynecol, 200,* 595.

30. Conde-Agudelo, A., Romero, R., & Kusanovic, J. P. (2011). Nifedipine in the management of preterm labor: A systematic review and metaanalysis. *Am J Obstet Gynecol, 204,* e1.

31. Conrad, K. P. (2010). Unveiling the vasodilatory actions and mechanisms of relaxin. *Hypertension, 56,* 2.

and early intervention, are crucial. The administration of uterotonic agents is recommended to prevent postpartum hemorrhage. The effectiveness of uterine massage for prevention of hemorrhage is undetermined.[42] Prevention of postpartum hemorrhage is facilitated by use of prophylactic oxytocin.[99] Management of uterine atony and postpartum hemorrhage aims at increasing uterine contractility with uterotonic medications along with hematology consultation.[24] If there is a lack of response to medical treatment along with persistence of uterine atony and hemorrhage, uterine suture compression or surgical intervention may be necessary.[24]

Under the influence of estrogens, the myometrium undergoes hypertrophy and hyperplasia during pregnancy with increases in cell cytoplasm and size. After delivery, excess intracellular proteins (especially actin and myosin) and cytoplasm within the myometrial cells are eliminated by autolysis with degradation by proteolytic enzymes and macrophages. As a result, the size of individual myometrial cells is markedly reduced without a significant reduction in the total number of cells. Initially, the endometrium resembles a large desquamating wound. The upper portion of the spongy endometrial layer is sloughed off with delivery of the placenta.

Regeneration of the uterine epithelial lining begins 2 to 3 days postpartum with differentiation of the remaining decidua into two layers, a superficial layer and a basal layer. The superficial layer of granulation tissue, which provides a barrier to infection, forms as leukocytes invade the remaining decidua. This layer gradually degenerates, becoming necrotic, and sloughs off in lochia. The basal layer, containing residual endometrial glands, remains intact and contributes to the new endometrium. By about 2 to 3 weeks, the endometrium has been restored and is similar to the nonpregnant endometrium in the proliferative phase of the menstrual cycle, except for remnants of hyalinized decidua with areas of leukocyte infiltration.[32] Healing at the placental site takes longer; regeneration occurs gradually over 6 weeks. After delivery, the placental site is a rough area 4 to 5 cm in diameter containing many thrombosed vessels. Fibroblasts invade the large blood vessels that supplied the intervillous spaces, and their lumen is obscured. Some of these vessels recanalize later with smaller lumens. The placental site heals by decidual sloughing and exfoliation and by growth of endometrial tissue.[32]

Lochia

The process of involution and restoration of the endometrium is reflected in the characteristics of lochia, the postpartum vaginal discharge. Lochia varies in amount and color as healing progresses. Three forms of lochia are observed, generally in the following pattern: rubra, serosa, and alba. Lochia rubra is red or red-brown with a fleshy odor and is seen during the first few days or through the first week postpartum. Lochia rubra contains blood from the placental site; pieces of amnion and chorion; and cellular elements from the decidua, vernix, lanugo, and meconium. Lochia serosa is a pinkish-brown discharge lasting approximately 2 to 4 weeks. Lochia serosa contains some blood, wound exudate, erythrocytes, leukocytes, cervical mucus, microorganisms, and shreds of decidual tissue. The lochia becomes progressively lighter in color. Lochia alba is whitish-yellow in color because it primarily contains leukocytes and decidual cells; it may continue for another few weeks, although not all women experience lochia alba. Overall lochia duration may last 4 to 6 weeks postpartum, which is a longer duration than traditionally described and may vary according to breastfeeding practice and parity.[28,60,91] Postpartum hemorrhage is defined as excessive bleeding through 6 weeks postpartum, although a clear definition of normal lochial discharge is lacking, which challenges assessment and appropriate course of action.[28] Lochia flow will go through the same phases after cesarean delivery but is considerably reduced because the lochia is wiped with sponges and some of the endometrial lining is removed during surgery.[71]

Cervix, Vagina, and Perineum

Immediately after a vaginal delivery, the cervix extends into the vagina and remains partly dilated, bruised, and edematous, with possible lacerations. During the first 12 to 18 hours, the cervix shortens and becomes firmer ("forming up") and, as measured by magnetic resonance imaging, has a mean length of 5.6 cm by 30 hours (versus 2.9 cm by 6 months).[101] By the second or third day, the cervix is dilated 2 to 3 cm and by 1 week the cervix is approximately 1 cm dilated. By 4 weeks, the external os appears as a small transverse slit, characteristic of multiparous women. By 6 weeks, there may still be evidence of stromal edema and round cell infiltrates, which may persist until 3 to 4 months.[32] Remodeling and involution of the cervix begin immediately postpartum to restore the cervical structure altered during cervical ripening and delivery. Remodeling occurs rapidly with an increase in fibroblasts, collagen, and proteoglycans. This process may be mediated by transforming growth factor-β (TGF-β) and other cytokines.[98]

After vaginal birth, the vagina is edematous and relaxed, with decreased tone and absence of rugae. The vagina gradually decreases in size and regains tone, although it does not fully return to its prepregnancy state. By 3 to 4 weeks, rugae reappear, and edema and vascularity have decreased. The vaginal epithelium is generally restored by 6 to 10 weeks postpartum.[32]

Perineal discomfort may result from perineal pain related to episiotomy, laceration, and trauma after vaginal birth. Routine use of episiotomies has significantly decreased since the 1990s when research documented the associated risks. Systematic reviews have shown that routine versus restrictive use of episiotomy is associated with a higher risk of perineal trauma and tears, need for suturing, complications, and increased pain and demonstrates no evidence of effective prevention or management of shoulder dystocia.[16,85] Although initial healing occurs in 2 to 3 weeks, the episiotomy site may take 4 to 6 months to completely heal. Based on clinical indication, use of skin adhesives may be a less painful nonsuturing alternative to addressing perineal trauma.[89] Antenatal digital perineal massage enhances the suppleness of the perineum, protecting the perineum from trauma and reducing the risk of episiotomy and chronic perineal pain and is therefore recommended to be taught to pregnant women to facilitate perineal preparation for birth.[7]

Urinary Function

Diuresis occurs during the postpartum period, reversing prenatal fluid retention. Overdistention of the bladder; prolonged labor; instrumental delivery; cesarean delivery; use of analgesics; or perineal, urethral, or bladder trauma may result in incomplete bladder emptying and urine retention, defined as lack of micturition within 6 hours of vaginal birth or 6 hours of removal of a catheter after cesarean delivery. Research has shown that nearly half of women who give birth vaginally experience postvoid residual bladder volume of at least 150 mL in the early postpartum period.[69] Management of maternal reports of urine retention in the early postpartum period include, as least invasive measures, provision of privacy, positioning, and immersion of the woman's hands in water. Catheterization and medication are more invasive options.[108] Urinary incontinence is associated with pregnancy and with trauma during the delivery process. Research has found that pelvic floor exercises can be effective in preventing and treating prenatal and postpartum urinary incontinence.[13] Changes in postpartum urinary function are described further in Chapter 11.

Physical Activity and Sexual Function

The postpartum period is characterized by physiologic changes and alterations in the maternal role that may affect physical activity and sexual function. Continuation or resumption of physical exercise promotes maternal well-being, physically and psychologically, and facilitates postpartum metabolic health and weight management.[37] Fatigue, postpartum anatomic and physiologic changes, lochia, perineal trauma, pain, decreased perineal tone, leaking or engorged breasts, the presence and stress of the new baby, adaptation to the demands of the new parental role, and psychological factors can modify physical and sexual function. Discomfort with sexual intercourse and difficulty with sexual function may result from perineal pain related to perineal trauma and decreased vaginal lubrication.[5] Reduced vaginal lubrication during lactation is associated with increased prolactin and resultant decreased estrogen levels. Breastfeeding may also enhance sexuality with increased breast size and sensitivity of the nipple and areola.[52] Recent research found that most women who resumed sexual intercourse by 6 weeks postpartum had not used contraception, highlighting the need to discuss postpartum contraception during the prenatal period.[92] Women who exclusively breastfeed may experience lactational amenorrhea. The timing of resumption of sexual intercourse should depend on maternal physical restoration (cessation of bleeding and absence of discomfort) and the emotional and psychological readiness of both partners,

taking into account traditional and cultural beliefs, attitudes, and preferences. Health care providers should be respectful of and sensitive to cultural and religious practices associated with sexuality during the postpartum period. Interventions include education and counseling regarding contraception, postpartum physical and sexual function, use of vaginal lubricants, alternate forms of intimacy, and pelvic floor exercises to strengthen and tone the perineal muscles.

ENDOCRINE CHANGES

Postpartum endocrine changes primarily occur secondary to fetoplacental hormonal withdrawal related to delivery of the infant and placenta and to increased production of prolactin. In general, most peptide hormones, enzymes, and other circulating proteins of placental origin reach nonpregnant levels by 6 weeks postpartum. Removal of placental hormones alters the physiologic function of many body systems, initiating return of those systems to their nonpregnant state. The rate at which placental hormones disappear from the maternal system depends on the half-life phases of the particular substance in maternal blood. There are two phases. The first half-life, which is relatively short, involves hormonal removal from the intravascular system; the second half-life involves the slower removal from the extravascular and intracellular space. For example, human chorionic somatomammotropin (hCS), also called *human placental lactogen (hPL)*, has a short second half-life and generally disappears by 1 to 2 days, whereas human chorionic gonadotropin (hCG) has a longer second half-life and can be detected for 3 to 4 weeks postpartum. Substances of fetoplacental origin, such as pregnancy-associated proteins, also disappear soon after delivery, whereas other proteins such as α-fetoprotein, derived from both placental and maternal sources, are present in maternal plasma for several weeks postpartum.[44] Endocrine changes related to mammary development in lactating and nonlactating women are summarized in Figure 5-1.

Estrogen and Progesterone

During pregnancy, estrogen promotes development of the mammary ductal system; progesterone promotes lobular and alveolar growth. The elevated levels of these hormones inhibit prolactin action, thereby inhibiting lactation. Because the placenta is the major source of estrogens and progesterone, these hormones disappear rapidly after delivery. Plasma estradiol (with a first half-life of 20 minutes and second half-life of 6 to 7 hours) reaches levels that are less than 2% of pregnancy values by 24 hours. By 1 to 3 days, estradiol levels are similar to those found during the follicular phase of the menstrual cycle (less than 100 pg/mL [367 pmol/L]), and unconjugated estriol is undetectable. Although the first and second half-lives of progesterone are short, progesterone levels do not fall as rapidly as estradiol levels because the corpus luteum continues to secrete progesterone during the first days after delivery. Generally, progesterone falls to levels similar to the luteal phase of the menstrual cycle (2 to 25 ng/mL [6.4 to

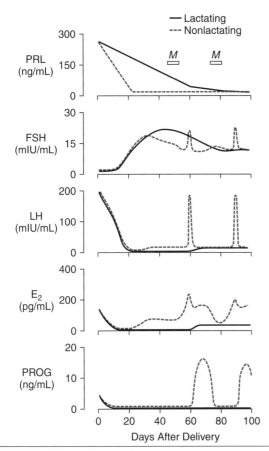

FIGURE 5-1 Changes in serum concentrations of pituitary and gonadal hormones in lactating and nonlactating women in the puerperium. In the top graph, the M boxes refer to menses in the nonlactating women. Changes in hormone levels associated with these menstrual periods are visible in the other graphs for nonlactating women. The lactating woman is still not menstruating. The elevated luteinizing hormone *(LH)* immediately postpartum is because of cross-reaction with assays of human chorionic gonadotropin and the estradiol (E$_2$) and progesterone *(PROG)* are of placental origin. *FSH,* Follicle-stimulating hormone; *PRL,* prolactin. (From Rebar, R.W. [2004]. The breast and the physiology of lactation. In R.K. Creasy, R. Resnik, & J.D. Iams. [Eds.]. *Maternal-fetal medicine: Principles and practice* [5th ed.]. Philadelphia: Saunders. Based on Rolland, R., de Jong, F.H., Schellekens, L.A., & Lequin R.M. [1975]. The role of prolactin in the restoration of ovarian function during the early postpartum period in the human female. Part I: A study during physiologic lactation. *Clin Endocrinol, 4,* 15.)

79.5 pmol/L]) by 24 to 48 hours and to the follicular phase (less than 1 ng/mL [3.2 pmol/L]) by 3 to 7 days.[44] Ovarian production of estrogens and progesterone is low during the first 2 weeks postpartum and gradually increases with resumption of gonadotropin secretion.

Pituitary Gonadotropin

Pregnancy suppresses the pituitary-hypothalamic-ovarian axis (see Chapter 2). Serum levels of follicle-stimulating hormone (FSH) and luteinizing hormone (LH) remain low during the first 2 weeks postpartum in both lactating and nonlactating women, gradually increasing with resumption

of pituitary function by 4 to 6 weeks. The basis for the initially sluggish pituitary response is unknown.[44,77]

Prolactin

Prolactin is a single-chain peptide hormone secreted in pulses by the anterior pituitary gland. Serum levels of prolactin dramatically increase during pregnancy (from 10 ng/mL to 200 ng/mL [434.8 to 8695.6 pmol/L]), working synergistically with other hormones to promote mammary development including lobular, alveolar, and nipple growth. Toward the end of pregnancy, estrogen stimulates the synthesis and secretion of prolactin by the anterior pituitary while dopamine inhibits prolactin secretion. A placental hormone, probably progesterone, inhibits the direct influence of prolactin on the breast during pregnancy, suppressing lactation. With the expulsion of the placenta at delivery, and the significant drop in progesterone, the transition to lactogenesis II occurs, with women experiencing increased milk production, often accompanied by a feeling of breast fullness. Postpartum prolactin levels remain elevated because of frequent infant suckling and nipple stimulation. In nonlactating women, prolactin levels fall into the high end of the nonpregnant range by 7 to 14 days.[77] Delayed lactogenesis II may result from retained placental fragments with the potential to secrete progesterone and further inhibit prolactin.[73] Breastfeeding women experience a gradual decreasing trend in serum prolactin surges after 6 weeks postpartum, even with continued breastfeeding. Patterns of prolactin secretion associated with lactation are described in "Physiology of Lactation."

Oxytocin

Oxytocin is an octapeptide hormone produced in the hypothalamus and stored and secreted by the posterior pituitary gland. The uterus becomes increasingly sensitive to oxytocin throughout pregnancy, probably as a result of increasing estrogens that mediate an increase in oxytocin receptors. Breastfeeding stimulates the release of oxytocin from the posterior pituitary into maternal blood. Oxytocin, in turn, stimulates the electrical and contractile activity in the myometrium by causing the myoepithelial cells of the uterus to contract and involute. Oxytocin also prompts contraction of the myoepithelial cells of the breast, resulting in milk ejection.[73]

RESUMPTION OF MENSTRUATION AND OVULATION

The early postpartum period tends to be a period of relative infertility for many women. Resumption of menstruation and ovulation varies among individual women, regardless of whether the woman is lactating, although there is a greater tendency for exclusively breastfeeding women to experience a longer period of anovulation and amenorrhea. Menstruation usually resumes by 6 weeks postpartum in nonlactating women, although research has found even earlier resumption.[45] The first postpartum menstrual cycle may be anovulatory, although nearly a third of these cycles are preceded by ovulation. That first cycle may also have inadequate luteal function, thereby decreasing fertility in the early postpartum period. Considering the possibility of resumption of ovulation in the early postpartum period, discussion of contraceptive options should be initiated prenatally or immediately postpartum.

Lactation is associated with a delay in resumption of menstruation and ovulation in response to infant suckling—a disruption in the normal pattern of GnRH secretion from the hypothalamus, resulting in lower levels of LH and FSH.[64] Although pulsatile secretion of LH is seen by 8 weeks postpartum, levels are low and of variable frequency with no preovulatory surge. With regular suckling, LH remains suppressed.[73] With decreased lactation frequency, ovulation resumes when GnRH secretion returns to normal and FSH stimulates follicular growth, which in turn increases estradiol and results in LH release, causing follicular rupture, egg release, and formation of the corpus luteum.[64]

Duration of lactational amenorrhea depends on the duration and frequency of breastfeeding and maternal amenorrhea. Therefore exclusive or nearly exclusive breastfeeding, at least 8 to 12 times per day with no formula supplementation, is a relatively reliable method for preventing pregnancy for the first 6 months postpartum, assuming the woman remains amenorrheic. This method of family planning is called the *lactational amenorrhea method (LAM)* and has been supported by research studies and the 1988 Bellagio Consensus.[50]

ANATOMY OF THE MAMMARY GLANDS

The breasts, or mammary glands, are modified exocrine glands consisting of epithelial glandular tissue with an extensive system of branching ducts surrounded by adipose tissue and supported by the pectoralis major muscles and the fibrous bands of the Cooper ligaments. The Cooper ligaments are suspensory and support the shape of the breast. The breasts are highly innervated with rich vascular and lymphatic systems. Each breast contains a range of 4 to 18 lobes and milk ducts arranged in a complex network with ducts that converge at the nipple.[83] The lobes consist of lobules containing clusters of alveoli, the site of milk synthesis and secretion. The alveolus consists of clusters of mammary epithelial secretory cells (lactocytes) surrounded by myoepithelial cells to form smooth muscle contractile units responsible for ejecting milk into the ducts from the lumen of the alveoli.[82] The ducts and alveoli are surrounded by a stroma of fibroblasts, adipocytes, blood vessels, plasma cells (B lymphocytes capable of producing immunoglobulins, especially secretory immunoglobulin A), and a few nerves.[73]

Research using ultrasound imaging demonstrated that there are not lactiferous sinuses under the areola; rather the ducts dilate for milk ejection.[83] Ducts serve to transport milk from the alveoli toward the nipple. The anterior and posterior medial branches of the internal mammary artery and the mammary branch of the lateral thoracic artery supply most of the blood to the breast. The internal thoracic, axillary, and cephalic veins drain the breast. Lymphatic drainage is conducted through the axillary and internal mammary nodes. The second through sixth intercostal nerves innervate the breast. The structure of milk production and ejection portions of the mammary glands is illustrated in Figure 5-2. The breast may be divided into four quadrants (lower inner, upper inner, lower outer, and upper outer with the adjacent tail of Spence) for purposes of mapping and descriptive location.

The nipple is surrounded by the areola. Both the nipple and areola are elastic and darker in pigmentation than the rest of the breast and become even darker during pregnancy and lactation, possibly providing a visual signal for the infant to latch. When not washed off, the mother's nipple and areola also attract the newborn immediately after delivery through the senses of taste and smell.[100] With suckling, the nipple and much of the areola are drawn into the infant's mouth, forming a teat. The stripping action of the infant's tongue against the hard palate, along with the infant's application of vacuum on the breast and the maternal milk ejection response, remove the milk.[33] Smooth muscle and elastic fibers in the areola and nipple form a sphincter to prevent milk loss when the infant is not suckling.[73]

Montgomery tubercles are sebaceous and lactiferous glands located around the areola. They are enlarged and elevated during pregnancy and lactation, providing lubrication and antisepsis. Washing the nipples with soap or antiseptic is usually contraindicated, because it can remove the protective secretions of the Montgomery tubercles, leading

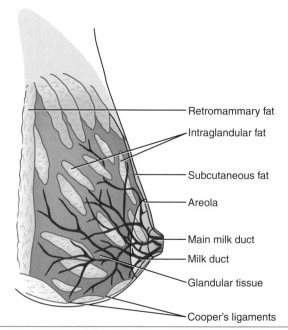

FIGURE 5-2   Side view of lactating breast. (From Ramsay, D.T., Kent, J.C., Hartmann, R.A. & Hartmann, P.E. [2005]. Anatomy of the lactating human breast redefined with ultrasound imaging. *J Anat, 206,* 531.)

Labels in figure:
- Retromammary fat
- Intraglandular fat
- Subcutaneous fat
- Areola
- Main milk duct
- Milk duct
- Glandular tissue
- Cooper's ligaments

to drying and cracking of the nipples and increasing the risk of infection.

PHYSIOLOGY OF LACTATION

Human milk is species-specific and promotes proper growth and development of nearly all infants. Lactation is a complex physiologic process involving integration of neuronal and endocrine mechanisms. Mammary development and lactation can be divided into phases: embryogenesis, mammogenesis (mammary growth during puberty and pregnancy), lactogenesis I and II

(secretory differentiation and secretory activation), lactogenesis III (maintenance of established milk secretion), and involution (cessation of lactation).[51,73,79] Hormonal influences on lactation are summarized in Table 5-1.

Embryogenesis

Mammary growth begins with development of the mammary band and streak in the fourth week of embryonic development, which progresses into the mammary ridge by the fifth week. The ectoderm continues to proliferate and undergo inward growth into the underlying mesoderm as the mammary

---

TABLE 5-1   Hormonal Contributions to Breast Development

HORMONE	ORIGIN	FUNCTION BEFORE AND DURING PREGNANCY	FUNCTION AFTER DELIVERY
Adrenocorticotropic hormone (ACTH)	Anterior pituitary	Blood levels gradually increase during pregnancy; stimulates adrenal to release corticosteroids	High level is believed necessary for maintenance of lactation
Estrogen	Ovary and placenta	Stimulates proliferation of glandular tissue and ducts in breast; probably stimulates pituitary to secrete PRL but inhibits PRL effects on breasts	Level in blood drops at parturition, which aids in initiating lactation; not important to lactation thereafter
Growth hormone	Anterior pituitary	Mediates mammogenesis and lactogenesis	May act with PRL in initiating lactation but appears to be most important in maintaining established lactation
Human chorionic somatomammotropin (hCS) (human placental lactogen [hPL])	Placenta	Like growth hormone in structure; stimulates mammary growth; associated with mobilization of free fatty acids and inhibition of peripheral glucose utilization and lactogenic action	Placental hormone not present after delivery
Oxytocin	Posterior pituitary	Generally no effect on mammary function; sensitivity of myoepithelial cells to oxytocin increases during pregnancy	Causes myoepithelial cells to contract, leading to milk ejection; release is inhibited by stresses such as fear, anxiety, embarrassment, pain, distraction; also causes uterine contraction and postpartum involution of the uterus
Progesterone	Ovary and placenta	With estrogen, stimulates proliferation of glandular tissue and ducts in breast; inhibits milk secretion	Blood level drops at parturition, which aids in initiating lactation; probably unimportant to lactation thereafter
Prolactin (PRL)	Anterior pituitary	Serum levels rise but estrogen suppresses its effect during pregnancy	Stimulates alveolar cells to produce milk; important in initiating and maintaining lactation; may also cause lactation infertility by suppressing release of FSH and LH from pituitary or by causing ovaries to be unresponsive to various psychogenic factors, stress, anesthesia, surgery, high serum osmolality, exercise, nipple stimulation, and sexual intercourse
Prolactin-inhibiting factor (PIF)	Hypothalamus	Suppresses release of PRL into blood; release stimulated by dopaminergic impulses (i.e., catecholamines)	Suppresses release of PRL from anterior pituitary; agents that increase PRL by decreasing catecholamines and thus PIF includes phenothiazines and reserpine
Thyrotropin-releasing hormone	Hypothalamus	Normally no effect on lactation	Stimulates release of PRL; can be used to maintain established lactation
Thyroxine	Thyroid	Normally no direct effect on lactation	Appears to be important in maintaining lactation either through some direct effect on the mammary glands or by control of metabolism

FSH, Follicle-stimulating hormone; *LH,* luteinizing hormone.
Adapted from Worthington-Roberts, B.S. & Williams, S.R. (1997). *Nutrition in pregnancy and lactation* (6th ed.). Madison, WI: Brown & Benchmark.

bud is formed. From the sixth week, mammary glands, milk ducts, and lobular branching gradually develop throughout embryonic growth. The continued proliferation of ingrowing ectodermal cells leads to the development of the branching mammary duct system. By 18 to 19 weeks, a bulb-shaped mammary bud is evident and extends into the mesenchyme, where fat pads are developing. The bud forms secondary buds, which will form the duct system in the mature breast. The secondary buds elongate and invade the fat pads, then branch and canalize to form the rudimentary ductal system.[74]

Mammogenesis

Mammogenesis involves mammary gland development that begins in fetal life, mediated by estrogen and growth hormone, and accelerates at puberty with ductal development, fatty tissue growth, lobuloalveolar development, and further maturation of the breasts. Alveolar development continues under the influence of the luteal phase of the menstrual cycle and in early pregnancy. There is development of terminal duct lobular units and alveoli formation under the influence of progesterone secreted by the ovaries during the luteal phase, as well as under the influence of estrogen and probably prolactin.[74] Because of exposure to maternal hormones, the newborn may experience transient breast swelling with possible secretion in the first few weeks after birth.

During pregnancy, beginning soon after conception, and continuing through the postpartum period, the breasts undergo additional changes, reaching full maturation. Lactogenesis I, characterized by mammary changes including secretory differentiation, occurs during pregnancy. External changes during pregnancy include increases in breast size and areolar pigmentation. The Montgomery tubercles enlarge and become more prominent, and the nipples become more erect. No special preparation of the nipples during pregnancy is necessary. Toward the end of pregnancy, it is normal for some women to experience some leaking of colostrum, although not all women do. The myoepithelial cells hypertrophy. The skin over the breasts appears thinner, the blood vessels are more prominent, and there is a twofold increase in blood flow to the breast. Much of the growth and development is a result of hormonal changes of the corpus luteum and placenta. During the first trimester, the ductal system proliferates and branches under the influence of estrogen, and lobular formation is enhanced by progesterone. The glandular tissue of the alveoli proliferates under the influence of hPL, hCG, and prolactin (see Table 5-1). Growth hormone and adrenocorticotropic hormone (ACTH) act synergistically with prolactin and progesterone to promote mammogenesis.

As pregnancy progresses, the epithelial cells of the alveoli differentiate into secretory cells capable of milk production and the number of alveoli increases. High levels of placental hormones, including progesterone, inhibit milk secretion during pregnancy. Fat droplets accumulate in the secretory cells; concurrently, breast interstitial tissue becomes infiltrated with

lymphocytes, plasma cells, and eosinophils. During the second and third trimesters, there is further lobular growth with formation of new alveoli and ducts and dilation of the lumens. Ductal arborization with development of extensive lobular clusters begins at midgestation. By the third month, prolactin stimulates production of colostrum, followed by the stimulation of its secretion by placental lactogen in the second trimester. Colostrum accumulates in the lumen. A pregnant woman will thus produce colostrum as early as 16 weeks (see "Human Milk for the Preterm Infant"). After birth, the alveolar epithelial cells continue to proliferate with synthesis of milk under the influence of increased levels of prolactin and the stimulus of suckling. An increase in required enzymes within the secretory cells precedes initial synthesis of milk components.

Lactogenesis

Lactogenesis, the initiation of milk production, involves a complex neuroendocrine process in which several hormones interact. Lactogenesis can be divided into three stages. Lactogenesis I occurs from early pregnancy to approximately the third postpartum day. This lactation initiation stage is not dependent on suckling or milk removal, but rather on the cascade of postpartum hormonal changes.[76] Only small amounts of milk are secreted at this time, as a result of the inhibitory effects of the placental hormones. Also during lactogenesis I, secretory differentiation takes place and there is a decrease in sodium; an increase in enzymes, proteins, and immunoglobulins; and an increase in the size of fat droplets in the mammary cells.[75] During the first few postpartum days, the first milk produced, colostrum, is unique in that it has relatively high concentrations of immunoglobulin A, lactoferrin, and oligosaccharide, which provide the newborn infant with protection against infection.

Lactogenesis II, also known as *secretory activation*, is initiated by delivery of the placenta and a significant drop in progesterone along with the increasing level of prolactin.[79] Typically, by days 2 to 4 postpartum, colostrum production continues while compositional changes occur and copious milk secretion begins, referred to as when a mother's "milk comes in," and milk composition shifts. Among the compositional changes are an increase in lactose and a decrease in sodium concentrations as volume increases. During the first postpartum day, the infant receives less than 100 mL of breast milk. By the fourth day, the amount of milk received by the infant increases to approximately 500 mL.[75] During the transition to lactogenesis II, junctions between mammary alveolar cells tighten. With frequent milk transfer, milk synthesis increases and milk production rises. With increased vascularity and fluid congestion in the early postpartum period, many women feel breast fullness and heaviness, which resolves with efficient and frequent milk removal through infant suckling, pumping, or hand expression. Pathologic engorgement occurs when there is inadequate milk removal resulting in milk stasis, swelling, pain, tenderness, and inflammation. Prolonged milk stasis triggers the feedback inhibitor of lactation (FIL), the autocrine inhibitory protein that controls and suppresses milk synthesis that may lead to decreased milk production.[47] Early and frequent suckling, pumping, and/or hand expression facilitates efficient milk production, especially as control of lactation changes from endocrine to autocrine, directed by milk removal.[25]

The autocrine control of mature milk production establishes lactogenesis III (or galactopoiesis). The milk production rate depends on the milk removal rate, in a supply-and-demand response through a feedback mechanism, and the hypothalamic-pituitary axis response regulating hormonal secretion, including prolactin and oxytocin. Suckling stimulates sensory nerves in the nipple and areola, sending messages to the hypothalamus to secrete prolactin and oxytocin. Prolactin stimulates milk synthesis and oxytocin stimulates contraction of the myoepithelial cells causing milk ejection or "let-down." Other hormones enhancing lactogenesis include growth hormone, thyroxine, and insulin, as demonstrated in Figure 5-3.[51] Growth hormone and insulin are important for the survival of alveolar cells and for stimulating glucose entry in the mammary epithelial cells to accelerate lipogenesis.

Breastfeeding frequently and on demand, at least 8 to 12 times in a 24-hour period, or frequent pumping when mother and infant are separated or unable to breastfeed, is usually effective in maintaining adequate milk supply. If milk supply is insufficient despite these efforts, maternal use of galactagogues may augment milk production.[110] Extended milk stasis causes increased pressure in the breast, leading to inflammation and decreased milk synthesis and inhibiting lactation. The introduction of formula supplementation also negatively affects lactation and is associated with shorter breastfeeding duration.[17] In nonlactating women, milk and lymphatic stasis may cause temporary distention and primary engorgement by 2 to 5 days postpartum. The treatment of engorgement for nonlactating women includes avoiding breast stimulation, abstaining from milk expression, application of cold compresses, and administration of antiinflammatory medication. Without stimulation by suckling and removal of milk, secretion of prolactin decreases and milk production ceases. Glandular tissue gradually returns to a resting state over the next few weeks, although the breasts do not completely return to their prepregnant state, because only some of the mammary epithelium formed during pregnancy is reabsorbed with involution.

Prolactin Patterns During Lactation

Milk production and release are controlled primarily by the effect of suckling on hormonal release via a complex neuroendocrine process. Suckling stimulates prolactin release from the anterior pituitary (Figure 5-4). Suckling also stimulates sensory nerve endings in the nipple and areola, sending impulses to the hypothalamus via the spinal cord. As a result, hypothalamic secretion of prolactin-inhibiting factor is suppressed, and adenohypophysis secretion of prolactin increases. Prolactin levels increase toward the end of a feeding, increasing the fat and protein content of milk and its volume.[77]

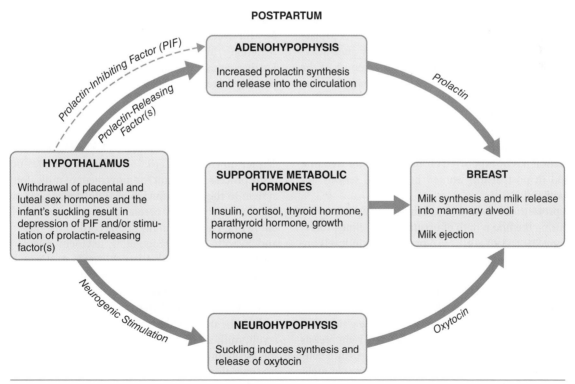

FIGURE 5-3 Hormonal preparation of the breast postpartum for lactation. (Modified from Vorherr, H. [1974]. *The breast.* New York: Academic Press; and Lawrence, R.A. & Lawrence, R.M. [2005]. *Breastfeeding: A guide for the medical profession* [6th ed.]. Philadelphia: Mosby.)

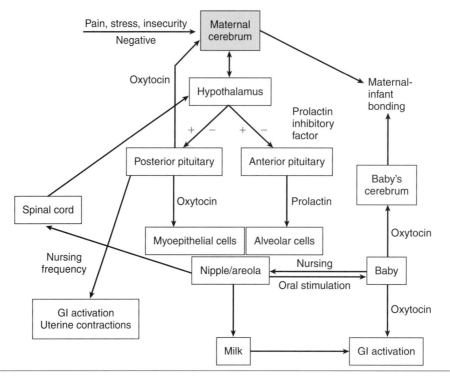

FIGURE 5-4 Endocrinology of lactogenesis. Oxytocin and the letdown reflex. *GI,* Gastrointestinal. (From Newton, E.R. [2017] Lactation and breastfeeding. In S.G. Gabbe, & J.R. Niebyl. [Eds.]. *Obstetrics: Normal and problem pregnancies* [7th ed.]. Philadelphia: Elsevier.)

Prolactin, acting synergistically with insulin and cortisol, stimulates the alveolar secretory cells to produce milk proteins and fat. However, lactation must be preceded by a fall in progesterone and estrogens, removing an inhibitory effect and facilitating response to prolactin. The number of prolactin receptors in breast tissue increases markedly after delivery. The decrease in hCS after expulsion or removal of the placenta may also facilitate prolactin action, in that hCS competes with prolactin for the same breast tissue receptors.[77] If lactation suppression is desired, the woman should abstain from breast stimulation, wear a supportive bra, and apply cold compresses throughout the day. The U.S. Food and Drug Administration has not approved bromocriptine for lactation suppression in postpartum women because of serious adverse outcomes.[36]

Serum prolactin levels are highest in the early postpartum period. During the first month of pregnancy, baseline prolactin levels are 119 ± 19.1 μg/L, and peak prolactin levels are 286 ± 22.6 μg/L in response to infant suckling stimulation.[21] Baseline and peak prolactin levels steadily decline by 6 months postpartum, although breastfeeding frequency and milk production may not be significantly different.[21] Prolactin peaks at approximately 45 minutes from the onset of suckling stimulus; no difference has been found between the left and right breasts in prolactin concentrations.[22] Prolactin circadian rhythm continues throughout lactation, manifesting higher levels at night when the rate of milk synthesis and the prolactin levels in the alveoli are highest, resulting in higher prolactin levels in the morning milk.[22]

As mentioned previously, although milk secretion depends on the endocrine system, such as prolactin secretion, there appears to be a more autocrine regulation of milk volume related to the rate of milk removal. Milk volume is mediated by FIL, which accumulates in the alveoli and inhibits protein secretion if milk is not efficiently removed from the breast. Furthermore, milk stasis causes reduced prolactin receptors, possibly decreasing cellular sensitivity to lactogenic hormones.[47] The rate of milk synthesis may also be regulated by the stretching of the alveolar cells.[76]

Oxytocin Release During Lactation

The let-down or milk ejection reflex is a complex neuroendocrine process important for movement of milk along the duct system to the nipple. Suckling stimulates sensory nerve endings in the nipple and areola. These impulses travel via afferent neural pathways in the spinal cord to the mesencephalon and hypothalamus, stimulating oxytocin release from the posterior pituitary gland (see Figure 5-4). Oxytocin stimulates contraction of the myoepithelial cells surrounding the alveoli (as well as uterine contractions), causing the let-down reflex. Contraction of the myoepithelial cells shortens and widens the ducts, enhancing milk flow to the nipples.[73] As a result, milk is ejected into the duct system and propelled to the lactiferous ducts. Oxytocin release and the let-down reflex may also be stimulated by thinking of the infant, hearing an infant crying, and experiencing orgasm, whereas it may be inhibited by stress through the hypothalamic-pituitary-adrenal (HPA) axis mechanism.[41]

Most of the milk fat is derived from the maternal circulation resulting from nutrition and from stored lipids, but some of the fat is synthesized in the mammary gland from glucose metabolism.[48] Milk fat is synthesized in the endoplasmic reticulum (see Figure 5-6) from precursors available within the secretory cell or obtained from maternal blood. The major constituents of milk fat are triglycerides (98%). Triglycerides are either obtained from maternal plasma or synthesized from intracellular carbohydrates (primarily glyceride and glucose). The triglycerides accumulate and coalesce to form larger fat droplets surrounded by a membrane rich in phospholipids and cholesterol. As fat droplets increase in size, they move to the membrane apex and become part of the milk fat globule.[63] Short-chain fatty acids are synthesized from acetate, whereas long-chain fatty acids are obtained from maternal plasma. There are more than 200 fatty acids in human milk; among their many functions, long-chain fatty acids contribute to neurodevelopment and short-chain fatty acids facilitate maturation of the gastrointestinal tract.[3] Human milk also contains enzymes to aid in fat digestion, including lingual lipase, gastric lipase, bile salt–stimulated lipase, and pancreatic lipase that aids in fat digestion, enhancing absorption, release of energy, and fat digestion.[80]

Protein Synthesis and Release

Protein components of human milk are critical to growth, development, and immunoprotection. Most proteins are synthesized in the mammary gland, and some are transported from maternal circulation. Human milk protein provides amino acids necessary for growth; protective factors such as immunoglobulins; bacteriostatic properties; bioactive factors and proteins to aid digestion and absorption, growth, and promotion of beneficial gut flora; and development of a protective gastrointestinal mucosal barrier.[55] Amino acid content is specific to the unique physiologic characteristics of the human newborn. For example, there is a higher proportion of docosahexaenoic acid (DHA) in preterm mothers' milk than in term mothers' milk, because it is needed for the less mature infants' neurodevelopment and function.[11]

Milk protein primarily consists of whey (alpha-lactalbumin; lactoferrin; serum albumin; and immunoglobulins sIgA, IgA, IgG, and IgM) and casein.[49] The concentrations of whey and casein in human milk are in a 60:40 ratio versus the 20:80 ratio in bovine milk. Although human milk has less total protein than bovine milk, the protein content in human milk is more bioavailable to the infant. Whey protein is easily digested, forming soft, flocculent curds. Protein content slowly decreases during the first 6 months of lactation. The protein content of colostrum is approximately double that of mature milk because of the higher concentration of essential amino acids and the increased abundance of antibodies such as secretory IgA and lactoferrin (see Chapter 13). Lactoferrin accounts for 15% to 20% of human milk protein and has bactericidal and antiviral function.[53]

Human milk also contains other nonprotein nitrogen components and protein factors. These components are used to synthesize nonessential amino acids; enhance gut maturation, growth, and nutrient absorption; or contribute to the immunologic properties of human milk (see Chapter 13). The proteins in human milk are used for nutrition, growth, and other functions such as immunoprotection. The proteins in artificial formula do not contain all the proteins available in human milk. To compensate for this absence, manufacturers add higher concentrations of total proteins, but the excess nitrogen resulting from protein metabolism may place an extra burden on the infant's kidneys.[55] Research and identification of some of the components of human milk motivate formula companies to augment their formula supplements. Formula supplements, however, cannot fully mimic the complexity and dynamic nature of human milk, a bioactive living tissue.[53] Examples of additional proteins and amino acids and their function in human milk include epidermal growth factors for gastrointestinal cellular development and tissue repair; lysozyme for destruction of gram-negative bacteria; amylase for digestion and absorption; carnitine for ketogenesis and thermogenesis; taurine involved in bile acid conjugation, neurotransmission, and neuromodulation; and glutamine and glutamic acid, providing energy substrates and neurotransmission in the brain.[1,54]

Human milk is rich in immunologic substances that provide passive immunity and protect the infant from infections (especially gastrointestinal and respiratory infections) (Table 5-3). It serves as an important facilitator of the initiation and development of the microflora in the infant gastrointestinal system, such as bifidus factors.[53] Human milk may protect against the development of allergies—both by reducing exposure of the infant to bovine milk allergens and by supplying secretory IgA, which reduces intestinal absorption of potentially antigenic proteins before gut closure at 6 to 9 months. In addition to immunoglobulins, protein lactoferrin in human milk is iron-binding and interrupts the activity of iron-dependent pathogens, modulates infant immune function, and kills pathogens together with lysozymes. Lysozymes are also bactericidal; they degrade the outer membrane of gram-positive bacteria.[54]

Human milk also contains other components including enzymes, growth factors, hormones, resistance factors, macrophages, vitamins, minerals, and trace elements. Although the amount of iron in human milk is lower than in bovine milk, it is more bioavailable to the infant because absorption is facilitated by lactose and ascorbic acid. Similarly, human milk's zinc is more bioavailable to the infant than the zinc in bovine milk. There are many components in human milk that have yet to be studied and their function yet to be understood. Considering this, and the fact that human milk provides active protection and growth factors for nearly all newborn infants, human milk remains the gold standard for infant nutrition.

Human Milk for the Preterm Infant

By 16 weeks' gestation, the breast is prepared for lactation. The milk of a woman who delivers a preterm infant (before

TABLE 5-3   Protective Components in Human Milk

IMMUNE PROTECTION	FUNCTION
sIgA, G, M D, E nonspecific protection	Specific antigen targeted antiinfective activity Antibacterial, antiviral, and antimicrobial-toxin, enhancing newborn's immune system maturation
Lactoferrin (500–600 mg/dL [6025–7230 μmol/L]); colostrum (50 mg/dL in mature milk)	Iron chelation: bacteriostatic for siderophilic bacteria and fungi; lactoferrin: 18-amino-acid loop has broad-spectrum antimicrobial action; antiviral activity (HIV, CMV, HSV): prevents viral penetration into cell; immunomodulating activity: reduced release of IL-1, IL-2, and IL-6 and TNF-α from monocytes and of PGE2 from macrophages; activation of NK cells, effect on complement activation and coagulation; antiadhesive for *Escherichia coli* and antiinvasive for *Shigella flexneri;* affects neonatal intestinal growth and recovery from injury; thereby reducing intestinal infection
Lysozyme (5–25 mg/dL [0.5–2.5 g/L]), increases with prolonged lactation	Bacterial lysis: hydrolysis of β1–4 link between N-acetyl-glucosamine and N-acetylmuramic acid in bacterial walls; immunomodulating activity; muramyl dipeptide enhances IgA production, macrophase activation; binding to bacterial lipopolysaccharides: reduces endotoxic effect
κ-casein (<100 mg/dL)	Antiadhesive: inhibits binding of *Helicobacter pylori* to human gastric mucosa and *Streptococcus pneumoniae* and *Haemophilus influenzae* to human respiratory tract epithelial cells; casein macropeptide is a strong growth promoting factor for *Bifidobacterium bifidum*
MINOR NUTRIENTS	
Nucleotides	Enhance: T-cell maturation, NK cell activity, antibody response to certain vaccines, intestinal maturation and repair after diarrhea
VITAMINS	
A (β-carotene)	Antiinflammatory (scavenging of oxygen radicals)
C (ascorbic acid)	Antiinflammatory (scavenging of oxygen radicals)
E (α-tocopherol)	Antiinflammatory (scavenging of oxygen radicals)
ENZYMES	
Bile salt dependent lipase	Production of FFA with antiprotozoan and antibacterial activity
Catalase	Antiinflammatory (degrades H_2O_2)
Glutathione peroxidase	Antiinflammatory (prevents lipid peroxidation)
PAF: acetylhydrolase	Protects against necrotizing enterocolitis (hydrolysis of PAF)
HORMONES	
Prolactin	Enhances the development of B and T lymphocytes, affects differentiation of intestinal lymphoid tissue
Cortisol, thyroxine, insulin and growth factors	Promote maturation of the newborn's intestine and development of intestinal host-defense mechanism
CELLS	
Macrophages, PMNs, and lymphocytes	Microbial phagocytosis, production of lymphokines and cytokines, interaction with and enhancement of other protective agents
Cytokines	Modulate functions and maturation of the immune system

CMV, Cytomegalovirus; *FFA,* free fatty acid; *HIV,* human immunodeficiency virus; *HSV,* herpes simplex virus; *IL,* interleukin; *NK,* natural killer; *PAF,* platelet activating factor; *PGE2,* prostaglandin E2; *PMN,* polymorphonuclear; *TNF-α,* tumor necrosis factor-α.
Adapted from Hamosh, M. (2001). Bioactive factors in human milk. *Pediatr Clin North Am, 48,* 72.

37 weeks gestation) differs from that of a woman who delivers at term. Preterm breast milk is preferred for preterm infants because it has higher protein content and antiinfective properties, including secretory IgA and lactoferrin, fatty acids (such as DHA), oligosaccharides, fat, sodium, chloride, and iron content.[11,68] The proportions of fat and fatty acids are higher in milk from mothers of preterm infants born at earlier gestations.[66] The bioactive factors in human milk support the preterm infant's immature immune system. When fed human milk rather than formula, preterm infants better tolerate feedings and have lower rates of bacterial, viral, and protozoan infections including necrotizing enterocolitis (NEC), an especially life-threatening infection for preterm infants.[87,95]

Considering the high nutritional requirements of preterm infants under 1800 g and the lower presence of some components in preterm human milk, preterm milk should be fortified with protein, vitamins, and minerals.[68] Recent research showed lower rates of intestinal inflammation, NEC, and neonatal mortality among extremely low birth weight infants who received human milk exclusively, which supports the preference of human-milk based fortifiers rather than bovine-based fortifiers.[68,86] Use of human milk and human milk fortifiers for feeding low-birth-weight infants is discussed in Chapter 12.

During early lactation, increasing the frequency of milk expression is important in establishing adequate milk production. This is especially true for the mother of a preterm infant, because the infant is often transferred to the neonatal intensive care unit and is not located near the mother. Furthermore, the infant may be unable to tolerate enteral feedings or may have difficulty with the techniques needed for breast-feeding. Early and frequent milk expression with a double pump along with skin-to-skin contact are recommended to help establish and maintain milk supply.[27]

NUTRITION DURING THE POSTPARTUM PERIOD AND LACTATION

Adequate nutrition and fluid intake are necessary to promote healing and restoration during the postpartum period. Lactating women should drink 600 to 700 mL additional nutritional fluids per day, largely water, with extra attention to environmental and seasonal factors.[57] Maternal basal metabolic rate and cardiac output are greater during lactation, with increased blood flow to the liver and gastrointestinal system to meet demands for specific nutrients and precursors as well as the redistribution of blood to augment the supply of nutrients and precursors to the mammary glands, increasing nutritional demand on the breastfeeding woman. Exclusive breastfeeding utilizes approximately 625 kcal daily with approximately 170 kcal provided by maternal fat stores from pregnancy.[15] Additional nutrition may be required for undernourished women or women breastfeeding multiple children. Once lactation is established, an overweight or obese woman may restrict her caloric intake by 500 kcal per day to facilitate postpartum weight loss without negatively affecting the growth of the breastfed infant.[56] Guidance and consultation on a healthy approach to postpartum weight loss in the breastfeeding woman is recommended.

Advice on maternal food intake to prevent allergic disease has changed in recent years. There is now evidence that fetal and infant exposure to a range of potential allergens via the mother and breast milk helps to develop normal immune tolerance. Although there are some inconsistencies among studies, the preponderance of research now indicates that pregnant and lactating women do not need to avoid traditional allergens unless they themselves are allergic to the food.[70,107]

Maternal diet influences water-soluble vitamins because they easily move from serum to milk. Fat-soluble vitamins are stored in fat and are more difficult to adjust by diet. Thus vitamin D supplementation is recommended for breastfed infants of women with insufficient vitamin D stores, especially those insufficiently exposed to ultraviolet light.[102] When maternal vitamin D intake is sufficient, vitamin D transfer via breast milk will meet infant needs, although doses up to ten times the current recommended intake are needed to produce sufficient transfer from mother to infant.[96] Women who restrict their dairy intake should be assessed for possible nutrient deficiencies, especially calcium and vitamin D.[59] Cultural practices such as fasting may also affect the quality of a woman's milk and should be carefully considered and discussed in a respectful and health-promotional manner.[81] Changes in nutritional requirements during lactation are summarized in Table 5-4.

TABLE 5-4 Recommended Daily Dietary Allowances for Lactation

	FIRST 6 MONTHS	SECOND 6 MONTHS
Energy (kcal)	500+	500+
Protein (gm)	65	62
Vitamin A (RE*)	1300	1200
Vitamin D (mcg)	10	10
Vitamin E activity (mg αTE)[†]	12	11
Ascorbic acid (mg)	95	90
Folacin (mcg)	280	260
Niacin (mg)[‡]	20	20
Riboflavin (mg)	1.8	1.7
Thiamin (mg)	1.6	1.6
Vitamin B_6 (mg)	2.1	2.1
Vitamin B_{12} (mcg)	2.6	2.6
Calcium (mg)	1200	1200
Phosphorus (mg)	1200	1200
Iodine (mcg)	200	200
Iron (mg)	15	15
Magnesium (mg)	355	340
Zinc (mg)	19	16

*RE, Retinol equivalent.
†α-Tocopherol equivalents: 1 mg d-α-tocopherol = 1 αTE.
‡Although allowances are expressed as niacin, it is recognized that on average, 1 mg of niacin is derived from 60 mg of dietary tryptophan.
Modified from Food and Nutrition Board, National Research Council. (1989). *Recommended dietary allowances* (10th ed.). Washington, DC: Government Printing Office; Worthington-Roberts, B.S. & Williams, S.R. (1997). *Nutrition in pregnancy and lactation* (6th ed.). Madison, WI: Brown & Benchmark.

COMMON BREASTFEEDING PROBLEMS

Breastfeeding can be challenging, especially for primiparous and first-time breastfeeding women during the initial few weeks, and any difficulties can reduce the breastfeeding rate drastically. There are many physical, physiologic, psychosocial, and cultural factors that contribute to exclusive breastfeeding and continued breastfeeding duration that should be considered when addressing breastfeeding for mother-infant dyads. Early education, support, and guidance are vital to help prevent or minimize problems.[8] Well before the onset of lactation, the health care provider should discuss with pregnant women, or women who intend to become pregnant, the value of breastfeeding, the important role exclusive breastfeeding plays in the promotion of neonatal development and neonatal health, and the mechanisms of lactation. Health care providers should encourage lactating mothers to seek support and assess previous difficulties and any potential for future problems with breastfeeding and provide anticipatory guidance.

Use of formula in the early postpartum period has been associated with premature termination of breastfeeding, even among women who had intended to exclusively breastfeed; even one bottle of formula can diminish the milk supply.[17] Researchers now believe that diet can be used to alter the gut microbiome; significant differences in gut microbiota composition and activity among breastfed, partially formula fed, and exclusively formula fed children are now recognized.[34] Early skin-to-skin contact is associated with improved lactation outcomes for women who give birth vaginally or by cesarean section.[67,93] Women who deliver by cesarean section may face additional difficulties with breastfeeding, including pain, positional restrictions, and fatigue. Early assistance with positioning and latching, as well as ensuring appropriate pain management, are key to the success of postcesarean breastfeeding. Early skin-to-skin contact is especially important to facilitate breastfeeding after a mother has undergone a cesarean section, because it reduces maternal oxidative stress and increases exclusive breastfeeding rates among these women.[14,109]

Minimizing the separation between the mother and her infant, whatever the mode of delivery, can help facilitate the breastfeeding process. For maternal-infant dyads experiencing separation, such as infants who have been admitted to the special care nursery or neonatal intensive care unit, the health care provider should recommend and guide regular pumping with a hospital-grade breast pump from the first postpartum day. A mother who is separated from her infant should pump for 10 to 15 minutes every 3 to 4 hours around the clock to stimulate milk production, although colostrum expression on the first postpartum day may best be accomplished through hand expression, because colostrum is viscous. The expressed milk should be provided to the infant or stored for future use.

For women who have a history of smoking or live in an environment with smoking exposure, providing clear messages about the importance of reducing and eliminating smoking, along with practical advice and information about resources for assistance, will promote healthier outcomes for both the mother and her infant. Mothers are customarily motivated during the prenatal and postpartum periods to modify lifestyle behaviors, such as reducing or eliminating negative behaviors and exposures and engaging in healthy, positive activities such as breastfeeding. This period thus offers "teachable moments."

Descriptions and treatments of specific, common breastfeeding problems are discussed here, but women encountering such problems should seek the advice of a health care professional specializing in lactation.

Milk stasis, caused by infrequent, insufficient, or missed feedings, may lead to breast engorgement. Frequent and sufficient suckling or milk expression, via pumping or by hand, reduces the congestion and provides relief, along with proper use of antiinflammatory medication. Application of warm compresses 20 minutes before breastfeeding promotes milk flow. Immediately before breastfeeding, brief milk expression reduces areolar distention related to engorgement, thereby facilitating infant latching. Application of cold packs for 20 minutes after breastfeeding promotes vasoconstriction and reduces swelling.[58] Untreated and extended milk stasis causes increased pressure in the breast and decreases capillary blood flow, reducing milk synthesis and inhibiting lactation. Extended insufficient breast stimulation, by lack of either infant suckling or milk expression, will reduce milk synthesis and inhibit lactation. Increasing frequency of breast stimulation through increased breastfeeding frequency or pumping often resolves insufficient milk production,

although some women require use of galactagogues to augment milk production. Milk expression between breastfeeding sessions should be avoided, as it may overstimulate milk production and lead to breast engorgement.

Mastitis, or breast infection, may result from untreated or unresolved engorgement, a plugged duct, milk stasis, breast or nipple trauma such as cracked nipples providing entry for infection, compromised immune status, or extreme fatigue. Common symptoms of mastitis are fatigue, general malaise, fever, and breast tenderness. A woman with mastitis should rest; drink fluids; and take antiinflammatory, antibiotic, and probiotic medications for the full course of treatment as prescribed by her health care provider. In addition, she should apply moist heat before breastfeeding and continue breastfeeding or expressing milk from the affected breast(s) to minimize milk stasis, preferably coordinated with the infant's feeding times, and apply cold compresses upon concluding the breastfeeding session.

Many women experience sore nipples during the first week of breastfeeding. It is crucial to identify the source of the problem as early as possible and provide appropriate treatment to mitigate the possibility of premature abandonment of breastfeeding. Sore nipples may be related to a host of maternal or infant factors, including challenging infant anatomy (e.g., ankyloglossia), challenging maternal anatomy (e.g., inverted nipples), improper latching or positioning, dysfunctional infant suckling, infections (e.g., candidiasis), skin conditions (e.g., eczema), other conditions (e.g., Raynaud syndrome), and other factors.

Consultation with expert resources regarding maternal medication during lactation is important, because medication may transfer into milk (see Chapter 7). The amount of drug secreted into human milk, or the ability of a drug to enter the milk, depends on the drug's lipid solubility, molecular weight, protein binding, ability to pass through the brain–blood barrier, and maternal plasma concentration.[36] Continually updated resources detailing the safety of consuming specific medications during lactation include Thomas Hale's *Medications and Mothers Milk* and the free National Institutes of Health online database, *LactMed*. Consideration of alternative, safer medications for the breastfeeding mother may preserve the breastfeeding relationship when a mother is required to take medication that is contraindicated for breastfeeding.[36] Maternal ingestion of alcohol should be avoided during lactation, because it has been found to significantly increase the risk of fetal alcohol spectrum disorder.[61]

SOCIAL AND CULTURAL BARRIERS TO BREASTFEEDING

Lactation research in various Western populations points to the importance of prenatal and postpartum lactation support from health care providers, such as that supported by the Baby Friendly Hospital Initiative, and from the woman's partner in promoting successful breastfeeding outcomes.[12,39,65] However, lactation physiology and the clinical aspects of breastfeeding management are often lacking in healthcare education and training, affecting the ability of providers to adequately support and advise patients who encounter difficulties.[20] Breastfeeding is a learned behavior. In cultures that frown on "breastfeeding in public," women rarely have the opportunity to observe other women breastfeeding, making successful breastfeeding more difficult.[104] The length of paid maternity leave and the timing of a woman's return to work after giving birth affect breastfeeding success. The longer women are able to postpone their return to work, the higher their odds of exclusively or predominantly breastfeeding beyond 3 months.[35,78]

In the United States women who belong to racial and ethnic minorities, among whom the benefits of breastfeeding may be significant for both themselves and their infants, have lower breastfeeding rates than the general public while experiencing disproportionately higher rates of diabetes, obesity, and cardiovascular disease. Breastfeeding barriers that are unique to minority women include lack of cultural acceptance and support of breastfeeding, lack of support at work, and lack of access to appropriate information. Barriers that affect African American mothers in particular include historical challenges that have shaped negative perceptions of breastfeeding.[46] Maternal-infant dyads who participate in the Supplemental Nutrition Program for Women, Infants, and Children (WIC) have lower 6-month overall breastfeeding rates and 3-month exclusive breastfeeding rates than nonparticipants.[29,40]

The marketing of breast milk substitutes negatively affects breastfeeding. The global sale of formula in 2014 of $44.8 billion illustrates the hold of the formula industry on infant feeding. With timely, knowledgeable interventions and the provision of support to mothers, breastfeeding rates and practices improve rapidly. Whether a mother is able to successfully breastfeed is not her sole responsibility. Breastfeeding success is a shared societal responsibility.[84]

SUMMARY

The postpartum period is a time of rapid and complex change as the woman recovers from labor and delivery and undergoes reversal of the anatomic, physiologic, and endocrine changes of pregnancy, and undergoes the anatomic, physiologic, and endocrine changes to support lactation. These changes provide the background for the new mother's physical function, sense of well-being, and adaptation to her new role and her infant. Understanding of the physiologic basis of lactation is essential in intervening appropriately to support the lactating woman and assisting with problems. Clinical recommendations related to postpartum involutional changes are summarized in Box 5-1.

BOX 5-1 Recommendations for Clinical Practice Related to Involutional Changes and Lactation

Recognize and monitor the progress of normal postpartum involutional changes for each of the reproductive organs (pp. 142-144).

Observe for signs of uterine subinvolution, hemorrhage, and infection (pp. 142-143).

Monitor color, amount, and characteristics of lochia flow (p. 143).

Teach postpartum women the physiologic and anatomic changes to expect during the postpartum period (pp. 142-144).

Teach women signs and symptoms of complications and infection (pp. 142-143).

Provide pain management and comfort techniques to postpartum women experiencing afterpains (p. 142).

Counsel women regarding urinary system changes postpartum (p. 144 and Chapter 11).

Counsel women and their partners regarding changes in vaginal tone and lubrication postpartum (p. 144).

Counsel women and their partners regarding resumption of postpartum sexual activity (p. 144).

Counsel lactating and nonlactating women regarding the expected timing for resumption of menstruation and ovulation and how breastfeeding affects that timing (pp. 145-146).

Counsel women regarding methods and risks of family planning (including lactational amenorrhea method) to reduce the risk of unplanned pregnancy (pp. 145-146).

Counsel women regarding the value of breastfeeding and human milk and the risks of not breastfeeding (pp. 151-159).

Teach women the physiology of lactation and milk production (pp. 147-151).

Encourage and facilitate early initiation of breastfeeding after vaginal birth (pp. 151-158).

Encourage and facilitate early initiation of breastfeeding after cesarean delivery (pp. 157-158).

Evaluate women for potential and past difficulties breastfeeding and provide anticipatory guidance (pp. 157-159)

Encourage frequent breastfeeding (on demand) or milk expression (pp. 157-159).

Recognize breast engorgement and implement interventions appropriate for breastfeeding and nonbreastfeeding women (pp. 148-149, 158).

Teach women interventions to reduce the risk of milk stasis, engorgement, and infection (pp. 148-149, 158).

Assist women who are pumping to increase their milk volume by increasing the frequency of pumping as well as other lactation promotional activities (pp. 156-158).

Provide women who are pumping with information on safe milk expression and storage to minimize nutrient and antiinfective factor loss (pp. 156-158).

Counsel women to abstain from alcohol and tobacco intake during lactation and to consult with a health care provider regarding medication during lactation (p. 158 and Chapter 7).

Learn the composition of human milk and the factors that influence composition and volume (pp. 153-155).

Learn the advantages and limitations of human milk for preterm infants (pp. 155-157 and Chapter 12).

Counsel and train mothers of preterm infants to provide expressed milk (pp. 155-159).

Support breastfeeding in mothers of term and preterm infants (pp. 155-159).

Provide support and counseling to breastfeeding women who are facing barriers to the breastfeeding process (pp. 157-159).

Assess nutritional status and counsel women regarding nutritional needs postpartum (p. 157 and Table 5-4).

References

1. Agostoni, C., et al. (2000). Free amino acid content in standard infant formulas: Comparison with human milk. *J Am Coll Nutr, 19*, 434.

2. American Academy of Pediatrics (AAP). (2012). Breastfeeding and the use of human milk. *Pediatrics, 129*, e827.

3. Andreas, N. J., Kampmann, B., & Mehring Le-Doare, K. (2015). Human breast milk: a review on its composition and bioactivity. *Early Hum Dev, 91*, 629.

4. Ballard, O., & Morrow, A. L. (2013). Human milk composition: nutrients and bioactive factors. *Pediatr Clin North Am, 60*, 49.

5. Barbara, G., et al. (2016). Impact of mode of delivery on postpartum sexual functioning: spontaneous vaginal delivery and operative vaginal delivery vs. cesarean section. *J Sex Med, 13*, 393.

6. Bateman, B. T., et al. (2010). The epidemiology of postpartum hemorrhage in a large, nationwide sample of deliveries. *Anesth Analg, 110*, 1368.

7. Beckmann, M. M., & Stock, O. M. (2013). Antenatal perineal massage for reducing perineal trauma. *Cochrane Database Syst Rev, 2013*(4), CD005123.

8. Bergmann, R. L., et al. (2014). Breastfeeding is natural but not always easy: intervention for common medical problems of breastfeeding mothers—a review of the scientific evidence. *J Perinat Med, 42*, 9.

9. Bode, L., et al. (2014). It's alive: microbes and cells in human milk and their potential benefits to mother and infant. *Adv Nutr, 5*, 571.

10. Bode, L. (2015). The functional biology of human milk oligosaccharides. *Early Hum Dev, 91*, 619.

11. Bokor, S., Koletzko, B., & Decsi, T. (2007). Systematic review of fatty acid composition of human milk from mothers of preterm compared to full-term infants. *Ann Nutr Metab, 51*, 550.

12. Bonuck, K., et al. (2014). Effect of primary care intervention on breastfeeding duration and intensity. *Am J Public Health, 104*, S119.

13. Boyle, R., et al. (2014). Pelvic floor muscle training for prevention and treatment of urinary and fecal incontinence in antenatal and postnatal women: a short version Cochrane review. *Neurourol Urodyn, 33*, 269.

14. Brady, K., Bulpitt, D., & Chiarelli, C. (2014). An interprofessional quality improvement project to implement maternal/infant skin-to-skin contact during cesarean delivery. *J Obstet Gynecol Neonatal Nursing, 43*, 488.

15. Butte, N. F., & King, J. C. (2005). Energy requirements during pregnancy and lactation. *Public Health Nutr, 8*, 1010.

16. Carroli, G., & Mignini, L. (2009). Episiotomy for vaginal birth. *Cochrane Database Syst Rev, 2009*(1), CD000081.

17. Chantry, C. J., et al. (2014). In-hospital formula use increases early breastfeeding cessation among first-time mothers intending to exclusively breastfeed. *J Pediatr, 164*, 1339.

18. Chertok, I. R., Luo, J., & Culp, S. (2011). Intent to breastfeed: A population-based perspective. *Breastfeed Med, 6*, 125.

19. Clapp, M. A., et al. (2016). A multi-state analysis of postpartum readmissions in the United States. *Obstet Gynecol, 127*, S11.

20. Clifford, J., & McIntyre, E. (2008). Who supports breastfeeding? *Breastfeeding Rev, 16*, 9.

21. Cox, D. B., Owens, R. A., & Hartmann, P. E. (1996). Blood and milk prolactin and the rate of milk synthesis in women. *Exp Physiol, 81*, 1007.

22. Cregan, M. D., Mitoulas, L. R., & Hartmann, P. E. (2002). Milk prolactin, feed volume and duration between feeds in women breastfeeding their full-term infants over a 24 h period. *Exp Physiol, 87*, 207.

23. Cunningham, F. G., et al. (2014). *Williams Obstetrics* (24th ed.). New York: McGraw-Hill.

24. Dahlke, J. D., et al. (2015). Prevention and management of postpartum hemorrhage: a comparison of 4 national guidelines. *Am J Obstet Gynecol, 213*, 76.e1.

25. Daly, S. E., & Hartmann, P. E. (1995). Infant demand and milk supply. Part 1: Infant demand and milk production in lactating women. *J Hum Lact, 11*, 21.

26. Fetherson, C. M., Lai, C. T., & Hartmann, P. E. (2006). Relationships between symptoms and changes in breast physiology during lactation mastitis. *Breastfeed Med, 1*, 136.

27. Fewtrell, M. S., et al. (2016). Predictors of expressed breast milk volume in mothers expressing milk for their preterm infant. *Arch Dis Child Fetal Neonatal Ed*, [Epub ahead of print].

28. Fletcher, S., Grotegut, C. A., & James, A. H. (2012). Lochia patterns among normal women: A systematic review. *J Womens Health, 21*, 1290.

29. Francescon, J., Kling, D., Haile, Z., & Chertok, I. R. (2016). Association between WIC enrollment and exclusive breastfeeding at three months postpartum among low-income women. *J Am Osteopath Assoc, 116*, 430–439.

30. Francois, K. E., & Foley, M. R. (2017). Antepartum and postpartum hemorrhage. In S. G. Gabbe, et al. (Eds.), *Obstetrics: normal and problem pregnancies* (7th ed.). Philadelphia: Elsevier.

31. Frei, S., et al. (2010). Puerperal symphysis fundus distance: normal values. *J Perinat Med, 38*, 173.

32. Gabbe, S. G., et al. (2017). *Obstetrics: normal and problem pregnancies* (7th ed.). Philadelphia: Elsevier.

33. Geddes, D. T. (2007). Inside the lactating breast: the latest anatomy research. *J Midwifery Womens Health, 52*, 556.

34. Gomez-Gallego, C., et al. (2016). The human milk microbiome and factors influencing its composition and activity. *Semin Fetal Neonatal Med, 21*, 400.

35. Guendelman, S., et al. (2009). Juggling work and breastfeeding: Effect of maternity leave and occupational characteristics. *Pediatrics, 123*, e28.

36. Hale, T. W. & Rowe H.F. (2017). *Medications and Mothers' Milk* (17th ed.). New York: Springer Publishing.

37. Harrison, C. L., et al. (2016). The role of physical activity in preconception, pregnancy, and postpartum health. *Semin Reprod Med, 34*, e28.

38. Hassiotou, F., & Geddes, D. T. (2015). Immune cell-mediated protection of the mammary gland and the infant during breastfeeding. *Adv Nutr, 6*, 267.

39. Hawkins, S. S., et al. (2015). Evaluating the impact of the Baby-Friendly Hospital Initiative on breast-feeding rates: a multi-state analysis. *Public Health Nutr, 18*, 189.

40. Hedberg, I. C. (2013). Barriers to breastfeeding in the WIC population. *MCN Am J Matern Child Nurs, 38*, 244.

41. Heinrichs, M., Neumann, I., & Ehlert, U. (2002). Lactation and stress: Protective effects of breast-feeding in humans. *Stress, 5*, 195.

42. Hofmeyr, G. J., Abdel-Aleem, H., & Abdel-Aleem, M. A. (2013). Uterine massage for preventing postpartum haemorrhage. *Cochrane Database Syst Rev, 2013*(3), CD006431.

43. Horta, B. L., & Victora, C. G. (2013). *Long-term effects of breastfeeding: a systematic review*. Geneva: World Health Organization.

44. Isley, M. K., & Katz, V. (2017). Postpartum care and longterm health considerations. In S. G. Gabbe, et al. (Eds.), *Obstetrics: Normal and Problem Pregnancies* (7th ed.). Philadelphia: Elsevier.

45. Jackson, E., & Glasier, A. (2011). Return of ovulation and menses in postpartum non-lactating women. *Obstet Gynecol, 117*, 657.

46. Jones, K. M., et al. (2015). Racial and ethnic disparities in breastfeeding. *Breastfeeding Med, 10*, 186.

47. Knight, C. H., Peaker, M., & Wilde, C. J. (1998). Local control of mammary development and function. *Rev Reprod, 3*, 104.

48. Koletzko, B., et al. (2001). Physiological aspects of human milk lipids. *Early Hum Dev, 65*, S3.

49. Kunz, C., et al. (1999). Nutritional and biochemical properties of human milk: Part I. General aspects, proteins, and carbohydrates. *Clin Perinatol, 26*, 307.

50. Labbok, M. H. (2015). Postpartum sexuality and the lactational amenorrhea method for contraception. *Clin Obstet Gynecol, 58*, 915.

51. Lawrence, R. M., & Lawrence, R. A. (2009). The breast and the physiology of lactation. In R. K. Creasy, et al. (Eds.), *Creasy and Resnik's maternal-fetal medicine: principles and practice* (6th ed.). Philadelphia: Saunders.

52. Leeman, L. M., & Rogers, R. C. (2012). Sex after childbirth: postpartum sexual function. *Obstet Gynecol, 119*, 647.

53. Lonnerdal, B. (2014). Infant formula and infant nutrition: bioactive proteins of human milk and implications for composition of infant formulas. *Am J Clin Nutr, 99*, 712S.

54. Lonnerdal, B. (2016). Bioactive proteins in human milk: health, nutrition, and implications for infant formulas. *J Pediatr, 173*, S4.

55. Lopez Alvarez, M. J. (2007). Proteins in human milk. *Breastfeeding Review, 15*, 5.

56. Lovelady, C. A. (2004). The impact of energy restriction and exercise in lactating women. *Adv Exp Med Bio, 554*, 115.

57. Mahdavi, R., Nikniaz, L., & Arefhosseini, S. (2009). Energy, fluids intake and beverages consumption pattern among lactating women in Tabriz, Iran. *Pakistan J Nutr, 8*, 69.

58. Mangesi, L., & Zakarija-Grkovic, I. (2016). Treatment for breast engorgement during lactation. *Cochrane Database Syst Rev, 2016*(6), CD006946.

59. Mannion, C. A., et al. (2007). Lactating women restricting milk are low on select nutrients. *J Am Coll Nutr, 26,* 149.

60. Marchant, S., et al. (1999). A survey of women's experienced vaginal loss from 24 hours to three months after childbirth (the BliPP Study). *Midwifery, 15,* 72.

61. May, P. A., et al. (2016). Breastfeeding and maternal alcohol use: prevalence and effects on child outcomes and fetal alcohol spectrum disorders. *Reprod Toxicol, 63,* 13.

62. McClure, C. K., et al. (2012). Maternal visceral adiposity by consistency of lactation. *Matern Child Health J, 16,* 316.

63. McManaman, J. L., & Neville, M. C. (2003). Mammary physiology and milk secretion. *Adv Drug Deliv Rev, 55,* 629.

64. McNeilly, A. S. (2001). Neuroendocrine changes and fertility in breast-feeding women. *Prog Brain Res, 133,* 207.

65. Mitchell-Box, K. M., & Braun, K. L. (2013). Impact of male-partner-focused interventions on breastfeeding initiation, exclusivity, and continuation. *J Hum Lact, 29,* 473.

66. Molto-Puigmarti, C., et al. (2011). Differences in fat content and fatty acid proportions among colostrum, transitional, and mature milk from women delivering very preterm, preterm, and term infants. *Clin Nutr, 30,* 116.

67. Moore, E. R., et al. (2012). Early skin-to-skin contact for mothers and their healthy newborn infants. *Cochrane Database Syst Rev, 2012*(16), CD003519.

68. Moro, G. E., et al. (2015). XII. Human milk in feeding premature infants: consensus statement. *J Pediatr Gastroenterol Nutr, 61,* S16.

69. Mulder, F. E. M., et al. (2016). Delivery-related risk factors for covert postpartum urinary retention after vaginal delivery. *Int Urogynecol J, 27,* 55.

70. Munblit, D., Boyle, R. J., & Warner, J. O. (2015). Factors affecting breast milk composition and potential consequences for development of the allergic phenotype. *Clin Exp Allergy, 45,* 583.

71. Murray, S. S., & McKinney, E. S. (2014). *Foundations of Maternal-Newborn and Women's Health Nursing.* St. Louis: Elsevier.

72. Negishi, H., et al. (1999). Changes in uterine size after vaginal delivery and cesarean section determined by vaginal sonography in the puerperium. *Arch Gynecol Obstet, 263,* 13.

73. Neville, M. C. (1999). Physiology of lactation. *Clin Perinatol, 26,* 251.

74. Neville, M. C. (2001). Anatomy and physiology of lactation. *Pediatr Clin North Am, 48,* 13.

75. Neville, M. C., & Morton, J. (2001). Physiology and endocrine changes underlying human lactogenesis II. *J Nutr, 131,* 3005S.

76. Neville, M. C., Morton, J., & Umemura, S. (2001). Lactogenesis: the transition from pregnancy to lactation. *Pediatr Clin North Am, 48,* 35.

77. Newton, E. R. (2017). Lactation and breastfeeding. In S. G. Gabbe, et al. (Eds.), *Obstetrics: normal and problem pregnancies* (7th ed.). Philadelphia: Elsevier.

78. Ogbuanu, C., et al. (2011). The effect of maternity leave length and time of return to work on breastfeeding. *Pediatrics, 127,* e1414.

79. Pang, W. W., & Hartmann, P. E. (2007). Initiation of human lactation: secretory differentiation and secretory activation. *J Mammary Gland Biol Neoplasia, 12,* 211.

80. Picciano, M. F. (2001). Nutrient composition of human milk. *Pediatr Clin North Am, 48,* 53.

81. Rakicioglu, N., et al. (2006). The effect of Ramadan on maternal nutrition and composition of breast milk. *Pediatr Int, 48,* 278.

82. Ramsay, D. T., et al. (2004). Ultrasound imaging of milk ejection in the breast of lactating women. *Pediatrics, 113,* 361.

83. Ramsay, D. T., et al. (2005). Anatomy of the lactating human breast redefined with ultrasound imaging. *J Anat, 206,* 525.

84. Rollins, N. C. (2016). Why invest, and what it will take to improve breastfeeding practices? *Lancet, 387,* 491.

85. Sagi-Daim, L., & Sagi, S. (2015). The role of episiotomy in prevention and management of shoulder dystocia: a systematic review. *Obstet Gynecol Surv, 70,* 354.

86. Schanler, R. J. (2015). Fortification of human milk with human milk components. *J Pediatr Gastroenterol Nutr, 61,* S9.

87. Schurr, P., & Perkins, E. M. (2008). The relationship between feeding and necrotizing enterocolitis in very low birth weight infants. *Neonatal Netw, 27,* 397.

88. Schwarz, E. B., et al. (2010). Lactation and maternal risk of type 2 diabetes: a population-based study. *Am J Med, 123,* 863.e1.

89. Seijmonsbergen-Schermers, A. E., et al. (2015). Nonsuturing or skin adhesives versus suturing of the perineal skin after childbirth: a systematic review. *Birth, 42,* 100.

90. Sentilhes, L., et al. (2016). Postpartum hemorrhage: guidelines for clinical practice from the French College of Gynaecologists and Obstetricians (CNGOF) in collaboration with the French Society of Anesthesiology and Intensive Care (SFAR). *Eur J Obstet Gynecol Reprod Biol, 198,* 12.

91. Sherman, D., et al. (1999). Characteristics of normal lochia. *Am J Perinatol, 16,* 399.

92. Sok, C., et al. (2016). Sexual behavior, satisfaction, and contraceptive use among postpartum women. *J Midwifery Women Health, 61,* 158.

93. Stevens, J., et al. (2014). Immediate or early skin-to-skin contact after a Caesarean section: a review of the literature. *Matern Child Nutr, 10,* 456.

94. Stuebe, A. (2009). The risks of not breastfeeding for mothers and infants. *Rev Obstet Gynecol, 2,* 222.

95. Sullivan, S., et al. (2010). An exclusively human milk-based diet is associated with a lower rate of necrotizing enterocolitis than a diet of human milk and bovine milk-based products. *J Pediatr, 156,* 562.

96. Thiele, D. K., Senti, J. L., & Anderson, C. M. (2013). Maternal vitamin D supplementation to meet the needs of the breastfed infant: a systematic review. *J Hum Lac, 29,* 163.

97. Victora, C. G., et al. (2016). Breastfeeding in the 21st century: epidemiology, mechanisms, and lifelong effect. *Lancet, 387,* 475.

98. Westergren-Thorsson, G., et al. (1998). Differential expressions of mRNA for proteoglycans, collagens, and transforming growth factor-beta in the human cervix during pregnancy and involution. *Biochem Biophys Acta, 1406,* 203.

99. Westhoff, G., Cotter, A. M., & Tolosa, J. E. (2013). Prophylactic oxytocin for the third stage of labour to prevent postpartum haemorrhage. *Cochrane Database Syst Rev, 2013*(10), CD001808.

100. Widstrom, A. M., et al. (2011). Newborn behavior to locate the breast when skin-to-skin: A possible method for enabling early self-regulation. *Acta Paediatr, 100,* 79.

101. Willms, A. B., et al. (1995). Anatomic changes in the pelvis after uncomplicated vaginal delivery: Evaluation with serial MR imaging. *Radiology, 195,* 91.

102. Wilson, P. R., & Pugh, L. C. (2005). Promoting nutrition in breastfeeding women. *J Obstet Gynecol Neonatal Nurs, 34,* 120.

103. Wojcik, K. Y., et al. (2009). Macronutrient analysis of a nationwide sample of donor breast milk. *J Am Dietetic Association, 109,* 137.

104. Wolf, J. H. (2008). Got Milk? Not in Public! *Intl Breastfeeding J, 3,* 11.

105. World Health Organization (WHO). (1998). *Evidence for the Ten Steps to Successful Breastfeeding (revised).* Geneva: World Health Organization.

106. World Health Organization (WHO) & UNICEF. (2003). *Global Strategy for Infant and Child Feeding.* Geneva: World Health Organization.

107. Wyness, L. (2014). Nutrition in early life and the risk of asthma and allergic disease. *Br J Community Nurs, 7,* S28.

108. Yip, S. K., et al. (2004). Postpartum urinary retention. *Acta Obstet Gynecol Scand, 83,* 881.

109. Yuksel, B., et al. (2015). Immediate breastfeeding and skin-to-skin contact during cesarean section decreases maternal oxidative stress, a prospective randomized case-controlled study. *J Matern Fetal Neonatal Med, 29,* 2691.

110. Zuppa, A. A., et al. (2010). Safety and efficacy of galactogogues: substances that induce, maintain and increase breast milk production. *J Pharm Pharm Sci, 13,* 162.

Fetal Assessment

Tekoa L. King

Fetal growth and development are dependent on adequate exchange of gases and nutrients within the placenta throughout the course of pregnancy. Fetal well-being in utero can be assessed via clinical measurement of the maternal fundal height, ultrasound measurement of fetal morphologic features, and tests of other biophysical parameters such as the fetal heart rate (FHR), amniotic fluid indices, and fetal movement. During labor, fetal oxygenation is monitored indirectly via assessment of FHR characteristics and patterns that develop over time. The status of fetal oxygenation can be measured directly via fetal scalp sampling and newborn umbilical cord gas analysis. This chapter reviews the physiology of fetal heart function, acid-base exchange, the fetal response to hypoxia, FHR patterns that occur during labor, and clinical implications for surveillance of the fetus during pregnancy, labor, and birth. First and second trimester genetic screening and diagnostic techniques are described in Chapter 3.

PHYSIOLOGY OF FETAL HEART FUNCTION

The average baseline FHR in a healthy fetus at 20 weeks is 155 beats per minute (bpm) with a range of 110 to 180 bpm. This baseline rate is determined by the depolarization rate of the sinoatrial (SA) node, which is actively inhibited by tonic parasympathetic input. As the parasympathetic system matures with advancing gestational age, the resting heart rate decreases.[70] At term, the average FHR is 140 beats per minute and the normal range is 110 to 160 bpm.[70]

Autonomic Control of Fetal Heart Rate

The fetal heart has a pacemaker in the SA node that causes rhythmic contractions. The intrinsic pace is set by the SA node in the right atrium, which produces the fastest rate.[77] The average FHR is the result of several factors that modulate this intrinsic rate, including vagal stimulation at the SA node, sympathetic innervation, and feedback from baroreceptors and chemoreceptors. Vagal stimulation causes a decrease in the rate of firing of the SA node and slows the rate of transmission from the atria to the ventricles, which results in a slower heart rate. Although the fetal heart is innervated by the sympathetic system as well, parasympathetic (vagal) input maintains a baseline rate. The parasympathetic stimulation

becomes dominant over sympathetic input as the fetus develops, which is why the FHR is initially faster when first detectable and slows as the fetus matures. The sympathetic nervous system innervates the heart muscle in the atria and ventricles and provides a reserve to improve the heart's pumping ability during intermittent stress. Other humoral factors, such as catecholamines, vasopressin, angiotensin II, and prostaglandins can also stimulate an increase or decrease in parasympathetic or sympathetic activity.[70]

Central Nervous System Influences

In addition to the tonic effect on the SA node that determines the baseline FHR, vagal stimulation induces variability in the time interval between each heart beat secondary to influences on the vagus in the central nervous system. These influences include baroreceptors, chemoreceptors, and other central nervous system functions. The central nervous system also influences the FHR via an integrative center in the medulla oblongata where the vagus nerve originates (Figure 6-1). Because the medulla oblongata is near the respiratory center, the FHR may occasionally increase with inspiration and decrease with expiration. During fetal sleep, variation in the timing between each FHR diminishes and the variability has less amplitude. During fetal movement, the heart rate increases and a brief acceleration occurs.

Baroreceptors and Chemoreceptors

Baroreceptor reflexes in the aortic arch and carotid arteries are sensitive to changes in systemic arterial pressure (Figure 6-2). Baroreceptors are stimulated by the increase in blood pressure that occurs if umbilical cord circulation is occluded, which causes an increase in afterload.[6] This increase in pressure and baroreceptor stimulation initiates a rapid neural reflex to the midbrain, which stimulates the vagus to slow the FHR, which results in fetal bradycardia.[69,92] For example, rapid complete occlusion of the umbilical cord during labor causes an immediate rise in arterial pressure and rapid bradycardic response, secondary to baroreceptor stimulation.[38,66]

Chemoreceptors are present in the carotid artery, carotid sinus, and aorta. When the chemoreceptors detect hypoxemia (a decrease in circulating oxygen) or hypercapnia (an increase in carbon dioxide), they stimulate a vagally mediated reflex

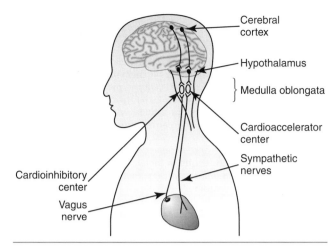

FIGURE 6-1 Cerebral influences on fetal heart rate. (From Parer, J.T. [1976]. Physiological regulation of fetal heart rate. *J Obstet Gynecol Neonatal Nurs, 5,* 265.)

bradycardia and a slight increase in blood pressure.[92] The chemoreceptor response is slower than the baroreceptor response. After chemoreceptor detection of a decrease in the Po_2, the fall in FHR is slower. Baroreceptors and chemoreceptors are described further in Box 6-1.

FETAL ACID-BASE PHYSIOLOGY

Table 6-1 lists definitions for terms used to describe acid-base physiology. During aerobic or oxidative metabolism, the fetus forms carbonic acid (H_2CO_3) via hydration of CO_2. Carbonic acid dissociates into H_2O and CO_2, and CO_2 easily diffuses across the placental membranes into the maternal venous circulation in the intervillous space. During anaerobic metabolism, which occurs when there is insufficient oxygen for complete oxidation of glucose for production of adenosine triphosphate (ATP), noncarbonic metabolic acids such as lactic acid ($C_3H_6O_3$) are produced. These acids are not cleared quickly by the kidneys secondary to the immature renal function in the fetus, and they do not diffuse quickly across the placental membranes into the maternal circulation.[17] Under normal conditions, buffers such as bicarbonate (HCO_3) and hemoglobin maintain the pH within the fetal circulation within a narrow range.[8] If oxygen is not available and anaerobic metabolism continues, noncarbonic acids accumulate in the fetal circulation, bicarbonate is used up, the pH falls, and metabolic acidosis develops. Normal metabolic activities fail when the pH falls below critical levels.

UTEROPLACENTAL CIRCULATION AND GAS EXCHANGE

Fetal "respiration," or transfer of oxygen and carbon dioxide between fetal and maternal circulations, depends on (1) adequate uterine blood flow into the intervillous space; (2) sufficient placental area available for gas and nutrient exchange; (3) efficient diffusion of oxygen, carbon dioxide, and nutrients across the membranes that separate fetal and maternal blood (see Chapter 3); and (4) unimpaired circulation within

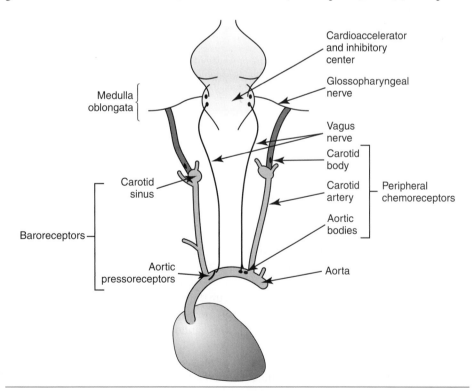

FIGURE 6-2 The peripheral chemoreceptors and baroreceptors and their input to the cardiac integrating center in the medulla oblongata. (From Parer, J.T. [1976]. Physiological regulation of fetal heart rate. *J Obstet Gynecol Neonatal Nurs, 5,* 265.)

BOX 6-1   Baroreceptors and Chemoreceptors

Baroreceptors and chemoreceptors are part of the homeostatic negative feedback mechanisms that regulate blood pressure. Chemoreceptors are also involved in regulating the respiratory rate.

Baroreceptors (see Figure 6-2) are sensory nerve endings located in the walls of most major arteries in the neck and chest. They are stimulated by changes in pressure. When arterial blood pressure increases and the walls of an artery stretch, the baroreceptors send signals to (1) the vasomotor center, which results in a reflex vasodilation, and (2) the vagus nerve, which results in vagally mediated bradycardia. The combination of vasodilation and slower heart rate decreases blood pressure.

Chemoreceptors (see Figure 6-2) are sensory nerve endings located peripherally near the baroreceptors in the carotid sinus and aortic arch and centrally in the medulla oblongata. Chemoreceptors are stimulated by changes in blood oxygen and carbon dioxide tension. In adults, when hypoxemia or hypercarbia is detected by the central chemoreceptors, a reflex is initiated that results in (1) vasomotor stimulation, which causes vasoconstriction and increased blood pressure, and (2) vagal inhibition, which results in tachycardia. In a fetus, central and peripheral chemoreceptor stimulation results in hypertension and bradycardia.

TABLE 6-1   Terms Related to Acid-Base Physiology

Acidemia	Increased concentration of hydrogen ions in the blood.
Acidosis	Increased concentration of hydrogen ions in the tissue.
Aerobic metabolism	Metabolism of glucose using oxygen. The end-products of aerobic metabolism are large amounts of energy (38 ATP molecules, H_2O, and CO_2).
Anaerobic metabolism	Metabolism of glucose without the use of oxygen. Glucose breaks down partially and the end-products are a small amount of energy (2 ATP molecules) and lactic acid.
Asphyxia	From the Greek word for "pulseless." Asphyxia is characterized by profound acidemia that is both metabolic and respiratory in nature. Some authors say the diagnosis of asphyxia is based on evidence of ischemia and organ dysfunction, but this is not universal. In fact, discrimination between metabolic acidemia and asphyxia is not well defined.
Base	A substance that is capable of accepting hydrogen ions, thereby decreasing acidity.
Base excess (BE)	The amount of base or HCO_3^- that is left available for buffering. A BE of -8 means there is less BE available than a value of -4. The lower BE implies a greater degree of anaerobic metabolism and more production of acids.
Bicarbonate (bicarb)	HCO_3^- is the base or hydrogen acceptor that is part of the primary buffering system within the blood.
Buffer	A chemical substance that is both a weak acid and salt. Buffers can absorb or give up hydrogen ions, thereby maintaining a constant pH value. The primary buffer involved in fetal oxygenation is HCO_3^-.
Hypercapnia	Excessive carbon dioxide in blood.
Hypoxia	Decreased oxygen in tissue.
Hypoxemia	Decreased oxygen content in blood.
Metabolic acidosis	Low bicarbonate (low base excess) in the presence of normal P_{CO_2} values.
pH	pH refers to the concentration of hydrogen ions in blood. The term pH refers to "puissance hydrogen," which is French for strength (or power) of hydrogen. The term pH was devised by the Danish biochemist S.P. Sorenson in 1909. A pH of 7.0 is the same as 0.0000001 moles per liter of hydrogen ions, whereas 0.01 moles/liter is written as a pH of 2.
Respiratory acidosis	High P_{CO_2} with normal bicarbonate levels. Found in acute cord compression before anaerobic metabolism has started.

From King, T.L. & Parer, J.T. (2000). The physiology of fetal heart rate patterns and perinatal asphyxia. *J Perinat Neonatal Nurs, 14*, 19. Original table modified from references 4, 13, 28, and 70.

the umbilical vein that returns oxygenated blood to the fetus. Current knowledge about the fetal response to changes in placental function and gas exchange comes largely from studies of pregnant sheep, the animal in which gestational physiology most closely reflects that of humans.[7]

Uterine Blood Flow in the Intervillous Space

Approximately 500 to 800 mL of blood flows to the uterus each minute.[12] Between 70% and 90% of the uterine blood flow circulates through the intervillous space, and the volume of blood that reaches the intervillous space is dependent on adequate flow through the maternal spiral arteries in the uterine endometrium. Maternal hypotension, hypertension,

and/or uterine contractions can decrease blood flow into the intervillous space. The maternal spiral arteries run perpendicular to uterine muscle, and the maternal veins are usually parallel to the uterine wall; thus uterine contractions that occur during labor cause vasoconstriction, which temporarily interrupts blood flow in and out of the intervillous space. Both inflow and outflow tracts are affected. During uterine contractions, the volume of maternal blood in the intervillous space that is available for continued gas exchange remains the same or slightly more than the volume present during uterine quiescence.[9,39]

Because the spiral arteries are maximally dilated during pregnancy and have lost some of their ability to "autoregulate" or constrict if pressure in the vessel drops, there is little physiologic function that can increase uterine blood flow. However, maximal uterine blood flow can be facilitated and events known to decrease uterine blood flow can be avoided. For example, two interventions that maximize blood flow to the uterus are side-lying positions (prevents compression of the inferior vena cava) and administration of tocolytics (temporarily decreases uterine contractions).

Umbilical Blood Flow

The two umbilical arteries and one umbilical vein spiral through a matrix of a specialized connective tissue called Wharton jelly within the umbilical cord. The umbilical cord is normally lighter than any of the fetal parts and generally moves freely within the amniotic fluid. However, the cord can be compressed during uterine contractions. Recurrent cord compression can result in the development of acidosis if oxygen and carbon dioxide transfer are significantly impeded enough to cause the fetus to shift to anaerobic metabolism, which generates lactic acid.[90]

Placental Area

The placental area available for exchange of gases and nutrients is approximately 1.8 m^2.[70] Several mechanisms can adversely affect the available villous surface. Abruptio placenta or uterine rupture causes an acute decrease in placental area. Fetal survival in these situations depends on the percentage of placental tissue that remains, the reserve of the individual fetus, and the rapidity of clinical response. Chronic maternal conditions such as hypertension, preeclampsia, diabetes, and/or renal disease are characterized by small artery dysfunction, which can result in reduced placental growth, placental infarcts, and chronic intrauterine fetal growth restriction. Finally, infection within the placenta can cause a reduction in placental size and alter transfer of oxygen and nutrients (see Chapter 3).

Transfer of Oxygen and Carbon Dioxide

Diffusion of oxygen and carbon dioxide across the membranes that separate maternal and fetal blood in the intervillous space occurs quickly. Factors that affect the rate of maternal-to-fetal gas exchange in the intervillous space include maternal and fetal oxygen-hemoglobin dissociation curves, the Bohr effect (see Box 10-1), maternal and fetal hemoglobin concentrations, and the oxygen affinity of fetal hemoglobin (see Chapter 8). Carbon dioxide transfer is affected by hydrogen ion concentration and the Haldane effect.

Oxygen Transfer

The Po$_2$ in maternal arteries that supply the intervillous space is 30 to 35 mm Hg (3.99 to 4.65 kPa), which is similar to the average Po$_2$ in maternal capillaries.[7] Thus the Po$_2$ in the fetal umbilical vein, which delivers oxygenated blood to the fetus, is approximately the same as the average Po$_2$ in maternal veins.[12] Despite an arterial partial pressure of oxygen that is lower than the Po$_2$ in adult arteries, the fetus has several physiologic mechanisms that support sufficient oxygenation.

First, the fetal oxygen-hemoglobin dissociation curve is to the left of the adult curve, because fetal hemoglobin (HbF) has a higher affinity for oxygen compared with adult hemoglobin. The pH of blood on the maternal side of the intervillous space drops and becomes more acidic when oxygen is released and fetal metabolites enter the maternal circulation. This shifts the maternal oxygen-hemoglobin dissociation curve to the right (the Bohr effect), which further encourages the transfer of oxygen from the mother to the fetus. As the fetus gives up carbon dioxide, the pH in the fetal compartment rises and becomes more alkaline, shifting the fetal dissociation curve to the left, which facilitates oxygen uptake by the fetus. This movement of hydrogen ions results in a displacement of both dissociation curves, moving them further apart (double Bohr effect). As the distance between the two curves increases, oxygen transfers at a faster rate from maternal blood to fetal blood. This process is unique to the placenta.

Second, in addition to a higher affinity for oxygen, the fetus has an increased number of red blood cells and thus more hemoglobin (approximately 15 g/dL [150 g/L] versus an average of 12 g/dL [120 g/L] in adults). Third, the fetus has more capillaries per unit of tissue. Fourth, HbF is functionally different than adult hemoglobin in a way that allows it to bind to oxygen more efficently.[89] Finally, the anatomic shunts in the fetal circulation (see Chapter 9) support direct delivery of oxygenated blood to vital organs. The combination of these factors results in a higher oxygen-carrying capacity compared with the oxygen carrying capacity of the mother. Usual fetal blood gases are listed in Table 10-4.

Maternal hypoxia (especially a Po$_2$ below 60 mm Hg [7.98 kPa]) can have significant consequences for the fetus. In this situation, the maternal oxygen-hemoglobin dissociation curve shifts to the left (toward the fetal curve), decreasing oxygen availability to the fetus.[16] Maternal hyperventilation, which results in decreased Pco$_2$, can also lead to decreased fetal oxygenation by shifting the maternal oxygen-hemoglobin dissociation curve to the left.

Carbon Dioxide Transfer

Carbon dioxide is transported in blood dissolved in plasma, as bicarbonate, or bound to the globin part of hemoglobin. The rate at which the maternal circulation can take up carbon dioxide is dependent on the amount of maternal hemoglobin that is not combined with oxygen. Uncombined hemoglobin is free to buffer the hydrogen ions formed by the dissociation of carbonic acid. As maternal hemoglobin gives up oxygen, it is able to accept increased amounts of carbon dioxide (the Haldane effect). The fetus gives up carbon dioxide as oxygen is accepted, without altering the local Paco$_2$ levels. This double Haldane effect is unique to the placenta and is probably responsible for half the transplacental carbon dioxide transfer.

Summary of Fetal Respiration

Uterine and umbilical blood flow are the most important components of uteroplacental gas exchange, or fetal "respiration."

Oxygen and carbon dioxide readily diffuse across the membranes separating fetal and maternal circulations. Rarely, an increased fetal need for oxygen occurs in the presence of infection, fetal anemia, or if the fetus is exposed to decreased maternal P_{O_2}, which can occur if the mother experiences cardiopulmonary disease, severe anemia, or acute trauma.

FETAL RESPONSE TO HYPOXIA

The fetus is normally able to maintain aerobic metabolism during the transient decreases in oxygenation that are common when there is a temporary interruption in uterine or umbilical blood flow because of the physiologic mechanisms described. In addition, the fetus has several compensatory mechanisms that facilitate oxygenation of critical organs during periods of hypoxia, listed in Box 6-2.[29,85,94]

Aerobic metabolism will be maintained until the available oxygen in the intervillous space falls to approximately 50% of normal levels.[12] In addition to increasing the efficiency of

---

BOX 6-2   Fetal Compensatory Responses to Hypoxia

Acute Hypoxia: "Brain Sparing" Effect
- Increased efficiency of oxygen extraction
- Redistribution of blood flow to shunt more blood to heart, brain, and adrenal glands, and blood flow in organs such as kidneys, gut, and striated muscle vasoconstricts
- Fetal heart rate bradycardia response, which slows the speed of cardiac blood flow, enhancing myocardial oxygen extraction and increasing diastolic volume, which preserves cardiac output
- Anaerobic metabolism

Chronic Hypoxia
- Increase in nucleated red blood cells
- Limited growth, which can result in intrauterine growth restriction
- Slowing or cessation of fetal breathing and fetal movements

---

oxygen extraction, transient hypoxemia initiates a redistribution of blood flow so that blood is preferentially shunted to the heart, brain, and adrenal glands (increased twofold to threefold) and blood flow to the gut, spleen, kidneys, and limbs is decreased (Figure 6-3).[29,43] In addition, fetal breathing ceases and the FHR slows as a response to hypoxia, which decreases oxygen consumption. Together these compensatory mechanisms are referred to as the "brain sparing effect" and maintain blood flow and oxygenation in the organs that are critical for survival if hypoxia is not severe.[29]

Acute Fetal Hypoxia

If the normal compensatory mechanisms are not sufficient to allow the fetus to maintain aerobic metabolism, anaerobic metabolism will ensue.[13] Oxygen uptake by fetal hemoglobin becomes less efficient as the pH decreases. The change from aerobic metabolism to anaerobic metabolism results in the production of lactic acid, which does not cross the placenta into the maternal circulation fast. The build-up of lactic acid in the fetal circulation sets the stage for the development of a metabolic acidosis. If normal fetal oxygenation does not resume, metabolic acidosis will progress to asphyxia, which interrupts metabolic processes. If this occurs, the adaptive mechanisms fail and arterial oxygenation will fall below critical levels, resulting in myocardial depression and loss of autoregulation in cerebral blood flow (see Chapter 15). The brain becomes ischemic in the presence of passive-pressure circulation.[51,71,78,84] Thus the cause of central nervous system injury is from both hypoxia and ischemia.

Chronic Fetal Hypoxemia

Chronic reductions in uteroplacental perfusion stimulate hematopoiesis via renal production of erythropoietin. This leads to an increase in nucleated red blood cells that can be measured in the neonate.[82] Chronic hypoxia also causes the fetus to limit the oxygen-consuming processes, which can result in growth and behavioral complications. Oxygen-consuming activities such as protein synthesis must be curtailed to direct

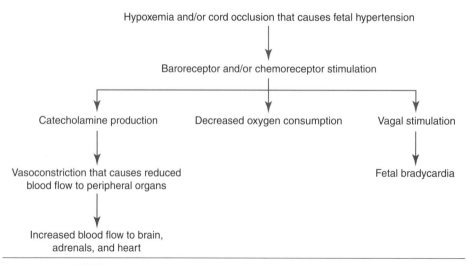

FIGURE 6-3   Fetal compensatory response to transient hypoxemia.

Tachycardia

Fetal tachycardia (baseline higher than 160 bpm for 10 minutes or more) can occur secondary to several fetal and maternal conditions. In term fetuses, short periods of tachycardia are a normal compensatory response to transient hypoxemia and are often seen for a brief period after a prolonged FHR deceleration. These periods of tachycardia are probably caused by a transient rise in catecholamine levels.

The most common cause of sustained tachycardia during labor in a term fetus is maternal infection, specifically chorioamnionitis.[10] Fetal tachycardia is present in 16% to 38% of cases of chorioamnionitis.[57] Fetal tachycardia can also be seen after sublethal hypoxic events that cause catecholamine release and sympathetic stimulation.

Other sources of fetal tachycardia are the use of β-sympathomimetic agents (to inhibit uterine contractions), ephedrine given to correct maternal hypotension after induction of epidural anesthesia, fetal anemia (Rh isoimmunization), acute fetal blood loss (placental abruption), or an abnormal fetal conduction system (fetal arrhythmia).

Bradycardia

Bradycardia is a sustained FHR of less than 110 bpm for longer than 10 minutes.[50] Bradycardia is the initial fetal response to acute hypoxemia or elevated blood pressure secondary to cord occlusion. Nonasphyxial causes of bradycardia include heart block and hypothermia.[35]

A few otherwise normal fetuses have a heart rate below 110 bpm that appears to be a normal variant. A transient fetal bradycardia commonly follows administration of intrathecal opioids or local anesthetics for epidural analgesia during labor.[27] The cause of this bradycardia is indirect in that the bradycardia is secondary to an interruption of uteroplacental circulation that occurs by one of two pathways: First, the rapid decline in circulating maternal catecholamines that accompanies pain relief can result in uterine hypertonus. Second, the induction of maternal hypotension after a regional blockade can cause a decrease in uteroplacental blood flow.

End-stage bradycardias at the end of the second stage of labor, in which the FHR remains higher than 80 bpm and FHR variability is usually retained, are not associated with newborn acidemia.

An acute terminal bradycardia can be caused by (1) a decrease in umbilical blood flow (cord compression, cord prolapse), (2) decreased placental exchange area (abruptio placentae, uterine rupture), (3) impaired uterine blood flow (acute maternal hypotension or excessive uterine contractions), or (4) decreased maternal oxygenation (apnea secondary to seizures).[46] If the FHR is less than 80 bpm, the FHR variability will diminish; this pattern is highly associated with newborn metabolic acidemia.[42,91]

Periodic and Episodic Fetal Heart Rate Decelerations

FHR decelerations are classified as early, late, or variable. This classifications scheme is characterized by the onset of the waveform, which is either "abrupt" or "gradual."[50,65] Periodic FHR decelerations are associated with uterine contractions. Episodic decelerations may or may not be associated with uterine contractions. Late and early decelerations are periodic, whereas variable decelerations may be periodic or episodic. The researchers who initially identified FHR decelerations named them on the basis of their appearance and relationship to uterine contractions, and not on the basis of their etiology or their relationship to fetal acidemia.[11,32] The etiology and relationship between FHR decelerations and fetal acidemia is a continued subject of research.

Early Decelerations

Early decelerations have a gradual waveform that mimics the start, peak, and resolution of a uterine contraction. The nadir of the deceleration occurs at the same time as the peak of the uterine contractions. These decelerations are not common. When they do occur, they generally appear during the active phase of the first stage of labor and they do not persist. Early decelerations are always associated with moderate FHR variability, and they are not associated with fetal acidemia.[50]

The exact physiologic mechanism responsible for early decelerations had not been conclusively determined. One theory is that early decelerations are the result of a physiologic chain of events that begins with head compression during a uterine contraction, which leads to a reduction in cerebral blood flow, hypercapnia, and hypoxemia. However, head compression triggers a vagal response and rapid bradycardia, so this putative etiology is not evidence-based. Some experts believe early decelerations may also be a benign variant of late reflex decelerations.

Late Decelerations

Late decelerations have a gradual waveform. They characteristically begin a few seconds after a contraction starts, reach their nadir 20 to 90 seconds after the peak of the contraction, and have a slow recovery phase (Figure 6-7).[50,65] These decelerations can be recurrent, occurring with each contraction over a period of time. Late decelerations are believed to be secondary to hypoxemia detected by chemoreceptors in the carotid artery, carotid sinus, and aortic arch.[63] The nadir of the fetal bradycardia is "late" in that it follows the peak of the uterine contraction (see Figure 6-7). An interruption in uteroplacental blood flow (e.g., uterine contraction) sufficient to impair oxygen transfer to the fetus initiates this response. The available oxygen in the intervillous space declines without blood flow. The fetal capillaries in the placenta therefore receive less oxygen. The relatively deoxygenated blood then circulates through the umbilical vein and fetal heart before reaching the chemoreceptors. The chemoreceptor reflex is thus slightly slower than the baroreceptor reflex, and the onset of the FHR deceleration is gradual.

Late decelerations can occur in the presence of moderate variability or minimal or absent variability.[74] Late decelerations with variability may be seen secondary to a transient drop in oxygenation, such as decreased uterine blood flow

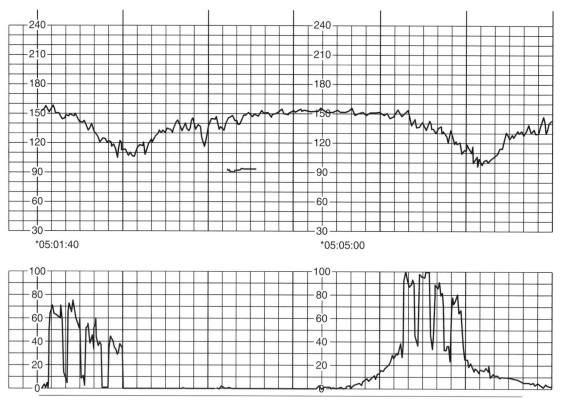

FIGURE 6-7   Late decelerations. The upper graph is fetal heart rate; the lower graph is uterine pressure.

during maternal hypotension, in a previously well-oxygenated fetus; these late decelerations are not associated with significant fetal acidemia.[72] Late decelerations with minimal or absent variability occur when the amount of oxygen in blood coming from the placenta cannot support fetal myocardial function. Thus late decelerations in the presence of absent or minimal variability are associated with an increased risk of significant fetal acidemia.[50,72] A fetus with decreased placental reserve, such as in preeclampsia or fetal growth restriction, is more likely to develop late decelerations during labor.[21]

Variable Decelerations

Variable decelerations can be inconsistent in timing compared with uterine contractions (Figure 6-8). These decelerations have an abrupt onset (less than 30 seconds from onset to nadir), and they may be periodic (associated with a uterine contraction) or episodic (not associated with a uterine contraction). The clinical implications of variable decelerations are related to the depth and duration of the deceleration.[72] The theorized physiology of variable decelerations is as follows: Partial compression of the umbilical cord results first in hypotension secondary to umbilical vein compression that causes a chemoreceptor-stimulated bradycardia.[6] The umbilical vein is larger and less protected by Wharton jelly; thus it is more vulnerable to compression than the umbilical arteries.[18] Full compression results in fetal hypertension and a baroreceptor response that causes an abrupt bradycardia.[6] Head compression can also cause vagal stimulation and bradycardia.[6] These differing etiologic pathways may partially

explain the wide variability in shape and duration of variable decelerations. Finally, recurrent severe variable decelerations can interrupt blood flow sufficiently to disallow normal exchange of oxygen and carbon dioxide, which can lead to metabolic acidosis and ultimately asphyxia.

Sinusoidal Pattern

A true sinusoidal FHR pattern is rare. This is a smooth, wavelike baseline with a frequency of approximately 3 to 6 waves per minute, amplitude of up to 30 bpm, and an absence of short-term variability.[50,65] The pattern is associated with severe fetal anemia, such as the anemia that occurs with Rh sensitization or fetal bleeding from a vasa previa. It is occasionally seen just before intrapartum demise and in fetuses with cardiac anomalies. A true sinusoidal pattern is an ominous sign indicating that the fetus is in marked jeopardy.[58] Pseudosinusoidal patterns have a similar wavelike look, but these patterns have short-term variability and are not associated with fetal compromise. They are often seen after maternal administration of intravenous opioids.[58]

Fetal Heart Rate Pattern Evolution

The FHR "pattern evolution" that is typically associated with developing metabolic acidosis during the course of labor is a decrease in FHR baseline variability with recurrent variable or late decelerations that are increasing in depth and duration (Figure 6-9).[72] In a previously healthy fetus, the development of significant metabolic acidosis occurs over a period of an hour to 90 minutes once this pattern starts to evolve.[72]

a fetal heart rate pattern with a normal baseline rate, moderate variability, and no variable or late decelerations. This FHR pattern reliably predicts the absence of fetal hypoxemia. Conversely Category III FHR patterns are the four FHR patterns that reliably predict hypoxia or impending fetal asphyxia (see Table 6-2).[50,72] The positive predictive value of late decelerations with absent or minimal variability for predicting umbilical arterial base deficit greater than 16 mEq/L (mmol/L) is approximately 18%.[49] Category II FHR patterns are all other patterns that are indeterminate with regard to their relationship to fetal acidemia. Ongoing research is being conducted that subdivides Category II FHR patterns, and these subdivisions may be used in clinical practice as more knowledge is obtained about their relationship to fetal acidemia.[15,73,84]

Therapeutic Interventions

Therapeutic interventions used to improve fetal oxygenation in the presence of Category II or Category II FHR patterns during labor include administration of an intravenous bolus, lateral positioning, oxygen therapy, tocolytic administration, any position other than supine, amnioinfusion, and pushing during every other contraction in the second stage.

Amnioinfusion and lateral positioning may relieve cord compression. Administration of oxygen at 10 L/minute with a nonrebreather facemask will increase the fetal oxygen saturation as measured with pulse oximetry.[83] Maternal oxygen therapy during the intrapartum period is useful in treating presumed fetal hypoxemia, even though the fetal Po_2 does not increase as dramatically as that of the mother given the differences in the oxygen-hemoglobin dissociation curve between the fetus and mother. Administration of oxygen to the mother increases maternal arterial Po_2, increasing the gradient between maternal and fetal values in the placenta. This increases oxygen transfer to the fetus, increasing fetal oxygen content and fetal cerebral oxygenation.[1,83]

SUMMARY

The fetal response to an oxygen deficit is the result of interaction between the degree of the stress and the responsiveness and reserve of the individual fetus. Some fetuses are more intolerant to hypoxic stress than others. Fetuses with less placental reserve (e.g., fetal growth restriction, maternal hypertension, postdates) are less able to maintain normal oxygenation during hypoxemia.[56] This maxim is the basis for the screening criteria for antepartum fetal surveillance. However, the concept of a continuum of causality, in the sense that a small amount of asphyxia causes a small amount of damage and a larger amount causes more severe damage, is not certain.[48] Rather, there appears to be a degree of hypoxia that can be tolerated without adverse effects over a varied period of time, and when this degree or duration is exceeded, the threshold for metabolic acidemia is reached and the chain of adverse physiologic effects will proceed.[25] Given this wide biologic variability in the fetal response to hypoxia, the biochemical indexes that signal decompensation from physiologic adaptation to pathologic consequences have not been determined.[71] In clinical terms, the degree of metabolic acidemia that causes irreversible damage has not been defined. Antepartum and intrapartum fetal assessment techniques designed to assess the presence or absence of fetal acidemia continue to be developed as knowledge of fetal physiology and the fetal response to hypoxia is discovered. Recommendations for clinical practice related to fetal assessment are summarized in Box 6-3.

BOX 6-3   Recommendations for Clinical Practice Related to Fetal Assessment

Understand that the fetal heart rate is highly sensitive to changes in oxygenation and blood pressure (p. 162).

Recognize the fetal response to hypoxemia: bradycardia and a decrease in beat-to-beat variability (pp. 166-167, 169-171).

Understand that fetal heart rate variability is the key reflection of intact cerebral oxygenation (pp. 168-169).

Recognize the normal baseline rate, moderate variability, and accelerations and understand that these features are highly predictive of fetal well-being (pp. 169-170).

Monitor minimal fetal heart rate variability, which may be idiopathic or may be secondary to fetal sleep; maternal administration of opiates, corticosteroids, and other drugs; or developing metabolic acidosis (p. 170).

Identify periodic fetal heart rate patterns that are most likely to be associated with fetal acidosis (late decelerations [mild or severe] and severe variable decelerations in the presence of absent variability), which are a significant risk for newborn acidemia (pp. 171-173).

Recognize typical fetal heart rate pattern evolutions that are associated with the development of metabolic acidosis (tachycardia with decreased variability and increasing severity of variable or late decelerations) (pp. 171-173).

Identify the criteria necessary to determine an intrapartum etiology for neonatal encephalopathy (pp. 167-168).

Collect umbilical cord gases on any newborn who might be at risk for intrapartum asphyxia (pp. 168-169).

Understand the efficacy and indications for antenatal surveillance tests: nonstress test, contraction stress test, biophysical profile, umbilical artery Doppler velocimetry (pp. 173-176).

Identify appropriate intrapartum resuscitation techniques that are efficacious in improving fetal oxygen saturation in the presence of periodic fetal heart rate decelerations (p. 177).

References

1. Aldrich, C. J., et al. (1994). The effect of maternal oxygen administration on human fetal cerebral oxygenation measured during labor by near infrared spectroscopy. *Br J Obstet Gynecol, 101*, 509.
2. Alfirevic, Z., Devane, D., & Gyte, G. M. L. (2006). Continuous cardiotocography (CTG) as a form of electronic fetal monitoring (EFM) for fetal assessment during labour. *Cochrane Database of Syst Rev, 2006*(3), CD006066.
3. Alfirevic, Z., Stampalija, T., & Gyte, G. M. L. (2010). Fetal and umbilical Doppler ultrasound in high-risk pregnancies. *Cochrane Database of Systematic Reviews, 2010*(1), CD007529.
4. American College of Obstetricians and Gynecologists. (1996). Umbilical artery blood acid-base analysis. Technical Bulletin #216. *Int J Gynaecol Obstet, 52*, 305.
5. American College of Obstetricians and Gynecologists. (2010). Management of Intrapartum Fetal Heart Rate Tracings. Practice Bulletin Number 116 (November). *Obstet Gynecol, 116*, 1232.
6. Ball, R. H., & Parer, J. T. (1992). The physiologic mechanisms of variable decelerations. *Am J Obstet Gynecol, 166*, 1683.
7. Bennet, L. A., & Gunn, A. J. (2009). The fetal heart rate responses to hypoxia: Insight from animal models. *Clinics in Perinatology, 36*, 655.
8. Blechner, J. N. (1993). Maternal fetal acid base physiology. *Clin Obstet Gynecol, 36*, 3.
9. Bleker, O. P., et al. (1975). Intervillous space during uterine contractions in human subjects: An ultrasonic study. *Am J Obstet Gynecol, 123*, 697.
10. Burke, C., & Chin, E. G. (2016). Chorioamnionitis at term. *J Perinat Neonat Nurs, 30*, 106.
11. Caldeyro-Barcia, R., et al. (1966). Control of human fetal heart rate during labor. In D. E. Casseles (Ed.), *The heart and circulation in the newborn infant*. New York: Grune & Stratton.
12. Carter, A. M. (2015). Placental gas exchange and the oxygen supply to the fetus. *Comprehensive Physiology, 5*, 1381.
13. Carter, B. S., Havercamp, A. D., & Merenstein, G. B. (1993). The definition of acute perinatal asphyxia. *Clin Perinatol, 20*, 287.
14. Clark, S. L., Gimovsky, M. L., & Miller, F. C. (1982). Fetal heart rate response to scalp sampling. *Am J Obstet Gynecol, 144*, 706.
15. Clark, S. L., et al. (2014). Recognition and response to electronic fetal heart rate patterns – impact on newborn outcomes and primary cesarean delivery rate in women undergoing induction of labor. *Am J Obstet Gynecol, 212*, 494e1.
16. Cousins, L. (1999). Fetal oxygenation, assessment of fetal well-being, and obstetric management of the pregnant patient with asthma. *J Allergy Clin Immunol, 103*, S343.
17. de Haan, H. H., & Hasaart, T. H. (1995). Neuronal death after perinatal asphyxia. *Eur J Obstet Gynecol, 61*, 123.
18. de Laat, M. W. (2005). The umbilical coiling index, a review of the literature. *J Matern Fetal Neonatal Med, 17*, 93.

19. D'Elia, A., et al. (2001). Spontaneous motor activity in normal fetuses. *Early Hum Dev, 65*, 139.
20. Devoe, L. D. (2008). Antenatal fetal assessment: Contraction stress test, nonstress test, vibroacoustic stimulation, amniotic fluid volume, biophysical profile, and modified biophysical profile—An overview. *Semin Perinatol, 32*, 247.
21. Epplin, K. A., et al. (2015). Effect of growth restriction on fetal heart rate patterns in the second stage of labor. *Am J Perinatol, 32*, 873.
22. Espinoza, M. F., & Parer, J. T. (1991). Mechanisms of asphyxial brain damage and possible pharmacologic interventions. *Am J Obstet Gynecol, 164*, 1582.
23. Everett, T. R., & Pebbles, D. M. (2015). Antenatal tests of fetal wellbeing. *Semin Fetal Neonatal Med, 20*, 138.
24. Fahey, J., & King, T. L. (2005). Intrauterine asphyxia: Clinical implications for providers of intrapartum care. *J Midwifery Women's Health, 50*, 498.
25. Freeman, J. M. (1985). *Prenatal and perinatal factors associated with brain disorders. National Institute of Child Health and Human Development.* NIH Publication 85-1149. Washington, DC: National Institutes of Health.
26. Froen, J. F., et al. (2008). Fetal movement assessment. *Semin Perinatol, 32*, 243.
27. Gaiser, R. R., et al. (2005). Predicting prolonged fetal heart rate deceleration following intrathecal fentanyl/bupivacaine. *Int J Obstet Anesth, 14*, 208.
28. Gilstrap, L. C., & Cunningham, G. (1994). *Umbilical cord blood acid-base analysis. Supplement #4 Williams' obstetrics* (19th ed.). Raritan, NJ: Ortho Pharmaceutical Corp.
29. Giussaini, D. A. (2016). The fetal brain sparing response to hypoxia; physiological mechanisms. *J Physiol, 594*, 1215.
30. Graham, E. M., et al. (2008). A systematic review of the role of intrapartum ischemia in the causation of neonatal encephalopathy. *Am J Obstet Gynecol, 199*, 587.
31. Helwig, J. T., et al. (1996). Umbilical cord blood acid base state: What is normal? *Am J Obstet Gynecol, 174*, 1807.
32. Hon, E. H., & Quilligan, E. J. (1967). The classification of fetal heart rate. *Conn Med, 31*, 779.
33. Huddleston, J. F. (2002). Continued utility of the contraction stress test? *Clin Obstet Gynecol, 45*, 1005.
34. Jackson, J. R., et al. (2003). The effect of glucocorticosteroid administration on fetal movements and biophysical profile scores in normal pregnancies. *J Matern Fetal Neonatal Med, 13*, 50.
35. Jaeggi, E., & Ohman, A. (2016). Fetal and neonatal arrhythmias. *Clin Perinatol, 46*, 99.
36. Jang, D. G., et al. (2011). Perinatal outcomes and maternal clinical characteristics in IUGR with absent or reversed end-diastolic flow velocity in the umbilical artery. *Arch Gynecol Obstet, 284*, 73.
37. Jansson, L. M., Dipietro, J., & Elko, A. (2005). Fetal response to maternal methadone administration. *Am J Obstet Gynecol, 193*, 611.

38. Jensen, A., et al. (1999). Dynamics of fetal circulatory responses to hypoxia and asphyxia. *Eur J Obstet Gynecol Reprod Biol, 84*, 155.
39. Jones, N. W., et al. (2009). Changes in myometrial 'perfusion' during normal labor as visualized by three-dimensional power Doppler angiography. *Ultrasound Obstet Gynecol, 33*, 307.
40. King, T.L., & Parer, J.T. (2000). The physiology of fetal heart rate patterns and perinatal asphyxia. *J Perinat Neonatal Nurs, 14*, 19.
41. Kitlinski, M. L., Kallen, K., & Marsal, K. (2003). Gestational age-dependent reference values for pH in umbilical cord arterial blood at term. *Obstet Gynecol, 102*, 338.
42. Kodama, Y., et al. (2009). Intrapartum fetal heart rate patterns in infants (> 34 weeks) with poor neurological outcome. *Early Human Development, 85*, 235.
43. Lagercrantz, H., & Slokin, T. A. (1986). The "stress" of being born. *Sci Am, 254*, 100.
44. Lai, M. C., & Yang, S. N. (2011). Perinatal hypoxic-ischemic encephalopathy. *J Biomed Biotechnol, 2011*, 609813.
45. Lalor, J. G., et al. (2008). Biophysical profile for fetal assessment in high risk pregnancies. *Cochrane Database of Syst Rev, 2008*(1), CD000038.
46. Leung, A. S., Leung, E. K., & Paul, R. H. (1993). Uterine rupture after previous cesarean delivery: Maternal and fetal consequences. *Am J Obstet Gynecol, 169*, 945.
47. Levine, T. A., et al. (2015). Early childhood neurodevelopment after intrauterine growth restriction: a systematic review. *Pediatrics, 135*, 126.
48. Low, J. A., et al. (1988). Motor and cognitive deficits after intrapartum asphyxia in the mature fetus. *Am J Obstet Gynecol, 158*, 356.
49. Low, J. A., Victory, R., & Derrick, E. L. (1999). Predictive value of electronic fetal monitoring for intrapartum fetal asphyxia with metabolic acidosis. *Obstet Gynecol, 93*, 285.
50. Macones, G. A., et al. (2008). The 2008 National Institute of Child Health and Human Development Research Workshop Report on Electronic fetal heart rate monitoring. *Obstet Gynecol, 112*, 661 and *JOGNN, 37*, 510.
51. Mallard, E. C., et al. (1995). Neuronal death in the developing brain following intrauterine asphyxia. *Reprod Fertil Dev, 7*, 647.
52. Mangesi, L., et al. (2015). Fetal movement counting for assessment of fetal wellbeing. *Cochrane Database of Syst Rev, 2015*(10), CD004909.
53. Manning, F. A. (2002). Fetal biophysical profile: A critical appraisal. *Clin Obstet Gynecol, 45*, 975.
54. Manning, F. A. (2009). Antepartum fetal testing: A critical appraisal. *Curr Opin Obstet Gynecol, 21*, 348.
55. McLean, C., & Ferriero, D. (2004). Mechanisms of hypoxic ischemic injury in the term infant. *Semin Perinatol, 28*, 425.
56. Miller, J., Turan, S., & Baschat, A. A. (2008). Fetal growth restriction. *Semin Perinatol, 32*, 274.
57. Miyake, H., Nakai, A., & Takeshita, T. (2008). Fetal heart rate monitoring as a

predictor of histopathologic chorioamnionitis in the third trimester. *J Nippon Med Sch*, *75*, 106.

58. Modanlou, H. D., & Murata, Y. (2004). Sinusoidal heart rate pattern: Reappraisal of its definition and clinical significance. *J Obstet Gynaecol Res*, *30*, 169.

59. Moore, T. R., & Piacquadio, K. (1989). A prospective evaluation of fetal movement screening to reduce the incidence of antepartum fetal death. *Am J Obstet Gynecol*, *160*, 1075.

60. Moore, T. R. (2011). The role of amniotic fluid assessment in evaluating fetal wellbeing. *Clin Perinatol*, *38*, 33.

61. Morrow, R. J., et al. (1989). Effect of placental embolization on the umbilical arterial velocity waveform in fetal sheep. *Am J Obstet Gynecol*, *161*, 1055.

62. Murray, E., et al. (2015). Differential effect of intrauterine growth restriction on childhood normal development: a systematic review. *BJOG*, *122*, 1062.

63. Myers, R. E., Mueller-Heubach, E., & Adamsons, K. (1973). Predictability of the state of fetal oxygenation from a quantitative analysis of the components of late deceleration. *Am J Obstet Gynecol*, *115*, 1083.

64. Nageotte, M. P., et al. (1994). Perinatal outcome with the modified biophysical profile. *Am J Obstet Gynecol*, *170*, 1672.

65. National Institute of Child Health and Human Development Research Planning Workshop. (1997). Electronic fetal heart rate monitoring: Research guidelines for interpretation. *Am J Obstet Gynecol*, *17*, 1385.

66. Nordstrom, L. (2001). Lactate measurements in scalp and cord arterial blood. *Curr Opin Obstet Gynecol*, *13*, 141.

67. O'Brien-Abel, N. E., & Benedetti, T. J. (1992). Saltatory fetal heart rate pattern. *J Perinatol*, *12*, 13.

68. Oyelese, Y., & Vintzileos, A. M. (2011). The uses and limitations of the fetal biophysical profile. *Clin Perinatol*, *38*, 47.

69. Parer, J. T. (1976). Physiological regulation of fetal heart rate. *J Obstet Gynecol Neonatal Nurs*, *5*, 265.

70. Parer, J. T. (1997). *Handbook of fetal heart rate monitoring* (2nd ed.). Philadelphia: Saunders.

71. Parer, J. T. (1998). Effects of fetal asphyxia on brain cell structure and function: Limits of tolerance. *Comp Biochem Physiol*, *199A*, 711.

72. Parer, J. T., et al. (2006). Fetal acidemia and electronic fetal heart rate patterns: Is there evidence of an association? *J Matern Fetal Neonatal Med*, *19*, 289.

73. Parer, J. T., & Ikeda, T. (2007). A framework for standardized management of intrapartum fetal heart rate patterns. *Am J Obstet Gynecol*, *197*, 26e.1.

74. Parer, J. T., & King, T. L. (1999). Whither fetal heart rate monitoring? *Obstet Gynecol Fertil*, *22*, 149.

75. Pearlman, M., & Shah, P. S. (2011). Hypoxic-ischemic encephalopathy: Challenges in outcome and prediction. *J of Pediatrics*, *158*, e51.

76. Pearson, J. F., & Weaver, J. B. (1976). Fetal activity and fetal wellbeing: An evaluation. *Br Med J*, *1*(6021), 1305.

77. Pillai, M., & James, D. (1990). The development of fetal heart rate patterns during normal pregnancy. *Obstet Gynecol*, *76*, 812.

78. Rivkin, M. J. (1997). Hypoxic-ischemic brain injury in the term newborn. *Clin Perinatol*, *24*, 607.

79. Ross, M. G., & Gala, R. (2002). Use of umbilical artery base excess: Algorithm for the timing of hypoxic injury. *Am J Obstet Gynecol*, *187*, 1.

80. Rotmensch, S., et al. (2005). Effect of betamethasone administration on fetal heart rate tracing: A blinded longitudinal study. *Fetal Diagn Ther*, *20*, 371.

81. Signore, C., Freeman, R. K., & Spong, C. Y. (2009). Antenatal testing—a reevaluation. *Obstet Gynecol*, *113*, 687.

82. Silva, A. M., et al. (2006). Neonatal nucleated red blood cells and the prediction of cerebral white matter injury in preterm infants. *Obstet Gynecol*, *107*, 550.

83. Simpson, K. R. (2008). Intrauterine resuscitation during labor: Should maternal oxygen administration be a first-line measure? *Semin Fetal Neonatal Med*, *13*, 362.

84. Soncini, E., et al. (2014). Intrapartum fetal heart rate monitoring: evaluation of a standardized system of interpretation for prediction of metabolic acidosis at delivery and neonatal neurologic morbidity. *J Matern Fetal Neonatal Med*, *27*, 1465.

85. Task Force on Neonatal Encephalopathy and Cerebral Palsy. (2014). *Neonatal encephalopathy and Neurologic Outcome: American College of Obstetricians and Gynecologists (ACOG) and the American Academy of Pediatrics*. Washington, DC: ACOG.

86. Vintzileos, A. M., et al. (1987). The relationship between fetal biophysical profile and cord pH in patients undergoing cesarean section before the onset of labor. *Obstet Gynecol*, *70*, 196.

87. Vintzileos, A. M., et al. (1991). Relationship between fetal biophysical activities and umbilical cord blood gas values. *Am J Obstet Gynecol*, *165*, 707. Erratum in: Am J Obstet Gynecol, 1992 Feb;166(2), 772. Am J Obstet Gynecol, 1992 Apr;166(4), 1313.

88. Von Steinburg, S. P., et al. (2013). What is the "normal" fetal heart rate? *Peer J*, *1*, e82.

89. Walker, J., & Trunbull, E. P. N. (1953). Haemoglobin and red cells in the human foetus and their relation to the oxygen content of the blood in the vessels of the umbilical cord. *Lancet*, *2*, 312.

90. Westgate, J. A., et al. (2007). The intrapartum deceleration in center stage: A physiologic approach to the interpretation of fetal heart rate changes in labor. *Am J Obstet Gynecol*, *197*, 236.e1.

91. Williams, K. P., & Galerneau, F. (2003). Intrapartum fetal heart rate patterns in the prediction of neonatal acidemia. *Am J Obstet Gynecol*, *188*, 850.

92. Wood, C. E., & Tong, H. (1999). Central nervous system regulation of reflex responses to hypotension during fetal life. *Am J Physiol Regul Integr Comp Physiol*, *277*, R1541.

93. Wu, Y. (2012). Brain Injury in Newborn Babies: We can't afford to get it wrong. *Annals of Neurology*, *12*, 151.

94. Zhu, M. Y., et al. (2016). The hemodynamics of late-onset-intrauterine growth restriction. *Am J Obstet Gynecol*, *214*, 367e1.

Pharmacology and Pharmacokinetics During the Perinatal Period

Pharmacologic therapy for the pregnant woman, fetus, neonate, and lactating woman is one of the most challenging therapies in health care. Pharmacologic treatment during pregnancy is unique in that a drug taken by one person (pregnant woman) may significantly affect another (embryo or fetus). Maternal handling of drugs may be altered by the normal physiologic changes of pregnancy, such as increased plasma volume, altered gastrointestinal (GI) motility, and changes in plasma components and renal function. These changes influence plasma levels, half-lives, and distribution and elimination of many drugs; may increase the risk of either subtherapeutic or toxic drug levels; and affect susceptibility to exposures from environmental toxins.[96]

Fetal drug exposure may be inadvertent (secondary to maternal treatment) or intended (treatment of fetus via treatment of mother). For many years it was believed that the placental barrier shielded the fetus from many drugs and other potentially harmful substances. However, the placenta provides little protection for the fetus from many drugs. The placenta and fetus are able to metabolize some agents; however, postmenstrual age (PMA) and maturation of hepatic enzyme systems influence the efficiency of these processes. Many maternal drugs are present in the fetus in lower levels than are seen in the mother, but some drugs may be found at higher levels in the fetus. Fetal effects of maternal drugs can range from no effect to pregnancy loss to teratogenesis with structural or functional changes, to alterations in later growth and development.

Pharmacologic therapy of the neonate is complex, and consideration of age-related maturation (ontogeny) is critical for understanding drug responses.[5,38] Hepatic metabolism and renal excretion are the major methods of drug elimination, and these change rapidly over the first weeks after birth. This challenge is magnified in preterm infants in whom maturation of hepatic and renal systems is changing based on both PMA and postbirth age. This can lead to significant changes in drug handling, sometimes within a few days or weeks.

Many drugs cross the blood-milk barrier in the lactating woman and have the potential to affect the infant. The amount of drug reaching the nursing infant is influenced by maternal drug handling, mode of administration, and maternal serum levels at time of feeding. However, drugs generally reach breast milk in significantly lower quantities than drugs reach the fetus across the placenta.

PHARMACOKINETICS

Pharmacokinetics refers to the processes involved in drug absorption, distribution, metabolism and biotransformation, and excretion (Figure 7-1). Site of absorption depends on route of administration (e.g., oral, intramuscular, intravenous, topical, inhaled). Drugs are carried in the blood, either bound to plasma proteins or as free drug. Protein-bound drugs provide a reservoir for future use, whereas free drug is the active component available to interact with the target cell. Biotransformation occurs primarily in the liver with a series of enzymatic reactions to modify and convert the drug into more polar (water-soluble) compounds. Intermediary steps in biotransformation may result in active metabolites. For example, codeine is demethylated to morphine, and in the neonate theophylline is methylated to caffeine.[31] Biotransformation also takes place in the lungs, intestinal mucosa, and kidneys. Hepatic biotransformation occurs in two phases. Phase I (nonsynthetic reactions) takes place primarily in the microsomes, although some occurs in the mitochondria and cytosol. Phase I reactions modify the activity of a drug. Phase I enzymes include the cytochrome P450 (CYP450) monooxygenase system. The enzymes of this system are indicated by the prefix CYP (cytochrome) followed by a series of numbers and letters (e.g., CYP1A2, CYP3A4, CYP2D6). Phase II (synthetic) reactions require adenosine triphosphate (ATP) and, except for glucuronidation, are extramicrosomal.[31] Phase II reactions generally inactivate the drugs by converting them to more polar substances. Table 7-1 provides examples of drugs metabolized by various phase I and phase II reactions. Not all drugs undergo hepatic metabolism before elimination; some drugs are excreted directly via the kidneys.

The term *drug* is used generically in this chapter to refer to prescription and nonprescription pharmacologic agents, herbal agents, and vitamins, as well as drugs of abuse. In addition, the principles that govern placental transfer of drugs are also applicable to transfer of chemicals, food additives,

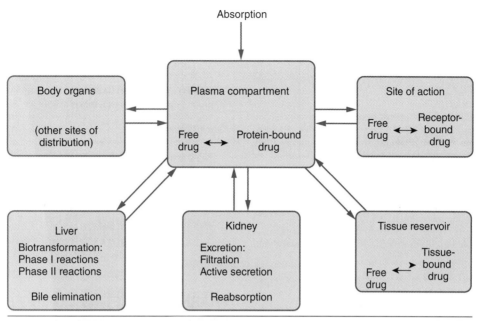

FIGURE 7-1   Possible disposition of drugs throughout various compartments in the body. (From Chemtob, S. [2004]. Basic pharmacologic principles. In R.A. Polin, W.W. Fox, & S.H. Abman [Eds.]. *Fetal and neonatal physiology* [3rd ed.]. Philadelphia: Saunders.)

TABLE 7-1   Biotransformation Reactions

REACTION	EXAMPLES OF DRUG SUBSTRATES
PHASE I (NONSYNTHETIC REACTIONS)	
Oxidation	Phenytoin, phenobarbital, ibuprofen, acetaminophen, morphine, codeine, diazepam, cimetidine
Reduction	Chloramphenicol, ethanol
Hydrolysis	Acetylsalicylic acid, indomethacin
PHASE II (SYNTHETIC REACTIONS: CONJUGATIONS)	
Glucuronide conjugation	Morphine, acetaminophen
Glycine conjugation	Salicylic acid
Sulfate conjugation	Acetaminophen, α-methyldopa
Glutathione conjugation	Ethacrynic acid
Methylation	Dopamine, epinephrine
Acetylation	Sulfonamides, clonazepam

Adapted from Chemtob, S. (2004). Basic pharmacologic principles. In R.A. Polin, W.W. Fox, & S.H. Abman (Eds.). *Fetal and neonatal physiology* (3rd ed.). Philadelphia: Saunders.

and environmental agents. Definitions of common terms used in pharmacokinetics are summarized in Box 7-1.

PHARMACOGENETICS AND PHARMACOGENOMICS

Variations in drug pharmacokinetics and pharmacodynamics occur among individuals at all ages, even with similar doses of a given medication, because of extrinsic (diet, environment, other therapies) and intrinsic (development, genetic constitution, diseases) factors.[101] Both inherited differences in drug metabolism

(influencing enzyme activity and level and receptor sensitivity) and genetic polymorphisms influence individual drug response, drug therapeutic effectiveness, efficiency of drug elimination, and the risk of side effects and adverse reactions.[5,50,38] Currently much research focuses on understanding these factors, especially the contributions of individual genetic polymorphisms (see Chapter 1). This has led to new fields of study such as pharmacogenetics and pharmacogenomics. Pharmacogenetics is the study of "genetic variations that give rise to interindividual responses to drugs,"[101] whereas pharmacogenomics integrates pharmacology and genomics into "the broader application of genome-wide technologies and strategies to identify both disease processes that represent new targets for drug development and factors predictive of therapeutic efficacy and risk of adverse drug reactions."[101] Thus pharmacogenetics examines genetically determined individual responses to drug therapy, whereas pharmacogenomics examines the influence of deoxyribonucleic acid (DNA) sequence variations on drug effects.[7,38]

Genetic polymorphisms are small variations in an individual's genome that may either be nonfunctional (have no effect on the individual) or modify expression of a protein that may alter the effects of exposures to environmental health hazards or result in individual differences in responses to drugs (changing efficacy, risk of adverse effects, or therapeutic dosing regimens).[81,101] Drug-metabolizing enzymes, transporters, and receptors are genetically determined. Single nucleotide polymorphisms (SNP) in any of these can affect drug concentrations and responses.[51] Understanding of these variations, which is just beginning, can individualize pharmacologic management.[7,38,51,84,101]

BOX 7-1   Definitions of Selected Terms Used in Pharmacokinetics

---

Pharmacokinetics is the study of drug disposition over time and includes absorption, distribution, metabolism, and excretion.

Pharmacodynamics is the study of physiologic and biological responses to a given agent.

Developmental pharmacodynamics examines the effects of age-related structural and functional maturation on response to pharmacotherapy.

Volume of distribution (Vd) is the distribution of a drug in the body. The greater the Vd, the longer it will take the drug to be cleared from the body. Drugs can be distributed in body water and fat compartments, or bound to plasma proteins or tissue.

Half-life is the time for the blood concentration of a drug to decline by 50%. There may be two half-lives calculated for drugs given intravenously: the initial or distribution half-life and the terminal or elimination half-life.

Oral bioavailability is the ability of a drug taken orally to reach the systemic circulation. A drug with high oral bioavailability moves readily from the gastrointestinal tract to the systemic circulation.

Protein binding is the percentage of the drug that is normally bound to plasma proteins. The two main drug-binding proteins are albumin and α1-acid glycoprotein.

Free drug is the fraction of drug that is unbound in plasma. Free drug can move across the placenta or blood-milk barrier; bound drug cannot.

Clearance is the amount of a drug that is cleared from the plasma by hepatic and renal systems in a given unit of time. Hepatic and renal clearance can be calculated separately.

Molecular weight (MW) is the weight of the drug in daltons. The smaller the MW, the more readily a substance can cross cell membranes. Very small substances (MW less than 100–200 daltons) may be able to move though pores in the cell membrane.

pKa is the pH at which a drug is 50% ionized. Ionized drugs do not cross cell membranes (including the placenta and the blood-milk barrier) as readily.

During pregnancy, these individual differences may occur in the mother, fetus, placental, or any combination of these to influence the expression of specific genes involved in biotransformation, amount and activity of enzymes produced, and thus levels of the drug and potential risks.[81] Similar differences are seen after birth. For example, pregnant and lactating women and their offspring have reported to have differing responses with opioid pain management, antihypertensive therapy, tocolytics, antenatal corticosteroids, and drugs used to treat nausea and vomiting of pregnancy.[52,130] The differential benefits seen with use of antenatal corticosteroids may result from SNPs in either the mother or fetus or both.[38,51] Difference in clearance of nifedipine is related to genetic variations in the CYP3A5 gene.[52] Some women have minimal activity of CYP2D6 (demethylates codeine to form morphine), whereas others have multiple copies and thus increased activity of this enzyme. If treated with codeine while breastfeeding, women with high CYP2D6 activity produce excess morphine that will be transferred to the infant, whereas women with low activity may find codeine minimally effective in treating their pain.[130]

Genetic differences in placental transporters and in maternal and fetal genes for activity or level of enzymes that metabolize opiates may influence the fetal exposure, the incidence and severity of neonatal abstinence syndrome, and response to therapy in the newborn.[84] Applying knowledge of specific receptor polymorphisms for drugs used to treat neonatal opiate withdrawal in individual infants was found to decrease the length of stay.[129] Genetic polymorphisms in transporter proteins, messenger ribonucleic acid (mRNA) expression, and protein expression can alter the risk of birth defects with maternal environmental exposures.[34] In neonates, not all differential responses in drug metabolism are related to the effects of SNP; responses are also influenced by developmental differences in levels and activity of drug-metabolizing enzymes.[130]

PHARMACOKINETICS DURING PREGNANCY
Drug Use During Pregnancy

Use of prescribed drugs, over-the-counter drugs, and herbal agents is common during pregnancy.[33,35,128,139] A survey of drug use by 14,000 pregnant women in 22 countries found that 86% of these women took some medication during pregnancy, with each woman taking an average of 2.9 medications (range, 1–15).[79] Mitchell and associates reviewed drug use during pregnancy between 1976 and 2008. They found that (1) average use of prescribed and over-the-counter drugs increased over these years from 2.5 to 4.2; (2) use of prescribed drugs increased 63% during the first trimester and most women took at least one prescribed drug; and (3) less than 1% of pregnant women took an antidepressant in 1988 to 1990 versus 7.5% in 2006 to 2008.[93] In the United States an estimated 64% of pregnant women are prescribed at least one drug during pregnancy for treatment of an acute or chronic condition.[139] Drugs most often prescribed in the first trimester were not necessarily drugs for which teratogenic effects have been studied and included drugs with potential fetal risk.[35,128] For many of these medications little pharmacokinetic data are available for pregnant women.[128,139] There are even fewer studies on the safety and efficacy of herbal therapies.[33,71] A multinational study (n = 26,731) reported that 29.3% of pregnant women used herbal agents during pregnancy. Most of these women (89%) used one or more of 126 specific herbal medications; of these agents, 20% were classified as contraindicated, 47.4% were classified as safe, and 31.6% were classified as requiring caution during pregnancy.[71]

Adherence to prescribed drug regimens is a problem during pregnancy, with up to 50% of women either not taking a prescribed drug or stopping before receiving a full course of the drug.[77,107] This can lead to maternal risks, especially in women with chronic diseases.[77,107] Peterson et al. found that antidepressants were more likely to be discontinued by pregnant than nonpregnant women, often leading to increased depression and other complications.[107] Problems with adherence stem primarily from concerns about teratogenic effects. Most women overestimate the teratogenic risks of common agents.[74] For example, in one study women personally estimated that the risk of having a baby with a birth defect was 25% (which is the risk associated with a potent teratogen such as thalidomide). After counseling, however, they more correctly estimated the risk at 5%.[74] The background risk of a birth defect for the general population is 3% to 5%. However, the risk may be higher or lower for an individual woman depending on factors such as her health status, teratogen exposures, and genetic makeup.

Several principles have been identified to guide drug therapy during pregnancy: (1) avoid medications in the first trimester whenever possible; (2) anyone prescribing drugs for a woman of childbearing age must consider a potential pregnancy before prescribing; (3) women receiving long-term drug therapy require counseling before pregnancy of the potential implications and risks; (4) a necessary treatment should not be stopped without good reason; (5) drugs may have altered effects during pregnancy (e.g., the increased metabolism of methicillin or increased renal elimination of digoxin may result in decreased levels, resulting in the need for higher doses); (6) use single-action, short-acting medications rather than long-acting or combination drugs; (7) use the lowest effective dose of the safest available medication; (8) use drugs only if the benefits outweigh the risks; (9) use alternate routes of administration if available (i.e., topical or inhaled rather than systemic agents); (10) select drugs that have a history of use during pregnancy without adverse effects, rather than the "latest" drug; and (11) use doses at the low end of the normal dose range with the understanding that for some drugs (e.g., digoxin, phenytoin, lithium), the woman's usual dose may need to be increased because of increased volume of distribution (Vd) and clearance of these agents during pregnancy.[79,113] These principles also apply to all women of childbearing age and to preconceptional and interconceptional use of drugs, because approximately half of all pregnancies are unplanned and critical developmental processes occur before most women realize they are pregnant.[79]

Alterations in Drug Absorption, Distribution, Metabolism, and Excretion During Pregnancy

Maternal responses to drugs during pregnancy are influenced by both maternal physiology and the presence of the placental-fetal unit.[86] Variations in handling of specific drugs by the pregnant woman may result from effects of the normal physiologic changes of pregnancy on drug absorption, distribution, metabolism, and excretion (Table 7-2). The presence of the placental-fetal compartment can also alter maternal pharmacokinetics.[86] For example, many antibiotics are lipid-soluble and may readily cross the placenta and become sequestered in the fetal compartment and thus be unavailable to the mother. This can lead to lower maternal levels.

Evidence regarding effects, effectiveness, and safety of many pharmacologic agents used during pregnancy is limited, because pregnant women are usually excluded from drug

TABLE 7-2	Influence of Pregnancy on Physiologic Aspects of Drug Disposition	
PHARMACOKINETIC PARAMETER	**CHANGE IN PREGNANCY**
ABSORPTION	
Intestinal motility	Decreased
Ventilation	Increased
Cardiac output	Increased
Blood flow to skin	Increased
DISTRIBUTION	
Plasma volume	Increased
Total body water	Increased
Plasma proteins	Decreased
Body fat	Increased
METABOLISM	
Hepatic metabolism	Increased or decreased
Extrahepatic metabolism	Increased or decreased
EXCRETION	
Uterine blood flow	Increased
Renal blood flow	Increased
Glomerular filtration rate	Increased
Ventilation	Increased

From McClary, J., Blumer, J.L., & Aranda, J.V., et al. (2011). Developmental pharmacology. In R.J. Martin, A.A. Fanaroff, & M.C. Walsh (Eds.). *Fanaroff and Martin's neonatal-perinatal medicine: Diseases of the fetus and infant* (9th ed.). Philadelphia: Mosby Elsevier.

trials. As a result, many drugs are not labeled for use in pregnancy, because the effects of the drug on the fetus are unknown.[74,91] This is protective for the fetus but may also limit benefits to the pregnant woman from these drugs. The net result of changes in drug handling during pregnancy depends on the individual drug, with both increases in levels (with need for a lower dose or less frequent dosing) and decreases in levels (with a need for a higher dose or more frequent dosing) seen (Table 7-3).[85] In general, both peak and steady-state serum concentrations are lower or unchanged in the pregnant woman.[21] Although changes may not be clinically significant, the efficacy and toxicity of drugs can be harder to predict because of the physiologic changes during pregnancy that have the potential to alter pharmacokinetics.[21] Variations in the direction of pharmacokinetic changes during pregnancy increases the complexity for the practitioner in choosing a specific pharmacologic agent and monitoring its effects. Many studies have significant methodological problems; for example, sample sizes may be small, the composition of the control group may vary (e.g., the group may include nonpregnant women, adult males, or the same subjects postpartum), women of various gestational ages may be grouped together, and dosing methods may vary.[36,85] Pregnancy exposure registries have been established to collect experiences with specific drugs or groups of drugs (such as antiepileptic agents) during pregnancy and fetal and neonatal outcomes (Box 7-2). Three types of drug registries have been established: individual academic sites; pharmaceutical drug company

TABLE 7-3   Summary of Pregnancy-Induced Changes in the Pharmacokinetics of Clinically Used Drugs

DRUG/PROBE	INDICATION	Effect on CL/F (%)[a] T_1	T_2	T_3	METABOLIZING-ENZYME ACTIVITY CHANGES
Caffeine*	CNS stimulant	↓ 33	↓ 48	↓ 65	
Theophylline	Asthma	↔	↔	↓ 34	↓ CYP1A2
Nicotine	Smoking cessation	NA	↑ 54	↑ 54	↑ CYP2A6
Phenytoin*,[b]	Epilepsy	↑ 43	↑ 51	↑ 61	↑ CYP2C9
Proguanil	Malaria	NA	↓ 60	↓ 60	↓ CYP2C19
Metoprolol*	Hypertension	NA	NA	↑ 459	
Dextromethorphan[b]	Cough	↑ 26	↑ 35	↑ 48	↑ CYP2D6
Midazolam*	Sedation	NA	NA	↑ 99	
Indinavir	HIV infection	NA	NA	↑ 277	↑ CYP3A4
Glyburide	Diabetes	NA	NA	↑ 106	
Methadone	Addiction	NA	↑ 101	↑ 65	↑ CYP2B6
Labetalol	Hypertension	NA	↑ 30	↑ 30	↑ UGT1A1
Lamotrigine	Epilepsy	↑ 200	↑ 200	↑ 300	↑ UGT1A4
Zidovudine[c]	HIV infection	NA	NA	↔	↔ UGT2B7
Amoxicillin	Bacterial infection	NA	↑ 23	↑ 20	
Metformin*	Diabetes	↑ 22	↑ 28	↑ 11	↑ Renal CL
Digoxin*	Cardiac diseases	NA	NA	↑ 19	

Asterisk (*) indicates that the probe drug is commonly used to measure specific hepatic enzyme activity or transporter activity in vivo. ↓ indicates decrease. ↑ indicates increase. ↔ indicates no effect. *NA* indicates that the data are not available.
CL, Clearance; *CL/F,* apparent oral clearance, where *F* represents bioavailability; *CNS,* central nervous system; *CYP,* cytochrome P450; $T_{1/2/3}$, first/second/third trimester; *UGT,* uridine diphosphate glucuronosyltransferase.
[a]Mean percentage change relative to postpartum value.
[b]Phenytoin data are based on plasma trough concentration (total). Dextromethorphan data are based on urinary metabolic ratio (dextromethorphan/dextrorphan).
[c]Morphine intravenous clearance (mediated by UGT2B7), determined at time of delivery, was found to increase 59% compared with nonpregnant control data, suggesting increased UGT2B7 activity and/or increased hepatic blood flow.
Modified from Ke, A.B., Rostami-Hodjegan, A., Zhao, P., & Unadkat, J.D. (2014). Pharmacometrics in pregnancy: An unmet need. *Pharmacol Toxicol, 54,* 53.

BOX 7-2   Resources for Information on Drugs During Pregnancy and Lactation

BOOKS

Briggs, G., et al (2017). *Drugs in pregnancy and lactation* (11th ed.). Philadelphia: Wolters Kluwer.
Hale, T.W. & Rowe, H.F. (2017). *Medications and mother's milk* (17th ed.). New York, NY: Springer.
King, T.L. & Brucker, M.C. (2017). *Pharmacology for women's health* (2nd ed.). Boston: Jones & Bartlett.

INTERNET

American College of Occupational and Environmental Medicine (ACOEM) Reproductive and Developmental Hazard Management Guidance. Available at http://www.acoem.org/uploaded Files/Public_Affairs/Policies_And_Position_Statements/ Guidelines/Guidelines/Reproductive_and_Developmental_ Hazard_Management.pdf
FDA List of pregnancy exposure registries. Available at http://www. fda.gov/scienceresearch/specialtopics/womenshealthresearch/ ucm134848.htm

InfantRisk Center. Available at http://www.infantrisk.com/ or via the InfantRisk Helpline (806)352-2519.
LactAid: A new NLM database on drugs and lactation. National Library of Medicine, National Institutes of Health. Available at https://www.nlm.nih.gov/news/lactmed_announce_06.html. (Also available as an app.)
March of Dimes Professional Resources. Available at http://www. marchofdimes.com/professionals
Mother to Baby. Medications and more during pregnancy and lactations. Available at http://mothertobaby.org/
Pregnancy and Lactation Labeling. (2014). Available at https:// www.fda.gov/Drugs/DevelopmentApprovalProcess/ DevelopmentResources/Labeling/ucm093307.htm
Teratology Information System (TERIS). Available at http://depts. washington.edu/terisweb/teris/

sites; and population-based sites (from individual countries or a group of countries).[25]

Drug Absorption

Pulmonary, GI, and peripheral blood flow changes during pregnancy can alter absorption of drugs from the lungs, gut, and skin (see Chapters 9, 10, and 12). The increased minute ventilation that occurs in pregnancy can increase the rate of drug uptake across the alveoli.[86,89] As a result, the pulmonary system may have a greater role in drug and metabolite excretion during pregnancy. Alveolar uptake of inhalation agents is also influenced by changes in cardiac output, which leads to increased pulmonary blood flow and thus increased alveolar uptake. As a result, doses of volatile anesthetics (e.g., halothane, isoflurane, methoxyflurane) may need to be decreased to compensate for these changes in the pregnant women.[86,106] Inhaled aerosols such as antiinflammatories and bronchodilators may have enhanced absorption.

Absorption of oral medications is influenced by gastric acidity, gastric motility, presence of bile acids or mucus, nausea and vomiting of pregnancy (NVP), and intestinal transit time. During pregnancy there is altered intestinal emptying time, increased mucus, and decreased gastric and intestinal motility.[36] Decreased gastric motility can increase the oral bioavailability of slowly absorbed drugs (such as digoxin) by prolonging transit time and can decrease peak plasma levels of rapidly absorbed drugs. Factors altering GI function in pregnancy may initially delay, and then prolong, absorption of oral medications. Peak plasma levels may be lower, and the time to peak levels may be later than in nonpregnant women. These changes tend to peak in the third trimester.[73] Changes in pH affect ionization and absorption of drugs.[36,86,139] Decreased GI motility may alter initial absorption of oral antibiotics and lead to unpredictable patterns of intestinal absorption. Absorption of hydrophilic drugs may be enhanced because of the longer intestinal transit time (from delayed intestinal emptying and decreased motility). NVP can lead to decreased absorption because of decreases in peak concentrations and bioavailability.[139] Increased cardiac output and peripheral blood flow may increase the rate of absorption of drugs from the stomach and small intestine.[85] Iron chelates with some drugs taken concurrently, preventing absorption. However, even with these changes in GI function, the clinical effect for most drugs is not significant. This is because therapeutic windows are usually wide enough for drugs administered orally that these factors do not significantly alter therapeutic effects.

Cardiovascular and integumentary changes during pregnancy may lead to more rapid absorption of agents delivered via transdermal, intranasal, intravascular, epidural, and subcutaneous routes.[106] The increased extracellular water and peripheral blood flow to the skin during pregnancy may enhance absorption and alter distribution of topical agents. For example, topical and vaginal iodine-based preparations are not recommended during pregnancy because of the increased absorption of iodine. Iodine is of concern because it is actively transported across the placenta to the fetus, whose thyroid gland has a high avidity for this substance (see Chapter 19). Increased peripheral perfusion secondary to decreased peripheral vascular resistance and vasodilation may increase absorption of intramuscular drugs.[36]

Drug Distribution

The distribution of drugs within the body depends on many factors, including the amount of body water, which affects Vd; degree to which a drug is bound to plasma proteins or body tissues; and the presence of the fetal-placental unit (increases Vd). Thus for many drugs the Vd is increased during pregnancy because of the increased plasma volume, blood volume, cardiac output, total body water, and body mass.[21,36,139] The increased plasma and blood volumes, and thus Vd, may result in decreased drug levels in the central compartment, reduce serum levels of drugs, and necessitate larger loading doses.[89] Increases in total body water during pregnancy affect primarily water-soluble (polar) drugs that tend to stay in the extracellular space. Initial doses may need to be increased to achieve therapeutic concentrations; however, maternal doses for most drugs are not significantly altered, because drug steady state is influenced by bioavailability and clearance as well as Vd.[73] Because of changes in the Vd, some pregnant women may notice that their prepregnancy dose of a drug taken regularly, such as digoxin or phenytoin, may not achieve the same therapeutic effect during pregnancy.

Some lipid-soluble drugs (e.g., caffeine, diazepam, thiopental) have a longer half-life in the pregnant woman, whereas polar drugs (e.g., oxazepam, ampicillin) tend to have a shorter half-life.[54,89,132,139] The Vd for lipophilic drugs is increased during pregnancy because of the accumulation of fat, which may serve as a reservoir for some drugs via tissue binding.[36,85] Tissue binding is a mechanism by which a drug is removed from circulation and stored in tissue such as hair, bone, teeth, and adipose tissue. This mechanism can result in storage of significant quantities of a drug, because tissue storage sites may need to be saturated before there is sufficient free drug to be effective at receptor sites. Factors reducing maternal serum drug levels increase the risk of subtherapeutic drug levels. When the drug is discontinued, tissue deposits may give up their stores slowly, resulting in persistent drug effects. Because lipid-soluble drugs are stored in adipose tissue, the increased adipose tissue during pregnancy can lead to a slight decrease in the amount of free lipid-soluble drugs, such as sedatives and hypnotics, and persistence of drug effects ("hangover") after the drug has been discontinued.

Drugs in plasma are either unbound (free) or bound to plasma proteins, primarily albumin or α1-acid glycoprotein. The reduction in these plasma proteins during pregnancy may increase plasma levels of free (active) drug.[139] Albumin is the major binding protein for acidic drugs such as salicylates, anticonvulsants, nonsteroidal antiinflammatory agents, and some neutral drugs such as warfarin and diazepam.[86] Serum albumin levels fall during pregnancy, increasing the unbound or free drug fraction. Total plasma drug concentration stays the same during pregnancy, but the unbound fraction of albumin-bound drugs is greater; therefore the drug may be cleared faster or transported more rapidly across the placenta.[69,86,139] Increases in free drug do not necessarily lead to an increase in plasma levels of that drug if the increase in free drug is balanced by more rapid hepatic biotransformation or renal elimination.[36,86,106] However, for some drugs that are bound to albumin (such as many antiepileptic drugs), total and free drug concentrations may be altered, and doses may need to be adjusted during pregnancy. For example, phenytoin total plasma concentration is decreased by 55% to 65% and levels of free drug by 18% to 31% during pregnancy; carbamazepine total concentration is reduced 0% to 43% and free drug 0% to 28%; phenobarbital total concentration is reduced by 50% to 55%.[106] Thus when monitoring serum concentrations of drugs such as phenytoin during pregnancy, free versus total levels should be evaluated (many laboratories report free levels if specified when ordering).[36]

Free fatty acids and steroid hormones, both of which are increased in pregnancy, may compete with drugs for albumin binding sites, further increasing levels of unbound drug. The decrease in albumin, coupled with increases in free fatty acids and steroid hormones, are most prominent in late pregnancy. This change can result in unpredictable transient increases in free levels of some drugs, such as phenytoin, carbamazepine, sulfisoxazole, theophylline, and phenobarbital; the potential for more rapid elimination increases the risk of subtherapeutic maternal levels.[36,46] α1-Acid glycoprotein is the major protein for binding basic drugs such as local anesthetics, most opioids, and β-blockers. α1-Acid glycoprotein is decreased slightly during pregnancy.[10]

Changes in protein binding during pregnancy not only influence availability of free drug in the mother but also the amount of drug available to cross the placenta. This may alter fetal-to-maternal drug ratios, thus further altering placental transfer. Drugs with hepatic blood flow–limited biotransformation (e.g., propranolol, lidocaine) are rapidly eliminated in their first pass through the liver, regardless of whether they are bound or unbound.[21] Therefore even with the decreased protein binding in pregnancy, hepatic clearance and total drug concentration generally are not significantly altered, although concentrations of free drug, Vd, and half-life may increase. Conversely, with drugs whose hepatic biotransformation is independent of hepatic blood flow (e.g., warfarin, phenytoin), only the unbound fraction is removed by the liver. For these drugs, total drug concentrations may be lower than usual, with a decreased half-life and greater fluctuations in peak and trough levels.

Hepatic Drug Metabolism

The hepatic changes during pregnancy (see Chapter 12) can alter biotransformation of drugs by the liver and clearance of drugs from the maternal serum. Drugs that are primarily (greater than 70%) metabolized in their first pass through the liver (high extraction ratio) are usually cleared rapidly by the liver, because clearance of these drugs is dependent on hepatic blood flow. Hepatic elimination of drugs with high extraction ratios is generally unchanged because hepatic blood flow is not significantly altered in pregnancy. Drugs with low (less than 30%) first-pass hepatic clearance (low extraction ratio) are more dependent on liver enzyme systems. The rate of elimination of these drugs (e.g., theophylline, caffeine, and diazepam) is related to free drug levels and tends to be decreased in pregnancy, with increased half-lives. Hepatic elimination of other drugs—including many antibiotics, pancuronium, phenytoin, and acetaminophen—is increased in pregnant women.

Some liver enzymatic processes may be slower during pregnancy, delaying drug metabolism and degradation; other processes have increased activity. The CYP450 monooxygenase system phase I enzymes are essential for hepatic metabolism of drugs. Activity of the following are increased during pregnancy: CYP3A4 (50% to 100%), CYP2A6 (54% in second trimester and 20% in third trimester), CYP2D6 (50% by the third trimester), and CYP2C9 (20% in the third trimester).[10,77,124] Upregulation of CYP2C9 decreases plasma concentrations and increases clearance of phenytoin, nonsteroidal antiinflammatory agents, and some oral antidiabetic agents.[10,73,89,124] These agents may require increased dosing during pregnancy to achieve therapeutic concentrations.[124] However, any increases in dosages during pregnancy must be made with a consideration of whether the drug crosses the placenta and potential fetal effects.[124] The increased CYP2E1 activity, which metabolizes acetaminophen, ethanol, some anesthetics such is halothane, and many toxic chemicals, may also increase the risk of toxicity to environmental agents.[124]

Changes to CYP3A4, which may be caused by increased cortisol in pregnancy, may increase the metabolism of methadone, nifedipine, protease inhibitors, darunavir, and indinavir during pregnancy.[106,124] Darunavir and indinavir are antiretroviral drugs whose concentrations are reduced during pregnancy, so care with monitoring and alterations in dosage may be needed. Activity of CYP1A2, which is responsible for hepatic elimination of many drugs (such as caffeine, clozapine, and melatonin), is decreased (33% in the first, 50% in the second, and 65% in the third trimester), increasing the risk of drug toxicity; activity of CYP2C19 is also decreased (50%).[10,85,124] Because CYP1A2 is involved in clearance of caffeine, the decreased activity may lead to slower clearance and enhanced effects during pregnancy.[77,106,139]

Activity of phase II enzymes is also altered during pregnancy, including some of the uridine 5′-diphosphatase glucuronosyltransferase (UGT) enzymes.[106,124] For example, UGT1A4 (metabolizes lamotrigine) is increased 200% in the first and second trimesters and 300% in the third trimester; UGT2B7 (metabolizes digoxin and enoxaparin) is increased 50% to 200% by the third trimester.[10,89] As a result of the increased hepatic clearance, changes in dosing may be needed (based on drug level monitoring results).[89] Labetalol is also metabolized by UGT enzymes, the activity of which is increased during pregnancy, leading to an increase in hepatic clearance of up to 30% and a shorter half-life.[89] Some extrahepatic enzymes, particularly cholinesterase, are also decreased, which may alter the woman's response to neuromuscular agents.[28,36] For example, the decrease in pseudocholinesterase during pregnancy has been enough to impair breakdown of suxamethonium with subsequent prolonged paralysis after anesthesia in some women. The relative increase in hepatic metabolism and blood flow during pregnancy (as a consequence of the increased cardiac output) may increase clearance of polar drugs.[36] In general, slowly metabolized drugs that are cleared primarily by the liver tend to be cleared more slowly in pregnancy because of decreased enzymatic activity and the net decrease in liver blood flow. This may also increase the length of time potentially teratogenic intermediary metabolites remain in circulation.

Clearance and metabolism of drugs by the liver during pregnancy may also be influenced by the increases in steroid hormones that stimulate hepatic microsomal enzyme activity. For example, progesterone may induce enzyme activity

TABLE 7-5   Fetal and Maternal Protein Binding and Total Concentration Ratios of Selected Drugs During Late Human Gestation

DRUG	PRIMARY BINDING PROTEIN	BOUND IN MOTHER (%)	BOUND IN FETUS (%)	FETUS/MOTHER TOTAL PLASMA CONCENTRATION RATIO
Betamethasone	AGP	60	41	0.33
Bupivacaine	AGP	91	51	0.27
Diazepam	ALB	97	98.5	1.6
Lidocaine	AGP	64	24	0.66
Mepivacaine	AGP	55	36	0.71
N-desmethyldiazepam	ALB	95	97	1.7
Phenobarbital	ALB	41	36	1.0
Phenytoin	ALB	87	82	1.0
Salicylate	ALB	43	54	1.2

AGP, α1-Acid glycoprotein; *ALB*, albumin.
Adapted from Plonait, S.L. & Nau, H. (2012). Physiochemical and structural properties regulating placental drug transfer. In R.A. Polin, W.W. Fox, & S.H. Abman (Eds.). *Fetal and neonatal physiology* (4th ed.). Philadelphia: Saunders.

serum albumin levels decrease, greater free diazepam is present in maternal serum and, because this is a lipophilic drug, readily crosses the placenta. Thus by term, fetal diazepam levels are greater than maternal levels (Table 7-5).[8] This may increase the risk of neonatal hyperbilirubinemia in that diazepam competes with bilirubin for albumin binding (see "Neonatal Pharmacokinetics").

Placental Blood Flow. The rate of maternal blood flow to and through the intervillous space and fetal blood flow to and through the villi influence placental transfer, particularly of nonionized, lipophilic substances such as anticonvulsants, alcohol, and opioid derivatives. Contractions decrease transfer so drugs that cross rapidly and are given during a contraction may demonstrate decreased transfer to the fetus. Contractions may also delay clearance of drugs from the fetus.[123] In addition to uterine contractions, factors that may alter uteroplacental blood flow include maternal position; anesthesia; nicotine, β-lactams, ototoxics, and other drugs; emotional or physical stress; and degenerative changes within the placenta that are seen with hypertension, prolonged pregnancy, diabetes, or renal disease.[76]

Route of Administration. The route of administration can also affect placental transfer. For example, nalbuphine that is given intramuscularly results in fetal blood levels that are 80% of maternal venous levels; if it is given intravenously, fetal levels are three to six times greater than maternal levels.[86,104] Peak drug concentrations in the fetus (and the infant, if delivered after maternal administration) do not necessarily occur at the same time as in the mother. For example, fentanyl may be higher in the neonate than in the mother if given shortly before delivery.

Antibiotics are some of the most commonly prescribed drugs in pregnancy. Because antibiotics cross the placenta primarily by simple diffusion, rate-limiting factors include maternal-fetal concentration gradients, protein binding, MW, and other physicochemical characteristics of the drug; placental surface area; diffusing distance; and the degree to which the drug is bound to maternal plasma proteins.

Placental Metabolism of Drugs

The placenta has many enzyme systems, including various peptidases that can metabolize drugs, thus influencing transfer of specific substances from mother to fetus or fetus to mother.[123] Placental tissue expresses a variety of drug metabolizing enzymes including phase I (CYP1, CYP2, and CYP3) and phase II (GST, SULT1A1, SULT1A3, UGT1A, and UGT2B) enzymes that can break down agents to prevent them from entering fetal circulation.[110,139] CYP450 isoforms found in the placenta are at levels about half of those seen in the liver. The primary CYP450 isoforms seen in the placenta are CYP1A1/1A2, although other isoforms, including CYP2E1, CYP3A4, CYP3A7, and CYP4B1, have also been reported, although with low activity.[21,114,123] Expression of placental CYP1A1 increases with exposure to polychlorinated biphenyls (PCBs) or maternal cigarette smoking.[123] Phase II reactions including UGTs are also present during most of gestation.[106,131] UGT has a role in detoxifying endogenous and exogenous substances and in regulating steroid hormones produced in the trophoblast.[131] Glutathione S-transferase may help protect the placenta and fetus from oxidative stress and is also involved in placenta hormone metabolism.[131] These enzymes may increase with maternal nicotine or alcohol use, although alcohol dehydrogenase (a phase I reactant) is seen in low concentrations and is not inducible.[21,123,131]

Placental Influx and Efflux Transporters

Although many drugs cross the placenta by simple diffusion, some drugs use placental influx or efflux transporters. These transporters are located along the apical membrane of the microvillus brush border (facing maternal blood in the intervillous space) and on the syncytiotrophoblast basal membrane (facing the fetal connective tissue matrix and blood vessels in the villi) or on fetal capillary epithelium to facilitate movement of nutrients and other physiologic substances across the placenta.[41,60,61,103,106,110,123,126,139] Expression of transporters varies during gestation and are influenced by genetic and environmental stimuli, although as a group these transporters tend to have greater activity early in pregnancy than at term.[120] Genetic polymorphisms of transporter influx and efflux proteins many influence drug levels reaching the fetus and thus fetal drug response and risk of adverse reactions.[34,120]

Some drugs may also be transferred across the placenta by nutrient (influx) transporters, including glucose, carnitine, monoamine, and organic ion carriers.[106] For example, a folate transporter is involved with folate transfer and retinol-binding proteins with retinal (vitamin A) transfer across the placenta.[8] Nonphysiologic substances—some drugs, environmental pollutants, and toxins—if structurally similar to nutrients, may compete for nutrient transporters. The drugs that seem to be particularly able to use this method to cross the placenta include amphetamines, cocaine, cannabinoids, and nicotine and other substances from cigarettes.[44,131] By successfully competing with nutrients for these transporters, nutrient transfer is reduced and fetal growth and development altered. In addition, cephalosporins, ganciclovir, and corticosteroids cross by facilitated diffusion, probably by using carriers that normally transport dipeptides, hormones, and steroids.[103]

A role of placental efflux transporters is to remove steroids and other potentially toxic substances and thus protect the fetus.[61,73,76,106,110,123,131,139] Originally most of the transporters were identified in studies of multidrug resistance in tumors, as is reflected in some of their names. Examples of drug efflux transporters in the placenta include members of the ATP-binding cassette (ABC) group such as multidrug-resistant gene protein (MRP) 1, or P-gp; MRP-2; MRP-3; and breast cancer resistance protein (BCRP).[60,73,106,125,126,131] P-gp, MRP-2, and BCRP are located on the apical membrane of the syncytiotrophoblast cells facing maternal blood; MRP-1 and MRP-3 are on the basal or fetal side of the trophoblast (Figure 7-3).[47,61,73,110,126] Efflux transporters are also found on the gut, lung, and blood-brain barrier and help protect entry of substances into the body and brain. Efflux transporters are under hormonal regulation—for example, BCRP by estradiol and progesterone and P-gp by glucocorticoids.[126] Inflammation and infection may alter regulation of these transporters.[93]

Each transporter appears to have specific substrates for which they provide protection. P-gp exports cations, steroids, digoxin, cytotoxic drugs, some antibiotics, opioids, phenobarbital, erythromycin, phenytoin, verapamil, and other substances that enter the placenta back into maternal blood, thus reducing fetal exposure.[21,60,61,89,106,110] BCRP is involved in efflux of flavonoids, zidovudine, cimetidine, glyburide, nitrofurantoin, and the food-borne chemical carcinogen PhiP.[60,73,106] Some transporters may have bidirectional flow, which can allow xenobiotics to be transported across the placenta to the fetus.[73] Thus BCRP and P-gp can not only decrease the amount of drug reaching the fetus but enhance removal of any drug reaching the fetal circulation.[131] OCT3 is a bidirectional transporter that transports metformin, and as a result

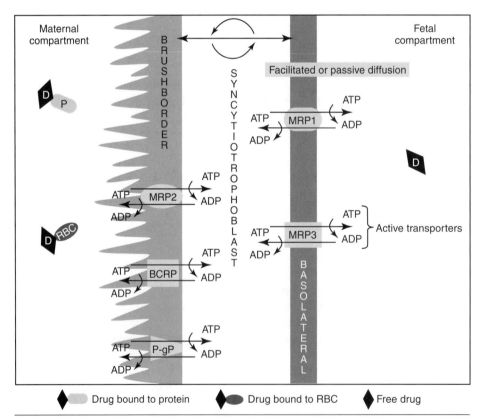

FIGURE 7-3   Transport across the placental barrier. *ADP,* Adenosine diphosphate; *ATP,* adenosine triphosphate; *BCRP,* breast cancer resistance protein; *D,* drug; *MRP,* multidrug-resistant gene protein; *P,* protein; *P-gP,* P-glycoprotein; *RBC,* red blood cell. (From Gedeon, C. & Koren, G. (2006). Designing pregnancy centered medications: Drugs which do not cross the human placenta. *Placenta, 27,* 862.)

TABLE 7-7   Summary of Developmentally Dependent Changes in Drug Disposition

PHYSIOLOGIC SYSTEM	AGE-RELATED TRENDS	PHARMACOKINETIC IMPLICATIONS	CLINICAL IMPLICATIONS
Gastrointestinal (GI) tract	Neonates and young infants: reduced and irregular peristalsis with prolonged gastric emptying time. Neonates: greater intragastric pH (>4) relative to infants. Infants: enhanced lower GI motility.	Slower rate of drug absorption (e.g., increased Tmax) without compensatory compromise in the extent of bioavailability. Reduced retention of suppository formulations.	Potential delay in the onset of drug action after oral administration. Potential for reduced extent of bioavailability from rectally administered drugs.
Integument	Neonates and young infants: thinner stratum corneum (neonates only), greater cutaneous perfusion, enhanced hydration and greater ratio of total body surface area to body mass.	Enhanced rate and extent of percutaneous drug absorption. Greater relative exposure of topically applied drugs compared with adults.	Enhanced percutaneous bioavailability and potential for toxicity. Need to reduce amount of drugs applied to skin.
Body compartments	Neonates and infants: decreased fat, decreased muscle mass, increased extracellular and total body water spaces.	Increased apparent volume of distribution for drugs distributed to body water spaces and reduced apparent volume of distribution for drugs that bind to muscle and/or fat.	Requirement of higher weight-normalized (i.e., mg/kg) drug doses to achieve therapeutic plasma drug concentrations.
Plasma protein binding	Neonates: decreased concentrations of albumin and α1-acid glycoprotein with reduced binding affinity for albumin-bound weak acids.	Increased unbound concentrations for highly protein-bound drugs with increased apparent volume of distribution and potential for toxicity if the amount of free drug increases in the body.	For highly bound (i.e., >70%) drugs, need to adjust dose to maintain plasma levels near the low end of the recommended "therapeutic range."
Drug metabolizing enzyme (DME) activity	Neonates and young infants: immature isoforms of cytochrome P450 and phase II enzymes with discordant patterns of developmental expression. Children 1–6 years: apparent increased activity for selected DMEs over adult normal values. Adolescents: attainment of adult activity after puberty.	Neonates and young infants: decreased plasma drug clearance early in life with an increase in apparent elimination half-life. Children 1–6 years: increased plasma drug clearance (i.e., reduced elimination half-life) for specific pharmacologic substrates of DMEs.	Neonates and young infants: increased drug dosing intervals and/or reduced maintenance doses. Children 1–6 years: for selected drugs, need to increase dose and/or shorten dose interval compared with usual adult dose.
Renal drug excretion	Neonates and young infants: decreased glomerular filtration rates (first 6 months) and active tubular secretion (first 12 months) with adult values attained by 24 months.	Neonates and young infants: accumulation of renally excreted drugs and/or active metabolites with reduced plasma clearance and increased elimination half-life, greatest during first 3 months of life.	Neonates and young infants: increased drug dosing intervals and/or reduced maintenance doses during the first 3 months of life.

From Rakhmanina, N.Y. & van den Anker, J.N. (2006). Pharmacological research in pediatrics: From neonates to adolescents. *Adv Drug Deliv Rev, 58,* 10.

Drug Absorption

Oral Agents

Absorption of oral medications in the neonate is altered by the following: (1) decreased bile salts and pancreatic enzymes; (2) slower gut transit time because of delayed gastric emptying and decreased motility; (3) mucus in the stomach; (4) differences in gastric and duodenal pH; (5) high levels of β-glucuronidase in the duodenum; (6) gut metabolic enzymes and drug transporters; (7) intestinal flora; and (8) intestinal surface area.[4,17,31,42,70,89,94] These alterations are more pronounced in preterm infants and those with intrauterine growth restriction (IUGR).[31,98] Oral drug absorption matures by 4 to 5 months of age.[17]

Decreased bile salts and pancreatic enzymes can result in poorer absorption of lipid-soluble substances such as vitamin K or drugs that must be hydrolyzed for absorption. Slower gut transit time because of delayed gastric emptying and decreased motility initially delays then prolongs absorption. Mucus in the stomach may also delay absorption. Differences in gastric and duodenal pH may partially or totally inactivate some drugs. Absorption of oral drugs by the neonate is also influenced by the drug's physicochemical characteristics. Drugs such as phenytoin, acetaminophen, and chloramphenicol are absorbed slowly and erratically, whereas penicillin and ampicillin are absorbed more efficiently than in adults because of the higher gastric pH in the neonate.[8] Other agents such as theophylline, digoxin, and diazepam have oral absorption patterns that are more similar to those in adults.

Gastric and duodenal pH influences drug solubility and ionization. An acid pH increases the absorption of acidic drugs (low pKa), because these drugs tend to stay in a non-ionized, lipid-soluble form. A higher pH enhances alkaline drug absorption and slows absorption of acidic drugs. Gastric pH is higher for the first 12 to 24 hours after birth, then gradually declines to adult values by 2 to 3 years.[42] Preterm infants who are less than 32 weeks' gestational age have decreased gastric acid secretion with a more alkaline pH and thus poorer absorption of weak acids and bases.[20,31,98] Gastric emptying is delayed for up to 6 to 8 hours in immature infants and is slower in all infants before 6 to 8 months. This may delay absorption and prolong the time to reach peak drug concentration.[20,70]

The neonate's duodenum has higher levels of β-glucuronidase, an enzyme that deconjugates drugs (e.g., indomethacin, chloramphenicol), and bilirubin (see Chapter 18) that the liver has metabolized via glucuronyl conjugation.[31,42,70,98] These drugs reenter the blood via the enterohepatic circulation (see Chapter 18) and must be remetabolized by the liver. This increases the half-life and prolongs activity of these drugs.[17,98] Oral absorption is also influenced by drug efflux transporter expression on the intestinal lining.[89,101] Membrane-bound transporter proteins may move drugs across the intestinal epithelium; immature transporters limit absorption.[24] Bioavailability is also influenced by intestinal microbiome, which varies depending on whether the infant is fed breast milk or formula.[42]

Intestinal absorption of drugs, gut transit time, and motility depend on perfusion and food intake. Better GI absorption occurs with drugs of low molecular weight (MW) that are nonionized and lipid-soluble.[98] An ill infant who is not being fed orally may have further impairment of gut function and erratic absorption of oral medications. Intestinal surface area is decreased with genetic disorders such as cystic fibrosis and disorders such as short bowel syndrome and necrotizing enterocolitis, thus reducing absorption.[20,98]

Intramuscular and Rectal Absorption

The infant's small muscle mass and alterations in peripheral perfusion influence intramuscular medications. Decreased muscle mass may limit use of intramuscular administration in very-low-birth-weight (VLBW) infants. Drugs given intramuscularly may have slower, more erratic absorption, depending on the infant's gestational age and health status. In the first few days after birth, muscle blood flow is decreased, slowing absorption.[20] Variations in muscle blood flow last for 2 to 3 weeks after birth.[42] Infants with respiratory problems or low cardiac output have decreased peripheral perfusion, leading to even slower and more erratic absorption of drugs given intramuscularly.[70] On the other hand, rectal administration may be more effective in neonates than in adults because the rectum in neonates is well vascularized.[42,70]

Skin Absorption

Percutaneous absorption of substances occurs via the cells of the stratum corneum (transepidermal route) or via the hair follicle–sebaceous gland complex (transappendageal route). The major pathway is most likely transepidermal, with diffusion of a substance through the stratum corneum and epidermis into the dermis and microcirculation. The subepidermal circulation is also readily accessible, enhancing rapid absorption. Preterm infants have greater skin absorption because their skin is thinner than that of term infants. VLBW infants have minimum to no stratum corneum and higher dermal water content (see Chapter 14).[70,98]

Neonates are at increased risk for toxic reactions from absorption of topically applied substances because of increased permeability and surface area per weight.[6] Skin metabolism is different in neonates, so drugs applied topically may result in the release of metabolites different from those that would occur if the drugs were given by other routes. This increases the risk of toxicity.[20,70] Occlusion of the skin (e.g., placement against the mattress) permits more complete absorption, with longer contact enhancing absorption of the substance. In preterm infants, percutaneous absorption occurs even more rapidly and completely as a result of the markedly increased skin permeability. Topical analgesic agents are more easily absorbed, increasing the risk of toxicity (see Chapter 14). Permeability of these agents, such as EMLA cream (lidocaine and prilocaine) is further increased in preterm infants in the first few weeks after birth.[98]

Neonatal toxicity secondary to the use of topical agents such as hexachlorophene, pentachlorophenol-containing laundry detergents, isopropyl alcohol, and povidone-iodine has been well documented.[20,23,28,70] Use of these substances can increase the risk of detrimental effects if not monitored carefully. Topical application of povidone-iodine (Betadine) yields significantly elevated levels of iodine in blood plasma if not removed completely from the skin after completion of invasive procedures (e.g., chest tube insertion, percutaneous line insertion).[20] Gentle cleansing of the skin with water reduces this risk.

Isopropyl alcohol is also absorbed through the skin. Alcohol use can result in dry skin, skin irritation, and skin burns. The concentration of the solution, duration of exposure, and condition of the exposed skin determine the effects of alcohol use. Tissue destruction occurs with the deesterifying of the skin and the disruption of the cell structure. Exposure, pressure, and decreased perfusion can contribute to the development of burns from alcohol and chlorhexidine, complicating fluid management and providing portals for infection.

Drug Distribution

The distribution of drugs is influenced by the infant's large extracellular fluid space, increased total body water, decreased fat, and decreased plasma protein content and binding. The blood-brain barrier is less well developed, which may result in increased amounts of drugs (especially lipid-soluble substances) reaching and being deposited in the brain.[101] The greater total body water and lower fat content in neonates increases the apparent Vd, especially for water-soluble substances.[98,121]

The altered Vd in the neonate may reduce peak volumes of drugs and delay excretion. Because of the increased extracellular water, higher doses per kilogram may be needed in the neonate for water-soluble drugs distributed in extracellular fluid. For example, an increased Vd is seen with drugs such as the right animal model, and the effects of maternal disease.[75,105] An example of the difficulty with recall bias occurred with Bendectin; women whose infants had defects recalled taking this drug, which was commonly used, in early pregnancy. Subsequent studies did not confirm a link between Bendectin and malformations.[59] Maternal pharmacologic therapy may be administered for an illness that itself leads to a defect or malformations or may produce maternal symptoms requiring treatment with a specific drug; several agents may interact with each other so that the combination is teratogenic rather than either individual drug; or the mother may be taking multiple drugs for different problems.[75]

Problems with human studies include difficulty studying cause and effect, lack of random sampling, lack of control over dosing and timing, and expense. Animal studies can also be problematic. Drug studies with animals may involve administration of large doses that exceed the usual therapeutic dose in humans. Selecting the appropriate animal model can be difficult. Drug kinetics and metabolism may differ between different species and between humans and animals.[22,75] For example, thalidomide, a potent teratogen in humans, did not produce limb reduction anomalies in the animal models used to study the drug before its release; subsequently, similar anomalies were seen in macaque monkeys. On the other hand, benzodiazepines cause oral clefts in some animal models but not in humans given clinically appropriate doses. Similarly, salicylates cause cardiac defects in some animal species but not humans. Most human teratogens have been discovered by either epidemiology studies or by health care professionals, not animal studies.[22] Dicke noted, "We will never be in a position to state that an environmental agent has no teratogenic potential. The most we can say is that an agent poses no measurable risk."[37]

Principles of Teratogenesis

General principles that govern the action of teratogens, originally outlined by Wilson,[134] include the following:

1. *Susceptibility to a teratogenic agent is dependent on the genotype of the embryo and the manner in which the agent interacts with environmental factors.*[37,134] The genetic makeup of the developing embryo is the environmental programmer to which the teratogenic agent is introduced. This programming means that the genes and extrinsic factors interact in varying degrees with varied responses in different individuals and species. Because individual sensitivity is dependent on the biochemical and morphologic makeup of that particular individual, data from animal models and sometimes even from studies on other individuals cannot always be applied. For example, individuals with a gene mutation that reduces levels of an enzyme needed to detoxify anticonvulsant drugs such as phenytoin are at greater risk of having a child with defects; gene polymorphisms of transforming growth factor-α and heavy maternal smoking increase the risk of oral clefts.[30]

2. *Susceptibility to teratogenic agents is dependent on the timing of the exposure and the developmental stage of the embryo.*[37,93,134] A basic precept of biology is that the more immature an organism is, the more susceptible that organism is to change.[134] This suggests that there is a critical period where teratogenic events have the greatest impact. The period of greatest susceptibility is during the first trimester, when cell differentiation and organogenesis are occurring. Structural and functional maturation continues throughout gestation and after birth, and therefore many systems remain susceptible to alterations in later development. Sometimes the specific period of vulnerability can be identified. For example, the hypoplastic limb defects seen with thalidomide occur only with exposure at 21 to 36 days after fertilization; valproic acid exposure results in a neural tube defect only with exposure between 14 and 27 days.[91,122]

The most likely period for structural defects to occur is during organogenesis, because exposure of the embryo to a teratogenic agent either during or before a critical stage in development of that organ can lead to anomalies.[95] The time of greatest susceptibility during development is defined as the time when the highest incidence of defects occurs (usually gross anatomic defects). Other defects, especially neurobehavioral and other functional defects, have peaks in sensitivity at different times during development. These periods of sensitivity vary depending on the timing and duration of the period of cell proliferation (e.g., brain growth and development extend into early childhood and thus are vulnerable for a longer period of time).[95,134]

Malformations resulting from incomplete morphogenesis within an organ usually originate before organ structure is complete. The exact time at which a specific defect occurs cannot be determined; it can be said only that a defect occurred at some time before a particular point. For example, anencephaly must occur before closure of the anterior neural tube (25 to 26 days), meningomyelocele before closure of the posterior neural tube (27 to 28 days), cleft palate before fusion of the secondary palate lateral shelves (10 weeks), cleft lip before closure of the lip (36 days), tracheoesophageal fistula before separation of the foregut into the trachea and primitive esophagus (30 days), ventricular septal defect before closure of the ventricular septum (6 weeks), transposition of the great vessels before development of the aorticopulmonary septum (34 days), diaphragmatic hernia before closure of the pleuroperitoneal canal (6 weeks), omphalocele before or during return of the gut to the abdomen (10 to 10.5 weeks), and imperforate anus before perforation of the anal membrane (8 weeks).[95]

3. *Teratogenic agents act in specific ways on cells or tissues to cause pathogenesis.*[37,134] Unfavorable factors within the environment are able to trigger changes in developing cells that alter their subsequent development. These changes are not specific to the type of causative factor, and initial changes may result in a variety of alterations within the embryo. These early changes may not be discernible, because they occur subcellularly at the molecular level.

Pathogenesis is the visible sign of cellular damage and may occur from cell necrosis or by secondary interference with cellular interactions—that is, by induction, adhesion, and migration; reduced biosynthesis of macromolecules; or accumulation of foreign materials, fluids, or blood.[37,134] A given teratogenic effect may be induced by a variety of agents. For example, a specific defect may result from infection, drug exposure, genetic alteration, an environmental toxin, or a combination of these factors.[37,134]

4. *The final manifestations of abnormal development are death, malformation, growth restriction, and functional disorders.*[37,134] For the early embryo a teratogenic event will most likely result in death. Once organogenesis begins, teratogenic events lead to malformation in the organs or organ systems. The teratogenic insult might also make the embryo more susceptible to death or general cell necrosis, resulting in a reduced cell mass and slower overall rate of growth. Functional defects may be diagnosed throughout infancy and childhood.

Before conception, damage can occur to the chromosomes of one or both parents, or new gene mutations may arise. Alterations in spermatogenesis; in seminal fluid or sperm transport in the male; or in oogenesis or the environment of the vagina, cervix, or uterus of the female may also alter development. Environmental toxins, such as heavy metals and chemicals, may influence hormonal changes that can alter the menstrual cycle, ovulation, and fertility.[118] Parental exposures before conception or even in previous generations can alter the genome. Changes before conception may arise from epigenetic mechanisms such as altered deoxyribonucleic acid (DNA) methylation, altered histone proteins, or differences in noncoding ribonucleic acid (RNA) expression (see Chapter 1) limiting gene expression. An example of a transgenerational effect is DES exposure. There is an increased risk of carcinoma, preterm birth, and infertility in daughters and sons and increased risk of hypospadias and preterm birth in grandchildren of women who took DES during pregnancy, probably transmitted by epigenetic and genetic processes.[39]

The preembryonic stage (conception to 14 days) is a time of little morphologic differentiation in specific organ systems. Exposure to teratogens during this period usually has an all-or-nothing effect; that is, either the damage is so severe that the zygote is aborted or there are no apparent effects.[25,91,113] However, this may be the time that syndromes affecting multiple organ systems arise. Teratogens or environmental disturbances may interfere with implantation of the blastocyst or cause death and early abortion. However, most congenital anomalies probably do not arise during this period, possibly because of the lack of cell differentiation, at least in the early part of this period. Many cells within the inner cell mass are not yet programmed to become specific structures. Thus damage to a few cells does not alter development if the preembryo is able to produce sufficient cells to restore the lost volume.[134] If a teratogen is potent or the dosage is high, the effect is death

or possibly mitotic disjunction during cleavage, with chromosomal alterations that subsequently cause malformation syndromes rather than local defects.[68] If only a few cells are damaged, development continues, although the genetically programmed schedule may be delayed.[95]

The period of organogenesis (15 to 60 days after conception) is a period of extreme sensitivity to teratogens; it is the period when many congenital malformations develop. Insults early in this period (15 to 30 days) are likely to result in death if the embryo is damaged. Early events in organ formation are generally most sensitive to external forces, although in some systems (e.g., the sensory organs), critical periods occur during relatively late stages. The more specialized the metabolic requirements of a group of cells, the more sensitive they are to deprivation and damage.[95,134]

From 11 weeks to term, the fetus becomes increasingly resistant to structural damage from toxic agents as the ability to produce major structural deviations is reduced as organ systems become organized. Thus once the definitive form and relationships within a system are established, gross anatomic defects are no longer possible. However, histogenesis continues and the function of organ systems can still be altered.[95,134] Defects can occur at the microscopic level, or neurobehavioral or other functional abilities can be altered, resulting in physiologic defects and delayed growth.[15] Insults during fetal life can lead to dysfunction such as brain damage or deafness, prematurity, growth restriction, stillbirth, infant death, or malignancy.

5. *Access to the embryo by environmental teratogens depends on the nature of the agent.*[37,39,134] There are several routes by which agents reach the embryo or fetus. Agents such as ultrasound, ionizing radiation, heat (see Chapter 20), and microwaves pass directly through maternal tissue without modification. Chemical agents or their metabolites reach developing tissues indirectly via transmission across the placenta. Whether these agents reach toxic or teratogenic concentrations depends on maternal dosage, rate of absorption, and maternal homeostatic capabilities as well as physical properties of the agent and the placenta. Pathogenic organisms may also reach the fetus by an ascending route via the vaginal canal and cervix (see Chapter 13). Agents also act indirectly on the fetus by inducing maternal pharmacologic effects or altering maternal physiology, affecting the fetal-placental unit or delivery of nutrients because of placental insufficiency.[15]

6. *As the dosage increases, manifestations of deviant development increase.*[37,134] There appears to be a threshold at which embryotoxicity occurs and damage is initiated. When the effect threshold is exceeded, cell damage or death exceeds restoration. For example, valproic acid increases the risk of neural tube defects, and the risk increases with increased dosage levels.[30] Sometimes the specific threshold cannot be determined, as is the case with alcohol. Different types of embryotoxicity exist for different thresholds.

Mechanisms of Teratogenesis

Proposed mechanisms of teratogenesis include the following:

1. *Gene mutation.* Mutation is the basis of heritable developmental defects and is the result of a change in the sequence of nucleotides. If the change appears in the germinal cell line (i.e., oocytes and spermatocytes), it is likely to be heritable. A mutation in a somatic cell will be passed to daughter somatic cells but cannot be transferred to the next generation. Gene mutations can result in biochemical or structural disorders or later development of malignancies (see Chapter 1).[134]

2. *Chromosome breaks and nondisjunction.* These alterations lead to excesses, deficiencies, or rearrangements of chromosomes or parts of chromosomes and can be transmitted to offspring. For example, sperm of men exposed to radiation or chemotherapy have increased numbers of chromosomal aberrations for at least 3 to 4 months (chemotherapy) up to 36 months (ionizing radiation).

3. *Mitotic interference and cell death.* Interference with mitosis can result from inhibition of DNA synthesis, prevention of spindle formation, or failure of chromosome separation. For example, aminopterin and methotrexate inhibit an enzyme needed during the cell cycle (see Chapter 1), leading to cell death during the S (DNA synthesis) phase.[30] Viruses and other infectious agents may also interfere with mitosis.

4. *Altered nucleic acid integrity or function.* These alterations occur secondary to biochemical changes that interfere with nucleic acid replication, transcription, natural base incorporation, or RNA translation and protein synthesis. Because processes such as protein synthesis are essential for survival of the embryo, interference usually results in death rather than malformation. DES acts on estrogen-responsive tissue by altering RNA, protein, and DNA synthesis with development of columnar epithelium not normally found in the vaginal area. This "foreign" tissue is at risk for later malignant degeneration.[30]

5. *Lack or excess of precursors, substrates, or coenzymes needed for biosynthesis.* These deficiencies result in slowed or altered growth and differentiation and occur because of dietary deficiencies, placental transfer failure, maternal absorption failure, or the presence of specific analogs or antagonists. Some agents, such as amphetamines, cocaine, cannabis, and nicotine, may occupy receptors for nutrients, thus decreasing transfer of critical substances and altering fetal growth and development.[44] Retinoic acid regulates expression of one of the developmental genes involved in craniofacial and axial skeleton development. Excess levels—as occurs with isotretinoin therapy—leads to malformations in these systems. Coumadin inhibits formation of substances needed for proteins to bind to calcium and can alter bone ossification with craniofacial and other skeletal anomalies.[30]

6. *Altered energy sources.* As a result of interference with energy pathways (glucose sources, glycolysis, citric acid cycle, terminal electron transport systems), the energy needs of the rapidly proliferating and synthesizing tissues of the embryo are not met. For example, biotin deficiency—seen with an inborn error of metabolism—decreases activity of a mitochondrial biotin-dependent enzyme.[30]

7. *Enzyme and growth factor inhibitions.* Inhibition of critical enzymes interferes with cell functioning, cellular repair, differentiation, and growth. Inadequate folic acid increases the risk of neural tube defects, especially if the deficiency occurs in women with an enzyme defect in folic acid metabolism. Thalidomide may inhibit angiogenesis and thus limb growth by decreasing critical growth factors such as insulin-like growth factor 1 and fibroblast growth factor.[122] Inhibition of alcohol dehydrogenases, needed to detoxify alcohol, alters retinoic acid metabolism similarly to the action of isotretinoin (which also leads to craniofacial and skeletal defects).[30]

8. *Osmolar imbalance.* These imbalances lead to pathogenesis by causing edema that impinges upon embryonic tissues.[134]

9. *Altered membrane characteristics.* These changes can result in abnormal membrane permeability and lead to osmolar imbalances and edema.[134]

10. *Altered cell and neuronal migration or central nervous system (CNS) organization.* These processes are influenced by neurotransmitters, especially monoamines (dopamine, serotonin, and norepinephrine). Inborn errors of metabolism—especially those involved with amino acid metabolism—alter CNS organization. Drugs, such as cocaine, that increase or reduce levels of neurotransmitters may alter migration or later organization of cortical neurons (see Chapter 15).[134]

Specific proposed teratogenic mechanisms associated with drugs are folate antagonism, oxidative stress, angiotensin-converting enzyme inhibition, angiotensin II receptor antagonism, cyclooygenase-1 and cyclooygenase-2 inhibition, 5-hydroxytryptamine-reuptake inhibition, and alterations in placental drug transporters.[133]

Effects of Drug Exposure in Utero

The fetus is a passive recipient of all drugs entering the mother's system. From laxatives and antacids to cocaine and heroin, all of these substances are chemicals that may have an effect on the fetus and newborn. Some classes of drugs are more significant to CNS development and function after birth than are others. Examples of drugs known to produce significant effects are ethanol, tobacco smoke, narcotics, amphetamines, and cocaine.

Cigarette Smoking

Smoking during pregnancy and its metabolites are "one of the leading preventable causes of adverse maternal and fetal outcomes."[97] Cigarette smoke contains many chemicals, many of which have been associated with adverse outcomes.[15,39,109] Nicotine is particularly important in adverse pregnancy outcomes.[19,97] Nicotine and cotinine readily cross the placenta, with fetal levels often exceeding maternal levels.[97,109] Nicotine may influence outcomes by binding to cholinergic receptors, leading to premature onset of cell differentiation and disrupting cell replication.[97] Nicotine can alter brain development and neurotransmitter systems, has vasoconstrictive effects on the placenta and fetus, alters placental structure (see Chapter 3), and may influence development.[15,109]

The effects of smoking include an increased risk of low birth weight and prematurity.[19,30,39,59,97,109] Smoking also increases pregnancy and placental complications (e.g., ectopic pregnancy, placental abruption, placenta previa, and miscarriage) and may alter fertility in both females and males.[30,39,97,109] Women who smoke during pregnancy are at increased risk for deep vein thrombosis, pulmonary embolism, and other cardiopulmonary complications.[109] Nicotine exposure increases the risk of altered cognitive and learning skills, sudden infant death syndrome, altered respiratory function, and increased respiratory infections in offspring.[39,97] Maternal genotype may influence the degree of fetal and neonatal effects.[109] Chronic exposure to secondhand smoke also reduces fetal growth and increases the risk of low birth weight. The effects of smoking on birth weight and other effects are dose-dependent, so the fewer cigarettes a woman smokes, the less likely her infant will be affected.[30]

Alcohol

Ethanol is one of the most commonly abused drugs during pregnancy, with specific teratogenic effects of fetal alcohol syndrome (FAS) seen in 0.5 to 2/1000 births.[132] Infants who were exposed to alcohol in utero are at increased risk for a range of fetal alcohol spectrum disorders (FASD) including FAS and other forms of alcohol-related damage.[39,43,67,88] These differential effects may be partially a result of variations in the metabolism of alcohol in the placenta by CYP2E1 and alcohol dehydrogenases.[109,131] Diagnosis of FAS requires the presence of prenatal or postnatal growth restriction, CNS involvement, and specific craniofacial features. Other forms of FASD seen in infants of women with a history of substantial alcohol intake during pregnancy include physical defects (e.g., congenital heart defects) without the characteristic facial features or mental and behavioral abnormalities without defects or facial features.[67]

Damage from ethanol may result from chromosomal damage or acetaldehyde (the placenta deoxidizes ethanol to this substance), which reaches 50% of maternal levels. Acetaldehyde affects cell membranes and cell migration, altering embryonic tissue organization with dysmorphic changes.[43] Alcohol interferes with transport of amino acids across the placenta and incorporation into proteins. This may limit the number of fetal cells and lead to fetal growth restriction.[43] Other mechanisms by which alcohol may influence fetal development are by alterations in prostaglandin and protein synthesis, hormone levels, hypoxia (because of decreased

placental blood flow and alterations in umbilical cord vessels), and altered brain morphology.[15] Decreased placental transfer of linoleic and docosahexanoic acid may also alter fetal growth and development.[131]

No level of drinking alcohol has been proven safe; drinking alcohol at any stage of pregnancy can affect the brain and other areas of development.[15,43,109] Current studies do not support identifying a "safe level" of alcohol consumption by pregnant women. FAS usually occurs in offspring of chronic alcohol abusers; however, FAS has occurred in women who drink less. Mild to moderate alcohol consumption during pregnancy has been associated with a range of later neurobehavioral effects, although the effects of moderate and light drinking are still not well understood.[15]

Marijuana

Marijuana use during pregnancy has been a continuing concern. The major psychoactive substance in marijuana is Δ-9-tetrahydrocannabinol (THC), which binds to specific receptors in the brain, lungs, liver, and kidneys. THC crosses both the placenta and blood-brain barrier. The placenta appears to limit transfer, so fetal marijuana levels tend to be less than maternal levels.[15] No specific patterns of malformations have been found with maternal marijuana use; effect on fetal growth is unclear, although lower birth weights have been reported.[15,59,109] A recent study found an increased risk of preterm birth but no other common pregnancy complications.[82] Long-term studies suggest children exposed to marijuana in utero have an increased risk of issues with problem-solving, spelling, reading performance, impulse control, visual memory, and attention during the school years.[15,137]

Opioids

Fetuses are not immune from developing chemical dependency. Neonatal abstinence syndrome (NAS) refers to particular withdrawal behaviors (CNS hypersensitivity, respiratory distress, autonomic dysfunction, and gastrointestinal [GI] disturbances) observed in neonates exposed to dependency-producing drugs in utero.[72] NAS is seen most commonly with maternal heroin or methadone use but can also occur with drugs such as oxycodone, hydrocodone, and codeine. The timing and severity of withdrawal are based on the type of drug, the mother's drug dosage, the length of time since the mother's last dose, the duration of exposure, the neonate's degree of immaturity, and the neonate's general health status. Symptoms usually appear within 72 hours after birth but can be seen as late as 2 to 4 weeks of age. The neonate's withdrawal responses may last from 6 days to 8 weeks, or longer.

Methadone has a long elimination half-life, which minimizes fluctuations in maternal serum levels and the risk of drug withdrawal in the fetus, reduces infant morbidity and mortality, and leads to less fetal growth restriction.[59] Withdrawal symptoms may be more common and severe in infants exposed to methadone, possibly because methadone accumulates in fat tissue and is released slowly.[59] A pregnant woman's volume of distribution (Vd) is increased, so many women need higher doses to prevent withdrawal.[32,59] Buprenorphine is a potent long-acting (72 hour) semisynthetic opioid with partial μ-receptor agonist and κ-receptor antagonist properties that is an alternative to methadone for the treatment of opiate-dependency. A multicenter international double-blinded study comparing buprenorphine with methadone treatment (n = 191) reported that neonates from mothers in the buprenorphine group required significantly less morphine, shorter hospital stay, and shorter duration of treatment for NAS. No significant differences were reported between groups in other outcomes or in rates of adverse events.[66]

The responses to drug withdrawal in neonates are similar to those in adults, but because of the nature of neurologic organization, the implications are more severe in neonates. NAS includes both physiologic and behavioral responses. Several scales have been developed to aid observation and measurement of the responses to neonatal abstinence. Interventions are initiated based on the severity of withdrawal as assessed by these scales. Withdrawal may be treated pharmacologically with drugs such as phenobarbital, morphine, and methadone.[59,72] Breastfeeding is not recommended if the woman is abusing opiates but is recommended for women receiving therapeutic methadone or buprenorphine and may decrease the amount of medication needed for NAS, although the infant's withdrawal may last longer.[80,109]

Cocaine and Amphetamines

Cocaine, amphetamine, and methamphetamine are central and peripheral stimulants that produce their effects by interfering with the reuptake of monoamines such as dopamine, norepinephrine, and serotonin at presynaptic adrenergic nerve terminals, thus increasing levels of these neurotransmitters at the neuronal junction (these transporters are inhibited by many antidepressants such as selective serotonin receptor reuptake inhibitors).[9,45,48,59,135] The excess monoamines result in prolonged neuronal activation, leading to characteristic neurobehavioral responses (because of binding to central receptors) and cardiovascular and motor effects (because of binding to peripheral receptors located in tissues innervated by the sympathetic nervous system).[15] Monoamines have a trophic role in CNS cell proliferation, neural migration, and organization. Thus exposure to elevated levels of monoamines may alter CNS organization, increasing the risk for later alterations in arousal and attention. Serotonin and norepinephrine receptors are found on the maternal-facing side of the placental syncytium. Inhibition increases serotonin and norepinephrine in the intervillous space, which may lead to uterine contractions, vasoconstriction, and decreased placental blood flow, thus increasing the risk of preterm labor and fetal growth restriction.[45,49,59,64]

The actions of cocaine and amphetamines are similar, causing intense sympathetic nervous system activity. Cocaine produces vasoconstriction, tachycardia, and elevation of blood pressure in addition to a sense of excitement and euphoria. Cocaine is lipid-soluble, low MW, and has low ionization and thus easily crosses the placenta. In the fetus, it produces increased motor activity and tachycardia; cocaine crosses the fetal blood-brain barrier. Cocaine competes with nutrients for monoamine transporters in the placenta.[44] By successfully competing with nutrients for these transporters, cocaine reduces nutrient transfer, which can lead to fetal growth restriction. Levels of cocaine are high in placental membranes, myometrium, and amniotic fluid, resulting in a reservoir that prolongs fetal exposure.[27] Drug enzyme genetic polymorphisms in both mother and fetus influence cocaine metabolism, leading to individual differences in responses.[59]

Vasoconstrictive effects with reduction in placental blood flow to the placenta are associated with a high incidence of placental abruption.[49] Blood flow to the fetus through the placenta is also reduced. In addition, the umbilical arteries constrict in response to cocaine. The resultant placental ischemia has been attributed as the cause of low birth weight, decreased body length, and smaller head circumference found among infants of cocaine-abusing mothers.[27,59] Cocaine also increases uterine irritability and results in contractions. Cocaine may cause cerebral infarcts in the fetus. Cocaine use during pregnancy also poses risks to the mother, including an increased risk of stroke, seizure, hypertensive crises, precipitous labor, preterm labor, and uterine rupture.[27]

After birth, cocaine does not produce withdrawal behaviors, per se, but its effect appears to be related to an alteration of neurobehavioral organization that probably results from its direct influence on the developing brain. Neonates exposed to cocaine in utero are irritable, tremulous, and difficult to soothe and have rapid respiratory and heart rates; these infants exhibit excessive motor activity, altered sleep-wake patterns, poor feeding, feeding intolerance, and diarrhea.[13,59,64] No increase in anomalies has been found in recent studies.[59,83] Later outcomes of prenatal cocaine exposure include catch-up growth by 1 to 2 years in many studies and an increased risk of behavior, attention, language development, and information-processing alterations in many studies of 4- to 14-year-olds.[59,64,83] Outcomes are related to cumulative effects of cocaine, environment, and possibly concomitant alcohol or other drug use.[83]

The half-life of cocaine is longer in fetuses and neonates than in adults because the enzyme systems governing the drug's metabolism are not mature; thus cocaine may persist in neonates for several days after birth. Cocaine passes easily into breast milk; active use of cocaine by a lactating mother may produce severe reactions and possibly death in a neonate. Cocaine has been found in breast milk as late as 36 hours after maternal use.

Neonatal symptoms from methamphetamine exposure are similar to those with cocaine, with neurobehavioral alterations (decreased arousal, increased stress, altered movements) reported.[64,83] Animal and human studies demonstrate an increased risk of adverse pregnancy outcome.[15,64] These infants are at increased risk of fetal distress, placental abruption, preterm birth, and a 2.5-fold increased risk of fetal growth restriction.[27,49,59,64,131] Breastfeeding is usually not recommended, because methamphetamines tend to concentrate in breast milk at levels 2.8 to 7.5 times higher than in maternal plasma.[109] Children usually achieve catch-up growth by 2 years, depending on environment.[83] Although few studies have been done on older children, available studies suggest similar findings to cocaine exposure.[83]

Drugs and Lactation

Most breastfeeding women take at least one drug during lactation.[12] Many pharmacologic agents and environmental pollutants (as well as alcohol, nicotine, and other abused drugs) can be found in human milk, although usually at levels lower than those in the mother. Often, breastfeeding is interrupted or discontinued for maternal therapy even though there are relatively few maternal medications that are not compatible with breastfeeding.[90,115] Even if the mother is taking drugs with potential risks, careful monitoring and strategies to minimize infant exposure often can be used so that the mother can decide to continue breastfeeding if she chooses. In general, serious side effects in infants are uncommon. Most adverse effects are seen in infants younger than 2 months of age and are uncommon after 6 months.[116]

The use of any pharmacologic agent by a breastfeeding woman should be carefully evaluated. Most drugs enter breast milk in some quantity, although few drugs are contraindicated during lactation.[25] Little is known about side effects of many less commonly used agents. Some drugs should be used with caution and only as absolutely needed by lactating women, with careful monitoring of both infant and mother. The nurse and the mother should be aware of potential hazards of any drug, for both mother and infant. There are many reviews of drugs used during breastfeeding and concerns or potential hazards of specific agents; many textbooks and online sites also cover these topics (see Box 7-2 on p. 184), such as LactMed (http://toxnet.nlm.nih.gov; also available as an app). Information regarding the risks of drugs taken during lactation that addresses clinical considerations, summarizes risk, and provides data to support this assessment is included in the revised FDA pregnancy-labeling requirements.[40,112]

Drugs taken by a nursing mother reach infants in much smaller amounts through breast milk than drugs taken by a pregnant woman reach the fetus across the placenta.[53,87] Drugs cross into breast milk across the milk-blood barrier via the following mechanisms: (1) transcellular diffusion of low-molecular-weight (less than 100 to 200 daltons), nonionized, lipid-soluble substances such as ethanol, which are pulled across by water flow; (2) intercellular movement of large molecules through spaces between alveolar cells; (3) passive diffusion across a concentration gradient; (4) carrier-mediated diffusion of polar substances; and (5) active movement via specific drug transporters.[16,53,90] A few drugs—nitrofurantoin, acyclovir, ranitidine, and iodine—are actively transported

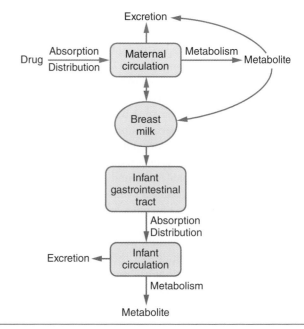

FIGURE 7-4 Steps involved in transfer of drugs from lactating mothers to nursing infants via breast milk. (From Reider, M.J. [1998]. Drug excretion during lactation. In R.A. Polin, W.W. Fox, & S.H. Abman [Eds.]. *Fetal and neonatal physiology* [3rd ed.]. Philadelphia: Saunders.)

across the blood-milk barrier into human milk by influx transporters.[12] Except for iodine, these agents do not usually reach clinically significant levels; iodine, however, can rise to elevated levels in the infant.[12] Figure 7-4 summarizes transfer of drugs from mother to infant. Figure 7-5 illustrates the movement of drugs at the blood-milk interface. Drugs move from the pregnant woman to the fetus directly from maternal blood to fetal blood, whereas drugs from the nursing mother to the infant pass from the mother's blood into milk and then to the infant's gut. In the infant's gut, the drug may be destroyed or absorption reduced because of limitations in GI absorption in infants, especially in the early months. In addition, there are more tissue layers between maternal blood and milk than between maternal and fetal blood across the placenta. This increases the diffusing distance and reduces the efficiency of transfer. Calculated doses of maternal drug received by the infant are generally significantly less than the standard therapeutic doses tolerated by infants without toxicity for most drugs.[53] Therefore some drugs that are not recommended during pregnancy may pose little risk during lactation.

Factors influencing the amount and rapidity of drug excretion into milk include drug dosage and duration; route of administration; drug physicochemical characteristics; blood level in maternal circulation; oral bioavailability; protein binding in maternal circulation; maternal physiology and drug handling; blood-milk barrier (see Figure 7-5); and infant physiology, drug handling, and maturity (see Table 7-7). Other infant factors to consider include the age of the infant, drug oral bioavailability, amount of milk intake,

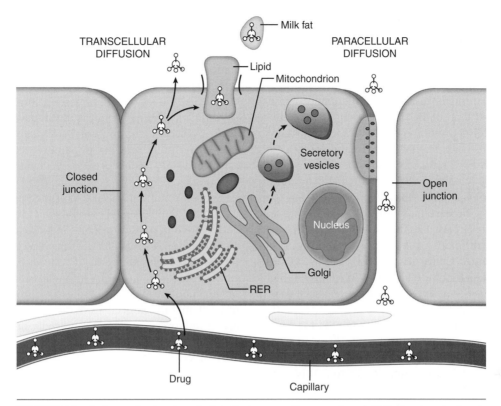

FIGURE 7-5 Pathways for drug transfer into the human milk compartment. *RER*, Rough endoplasmic reticulum. (From Hale, T.W., & Rowe, H.E. [2017]. *Medications and mothers' milk* [17th ed.]. New York, NY: Springer.)

and the record of the drug's use as a therapeutic agent in infants.[12,16,80,90] Characteristics of drugs most likely to cross into milk are agents that are lipid-soluble, have low MW, have a long half-life in the mother, have low protein binding, are given to the mother in large doses, or are used for chronic conditions or are used long term so that plasma levels are maintained at steady-state conditions.[12,86,89,90,124]

Infant drug exposure can be calculated by the milk-to-plasma ratio of a drug, percentage of maternal dose, relative infant dosage as a percentage of maternal dose, estimated infant serum concentration (using oral bioavailability or clearance in the infant), and the milk-plasma (M/P) ratio.[87] The M/P ratio ranges from 0.01 to 6.5 (averaging 0.5 to 1 for most drugs used during lactation).[12,115] Highly lipid-soluble and water-soluble substances with MW lower than 200 daltons generally have an M/P ratio near 1. High M/P ratios (greater than 1) are seen with weak bases and actively transported substances; a low M/P ratio (less than 1) is generally found with drugs that are weak acids or highly protein-bound substances.[80] Drugs with a low (less than 1) M/P ratio and high maternal and infant clearance rates generally have low risk of infant side effects. The M/P ratio assumes drug concentrations are constant and in equilibrium, which is often not valid, limiting clinical usefulness.[80,90]

Most drugs cross by passive or facilitated diffusion from higher to lower concentrations between maternal plasma and milk.[12] Some low MW drugs may also cross via membrane pores, whereas other substances such as immunoglobulins may pass between alveolar cells (see Figure 7-5).[53] The blood-milk barrier consists of the maternal capillary epithelium, mammary alveolar cell membrane, intracellular structures (including protein micelles and lipid vesicles), and the apical membrane of the mammary alveolar cell. The alveolar cell is a lipid barrier that reduces transfer of water-soluble and ionized drugs.[16] Therefore lipid-soluble drugs cross into milk more readily than water-soluble drugs, although this is somewhat influenced by MW. Concentration of drugs in milk may change with time from birth or during a feeding. For example, drugs such as diazepam and phenobarbital that are highly lipid-soluble may be more concentrated in hindmilk, which has four to five times greater lipid content than foremilk.[12,54] Lipid content is higher in mature milk versus colostrum; thus concentrations of lipid-soluble drugs may be reduced initially after birth.[87] Efflux transporters such as P-gp may transport some substances out of milk back to maternal plasma.[12]

Low MW substances such as ethanol rapidly diffuse across the tissue layers between maternal blood and milk. Water-soluble drugs with MWs less than 200 daltons can move across the blood-milk barrier via water-filled membrane pores.[87] Molecules greater than 200 daltons cannot pass through these pores and are transferred more slowly because they must first dissolve in the outer lipid membrane of the alveolar cell, diffuse across the cell, then dissolve in the apical membrane to reach milk. Substances with MWs larger than 800 daltons, such as insulin and heparin, generally do not cross into milk or do so very minimally.[12,80] Substances with higher MWs may cross in the first 4 to 10 days after delivery because of larger gaps between alveolar cells during this time.[53,80,91,103,115]

The major milk protein (α-lactalbumin) does not significantly bind drugs. One of the main serum drug-binding proteins (α1-acid glycoprotein) is not present in milk. Therefore the major milk drug-binding proteins are albumin and lactoferrin, which have markedly decreased binding compared with plasma proteins. Drugs that are highly bound in maternal blood (such as warfarin, which is 99% bound) are less likely to cross, because plasma levels of free drug are lower. If a drug is at least 85% bound in maternal blood, measurable concentrations of the drug are unlikely to be found in the infant.[10] Conversely, a drug such as lithium, which has no protein binding and a low MW, can reach high levels in milk.[10] Free drug levels of some agents (such as salicylates, phenytoin, and diazepam) may be increased in the mother in the first 5 to 7 weeks postpartum as the lower albumin levels of pregnancy gradually return to nonpregnant values.[80,87]

Milk pH (mean of 7 with a range of 6.8 to 7.3) is lower than blood pH.[80] Weak acids are highly ionized in maternal plasma and less likely to cross into milk. However, weak bases (e.g., erythromycin, iodides, antihistamines, barbiturates) tend to be transferred and are at equal or higher concentrations in milk than in maternal plasma.[87] Colostrum has a mean pH of 7.45, so it is more likely to have higher levels of basic drugs than mature milk.[53] Ion trapping may occur in milk. Weak bases are generally nonionized and readily cross into milk. As these drugs encounter the low milk pH, they become ionized. This creates a gradient toward movement of more of the drug into milk and reduces the ability of the drug to return across the blood-milk barrier to maternal blood.[12,16,87] Drugs with a pKa greater than 7.2 are most likely to be sequestered in milk.[12]

Steady-state concentrations of drugs in an infant are influenced by drug oral bioavailability, dose, and infant clearance. Drugs given to the mother via methods other than oral administration often have a low oral bioavailability. Drugs with high oral bioavailability may be sequestered in milk at high levels. Drugs with low oral bioavailability have only minimal milk transfer.[12,87] This reduces infant exposure, because the infant receives these drugs via milk into the gut. The amount of drugs reaching the nursing infant is also influenced by non–steady-state conditions. Milk is supplied on a continuous basis during sucking, so milk drug concentrations at time of feeding tend to reflect maternal plasma levels at that time. Concentrations of drugs in milk (including most narcotics) are independent of volume of milk.

Drugs may also affect lactation via either central or peripheral mechanisms to increase or reduce milk output.[12,53] Central mechanisms include increased or decreased oxytocin, prolactin, or CNS dopamine release. Increased dopamine depresses prolactin. Peripheral mechanisms act directly on the breast to alter milk production. Exogenous substances that increase milk production include thyrotropin-releasing hormone, domperidone (banned in United States by the FDA because of its association with cardiac arrhythmias), metoclopramide, and psychotropic agents such as reserpine, imipramine, and phenothiazine derivatives that interfere with dopamine release.[12] Nicotine, estrogens, and possibly pseudoephedrine may also depress lactation.[12]

Use of combination oral contraceptives by lactating women is controversial, with many differing opinions. Estrogen-containing oral contraceptives inhibit prolactin and have been associated with decreases in milk production, shorter overall length of time of breastfeeding, and slower infant weight gain, although this is not well documented and the available studies are limited and have significant methodological limitations.[12,16,53] The effects on breast milk production are reportedly most prominent in the first 4 to 6 weeks postpartum.[53] Although progestin only or combination agents have been considered safer, these have also been associated with reports of decreased milk synthesis in the first few months.[12,53] The World Health Organization and Centers for Disease Control and Prevention have each established guidelines for use of estrogen-only and progestin-only contraceptives by breastfeeding women.[29,136]

Minimizing Infant Drug Exposure

A drug with a high dose may be safe if given after feeding or before the infant's longest predictable sleep period. However, a normally safe drug may be problematic if given in a high dose or over a long duration. Most data on drug levels in milk are with mature milk, with minimal data on milk from mothers of preterm infants. These infants may be at greater risk for adverse effects from exposure to drugs in breast milk because of their immature hepatic and renal function. In addition, these infants are more likely to absorb large macromolecules across their immature gut (see Chapter 13).[54] Although the major concern is that the infant will receive a pharmacologically significant concentration of drug, other possible effects are allergic sensitivities and altered gut flora with antibiotics.

Suggestions for reducing the effects of drugs in breast milk on the infant include (1) using alternative forms of drugs within the same drug class that pass more poorly into milk, have shorter half-lives, or can be given via alternate routes (topical or inhaled); (2) using single components rather than compound drugs (e.g., a decongestant for allergy rather than a multisymptom drug); and (3) feeding the infant before taking the medication, thus avoiding feeding during peak plasma levels, which tend to occur 1 to 3 hours after a maternal oral dose.[14,53,54,80,87,91,103] Use of a short-acting form of the drug may reduce the risk of accumulation for drugs with concerns at high levels; however, use of preparations that can be given at longer intervals (once versus three to four times per day) may be a useful strategy for other agents.[14,53,54,80,87,91,103]

If the mother is taking a drug for which there are concerns about the potential for elevated infant plasma levels, drug levels may need to be monitored periodically. The infant should be monitored closely (growth pattern, sleep patterns, activity, alertness, behaviors, responsiveness, and general health). Breastfeeding may need to be temporarily discontinued when mothers are taking medication for diagnostic procedures or are taking drugs with a high potential for toxicity that are given once. In such cases, previously expressed milk or formula may be used. The timing for reinstitution of breastfeeding varies with the toxicity of the agent. For mild toxicity, resumption of nursing may be as soon as one to two maternal half-lives (50% to 75% elimination); for high toxicity, it may be necessary to wait for four to five maternal half-lives (94% to 97% elimination) or longer.[53,87] Rarely, breastfeeding may need to be discontinued if a highly toxic drug is necessary for maternal health, such as chemotherapy.

SUMMARY

Drug therapy for pregnant women, fetuses, neonates, and lactating women is a complex health challenge. Both pregnant women and neonates have alterations in drug absorption, distribution, metabolism, and elimination that increase the risk of subtherapeutic or toxic levels of individual drugs. An understanding of the principles influencing transfer of drugs across the placenta and into breast milk is critical to reducing risk in the fetus and young infant. Drug therapy for lactating women generally poses fewer risks to infants than therapy of pregnant women. However, the use of any pharmacologic agent for either pregnant or breastfeeding women must be carefully evaluated and drugs used with caution. Neonates present a unique challenge for pharmacologic therapy, not only because of their physiologic immaturity but also because their systems continue to undergo maturation during early infancy, so drug handling can change within a relatively short period. Recommendations for clinical practice related to perinatal pharmacology are listed in Box 7-4. Box 7-2 lists print and online resources for information about drugs in pregnancy and lactation.

BOX 7-4   Recommendations for Clinical Practice Related to Perinatal Pharmacology

Know the effects of physiologic alterations during pregnancy on pharmacokinetics (pp. 184-187 and Table 7-2).

Recognize the effects of altered gastrointestinal and hepatic function during pregnancy on drug absorption and metabolism (pp. 184-187).

Recognize the effects of altered body water, fat, and plasma proteins on drug distribution and binding during pregnancy (pp. 185-186).

Recognize the effects of altered renal function on drug elimination during pregnancy (p. 187).

Counsel women regarding the side effects of drugs and potential toxicity to mother, fetus, and neonate (pp. 182-183, 202-208).

Counsel women regarding planned fetal drug therapy (pp. 195-196).

Monitor and evaluate maternal responses to drugs for evidence of subtherapeutic doses (pp. 183-187, 193-194).

Know or verify the usual doses for medications given during pregnancy (pp. 183-187, 193-194).

Recognize the effects of maternal physiologic adaptations on the pharmacokinetics and potential toxicity to the woman and fetus of antibiotics (pp. 193-194).

Counsel women regarding the side effects of drugs used to treat specific chronic conditions and potential toxicity to the woman and fetus (pp. 183, 202-208).

Counsel women with chronic disorders regarding the effects of their disorder and its pharmacologic treatment during pregnancy and of treatment alternatives (pp. 183-187, 193-194).

Know the factors that influence distribution of drugs and other substances in the fetus (pp. 187-193 and Table 7-4).

Recognize critical periods of development and principles of teratogenesis (pp. 202-204 and Chapter 3).

Recognize risks associated with fetal exposure to drugs and other environmental agents during pregnancy (pp. 202-208).

Provide appropriate counseling and health teaching to promote optimal fetal development and health (pp. 202-208 and Chapter 3).

Provide counseling and health teaching to reduce exposure of the fetus to adverse environmental influences (pp. 202-208 and Chapter 3).

Counsel women regarding the use of drugs or exposure to other environmental agents during pregnancy (pp. 202-208).

Know the effects of neonatal physiology on pharmacokinetics (pp. 196-201 and Table 7-7).

Recognize the effects of immature gastrointestinal and hepatic function in neonates on drug absorption and metabolism (pp. 197-201).

Recognize the effects of altered body water, fat, and plasma proteins on drug distribution and binding in neonates (pp. 198-199).

Recognize the effects of maturation of liver enzyme systems on drug metabolism and risks of side effects in neonates (pp. 199-201).

Recognize the effects of immature renal function on drug elimination and risks of side effects in neonates (p. 201).

Know or verify the usual doses for drugs given during the neonatal period (pp. 197-201).

Recognize the side effects of drugs and potential toxicity to neonates (pp. 197-201).

Monitor and evaluate neonatal responses to drugs, including peak and trough and serum levels (pp. 198-201).

Know the factors that place neonates at risk for toxic responses to topically applied substances (p. 198, and Chapter 14).

Provide care to reduce the risk of topically applied substances (p. 198, and Chapter 14).

Counsel women regarding the use of medications during lactation (pp. 208-211).

Recognize the risks associated with use of pharmacologic agents by breastfeeding women (pp. 208-211).

Evaluate the need for use of specific drugs and counsel women regarding side effects (pp. 208-211).

Monitor and evaluate maternal and neonatal responses to drugs taken by breastfeeding women (pp. 208-211).

Institute interventions as appropriate to reduce the risks associated with specific drugs (pp. 210-211).

Assess infants for signs of intrauterine drug exposure from maternal substance abuse (pp. 205-208).

Know resources for obtaining information about risks of specific drugs during pregnancy and lactation (Box 7-2 on p. 184).

References

1. Abitbol, C. L., & Rodriguez, M. M. (2012). The long-term renal and cardiovascular consequences of prematurity. *Nat Rev Nephrol, 8,* 265.
2. Adam, M. P., Polifka, J. E., & Friedman, J. M. (2011). Evolving knowledge of the teratogenicity of medications in human pregnancy. *Am J Med Genet C Semin Med Genet, 157,* 175.
3. Allegaert, K. (2011). Mechanism based medicine in infancy: complex interplay between developmental pharmacology and pharmacogenetics. *Int J Clin Pharm, 33,* 473.
4. Allegaert, K. (2014). Tailored tools to improve pharmacotherapy in infants. *Expert Opin Drug Metab Toxicol, 10,* 1069.
5. Allegaert, K., & van den Anker, J. N. (2014). Clinical pharmacology in neonates: small size, huge variability. *Neonatology, 105,* 344.
6. Allegaert, K., van de Velde, M., & van den Anker, J. (2014). Neonatal clinical pharmacology. *Paediatr Anaesth, 24,* 30.
7. Allegaert, K., & van den Anker, J. (2015). Neonatal drug therapy: The first frontier of therapeutics for children. *Clin Pharmacol Ther, 98,* 288.
8. Allegaert, K., & Van Den Anker, J. N. (2017). Physiochemical and structural properties regulating placental drug transfer. In R. A. Polin, et al. (Eds.), *Fetal and neonatal physiology* (5th ed.). Philadelphia: Elsevier Saunders.
9. Alwan, S., & Friedman, J. M. (2009). Safety of selective serotonin reuptake inhibitors in pregnancy. *CNS Drugs, 23,* 493.
10. Anderson, G. D., & Carr, D. B. (2009). Effect of pregnancy on the pharmacokinetics of antihypertensive drugs. *Pharmacokinet, 48,* 159.
11. Anderson, G. D., & Lynn, A. M. (2009). Optimizing pediatric dosing: A developmental pharmacologic approach. *Pharmacotherapy, 29,* 680.
12. Baker, T. E., & Hale, T. W. (2017). Breastfeeding mothers. In T. L. King, M. C. Brucker, & M. C. (Eds.), *Pharmacology for women' health* (2nd ed.). Boston: Jones & Bartlett.
13. Bandstra, E. S., et al. (2010). Prenatal drug exposure: Infant and toddler outcomes. *J Addict Dis, 29,* 245.
14. Banta-Wright, S. (1997). Minimizing infant exposure to and risks from medications when breastfeeding. *J Perinat Neonat Nurs, 11,* 71.
15. Behnke, M., Smith, V. C., & Committee on Substance Abuse & Committee on Fetus and Newborn. (2013). Prenatal substance abuse: short- and long-term effects on the exposed fetus. *Pediatrics, 131,* e1009.
16. Berlin, C. M., Jr. (2011). The excretion of drugs and chemicals in human milk. In S. J. Yaffe & J. V. Aranda (Eds.), *Neonatal and pediatric pharmacology: Therapeutic principles in practice* (4th ed.). Philadelphia: Lippincott Williams & Wilkins.
17. Bhosle, V. K., et al. (2017). Basic pharmacologic principles. In R. A. Polin, et al. (Eds.), *Fetal and neonatal physiology* (5th ed.). Philadelphia: Elsevier Saunders.
18. Blackburn, S. (2008). Fetal pharmacotherapy. *J Perinatal and Neonatal Nursing, 22,* 264.
19. Blood-Siegfried, J., & Rende, E. K. (2010). The long-term effects of prenatal nicotine exposure on neurologic development. *J Midwifery Womens Health, 55,* 143.
20. Blumer, J. L., & Reed, M. D. (2011). Principles of neonatal pharmacology. In S. J. Yaffe & J. V. Aranda (Eds.), *Neonatal and pediatric pharmacology: Therapeutic principles in practice* (4th ed.). Philadelphia: Lippincott Williams & Wilkins.
21. Boskovic, R., & Koren, G. (2005). Placenta transfer of drugs. In S. J. Yaffe & J. V. Aranda (Eds.), *Neonatal and pediatric pharmacology: Therapeutic principles in practice* (3rd ed.). Philadelphia: Lippincott Williams & Wilkins.
22. Brent, R. L. (2004). Utilization of animal studies to determine the effects and human risks of environmental toxicants (drugs, chemicals, and physical agents). *Pediatrics, 113,* 984.
23. Briggs, G., & Freeman, R. K. (2014). *Drugs in pregnancy and lactation* (10th ed.). Philadelphia: Wolters Kluwer.
24. Brouwer, K. L., et al. (2015). Pediatric Transporter Working Group. *Clin Pharmacol Ther, 98,* 266.
25. Buhimschi, C. S., & Weiner, C. P. (2009). Medications in pregnancy and lactation: Part 1. Teratology. *Obstet Gynecol, 113,* 166. Erratum in: Obstet Gynecol. 2009, 113,1377.
26. Burakgazi, E., Pollard, J., & Harden, C. (2011). The effect of pregnancy on seizure control and antiepileptic drugs in women with epilepsy. *Rev Neurol Dis, 8,* 16.
27. Cain, M. A., Bornick, P., & Whiteman, V. (2013). The maternal, fetal, and neonatal effects of cocaine exposure in pregnancy. *Clin Obstet Gynecol, 56,* 124.
28. Capparelli, E. V. (2011). Clinical pharmacotherapeutics in infants and children. In S. J. Yaffe & J. V. Aranda (Eds.), *Pediatric pharmacology: Therapeutic principles in practice* (4th ed.). Philadelphia: Saunders.
29. Centers for Disease Control and Prevention. (2010). U.S. medical eligibility criteria for contraceptive use. *MMWR, 59,* 1.
30. Chambers, C., & Scialli, A. R. (2014). Teratogenesis and environmental exposure. In R. K. Creasy, et al. (Eds.), *Creasy & Resnik's Maternal-fetal medicine: Principles and practice* (6th ed.). Philadelphia: Elsevier Saunders.
31. Chemtob, S., & Aranda, J. V. (2005). Pharmacology in the fetus & newborn. In A. R. Spitzer (Ed.), *Intensive care of the fetus and neonate* (2nd ed.). St. Louis: Mosby.
32. Cleary, B. J., et al. (2010). Methadone dose and neonatal abstinence syndrome—systematic review and meta-analysis. *Addiction, 105,* 2071.
33. Dante, G., et al. (2014). Herbal therapies in pregnancy: what works? *Curr Opin Obstet Gynecol, 26,* 83.
34. Daud, A. N., et al. (2014). Pharmacogenetics of drug-induced birth defects: the role of polymorphisms of placental transporter proteins. *Pharmacogenomics, 15,* 1029.
35. Daw, J. R., et al. (2011). Prescription drug use during pregnancy in developed countries: a systematic review. *Pharmacoepidemiol Drug Saf, 20,* 895.
36. Dawes, M., & Chowienczyk, P. J. (2001). Drugs in pregnancy. Pharmacokinetics in pregnancy. *Best Pract Res Clin Obstet Gynaecol, 15,* 819.
37. Dicke, J. M. (1989). Teratology: Principles and practice. *Med Clin North Am, 73,* 567.
38. Dotta, A., & Chukhlantseva, N. (2012). Ontogeny and drug metabolism in newborns. *J Matern Fetal Neonatal Med, 25*(Suppl. 4), 83.
39. Falck, A. J., et al. (2016). Adverse exposures to the fetus. In R. J. Martin, A. A. Fanaroff, & M. C. Walsh (Eds.), *Fanaroff and Martin's Neonatal-perinatal medicine: Diseases of the fetus and infant* (10th ed.). Philadelphia: Elsevier Saunders.
40. Federal Register. (2014). Content and format of labeling for human prescription drug and biological products; requirements for pregnancy and lactation labeling. https://www.gpo.gov/fdsys/pkg/FR-2014-12-04/pdf/FR-2014-12-04.pdf. Accessed 25.05.16.
41. Feghali, M. N., & Mattison, D. R. (2011). Clinical therapeutics in pregnancy. *J Biomed Biotechnol, 2011,* 783528.
42. Fernandez, E., et al. (2011). Factors and mechanisms for pharmacokinetic differences between pediatric population and adults. *Pharmaceutics, 3,* 53.
43. Frost, E. A., Gist, R. S., & Adriano, E. (2011). Drugs, alcohol, pregnancy, and the fetal alcohol syndrome. *Int Anesthesiol Clin, 49,* 119.
44. Ganapathy, V. (2000). Placental transporters relevant to drug distribution across the maternal-fetal interface. *J Pharmacol Exp Ther, 294,* 413.
45. Ganapathy, V. (2011). Drugs of abuse and human placenta. *Life Sci, 88,* 926.
46. Garland, M. (2017). Drug distribution during fetal life. In R. A. Polin, et al. (Eds.), *Fetal and neonatal physiology* (5th ed.). Philadelphia: Elsevier Saunders.
47. Gedeon, C., & Koren, G. (2006). Designing pregnancy centered medications: Drugs which do not cross the human placenta. *Placenta, 27,* 861.
48. Gentile, S. (2010). Neurodevelopmental effects of prenatal exposure to psychotropic medications. *Depress Anxiety, 27,* 675.
49. Gouin, K., et al. (2011). Effects of cocaine use during pregnancy on low birthweight and preterm birth: Systematic review and metaanalyses. *Am J Obstet Gynecol, 204,* 340.
50. Grant, D. M. (2017). Pharmacogenetics. In R. A. Polin, et al. (Eds.), *Fetal and neonatal physiology* (5th ed.). Philadelphia: Elsevier Saunders.
51. Haas, D. M., et al. (2012). The impact of drug metabolizing enzyme polymorphisms on outcomes after antenatal corticosteroid use. *Am J Obstet Gynecol, 206,* 447.e17.
52. Haas, D. M. (2014). Pharmacogenetics and individualizing drug treatment during pregnancy. *Pharmacogenomics, 15,* 69.
53. Hale, T., & Abbey, J. (2017). Drug transfer during breast feeding. In R. A. Polin, et al. (Eds.), *Fetal and neonatal physiology* (5th ed.). Philadelphia: Elsevier Saunders.
54. Hale, T. W., & Rowe, H. F. (2014). *Medications and mother's milk* (16th ed.). Amarillo, Texas: Hale Publishing.
55. Harden, C. L., et al. (2009). Practice parameter update: Management issues for women with epilepsy—focus on pregnancy (an evidence-based review): Teratogenesis and

perinatal outcomes: Report of the Quality Standards Subcommittee and Therapeutics and Technology Assessment Subcommittee of the American Academy of Neurology and American Epilepsy Society. *Neurology, 73*, 133.

56. Harden, C. L., et al. (2009). Practice parameter update: Management issues for women with epilepsy—focus on pregnancy (an evidence-based review): Vitamin K, folic acid, blood levels, and breastfeeding: Report of the Quality Standards Subcommittee and Therapeutics and Technology Assessment Subcommittee of the American Academy of Neurology and American Epilepsy Society. *Neurology, 73*, 142.

57. Hines, R. N. (2008). The ontogeny of drug metabolism enzymes and implications for adverse drug events. *Pharmacol Ther, 118*, 250.

58. Hines, R. N. (2013). Developmental expression of drug metabolizing enzymes: impact on disposition in neonates and young children. *Int J Pharm, 452*, 3.

59. Hudak, M. L. (2015). Infants with antenatal exposure to drugs. In R. J. Martin, A. A. Fanaroff, & M. C. Walsh (Eds.), *Fanaroff and Martin's neonatal-perinatal medicine: Diseases of the fetus and infant* (10th ed.). Philadelphia: Elsevier Saunders.

60. Hutson, J. R., Koren, G., & Matthews, S. G. (2010). Placental P-glycoprotein and breast cancer resistance protein: Influence of polymorphisms on fetal drug exposure and physiology. *Placenta, 31*, 351.

61. Iqbal, M., et al. (2012). Placental drug transporters and their role in fetal protection. *Placenta, 33*, 137.

62. Jacquemyn, Y., et al. (2015). The use of intravenous magnesium in non-preeclamptic pregnant women: fetal/neonatal neuroprotection. *Arch Gynecol Obstet, 291*, 969.

63. Jacqz-Aigrain, E., & Burtin, P. (1996). Clinical pharmacokinetics of sedatives in neonates. *Clin Pharmacokinet, 31*, 423.

64. Jansson, L. M., & Velez, M. L. (2011). Infants of drug-dependent mothers. *Pediatr Rev, 32*, 5.

65. John, E. G., & Guignard, J. P. (1998). Development of renal excretion of drugs during ontogeny. In R. A. Polin & W. W. Fox (Eds.), *Fetal and neonatal physiology* (2nd ed.). Philadelphia: Saunders.

66. Jones, H. E., et al. (2010). Neonatal abstinence syndrome after methadone or buprenorphine exposure. *N Engl J Med, 363*, 2320.

67. Jones, K. L. (2011). The effects of alcohol on fetal development. *Birth Defects Res C Embryo Today, 93*, 3.

68. Jones, K. L., & Jones, M. C. (2013). *Smith's recognizable patterns of human malformation* (7th ed.). Philadelphia: Elsevier Saunders.

69. Ke, A. B., et al. (2014). Pharmacometrics in pregnancy: An unmet need. *Annu Rev Pharmacol Toxicol, 54*, 53.

70. Kearns, G. L., et al. (2003). Developmental pharmacology—Drug disposition, action, and therapy in infants and children. *N Engl J Med, 349*, 1157.

71. Kennedy, D. A., et al. (2016). Safety classification of herbal medicines used in pregnancy in a multinational study. *Complement Altern Med, 16*, 102.

72. Kenner, C., & Amlung, S. (2000). *Nursing management of substance-dependent neonates: A continuing education module.* Des Plaines, IL: National Association of Neonatal Nurses.

73. Klieger, C., et al. (2009). Hypoglycemics: Pharmacokinetic considerations during pregnancy. *Ther Drug Monit, 31*, 533.

74. Koren, G., et al. (1989). Perception of teratogenic risk by pregnant women exposed to drugs and chemicals during the first trimester. *Am J Obstet Gynecol, 160*, 1190.

75. Koren, G., Paturszack, A., & Ito, S. (1998). Drugs in pregnancy. *N Engl J Med, 228*, 1128.

76. Koren, G., Klinger, G., & Ohlsson, A. (2002). Fetal pharmacotherapy. *Drugs, 62*, 757.

77. Koren, G. (2011). Pharmacokinetics in pregnancy: clinical significance. *J Popul Ther Clin Pharmacol, 18*, e523.

78. Lam, J., & Koren, G. (2014). P-glycoprotein in the developing human brain: a review of the effects of ontogeny on the safety of opioids in neonates. *Ther Drug Monit, 36*, 699.

79. Larrimore, W. L., & Petrie, K. L. (2000). Drug use during pregnancy and lactation. *Prim Care, 27*, 35.

80. Lawrence, R. A., & Lawrence, R. M. (2016). *Breastfeeding: A guide for the medical profession* (8th ed.). Philadelphia: Elsevier.

81. Leeder, J. S. (2009). Developmental pharmacogenetics: a general paradigm for application to neonatal pharmacology and toxicology. *Clin Pharmacol Ther, 86*, 678.

82. Leemaqz, S. Y., et al. (2016). Maternal marijuana use has independent effects on risk for spontaneous preterm birth but not other common late pregnancy complications. *Reprod Toxicol, 62*, 77.

83. Lester, B. M., & Lagasse, L. L. (2010). Children of addicted women. *J Addict Dis, 29*, 259.

84. Lewis, T., Dinh, J., & Leeder, J. S. (2015). Genetic determinants of fetal opiate exposure and risk of neonatal abstinence syndrome: Knowledge deficits and prospects for future research. *Clin Pharmacol Ther, 98*, 309.

85. Little, B. B. (1999). Pharmacokinetics during pregnancy: Evidence-based maternal dose formulation. *Obstet Gynecol, 93*(5, Pt 2), 858.

86. Loebstein, R., Lalkin, A., & Koren, G. (1997). Pharmacokinetic changes during pregnancy and their clinical relevance. *Clin Pharmacokinet, 33*, 328.

87. Logsdon, B. A. (1997). Drug use during lactation. *J Am Pharm Assoc (Wash), NS37*, 407.

88. Manzo-Avalos, S., & Saavedra-Molina, A. (2010). Cellular and mitochondrial effects of alcohol consumption. *Int J Environ Res Public Health, 7*, 4281.

89. McClary, J. (2016). Principles of drug use in the fetus and neonate. In R. J. Martin, A. A. Fanaroff, & M. C. Walsh (Eds.), *Fanaroff and Martin's Neonatal-perinatal medicine: Diseases of the fetus and infant* (10th ed.). Philadelphia: Elsevier Saunders.

90. McClary, J. D. (2016). Principles of drug use during lactation. In R. J. Martin, A. A. Fanaroff, & M. C. Walsh (Eds.), *Fanaroff and Martin's Neonatal-perinatal medicine: Diseases of the fetus and infant* (10th ed.). Philadelphia: Elsevier Saunders.

91. Mehta, N., & Larson, L. (2011). Pharmacotherapy in pregnancy and lactation. *Clin Chest Med, 32*, 43.

92. Miller, W. L. (2015). Fetal endocrine therapy for congenital adrenal hyperplasia should not be done. *Best Pract Res Clin Endocrinol Metab, 29*, 469.

93. Mitchell, A. A., et al. (2011). Medication use during pregnancy, with particular focus on prescription drugs: 1976-2008. National Birth Defects Prevention Study. *Am J Obstet Gynecol, 205*, e1.

94. Mooij, M. G., et al. (2012). Ontogeny of oral drug absorption processes in children. *Expert Opin Drug Metab Toxicol, 8*, 1293.

95. Moore, K. L., Persaud, T. V. N., & Torchia, M. G. (2015). *The developing human: Clinically oriented embryology* (10th ed.). Philadelphia: Elsevier Saunders.

96. Moya, J., et al. (2014). A review of physiological and behavioral changes during pregnancy and lactation: Potential exposure factors and data gaps. *J Expo Sci Environ Epidemiol, 24*, 449.

97. Murin, S., Rafii, R., & Bilello, K. (2011). Smoking and smoking cessation in pregnancy. *Clin Chest Med, 32*, 75.

98. Nagourney, B. A., & Aranda, J. V. (1998). Physiologic differences of clinical significance. In R. A. Polin & W. W. Fox (Eds.), *Fetal and neonatal physiology* (2nd ed.). Philadelphia: W.B. Saunders.

99. Namouz-Haddad, S., & Koren, G. (2013). Fetal pharmacotherapy 2: fetal arrhythmia. *J Obstet Gynaecol Can, 35*, 1023.

100. Namouz-Haddad, S., & Koren, G. (2014). Fetal pharmacotherapy 4: fetal thyroid disorders. *J Obstet Gynaecol Can, 36*, 60.

101. Neville, K. A., et al. (2011). Developmental pharmacogenomics. *Paediatr Anaesth, 21*, 255.

102. Niebyl, J. R. (2003). Antibiotics and other anti-infective agents in pregnancy and lactation. *Am J Perinatol, 20*, 405.

103. Ostrea, E. M., Jr., Mantaring, J. B., 3rd., & Silvestre, M. A. (2004). Drugs that affect the fetus and newborn infant via the placenta or breast milk. *Pediatr Clin North Am, 51*, 539.

104. Pacifici, G. M., & Nottoli, R. (1995). Placental transfer of drugs administered to the mother. *Clin Pharmacokinet, 28*, 235.

105. Parisi, M. A., et al. (2011). We don't know what we don't study: The case for research on medication effects in pregnancy. *Am J Med Genet C Semin Med Genet, 157*, 247.

106. Pavek, P., Ceckova, M., & Staud, F. (2009). Variation of drug kinetics in pregnancy. *Curr Drug Metab, 10*, 520.

107. Petersen, I., et al. (2011). Pregnancy as a major determinant for discontinuation of antidepressants: An analysis of data from The Heath Improvement Network. *J Clin Psychiatry, 72*, 979.

108. Pineda, L. C., & Watt, K. M. (2015). New antibiotic dosing in infants. *Clin Perinatol, 42*, 167.

109. Prasad, M. R., & Jones, H. E. (2014). Substance abuse in pregnancy. In R. K. Creasy, et al. (Eds.), *Creasy & Resnik's Maternal-fetal medicine: Principles and practice* (6th ed.). Philadelphia: Elsevier Saunders.

110. Prouillac, C., & Lecoeur, S. (2010). The role of the placenta in fetal exposure to xenobiotics: importance of membrane transporters and human models for transfer studies. *Drug Metab Dispos, 38,* 1623.

111. Rakhmanina, N. Y., & van den Anker, J. N. (2006). Pharmacological research in pediatrics: From neonates to adolescents. *Adv Drug Deliv Rev, 58,* 4.

112. Ramoz, L. L., & Patel-Shori, N. M. (2014). Recent changes in pregnancy and lactation labeling: retirement of risk categories. *Pharmacotherapy, 34,* 389.

113. Rayburn, W. F., & Amanze, A. C. (2008). Prescribing medications safely during pregnancy. *Med Clin North Am, 92,* 1227.

114. Ring, J. A., et al. (1999). Fetal hepatic drug elimination. *Pharmacol Ther, 84,* 429.

115. Rowe, H., Baker, T., & Hale, T. W. (2015). Maternal medication, drug use, and breast-feeding. *Child Adolesc Psychiatr Clin N Am, 24,* 1.

116. Sachs, H. C., & Committee On Drugs. (2013). The transfer of drugs and therapeutics into human breast milk: an update on selected topics. *Pediatrics, 132,* e796.

117. Schreuder, M. F., Bueters, R. R., & Allegaert, K. (2014). The interplay between drugs and the kidney in premature neonates. *Pediatr Nephrol, 29,* 2083.

118. Sengupta, P., et al. (2015). Metals and female reproductive toxicity. *Hum Exp Toxicol, 34,* 679.

119. Smits, A., Annaert, P., & Allegaert, K. (2013). Drug disposition and clinical practice in neonates: cross talk between developmental physiology and pharmacology. *Int J Pharm, 452,* 8.

120. Staud, F., & Ceckova, M. (2015). Regulation of drug transporter expression and function in the placenta. *Expert Opin Drug Metab Toxicol, 11,* 533.

121. Steinberg, C., & Notterman, D. A. (1994). Pharmacokinetics of cardiovascular drugs in children: Inotropes and vasopressors. *Clin Pharmacokinet, 27,* 345.

122. Stephens, T. D., et al. (2000). Mechanism of action in thalidomide teratogenesis. *Biochem Pharmacol, 59,* 1489.

123. Syme, M. R., Paxton, J. W., & Keelan, J. A. (2004). Drug transfer and metabolism by the human placenta. *Clin Pharmacokinet, 43,* 487.

124. Tasnif, Y., Morado, J., & Hebert, M. F. (2016). Pregnancy-related pharmacokinetic changes. *Clin Pharmacol Ther, 100,* 53.

125. Tomi, M., Nishimura, T., & Nakashima, E. (2011). Mother-to-fetal transfer of antiviral drugs and the involvement of transporters at the placental barrier. *J Pharm Sci, 100,* 3708.

126. Vähäkangas, K., & Myllynen, P. (2009). Drug transporters in the human blood-placental barrier. *Br J Pharmacol, 158,* 665.

127. van den Anker, J., & Allegaerti, K. (2011). Renal function and excretion of drugs in the newborn. In S. J. Yaffe & J. V. Aranda (Eds.), *Neonatal and pediatric pharmacology: Therapeutic principles in practice* (4th ed.). Philadelphia: Lippincott Williams & Wilkins.

128. van Gelder, M. M., de Jong-van den Berg, L. T., & Roeleveld, N. (2014). Drugs associated with teratogenic mechanisms. Part II: a literature review of the evidence on human risks. *Hum Reprod, 29,* 168.

129. Wachman, E. M., et al. (2013). Association of OPRM1 and COMT single-nucleotide polymorphisms with hospital length of stay and treatment of neonatal abstinence syndrome. *JAMA, 309,* 1821.

130. Ward, R. M., Stiers, J., & Buchi, K. (2015). Neonatal medications. *Pediatr Clin North Am, 62,* 525.

131. Weier, N., et al. (2008). Placental drug disposition and its clinical implications. *Curr Drug Metab, 9,* 106.

132. Weiner, C., & Buhimschi, C. (2009). *Drugs for pregnant and lactating women* (2nd ed.). London: Churchill Livingstone.

133. Wilffert, B., et al. (2011). Pharmacogenetics of drug-induced birth defects: What is known so far? *Pharmacogenomics, 12,* 547.

134. Wilson, J. G. (1977). Current status of teratology: General principles and mechanisms derived from animal studies. In J. G. Wilson & F. C. Fraser (Eds.), *Handbook of teratology: General principles and etiology.* New York: Plenum.

135. Wisner, K. L., et al. (2009). Major depression and antidepressant treatment: Impact on pregnancy and neonatal outcomes. *Am J Psychiatry, 166,* 557.

136. World Health Organization medical eligibility criteria for contraceptive use. (5th ed., 2015). http://apps.who.int/iris/bitstream/10665/181468/1/9789241549158_eng.pdf. Accessed 25.05.16.

137. Wu, C-S., et al. (2011). Lasting impacts of prenatal cannabis exposure and the role of endogenous cannabinoids in the developing brain. *Future Neurol, 6,* 459.

138. Zeng, X., et al. (2016). Effects and safety of magnesium sulfate on neuroprotection: a meta-analysis based on PRISMA guidelines. *Medicine (Baltimore), 95,* e2451.

139. Zhao, Y., Hebert, M. F., & Venkataramanan, R. (2014). Basic obstetric pharmacology. *Semin Perinatol, 38,* 475.

Hematologic and Hemostatic Systems

The hematologic system encompasses blood and plasma volume, the constituents of plasma, and the formation and function of blood cellular components. Hemostasis involves mechanisms that result in the formation and removal of fibrin clots. Pregnancy and the neonatal period are associated with significant changes in these processes, increasing the risk for anemia and alterations in hemostasis such as thromboembolism and consumptive coagulopathies. This chapter examines alterations in the hematologic system and hemostasis during the perinatal period and their implications for the mother, fetus, and neonate.

MATERNAL PHYSIOLOGIC ADAPTATIONS

The significant changes in the hematologic system and hemostasis during pregnancy have a protective role for maternal homeostasis and are important for fetal development. These changes are also critical in allowing the mother to tolerate blood loss and placental separation at delivery. The maternal adaptations also increase the risk for complications such as thromboembolism, iron deficiency anemia, and coagulopathies.

Antepartum Period

Most hematologic parameters, including blood and plasma volume, cellular components, plasma constituents, and coagulation factors, are altered during pregnancy. These changes are reflected in progressive changes in many common hematologic laboratory values. As a result, it is essential to recognize the normal range of laboratory values and usual patterns of change during pregnancy and to evaluate findings in conjunction with clinical data and previous values to distinguish between normal adaptations and pathologic alterations. Reference values for many parameters are available[1] (these are also available online at http://perinatology.com/Reference/Reference%20Ranges/Reference%20for%20Serum.htm).

Changes in Blood and Plasma Volume

Among the most significant hematologic changes during pregnancy are increases in blood and plasma volume (Figure 8-1). These changes result in the hypervolemia of pregnancy, which is in turn responsible for many of the alterations in blood cellular components and plasma constituents. Maternal circulating blood volume increases by 40% to 50%, with individual variations.[7,39,83] The increased blood volume results from an increase in plasma volume that is followed by an increase in the total red blood cell (RBC) volume. Blood volume changes begin at 6 to 8 weeks, increases by about 15% by 12 weeks, peaks at 32 to 34 weeks at values about 1200 to 1600 mL higher than in nonpregnant women, then reach a plateau or decrease slightly to term.[7,39,65,83,116]

Plasma volume increases progressively beginning at 6 to 8 weeks to values approximately 45% (range, 40% to 60%) above nonpregnant values.[7,51,83,116,150,174] Plasma volume increases rapidly during the second trimester, followed by a slower but progressive increase that reaches its maximum of 4700 to 5200 mL around 30 to 32 weeks.[7,83,116,148] The enlarged plasma volume is accommodated by the vasculature of the uterus, breasts, muscles, kidneys, and skin. The increased volume leads to a relative hemodilution with a net decrease in RBC volume and total circulating plasma proteins.

Plasma volume, placental mass, and birth weight are positively correlated.[51,67] Fetal growth correlates more closely with maternal plasma volume increases; alterations in the usual increase in plasma volume are associated with pregnancy complications. A greater-than-normal increase in plasma volume has been observed in multiparous women (probably related to a tendency for higher weight infants) and with maternal obesity, large-for-gestational-age infants, prolonged pregnancy, and multiple gestation.[51]

In twin pregnancies, plasma volume increases up to 70% over nonpregnant values, with further elevations seen in women with triplets and other multiple pregnancies.[29,51] The lower-than-expected hematocrit seen in these women may be caused by hemodilution from excessive plasma volume and may not indicate a problem with erythropoiesis per se. Preeclampsia is associated with a reduction in the expected increase in plasma volume in most studies (see Chapter 9).[99,116] This may be caused by vasoconstriction altering the intravascular compartment or a more "leaky" vasculature.

The etiology of plasma volume changes in pregnancy is believed to be related to the effects of nitric oxide–mediated vasodilation on the renin-angiotensin-aldosterone system and subsequent sodium and water retention (see Chapter 11).[116]

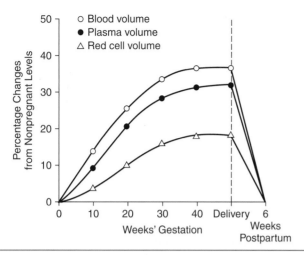

FIGURE 8-1   Changes in blood volume, plasma volume, and red blood cell volume during pregnancy and postpartum. (From Peck, T.M. & Arias, F. [1979]. Hematologic changes associated with pregnancy. *Clin Obstet Gynecol, 22,* 788.)

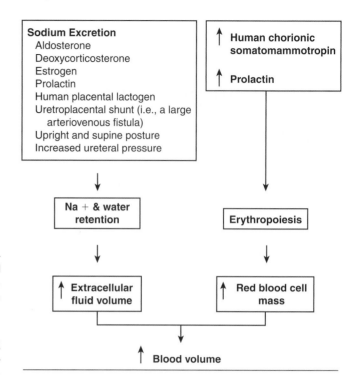

FIGURE 8-2   Potential mechanisms of hypervolemia during pregnancy. (From Ouzounian, J.G. & Elkayam, U. [2012]. Physiologic changes during normal pregnancy and delivery. *Cardiol Clin, 30,* 317.)

These changes are also influenced by hormonal effects and alterations in fluid balance and in the renal and cardiovascular systems during pregnancy. Hormonal influences, especially the effects of progesterone, on the vasculature of the venous system lead to decreased venous tone, increased capacity of the veins and venules, and decreased vascular resistance. These changes allow the vasculature to accommodate the increased blood volume. Estrogen and progesterone influence plasma renin activity and aldosterone levels, resulting in retention of sodium and an increase in total body water.[67] Most of this extra water is extracellular and available to contribute to the increased plasma volume. Potential mechanisms for hypervolemia during pregnancy are summarized in Figure 8-2. Changes in plasma volume have also been linked to a mechanical effect, with the low-resistance uteroplacental circulation acting as an arteriovenous shunt. This shunt provides physical space to accommodate the increased cardiac output and corresponding change in plasma volume.[29,67]

Increased plasma volume and hypervolemia reduce blood viscosity. Hypervolemia also leads to hemodilution and changes in plasma protein and blood cellular components, which further reduce viscosity. Blood viscosity decreases approximately 20% during the first two trimesters. During the third trimester, viscosity may increase slightly. The decreased viscosity reduces resistance to flow and the cardiac effort needed, thus conserving maternal energy resources.[29]

Changes in Blood Cellular Components

The principal change in blood cellular components during pregnancy is an increase in RBC volume. This alteration, in conjunction with changes in plasma volume, is reflected in changes in the hemoglobin and hematocrit. Changes in blood cellular components are summarized in Table 8-1.

Changes in Red Blood Cells. The total RBC volume increases by 20% to 30% (250 to 450 mL) during pregnancy, reaching maximum values by term.[41,51,83,116,150] Changes in RBC volume

result from increased circulating erythropoietin (Epo), which stimulates erythropoiesis and accelerated RBC production. Epo rises during the last two trimesters in response to the effects of progesterone and human chorionic somatomammotropin (hCS; also known as *human placental lactogen*). The Epo rise is not a result of a decrease in oxygen-carrying capacity (this is the usual stimulus for Epo production in nonpregnant individuals).[51,116] The magnitude of change in RBC volume varies and is influenced by the woman's iron stores.[29] The increase in RBCs also reflects the increase in oxygen demands (which rise 15%) during pregnancy.[165]

The increase in erythropoiesis and total RBC volume begins during the first trimester.[51,83] The increase occurs at a relatively constant rate, but slower than changes in plasma volume, and may accelerate slightly during the third trimester.[51,67] Hemodilution is maximal at 30 to 34 weeks and leads to a lower hemoglobin, hematocrit, and RBC count.[7] The increased RBC production results in a moderate erythroid hyperplasia of the bone marrow and an increase in the reticulocyte count.

RBC 2,3-diphosphoglycerate (2,3-DPG) rises beginning early in pregnancy and leads to a gradual shift to the right of the maternal oxygen-hemoglobin dissociation curve (see Chapter 10). This reduces the affinity of maternal hemoglobin for oxygen (see Box 10-1) and favors release of oxygen in the peripheral tissues, including the intervillous space, which facilitates oxygen transfer from mother to fetus and fetal growth.[51,67,116] Alterations in placental function that occur with disorders such as preeclampsia, chronic renal disease, diabetes, and severe anemia can decrease oxygen transfer across the placenta. The fetus may develop chronic hypoxia,

TABLE 8-1 Changes in Blood Cellular Components During Pregnancy

COMPONENT	CHANGE	PATTERN OF CHANGE	BASIS FOR CHANGE	INTRAPARTUM CHANGES	POSTPARTUM CHANGES
Red blood cells (RBCs)	Increases 20%–30% (250–450 mL)	Slow, continuous increase beginning in first trimester; may accelerate slightly in third trimester	Erythropoietin stimulated by human chorionic somato-mammotropin progesterone, and prolactin	Slight increase because of slight hemo-concentration; 50% of increased RBCs lost at delivery	RBC production ceases temporarily; remainder of increased RBCs lost via normal catabolism
Hematocrit	Decreases 3%–5% to 33.8% at term (range, 33%–39%)	Decreases from second trimester as plasma volume peaks	Hemodilution		Returns to nonpregnant levels by 4–6 weeks as a result of RBC catabolism
Hemoglobin	Decreases 2%–10% to average of 12.5 g/dL (125 g/L with range of, 11–13 g/dL (110–113 g/L) at term	If iron and folate are adequate, little change to 16 weeks; lowest values at 16–22 weeks; slowly increases to term	Hemodilution; total body hemoglobin increases by 65–150 g	Slight increase as a result of stress and dehydration	Initial decrease; stabilizes at 2–4 days; nonpregnant values by 4–6 weeks
Reticulocytes	Increase 1%–2%	Gradual increase to third trimester	Increased RBC production		Increases slightly; nonpregnant values by 4–6 weeks
White blood cells	Increase 8% to 5000–12,000/mm^3 (up to 15,000/mm^3 seen)	Begins in second month; increase involves primarily neutrophils	Estrogen	Increase to 25,000–30,000/mm^3	Decrease to 6000–10,000/mm^3; normal values by 4–7 days
Eosinophils	Probably increase slightly	Variable	Hemodilution	Disappear from peripheral blood	By 3 days return to peripheral blood
Platelets	May decrease slightly but within normal adult ranges; usual range 150,000–400,000/mm^3	Variable	Hemodilution	20% decrease with placental separation	Increase by 3–5 days with gradual return to nonpregnant levels
Erythrocyte sedimentation rate	Increases	Progressive	Increased plasma globulin and fibrinogen	Increases	Initially 55–80 mm/hr; peaks 1–2 days postpartum

with stimulation of Epo production, increased erythropoiesis, polycythemia, and increased neonatal morbidity.

The mean cell diameter and thickness of the RBCs also change, resulting in a cell that is more spherical in shape. Because the increase in plasma volume is three times greater than the RBC volume increase, the net result is a decrease in the total RBC count, hemoglobin, and hematocrit (see Tables 8-1 and 8-2). Changes in the mean corpuscular volume (MCV) and mean corpuscular hemoglobin volume (MCHV) are related to iron status. In women with adequate iron, the MCV and MCHV are relatively stable; in iron-deficient women, these values may decrease.[83,165]

The hemoglobin and hematocrit decrease from the second trimester on as plasma volume peaks. Thus although total body hemoglobin increases 85 to 150 g in pregnancy, net hemoglobin decreases because the changes in plasma volume occur more rapidly than changes in RBC volume. Even with adequate iron supplementation, the hemoglobin decreases about 2 g/dL (20 g/L) to a mean of about 11.6 g/dL (116 g/L) in the second trimester as a result of hemodilution.[69] At term the hemoglobin averages 12.5 g/dL (125 g/L), with a range of 11 to 13 g/dL (110 to 130 g/L) versus a mean of 14 ± 2 (140 ± 20 g/L) for nonpregnant females.[28,51] Approximately 5% of women have term hemoglobin values below 11 g/dL (110 g/L).[1] Values of 11 g/dL (110 g/L) (first and second trimesters) and 10.5 g/dL (105 g/L) (third trimester) have traditionally been used as the lowest acceptable values for screening pregnant women.[28,51] The mean hematocrit is 33.8% (range, 33% to 39%) at term.[51,83] The fall in the hematocrit may help protect the woman from thromboembolism by decreasing blood viscosity and enhancing perfusion.[116] A high hematocrit in a pregnant woman may indicate a low plasma volume and a relative hypovolemia. Changes in the hemoglobin and hematocrit in pregnant women are illustrated in Figure 8-3.

Changes in White Blood Cells and Platelets. Total white blood cell (WBC) volume increases slightly beginning in the second month and levels off during the second and third trimesters (see Table 8-1), ranging from 5000 to 12,000/mm^3, with values as high as 15,000/mm^3 reported.[83,116] The slight increase in WBC count is a result of neutrophilia with an elevation in mature leukocyte forms. A slight shift to the left may occur with occasional myelocytes and metamyelocytes

TABLE 8-2   Changes in Plasma Components During Pregnancy

COMPONENT	CHANGE	TIMING	BASIS	SIGNIFICANCE
Total plasma proteins	Decreases 10%–14%	Begins in first trimester	Estrogen/progesterone	Decreased colloid osmotic pressure (edema formation) Altered protein binding of calcium, drugs, and so on
Albumin	Total: 144 g Serum: 3.5 g	Begins in first trimester	Estrogen/progesterone Hemodilution	See above
Fibrinogen	Increases 50%–80%	First to third trimesters	Hemodilution	Alterations in hemostasis Decreased erythrocyte sedimentation rate
Globulin	Increases	First to third trimesters	Estrogen/progesterone	Decreased erythrocyte sedimentation rate
α- and β-globulin	Decreases	Progressive throughout pregnancy	Estrogen/progesterone	See individual globulins Facilitate transport of carbohydrates and lipids to placenta and fetus
γ-Globulin	Decreases	Third trimester	Estrogen/progesterone Transplacental passage of IgG beginning in second trimester	Fetal passive immunity Risk of transfer of potentially damaging antibodies (see Chapter 13)
Thyroxin-binding globulin	Increases	First trimester to term	Estrogen	Increased plasma T3 and T4
α1-Antitrypsin	Doubles	First trimester to peak in third trimester	Altered liver function	Protects lungs from deported trophoblast tissue
α2-Macroglobulin	Increases 20%		Altered liver function	Antiplasmin effect, which may predispose to DIC
Total serum lipids	Increases 40%–60%	Continuous to term	Human chorionic somato-mammotropin and altered metabolism	Maternal and fetal need for increased lipids (see Chapter 16)
Cholesterol	Increases up to 50%	Continuous to term	Estrogen, human chorionic somatomammotropin, cortisol, prolactin	Essential precursor for steroid hormones (e.g., estrogen, progesterone)
Phospholipids	Increases 37%	Continuous to term	Estrogen, human chorionic somatomammotropin, cortisol, prolactin	Major component of cell membranes needed for maternal and fetal growth
Serum electrolytes	Decreases 5–10 mg/L	First trimester	Hypervolemia and hemodilution Physiologic hyperventilation with increased CO_2 loss	Decreased plasma osmolarity by 8–10 mOsm/L during the first trimester
Serum ferritin	Decreases 30%	To 28 weeks (with adequate iron) or 30–32 weeks (without)	Hemoglobin synthesis (early) Fetal uptake (late)	Reflects decreasing iron stores
Transferrin	Increases 70%	Linear rise	Altered liver function	Facilitates Fe absorption and transport
Hepcidin	Decreases	Lowest in the third trimester	May be related to decreasing iron levels or other factors	Regulates serum iron bioavailability and enhances iron absorption

DIC, Disseminated intravascular coagulation; *Fe*, iron; *IgG*, immunoglobulin G.

seen on the peripheral smear.[83] Changes in leukocytes accompanying pregnancy are similar to changes that occur with physiologic stress, such as vigorous exercise, with return to the circulation of mature leukocytes that were previously shunted out of the circulatory system.[39] The basis for these changes is probably related to hormonal changes, because the neutrophil count normally increases slightly with the estrogen peak during the menstrual cycle and, in women who become pregnant, continues to increase after fertilization, peaking around 30 weeks then remaining stable to term.[51,83] Changes in other WBC forms are minimal (see Table 8-1).[83] Changes in lymphocytes are discussed in Chapter 13.

Platelet values do not change significantly during pregnancy.[1,63,83] A slight decrease in platelet count, probably a result of hemodilution, and an increase in platelet aggregation during the last 8 weeks of pregnancy has been reported, suggesting a low-grade activation and consumption of platelets.[7,62,63,83] In healthy pregnant women, platelet counts have generally not been reported at values below lower limits for normal nonpregnant women.[83] Mild to moderate thrombocytopenia (less than 150,000/mm³) has been reported in late pregnancy in some healthy pregnant women.[7,23,83,167] This may be caused by hemodilution, decreased platelet production, or increased turnover.[20] The usual range for platelet values in

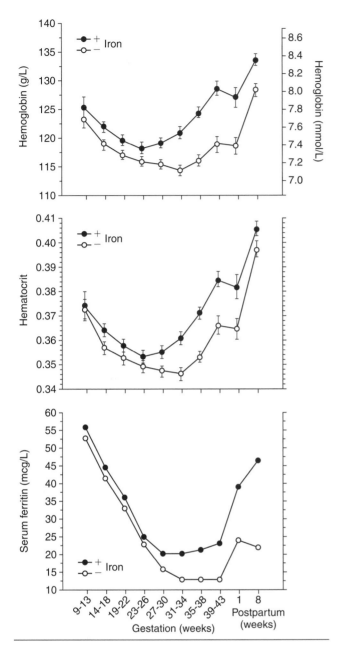

FIGURE 8-3 Variations in hemoglobin and hematocrit (mean ± standard error of the mean) and serum ferritin (median) in normal pregnancy and postpartum in placebo-treated and iron-treated women taking 66 mg ferrous iron daily. (From Milman, N., Bergholt T., Byg K.E., Eriksen L., & Graudal N. [1999]. Iron status and iron balance during pregnancy: A critical reappraisal of iron supplementation. *Acta Obstet Gynecol Scand, 78,* 749.)

pregnancy is 150,000 to 400,000/mm³, although some suggest a slightly lower limit of normal in the third trimester.[1,7]

Changes in Plasma Components

Many components of plasma—including plasma proteins, electrolytes, serum iron, lipids, and enzymes—change during pregnancy (see Table 8-2). Total plasma proteins decrease 10% to 14%, with much of the change occurring in the first trimester. Although there is an absolute increase in albumin concentration during the first trimester, there is a relative decrease

because of increased blood volume and hemodilution. Decreased albumin leads to a net decrease in colloid osmotic (oncotic) pressure, reducing the normal forces counteracting edema formation. Although edema formation in pregnancy is primarily caused by alterations in venous hydrostatic pressure, decreased oncotic pressure from the relative decrease in albumin is an important contributory factor.[13,39] Alterations in other plasma proteins are summarized in Table 8-2.

The alterations in plasma proteins alter protein binding of substances such as calcium, drugs, and anesthetic agents. Because many drugs are transported in the blood bound to albumin, doses of some drugs may need to be altered during pregnancy (see Chapter 7). Increased binding of substances such as calcium reduces the level of free calcium in the maternal plasma. As a result, calcium must be actively transported across the placenta to the fetus (see Chapter 17).

Serum iron decreases during pregnancy, especially after 28 weeks and in women without adequate iron stores. Iron needs during pregnancy are summarized in Table 8-3. Maternal iron needs are met with both heme and nonheme iron. Serum ferritin is a more precise indicator of reticuloendothelial iron stores. During pregnancy, 1 μg/L (2.5 pmol/L) serum ferritin represents 10 mg of stored iron.[25] Serum ferritin levels in pregnancy are 15 to 150 ng/mL (33.7 to 337 pmol/L).[51] In women without adequate iron, serum ferritin levels fall until 30 to 32 weeks and then stabilize. The greatest decrease in serum ferritin is between 12 and 25 weeks because of the rapid expansion of maternal RBC volume during this time (see Figure 8-3).[161] With adequate iron, serum ferritin levels stabilize by 28 weeks or slightly earlier, and may even rise near term.[13,51] Decreases in serum ferritin in early pregnancy result from mobilization of iron stores for maternal hemoglobin synthesis; later decreases are caused by increased fetal iron uptake. In multiparous women the decrease in serum ferritin occurs earlier and may be greater. Serum transferrin receptors (sTfR) are stable in the first trimester then increase, reflecting cellular iron demands and erythrocyte proliferation.[24,25] Hepcidin is a peptide hormone that regulates systemic iron bioavailability and mediates host defenses. Hepcidin levels are lower in pregnancy, with lowest levels in the third trimester, when fetal iron demands are greatest.[87] Inflammatory states during pregnancy

TABLE 8-3   Iron Requirements for Pregnancy

REQUIRED FOR	AVERAGE (mg)	RANGE (mg)
External iron loss	170	150–200
Expansion of red blood cell mass	450	200–600
Fetal iron	270	200–370
Iron in placenta and cord	90	30–170
Blood loss at delivery	150	90–310
Total requirement	980	580–1340
Requirement less red blood cell expansion	840	440–1050

From Roger, M.A. & Silver, R.M. (2014). Coagulation disorders in pregnancy. In R.K. Creasy, R. Resnik, J.D. Iams, C.J. Lockwood, T.R. Moore, & M.F. Greene. (Eds.). *Creasy & Resnik's maternal-fetal medicine: Principles and practice* (7th ed.). Philadelphia: Elsevier Saunders.)

such as maternal infection and preeclampsia are associated with higher hepcidin levels, which may compromise maternal and fetal iron bioavailability.[87]

Levels of serum lipids rise with marked elevations in cholesterol and phospholipids. Cholesterol is an essential precursor for steroid hormone production by the placenta; phospholipids are major components of cell membranes. The rise in serum lipids begins in the first trimester, increasing to 40% to 60% at term. Increases in serum alkaline phosphatase are a result of increased placental production. As a result, alkaline phosphatase levels are not useful in evaluating liver disorders during pregnancy. Serum cholinesterase activity decreases by 30%. Increased cholinesterase activity may lead to longer periods of paralysis if substances such as succinylcholine are used during surgical procedures.[13]

Changes in Coagulation Factors and Hemostasis

Pregnancy has been called an *acquired hypercoagulable state*, reflecting an increased risk for thrombosis and consumptive coagulopathies such as disseminated intravascular coagulation (DIC). Pregnancy is associated with increased clotting potential, decreased anticoagulants, and decreased fibrinolysis.[149] Hemostatic changes during pregnancy are believed to result in an ongoing low-grade activation of the coagulation system in the uteroplacental circulation, beginning as early as 11 to 15 weeks. This state of compensated intravascular coagulation is characterized by thrombin formation and local consumption of clotting factors in which component synthesis equals or exceeds consumption.[62] Figures 8-4 to 8-6 summarize coagulation and fibrinolysis.

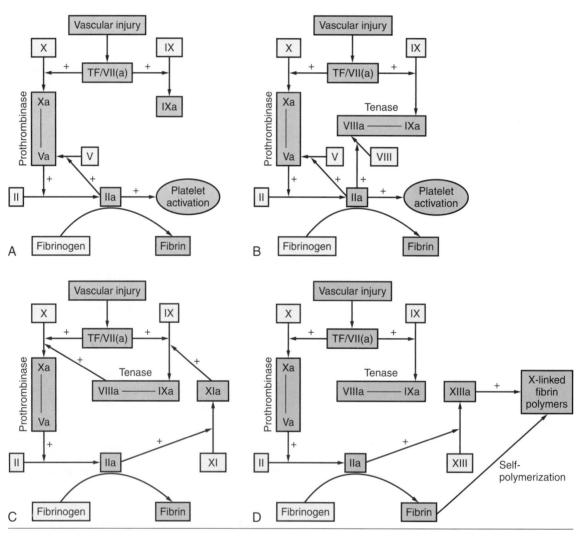

FIGURE 8-4 Fibrin plug formation. **A,** After vascular disruption, plasma factor VII binds to tissue factor *(TF)* to form the TF/VIIa, which activates both factor X and factor IX. Factor Xa binds to factor Va, which has been activated by thrombin factor (factor IIa) or released from platelet α-granules. The Xa/Va complex catalyzes the conversion of prothrombin (factor II) to thrombin, which, in turn, converts fibrinogen to fibrin and activates platelets. **B,** The clotting cascade is amplified by clotting reactions that occur on adjacent activated platelets. Locally generated factor IXa binds to factor VIIIa, which is activated by thrombin. The factor IXa/VIIIa complex then generates factor Xa. **C,** Coagulation is further boosted by the thrombin-mediated activation of factor XI to XIa, which also activates factor IX. Circulating TF-bearing microparticles may also bind to activate platelets at sites of vascular injury. **D,** The stable hemostatic plug is finally formed when fibrin monomers self-polymerize and are cross-linked by thrombin-activated factor XIIIa. (From Roger, M.A. & Silver, R.M. [2014]. Coagulation disorders in pregnancy. In R.K. Creasy, R. Resnik, J.D. Iams, C.J. Lockwood, T.R. Moore, & M.F. Greene. [Eds.]. Creasy & Resnik's maternal-fetal medicine: Principles and practice [7th ed.]. Philadelphia: Elsevier Saunders.)

evidence regarding prenatal supplementation to prevent iron deficiency anemia and improve maternal and fetal outcomes was inconclusive but may improve maternal hematologic indices.[161] Intermittent iron supplementation (one to three times per week) was found to be effective, although there was a greater risk of mild maternal anemia near term, and was associated with fewer maternal side effects.[136]

Although intestinal iron absorption increases in the second half of pregnancy (probably as a compensatory mechanism in response to increased iron demand), dietary sources and maternal stores alone may not be adequate to meet the increased demands of pregnancy. Iron stores affect iron absorption. Women who have good iron stores have minimal increases in absorption during the first trimester, then increase absorption during the second trimester. By later pregnancy, iron stores may be exhausted and iron needs met primarily from absorption.[100] Thus most women who have good iron stores before pregnancy and a diet high in bioavailable iron will not develop anemia if they are not supplemented.[83] However, iron stores in young, healthy nonpregnant women may be marginal to nonexistent.

Iron supplementation increases iron reserves and hemoglobin levels and decreases the risk of iron-deficiency anemia during pregnancy and postpartum, including women with good iron stores at the beginning of pregnancy.[116] Even with adequate nutrition, 10% to 20% of pregnant women will develop an iron deficiency.[69,70] General recommendations made by the Institute of Medicine (IOM) for iron supplementation during pregnancy are 30 mg ferrous iron (which is provided by 150 mg ferrous sulfate, 300 mg ferrous gluconate, or 100 mg ferrous fumarate) daily beginning at 12 weeks' gestation along with a well-balanced diet.[70] The need for iron can also be met with supplementation of 60 to 85 mg/day of elemental iron beginning at 20 to 28 weeks.[65,70,83] Although the IOM recommended supplementation only if serum ferritin levels were below 20 µg/L, the high cost of this screening has limited applicability.[70,83] Iron supplementation does not prevent or correct the normal decline in hemoglobin seen in pregnancy, but it can prevent depletion of stores, the first stage of iron-deficiency anemia.[69,193]

Anemia and Pregnancy

Anemia during pregnancy is generally defined as a hemoglobin below 11 g/dL (110 g/L) in the first and third trimesters and below 10.5 g/dL (105 g/L) in the second trimester.[65,148,174] Cut-off values for different populations are available.[148] The most common anemia encountered in pregnancy is iron-deficiency anemia, followed by megaloblastic anemia of pregnancy (folic acid deficiency), sickle cell disorders, and α- and β-thalassemia.[51] Changes in the hematologic system may influence the course of these disorders during pregnancy and alter fetal outcome. Anemia caused by iron or folate deficiency is a result of underproduction of RBCs and is associated with decreased reticulocytes. The normal hematologic changes along with altered nutritional needs during pregnancy increase the risk for these nutritional anemias.

In women with severe anemia (hemoglobin less than 6 to 8 mg/dL [60 to 80 g/L]), maternal arterial oxygen content and oxygen delivery to the fetus are decreased. The fetus attempts to adapt through increased placental blood flow, redistribution of blood within the fetal organs, increased RBC production (to increase the total oxygen-carrying capacity), and a decrease in the diffusing distance for oxygen across the placenta. Because fetuses have predominantly fetal hemoglobin, they cannot readily increase the availability of oxygen to the tissues by further altering the affinity of hemoglobin for oxygen. Although the fetus adapts, the cost may be high, with decreased growth and an increased mortality because of the lack of an adequate oxygen supply and nutrients. Several metaanalyses have found significant relationships between severe maternal anemia (hemoglobin less than 8.5 g/dL [85 g/L]) in early pregnancy and preterm birth, but not with small-for-gestational-age infants.[60,154,193] Conversely, an elevated hemoglobin (greater than 13 to 14.5 g/dL [130 to 145 g/L]) in early pregnancy is associated with stillbirth and small-for-gestational-age infants, perhaps because the increased hemoglobin is a result of a reduction in the usual increase in plasma volume and thus reduced blood flow to the intervillous space.[25,165]

Iron-Deficiency Anemia

The most common cause of anemia during pregnancy is iron-deficiency anemia, accounting for approximately 75% of women with anemia.[28,65,83] The prevalence of iron-deficiency anemia during pregnancy is 14% to 52% if the woman is not taking prenatal supplements and 0% to 25% in those taking supplements.[25] Maternal risks of iron-deficiency anemia include cardiovascular strain, altered performance, decreased peripartal blood reserves, and increased risk of transfusion with delivery; fetal risks include growth restriction, prematurity, infection, and alterations in developmental and metabolic programming.[24,108] Generally this form of anemia is preventable or easily treated with iron supplements.

Hematologic changes in pregnancy can make diagnosis of iron-deficiency anemia more difficult.[51] Total iron-binding capacity and serum iron often fall during pregnancy, as well as with iron-deficiency anemia. A useful test for iron deficiency in a pregnant woman is measurement of serum ferritin levels, which correlate well with iron stores during pregnancy.[51] Serum ferritin levels lower than 12 µg/L with a low hemoglobin indicate iron-deficiency anemia, which can be treated with ferrous sulfate until the hemoglobin returns to levels normal for the stage of gestation.[51,69] Because ferritin is an acute-phase reactant, falsely high levels may occur with infection. Therefore higher serum ferritin levels may indicate deficiency if infection is present.[51]

In general, even with significant maternal iron deficiency, the fetus will often be protected and receive adequate stores at cost to the mother. However, if the mother is severely iron deficient and anemic, the fetus may have decreased RBC volume, hemoglobin, iron stores, and cord ferritin levels and an increased risk of iron deficiency during infancy.[24,29,51,83,108]

Iron-deficiency anemia before midpregnancy is associated with an increased risk of low birth weight, preterm birth, and perinatal mortality.[51,69,96,116]

Megaloblastic Anemia

Megaloblastic anemia in a nonpregnant woman is usually caused by folic acid or vitamin B_{12} deficiency. Folic acid deficiency is the most common cause of megaloblastic anemia encountered during pregnancy. Vitamin B_{12} deficiency with pregnancy is less common because (1) stores of vitamin B_{12} are normally large (most women have a 2- to 3-year store in their liver), so deficient states take years to develop; (2) vitamin B_{12} is used for deoxyribonucleic acid (DNA) replication, so a severe deficiency usually leads to infertility; and (3) vitamin B_{12} deficiency is usually caused by pernicious anemia, a disorder seen primarily in older women.[51,83] Vitamin B_{12} dietary deficiency in pregnancy most often occurs with a vegan diet. Vitamin B_{12} deficiency may be misdiagnosed in pregnant women, because serum vitamin B_{12} levels fall with the expanded plasma volume and consequent hemodilution.[51]

Folate demands increase threefold during pregnancy from 50 μg/day to 300 to 500 μg/day during pregnancy.[83] Because folic acid is essential for DNA synthesis and cell duplication, folate is needed for growth of the fetus and placenta as well as for maternal RBC production. Folate requirements increase throughout pregnancy and are higher in multiple pregnancy.[51] Maternal serum folate levels fall during pregnancy, and women with an inadequate dietary intake need supplements. Prenatal vitamins generally contain 1 g of folate; increased levels are needed for individuals with hematolytic disorders. The changes in folate metabolism during pregnancy are caused by decreased serum folate and RBCs, increased plasma clearance, increased urinary excretion, and altered histidine metabolism.[90]

Severe folic acid deficiency has been associated with fetal malformations, preeclampsia, abruptio placenta, prematurity, and low birth weight.[51] Maternal folate deficiency increases the risk of neural tube defects (NTDs) and has been associated with an increased risk of cleft lip and palate and preterm birth.[46,51,83,176] Recent Cochrane metaanalyses confirmed that daily folic acid supplementation reduced the risk of neural tube defects but did not find clear evidence on other birth defects nor in reducing the risk of preterm birth in all populations.[46,90] Supplementation is recommended for all women of childbearing age to reduce the risk of neural tube defects. Supplementation should begin before pregnancy, because NTDs occur early in the first trimester (see Chapter 15).[176] In later pregnancy, the fetus has higher levels of folate and elevated folate-binding protein, which protects against fetal folate deficiency; even with low maternal folate levels, neonatal cord levels are usually within normal limits.

Sickle Cell Disease

Sickle cell disease is a group of disorders that involve mutations in the genes that determine hemoglobin β-chain structure.

In women with sickle cell anemia, tissue deoxygenation or acidosis triggers structural changes in the sickle hemoglobin (HbS), so the RBCs take on a half-moon or sickle appearance. The sickled cells can obstruct blood flow in the microvasculature. The areas most susceptible to obstruction are those characterized by slow flow and high oxygen extraction such as the spleen, bone marrow, and placenta. Obstruction leads to venous stasis, further deoxygenation, platelet aggregation, hypoxia, acidosis, further sickling, and eventually infarction.[51,83]

A woman with sickle cell anemia normally has a lower hemoglobin level (7 to 8 g/dL [70 to 80 g/L]) and oxygen-carrying capacities, to which her system has adjusted. Pregnancy places both the woman and her infant at greater risk for complications in part because of the effects of hematologic, cardiovascular, renal, and respiratory changes during pregnancy.[132,150] As plasma volume increases during pregnancy, the woman may become more anemic and experience an increased risk of sickling attacks.[118] Sickle cell crises are triggered by physical or emotional stress, which may be caused by infection, trauma, hypoxia, and pregnancy. Crises in pregnancy and postpartum may be related to the hypercoagulable state, increased susceptibility to infection, or vascular stress.[118,150] The rapid hemodynamic changes postpartum often precipitate crises, especially if associated with a long or difficult labor and delivery.[83] Fetal and neonatal complications such as prematurity and fetal growth restriction may arise because of placental infarction and fetal hypoxia. Fetal hypoxia results from decreased oxygen transport caused by the abnormal biochemistry of the maternal hemoglobin and the loss of functional placental tissue for gas and nutrient exchange caused by the infarctions.[51,83]

Thalassemias

Thalassemia is a disorder in the synthesis of either the α or β peptide chains of the hemoglobin molecule. This leads to alterations in the RBC membrane and decreased RBC life span. α-Thalassemia is an alteration in the production of α chains, in which one or more of the four genes on chromosome 16 that are involved in α-chain production are altered or deleted. Phenotype and severity depend on how many genes are involved and whether the genes are deleted (nonfunctional) or present but with altered function.[178] Most pregnant women with α-thalassemia have one or two genes affected and have either a silent presentation or mild anemia.[83,178] If all four α-chain genes are missing, the fetus cannot synthesize either normal fetal hemoglobin (composed of two α- and two γ-chains) nor adult hemoglobin (composed of two α- and two β-chains). Infants develop high-output cardiac failure or hydrops fetalis and are often stillborn or die shortly after birth. Intrauterine transfusions are associated with decreased perinatal mortality and morbidity. These infants currently require lifelong transfusion therapy; however, stem cell transplants have been reported to be effective in treating this disorder.[178]

β-Thalassemia minor is a common β-thalassemia during pregnancy. Many females with thalassemia major (Cooley anemia) die in childhood or adolescence; those who survive are often amenorrheic and infertile.[51,83] Some pregnancies have occurred in these women, with an increased risk of fetal loss.[51] Women with β-thalassemia minor have a mild hypochromic, microcytic anemia but are usually healthy otherwise and generally do not have increased maternal or infant morbidity if their condition is stable.[83] With the plasma volume expansion that accompanies pregnancy, they may develop a more pronounced anemia, but they generally require only supportive care.[174] Women with β-thalassemia intermedia may develop a more severe anemia during pregnancy, especially in the second and third trimesters, and may require transfusion therapy.[22]

Thromboembolism and Pregnancy

The hypercoagulable state of pregnancy is crucial in protecting the mother against excessive blood loss with delivery and placental separation. However, the hypercoagulable state is also a disadvantage because it significantly increases the risk of thromboembolic disorders during pregnancy and postpartum. Venous thromboembolism (VTE) is a leading cause of maternal mortality in the United States.[92]

The risk of VTE increases up to sixfold during pregnancy.[92,104] The risk increases with parity and age and is nine times higher among women with cesarean deliveries than among women who give birth vaginally.[180] VTE is more common antepartum than postpartum; however, the risk of developing VTE is four times greater postpartum.[144,148,180] VTE includes both deep vein thrombosis (DVT) and pulmonary emboli, which usually result from dislodged thrombi in the lower extremities. Pulmonary embolism occurs in 1 in 2000 pregnancies and is a major cause of maternal mortality.[62,92] Most pulmonary emboli develop postpartum and are associated with cesarean section.[92]

The three factors (Virchow triad) that predispose to thromboembolic disorders (stasis, altered coagulation, and vascular damage) are all present or potentially present during pregnancy.[92] Most (98%) DVT arise in the lower extremities.[149] During pregnancy, increased venous capacitance (caused by the effects of progesterone and local endothelial production of prostacyclin [PGI$_2$] and nitric oxide) leads to increased distensibility, decreased flow in the lower extremities, and venous stasis.[149] By late pregnancy, the velocity of venous blood flow in the lower extremities has been reduced by half, and venous pressure has risen an average of 10 mm Hg (1.33 kPa).[62,92,104] The blood flow velocity decreases by early in the second trimester, with a nadir from 34 weeks to term that does not return to prepregnant values until 6 or more weeks after delivery. In addition, the diameter of the major leg veins increases, more so on the left than the right. During pregnancy, up to 80% of DVT occur on the left (versus 55% in nonpregnant women).[92,128,144] This is because of pulsatile compression of the left iliac vein by the right iliac vein and ovarian artery.[149]

The hypercoagulable state during pregnancy induces a prothrombotic state, increasing the risk of clot formation.[149] The increased fibrinogen, coagulation factors, and decreased protein S and resistance to activated protein C increase thrombin generation, decrease endogenous anticoagulants, and impair fibrinolysis.[7,80] If a clot develops, the decreased fibrinolytic activity and increased PAI-1 and PAI-2 (which inhibit clot lysis) impedes fibrin removal and clot lysis.[92] An increase in the incidence of VTEs is seen during the third trimester when fibrinolytic activity decreases. Finally, the potential for localized vascular damage to the pelvic blood vessels with release of tissue factor exists with venous distension in late pregnancy and with delivery, particularly with cesarean section.[149] Further decreases in protein S after cesarean delivery or with infection may increase the risk of pulmonary emboli postpartum.[92] VTE is also increased with obesity; increased parity; increased maternal age; prolonged bed rest; and in women with thrombophilia, antiphospholipid syndrome, anemia, artificial heart valves, or preeclampsia (because of exaggeration of the hypercoagulable state).[104,112] Once a thrombus develops, it is more likely that it will extend if the predisposing factors persist over time, as occurs with pregnancy. Women with a history of VTE either before or during pregnancy, especially if associated with thrombophilia, have an increased risk of developing a similar disorder in subsequent pregnancies. Ambulation soon after delivery decreases venous stasis and the risk of VTE.

In pregnant women with VTEs the anticoagulant therapy of choice is usually low-molecular-weight heparin, which has fewer complications than unfractionated heparin; the molecular weight of heparin prevents placental transfer.[92] Heparin doses may need to be increased as pregnancy progresses, particularly during the third trimester. Changes in heparin requirements have been related to increasing plasma volume and renal clearance and to the presence of a placental heparinase enzyme. Heparin doses may need to be decreased in women who develop significant alterations in renal function or in whom plasma volume changes are reduced.[149] Warfarin sulfate inhibits vitamin K–dependent coagulation factors. These agents cross the placenta, whereas vitamin K–dependent coagulation factors do not, impairing fetal coagulation and increasing the risk of fetal and neonatal hemorrhage.[107] The risk of fetal bleeding and intracranial hemorrhage is especially high during labor. Warfarin has also been associated with an increased risk of abortion and with a specific syndrome of fetal anomalies involving the face, eyes, bones, and central nervous system, if given in the first 11 to 13 weeks of gestation.[107] These abnormalities may be a result of inhibition of vitamin K–dependent proteins (osteocalcins) involved in bone development.

Platelet and Coagulation Disorders During Pregnancy

Thrombophilias are being increasingly regarded as having potential roles in the pathophysiology of preeclampsia, fetal growth restriction, and miscarriage because of the effects of thrombotic changes in the placental bed.[160] Changes in pregnancy may exacerbate the effects of inherited thrombophilias such as the factor V Leiden and prothrombin gene variants and deficiencies of protein C and S and increase the risk of pregnancy complications.[149] Women with these disorders may develop clinical signs for the first time during pregnancy.[160] The most common acquired thrombophilic disorder is antiphospholipid syndrome (APS), an autoimmune disorder seen in 0.2% to 2% of pregnant women.[149,151] In this disorder, antibodies are produced that promote thrombosis. APS involves activation of endothelial cells, monocytes, and platelets by the antiphospholipid antibodies.[151] Women with APS have an increased risk of arterial and venous thrombosis, autoimmune thrombocytopenia, recurrent miscarriage, and fetal loss.[44,151] Treatment with heparin or low-dose aspirin can reduce fetal loss.[44,151]

Antiphospholipid antibodies such as lupus anticoagulant and anticardiolipin are also seen in pregnancies complicated by preeclampsia, fetal growth restriction, placental insufficiency, placental abruption, and preterm birth.[44,149,160] The increase in fetal loss with antiphospholipid antibodies is believed to be caused by an increase in the thromboxane-to-prostacyclin ratio in the decidua and placenta, leading to increased platelet activation, vasoconstriction, placental thrombosis and infarct, and subsequent fetal death.[149]

The most common inherited bleeding disorder in pregnant women is von Willebrand disease (vWD). Because vWF is important in platelet adhesion at the site of injury and stabilizing factor VIII, pregnant women with vWD are at increased risk of bleeding and postpartum hemorrhage.[148]

Pregnancy may also be complicated by thrombocytopenia, including primary immune thrombocytopenia or idiopathic thrombocytopenia purpura (ITP) and alloimmune thrombocytopenia (AIT). ITP is the most common gestational thrombocytopenia and is seen in 6% to 10% of pregnant women.[148] ITP can develop during pregnancy or secondary to disorders such as systemic lupus erythematosus. Women with ITP have platelet levels below 100,000 cell/mm³ because of platelet destruction by an antiplatelet antibody.[40,149] The course of ITP is generally not significantly altered by pregnancy, but pregnancy may be affected by ITP with an increased risk of hemorrhage and passage of IgG antiplatelet antibodies to the fetus with decreased fetal platelet levels.[40,148,149] Although the fetus has a slight increase in intracranial hemorrhage, generally both fetus and neonate do well.[92] However, AIT involves maternal alloimmunization against fetal platelet antigens and can be life-threatening to the fetus and neonate because of the risk of thrombocytopenia, bleeding, and intracranial hemorrhage. With AIT the mother develops specific IgG antibodies against fetal platelet antigens that then cross the placenta and destroy fetal platelets (see Chapter 13).[44,148]

Pregnancy is characterized by increases in fibrinolytic activity, plasminogen and plasminogen activators in the uterus, and an ongoing low-grade activation of the coagulation system within the uteroplacental circulation. As a result, events such as extravasation of blood into the myometrium

or rupture of blood vessels in the area can activate the fibrinolytic system and lead to a consumptive coagulopathy.[13] The risk of coagulopathies such as disseminated intravascular coagulation (DIC) is higher during pregnancy, particularly in association with placental abruption, severe preeclampsia, HELLP (hemolysis, elevated liver enzymes, low platelet count) syndrome, eclampsia, intrauterine fetal death, amniotic fluid embolism, or septic abortion.[55] These events result in one or more of the processes commonly associated with intravascular coagulation: release of tissue factor and activation clotting (preeclampsia, eclampsia), endothelial injury with activation of coagulation (placental abruption, fetal death), or shock and stasis (amniotic fluid embolism, gram-negative sepsis).[55,83] Many of these complications trigger the formation of tissue factor or endotoxins, thus inducing thrombin formation. The resulting activation of the coagulation pathway (see Figure 8-4) leads to uncontrolled thrombin formation, depletion of fibrinogen, and increased fibrinolytic activity.[62,148]

DIC arises from inappropriate activation of normal clotting processes within the circulation with intravascular consumption of procoagulant proteins, clotting factors, and platelets; formation of fibrin clots within the vascular bed; production of anticoagulants; and activation of fibrinolysis. As a result, the normal balance between the coagulation and fibrinolytic systems is disrupted. Initiating events include the release of proinflammatory cytokines, especially interleukin-6 (IL-6) and tumor necrosis factor-α (TNF-α). IL-6 increases fibrin formation; TNF-α inhibits natural anticoagulants such as proteins C and S and antithrombin and activates fibrinolysis by increasing PAI-1.[73] Consumption of the clotting factors can lead to hemorrhage and shock. As clots are formed and fibrin is deposited in the microcirculation, further cell (tissue) injury occurs, triggering further coagulation and eventual depletion of plasma clotting factors. These fibrin clots may also cause intravascular obstruction and infarction. Activation of clotting also activates the fibrinolytic system, which leads to formation of fibrin-fibrinogen degradation products or fibrin split products. These fibrin degradation products further inhibit coagulation and decrease platelet function.[55,145]

SUMMARY

The hematologic and hemostatic systems undergo significant alterations during pregnancy that promote maternal adaptation but also influence interpretation of laboratory values and increase the risk of thromboembolic insults and coagulopathies. Because of the significant risks associated with these events, appropriate measurement, observation, data gathering, and evaluation are essential. Changes in the hematologic system during pregnancy are also critical for fetal homeostasis. Maternal hypervolemia promotes delivery of oxygen and nutrients to the fetus; changes in serum albumin may influence the availability of both nutrients and potentially harmful substances. The fetus can affect maternal status, as is the case with iron metabolism and needs. Clinical recommendations for nurses working with pregnant women based on changes in the hematologic and hemostasic systems are summarized in Box 8-1.

BOX 8-1   Recommendations for Clinical Practice Related to Changes in the Hematologic and Hemostatic Systems in Pregnant Women

Recognize usual hematologic values and patterns of change during pregnancy and postpartum (pp. 215-224 and Tables 8-1–8-3).

Recognize that isolated laboratory values must be evaluated in light of clinical findings and previous values (pp. 215-224).

Assess maternal nutritional status in relation to iron, folate, and vitamins, and provide nutritional counseling (pp. 224-226).

Monitor hematocrit and hemoglobin values throughout pregnancy (pp. 217, 224-226).

Know the patterns of change in plasma and blood volume during pregnancy and the postpartum period (pp. 215-216, 225).

Monitor and counsel women with cardiac problems, paying particular attention to periods when blood and plasma volume increases significantly (pp. 215-216, 225 and Chapter 9).

Monitor for and teach pregnant woman to recognize the signs of thromboembolism (p. 227).

Recognize risk factors for the development of thromboembolism (p. 227).

Encourage ambulation soon after delivery to reduce the risk of thromboembolism (p. 227).

Recognize risk factors for development of altered platelets or hemostasis (pp. 227-228).

Evaluate maternal responses to prescribed drugs for signs of subtherapeutic levels or side effects (p. 219 and Chapter 7).

Counsel women regarding the effects of plasma volume increases and decreased plasma proteins on drug levels during pregnancy (pp. 215-216, 219 and Chapter 7).

Recognize factors that may alter indicators of infection during the intrapartum and early postpartum period (p. 222).

DEVELOPMENT OF THE HEMATOLOGIC SYSTEM IN THE FETUS

The hematologic system arises early in gestation and along with the primitive cardiovascular system is one of the earliest systems to achieve some functional capacity. The hematologic system is critical for the well-being of the fetus through transport of nutrients and oxygen and removal of waste products. Fetal red blood cells (RBCs), white blood cells (WBCs), and platelets are often found in the maternal circulation. Fetomaternal transfusion occurs in an estimated 50% of pregnancies, although this generally involves a small volume. RBCs can pass as early as 4 to 6 weeks. Later, antigens on some of these cells may stimulate maternal antibody production against the fetal cells, which can lead to fetal anemia, neutropenia, or thrombocytopenia (see Chapter 13). Fetal iron requirements are discussed on pages 232-233.

Formation of Blood Cells

Blood cells first appear in the yolk sac and can be found as early as 14 to 19 days' gestation.[47] By about 6 weeks' gestation, hematopoietic stem cells are found in the developing liver and later migrate from there to the bone marrow.[189] Hematopoiesis in the fetus is under the influence of many hematopoietic growth factors and can be divided into three periods: mesoblastic, hepatic, and myeloid. In all sites, cells arise from stem cells derived from mesoderm tissues. Primitive cells arise first, followed by definitive cells. Embryonic and fetal hematopoietic stem cells are pluripotent cells that can reproduce and repopulate in adults better than adult stem cells. Thus these fetal cells have greater potential for transplant with lower risk of graft failure.[26,41,189] Embryonic and fetal stem cells also have the ability to differentiate into cells of different tissues types, not just hematopoietic cells, depending on environment.[129]

During the mesoblastic period (from 14 to 19 days to a peak at 6 weeks' gestation), blood cells are formed in blood islands in the secondary yolk sac. The secondary yolk sac arises at 12 to 15 days and is a site of early protein synthesis, nutrient transfer, and hematopoiesis. Peripheral cells in these islands form primitive blood vessels; central cells develop into hematoblasts (primitive RBCs).[26,138] Although only RBCs and macrophages are produced in the yolk sac, the yolk sac stem cells are all multipotential.[76] Blood formation in the yolk sac is maximal from 2 to 10 weeks and disappears by the third month.[3,42] Another site of early blood formation during this period is the ventral aspect of the aorta in the periumbilical area. Hematopoiesis occurs in this area until 28 to 40 days' gestation.[26,48,76,173]

The hepatic period begins during the fifth to sixth week, shortly after the onset of circulation during weeks 4 to 5. This period peaks from 6 to 18 weeks. Thus from 3 to 5 months the liver is the major source of fetal blood cells, although some blood formation continues in this site through the first week after birth. Liver mass increases 40-fold after liver hematopoiesis begins, and at 11 to 12 weeks' gestation, hematopoietic cells make up 60% of the liver.[41,76] The predominant cells produced by the liver are normoblastic erythrocytes, although megakaryocytes, granulocytes, and lymphocytes are also produced.[138] Hematopoiesis can be detected in the spleen, omentum, and thymus during the third month and shortly thereafter in the lymph nodes. Blood formation in the spleen, initially producing erythrocytes and later lymphocytes, declines after 4 to 5 months' gestation.[126]

Extramedullary erythropoiesis may continue in the liver and spleen and develop in other organs, including the adrenal glands, pancreas, thyroid, endocardium, skin, and brain, after bone marrow is established.[76] This may occur with any event resulting in reduced bone marrow function, as can occur with rubella or parvovirus B19 infection. When this occurs in the skin, it can be seen as the "blueberry muffin" rash.[76]

The thymus and lymph nodes become seeded with stem cells by the fourth month. These structures are primarily involved in lymphopoiesis but are also involved in maturation and activation of the immature WBCs that develop from myeloid stem cells.[26,130]

The myeloid period begins at about 18 weeks, with eventual production of all types of blood cells.[3,41,76] Centers for blood formation arise in mesenchymal tissues and invade cavities produced during bone formation (see Chapter 17). Initially bone marrow produces granulocytes and megakaryocytes. After liver erythropoiesis declines, bone marrow erythropoiesis increases. The major area of blood production is the fatty marrow in the core of the long bones. Large fat cells are not found in fetal marrow as they are in adults, suggesting that fetal marrow is functioning at full hematopoietic capacity under homeostatic conditions.

The long bones of the fetus and newborn are cartilaginous, and their relative marrow volume is smaller than in older individuals. As a result, the only way the fetus or newborn can significantly increase production of blood cells is by either reactivation or persistence of extramedullary hematopoiesis in the abdominal viscera, such as the liver and spleen. This extramedullary erythropoiesis is responsible for much of the hepatosplenomegaly seen in infants with erythroblastosis fetalis.[50]

All blood cells arise from pluripotent stem cells under the influence of various cytokines and growth factors for specific cell lineages (Figure 8-8). Fetal and postbirth hematopoiesis are mediated by hematopoietic growth factors and cytokines, including stem cell factors, interleukin (IL)-1, IL-4, IL-6, IL-9, erythropoietin (Epo), macrophage colony-stimulating factor (M-CSF), granulocyte colony-stimulating factor (G-CSF), thrombopoietin, and possibly insulin and insulin-like growth factors.[41,47,76,138] Hematopoietic growth factors are either non–cell-lineage or cell-lineage specific. Non–cell-lineage–specific growth factors such as IL-3 and granulocyte-macrophage colony-stimulating factor (GM-CSF) stimulate a variety of progenitor cells. Cell-lineage–specific growth factors stimulate differential maturation of granulocytes (G-CSF), monocytes (M-CSF), or erythrocytes.[47,76] Epo and other hematopoietic growth factors also appear to be important in development of other systems (including cardiovascular, gastrointestinal, and brain) both before and after birth.[89,187]

Development of Red Blood Cells

Fetal RBC production is independent of the mother. The initial RBCs are primitive nucleated megaloblasts that appear at 3 to 4 weeks' gestation, followed by normative megaloblastic erythropoiesis at 6 weeks. The primitive nucleated cells contain embryonic hemoglobin and are not dependent on Epo. The definitive fetal RBC, produced initially in the liver, contains primarily fetal hemoglobin (HbF) and is regulated

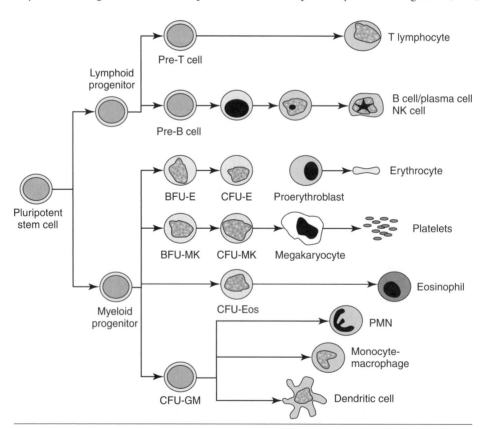

FIGURE 8-8   Overview of hematopoiesis. Hematopoietic lineages are outlined. *BFU,* Burst forming unit; *CFU,* colony forming unit; *E,* erythroid; *Eos,* eosinophil; *GM,* granulocyte-macrophage; *MK,* megakaryocyte; *NK,* natural killer cell; *PMN,* polymorphonuclear. (From Nguyen-Vermillion, A. & Juul, S. [2012]. Developmental biology of the hematologic system. In C.A. Gleason & S. Devaskar [Eds.]. *Avery's diseases of the newborn* [9th ed.]. Philadelphia: Saunders.)

by Epo.[1,41,138] By 10 weeks, the latter cells constitute 90% of the RBC volume. The early cells are large nucleated cells with increased deformability. With increasing gestation, hemoglobin, hematocrit, and total RBC count increases, whereas numbers of nucleated RBCs, mean corpuscular volume, cell diameter, mean corpuscular hemoglobin volume, reticulocytes, and proportion of immature cell forms decrease.[76,130] Yolk sac cells differentiate intravascularly, whereas erythroblasts in the liver and bone marrow mature attached to macrophages in blood islands.

Epo does not cross the placenta, so fetal erythropoiesis is endogenously controlled.[26,76] Fetal Epo increases from 19 weeks to term and is produced primarily in the liver but also in the spleen, rather than in the kidneys. Increasing amounts of Epo are produced in the kidneys from 20 weeks, and especially from 30 weeks to term as the kidneys mature.[41,76] The shift from liver to renal Epo production after 30 weeks is believed to result from increased Epo expression in interstitial cells along with renal growth and maturation. Epo inhibits the death of erythroid precursors and stimulates development and differentiation of these precursors. Epo levels are elevated with fetal hypoxia, anemia, and placental insufficiency and in infants of insulin-dependent diabetic mothers.[41]

Development of White Blood Cells and Platelets

Formation of WBCs begins in the liver at 5 weeks, although a few macrophages are produced in the yolk sac, followed by the thymus (8 to 9 weeks), spleen (11 weeks), and lymph nodes (12 weeks).[76] Significant numbers are not produced until the myeloid period. Initially, erythropoiesis is greater than granulopoiesis; however, by 10 to 12 weeks, granulopoiesis predominates, and by 21 weeks the adult ratio of granulopoiesis to erythropoiesis is seen. Circulating granulocytes increase rapidly during the third trimester. The neutrophil count doubles from 14 to 18 weeks' gestation and increases fourfold from 24 to 32 weeks.[101] At birth, numbers of WBCs are equal to or greater than those found in adults. Eosinophils appear by 10 weeks, increasing to 5% of total marrow cells by 21 weeks. Basophils also appear by 10 weeks, but levels remain low. Monocytes are found in the yolk sac by 3 to 4 weeks and initially are the most prominent cells in liver hematopoietic tissue, then decrease to birth. Circulating monocytes are seen at 5 to 6 months' gestation.[86] Macrophage levels peak at 10 to 16 weeks; monocyte levels peak by 12 to 16 weeks.

Lymphocytes are formed in the fetal liver and lymphoid plexuses initially, then in the thymus (7 to 10 weeks) and spleen and bone marrow (10 to 12 weeks).[76] The numbers of circulating lymphocytes increase rapidly to peak at 20 weeks (10,000 mm³), then decline to 3000/mm³ by term.[130] Megakaryocytes are found by 5 weeks in the yolk sac, by 8 to 9 weeks in the circulation, in the liver and spleen by 10 weeks, and are within adult ranges by 22 weeks, increasing further to term.[133,164] Thrombopoietin, produced primarily in the liver and kidneys, is the major factor controlling platelet production.[76]

Formation of Hemoglobin

Hemoglobin synthesis, under the influence of many hematopoietic growth factors, begins around 14 days' gestation. Several forms of hemoglobin (Hb) are found in the embryo and fetus (Figure 8-9). Two pairs of polypeptide chains form each of the different hemoglobin types (Table 8-4). Most forms have two α or α-like globulin chains (controlled by genes on chromosome 16). The primitive embryonic varieties formed in the yolk sac are Gower 1 (seen at less than 5 weeks' gestation), followed by Gower 2 and Hb Portland (seen between 5 and 10 to 12 weeks' gestation).[41,138] Two points of hemoglobin switching occur during development: the first is the switch from embryonic hemoglobin to fetal hemoglobin (HbF); the second is the switch from HbF to adult hemoglobin (HbA).[14]

The predominant hemoglobin from 10 to 12 weeks to term is HbF, which consists of a pair of α chains and a pair of γ chains. HbA, which consists of pairs of α and β chains (controlled by genes on chromosome 11), appears after 6 to 8 weeks and increases rapidly after 16 to 20 weeks' gestation.[130] By 30 to 32 weeks, 90% to 95% of the hemoglobin is HbF. After this point, the amount of HbF begins to slowly decline to 84% at 34 weeks and 60% to 80% by term.[137] Simultaneously, levels of HbA increase along with the total body hemoglobin mass.[130] The switch from fetal to adult hemoglobin synthesis is related to postmenstrual, not postbirth, age. Synthesis of HbA and HbF is not significantly affected by intrauterine transfusions or exchange transfusions after birth.

All forms of hemoglobin have similar functions but vary in their oxygen affinity, with earlier forms having greater affinity.[41] HbF has a greater affinity for oxygen because HbF does not bind 2,3-diphosphoglycerate (2,3-DPG) as effectively as does HbA. Increased affinity facilitates oxygen transfer across the placenta but reduces oxygen release to the tissues. Fetal hemoglobin has several other unique properties. HbF is more resistant to acid elution and can be oxidized to methemoglobin more readily, increasing the susceptibility of newborns to methemoglobinemia.

The resistance of fetal hemoglobin to acid elution is the basis for tests such as the Kleihauer-Betke techniques used to detect fetal cells in maternal blood. These tests may be unreliable as a measure of fetal cells if maternal HbF is elevated or with ABO incompatibility. In the presence of ABO incompatibility, fetal cells may be destroyed by maternal antibody and cleared from the mother's circulation. HbF is seen in adults but has a different amino acid at position 136 on the γ chain.[26] Altered levels of HbF are seen in women with sickle cell anemia, thalassemia minor, hydatidiform mole, and leukemia and in a pregnancy-induced elevation of HbF. Fetal cells may still be identified, because with elevated maternal HbF there tend to be many cells with varying amounts of HbF and the fewer fetal cells have consistently high HbF concentrations.[50]

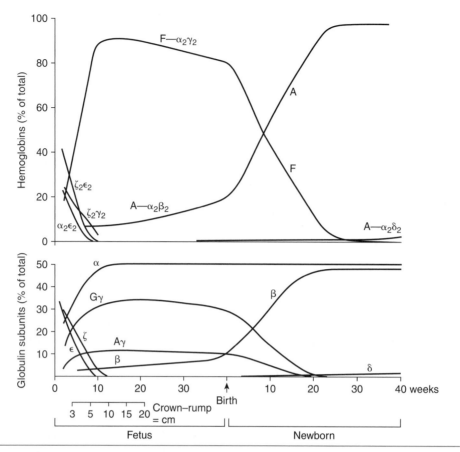

FIGURE 8-9 Development of hemoglobin in the fetus and newborn. The relative proportions of each globulin chain produced at each stage of gestation are shown. Refer to Table 8-4 for descriptions of the different types of hemoglobin. (Adapted from Bunn, H.F. & Forger, B.G. [1986]. *Hemoglobin: Molecular, genetic and clinical aspects*. Philadelphia: Saunders.)

TABLE 8-4 Human Hemoglobins Expressed During Development

HEMOGLOBIN (Hb)	GLOBULIN CHAIN COMPOSITION	STAGE OF EXPRESSION	PRIMARY SITE OF PRODUCTION
Hb Gower 1	Zeta$_2$ epsilon$_2$ ($\zeta_2\epsilon_2$)	Embryonic	Yolk sac
Hb Gower 2	Alpha$_1$ epsilon$_2$ ($\alpha_1\epsilon_2$)	Embryonic	Yolk sac
Hb Portland	Zeta$_2$ gamma$_2$ ($\zeta_2\gamma_2$)	Embryonic	Yolk sac
HbF	Alpha$_2$ gamma$_2$ ($\alpha_2\gamma_2$)	Fetal	Liver
HbA	Alpha$_2$ beta$_2$ ($\alpha_2\beta_2$)	Adult	Bone marrow
HbA2	Alpha$_2$ delta$_2$ ($\alpha_2\delta_2$)	Adult (minor)	Bone marrow
Hb Barts	Gamma$_4$ (γ_4)	Fetal	Alpha thalassemia
Hb H	Beta$_4$ (β_4)	Adult	Alpha thalassemia

From Diab, Y. & Luchtman-Jones, L. (2015). Hematologic and oncologic problems in the fetus and newborn. In R.J. Martin, A.A. Fanaroff, & M.C. Walsh (Eds.). *Fanaroff and Martin's neonatal-perinatal medicine: Diseases of the fetus and infant* (10th ed.). Philadelphia: Saunders.

Fetal Iron Requirements

Fetal iron content is 75 mg/kg by the third trimester.[96,142] The majority (75%) of fetal iron is found in hemoglobin, with about 7 mg/kg in tissues and 10 mg/kg stored in the liver and spleen.[142] The stored iron doubles during the last weeks of gestation.[25] Iron is transferred across the placenta against a concentration gradient from mother to fetus via transferrin.[25] Maternal transferrin releases its iron in the intervillous space. The iron is taken up by transferrin receptors located on the surface of syncytiotrophoblast cells facing maternal blood and is actively transported across the syncytiotrophoblast and cytotrophoblast by a series of iron transporters.[83,87,142,190] Iron transported across the placenta can be stored in the placenta as ferritin or enter fetal circulation, where it attaches to fetal serum transferrin.[25,87] Fetal transferrin is synthesized by the fetal liver beginning about 29 to 30 days' gestation.[130]

By the end of pregnancy, 90% of the maternal transferrin-bound iron is delivered to the placenta.[142] Placental transferrin receptor density is believed to be the major determinant of placental iron transfer.[190] Increased expression of placental transferrin receptors (which facilitate iron uptake by the placenta) is seen with low maternal stores, low fetal stores, and with adolescents (who have increased iron needs because of their own growth and development).[25,190] This compensatory mechanism enhances uptake of iron by the placenta, meeting fetal needs at the expense of the mother. Another mechanism that increases iron availability for the fetus is increased maternal iron absorption.[83]

With fetal growth the rate of iron transfer across the placenta increases and fetal serum ferritin levels increase from 24 to 40 weeks.[49] Thus transport of iron from mother to fetus is greatest during the last few months of gestation and can reach 5.6 mg/day in late pregnancy.[25] Serum iron and ferritin levels in cord blood are higher than in maternal blood and have been related to maternal hemoglobin or ferritin in most but not all studies. Cord blood serum ferritin levels are lower (but usually still within normal limits) in infants of iron-deficient mothers, reflecting lower fetal iron stores. These infants are reported to have reduced iron stores and an increased risk of anemia in the first year.[142] The fetus begins to produce hepcidin (a major regulator of iron bioavailability) in the first trimester. Fetal hepcidin is independent of the mother and may be involved in placental iron transport proteins.[25]

Development of the Hemostatic System

The hemostatic and fibrinolytic systems develop simultaneously. Most procoagulant and anticoagulant proteins are produced by the fetal liver beginning around 5 weeks' gestation and are measurable in fetal plasma by 10 weeks' gestation, although levels are very low.[72,73] Fetal blood demonstrates clotting ability by 11 to 12 weeks.[62] Fibrinogen synthesis in the liver begins at 5 weeks. Fibrinogen can be found in the plasma by 12 to 13 weeks, reaching adult values by 30 weeks.[166] The placenta is rich in tissue factor (TF), which also plays a role in angiogenesis, cell signaling, and embryogenesis. Thus the placenta is able to respond rapidly to insults with initiation of clotting.[16,62,155] This helps protect the fetus from significant blood loss. Vitamin K levels are 30% of adult values by the end of the second trimester and 50% by term.[166]

Fibrinolytic activity can be demonstrated at 12 to 13 weeks' gestation. The whole blood clotting time in the fetus is relatively short, and the fetus is in a hypercoagulable state during the first and second trimesters. Fibrinolytic activity in the fetus is increased even though levels of blood plasminogen are low, because of increased tissue plasminogen activator (tPA) or decreased inhibitor or both.[62] The elevated fibrinolytic activity may help protect and maintain the extensive fetal capillary circulation within the placental villi.

NEONATAL PHYSIOLOGY

The neonate experiences significant alterations in the hematologic system and hemostasis. Among these differences are the structural and functional alterations in the neonatal red blood cell (RBC) and the potential effects of HbF on oxygen delivery to the tissues. Variations are also seen in blood volume and blood cellular components and in hemostasis parameters. These alterations increase the risk for anemia, thromboembolism, and coagulopathies in the neonate.

Transitional Events

A major transitional event for the neonate is removal of the placental circulation with clamping of the umbilical cord. The timing of umbilical cord clamping influences the amount of placental transfusion and subsequent plasma and RBC volume of the neonate. At term, fetal blood volume is approximately 70 to 80 mL/kg; placental blood volume accounts for 30% of this volume.[109] At 30 weeks' gestation, about one half of this volume is in the fetal circulation, increasing to two thirds by term; the remainder is in the placenta.[36,182]

Flow in the umbilical arteries and umbilical vein continues longer after birth than previously believed and is unrelated to cessation of cord pulsations.[21,85] In a study in which cord clamping was delayed and the infant was placed on the mother's chest after birth, flow in the umbilical vein (UV) was found to be intermittent or continuous, increasing during inspiration; in a few infants there was no UV flow after birth. Flow in umbilical arteries was pulsatile, absent in 17%, but in most was unidirectional or bidirectional (because of uterine contractions) and often continued after cord pulsations ceased.[21] Thus using cessation of pulsations as a guide for when to clamp the cord needs further investigation. The position of the infant in relation to the placenta can influence placental transfusion; however, recent studies have found no adverse effects of placing the infant on the mother's abdomen or chest.[85,188]

The timing of umbilical cord clamping and the magnitude of placental transfusion has physiologic and clinical effects on many body systems. Delayed cord clamping is beneficial for promoting cardiopulmonary transition and increasing blood volume at birth to prevent low blood pressures and cardiac output.[85] Lung aeration after birth simulates increased pulmonary blood flow, removal of lung fluid, and circulatory changes (see Chapters 9 and 10). Clamping the umbilical cord after lung aeration begins reduces the risks of swings in cardiac output, increased arterial pressures, and increased cerebral blood flow and pressure. By delaying cord clamping lung aeration and pulmonary blood flow can begin to increase so that as the cord is clamped, the additional volume can be accommodated without large swings in cerebral blood flow and arterial pressures.[85] Early clamping may deprive infants of blood that has an important role in opening the lungs, increasing pulmonary perfusion, enhancing lung fluid clearance, and improving oxygen delivery to the infant's tissues.[10,109,182] Thus, early cord clamping may interfere with completion of normal physiologic transition at birth, resulting in a 25% to 30% decrease in blood volume.[109] With birth the amount of cardiac output going to the lungs must increase up to 45% for transition to air breathing.[36] In preterm infants, early cord clamping may lead to hypovolemia, with reduction in RBCs and thus decreased oxygen-carrying capacity, oxygen delivery, and pulmonary blood flow, limiting lung expansion.[182]

Delayed cord clamping is currently recommended when feasible, although there are variations in what constitutes "delayed," the ideal timing, and the safety of milking the cord.[5,21,85,186] Delayed cord clamping allows for passive flow, whereas milking the cord is an active, more rapid transfer. A recent metaanalysis found no adverse effects with milking the cord, but the numbers of studies are limited.[4] Delayed cord clamping increased blood volume, RBCs, postbirth hematocrit, total body iron, and iron stores at 6 months and was associated with improved motor function at 18 to 22 months.[25,96,110,141] In addition, delayed cord clamping (between 30 and 180 seconds) in preterm infants has been found to decrease the need for blood transfusions and vasopressors, improve tissue oxygenation, and reduce the incidence of intraventricular hemorrhage and sepsis.[8,9,30,36,53,66,110,140,141,188] Others have reported that delayed clamping in preterm infants reduced exogenous surfactant needs, improved cerebral oxygenation, and led to fewer days on ventilator support.[168,175] The risks of delayed cord clamping reported have been a slight increase in polycythemia, which was generally not symptomatic and required no treatment, and a slight increase in the need for phototherapy in some studies.[36,53,66]

Changes in Hematologic Parameters

Hematologic parameters differ in neonates compared with adults and change rapidly during the first week after birth. Considerable variation may be noted between individual infants and within the same infant over time.[195] Values for infants of varying gestational and postbirth ages can be found in neonatology texts.[47,50,105,189]

Blood Volume

Blood volume averages about 80 to 100 mL/kg in term infants and 90 to 105 mL/kg in preterm infants.[124] Variations in blood volume at birth are primarily related to placental transfusion and gestational age. Total combined fetal and placental blood volume is 115 mL/kg in term infants and 150 mL/kg at 26 weeks.[79] The higher blood volume of preterm infants is caused by increased plasma volume. Plasma volume decreases with gestation.[124]

Red Blood Cells

RBC counts are 4.6 to 5.2 million/mm³ at birth, increasing by about 500,000 in the initial hours after birth, then falling to cord blood levels by the end of the first week.[105,130,189] RBC mass is lower with decreasing gestational age.[138] Nucleated RBCs are seen in most newborns during the first 24 hours, perhaps as a response to the stresses of delivery, disappearing by 3 to 4 days in term infants and by 1 week in most preterm infants.[138] Increased numbers of nucleated RBCs are found in more immature infants (and may persist beyond the first week) and in infants with Down syndrome or congenital anomalies.[130] Nucleated RBCs are also seen in neonates as an acute stress response to asphyxia, with anemia, and after hemorrhage. In older individuals, these cells are rare and associated with abnormal erythropoiesis.[195] The erythrocyte sedimentation rate (ESR) is decreased in neonates because of alterations

in plasma viscosity, protein content, and hematocrit. The RBC count of neonates differs from that of adults. These differences and their implications are summarized in Table 8-5.

Hemoglobin and Hematocrit

Hemoglobin levels are higher in newborns, ranging from 13.5 to 20.1 g/dL (135 to 201 g/L), with most in the 16.6 to 17.5 g/dL (166 to 175 g/L) range.[96,105,130,189] Hemoglobin levels increase by up to 6 g/dL (60 g/L) within the first hours after birth. This increase results from a shift in fluid distribution after birth—with a decrease in plasma volume and a net increase in RBCs—and partially compensates for placental transfusion.[1] Levels peak at 4 to 6 hours, then slowly decrease over the next 12 to 18 hours and are similar to birth values by

TABLE 8-5	Characteristics of Neonatal Red Blood Cells and Their Implications
RED BLOOD CELL CHARACTERISTIC	**CLINICAL IMPLICATION**
Macrocytosis with increased mean cellular diameter and mean corpuscular volume	More susceptible to damage in small capillaries; increased RBC turnover
Increased permeability to sodium and potassium	Increased risk of cell lysis as a result of osmotic changes
Altered enzyme activity with increased glucose utilization	Risk of hypoglycemia, especially in infants with low glucose stores or altered glucose metabolism with a tendency toward polycythemia (i.e., IDMs, SGA infants)
Increased ATP utilization	Higher energy (glucose) needs and oxygen consumption
Decreased survival time (60–80 days for term infants and 30–50 days for VLBW infants versus 120 days for adults)	Increased RBC turnover rate; proportionately greater amounts of bilirubin produced
Increased receptor sites for substances such as insulin and digoxin	Insulin receptor sites facilitate increased glucose uptake; digoxin sites contribute to greater tolerance for digoxin
Increased fetal hemoglobin and less adult hemoglobin	Increased affinity of hemoglobin for oxygen with less ready release to tissues
Increased RBC count at birth (4.6–5.2 million/mm³, falling to 3–4 million/mm³ by 2–3 months of age)	Increased RBC turnover rate and bilirubin production
Increased phospholipid, cholesterol, and total lipid content	Increased risk of lipid peroxidation and hemolysis (cholesterol may provide protection against hemolysis)
Decreased catalase glutathione peroxidase	Increased susceptibility to oxidative injury and decreased RBC life span
Increased fragility, decreased deformability, and increased variety and frequency of morphologic abnormalities	Increased susceptibility to damage, especially in microcirculation; increased RBC turnover
Increased free intracellular iron	May lead to decreased RBC survival

Data compiled from references 33, 42, 48, 50, 105, 126, 130.
ATP, Adenosine triphosphate; *IDM,* infant of a diabetic mother; *RBC,* red blood cell; *SGA,* small for gestational age; *VLBW,* very low birth weight.

24 hours of age.[2,33] Hemoglobin levels fall further in the first few months (see "Physiologic Anemia of Infancy").

The hemoglobin concentration decreases by the end of the first week to values similar to cord blood levels. Higher hemoglobin levels are seen in infants with severe hypoxia, in some infants with fetal growth restriction, and in postterm infants, possibly as a compensatory mechanism to increase oxygen availability to the tissues. Lower hemoglobin levels are found in preterm infants. An elevation of either the reticulocyte count or the number of nucleated RBCs above normal values in any infant, regardless of the hemoglobin level, suggests a compensatory response and may indicate anemia.[105,130,189]

Cord blood at term contains 60% to 80% HbF, 15% to 40% HbA, and less than 1.8% hemoglobin A_2 (a minor normal adult form). A fourth type, Hb Bart (less than 0.5%), is seen in small amounts in some infants. Cord blood hemoglobin levels vary with gestational age. Preterm infants have a greater percentage of HbF than term infants.

HbF does not bind 2,3-DPG as readily as does adult hemoglobin (HbA), shifting the oxygen-hemoglobin dissociation curve of the fetus and newborn to the left (see Box 10-1). Increased concentrations of HbF are seen in infants that are small for gestational age (SGA) and other infants who have experienced chronic hypoxia in utero, probably because of a delay in the normal switch to synthesis of HbA at about 32 weeks' gestation.[50,166] Alterations in HbF are usually not seen in infants with acute intrapartum hypoxia, because the more recent onset of this condition does not allow the infant sufficient time to compensate.[130] The increased HbF seen in infants with trisomy 13 during the first 2 years of life is also believed to be caused by a delay in HbA synthesis. Decreased HbF is also seen in infants with Down syndrome. Increased HbA is found in infants with erythroblastosis fetalis because of rapid destruction of older RBCs containing HbF and replacement by new cells containing higher concentrations of HbA.[130]

Hematocrit levels increase in the first few hours or days because of the movement of fluid from intravascular to interstitial spaces. The hematocrit falls again to levels near cord blood values by the end of the first week and further over the first months (see "Physiologic Anemia of Infancy").[31]

2,3-Diphosphoglycerate

Although 2,3-DPG levels at birth in term infants are similar to those in adults, the 2,3-DPG of infants is less stable than that of adults. Concentrations of 2,3-DPG may fall the first week but increase by the time the infant is 2 to 3 weeks of age.[126] The P_{50} (the Po_2 at which 50% of the hemoglobin is saturated with oxygen) is decreased at birth but gradually increases during the first week after birth.[195] This change in the P_{50} primarily results from an increase in 2,3-DPG rather than in the percentage of HbF. Compared with term infants, preterm infants have a lower P_{50}, decreased concentrations of 2,3-DPG, and increased amounts of HbF. Therefore in the initial few weeks after birth, the functioning DPG fraction in preterm infants is significantly reduced.[45,126,195]

Erythropoietin

Erythropoietin (Epo) is an essential glycoprotein growth factor for erythropoiesis. Epo levels are higher at birth than in adults and higher in term infants than in preterm infants. After the first day, Epo levels fall, and plasma levels in healthy term infants reach a nadir around 4 weeks of age (6 weeks in preterm infants).[47] Stimulation of Epo production at that point coincides with the resumption of bone marrow activity and RBC production (see "Physiologic Anemia of Infancy"). Epo levels remain low for longer periods in preterm infants.[47] In preterm infants, the liver is still the main site of Epo production, because the switch to renal Epo production is related to postmenstrual age rather than postbirth age.[169] Hepatocyte production of Epo in response to hypoxic stimulation is only 10% of that produced by renal cells. In addition, the liver requires more prolonged hypoxic stimulation to produce Epo. In preterm infants, this increases the risk of anemia, but it may also protect from polycythemia.[41]

Elevated levels of Epo are found at birth in infants with Down syndrome, growth restriction, or anemia secondary to erythroblastosis fetalis and in those born to women with diabetes or preeclampsia. In the first 24 hours, Epo is elevated in infants with severe anemia or cyanotic congenital heart defects or after hypoxia.[47] The increased levels result from decreased oxygen-carrying capacity (anemia) or low arterial oxygen saturations (congenital heart defects), which stimulate continued production of Epo. Epo is also believed to be important in maturation of the gut and neurologic development.[76,89,106,187,191]

Reticulocytes

The reticulocyte count is elevated at birth, probably because of the elevated Epo levels, ranging from 3% to 7% (absolute values of 200,000 to 400,000/μL [200 to 400 10^9/L]) in term infants and up to 8% to 10% (absolute values of 400,000 to 500,000/μL [400 to 500 10^9/L]) in preterm infants.[31,33] The reticulocyte count decreases markedly to 0% to 1% (absolute values of 0 to 50,000/μL [0 to 50 10^9/L]) by 1 week of age as RBC production decreases and continues to fall over the first few months (see "Physiologic Anemia of Infancy").[31,33]

Iron and Serum Ferritin

Maturity, birth weight, and hemoglobin level determine the iron status of the neonate. Cord serum ferritin levels at term are higher than maternal values and rise further in the first 24 hours with RBC catabolism and release of hemoglobin iron. Cord serum ferritin levels increase with increasing gestational age to 170 μg/L at term.[49] Cord hemoglobin and serum ferritin levels are inversely related. At birth the serum folate level of the neonate is also higher than that in maternal blood. Stores in preterm infants are lower and more rapidly depleted in the first months because of rapid growth. For example, a term infant with a birth weight of 3500 g has 262.5 mg of total body iron, whereas a very-low-birth-weight (VLBW) infant with a birth weight of 500 g has only 37.5 mg.[49] Iron in breast milk is better absorbed than iron in formula, probably because of the interaction of the iron-binding protein lactoferrin in human milk and lactoferrin-specific receptors on intestinal cell apical membranes.[96]

White Blood Cells

There are two pools of WBCs in the body, a circulating pool and marginated cells. Cells usually circulate in blood for about 6 to 8 hours and survive for another 24 hours in tissues. The WBC count ranges from 10,000 to 26,000/mm^3 in term infants and from 6000 to 19,000/mm^3 in preterm infants. The physiologic decrease in WBCs in the first 4 hours postbirth is believed to be caused by the corticosteroid surge with birth.[48] The number of cells increases during the first 12 to 24 hours, then gradually decreases to 6000 to 15,000/mm^3 (mean of 12,000/mm^3) by 4 to 5 days in both term and preterm infants.[130] The initial increase in WBCs is because of displacement of cells from the margins of larger vessels or bone marrow mobilization of the existing neutrophil pool (similar to changes seen in adults after strenuous exercise) because of the stress of labor and delivery rather than an increase in WBC production rate.[62,138]

Initially, up to 60% of the WBCs may be neutrophils, with a variety of immature forms. During the first 3 to 4 days, the neutrophil count is higher in preterm than in term infants. Reference limits for neutrophil counts in neonates were published by Manroe et al. and Mouzinho et al.[103,119] In term infants, neutrophils peak at 8 to 12 hours at 7800 to 14,500 cells/mm^3, although individual variations can be seen in otherwise healthy infants.[86,119,138] Values less than 3000 in the first 48 hours and less than 1500 after that are abnormal.[86] VLBW infants show a similar peak, but the peak occurs later (at 18 to 20 hours). In preterm infants, the lower limit for normal values is 2200 in the first 12 to 24 hours and less than 1100 after 60 hours.[86] Immature forms of neutrophils (e.g., bands, metamyelocytes, myelocytes) may be seen in healthy neonates during the first 2 to 3 days.[103] The number of monocytes increases slightly during the first 12 hours, then gradually decreases. A study done at altitude found similar findings in the first 70 hours after birth, but with slightly higher upper and lower limits at both birth and 72 hours and peak values at 8 hours.[156]

Eosinophil counts in neonates show great individual variation, with reported values ranging from 19 to 851 cells/mm^3 in term infants in the first 12 hours and increasing during the first 4 to 5 days of life to 100 to 2500 cells/mm^3.[50] Eosinophilia (more than 700/mm^3) is more common in preterm infants during the first few weeks, with 75% having values greater than 700/mm^3. Disappearance of eosinophils from the peripheral circulation has been noted before death.

Monocytes range from 0 to 2000 cells/mm^3 at birth, peaking at 12 to 24 hours, then falling to 450 to 600 in the first week.[86] After circulating in the blood for about 72 hours, monocytes migrate into the tissues and become macrophages.

Platelets

In term and healthy preterm infants, platelet counts are similar to those in adults, ranging from 150,000 to 450,000/mm^3. Age-related reference ranges are available.[113,164] Preterm infants tend to have values slightly lower than term infants, but still within normal range.[31,88,164] Platelet counts increase by the end of the first month in both term and preterm infants. Higher levels may persist for the first 3 months in preterm infants. Platelet counts below 150,000/mm^3 are abnormal in neonates.[50,166] Neonatal megakaryocytes are small and generate fewer platelets than in adults. The normal (i.e., similar to adult values) platelet count in neonates is probably because of the increased proliferative rate by these smaller cells.[88,163,164] The platelet life span in healthy infants is similar to that of adults.[88] Thrombopoietin levels are three to four times higher than in adults, increasing on day 2, then decreasing to cord blood levels by 1 month.[164] The response of thrombopoietin to thrombocytopenia is reduced with decreasing gestational age.[88]

Neonatal platelets have a decreased functional reserve capacity and hypoactive response to stimuli in the first few days.[146] Neonatal platelets have reduced granule secretions, decreased fibrinogen-binding site expression, fewer microtubule structures, and hypoactivity in the first 2 to 4 weeks, reducing clot strength.[146] Platelet aggregation, adhesion, and release of substances that enhance the clotting cascade may also be altered.[59,133,164] Platelet function tends to be generally normal, however, because of enhanced von Willebrand factor (vWF) activity.[177] However, if the infant is ill or immature, these limitations increase the risk of bleeding and coagulopathy. Coagulation in the neonate may be impaired by maternal drugs such as aspirin that alter platelet aggregation and factor XII (contact factor) activity.[163]

Alterations in Hemostasis

Neonatal hemostasis is altered and characterized by a low reserve capacity. Values for all components are related to gestational age and change gradually after birth, necessitating use of postbirth- and gestational age–dependent reference tables for accurate assessment of individual parameters.[52,88,115] The hemostatic system is illustrated in Figures 8-4, 8-5 and 8-6.

Coagulation

Levels of both procoagulant proteins and natural anticoagulants are lower in neonates. The clotting cascade is illustrated in Figure 8-4. Vitamin K–dependent clotting factors II (prothrombin), VII, IX, and X are approximately 50% of adult plasma values at birth and in the early weeks after birth.[52,59,88,72] This reduction is greater in preterm infants, because concentrations of vitamin K–dependent factors are related to gestational age. Contact factors involved in the initiation of the clotting cascade are at less than 50% of adult plasma values at birth.[59,88] This leads to the prolonged activated partial thromboplastin time seen in neonates.[59] Neonatal fibrinogen levels are similar to those in adults or slightly increased at birth, although fetal forms of fibrinogen (with higher sialic acid levels and decreased cross-linking ability) may be present.[48,72,115,133] Plasma concentrations of vWF are increased at birth and remain high for the first 3 months.[47,115] Factors V, VIII, and XIII levels are close to adult values.[115] As a result of these changes, thrombin generation is 50% of adult capacity, resulting in resistance to heparin and an increased risk of hemorrhage.[88] Activity is further diminished with decreasing gestational age and in severely ill neonates.

Inhibitors of coagulation are also altered (see Figure 8-5). Levels of antithrombin (a protease inhibitor that neutralizes activated clotting factors) and heparin cofactor II (HCII) are at 50% of adult values.[52,72,88] Antithrombin also has angiogenic properties, which may be why it is lower in the newborn.[48,72] Protein C and S (inhibitors of factors VII and V and the vitamin K–dependent factors) are also decreased. Protein C is decreased to 35% (17% to 53%) and protein S to 36% (12% to 60%) of adult values.[82] Protein C is found in a fetal form in neonatal circulation. Protein S is found primarily in a free form in neonates (versus protein-bound as in adults) because of absence of its binding protein. This is an advantage for neonates, because the increased levels of free protein S result in net activity that is 75% of adult values even though absolute values are closer to one third of adult levels.[52,82] Fetal forms of fibrinogen and protein C may be present and alter thrombin generation and regulation.[72] Levels of another inhibitor, α1-macroglobin, are elevated to twice adult values, which may help compensate

for the alterations in antithrombin, protein C, protein S, and heparin cofactor II.[52,59,88,133] Possible mechanisms for these alterations in coagulation include decreased factor synthesis, accelerated clearance (because of the accelerated basal metabolic rate), and activation and increased consumption of coagulation components at birth.[52] These changes increase the risk for hypercoagulable states and thrombin formation.[62,166] Inhibition of thrombin is slower in newborns but is balanced by increased binding of thrombin by the elevated α1-macroglobin.[72,73] This protein increases further by 6 months and remains high into the third decade.[72] Edstrom and colleagues note that "thrombin generation in neonates is similar to that in adults receiving therapeutic doses of warfarin or heparin."[52, p. 243]

Prothrombin time (PT), thrombin time (TT), and activated partial thromboplastin time (aPTT) are prolonged, more so with decreasing gestational age.[73] However, specific values for these tests vary between laboratories and with differences in cord versus neonatal samples, reagents used, and assay conditions. Reference values are available for term and preterm infants of varying postbirth ages.[52,88,113] Table 8-6

TABLE 8-6 Developmental Hemostasis: Age-Related Differences in Hemostatic Factors

	PRETERM NEONATES VERSUS TERM NEONATES	NEONATES VERSUS OLDER CHILDREN/ADULTS	APPROXIMATE AGE OF ADULT VALUES[a]
PRIMARY HEMOSTASIS			
Platelet count	Decreased (<32 weeks)	Same	
Platelet function	Decreased	Decreased[b]	2–4 weeks
% reticulated platelets	Higher	Higher	NA
vWF level	NA	Higher	3 months
vwF large multimers	NA	Higher	3 months
COAGULATION FACTORS			
FII, FVII, FIX, FX	Lower	Lower	16 years
FV	Lower	Same or lower	16 years
FIII	Higher	Same or lower	1 month[c]
FXI	Lower	Lower	1 year
FXII	Lower	Lower	16 year
Fibrinogen levels	Same	Same	
Fibrinogen function	NA	Decreased	5 year
REGULATION OF COAGULATION			
Antithrombin	Lower	Lower	3 months
Protein C	Lower	Lower	16 years
Total protein S	Lower	Lower	1 month
Free protein S	NA	Higher	NA
APCR generation	NA	Reduced	NA
Free TFPI	NA	Lower	Adult
FIBRINOLYSIS			
Plasminogen level	Lower	Lower	6 months
Plasminogen function	NA	Decreased	NA
tPA	Same	Higher	5 days
α2-antiplasmin	Lower	Lower	5 days
α2 macroglobulin	Same	Higher	Adult
PAI	Same[d]	Same or higher	5 days

[a]Maximum age reported.
[b]Decreased response was reported to agonists such as thrombin, collagen, epinephrine, and thrombin activation peptide as tested by flow cytometry.
[c]Lower levels compared with adults are reported from 1 month to 16 years of age.
[d]Higher levels in extremely preterm neonates on day 10 compared with older preterm or term neonates.
APCR, Activated protein C resistance; *NA,* not available; *TFPI,* tissue factor pathway indicator; *tPA,* tissue plasminogen activator.
From Revel-Vilk, S. (2012). The conundrum of neonatal coagulopathy. *Hematology Am Soc Hematol Educ Program, 2012,* 450.

provides an overview of age-related differences in hemastotic parameters. The difference in PT time reflects the decrease in vitamin K–dependent factors in newborns, whereas the altered aPTT is a reflection of decreases in both contact factors and vitamin K–dependent factors.[81] PT greater than 17 seconds at any gestational age or aPTT greater than 45 to 50 seconds in a term infant is of concern. aPTT is generally not a useful parameter in preterm infants. aPTT measures all coagulation factors except VII and XIII and is abnormal if any one factor is 20% to 40% of normal. aPTT is influenced unduly by decreases in the contact factors, such as are seen in many healthy preterm infants. TT is prolonged because of the presence of the fetal form of fibrinogen.[114] Despite the prolonged aPTT, PT, and TT, newborn whole blood clotting times are slightly shorter than adult values (mean of 80 ± 5.1 in term infants).[48,88,133] The mechanism for this paradoxical finding may represent a slight overbalance of the tendency toward thrombosis (decreased antithrombin and proteins C and S) compared with the physiologic hypocoagulability (low levels of factors II, VII, IX, and X) as well as increased vWF levels and function and the increased size and number of RBCs.[6,81,133] D-dimer is also increased in newborns.[72]

Fibrinolysis

Activity of the fibrinolytic system (see Figure 8-6) is transiently increased at birth with a decrease in plasmin generation.[59,88] In general, fibrinolysis is less effective in the newborn because of the presence of fetal plasminogen, low plasminogen (50% of adult values), and α2-antiplasmin (80% of adult values) and increased inhibitors of fibrinolysis: plasminogen activator inhibitor-1 (PAI-1) and tissue plasminogen activator (tPA).[59,88,133,115] Although cord blood levels of PAI-1 and tPA are low, they are released from tissues with birth and quickly rise.[115] Levels of PAI-1 and tPA are twice adult levels, decreasing by 5 days; PAI-1 increases again after 5 days to twice adult values by 6 months.[52] Fetal fibrinogen may also be more resistant to lysis than adult fibrinogen.[133] In addition, clearance of collagen debris, fibrin, and injured cells is delayed secondary to immaturity of the reticuloendothelial activating system and low levels of fibronectin (a glycoprotein involved in clearance of debris from tissue injury and inflammation). Alterations in healthy preterm infants are similar to or slightly less than those in term newborns. However, activity of the fibrinolytic mechanism may be significantly depressed in some infants, especially after a hypoxic-ischemic insult or in preterm infants (with severe respiratory distress syndrome), for at least the first 24 hours after birth and possibly longer. Plasminogen levels are 60% to 70% of adult values at birth and are decreased even further in SGA infants and some preterm infants, increasing the risk for hemostatic disorders.[52,88]

CLINICAL IMPLICATIONS FOR NEONATAL CARE

Alterations in the hematologic system and hemostasis in the neonate have a significant effect on neonatal adaptations to extrauterine life. These alterations, along with the changes that occur during the first few months of life, can influence interpretation of laboratory test results, lead to alterations such as physiologic anemia or hemorrhagic disease of the newborn, and increase the risk of thromboembolism and consumptive coagulopathies. This section discusses these implications and clinical issues such as physiologic anemia, vitamin K prophylaxis, anemia of prematurity, and related transfusion practices.

Factors Influencing Hematologic Parameters

Factors that influence blood values and their interpretation in neonates include the timing, site, and amount of blood sampled; placental transfusion; and infant growth rate.[50] The timing of blood sampling in relation to changes in hemoglobin and hematocrit during the first week of postnatal life and effects of placental transfusion are discussed earlier in this chapter. The detection of hemolysis can be more difficult because of the unique characteristics of neonates' hematologic system.[50,195]

Site of Sampling

The site of sampling can result in significant variations in values. Capillary hemoglobin values average 2 to 4 g/dL (20 to 40 g/L) higher than venous values, with differences up to 8 g/dL (80 g/L) reported; arterial values average 0.5 g/dL (5 g/L) above venous values and are probably of less clinical significance.[50,173] Hematocrit, hemoglobin, and red blood cell (RBC) counts from heel capillaries are 5% to 25% higher than venous or arterial values.[2,31] Differences are greatest with decreasing gestational age. A neonate's hematocrit does not reflect RBC mass as accurately as in an adult, with a correlation of 0.63 versus 0.78 in adults.[41] Poorer correlations are reported in ill and preterm infants who are growing rapidly and thus have increased circulating blood volumes.

Both sampling site and physical activity can alter white blood cell (WBC) counts. A mean capillary difference of 1.8×10^9/L has been found in neutrophil counts between capillary and arterial samples.[173] Using simultaneously drawn blood samples, arterial WBC counts were reported to be 75% of venous or capillary values.[31] These differences may be because of the pulsatile nature of arterial flow that moves larger cells to the periphery.[31] Intense crying or other events such as chest physiotherapy has been associated with an increase in WBC counts of up to 146% and a shift to the left in the differential count, with the appearance of more immature forms of WBCs in the peripheral circulation.[31] No differences were noted in platelet counts between umbilical artery catheter, venipuncture, and capillary heel stick samples.[173]

Differences between capillary and venous blood samples are a result of poorer circulation and venous stasis in the peripheral circulation. Differences between arterial and venous samples are believed to be caused by passage of plasma to the interstitial spaces in the capillary bed with later return to circulation via the lymphatic system.[173] Capillary and venous differences are more marked with decreasing gestational age; after a large placental transfusion; and in infants with acidosis, hypotension, or severe anemia.[50] The site of sampling is critical in interpreting hematologic values in neonates and should be recorded for all samples. Unfortunately, site-related differences are most marked in those infants for whom accurate determination of hematologic values is most critical.[130]

Iatrogenic Losses

Hematologic parameters are also influenced by iatrogenic losses, which can range from 10 to 40 mg/kg/week in the neonatal intensive care unit (NICU).[49] In the first 6 weeks after birth, infants in NICUs had a mean iatrogenic blood loss equivalent to 22.9 ± 10 mL of packed cells; 46% of these infants had cumulative losses that exceeded their circulating RBC mass at birth.[50] Iatrogenic blood losses were greater in ill than in healthy preterm infants (26.9 ± 9 mL versus 14.6 ± 5 mL). In VLBW infants, these losses were equivalent to a significant proportion of their circulating RBC mass (32.2 to 45.5 mL/kg in the preterm infant). Significant overdraws of blood (19% ± 1.8% above that required by the laboratory) for laboratory testing of NICU infants has been reported.[93] Another study found 54% of blood sent to the laboratory was discarded as waste.[27] The greatest overdraws were in the smallest and most critical infants. Removal of 1 mL of blood from a 1000-g infant is estimated to be equivalent to removing 70 mL from the average adult.[50] In addition, for each gram of hemoglobin removed, 3.46 mg of elemental iron is lost.[49] Accurate determination of true anemia versus "anemia" caused by blood loss is often dependent on accurate recording of the amount of blood that has been previously drawn for sampling.[50] Iatrogenic losses can be reduced by microsampling, careful monitoring of losses, avoiding overdraws, use of bedside or point-of-care sampling, and use of placenta (cord) blood for admission labs.[27,169,174] A recent study reported good concurrence between placenta blood and infant values.[27]

Growth Influences

Rapid weight gain results in an obligatory increase in total blood volume that often precedes any change in RBC mass.[130] The ensuing hemodilution can lead to a static or falling hemoglobin even with active erythropoiesis as evidenced by reticulocytosis. The correlation between RBC mass and hemoglobin is low during the first 6 weeks because of the effects of this hemodilution, so hemoglobin levels may not accurately reflect RBC mass.[50]

Alterations in Hemoglobin–Oxygen Affinity

The increased affinity of hemoglobin for oxygen is an advantage to fetuses in facilitating oxygen transfer across the placenta but may be a liability for neonates. Preterm infants who have higher levels of HbF and lower concentrations of 2,3-diphosphoglycerate (2,3-DPG) are more vulnerable. With increased affinity, oxygen is unloaded less rapidly and efficiently in the peripheral tissues. Therefore the newborn may be less able to respond to hypoxia by significantly increasing oxygen delivery to the tissues. The newborn is also lacking in some of the protective responses seen in adults. For example, in adults, but not in neonates, hypoxia tends to stimulate increased production of 2,3-DPG, a response that further facilitates oxygen release to the tissues.[130]

The measurement of arterial hemoglobin saturation (SaO_2) by pulse oximetry is generally as reliable in neonates (who have high levels of HbF) as it is in adults (whose hemoglobin is predominantly HbA). This occurs because pulse oximetry is a direct measure of percent saturation, whereas calculating saturation from PaO_2 requires consideration of the percent concentrations of HbA and HbF in the blood.[43] Pulse oximetry works on the principle of light absorbance. The light absorbed by the hemoglobin molecule is absorbed primarily by the heme portion (which is similar in both HbA and HbF) and not by the globulin chains (which are different in HbA and HbF). Infants with significant amounts of HbF can have a SaO_2 greater than 85% even with a low PaO_2; therefore infants on pulse oximeters must also have their PaO_2 levels regularly evaluated. Even if an infant is well saturated, PaO_2 levels must be kept within normal ranges, because this is the driving force for movement of oxygen from the blood to the tissues. In preterm infants with a higher percentage of HbF, a PaO_2 of 41 to 53 (5.46 to 7.06 kPa) is often high enough to provide an SaO_2 of 88% to 92%.[43,45]

Because the P_{50} (see Box 10-1) of preterm infants is lower than that of term infants, the progressive shift to the right of the oxygen–hemoglobin dissociation curve after birth is more gradual in preterm infants and is related to postmenstrual rather than postbirth age.[130] As a result, the oxygen-unloading capacity in a preterm infant who has not been transfused is reduced for at least the first 3 months.[195] In some circumstances, the shift to the left in the oxygen–hemoglobin dissociation curve may be an advantage to the infant by helping maintain oxygen delivery with severe hypoxemia and low cardiac output.[131]

Vitamin K Deficiency Bleeding

Newborns have reduced levels of all the vitamin K–dependent clotting factors (II, VII, IX, X) at birth, leading to a physiologic hypoprothrombinemia. The reduction in these factors is the consequence of poor placental transport of vitamin K to the fetus and lack of intestinal colonization by bacteria that normally synthesize vitamin K. The low vitamin K levels in a fetus may be a mechanism to control levels of other (noncoagulation-related) vitamin K–dependent proteins, which act as ligandins for cutaneous receptor enzymes that regulate growth in the fetus. Because normal fetal growth is carefully regulated within a narrow range, vitamin K levels may be kept low to prevent growth dysregulation.[71]

Neonatal vitamin K deficiency is characterized by low plasma vitamin K_1 (phylloquinone), low liver K_1, and a near absence of K_2 (menaquinone), the major vitamin K component in the liver.[58,71,196] Unless the infant is given vitamin K at birth, the deficiency intensifies in the first few days after birth as maternally-acquired vitamin K is catabolized (half-life is about 24 hours). This decline is more marked in infants who are breastfed, have a history of perinatal asphyxia, or are born to mothers on warfarin anticoagulants. Neonatal liver stores are one fifth those of adults, because placental transport of vitamin K is low. In addition, neonatal stores are composed primarily of K_1, which has a rapid turnover, especially with a diet such as breast milk that is low in vitamin K.[196] Stores gradually increase in the first month, more rapidly in infants who are formula fed rather than breastfed. This is because of both the increased levels of vitamin K in formula and differences in intestinal colonization. Formula-fed infants are colonized with bacteria that can produce K_2, whereas lactobacillus, the primary organism colonizing the intestine of breastfed infants, cannot. Vitamin K recycling by the liver is lower in preterm than term infants because of the lower enzyme activity in preterm infants.[35]

Because this decline in vitamin K after birth leads to a bleeding tendency in some newborns, prophylactic vitamin K is given after birth to prevent hemorrhagic disease of the newborn (HDN), also known as vitamin K deficiency bleeding (VKDB). VKDB involves bleeding from the gastrointestinal tract, umbilical cord, or circumcision site; oozing from puncture sites; and generalized ecchymosis. Although it is likely that many newborns do not need vitamin K at birth, VKDB usually occurs in infants without specific risk factors.[196] Therefore it is difficult to identify which infants need this prophylaxis and which do not, and clinical and research evidence clearly demonstrates the risk of hemorrhage in some infants. In countries where routine use of vitamin K was eliminated, the incidence of VKDB increased.[196] Thus prophylaxis at birth is recommended.

Three forms of VKDB have been described: early, classic, and late.[48,94,196] The early form occurs within 24 hours of birth and is seen primarily in infants of women on certain medications.[94] In addition to receiving the usual dose of vitamin K after birth, these infants must be assessed for signs of bleeding throughout the neonatal period.[88,133] Vitamin K–dependent clotting factors may be further reduced in infants of women taking anticoagulants (warfarin); long-term antibiotic therapy, especially antituberculosis medications (e.g., isoniazid, rifampin); or antiepileptic drugs such as carbamazepine, barbiturates, and phenytoin diphenylhydantoin (Dilantin) during pregnancy.[94] These agents tend to concentrate in the fetal liver and inhibit the action of vitamin K in the formation of precursor proteins for factors II, VII, IX, and X.[88] The incidence of bleeding in these infants has been reported as 6% to 12%.[94] A review of evidence for management of women with epilepsy concluded that there was insufficient evidence to determine whether mothers on antiepileptic drugs were actually at risk of increased bleeding, nor epileptic drugs were actually at risk of increased bleeding, nor

was there adequate evidence to determine whether maternal prenatal vitamin K supplementation reduced neonatal hemorrhage.[61]

The classic form of VKDB is seen at 24 hours to 7 days as the vitamin K deficiency intensifies.[48,94] The prevalence of VKDB is 0.4 to 1.7 per 100 if no vitamin K is given.[88,133] Laboratory findings include reduction in the vitamin K–dependent clotting factors, decreased prothrombin activity, and prolonged clotting time and PT.[88,133,196] Breastfed infants with delayed or insufficient intake are at higher risk if no prophylaxis is given, because breast milk has low levels of vitamin K. VKDB is rarely seen when prophylactic vitamin K is given.[94,139]

The late form of VKDB is uncommon (incidence of 1/15000 to 1/20,000) and usually is seen at 2 to 12 weeks in infants who did not receive vitamin K at birth, who received an inadequate oral dose and were breastfed, or who have hepatobiliary problems.[48,88,94,139] This form is also sometimes seen in infants with gastrointestinal disorders leading to fat malabsorption. Prophylactic vitamin K may be given to preterm and ill infants who are on prolonged antibiotic therapy (particularly with use of third-generation cephalosporins). Antibiotics may significantly reduce the normal intestinal bacterial flora essential for vitamin K synthesis and compete for vitamin K in the liver.

Vitamin K is not required for the synthesis of clotting factors per se but rather for the conversion of precursor proteins synthesized in the liver to activated proteins with coagulant properties.[42] This process (posttranslational γ-carboxylation) is needed for calcium binding, which is critical for activation of these factors. The hypoprothrombinemia commonly present at birth is secondary to decreased levels of the precursor proteins. Term neonates respond to prophylactic vitamin K administration at birth by achieving normal or near-normal PTs, although actual values of individual clotting factors may not reach adult values for several weeks or more. The response in preterm infants is less predictable, with minimal response to vitamin K seen in some VLBW infants because of an inability of the immature liver to synthesize adequate amounts of the precursor proteins.[130]

Physiologic Anemia of Infancy

Both term infants and preterm infants experience a decline in hemoglobin during the first few months after birth. This process has been termed *physiologic anemia of infancy* in term infants because the infant tolerates the change without any clinical difficulties. Preterm infants experience a similar phenomenon that leads to anemia of prematurity (see next section). Physiologic anemia of infancy results from postnatal suppression of hematopoiesis (Figure 8-10). Hematopoiesis is controlled by Epo, which increases when oxygen delivery to the tissues is reduced. This hormone stimulates the bone marrow to increase production of RBCs. The low fetal arterial oxygen tension stimulates Epo release, which leads to production of RBCs.

system.[72,114,146] Although neonates produce less thrombin, they do produce it faster than older individuals.[72] Prolonged clotting times and decreased clot firmness have been reported in infants with complex congenital heart disease.[146]

The risk for DIC is secondary to decreased levels of antithrombin and protein C, which normally protect against accelerated coagulation by neutralizing or inhibiting activated clotting factors. Other limitations that make the newborn more susceptible to DIC are a decreased capacity of the reticuloendothelial system to clear intermediary products of coagulation (which stimulate further coagulation and consumption of clotting factors), difficulty in maintaining adequate perfusion of small vessels (resulting in local accumulation of clotting factors and delayed clearance), hepatic immaturity (with delay in compensatory synthesis of essential clotting factors), and vulnerability to pathologic problems known to initiate DIC.[62,88] Even in preterm infants, the major risks for bleeding disorders or thrombosis are not the infant's physiologic limitations per se but rather the presence of other pathologic problems (for DIC) and trauma or indwelling lines (for thrombosis).[177]

Respiratory distress, sepsis, necrotizing enterocolitis, and other severe diseases are all associated with one or more of the processes that usually lead to intravascular coagulation: (1) release of tissue factor (sepsis; severe perinatal asphyxia; and other hypoxic-ischemic events such as severe respiratory distress syndrome, necrotizing enterocolitis, and central nervous system hemorrhage), (2) endothelial injury (viral infections), and (3) shock and venous stasis (severe disease that promotes local accumulation of clotting factors and decreased clearance by the liver of activated factors).[62,73,88,177]

Altered hemostasis in the ill VLBW infant—with release of tissue factor secondary to ischemic events in the germinal matrix microcirculation—may increase the risk of both intraventricular hemorrhage and extension of earlier hemorrhages.[62] Fibrinolytic activity in the periventricular area and germinal matrix is increased, leading to more rapid destruction of fibrin clots that might prevent further hemorrhage.

Thrombosis is also a risk during the neonatal period, usually because of health problems and use of intravascular catheters.[72,146] The three factors that predispose to thromboembolism (stasis, altered coagulation, and vascular damage) are present in some neonates. Infants with polycythemia and hyperviscosity have alterations in blood flow with increased platelet adhesion and thrombi formation in the microcirculation, especially in the bowel, kidneys, and extremities. This may explain the increased risk of renal vein thrombosis in infants of diabetic women, who also have a high incidence of polycythemia. An infant with shock or perinatal asphyxia also has altered flow with hypotension and stasis.[50] Vascular damage can occur before birth within placental vessels in association with maternal complications such as preeclampsia or after birth secondary to trauma from indwelling catheters.[130]

Catheters act as foreign bodies along which fibrin is deposited and thrombi form. Infants with catheters require close observation for vasospasm or emboli formation, especially in the extremities or buttocks.

Newborns are also at risk for thrombi caused by alterations in hemostasis, such as the shorter whole blood clotting time, increased levels of factors V and VIII, and altered function along with decreased levels of major naturally occurring anticoagulants (antithrombin and proteins C and S).[59,62,88] Antithrombin levels are further reduced in SGA infants, increasing their risk of thrombosis. The neonatal period is also characterized by decreased fibrinolytic activity, so once clots develop the infant is less able to remove fibrin and lyse the clots, and increased plasminogen activator inhibitor in plasma.[177]

MATURATIONAL CHANGES DURING INFANCY AND CHILDHOOD

Most of the maturational changes in the hematologic system occur during the first 6 to 12 months. The most significant changes are related to the decline in hemoglobin, with the resulting physiologic anemia of infancy, accumulation of higher concentrations of 2,3-diphosphoglycerate (2,3-DPG), and shift of the oxygen–hemoglobin dissociation curve to the right. An awareness of these changes in infancy is necessary for an appropriate evaluation and treatment of anemia and hypoxia.

Changes in Hematologic Parameters

Blood volume values per unit weight are higher than adult values for the first month or two, increasing the risk of hypovolemia.[130] The mean red blood cell (RBC) corpuscular volume and mean diameter decrease rapidly during the first week, followed by a gradual decrease to volumes similar to those of adult cells by 3 to 4 months, declining further to lower than adult by 4 to 6 months, then increasing to adult volumes by about 1 year.[31] RBC fragility also decreases and is similar to that of adults by 3 months. During the first 2 to 3 months, blood and total body hemoglobin levels decrease secondary to decreased RBC production, resulting in the physiologic anemia of infancy (see pp. 240-242).

Erythropoietin (Epo) production reaches adult levels by 10 to 12 weeks, and the switch from hepatic to renal Epo production is probably completed by several months of age.[41,76] Differences between capillary and venous hemoglobin levels persist until 3 months of age.[130] The hematocrit decreases to around 30% by 2 months, then increases to 35% by 1 year and to adult values in adolescence. Reticulocyte levels reach adult values by 2 years. Serum ferritin levels rise after birth and remain high for 4 to 6 weeks, with a mean of 356 ng/mL (800 pmol/L). After this time, levels fall to 30 ng/mL (67.4 pmol/L)—versus 39 ng/mL [87.6 pmol/L] in female adults and 140 ng/mL [314.6 pmol/L] in male adults—by 6 months and remain stable until early to midadolescence.[97,130]

RBC membrane characteristics are similar to those of adults by 4 to 6 weeks.[76]

With the occurrence of hypoxia, congestive heart failure, or other physiologic stressors, the liver and spleen in early childhood can resume active hematopoiesis and serve as alternative sites for RBC production.[97] During early childhood, blood cells are found in the bones of the tibia, femur, ribs, sternum, and vertebrae rather than in the axial skeleton as seen in adults. Blood tissue in long bones is gradually replaced by adipose tissue beginning at 3 years. By puberty the red marrow in these bones is found only in the upper ends of the humerus and femur, and it has disappeared by adulthood. Production of WBCs in the thymus ceases in early childhood. Megakaryocytes reach adult size by 2 years.[76] Activity of coagulation factors gradually increases during infancy and early childhood with the gradual evolution of hemostasis to adult parameters by adolescence (see Table 8-6).[6] During childhood, bleeding times remain longer than in adults.[6]

Changes in Oxygen–Hemoglobin Affinity

During the first 3 months after birth, the P_{50} gradually increases, and by 4 to 6 months the P_{50} and the oxygen–hemoglobin dissociation curve is similar to that of the adult.[195] From 8 to 11 months, the curve may actually be shifted slightly to the right of the adult curve because of increased blood organic phosphates along with changes in the concentrations of adult hemoglobin (HbA) and 2,3-DPG.[130] Fetal hemoglobin (HbF) concentrations decrease 3% to 4% per week during the first 6 months. By 4 months, HbF accounts for only 5% to 10% of the hemoglobin. Levels of HbF gradually decrease to adult levels (less than 2%) by 2 to 3 years. HbA_2 concentrations increase to adult levels of 2% to 3% by 5 to 6 months.

The gradual shift of the oxygen–hemoglobin dissociation curve during the first 6 months after birth is determined by the relative proportions of HbF to HbA and concentrations of 2,3-DPG. Infants with similar concentrations of HbF may have different P_{50} values if they have significantly different levels of 2,3-DPG. Similarly, infants with similar levels of 2,3-DPG may have different P_{50} values if concentrations of HbF are significantly different. Thus an infant with elevated levels of HbA and low levels of 2,3-DPG may have a P_{50} that is similar to that of another infant with high levels of HbF and 2,3-DPG.[50,130] This seeming paradox is explained by what Delivoria-Papadopoulous and colleagues called the *functioning DPG fraction:* The gradual decrease in affinity of hemoglobin for oxygen during the first 6 months after birth correlates with a fraction derived from multiplying the total RBC 2,3-DPG content by the percentage of HbA.[45] Thus two critical factors in determining the position of the oxygen–hemoglobin dissociation curve during infancy are the amount of HbA and the amount of 2,3-DPG. The rate of postnatal decline in fetal hemoglobin concentrations is generally not affected by persistent cyanosis secondary to cyanotic heart disease.[130]

SUMMARY

The hematologic and hemostatic systems undergo significant alterations during the neonatal period. Because of these changes, infants are at risk for anemia, thromboembolic insults, and coagulopathies. Many of the changes in the hematologic system encountered in neonates occur progressively over time. Therefore gestational and postbirth age, as well as health status, must be considered in evaluating and managing individual infants. Clinical recommendations for nurses working with neonates based on changes in the hematologic and hemostatic systems are summarized in Box 8-2.

BOX 8-2   **Recommendations for Clinical Practice Related to the Hematologic and Hemostatic Systems in Neonates**

Know normal parameters for hematologic values in preterm and term neonates and patterns of change during the neonatal period (pp. 233-238).

Recognize changes in hematocrit during the first few days postbirth because of fluid shifts (versus changes indicating pathologic processes) (pp. 233-235).

Monitor for problems for which the newborn is at increased risk because of alterations in the neonate's red blood cells (p. 234 and Table 8-5).

Recognize the effects of sampling site and physical activity (especially crying) on hematologic values (pp. 238-239).

Record the sampling site and infant activity each time blood is drawn (pp. 238-239).

Record the amount of blood drawn and other iatrogenic blood loss (pp. 239, 243).

Evaluate the amount of iatrogenic blood loss in light of an infant's blood volume (pp. 238-239, 243).

Ensure that vitamin K is given after birth (pp. 239-240).

Monitor for signs of vitamin K deficiency bleeding, especially in infants of mothers on anticonvulsants, anticoagulants, or long-term antibiotic therapy and in infants on long-term antibiotic therapy (p. 240).

Recognize laboratory and clinical signs associated with anemia in preterm and term neonates and with anemia is infancy (pp. 240-243).

Monitor for clinical signs of anemia, anemia of prematurity, and hemolysis (pp. 240-243).

Recognize and monitor for signs of bleeding and disseminated intravascular coagulation, especially in infants at risk (pp. 244-245).

Monitor Po_2 values regularly in infants on pulse oximetry and maintain within normal limits (p. 239).

Monitor Po_2 and for hyperoxia in infants after transfusions (especially with fresh blood, after multiple or exchange transfusions) (pp. 239, 243).

Recognize and monitor for signs of thromboembolism in infants with indwelling lines or who are hypotensive, polycythemic, or in shock (pp. 244-245).

Recognize and monitor infants at risk for polycythemia and hyperviscosity (pp. 243-244).

Ensure that term and preterm infants receive iron supplementation at recommended time points (p. 243).

References

1. Abbassi-Ghanavati, M., Greer, L. G., & Cunningham, F. G. (2009). Pregnancy and laboratory studies: a reference table for clinicians. *Obstet Gynecol, 114*, 1326.
2. Aher, S. M., & Ohlsson, A. (2014). Late erythropoietin for preventing red blood cell transfusion in preterm and/or low birth weight infants. *Cochrane Database Syst Rev, 2014*(4), CD004868.
3. Aher, S., Malwatkar, K., & Kadam, S. (2008). Neonatal anemia. *Semin Fetal Neonatal Med, 13*, 239.
4. Al-Wassia, H., & Shah, P. S. (2015). Efficacy and safety of umbilical cord milking at birth: a systematic review and meta-analysis. *JAMA Pediatr, 169*, 18.
5. American College of Obstetricians and Gynecologists. (2012). Committee Opinion No. 543: timing of umbilical cord clamping after birth. *Obstet Gynecol, 120*, 1522.
6. Andrew, M. (1995). Developmental hemostasis: Relevance to hemostatic problems during childhood. *Semin Thromb Hemost, 21*, 341.
7. Antony, K. M., et al. (2017). Maternal Physiology. In S. G. Gabbe, et al. (Eds.), *Normal and Problems Pregnancies* (7th ed.). Philadelphia: Elsevier.
8. Arca, G., et al. (2010). Timing of umbilical cord clamping: new thoughts on an old discussion. *J Matern Fetal Neonatal Med, 23*, 1274.
9. Backes, C. H., et al. (2014). Placental transfusion strategies in very preterm neonates: a systematic review and meta-analysis. *Obstet Gynecol, 124*, 47.
10. Baenziger, O., et al. (2007). The influence of the timing of cord clamping on postnatal cerebral oxygenation in preterm neonates: A randomized, controlled trial. *Pediatrics, 119*, 455.
11. Bain, A., & Blackburn, S. (2004). Issues in transfusing preterm infants in the NICU. *J Perinat Neonatal Nurs, 18*, 170.
12. Baker, R. D., Greer, F. R., & Committee on Nutrition American Academy of Pediatrics. (2010). Diagnosis and prevention of iron deficiency and iron-deficiency anemia in infants and young children (0-3 years of age). *Pediatrics, 126*, 1040.
13. Bassell, G. M., & Marx, G. F. (1981). Physiologic changes of normal pregnancy and parturition. In E. V. Cosmi (Ed.), *Obstetrical anesthesia and perinatology*. New York: Appleton-Century-Crofts.
14. Bauer, D. E., & Orkin, S. H. (2011). Update on fetal hemoglobin gene regulation in hemoglobinopathies. *Curr Opin Pediatr, 23*, 1.
15. Bell, E. F., et al. (2005). Randomized trial of liberal versus restrictive guidelines for red blood cell transfusions in preterm infants. *Pediatrics, 115*, 1685.
16. Bell, E. F. (2011). When to transfuse preterm babies. *Arch Dis Child Fetal Neonatal Ed, 93*, F469.
17. Berglund, S., Westrup, B., & Domellöf, M. (2010). Iron supplements reduce the risk of iron deficiency anemia in marginally low birth weight infants. *Pediatrics, 126*, e874.
18. Bishara, N., & Ohls, R. K. (2009). Current controversies in the management of anemia of prematurity. *Semin Perinatol, 33*, 29.
19. Blau, J., et al. (2011). Transfusion-related acute gut injury: Necrotizing enterocolitis in very low birth weight neonates after packed red blood cell transfusion. *J Pediatr, 158*, 403.
20. Boehlen, F., et al. (2000). Platelet count at term pregnancy: A reappraisal of the threshold. *Obstet Gynecol, 95*, 29.
21. Boere, I., et al. (2015). Umbilical blood flow patterns directly after birth before delayed cord clamping. *Arch Dis Child Fetal Neonatal Ed, 100*, F121.
22. Borgna-Pignatti, C., Marsella, M., & Zanforlin, N. (2010). The natural history of thalassemia intermedia. *Ann N Y Acad Sci, 1202*, 214.
23. Bremme, K. A. (2003). Haemostatic changes in pregnancy. *Best Pract Res Clin Haematol, 16*, 153.
24. Breymann, C. (2015). Iron deficiency anemia in pregnancy. *Semin Hematol, 52*, 339.
25. Cao, C., & O'Brien, K. O. (2013). Pregnancy and iron homeostasis: an update. *Nutr Rev, 71*, 35.
26. Carlson, B. M. (2013). *Human embryology and developmental biology* (5th ed.). Philadelphia: Elsevier Saunders.
27. Carroll, P. D., & Widness, J. A. (2012). Nonpharmacological, blood conservation techniques for preventing neonatal anemia–effective and promising strategies for reducing transfusion. *Semin Perinatol, 36*, 232.
28. Centers for Disease Control and Prevention. (1998). Recommendations to prevent and control iron deficiency anemia in the United States. *MMWR, 47*, 1.
29. Chesley, L. C. (1972). Plasma and red cell volumes during pregnancy. *Am J Obstet Gynecol, 112*, 440.
30. Chiruvolu, A., et al. (2015). Effect of delayed cord clamping on very preterm infants. *Am J Obstet Gynecol, 213*, 676.e1–7.
31. Christensen, R. D. (2000). Expected hematologic values for term and preterm neonates. In R. Christensen (Ed.), *Hematologic problems of the neonate*. Philadelphia: Saunders.
32. Christensen, R. D. (2011). Association between red blood cell transfusions and necrotizing enterocolitis. *J Pediatr, 158*, 349.
33. Christensen, R. D., et al. (2016). Reference intervals for reticulocyte parameters of infants during their first 90 days after birth. *J Perinatol, 36*, 61.
34. Clark, P. (2003). Changes of hemostasis variables during pregnancy. *Semin Vasc Med, 3*, 13.
35. Clarke, P. (2010). Vitamin K prophylaxis for preterm infants. *Early Hum Dev, 86*, 17.
36. Coggins, M., & Mercer, J. (2009). Delayed cord clamping: Advantages for infants. *Nurs Womens Health, 13*, 132.
37. Collard, K. J. (2009). Iron homeostasis in the neonate. *Pediatrics, 123*, 1208.
38. Collard, K. J. (2014). Transfusion related morbidity in premature babies: Possible mechanisms and implications for practice. *World J Clin Pediatr, 3*, 19.
39. Cunningham, F. G., et al. (2014). *Williams obstetrics* (24th ed.). New York: McGraw-Hill.
40. Curtis, B. R. (2015). Recent progress in understanding the pathogenesis of fetal and neonatal alloimmune thrombocytopenia. *Br J Haematol, 171*, 671.
41. Dame, C., & Juul, S. (2000). The switch from fetal to adult erythropoiesis. *Clin Perinatol, 27*, 507.
42. de Alarcón, P., et al. (2013). *Neonatal hematology* (2nd ed.). Cambridge, England: Cambridge University Press.
43. Deckardt, R., & Steward, D. J. (1984). Noninvasive arterial oxygen saturation versus transcutaneous oxygen tension monitoring in the preterm infant. *Crit Care Med, 12*, 935.
44. de Jesús, G. R., et al. (2014). Pregnancy morbidity in antiphospholipid syndrome: what is the impact of treatment? *Curr Rheumatol Rep, 16*, 403.
45. Delivoria-Papadopoulous, M., Roncevic, N. P., & Oski, F. A. (1971). Postnatal changes in oxygen transport of term, preterm, and sick infants: the role of 2,3-DPG and adult hemoglobin. *Pediatr Res, 5*, 235.
46. De-Regil, L. M., et al. (2015). Effects and safety of periconceptional oral folate supplementation for preventing birth defects. *Cochrane Database Syst Rev, 2015*(12), CD007950.
47. Diab, Y., & Luchtman-Jones, L. (2015). Hematologic and oncologic problems in the fetus and newborn. In R. J. Martin, A. A. Fanaroff, & M. C. Walsh (Eds.), *Fanaroff and Martin's Neonatal-perinatal medicine: Diseases of the fetus and infant* (10th ed.). Philadelphia: Elsevier Saunders.
48. Diaz-Miron, J., Miller, J., & Vogel, A. M. (2013). Neonatal hematology. *Semin Pediatr Surg, 22*, 199.
49. Domellöf, M., & Georgieff, M. K. (2015). Postdischarge Iron Requirements of the Preterm Infant. *J Pediatr, 167*, S31.
50. Dror Y., et al. (2016). Hematology. In M. G. Macdonald & M. M. K. Seshia (Eds.), *Avery's Neonatology: Pathophysiology and management of the newborn* (7th ed.). Philadelphia: Wolters Kluwer.
51. Duffy, T. P. (2004). Hematologic aspects of pregnancy. In G. N. Burrows, T. P. Duffy, & J. A. Copel (Eds.), *Medical complications during pregnancy* (6th ed.). Philadelphia: Saunders.
52. Edstrom, C. S., Christensen, R. D., & Andrew, M. (2000). Developmental aspects of blood hemostasis and disorders of coagulation and fibrinolysis in the neonatal period. In R. Christensen (Ed.), *Hematologic problems of the neonate*. Philadelphia: Saunders.
53. Eichenbaum-Pikser, G., & Zasloff, J. S. (2009). Delayed clamping of the umbilical cord: A review with implications for practice. *J Midwifery Womens Health, 54*, 321.
54. Elmahdy, H., et al. (2010). Human recombinant erythropoietin in asphyxia neonatorum: Pilot trial. *Pediatrics, 125*, e1135.
55. Erez, O., Mastrolia, S. A., & Thachil, J. (2015). Disseminated intravascular coagulation in pregnancy: insights in pathophysiology, diagnosis and management. *Am J Obstet Gynecol, 213*, 452.
56. Furman, L. M. (2011). Exclusively breastfed infants: Iron recommendations are premature. *Pediatrics, 127*, e1098.

57. Ghavam, S., et al. (2014). Effects of placental transfusion in extremely low birthweight infants: meta-analysis of long- and short-term outcomes. *Transfusion, 54*, 1192.

58. Greer, F. R. (2010). Vitamin K the basics—what's new? *Early Hum Dev, 86*, S43.

59. Guzzetta, N. A., & Miller, B. E. (2011). Principles of hemostasis in children: Models and maturation. *Paediatr Anaesth, 21*, 3.

60. Haider, B., et al. (2013). Anaemia, prenatal iron use, and risk of adverse pregnancy outcomes: systematic review and meta-analysis. *BMJ, 346*, 3443.

61. Harden, C. L., et al. (2009). Practice parameter update: Management issues for women with epilepsy—focus on pregnancy (an evidence-based review): Vitamin K, folic acid, blood levels, and breastfeeding: Report of the Quality Standards Subcommittee and Therapeutics and Technology Assessment Subcommittee of the American Academy of Neurology and American Epilepsy Society. *Neurology, 73*, 142.

62. Hathaway, W. E., & Bonnar, J. (1987). *Hemostatic disorders of the pregnant woman and newborn infant.* New York: Elsevier.

63. Hellgren, M. (2003). Hemostasis during normal pregnancy and puerperium. *Semin Thromb Hemost, 29*, 125.

64. Hernell, O., et al. (2015). Summary of current recommendations on iron provision and monitoring of iron status for breastfed and formula-fed infants in resource-rich and resource-constrained countries. *J Pediatr, 167*, S40.

65. Horowitz, K. M., Ingardia, C. J., & Borgida, A. F. (2013). Anemia in pregnancy. *Clin Lab Med, 33*, 281.

66. Hutton, E. K., & Hassan, E. S. (2007). Late vs early clamping of the umbilical cord in full-term neonates: Systematic review and meta-analysis of controlled trials. *JAMA, 297*, 1241.

67. Hytten, F. (1985). Blood volume changes in normal pregnancy. *Clin Hematol, 14*, 601.

68. Ibrahim, M., Ho, S. K., & Yeo, C. L. (2014). Restrictive versus liberal red blood cell transfusion thresholds in very low birth weight infants: a systematic review and meta-analysis. *J Paediatr Child Health, 50*, 122.

69. Institute of Medicine. (1990). *Nutrition during pregnancy.* Washington, DC: National Academy Press.

70. Institute of Medicine. (1993). *Iron deficiency anemia: Guidelines for prevention, detection, and management among U.S. children and women of childbearing age.* Washington, DC: National Academy Press.

71. Israels, L. G., et al. (1997). The riddle of vitamin K1 deficit in the newborn. *Semin Perinatol, 21*, 90.

72. Jaffray, J., & Young, G. (2013). Developmental hemostasis: clinical implications from the fetus to the adolescent. *Pediatr Clin North Am, 60*, 1407.

73. Jaffray, J., & Young, G. (2016). The bleeding newborn: A review of presentation, diagnosis, and management. *Semin Fetal Neonatal Med, 21*, 44.

74. Josephson, C. D., et al. (2010). Do red cell transfusions increase the risk of necrotizing enterocolitis in premature infants? *J Pediatr, 157*, 972.

75. Joy, R., et al. (2014). Early versus late enteral prophylactic iron supplementation in preterm very low birth weight infants: a randomized controlled trial. *Arch Dis Child Fetal Neonatal Ed, 99*, F105.

76. Juul, S. E. (2000). Nonhematopoietic aspects of hematopoietic growth factors in the fetus and newborn. In R. Christensen (Ed.), *Hematologic problems of the neonate.* Philadelphia: Saunders.

77. Juul, S. E., & Pet, G. C. (2015). Erythropoietin and neonatal neuroprotection. *Clin Perinatol, 42*, 469.

78. Kabra, N. S. (2003). Blood transfusion in preterm infants. *Arch Dis Child Fetal Neonatal Ed, 88*, F78.

79. Kakkilaya, V., et al. (2008). Effect of placental transfusion on the blood volume and clinical outcome of infants born by cesarean section. *Clin Perinatol, 35*, 561.

80. Katz, D., & Beilin, Y. (2015). Disorders of coagulation in pregnancy. *Br J Anaesth, 115*, S75.

81. Kenet, G., et al. (2010). Bleeding disorders in neonates. *Haemophilia, 16*, 168.

82. Khor, B., & Van Cott, E. M. (2009). Laboratory evaluation of hypercoagulability. *Clin Lab Med, 29*, 339.

83. Kilpatrick, S. J. (2014). Anemia and pregnancy. In R. K. Creasy, et al. (Eds.), *Creasy & Resnik's Maternal-fetal medicine: Principles and practice* (7th ed.). Philadelphia: Elsevier Saunders.

84. Kirpalani, H., et al. (2006). The Premature Infants in Need of Transfusion (PINT) study: a randomized, controlled trial of a restrictive (low) versus liberal (high) transfusion threshold for extremely low birth weight infants. *J Pediatr, 149*, 301.

85. Kluckow, M., & Hooper, S. B. (2015). Using physiology to guide time to cord clamping. *Semin Fetal Neonatal Med, 20*, 225.

86. Koenig, J. M., & Yoder, M. C. (2005). White blood cell disorders in the neonate. In A. R. Spitzer (Ed.), *Intensive care of the fetus & neonate* (2nd ed.). Philadelphia: Mosby.

87. Koenig, M. D., et al. (2014). Hepcidin and iron homeostasis during pregnancy. *Nutrients, 6*, 3062.

88. Kuhne, T., & Imbach, P. (1998). Neonatal platelet physiology and pathophysiology. *Eur J Pediatr, 157*, 87.

89. Kumral, A., et al. (2011). Erythropoietin in neonatal brain protection: the past, the present and the future. *Brain Development, 33*, 632.

90. Lassi, Z. S., et al. (2013). Folic acid supplementation during pregnancy for maternal health and pregnancy outcomes. *Cochrane Database Syst Rev, 2013*(3), CD006896.

91. Lemyre, B., Sample, M., & Lacaze-Masmonteil, T. (2015). Minimizing blood loss and the need for transfusions in very premature infants. Canadian Paediatric Society, Fetus and Newborn Committee. *Paediatr Child Health, 20*, 451.

92. Leung, A. N., & Lockwood, C. J. (2014). Thromboembolic disease in pregnancy. In R. K. Creasy, et al. (Eds.), *Creasy & Resnik's Maternal-fetal medicine: Principles and practice* (7th ed.). Philadelphia: Elsevier Saunders.

93. Lin, J. C., et al. (2000). Phlebotomy overdraw in the neonatal intensive care nursery. *Pediatrics, 106*, e19.

94. Lippi, G., & Franchini, M. (2011). Vitamin K in neonates: Facts and myths. *Blood Transfus, 9*, 4.

95. Liu, J., Yuan, E., & Lee, L. (2012). Gestational age-specific reference intervals for routine haemostatic assays during normal pregnancy. *Clin Chim Acta, 413*, 258.

96. Lönnerdal, B., Georgieff, M. K., & Hernell, O. (2015). Developmental physiology of iron absorption, homeostasis, and metabolism in the healthy term infant. *J Pediatr, 167*, S8.

97. Lowrey, G. H. (1986). *Growth and development of children.* Chicago: Year Book.

98. Luegenbiehl, D. L., et al. (1990). Standardized assessment of blood loss. *MCN Am J Matern Child Nurs, 15*, 241.

99. Luft, F. C., Gallery, E. D. M., & Lindheimer, M. D. (2009). Normal and abnormal volume homeostasis. In M. D. Lindheimer, J. M. Roberts, & F. G. Cunningham (Eds.), *Chesley's hypertensive disorders in pregnancy* (3rd ed.). San Diego: Academic Press Elsevier.

100. Lynch, S. R. (2000). The potential impact of iron supplementation during adolescence on iron status in pregnancy. *J Nutr, 120*, 448.

101. Maheshwari, A., & Christensen, R. D. (2017). Developmental granulocytopoiesis. In R. A. Polin, et al. (Eds.), *Fetal and neonatal physiology* (5th ed.). Philadelphia: Elsevier Saunders.

102. Mainie, P. (2008). Is there a role for erythropoietin in neonatal medicine? *Early Hum Dev, 84*, 525.

103. Manroe, B. L., et al. (1979). The neonatal blood count in health and disease. I. Reference values for neutrophil cells. *J Pediatr, 95*, 89.

104. Marik, P. E. (2010). Venous thromboembolism in pregnancy. *Clin Chest Med, 31*, 731.

105. Matthews, D. C., & Glader, B. E. (2012). Erythrocyte disorders in infancy. In C. A. Gleason & S. Devaskar (Eds.), *Avery's diseases of the newborn* (9th ed.). Philadelphia: Saunders.

106. McPherson, R. J., & Juul, S. E. (2010). Erythropoietin for infants with hypoxic-ischemic encephalopathy. *Curr Opin Pediatr, 22*, 139.

107. Mehndiratta, S., et al. (2010). Fetotoxicity of warfarin anticoagulation. *Arch Gynecol Obstet, 282*, 335.

108. Mei, Z., et al. (2011). Assessment of iron status in US pregnant women from the National Health and Nutrition Examination Survey (NHANES), 1999–2006. *Am J Clin Nutr, 93*, 1312.

109. Mercer, J. S., & Skovgaard, R. L. (2002). Neonatal transitional physiology: A new paradigm. *J Perinat Neonatal Nurs, 15*, 56.

110. Mercer, J. S., et al. (2016). Effects of placental transfusion on neonatal and 18 month outcomes in preterm infants: a randomized controlled trial. *J Pediatr, 168*, 50.

111. Milman, N. (2011). Postpartum anemia I: definition, prevalence, causes, and consequences. *Ann Hematol, 90*, 1247.

112. Mitic, G., et al. (2011). Clinical characteristics and type of thrombophilia in women with pregnancy-related venous thromboembolic disease. *Gynecol Obstet Invest, 72*, 103.

113. Monagle, P., Ignjatovic, V., & Savoia, H. (2010). Hemostasis in neonates and children: Pitfalls and dilemmas. *Blood Rev, 24*, 63.

114. Monagle, P., & Massicotte, P. (2011). Developmental haemostasis: secondary haemostasis. *Semin Fetal Neonatal Med, 16*, 294.

115. Monagle, P. (2017). Developmental hemostasis. In R. A. Polin, et al. (Eds.), *Fetal and neonatal physiology* (5th ed.). Philadelphia: Elsevier Saunders.

116. Monga, M., & Mastrobattista, J. M. (2014). Maternal cardiovascular, respiratory and renal adaptation to pregnancy. In R. K. Creasy, et al. (Eds.), *Creasy & Resnik's Maternal-fetal medicine: Principles and practice* (7th ed.). Philadelphia: Elsevier Saunders.

117. Montagnana, M., et al. (2010). Disseminated intravascular coagulation in obstetric and gynecologic disorders. *Semin Thromb Hemost, 36*, 404.

118. Morrison, J. C. (2013). Sickle cell crisis and pregnancy. *Semin Perinatol, 37*, 274.

119. Mouzinho, A., et al. (1994). Revised reference ranges for circulating neutrophils in very-low-birth-weight neonates. *Pediatrics, 94*, 76.

120. Natalucci, G., et al. (2016). Effect of early prophylactic high-dose recombinant human erythropoietin in very preterm infants on neurodevelopmental outcome at 2 Years. *Jama, 315*, 2079.

121. New, H. V., & British Committee for Standards in Haematology (BCSH), Transfusion Task Force. (2016). Guidelines on Transfusion for fetuses, neonates and older children. http://www.bcshguidelines.com/documents/2016-neonates-final.pdf; Accessed 11.06.16.

122. Nickel, R. S., & Josephson, C. D. (2015). Neonatal transfusion medicine: five major unanswered research questions for the twenty-first century. *Clin Perinatol, 42*, 499.

123. Nopoulos, P. C., et al. (2011). Long-term outcome of brain structure in premature infants: Effects of liberal vs. restricted red blood cell transfusions. *Arch Pediatr Adolesc Med, 165*, 443.

124. Ohls, R. K. (2000). Evaluation and treatment of anemia in the neonate. In R. Christensen (Ed.), *Hematologic problems of the neonate*. Philadelphia: Saunders.

125. Ohls, R. K., et al. (2016). Preschool assessment of preterm infants treated with darbepoetin and erythropoietin. *Pediatrics, 137*, 1.

126. Ohls, R. K. (2017). Developmental erythropoiesis. In R. A. Polin, et al. (Eds.), *Fetal and neonatal physiology* (5th ed.). Philadelphia: Elsevier Saunders.

127. Ohlsson, A., & Aher, S. M. (2014). Early erythropoietin for preventing red blood cell transfusion in preterm and/or low birth weight infants. *Cochrane Database Syst Rev, 2014*(4), CD004863.

128. O'Riordan, M. N., & Higgins, J. R. (2003). Haemostasis in normal and abnormal pregnancy. *Best Pract Res Clin Obstet Gynaecol, 17*, 385.

129. Orkin, S. H., & Zon, L. I. (2008). Hematopoiesis: An evolving paradigm for stem cell biology. *Cell, 132*, 631.

130. Orkin, S. H., & Nathan, D. G. (2009). *Nathan and Oski's Hematology of infancy and childhood* (7th ed.). Philadelphia: Saunders Elsevier.

131. Oski, F. A. (1979). Clinical implications of the oxygen-hemoglobin dissociation curve in the neonatal period. *Crit Care Med, 7*, 412.

132. Oteng-Ntim, E., et al. (2015). Adverse maternal and perinatal outcomes in pregnant women with sickle cell disease: systematic review and meta-analysis. *Blood, 125*, 3316.

133. Parker, R. I. (2005). Neonatal thrombosis, hemostasis and platelet disorders. In A. R. Spitzer (Ed.), *Intensive care of the fetus & neonate* (2nd ed.). Philadelphia: Mosby.

134. Paul, D. A., et al. (2011). Increased odds of necrotizing enterocolitis after transfusion of red blood cells in premature infants. *Pediatrics, 127*, 635.

135. Pena-Rosas, J. P., et al. (2015). Daily oral iron supplementation during pregnancy. *Cochrane Database Syst Rev, 2015*(7), CD004736.

136. Peña-Rosas, J. P., et al. (2015). Intermittent oral iron supplementation during pregnancy. *Cochrane Database Syst Rev, 2015*(10), CD009997.

137. Peri, K. G., et al. (1998). Quantitative correlation between globulin mRNAs and synthesis of fetal and adult hemoglobin during hemoglobin switchover in the perinatal period. *Pediatr Res, 43*, 504.

138. Proytcheva, M. A. (2009). Issues in neonatal cellular analysis. *Am J Clin Pathol, 131*, 560.

139. Puckett, R. M., & Offringa, M. (2000). Prophylactic vitamin K for vitamin K deficiency bleeding in neonates. *Cochrane Database Syst Rev, 2000*(4), CD002776.

140. Rabe, H., et al. (2012). Effect of timing of umbilical cord clamping and other strategies to influence placental transfusion at preterm birth on maternal and infant outcomes. *Cochrane Database Syst Rev, 2012*(8), CD003248.

141. Raju, T. N. (2013). Timing of umbilical cord clamping after birth for optimizing placental transfusion. *Curr Opin Pediatr, 25*, 180.

142. Rao, R., & Georgieff, M. K. (2007). Iron in fetal and neonatal nutrition. *Semin Fetal Neonatal Med, 12*, 54.

143. Rath, W. H. (2011). Postpartum hemorrhage—update on problems of definitions and diagnosis. *Acta Obstet Gynecol Scand, 90*, 421.

144. Ray, J. G., & Chan, W. S. (1999). Deep vein thrombosis during pregnancy and the puerperium: A meta-analysis of the period of risk and the leg of presentation. *Obstet Gynecol Surv, 54*, 265.

145. Réger, B., et al. (2013). Challenges in the evaluation of D-dimer and fibrinogen levels in pregnant women. *Thromb Res, 131*, e183.

146. Revel-Vilk, S. (2012). The conundrum of neonatal coagulopathy. *Hematology Am Soc Hematol Educ Program, 2012*, 450.

147. Richter, C., et al. (1995). Erythropoiesis in the perinatal postpartum period. *J Perinat Med, 23*, 51.

148. Rodger, M., et al. (2015). Haematological problems in obstetrics. *Best Pract Res Clin Obstet Gynaecol, 29*, 671.

149. Roger, M. A., & Silver, R. M. (2014). Coagulation disorders in pregnancy. In R. K. Creasy, et al. (Eds.), *Creasy & Resnik's Maternal-fetal medicine: Principles and practice* (7th ed.). Philadelphia: Elsevier Saunders.

150. Rogers, D. T., & Molokie, R. (2010). Sickle cell disease in pregnancy. *Obstet Gynecol Clin North Am, 37*, 223.

151. Ruiz-Irastorza, G., et al. (2010). Antiphospholipid syndrome. *Lancet, 376*, 1498.

152. Sanghvi, T. G., Harvey, P. W., & Wainwright, E. (2010). Maternal iron-folic acid supplementation programs: Evidence of impact and implementation. *Food Nutr Bull, 31*, S100.

153. Sarker, S., & Rosenkranz, T. S. (2008). Neonatal polycythemia and hyperviscosity. *Semin Fetal Neonatal Med, 13*, 248.

154. Scanlon, K. S., et al. (2000). High and low hemoglobin levels during pregnancy: Differential risks for preterm birth and small for gestational age. *Obstet Gynecol, 96*, 741.

155. Schanler, R. J., et al. (2011). Concerns with early universal iron supplementation of breastfeeding infants. *Pediatrics, 127*, e1097.

156. Schmutz, N., et al. (2008). Expected ranges for blood neutrophil concentrations of neonates: the Manroe and Mouzinho charts revisited. *J Perinatol, 28*, 275.

157. Scholl, T. O. (2011). Maternal iron status: relation to fetal growth, length of gestation, and iron endowment of the neonate. *Nutr Rev, 69*, S23.

158. Sehgal, A., & Francis, J. V. (2011). Hemodynamic alterations associated with polycythemia and partial exchange transfusion. *J Perinatol, 31*, 143.

159. Siddappa, A. M., et al. (2007). The assessment of newborn iron stores at birth: A review of the literature and standards for ferritin concentrations. *Neonatology, 92*, 73.

160. Simcox, L. E., et al. (2015). Thrombophilia and pregnancy complications. *Int J Mol Sci, 16*, 28418.

161. Siu, A. L., et al. (2015). Screening for iron deficiency anemia and iron supplementation in pregnant women to improve maternal health and birth outcomes: U.S. Preventative Services Task Force Recommendation Statement. *Ann Intern Med, 163*, 529.

162. Sloan, S. R. (2011). Neonatal transfusion review. *Paediatr Anaesth, 21*, 25.

163. Sola, M. C., & Rimsza, L. M. (2002). Mechanisms underlying thrombocytopenia in the neonatal intensive care unit. *Acta Paediatr Suppl, 91*, 66.

164. Sola-Visner, M., & Ramsey, H. (2017). Developmental megakaryocytopoiesis. In R. A. Polin, et al. (Eds.), *Fetal and neonatal physiology* (5th ed.). Philadelphia: Elsevier Saunders.

165. Stephansson, O., et al. (2000). Maternal hemoglobin concentration during pregnancy and risk of stillbirth. *JAMA, 284*, 2611.

166. Stockman, J. A. (1990). Fetal hematology. In R. D. Eden & F. H. Boehm (Eds.), *Assessment and care of the fetus*. Norwalk, CT: Appleton & Lange.

167. Stoltzfus, R. J. (2011). Iron interventions for women and children in low-income countries. *J Nutr, 141,* 756S.

168. Strauss, R. G., et al. (2008). A randomized clinical trial comparing immediate versus delayed clamping of the umbilical cord in preterm infants: Short-term clinical and laboratory endpoints. *Transfusion, 48,* 658.

169. Strauss, R. G. (2010). Anaemia of prematurity: Pathophysiology and treatment. *Blood Rev, 24,* 221.

170. Strauss, R. G., & Widness, J. A. (2010). Is there a role for autologous/placental red blood cell transfusions in the anemia of prematurity? *Transfus Med Rev, 24,* 125.

171. Strunk, T., Hartel, C., & Schultz, C. (2004). Does erythropoietin protect the preterm brain? *Arch Dis Child Fetal Neonatal Ed, 89,* F364.

172. Szecsi, P. B., et al. (2010). Haemostatic reference intervals in pregnancy. *Thromb Haemost, 103,* 718.

173. Thurlbeck, S. M., & McIntosh, N. (1987). Preterm blood counts vary with sampling site. *Arch Dis Child, 62,* 74.

174. Tsatalas, C., et al. (2009). Pregnancy in beta-thalassemia trait carriers: An uneventful journey. *Hematology, 14,* 301.

175. Ultee, C. A., et al. (2008). Delayed cord clamping in preterm infants delivered at 34-36 weeks' gestation: A randomized controlled trial. *Arch Dis Child Fetal Neonatal Ed, 93,* F20.

176. U.S. Preventative Services Task Force. (2009). Folic acid to prevent neural tube defects. http://www.uspreventiveservices-taskforce.org/Page/Document/Update-SummaryFinal/folic-acid-to-prevent-neural-tube-defects-preventive-medication; Accessed 08.06.16.

177. Veldman, A., et al. (2010). Disseminated intravascular coagulation in term and preterm neonates. *Semin Thromb Hemost, 36,* 419.

178. Vichinsky, E. (2010). Complexity of alpha thalassemia: growing health problem with new approaches to screening, diagnosis, and therapy. *Ann N Y Acad Sci, 1202,* 180.

179. Von Kohorn, I., & Ehrenkranz, R. A. (2009). Anemia in the preterm infant: erythropoietin versus erythrocyte transfusion—it's not that simple. *Clin Perinatol, 36,* 111.

180. Walker, I. D. (2003). Venous and arterial thrombosis during pregnancy: Epidemiology. *Semin Vasc Med, 3,* 25.

181. Wang, H., Zhang, L., & Jin, Y. (2015). A meta-analysis of the protective effect of recombinant human erythropoietin (rhEPO) for neurodevelopment in preterm infants. *Cell Biochem Biophys, 71,* 795.

182. Wardrop, C. A., & Holland, B. M. (1995). The roles and vital importance of placental blood to the newborn infant. *J Perinat Med, 23,* 139.

183. Werner, E. J. (1995). Neonatal polycythemia and hyperviscosity. *Clin Perinatol, 23,* 693.

184. Whyte, R. K., et al. PINTOS Study Group. (2009). Neurodevelopmental outcome of extremely low birth weight infants randomly assigned to restrictive or liberal hemoglobin thresholds for blood transfusion. *Pediatrics, 123,* 207.

185. World Health Organization. (2012). *Daily iron and folic acid supplementation in pregnant women.* Geneva: World Health.

186. Wycoff, M. H., et al. (2015). Part 13: Neonatal resuscitation: 2015 American Heart Association Guidelines Update Cardiopulmonary Resuscitation and Emergency Cardiovascular Care. *Circulation, 132,* S543.

187. Xiong, T., et al. (2011). Erythropoietin for neonatal brain injury: Opportunity and challenge. *Int J Dev Neurosci, 29,* 583.

188. Yao, A. C., & Lind J. (1982). *Placental transfusion.* Springfield, IL: Charles C Thomas.

189. Young, G. (2012). Hemostatic disorders of the newborn. In C. A. Gleason & S. Devaskar (Eds.), *Avery's diseases of the newborn* (9th ed.). Philadelphia: Saunders.

190. Young, M. F., et al. (2010). Impact of maternal and neonatal iron status on placental transferrin receptor expression in pregnant adolescents. *Placenta, 31,* 1010.

191. Zhu, C., et al. (2009). Erythropoietin improved neurologic outcomes in newborns with hypoxic-ischemic encephalopathy. *Pediatrics, 124,* e218.

192. Ziegler, E. E., Nelson, S. E., & Jeter, J. M. (2009). Iron status of breastfed infants is improved equally by medicinal iron and iron-fortified cereal. *Am J Clin Nutr, 90,* 76.

193. Ziegler, E. E., Nelson, S. E., & Jeter, J. M. (2009). Iron supplementation of breastfed infants from an early age. *Am J Clin Nutr, 89,* 525.

194. Ziegler, E. E., et al. (2011). Dry cereals fortified with electrolytic iron or ferrous fumarate are equally effective in breast-fed infants. *J Nutr, 141,* 243.

195. Zipursky, A. (1987). Hematology of the newborn infant. In L. Stern & P. Vert (Eds.), *Neonatal medicine.* New York: Masson.

196. Zipursky, A. (1999). Prevention of vitamin K deficiency bleeding in newborns. *Br J Haematol, 104,* 430.

autotransfusion of uteroplacental blood back into maternal circulation, and decreased SVR and vascular capacitance from contraction of the muscular uterus and absence of placental blood flow.[89,145] Mobilization of extracellular fluid improves venous return to the heart and is reflected in an increase in left atrial size at 1 to 3 days.[111] The increased return to the heart contributes to the higher central venous pressure that occurs postpartum. Maternal hypervolemia during pregnancy acts as a protective mechanism for excessive blood loss at delivery (see Chapter 8).

During the first week after delivery, up to 2 L of body fluid is mobilized and excreted. This results in a 3-kg weight loss. Diuresis (to dissipate the increased extracellular fluid) occurs between day 2 and day 5.[135] ANP and BNP increase postpartum, and their diuretic effects help mediate the maternal diuresis.[124] Without the diuresis of mobilized extracellular fluid, increased pulmonary wedge pressures and pulmonary edema can result.[32,89] The latter may be encountered in women with preeclampsia or heart disease who do not undergo normal patterns of diuresis.

Stroke volume and thus cardiac output remain elevated for at least 48 hours after delivery.[135] This increase is probably because of increased venous return with loss of uterine blood flow and mobilization of interstitial fluid .[111,135] Left atrial size increases over the first 1 to 3 days postpartum, probably because of the increased venous return with mobilization of fluid.[111] Cardiac output decreases by 30% by 2 weeks postpartum then gradually decreases to nonpregnant values by 6 to 12 weeks in most women but may last up to 24 weeks in some women.[24,111,135]

Most of the other cardiovascular system changes resolve by 6 to 8 weeks postpartum. Left atrial size and heart rate reach prepregnancy values by 10 days postpartum and LV size by 4 to 6 months.[111] However, in some women, stroke volume, cardiac output, end-diastolic volume, and SVR may remain elevated for up to 12 to 24 weeks or longer.[111,135] SVR and aortic enlargement reach prepregnant levels by around 16 weeks.[96,145,168] LV wall muscle mass gradually decreases over the first 6 months postpartum.[66] The audible vibrations caused by ejection of blood from the RV into the pulmonary trunk or from the LV into the brachiocephalic arteries at the point of branching from the aortic arch usually disappear by postpartum day 8. For approximately 20% of women, the systolic murmur persists beyond 4 weeks postpartum. The intensity of the murmur does, however, decrease by day 8, even if it does not disappear.[125,135]

CLINICAL IMPLICATIONS FOR THE PREGNANT WOMAN AND HER FETUS

The effects of pregnancy on the cardiovascular system can influence the ability of the woman to carry on the activities of daily living, exercise, or be comfortable in various positions. Because the maternal circulatory system is the lifeline for the fetus to receive oxygen and nutrients, hemodynamic alterations can affect the well-being of the fetus. Some of the changes experienced are exaggerations of normal and have little effect on the fetus; however, disease states may result in significant growth alterations or potentiate hypoxic episodes.

Arrhythmias

Many pregnant women experience rhythm disruptions that become more intense during the second and third trimesters.[40,52,86] Most of these arrhythmias are benign and are not indicative of heart disease. The most common (seen in 50% to 60%) are simple ventricular or atrial ectopy.[40] The woman may describe skipped beats, momentary pressure in the neck or chest, or extra beats. These are usually representative of premature ventricular contractions and require no further treatment. Extra systoles or supraventricular tachycardia may also occur in some women.[18] The reason for the increase in arrhythmias may be related to the electrophysiologic effects of hormones, increased sympathetic nervous system activity, hemodynamic alterations, increased potassium, or in some cases, underlying cardiac disease.[52] In addition, atrial stretching (from changes in cardiac output, plasma volume, and heart wall tension) and estrogen may lower the threshold for arrhythmias.[66,86] Most arrhythmias are neither life-threatening nor a result of structural defects.[27]

Occasionally cardiac problems may present during pregnancy, so arrhythmias should be evaluated and managed in a manner similar to that in nonpregnant women. Hemodynamically significant arrhythmias can result in increased catecholamine levels and volume shifts and may reduce uteroplacental blood flow.[86] Awareness of the increased heart rate can be uncomfortable for some women. True tachycardia, such as paroxysmal atrial tachycardia or paroxysmal atrial fibrillation, may be evident for the first time during pregnancy. This may be frightening for the woman. Taking a deep breath, coughing, or the Valsalva maneuver may result in a slowing or conversion of the heart rate into a more normal pattern.

Supine Hypotension

Orthostatic stress generated by changes in position (from recumbent to sitting to standing) is associated with acute hemodynamic changes. Blood pools in dependent vessels, which reduces venous return and decreases cardiac output and blood pressure with increasing orthostatic stress. Heart rate and SVR increase; mean arterial pressure changes, however, are usually not significant. Decreased baroreflex sensitivity during pregnancy leads to blunted reflex activation of the sympathetic nervous system and inadequate peripheral vasoconstriction.[22]

The gravid uterus is also associated with a significant amount of vena cava blood flow obstruction in the supine position. Approximately 90% of gravid women experience obstruction of the inferior vena cava in the supine position in late pregnancy, but rarely does this lead to hypotension or other symptoms. Late in pregnancy, but before the fetal presenting part becomes engaged, the uterus is mobile enough to fall back against the inferior vena cava in the supine

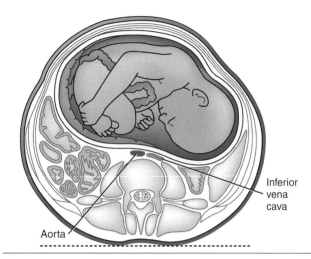

FIGURE 9-6   The pregnant uterus compressing the aorta and the inferior vena cava (aortocaval compression) with the patient in the supine position. (From Cohen, W.R., Acker, D.B., & Friedman, E.A. [Eds.]. [1989]. *Management of labor* [2nd ed.]. Rockville, MD: Aspen.)

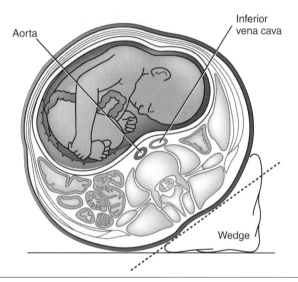

FIGURE 9-7   Uterine displacement with a wedge under the hip to relieve aortocaval compression. (From Cohen, W.R., Acker, D.B., & Friedman, E.A. [Eds.]. [1989]. *Management of labor* [2nd ed.]. Rockville, MD: Aspen.)

position (Figure 9-6). This results in vena cava tamponade. Vascular compression may also be applied to the aorta and its branches. In most women, paravertebral collateral circulation develops during pregnancy. This, along with the dilated uteroovarian circulation, permits blood flow from the legs and pelvis to bypass the vena cava.[89,124] These changes are reversed in the left lateral position (Figure 9-7), which displaces the uterus to the left and off the vena cava. In the supine position the aorta may also be compressed (see Figure 9-6), which can also alter arterial blood pressure.[32]

Usually the fall in cardiac output from a posture change is compensated for by an increase in systemic peripheral resistance. This allows systemic blood pressure and heart rate to remain unchanged.[164] However, up to 8% of pregnant women

may experience a significant decrease in heart rate and blood pressure in the supine position, leading to symptoms of weakness, lightheadedness, nausea, dizziness, or syncope.[111] This is referred to as *supine hypotensive syndrome of pregnancy* and is usually corrected when position is changed.[32,111] These women may be more vulnerable because of inadequate paravertebral collateral blood supply.[111]

Exercise During Pregnancy: Cardiovascular Effects

Exercise has significant benefits for the mother and fetus. Regular aerobic exercise done two to three times per week maintains or improves maternal fitness during pregnancy. Fit women have been shown to have shorter labors and fewer perinatal complications.[5,54,136] Despite the many benefits of and recommendations for physical activity during pregnancy, pregnant women tend to be sedentary for about 60% of the day.[35] Concerns regarding exercise during pregnancy include the effects on the fetus and mother, including the risks of hyperthermia (see Chapter 20) and increased cardiac workload. These concerns, however, have not been substantiated for women with uncomplicated pregnancies or for most women with certain common pregnancy complications.[5]

Physiologic Responses to Exercise During Pregnancy

Physiologic responses to exercise include increased oxygen consumption, redistribution of blood, altered venous pooling, and changes in cardiac output and stroke volume. With submaximal exercise, minute ventilation, cardiac output, and heart rate are greater in pregnant versus nonpregnant women.[62,105,123] Both aerobic exercise and resistance training increase cardiac output, stroke volume, and heart rate with minimal changes on blood pressure.[162] Aerobic capacity is similar in pregnant and nonpregnant women, although the amount of work that can be done is somewhat reduced during pregnancy.[35] Both exercise and pregnancy increase oxygen consumption and the need for energy substrate by different tissues. Respiratory system responses to exercise during pregnancy are discussed in Chapter 10.

Blood flow is redistributed during exercise, moving blood away from the viscera, uterus, and ovaries to the skin and skeletal muscles.[28,170] Greater intensity and duration of exercise is associated with increased redistribution of blood to the skin and muscles.[59] The limitation in substrate delivery to the fetus could potentially have adverse effects resulting in fetal hypoxia; however, to cause such changes, the reduction in uterine blood flow has to exceed 50%. In healthy pregnant women, these occurrences would be rare, more likely during strenuous, prolonged exercise.[29,109] Therefore under normal conditions enough oxygen is available to the uterus to meet uterine and fetal demands.[35] Compensatory mechanisms help maintain oxygen availability during maternal exercise; blood flow is selectively distributed to the placenta at the expense of the myometrium.[19,59] Thus the decrease in placental blood flow is significantly less than the decrease in uterine blood flow.[59]

Maternal hematocrit rises during exercise. This increases maternal oxygen-carrying capacity. Uterine oxygen uptake increases during exercise to maintain a stable oxygen consumption level.[59] Maternal ventricular performance is maintained with exercise. In response to strenuous exercise in early pregnancy, the LV adapts by increasing its contractile reserve; in late pregnancy, the LV adapts by increasing preload reserve.[19]

Along with the redistribution of weight that occurs with the anterior displacement of the uterus, the progressive enlargement of the fetus and uterus can lead to alterations in venous blood return. The woman may experience dizziness because of poor venous return and resultant orthostatic hypotension. Altered cardiac return may modify blood flow to the uterus and place the fetus at risk for hypoxia. Therefore certain positions and activities may need to be modified in exercise regimens.

Pregnancy increases the workload of the heart, although in most pregnancies the cardiac reserve is adequate to meet these demands. The maximal cardiac output is achieved at a lower level of work in pregnant women because the resting cardiac output is higher.[102,145] During early pregnancy, exercise is associated with further increases in stroke volume and cardiac output.[62] As pregnancy progresses, the cardiac output changes less with exercise.[102,123] These changes in later pregnancy may be a result of increased peripheral pooling rather than a progressive decline in circulatory reserve as pregnancy progresses. Decreased exercise tolerance with fatigue and dyspnea is also noted in later pregnancy. Maternal exercise is also associated with a significant increase in circulating catecholamines. Under normal circumstances, the placenta is very efficient in metabolizing catecholamines, and only 10% to 15% reach the fetus.[109,123]

The usual fetal response to maternal exercise is an increase in heart rate by 10 to 30 beats per minute.[5] This increase may be a result of decreased placental blood flow, stimulation of maternal vasoactive hormones, or exercise-induced uterine contractions.[54,136] These changes are independent of gestational age and intensity of maternal exercise. Immediately after exercise and during the next 5 minutes, the fetal heart rate (FHR) remains elevated regardless of the type of exercise. Within 15 minutes, the FHR drops to preexercise values in women engaged in mild to moderate exercise activities. For women engaged in strenuous activities, the FHR may not return to baseline for up to 30 minutes.[54,109,136] In some women, transient fetal bradycardia (usually mild at 100 to 119 beats per minute) has been reported after maximal exercise (heart rate greater than 180 beats per minute), possibly because of a rapid increase in catecholamines.[148] These episodes of bradycardia did not compromise fetal outcome.[79,109]

Benefits and Recommendations

Regular exercise during pregnancy has many maternal benefits, including maintenance of fitness; improved cardiovascular function; control of blood pressure; improved metabolic efficiency; decreased backaches, fatigue, and shortness of breath; shorter labors; decreased clot formation and varicosities; feelings of wellness; prevention of excessive weight gain and fat deposition; decreased leg cramps; decreased leg edema; and more rapid postpartum recovery.[5,27-29,54,59,102-105,113,136,157,162] Women with conditioning before pregnancy demonstrate improved metabolic effects with exercise during pregnancy compared with unconditioned women.[28] Maternal risks of exercise include musculoskeletal injury, risk of cardiovascular complications, hypoglycemia, and uterine contractions.[59,105] The most common maternal risk is musculoskeletal because of lower extremity edema, joint laxity, and other musculoskeletal changes seen during pregnancy (see Chapter 15).[5] If the woman continues resistance training, she should avoid supine exercises because of concerns about vena cava compression.[130]

Fetal benefits may include better growth, improved stress tolerance, maturation of autonomic control, and enhanced neurobehavioral maturation, with a leaner body composition at 5 years of age.[29,30,105,162] "The fetus responds to, but is not distressed from, maternal aerobic exercise."[162] Mild to moderate aerobic exercise (to 50% to 85% of maximum) has not been demonstrated to increase spontaneous abortions but does decrease length of labor, number of cesarean births, fetal fat mass (and thus mean birth weight), and number of episodes of fetal distress.[5,28,54,170] No significant effects between maternal exercise and birth weight have been found in metaanalyses.[5] Women who exercised vigorously during the last trimester had infants with birth weights 200 g to 400 g lower, but no increase in fetal growth restriction.[5] There are fewer studies examining fetal response to resistance and circuit (combination of aerobic and resistance) training, but adverse pregnancy outcomes have not been reported.[162] Thirty minutes of strenuous exercise (in the second trimester) has been reported to be well tolerated by mothers and fetuses.[158]

The American College of Obstetricians and Gynecologists (ACOG) recommends as a goal "moderate-intensity exercise for at least 20 to 30 minutes per day on most or all days of the week" with adjustments as medically indicated.[5] An exercise program developed during pregnancy should be continued postpartum.[5] Sedentary women are encouraged to begin an exercise program in consultation with their health care provider. Individualized programs can also be developed for women with obstetric or medical comorbidities after medical consultation and evaluation.[5] Suggested activities during pregnancy include swimming, biking, aerobic walking, stretching, and normal walking. Weight-bearing exercises increase energy expenditure during pregnancy, whereas weight-supported exercises (biking, swimming) do not.[123] Swimming and aquatic exercises have particular benefits during pregnancy. Heart rate and vital capacity changes are reduced and stroke volume is increased during exercise in water.[79] Hydrostatic pressure moves extravascular fluid back into the vascular space, reducing fluid retention and enhancing diuresis.[59] The water reduces thermal changes with exercise by acting as a thermoregulatory buffer around the woman.[59]

In general, aerobic exercise, resistance training, and circuit training have all been found to be beneficial for pregnant women.[102] Prenatal yoga has been found to decrease anxiety, reduce back pain, reduce sleep disturbances, and possibly improve fetal growth and stress responses.[11] Vigorous exercise should not be performed in hot, humid weather or during a period of febrile illness, and body temperature should never exceed 40° C (104° F) (see Chapter 20).[5] Because of these concerns, hot yoga is not recommended.[5] Pregnant women should avoid sports with a high risk of blunt abdominal trauma, such as contact sports, those with a high risk of falling, scuba diving, and sky diving.[5,19]

Studies on elite athletes with high-intensity exercise during pregnancy are limited, although data support the safety of training during pregnancy.[5,19,130] ACOG recommends these athletes be closely monitored, "avoiding hyperthermia, maintaining proper hydration, and sustaining adequate caloric intake to prevent weight loss, which may adversely affect fetal growth."[5] Recommendations are being developed by an International Olympic Committee consensus group for recreational and elite athletes involved in strenuous exercise.[19]

At no time should exercise be continued if pain or contractions are experienced. The primary health care provider should be contacted if bleeding, dizziness, shortness of breath, palpitations, faintness, tachycardia, back pain, pubic pain, or difficulty in walking is experienced. Women designated as high risk for preterm labor need to receive special counseling regarding not only appropriate activity levels but also signs and symptoms of labor.[5] Exercise programs for women at risk for gestational diabetes mellitus or preeclampsia have been shown to be a useful adjunct therapy and may also decrease the risk of developing these disorders.[5,10,142,144]

Multiple Pregnancy

A woman with a multiple pregnancy is subject to a higher risk of morbidity and mortality. The increased production of estriol, progesterone, and human chorionic somatomammotropin in these women results in greater volume expansion and weight gain. Whereas plasma volume is increased by about 50% in single pregnancies, in twins there is an increase of up to 65%, with further elevations seen in women with higher order multiples.[111] There is also a higher RBC volume, increased hemodilution of iron and folate, and an exaggerated physiologic anemia. The hemodilution may be caused by a greater increase in total body volume or a greater demand for iron or folic acid.[125]

The increase in maternal cardiac output, stroke volume, and heart rate is also greater in multiple pregnancies than that found in singletons.[98,145] The change in cardiac output suggests decreased cardiovascular reserve. Characteristic changes in blood pressure with a multiple pregnancy include a lowered diastolic pressure at 20 weeks, followed by a greater rise in diastolic pressure between midpregnancy and delivery.[98,125]

Mothers with multiple pregnancies are at greater risk for preterm labor, preeclampsia, placenta previa, placental abruption, anemia, hyperemesis gravidarum, and postpartum hemorrhage. The length of labor is similar in twin and singleton pregnancies, although with twins the active phase is longer and the latent phase is shorter. Labor may be more difficult, possibly because of uterine overdistention and an increased incidence of malpresentation. Blood loss is greater than that in a single delivery, and hemorrhage is more common because of uterine atony and sudden decompression of the overdistended uterus. There is also a slightly higher incidence of vasa previa and placenta previa, increasing the possibility of hemorrhage at delivery. The risk of preeclampsia is greater in twin than in singleton pregnancies, possibly related to the larger placental mass found with twin pregnancies.[125]

Cardiac Disease and Pregnancy

Cardiac disease affects about 1% (range 0.1% to 4%) of pregnant women and accounts for 15% of pregnancy-related maternal morbidity.[27,48,171] The incidence of pregnant women with cardiac disease is slowly increasing as improved management and technical capabilities for both the mother and fetus make it possible to sustain pregnancy in those who previously would have been advised to terminate or avoid pregnancy.[38] Corrective surgery for infants and children with congenital heart disease has increased the number of these women who are now of childbearing age. In addition, the incidence of heart disease increases in women who wait until their 40s or later to have children. However, congenital lesions are more common in pregnant women than adult-onset cardiac abnormalities.[38] Adult-onset cardiac problems may be the result of ischemic heart disease, cardiomyopathies (including peripartum cardiomyopathy), coronary artery disease, aortic dissection, or valvular disease.[38]

The profound alterations in the cardiorespiratory system and hemodynamics during pregnancy can result in death or disability to women who have underlying heart disease. Many early symptoms of cardiac disease, such as fatigue, dyspnea on exertion, dependent edema, presyncope (caused by pressure on the inferior vena cava), and palpitations are normal findings in pregnancy.[18,48] Thus the diagnosis of cardiac disease may be delayed in women who present with symptoms of cardiac disorders for the first time during pregnancy.

Women with cardiac diseases associated with fixed lesions often do not tolerate the volume increase because the stenotic area cannot accommodate the increased flow. When blood volume reaches its peak, the potential for congestive heart failure (CHF) increases. The increased heart rate shortens the diastolic filling time, thereby preventing adequate filling of the heart. This combined with the decrease in SVR may result in a drop in blood pressure, increased fatigue, dizziness, and reduced uterine blood flow.

At delivery the risk for CHF is further increased by the increase in blood volume. Acute pulmonary edema may occur. Applying pressure to the abdomen can slow the blood return to the heart and facilitate cardiovascular stabilization.

If the heart is unable to compensate for the decrease in SVR, the blood pressure falls. Maintenance of blood pressure can be attempted by administration of chronotropic and alpha pressor agents. Epidural and spinal anesthesia may further decrease SVR and should be used with caution in these patients. The increased cardiac load with the marked increase in cardiac output immediately after delivery may significantly increase ventricular filling pressures and stroke volume, increasing the risk of clinical deterioration.[33,171]

Pregnancy is particularly dangerous and may be contraindicated for women who have Eisenmenger syndrome, peripartum cardiomyopathy, severe primary pulmonary hypertension, aortic stenosis, coarctation of the aorta, Marfan syndrome, and hemodynamically significant mitral stenosis (Table 9-3).[18] The presence of a cardiac lesion involving pulmonary hypertension during pregnancy carries a risk of maternal mortality somewhere between 30% and 50%. Pregnancy may also aggravate preexisting cardiac conditions such that damage is extensive and recovery to prepregnancy levels is not possible. In addition, pregnancy may result in maternal heart disease (e.g., peripartum cardiomyopathy).[18,27,33,65]

The fetus must be monitored closely during pregnancy in a woman with cardiac disease. Fetal well-being and growth are dependent on a continuous flow of well-oxygenated blood to the uterus. When this supply is reduced or interrupted or oxygenation is decreased, the fetus is at risk for altered growth and development and for increased mortality.[33] In addition, the fetus is at increased risk (3% to 12% depending on the defect versus 0.8% in the general population) of being born with a congenital heart defect if either parent has congenital heart disease, because this can be a multifactorial disorder (see Chapter 1).[33] If the mother is the affected parent, she adds an environmental risk (altered hemodynamics during pregnancy) as well as a genetic risk for her infant.

All of these factors and the risk to the mother and fetus should be discussed in depth with couples before pregnancy. Preconception counseling allows the risks to the mother and fetus, effects of pregnancy on the mother's condition, potential problems and treatment options to be explored, and the woman's current health status to be evaluated.[171] Surgical correction or palliative procedures are generally recommended to be done before pregnancy, followed by several months to a year of recovery time.[18]

Obstructive Lesions

Obstructive lesions are basically stenotic in nature. The main concern is an obstruction of flow causing an elevation of pressure proximal to the obstructive lesion and a decrease in flow distal to the stenotic area. Pulmonary stenosis without septal defect, coarctation of the aorta, aortic stenosis, mitral stenosis, and tricuspid stenosis are included in this group. Mitral valve stenosis, regurgitation, and prolapse are presented as examples.

Mitral Stenosis. Mitral stenosis is caused almost exclusively by rheumatic heart disease and, although not common in North America, is an issue in many parts of the world.[48] The stenotic valve restricts cardiac output, resulting in fatigue, which is the most common symptom. The obstruction of left atrial outflow leads to pressure elevations in the left atrium, pulmonary veins, and pulmonary capillaries, causing severe pulmonary congestion. Risk of death is greatest in the third trimester and postpartum.[18] About one fourth of women experience their first symptoms with pregnancy.[27]

The increased blood volume, cardiac output, and heart rate of pregnancy, along with the fluid retention, may lead to an increase in symptoms, especially after 20 weeks.[27] Signs of pulmonary congestion usually occur by 20 to 24 weeks, because intravascular volumes begin to peak and stabilize around 30 weeks.[48] The increase in cardiac output, plasma volume, and heart rate peak by this time, decrease diastolic filling time in the LV, and increase the pressure gradient across the mitral valve.[27] An exacerbation may occur at the time of delivery in response to increased pulmonary wedge pressure if there is prolonged tachycardia. The first 24 hours after delivery is a time of increased vulnerability in these women because of intravascular fluid shifts.[27] The risk of maternal and neonatal complications is higher in women with abnormal functional capacity, cyanosis, or left-sided valve obstruction and is increased with maternal smoking, maternal age younger than 20 years or older than 35 years, multiple pregnancy, and anticoagulant therapy.[27,48] The supine position should be avoided. If severe mitral stenosis is diagnosed, mitral commissurotomy is advised before conception.[18]

Mitral Regurgitation. Mitral regurgitation may result from rheumatic heart disease; however, there are numerous other conditions that can lead to its development, including congenital heart disease, hypertension, ischemia, and idiopathic myocardial disease.[18] Prolapse of the mitral valve during systole allows for regurgitation of blood back into the left atrium. Fatigue results. If it is severe, pulmonary congestion can occur. These women have a propensity for atrial fibrillation and left atrial thrombus formation. Individuals with mitral regurgitation may be asymptomatic for extended periods of time. Pregnancy is usually well tolerated by women with mild regurgitation, and the development of CHF is rare.

Mitral Valve Prolapse. Mitral valve prolapse (MVP) is one of the most common congenital heart lesions. Most women

TABLE 9-3 High-Risk Maternal Cardiovascular Conditions

DISORDER	ESTIMATED MATERNAL MORTALITY RATE (%)
Aortic valve stenosis	10–20
Coarctation of the aorta	5
Marfan syndrome	10–20
Peripartum cardiomyopathy	15–60
Severe pulmonary hypertension	50
Tetralogy of Fallot	10

From Blanchard, D.G. & Daniels, L.B. (2014). Cardiac disease. In R.K. Creasy, R. Resnik, J.D. Iams, C.J. Lockwood, T.R. Moore, & M.F. Greene. (Eds.). *Creasy & Resnik's maternal-fetal medicine: Principles and practice* (7th ed.). Philadelphia: Saunders, p. 854.

with MVP are asymptomatic and tolerate pregnancy well; in fact, there is evidence that pregnancy may actually improve hemodynamics and symptoms in some women. Although rare, complications associated with MVP (arrhythmias, infective endocarditis, and cerebral ischemic events) may result in serious complications during pregnancy. MVP can be both a primary disease lesion and a secondary pathology associated with connective tissue diseases or cardiac disease that reduces the size of the LV. The latter includes syndromes such as Marfan syndrome, pseudoxanthoma elasticum, and osteogenesis imperfecta.

The hemodynamic changes of pregnancy can reduce the clinical signs of MVP by decreasing audible murmurs (usually a late systolic murmur associated with a click), possibly by increasing the LV end-diastolic volume and favorably realigning the mitral valve complex. The decrease in peripheral vascular resistance relieves the mitral insufficiency, thereby reducing the murmur. Once these parameters return to normal in the postpartum period, the auscultatory findings of MVP return. These changes are also reflected on echocardiography. In most situations, pregnancy is tolerated well in women with MVP, especially if there is no mitral valve regurgitation, with good maternal and fetal outcomes.[48] The woman may experience an increase in palpitations, lightheadedness, dizziness, fainting with prolonged standing, arrhythmias, or chest pains that may require medical intervention.[18]

Left-to-Right Shunts

Left-to-right shunts are characterized by recirculation of oxygenated blood through the lungs, bypassing the peripheral circulation. This can occur through an atrial septal defect (ASD), ventricular septal defect (VSD), or a patent ductus arteriosus (PDA). In most patients born with these defects, the defect has either closed on its own during childhood or corrective surgery has been performed to reduce the defect. A residual defect may remain, however.

The magnitude of the left-to-right shunt is dependent on the ratio of resistance in the systemic and pulmonary vascular circuits. During pregnancy, both circuits have a decline in resistance (see Table 9-1), so there is usually no significant change if shunting occurs. If pulmonary vascular disease exists, the normal fall in pulmonary vascular resistance (PVR) may not occur. Cyanosis rarely occurs with these defects unless significant pulmonary hypertension or RV failure develops. Pregnancy does not seem to precipitate these events, however.

Atrial Septal Defect. An uncorrected ASD is usually asymptomatic but may become symptomatic for the first time in pregnancy.[18,27] The most common complications are arrhythmias, pulmonary hypertension, and heart failure. The hypervolemia of pregnancy increases the left-to-right shunt through the ASD, thereby creating an additional burden on the RV. This additional load is usually tolerated well by most women, although up to 15% fetal loss has been reported.[27] If the additional load is not well tolerated, which usually occurs

if the woman has pulmonary hypertension, chronic atrial fibrillation, or RV dysfunction, RV failure occurs, leading to marked peripheral edema, atrial arrhythmias, pulmonary hypertension, and paradoxical systemic emboli across the septal defect.[18,33]

Ventricular Septal Defect. A VSD can occur either as an isolated lesion or in conjunction with other congenital cardiac anomalies (such as tetralogy of Fallot [TOF], transposition of the great vessels, or coarctation of the aorta). Most VSDs have closed or been repaired before pregnancy. The size of the defect determines the degree of shunting, tolerance to the additional burden of pregnancy, and prognosis.[48] Small defects are usually tolerated well.[18,27] Large VSDs often lead to CHF, arrhythmias, or development of pulmonary hypertension or Eisenmenger syndrome with increased maternal and fetal mortality.[18,27] These women are often counseled to avoid becoming pregnant.[18] A large VSD is often associated with some degree of aortic regurgitation, which contributes to the risk of CHF during pregnancy.

Right-to-Left Shunts

Right-to-left shunts are characterized by shunting of blood from the systemic venous circulation to the arterial circulation without oxygenation. Right-to-left shunting occurs through an ASD, VSD, or PDA when the PVR rises so that it exceeds the SVR or when an obstruction to RV outflow exists. These women present with cyanosis, clubbing of the fingers, and RV hypertrophy. Conditions include Eisenmenger syndrome, TOF, and primary pulmonary hypertension.

Eisenmenger Syndrome. Eisenmenger syndrome combines the presence of a congenital communication between systemic and pulmonary circulations with progressive pulmonary hypertension that leads to shunt reversal or bidirectional flow. It is often associated with VSD or PDA. During pregnancy the increased plasma volume increases the burden on the compromised heart.[18] The decreased SVR increases the degree of right-to-left shunting, which reduces pulmonary perfusion, leading to hypoxemia and maternal and fetal compromise.[18,33,48,58] Systemic hypotension leads to decreased RV filling pressures, which may be insufficient to perfuse the pulmonary bed, when high PVR exists. The result may be the onset of sudden and profound hypoxemia. Hemorrhage or complications of conduction anesthesia (hypovolemia) may precipitate hypoxemia and lead to death during the intrapartum period.[18,48]

The fetal and maternal mortality rate for pregnant women with Eisenmenger syndrome can be 30% and up to 50% when pulmonary hypertension is associated with a VSD.[27,171] Death is usually from right ventricular failure with cardiogenic shock.[27] Maternal mortality is greatest during parturition and early postpartum.[18,170] Because of the high mortality rate, women are usually discouraged from becoming pregnant, and pregnancy termination is usually recommended. If gestation continues, hospitalization, continuous oxygen administration, and the use of pulmonary vasodilators are recommended. During labor it is essential to maintain an adequate fluid load to maintain venous return and right ventricular filling.[27] However, maintaining a preload edge to protect against unexpected blood loss may risk tipping the scales toward pulmonary edema. Only about one-fourth of pregnancies in women with this disorder continue to term, and approximately one-third of the infants are growth restricted.[170]

Tetralogy of Fallot. TOF is the most common cause of right-to-left shunting. TOF includes a combination of VSD, pulmonary valve stenosis, RV hypertrophy, and rightward displacement of the aortic root. PVR is normal. Surgical correction usually occurs during infancy, although there may be residual shunting after correction. Pregnancy outcome is relatively good for those individuals who have undergone surgical correction who have good ventricular function and no significant right ventricular outflow tract obstruction.[18,58,161] Women with right ventricular dysfunction, significant pulmonary hypertension, and hypoxemia are at increased risk of cardiac complications with pregnancy.[48] In pregnant women with uncorrected VSDs, the decrease in systemic vascular resistance (SVR) leads to increases in right-to-left shunting and cyanosis.[27] This can be complicated by intrapartum blood loss, leading to systemic hypotension. Therefore careful monitoring of fluid status is warranted.[18]

Pulmonary Artery Hypertension. Severe pulmonary hypertension associated with pregnancy carries a 30% to 50% maternal mortality rate and up to 40% fetal mortality rate if the mother survives.[48] Deterioration of cardiac function with right heart failure usually begins in the second trimester.[33] Significant pulmonary hypertension is a contraindication to pregnancy, and pregnancy should be prevented or termination recommended if it occurs. If termination is not possible, physical activity should be curtailed and supine positioning avoided during late gestation. Careful monitoring of oxygenation and fluid status at the time of labor and delivery is essential to identify problems early and intervene appropriately.[27,38]

Marfan Syndrome

Marfan syndrome is an autosomal dominant disorder of connective tissue whose clinical manifestations include skeletal, ocular, and cardiovascular abnormalities. Aortic dilation is one of these manifestations. Complications that can result include aneurysm formation and rupture, aortic dissection, and aortic regurgitation. Structural changes in the aortic wall because of high estrogen levels predispose pregnant women with Marfan syndrome to aortic dissection.[166,168] Rupture is more likely to occur in the third trimester or in the first stage of labor.[18,161] Counseling regarding the risk of inheritance and the potential maternal complications should be given before conception if possible. If pregnancy occurs, the use of long-acting β-blockers to decrease pulsatile pressure on the aortic wall is indicated, along with limitations on physical activity and preventing hypertensive complications.[18] Women with Marfan syndrome are also at increased risk of fetal complications including fetal growth restriction, small-for-gestational-age infants, miscarriage, and premature rupture of the membranes.[166,168]

Peripartum Cardiomyopathy

Peripartum cardiomyopathy is a form of dilated cardiomyopathy seen in women without a previous history of heart disease that develops during the last month of pregnancy or up to 5 months postpartum; it is seen most often in the first 2 months postpartum.[18,33,38,48] In dilated cardiomyopathy the cardiac chambers become significantly dilated with a hypokinetic LV and progressive decrease in LV function. Peripartum cardiomyopathy has a frequency of 1 in 3000 to 1 in 4000 live births, with recurrence risk in subsequent pregnancies of up to 50%.[18,33,48] This disorder has a variable and unpredictable clinical course. Generally 30% to 50% of women demonstrate partial recovery with persistence of some cardiac dysfunction; 20% develop deteriorating cardiac function to the point of needing a heart transplant.[18,93] In women with partial recovery, cardiac function may improve over time.[18,93] The cause of peripartum cardiomyopathy is unknown. It is not clear whether the pregnancy and postpartum state causes the disorder or aggravates an underlying cardiomyopathy process.[18,33,65] The risk of developing peripartum cardiomyopathy is higher with increased maternal age, chronic hypertension, multiple gestation, multiparity, and preeclampisa.[33,38,65]

Hypertensive Disorders

Hypertensive disorders are one of the most common complications of pregnancy and a leading cause of maternal mortality.[92] Hypertension during pregnancy is classified as (1) chronic hypertension, (2) preeclampsia, (3) preeclampsia superimposed on chronic hypertension, and (4) gestational hypertension.[117] Definitions of these disorders have been recently updated by several groups to reduce reliance on proteinuria as a diagnostic criteria, and to further describe different subtypes (including criteria for severe preeclampsia) based on current research and practice.[4,78,162]

Chronic hypertension is hypertension that is present before pregnancy or that is diagnosed before 20 weeks' gestation.[4,158] Maternal–fetal complications of chronic hypertension include superimposed preeclampsia, abruptio placentae, stroke, preterm delivery, stillbirth, low birth weight, and neonatal loss. Perinatal mortality is two to four times higher.[69,100] Nonpregnant women with chronic hypertension generally have decreased renal plasma flow (RPF) and GFR, with an exaggerated excretion of sodium in response to a salt load. During early pregnancy, RPF and GFR increase, but the total increase by late pregnancy is less than in normotensive pregnant women. With increased blood pressure, fluid moves from the vascular to the extravascular spaces, and the blood becomes hemoconcentrated with further reductions in RPF and GFR. Vasoconstriction may reduce uteroplacental perfusion, with alterations in fetal growth.[69,100]

Preeclampsia

Preeclampsia is a hypertensive, multisystem disorder characterized by hypertension with or without proteinuria.[69,110] Preeclampsia is defined as blood pressure of 140 mm Hg

(18.62 kPa) or more systolic or 90 mm Hg (11.97 kPa) or more diastolic after 20 weeks' gestation in a woman who was normotensive before 20 weeks' gestation or 160 mm (21.33 kPa) or more systolic or 105 mm Hg (13.99 kPa) or more diastolic within a short renal interval.[4,78,133,162] In addition, the blood pressure changes are accompanied by evidence of proteinuria or, if proteinuria is absent, onset of one of the following severe features: thrombocytopenia, renal insufficiency, impaired liver function, pulmonary edema, or cerebral or visual symptoms.[4,133] The revised classification subdivides preeclampsia into presentations with and without severe features.[4] Increases in preeclampsia incidence in recent years are believed to be related to the increased prevalence of hypertension, diabetes, and obesity; increasing maternal age; and increased multiple gestations with assisted reproductive technologies.[69] Changes in different organ systems that result from preeclampsia are summarized in Table 9-4.

Preeclampsia is a progressive disorder, progressing at different rates in individual women.[4] Women with preeclampsia may develop seizures (eclampsia) or a variant with abnormal liver function and thrombocytopenia known as *HELLP syndrome*. The term *HELLP* comes from this syndrome's characteristic clinical findings: hemolysis (H), elevated liver enzymes (EL), and a low platelet (LP) count. This syndrome occurs in 0.5% to 0.9% of all pregnancies and in 10% to 20% of women with severe preeclampsia.[81] The recurrence risk for preeclampsia in subsequent pregnancies is 7% to 29%.[69] Low-dose aspirin therapy has been used in at-risk women to reduce the incidence of preeclampsia.[63] Women with preeclampsia are at increased risk of later cardiovascular disease and stroke.[69,78,149] The risk is increased twofold in all women with preeclampsia and eightfold to ninefold in those who deliver before 34 weeks' gestation.[78]

"Placental and maternal factors interact to develop preeclampsia. Originating in the placenta as a result of decreased trophoblast invasion, ischemia leads to oxidative stress and a continuum of events which adversely affect the maternal vasculature leading to hypertension and proteinuria."[115,p. 380] Preeclampsia is characterized by increased SVR; enhanced platelet aggregation; activation of the coagulation system; endothelial cell dysfunction; pathologic changes and decreased perfusion to most organ systems, especially the liver, kidney, brain, and placenta, secondary to vasoconstriction; increased sensitivity to pressors, including

TABLE 9-4   Findings and Clinical Manifestations of Preeclampsia

SYSTEM	FINDINGS	CLINICAL MANIFESTATIONS
Cardiovascular	Increased cardiac output (CO) and systemic vasoconstriction/vascular resistance	Systemic hypertension
	Increased hydrostasis present	Generalized edema
	High CO and hypertension	Increased hemolysis
	Increased responsiveness to vasopressors/increased angiotensin II sensitivity	Systemic hypertension
Uteroplacental	Uteroplacental insufficiency	Fetal somatic growth deficiency; fetal hypoxemia and distress
	Decidual ischemia	Abruptio placentae; placental infarcts
	Decidual thrombosis	Thrombocytopenia
Renal	Decreased renal blood flow and glomerular filtration rate; endothelial damage	Proteinuria; elevated creatinine and decreased creatinine clearance; oliguria
		Altered handling of protein, calcium, uric acid, sodium
	Altered renin-angiotensin-aldosterone system; increased angiotensin II responsiveness in tubular vasculature	Elevated uric acid
		Sodium retention
	All of the above	Renal tubular necrosis and renal failure
Cerebrovascular	Cerebral motor ischemia	Generalized grand mal seizures (eclampsia)
	High cerebral perfusion pressure with regional edema	Cerebral hemorrhage
		Headaches, seizures
	Cerebral edema	Headaches, seizures, coma
	Regional ischemia	Visual symptoms including risk of central blindness; loss of speech
Hepatic	Ischemic and hepatic cellular injury; vasospasm	Elevated liver enzymes
		Epigastric or right upper quadrant pain
	Mitochondrial injury	Intracellular fatty deposition
Hematologic	Intravascular hemolysis	Elevated free hemoglobin and iron-decreased haptoglobin levels
	Endothelial dysfunction	Risk of coagulation disorders
		Altered sensitivity to angiotensin II
		Altered vascular responses
	Altered coagulation	Coagulation disorders
	Decidual thrombosis, release of fibrin degradation products	Thrombocytopenia; antiplatelet antibodies

Updated from Shah, D.M. (2011). Hypertensive disorder of pregnancy. In R.J. Martin, A.A. Fanaroff, & M.C. Walsh. (Eds.). *Fanaroff and Martin's neonatal-perinatal medicine: Diseases of the fetus and infant* (9th ed.). Philadelphia: Mosby, p. 280.

angiotensin II; and a reduction in the usual increase in plasma volume because of a loss of fluid from the vascular space.[69,70,100,133,152] Factors predisposing to preeclampsia include conditions in which oxygen demand is increased (multiple pregnancy, molar pregnancy, or an edematous placenta) or conditions with decreased oxygen transfer (primipara, microvascular disease, chronic hypertension, diabetes, collagen disorders, or abnormal placentation).[70,100,110,137] The net result of these factors is a direct or relative placental hypoperfusion. Thus altered uteroplacental perfusion is an early event in the pathogenesis of preeclampsia, possibly because of oxidative stress, inflammation, and ischemia-reperfusion.[4] In addition, many of these factors are also associated with increased fetal antigen load (i.e., multiple pregnancy, hydrops, molar pregnancy, or other increased placental mass) or inflammatory response (rheumatoid disease, infection), supporting an immunologic basis for preeclampsia.[110] An immunologic basis is also supported by the greater frequency of classic preeclampsia in first pregnancies with limited exposure of the mother's system to paternal sperm, and thus the paternal antigens expressed on fetal tissues, or in multiparous women with new partners (see Chapter 13).[69,139]

Although the exact pathogenesis of preeclampsia is still unclear, it involves events early in pregnancy followed by maternal multisystem involvement with endothelial dysfunction.[69,134,138] "The insult to the placenta is proposed as an immunologically initiated alteration in trophoblast function, and the reduction in trophoblast invasion leads to failed vascular remodeling of the maternal spiral arteries that perfuse the placenta. The resulting reduced perfusion and increased velocity of blood perfusing the intervillous space alter placental function. The altered placental function leads to maternal disease through putative primary mediators, including oxidative and endoplasmic reticulum stress and inflammation, and secondary mediators that include modifiers of endothelial function and angiogenesis."[4,p. 1131] Factors believed to mediate the pathogenesis of preeclampsia are discussed in this section.

Inadequate remodeling of maternal uterine spiral arteries is an early pathogenic event.[24,36,110,133,137,138,152] Normally extravillous trophoblast cells from the placenta migrate into the uterine spiral arteries in both the decidua and myometrium. These trophoblast cells remodel the maternal spiral arteries so that little vascular smooth muscle tissue, neural elements, and elastic matrix remain.[69] The spiral arteries become large, flaccid uteroplacental vessels establishing a low-resistance circuit that enhances blood supply to the fetus and placenta. This remodeling process is described in Chapter 3 and Figure 3-10. In preeclampsia the remodeling is incomplete and often confined to the decidual portion of the blood vessels, with 30% to 50% of the vessels in the myometrium and their adrenergic nerve supply left intact.[43,95,137] The result is that the spiral arteries remain thick-walled and muscular, leading to inadequate placental flow and thus reduced oxygen delivery to the placenta.

The basis for this defect in preeclampsia is unclear. It may be a primary defect in invasive trophoblast or due to altered endometrial metabolism or expression of vasculogenic or angiogenic factors.[43] Alterations in implantation and remodeling of maternal spiral arteries may be secondary to maternal–fetal immune maladaptation at the maternal–fetal interface (see Chapter 13) because of oxidative stress, endothelial activation, vascular disease, and hypertension in response to placental ischemia.[69,78] This may be a result of genetic factors or maternal disease that alters maternal antioxidant enzymes or increases sensitivity to oxidative stress. A similar lack of spiral artery change is seen without preeclampsia in some forms of fetal growth restriction and in some women with preterm labor.[95]

Oxidative stress secondary to hypoxia (because of altered perfusion) occurs at the maternal–fetal interface. Plasma lipoproteins, nonesterified fatty acids, and low-density lipoproteins are elevated in women with preeclampsia.[36] These provide increased substrate for lipid peroxidation. Decreased placental perfusion may also increase lipid peroxidation with release of oxygen radicals without adequate counteracting antioxidant enzymes.[36] This damages maternal vascular endothelium with activation of neutrophils and macrophages (inflammatory response). Women with preeclampsia have a greater rate of lipid peroxidation, release of reactive oxygen species (free radicals), and lower levels of antioxidants that may contribute to endothelial dysfunction.[69,138]

Release of antiangiogenic factors into maternal circulation by the oxidatively stressed placenta stimulates a generalized systemic inflammatory response leading to further endothelial dysfunction.[134] These antiangiogenic factors include soluble FMS-like tyrosine kinase-1 (s-FLT-1), soluble endoglin (sEng), and syncytiotrophoblast membrane fragments.[115,155] Levels of s-FLT-1, a receptor for vascular endothelial growth factor (VEGF) and sEng, an antiangiogenic factor that inhibits transforming growth factor-β signaling, increase with preeclampsia.[70,115,155] These factors along with others interact with and may damage the maternal vasculature, resulting in an inflammatory response, increased maternal vasculature resistance, and vascular dysfunction.[115] These substances bind VEGF and placental growth factors (PlGF), decreasing free levels of these factors, thus preventing their action on systemic endothelium, leading to endothelial dysfunction.[70,110,115,134,155] Levels of endothelin-1, a potent endothelial-derived vasoconstrictor, and its receptors also increase with preeclampsia.[78]

Thus alterations in implantation and spiral artery remodeling decrease uteroplacental perfusion, placental ischemia, and alterations in maternal vascular endothelium.[100] Placental ischemia stimulates release of cytokines that disrupt endothelial function by inducing structural and functional changes in endothelial cells, enhancing endothelin production and decreasing acetylcholine-induced vasodilation. The endothelium is a single layer of epithelium lining the blood vessels and in direct contact with blood. The endothelium releases factors to maintain vascular tone, enhance permeability, control plasma lipids, inhibit white blood cell adhesion and migration, inhibit platelet activation and aggregation, and inhibit smooth muscle proliferation and migration (to prevent atherosclerotic changes).[1] Normally antithrombic, antiproliferative, vasodilating substances (e.g., nitric oxide, prostacyclin [or PGI_2]) are in a homeostatic balance with vasoconstrictive, prothrombic, proliferative factors (e.g., thromboxane A_2, endothelin, platelet-activating factor, superoxide, angiotensin II).

The balance within the uteroplacental circulation normally favors vasodilation. In women with preeclampsia, this balance is disrupted. Endothelial dysfunction leads to altered control of vascular tone (hypertension), increased glomerular permeability (proteinuria), altered procoagulant/anticoagulant ratio (coagulopathy), endothelial injury, and vasoconstriction (liver dysfunction).[69,100] Markers of endothelial dysfunction found in women with preeclampsia include alteration in the procoagulant/anticoagulant ratio; increased fibronectin; enhanced platelet activation; alterations in vasomediators such as nitric oxide, endothelin, PGs, and cytokines; factor VIII antigen; thrombomodulin; and VEGF.

Substances such as cellular fibronectin, growth factors, vascular cell adhesion molecules, factor VIII, antigen, and other peptides released after endothelial injury are elevated in preeclampsia.[115] The woman with preeclampsia has increased responsiveness to angiotensin II, leading to increased vascular resistance and eventually vasoconstriction, hypoxemia, and cell damage in various organs (see Table 9-4).[69] This leads to further endothelial damage aggravated by oxidative stress.

Genetics plays a role in preeclampsia, but the exact pattern of inheritance is unclear. Preeclampsia is more common in daughters of women who had preeclampsia and in pregnancies fathered by sons of women with preeclampsia.[70,100,138] Models of inheritance that have been proposed include a maternal dominant gene with reduced penetrance, maternal and fetal gene interaction, mitochondrial inheritance, or a gene–environment interaction increasing susceptibility.[163] Preeclampsia has been associated with genes on various chromosomes including 2q, 5q, and 13q; HELLP is associated with genes on chromosome 12q.[56]

SUMMARY

The cardiovascular changes associated with pregnancy are significant although well tolerated by most women. Maternal and fetal risks occur when underlying cardiovascular or pulmonary disease processes are compounded with the changes incurred during pregnancy. Cardiovascular problems increase maternal morbidity and mortality and can compromise the health and well-being of the fetus. Careful assessment and ongoing monitoring of cardiovascular status throughout the prenatal, intrapartum, and postpartum periods are essential for early identification and prompt intervention, thereby improving maternal and neonatal outcomes. Box 9-1 summarizes clinical implications related to the cardiovascular system during pregnancy.

DEVELOPMENT OF THE CARDIOVASCULAR SYSTEM IN THE FETUS

The cardiovascular system is the first system in the embryo to begin to function. The need for substrates to support the rapid growth and development of the embryo necessitates the early development of a system that transports nutritional elements and metabolic byproducts to and from the cells of the body. Initially the embryo is small enough that diffusion

---

BOX 9-1   Recommendations for Clinical Practice Related to the Cardiovascular System in Pregnant Women

Recognize usual cardiovascular and hemodynamic patterns of change during pregnancy (pp. 251-258, Table 9-1).

Assess maternal cardiovascular changes throughout pregnancy (pp. 251-258).

Counsel women on normal cardiovascular changes and anticipated symptoms associated with those changes (pp. 251-258).

Counsel women in the third trimester to use the lateral recumbent position (pp. 259-260 and Figures 9-6 and 9-7).

Assess and closely monitor women at risk for and with preeclampsia throughout pregnancy (pp. 265-268).

Encourage moderate-intensity exercise on a regular basis during pregnancy (pp. 260-262).

Encourage sedentary women to begin an exercise program (pp. 260-262).

Counsel women with complications to be medically evaluated before beginning an exercise program (pp. 261-262).

Recommend interval-type exercises rather than long continuous exercise (pp. 261-262).

Provide counseling and regularly evaluate pregnant women who start a progressive exercise program during pregnancy (pp. 261-262).

Teach women self-uterine palpation to assess for uterine contractions during exercise (pp. 261-262).

Advise cessation of exercise if contractions, pain, or bleeding occurs (pp. 261-262).

Recognize usual changes in heart sounds and rhythms during pregnancy. (pp. 257, 259).

Monitor vascular volume status carefully during the intrapartum and postpartum periods (pp. 258-259).

Evaluate blood loss and fundal tone postpartum (pp. 258-259).

Monitor for signs of congestive heart failure in women with cardiac disease, especially in the second half of pregnancy and during the intrapartum and immediate postpartum periods (pp. 253, 258-259, 262-263).

Assess maternal activity tolerance in women with cardiac disease and discuss management of daily activities (pp. 262-265).

Teach women with cardiac disease the signs and symptoms of cardiovascular decompensation (pp. 262-265).

of nutrients can meet the demands of the cells; however, because of the exponential growth of the embryo, demand for nutrients quickly increases. Blood can be seen circulating through the embryonic body as early as the end of the third week.[112] Each of the developing regions of the embryo requires different amounts of circulatory support at various times throughout gestation; therefore the pattern of vessel development is markedly different from one region to the next, depending on the demand.[26]

The cardiovascular system is composed of the heart and the blood vessels. Their development is both independent and contiguous, with the final product being a closed system that continuously circulates a given blood volume. Although considered separately here, development of the two elements of the system (heart and vessels) occurs simultaneously. Major landmarks in the development of the cardiovascular system are summarized in Table 9-5.

Anatomic Development

Cardiogenesis is a complex process that is controlled by a complex cascade of factors at each step of cardiogenesis, including members of the transforming growth factor-β (TGF-β) and fibroblast growth factor families, retinoic acid, and many other transcriptional and signaling factors.[20,114] The GATA family of zinc finger probes is also critical for cardiac formation.[57,169] Hypoxia-inducible factor 1 and vascular endothelial growth factor (VEGF) are important in signaling fetal heart formation, development of the outflow tract, and

TABLE 9-5   Timelines in Normal and Abnormal Cardiac Development

NORMAL TIME	DEVELOPMENTAL EVENTS	MALFORMATIONS ARISING DURING PERIOD
18 days	Horseshoe-shaped cardiac primordium appears.	Lethal mutations
20 days	Bilateral cardia primordial fuse.	Cardia bifida (experimental)
	Cardiac jelly appears.	
	Aortic arch is forming.	
	Heart is looping into S shape.	Dextrocardia
22 days	Heart begins to beat.	
	Dorsal mesocardium is breaking down.	
	Aortic arches I and II are forming.	
	Atria are beginning to bulge.	
24 days	Right and left ventricles act like two pumps in series.	
	Outflow tract is distinguished from right ventricle.	
	Sinus venosus is being incorporated into right atrium.	Venous inflow malformations
	Endocardial cushions appear.	Persistent atrioventricular canal
	Septum primum appears between right and left atria.	Common atrium
Late in week 4	Muscular interventricular septum is forming.	Common ventricle
	Truncoconal ridges are forming.	Persistent truncus arteriosus
	Aortic arch I is regressing.	
	Aortic arch III is forming.	
	Aortic arch IV is forming.	
	Endocardial cushions are coming together, forming right and left atrioventricular canals.	Persistent atrioventricular canal
	Further growth of interatrial septum primum and muscular interventricular septum occurs.	Muscular ventricular septal defects
	Truncus arteriosus is dividing into aorta and pulmonary artery.	Transposition of the great vessels; aortic and pulmonary stenosis or atresia
Early in week 5	Atrioventricular bundle is forming; there is possible neurogenic control of heart beat.	Aberrant pulmonary drainage
	Pulmonary veins are being incorporated into the atrium.	
	Aortic arches I and II have regressed.	
	Aortic arches III and IV have formed.	
	Aortic arch VI is forming.	
	Conduction system forms.	
	Endocardial cushions fuse.	
	Interatrial foramen secundum is forming.	
Late in week 5 to early in week 6	Interatrial septum primum is almost contacting endocardial cushions.	Low atrial septal defects
	Membranous part of interventricular septum starts to form.	Membranous interventricular septal defects
	Semilunar valves begin to form.	Aortic and pulmonary vascular stenosis
	Interatrial foramen secundum is large.	High atrial septal defects
	Interatrial septum secundum starts to form.	
Late in week 6	Atrioventricular valves and papillary muscles are forming.	Tricuspid or mitral valve stenosis or atresia
	Interventricular septum is almost complete.	Membranous interventricular septal defects
	Coronary circulation is becoming established.	
8–9 weeks	Membranous part of interventricular septum is complete.	Membranous interventricular septal defect

From Carlson, B.M. (2013). *Human embryology and developmental biology* (5th ed.). Philadelphia: Saunders.

coronary vessel growth.[127] Septation of the heart involves signaling between myocardial and endothelial cells by growth factors TGF-β, VEGF, extracellular matrix molecules, and homeobox genes (see Chapter 3).[20,169] Examples of other transcription factors that influence gene expression and cardiogenesis include helix-loop-helix proteins, MADS box proteins, Nkx2-5, and mEF-2.[20,169]

Development of the Primitive Heart

Heart cell precursors arise from three sources: (1) mesoderm (forming most of the myocardium of the atria and ventricles and outflow track); (2) pericardium (forming the epicardium, fibroblasts, vascular smooth muscle cells, coronary vessels endothelium, and some myocytes); and (3) cardiac neural crest (forming distal smooth muscle of the outflow tract, cardiac aorticopulmonary tract, and autonomic nervous system).[20,51] The mesoderm consists of primary and secondary heart fields. The primary heart field or cardiac crescent forms the left ventricle and atria; the secondary heart field forms the right ventricle, outflow tract, and pericardium.[20,26] Mesenchyme cells known as the angioblastic tissue are derived from the lateral mesoderm and

appear early in the third week.[169] These cells appear as scattered, small masses at the anterior margin of the embryonic disk cranial to the neural plate (see Figure 15-4). The cells coalesce to form a plexus of endothelial vessels that fuse to form two longitudinal cellular strands called *cardiogenic cords.* These cords can be seen ventral to the coelomic cavity at the end of the third week. These cords canalize to form two thin-walled tubes—the endocardial heart tubes. As the embryo undergoes lateral folding, the tubes come into proximity and fusion occurs in a cranial-to-caudal direction (Figure 9-8, *A* through *C*). Fusion results in a single tube that will eventually form the endocardium.[20,26,99,112] Formation of the heart tube is influenced by surrounding neural and endodermal tissues.[169]

At this stage the mesenchymal tissue around the endocardial tube thickens to form the myoepicardial mantle. An extracellular matrix separates the inner endothelial tube from the thicker outer mesenchymal tube, resulting in the appearance of a tube within a tube (see Figure 9-8, *C*). The inner tube becomes the endothelial lining of the heart (endocardium), and the myoepicardial mantle develops into the myocardium.[51,112,169] The outflow tract and sinus

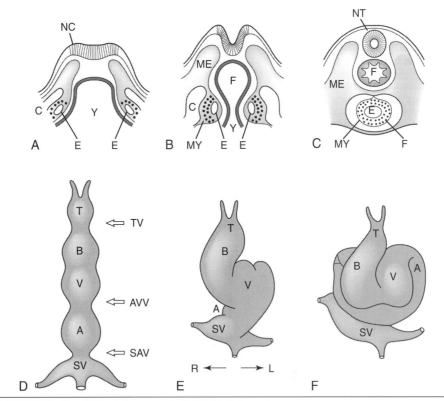

FIGURE 9-8   Development of the heart. Transverse sections **(A)** paired endocardial and myoepicardial tubes on either side of body **(B)** these paired tubes move toward each other with embryo folding and when fused results in a single straight cardiac tube **(C). (D)** Simple tubular heart. **(E)** Early looping to the left side. **(F)** Established looping with definition of unseptated cardiac chambers. The *open arrows* indicate the valve sites. *A,* Atrium; *AVV,* atrioventricular valve; *B,* bulbus cordis; *C,* Coelomic cavity; *E,* endocardial tubes; *F,* foregut; *ME,* mesoderm; *MY,* myocardium; *NC,* neural crest; *NT,* neural tube; *SAV,* sinoatrial valve; *SV,* sinus venosus; *T,* truncus arteriosus; *TV,* truncal valve; *Y,* yolk sac. (From Reller, M.D., McDonald, R.W., Gerlis, L.M., &Thornburg, K.L. [1991]. Cardiac embryology: Basic review and clinical correlations. *J Am Soc Echocardiogr, 4,* 519.)

venosus form later at the distal end of this tube. The epicardium appears after septation of the heart has begun. The epicardium forms from epithelial tissue that spreads over the myocardium. Epicardial cells invade the myocardium to give rise to fibroblast cells, smooth muscle cells, and the coronary vasculature.[20,114,169] The epicardium also has a role in signaling cardiomyocytes and differentiation of Purkinje fibers.[57]

With cranial folding, the pericardial cavity and heart rotate on the transverse axis almost 180 degrees to lie ventral to the foregut and caudal to the oropharyngeal membrane. The septum transversum is therefore positioned between the pericardial cavity and the yolk sac (see Figure 12-6), and the heart is then situated in a definitive pericardial cavity.[26,112] The primitive heart, consisting of the endothelial tube and myoepicardial mantle, passes craniocaudally through the pericardial cavity and is fixed to the pericardial wall only at the venous entrance (caudal end) and at the arterial outlet (cranial end). The cardiac tube begins to beat around 22 to 23 days, initially at less than 40 beats per minute, moving blood from the caudal venous end to the cranial arterial end.[26] At this time, fetal vascular genesis also begins.

Differentiation of the heart regions begins and alternating dilations and constrictions can be identified (Figure 9-8, *D* through *F*). The first areas to appear include the bulbus cordis, ventricle, and atrium. The truncus arteriosus and sinus venosus follow.[112] The truncus arteriosus lies above and is connected to the bulbus cordis. The aortic sac from which the aortic arches arise is included in the truncus arteriosus. The large sinus venosus receives the umbilical, vitelline, and common cardinal veins from the primitive placenta, yolk sac, and embryo, respectively.[26,112]

During this differentiation stage, there is rapid growth of the cardiac tube as well. Because the ends are held fixed and the bulboventricular portion of the tube grows more rapidly (doubling its length from day 21 to day 25) than the surrounding cavity, the tube bends upon itself and forms a U-shaped loop that has its convexity directed forward and to the right. Continued growth results in an S-shaped curve that nearly fills the pericardial cavity (see Figure 9-8, *E* and *F*).

The separation of the atrium and sinus venosus from the septum transversum positions the atrium dorsal and to the left of the bulboventricular loop; the sinus venosus lies dorsal to the atrium. The right and left horns of the sinus venosus now partially fuse to form a single cavity that opens into the atrial cavity via the sinoatrial orifice. The right horn of the sinus venosus becomes incorporated into the right atrium. Most of the wall of the left atrium is derived from the primitive pulmonary vein. The vein develops to the left of the septum primum (see "Septation of the Heart") and is an outgrowth of the dorsal atrial wall. However, as the atrium expands, the vein is progressively incorporated into the wall of the atrium.[26,112]

The heart is still a single tube except at the caudal end, where the remaining unfused portions of the right and left horns of the sinus venosus lie. The three pairs of symmetric veins that return blood to the horns are the veins of the placenta (umbilical), yolk sac (vitelline), and embryonic body (cardinal). The vitelline vessels soon develop asymmetrically, with the left vein undergoing retrogression. At 33 to 34 days, the right umbilical vein atrophies and disappears. The left horn of the sinus venosus also becomes much smaller as the veins in the septum transversum rearrange. Eventually the left sinus venosus becomes the coronary sinus.[26,112]

During the rearrangement of vessels, the ductus venosus (DV) is formed. This shunt between the left umbilical vein and the right hepatocardiac channel allows some of the blood from the developing placenta to bypass the liver sinusoids and flow directly into the heart via the inferior vena cava (see "Fetal Circulation"). This results in an enlargement of the right horn of the sinus venosus and a change in the position of the sinoatrial orifice. The latter is positioned to the right side of the dorsal surface and is converted to a vertical alignment. The margins are now projected into the atrium and compose the right and left venous valves.[26]

The atrium, ventricle, and bulbus cordis continue to expand rapidly with changes in position. The atrium expands transversely, extending laterally and ventrally, and appears on either side of the bulbus cordis. This results in the atria being deeply grooved. Further growth results in the right and left auricular appendages being formed. At the same time, the bulboventricular sulcus dissipates with the growth of these structures. Eventually the caudal portion of the bulbus becomes part of the ventricle. The ventricle gradually moves to the left and ends up on the ventral surface of the heart. This change defines the atrioventricular canal.[26]

Septation of the Heart

Septation of the atrioventricular canal, the atrium, and the ventricle begins in the middle of the fourth week and is complete by the sixth week. Development of the septa involves a cascade of multiple transcription factors, cell types, and tissues. Alterations in any of these can result in septal defects, some of the most common congenital heart defects.[169] The changes in shape and position of the heart tube, as described earlier, facilitate the partitioning of these structures. The process of septation takes place while the heart continues to pump and blood continues to move unidirectionally through the tube. The subdivision of the heart into right and left compartments occurs simultaneously in the various regions of the heart; however, all of the processes must be integrated so that normal functional development occurs.

Atrioventricular Canal. The atrium leads into the ventricle via a narrow atrioventricular canal. During the fourth week the endocardium proliferates to produce dorsal and ventral bulges in the wall of the atrioventricular canal (Figure 9-9). These swellings are the atrioventricular endocardial cushions, which function as primitive valves.[26] Mesenchymal cells invade the swellings, which results in the growth of the cushions toward each other. Fusion of the cushions occurs, leading to right and left atrioventricular canals.[99,112] Failure of septation results in atrioventricular canal defects and Ebstein anomaly and can

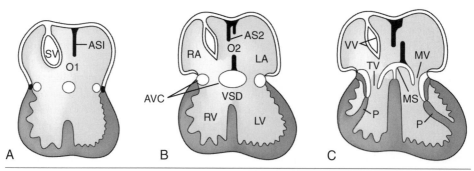

FIGURE 9-9   Coronal sections of the heart demonstrating changes in cardiac chamber septation. **(A)** Early stage, commencing atrial and ventricular septation. **(B)** Atrial ostium primum closed, ostium secundum forming, and ventricular septum incomplete. **(C)** Septation complete and membranous septum formed. The atrioventricular valves have been formed by atrioventricular (endocardial) cushion tissue and delamination of the myocardium. *AS1,* Atrial septum primum; *AS2,* atrial septum secundum; *AVC,* atrioventricular cushion; *LA,* left atrium; *LV,* left ventricle; *MS,* membranous septum; *MV,* mitral valve; *O1,* atrial ostium primum; *O2,* atrium ostium secundum; *P,* papillary muscles; *RA,* right atrium; *RV,* right ventricle; *SV,* sinus venosus; *TV,* tricuspid valve; *VSD,* ventricular septal defect; *VV,* venous valves. (From Reller, M.D., McDonald, R.W., Gerlis, L.M., & Thornburg, K.L. [1991]. Cardiac embryology: Basic review and clinical correlations. *J Am Soc Echocardiogr, 4*[5], 519.)

alter formation of the heart valves, the membranous portion of the ventricular septum, and the atrial septation.[51,57,169]

Atria. A thin, crescent-shaped septum (septum primum, which arises from the secondary heart field) begins to grow downward from the roof of the atrium during the fourth week. Initially a large opening exists between the caudal free edge of the septum and the endocardial cushions; this is the foramen primum.[51] This allows oxygenated blood that is returned to the right atrium from the placenta to pass to the left atrium and be distributed to the systemic circulation. The opening progressively gets smaller and is eventually obliterated when the septum primum fuses with the endocardial cushions. Before the septum primum reaches the atrioventricular cushions, however, a second interatrial communication forms as the result of multiple perforations that coalesce in the upper part of the septum. This is the foramen secundum.[99,112]

A second, thicker septum (septum secundum) begins to develop just to the right of the septum primum. This septum is also crescent-shaped, but it grows only until it overlaps the foramen secundum. The partition is incomplete, and an oval opening, the foramen ovale, is left.[26,112] The upper portion of the septum primum regresses, whereas the lower segment (attached to the endocardial cushions) remains, serving as a flap valve for the foramen ovale. Before birth this valve allows directed blood to move freely from the right to the left atrium. However, flow from the left to the right is prevented by apposition of the thin flexible septum primum to the rigid septum secundum after birth. This results in fusion of the septa and eventual anatomic closure of the foramen ovale. Atrial septation is illustrated in Figure 9-9.

Ventricles. The interventricular septum consists of muscular and membranous portions. Division of the bulboventricular cavity is first indicated by a sagittal muscular ridge appearing on the floor of the ventricle near the apex; this is the interventricular septum. At first the septum appears to lengthen as a result of the dilation of the lateral halves of the ventricle. Later there is active proliferation of the septal tissue as the muscular portion of the interventricular septum forms.[26,112] Communication between the right and left sides of the ventricle is maintained until the bulbar ridges fuse. This closure is the result of fusion of subendocardial tissue from the bulbar ridges with the atrioventricular cushions.[112]

The membranous portion of the ventricular septum is derived from tissue that extends from the right side of the endocardial cushions. This eventually fuses with the aorticopulmonary septum of the truncus arteriosus and the muscular interventricular septum. Closure of the interventricular foramen results in the pulmonary trunk being in communication with the right ventricle (RV) and the aorta with the left ventricle (LV) (see Figure 9-9).[112]

Bulbus Cordis and Truncus Arteriosus. Before the interventricular septum has developed completely, spiral subendocardial thickenings appear in the distal part of the bulbus cordis. These are the bulbar ridges, which can be seen during the fifth week of gestation. Initially these ridges are composed of cardiac jelly, but they are later invaded by mesenchymal and cardiac neural crest cell. Failure of neural crest cells to migrate from the cranial to cardiac region can lead to congenital heart defects such as tricuspid atresia, truncus arteriosus, and aortic arch anomalies.[169] In the proximal part of the bulbus, the ridges are located on the ventral and dorsal walls, whereas in the distal portion they are attached to the lateral walls. The distal portion of the bulbus is continuous with the truncus arteriosus, which develops truncal ridges that match those of the bulbus cordis. The growth and fusion of these ridges during the eighth week results in the spiral aorticopulmonary septum (Figure 9-10). The spiral effect may result from the streaming of blood from the ventricles through the truncus during septum development. The result is the creation of two channels: the pulmonary trunk and the aorta. The bulbus cordis is gradually incorporated into the ventricles.[26,112]

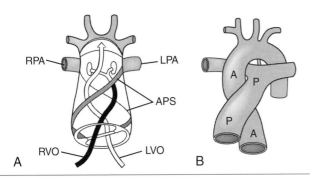

Cardiac Valves. Part of the septation process involves the development of the cardiac valves. This includes the development of the semilunar valves of the aorta and the pulmonary artery and the atrioventricular valves (tricuspid and mitral valves). The cellular and molecular mechanisms that control heart valve cell differentiation are similar to those involved in the formation of cartilage, tendons, and bones.[91]

The semilunar valves develop from a swelling of subendothelial tissue that appears on each side of the ventricular end of the bulbar ridges. These swellings consist of loose connective tissue covered by endothelium. Eventually the swellings become hollowed out and reshaped to form three thin-walled cusps.[20,26,112] The atrioventricular valves develop from local proliferation of subendocardial tissue as well as from connective tissue under the endocardium of the atrioventricular canals. These, too, become hollowed out, but on the ventricular side. The atrioventricular valves remain connected to the ventricular wall via muscular strands that are both papillary muscles and chordae tendineae. The mitral valve develops two cusps; the tricuspid has three.[26,99,112]

Conducting System

The conducting system is derived from modified atrial and ventricular myocytes.[26] The initial pacemaker of the cardiac muscle is located in the caudal part of the left cardiac tube. Because the muscle layers of the atrium and ventricle are continuous, this temporary pacemaker is effective in controlling contractions throughout the primitive heart. Once the sinus venosus develops, the excitatory center (sinoatrial node) is found in the right wall. This node is incorporated into the right atrium along with the sinus venosus, where it lies near the entrance of the superior vena cava.[26,112]

Once the sinus venosus is incorporated into the atrium, cells from the left wall of the sinus venosus can be found in the base of the interatrial septum. When combined with cells from the atrioventricular canal, the atrioventricular node and the bundle of His are formed. These structures can be identified in embryos early in the second month of gestation.[26,112]

The Purkinje fibers constitute one of the most unusual features of the heart muscle. These cells are responsible for the initiation and propagation of the cardiac impulse and ensuring a regular contraction sequence within the organ. Although they are cardiac muscle cells, they are specialized through differentiation for conduction rather than contraction. These cells have fewer fibrils and are larger in diameter than the rest of the cardiac muscle cells. Purkinje cells are located external to the endocardium and run without interruption from the atrium to the ventricle as the atrioventricular bundle.[26] A fibrous band of connective tissue eventually separates the muscles of the atria and ventricles. This results in the atrioventricular node and bundle of His being the only conductive pathways between the upper and lower halves of the heart.

Initially the heart rate is slower than 40 beats per minute, increasing to around 110 at 7 weeks and 170 at 9 to 10 weeks; between 20 and 40 weeks' gestation, heart rates range from 110 to 180 beats per minute with a maximum beat to beat variability of 15.[151] Immaturity of the conducting system can result in high rates of atrial premature beats, which are usually benign but can occasionally be associated with an underlying cardiac disorder.[151]

Vasculature

Blood vessels consist of an endothelial lining stabilized by an outer coat of connective tissue. The formation of blood vessels involves either vasculogenesis or angiogenesis. Vasculogenesis is the "process by which endothelial progenitor cells are recruited and differentiate into mature endothelial cells to form new blood vessels."[49,p. 1293] Angiogenesis involves the sprouting of new blood vessels from existing ones.[49] In most organ systems, both processes are involved.

The earliest vessels are derived from angioblastic tissue, which differentiates from the mesenchyme that covers the yolk sac, within the connecting stalk and in the wall of the chorionic sac. The impetus for vascular differentiation seems to be the reduction of nutrients within the yolk sac, which leads to an urgent need for a vascular system to supply nutrients to the cells.[26,57,112]

Masses of isolated angioblasts come together and form blood islands (hemangioblasts), which can develop into endothelial cells, hematopoietic stem cells, or vascular smooth muscle cells.[26] Soon spaces can be seen in these islands, around which the angioblasts will arrange themselves. This results in lumen formation and the development of a primitive endothelial layer. The isolated vessels fuse to form a network of channels and extend to adjacent areas either through growth (endothelial budding) or by fusion with other independently formed vessels. Mesenchymal cells surrounding the primitive endothelial vessels differentiate into the muscle and connective tissue layers of the vessels.[112]

Endothelial tissue first appears in the yolk sac wall as isolated cellular cords that develop a lumen. As these vessels join together, a network of endothelial vitelline vessels is formed. By extension and growth the network progressively reaches the embryonic body.[26] Primitive plasma and blood cells are developed from endothelial cells trapped within the vessels of the yolk sac and allantois. Blood formation in the embryo begins in the liver after 5 to 6 weeks (see Chapter 8).[26,112] Early hematopoiesis also occurs in the aortic ventral wall and aortic–genital ridge–mesonephric area.[26] Hematopoietic cells in this area later move to the liver, yolk sac, and placenta.

The endothelial lining of vessels develops before circulation begins. However, once circulation begins, the hemodynamics of blood flow influences the growth of the endothelium and the differentiation of the other parts of the vessel wall. The developing organs and the temporal sequence and metabolic demands of those organs may also influence the differentiation of vessels.[26]

Early vessels seen within the embryonic body develop in mesodermal areas in different regions of the body via vasculogenesis and angiogenesis to form a diffuse network that runs throughout the embryonic mesenchyme.[26] As tissues and organs differentiate, the regional networks elaborate to meet metabolic demands. The earliest vessels are simple endothelial tubes; differentiation of arteries from veins is not possible at this time. As development continues, the tunica media and tunica adventitia of the definitive arteries and veins arise from mesenchymal tissue.[26]

Development of the vasculature is influenced by many growth factors including bone morphogenetic protein 5 (BMP5), which stimulates blood island formation; VEGF and its receptor (VEGFR-1); epidermal growth factor (EGF); angiopoietin 1 and its receptor; TGF-β; platelet derived growth factor; and myocardin.[26,128] VEGF has neuroprotective and neurotropic functions; influences smooth muscle differentiation, growth, and organization of contractile proteins; and mediates hypoxic-mediated vascular remodeling.[128] EGF synthesis and release is influenced by low oxygen tensions that occur in the fetus to stimulate VEGF release and function.[128] Myocardin is the master regulator of smooth muscle formation.[26] Different signaling cascades, ligands, and receptors are expressed by cells that will become arteries versus veins. VEGF serves as the patterning agent for blood vessel development.[26]

Arteries. The aortic arches are essential in the primitive circulatory system. These vessels arise from the aortic sac and terminate in the dorsal aorta. A total of five pairs develop; however, the third, fourth, and fifth arches are the only ones to contribute to the great vessels. By the end of the eighth week, the adult pattern has been established.[112] The coronary arteries arise from epicardium; their smooth muscle cells are derived from mesoderm.[20,26]

The right and left dorsal aortae are the primary embryonic arteries. Initially these vessels are continuations of the endocardial tubes and can be divided into three portions: a short, ventral, ascending portion that supplies blood to the forebrain; a primitive first aortic arch that lies in the mesenchyme of the mandibular arch (pharynx); and a relatively long, descending portion that distributes blood to the embryonic body, yolk sac, and chorion via the segmental plexuses, vitelline vessels, and umbilical branches, respectively. The paired dorsal aortae initially run the length of the embryo. As development continues, the two fuse just caudal to the branchial region so that there is only a single midline vessel in the caudal part of the embryo.[26]

There are three major arterial branches that run off the dorsal aorta above the level of right and left aortic fusion. The intersegmental arteries are a group of 30 or more vessels that pass between and carry blood to the somites and their derivatives, which will form the muscular and bony elements of this region. In the cervical region the first seven intersegmental arteries are connected by a longitudinal anastomosis that forms the vertebral artery. The proximal segments of the first six arteries disappear, and the seventh intersegmental artery becomes the subclavian artery.[112]

The somatic arteries also arise from this group of vessels. Eventually the intercostal arteries, lumbar arteries, common iliac arteries, and lateral sacral arteries can be identified.[112] The midline branches of the dorsal aorta run to the yolk sac, allantois, and chorion. There are two main groups: the lateral branches and the ventral branches. The ventral or vitelline arteries supply the yolk sac and the gut. These vessels will eventually be reduced to three persisting vessels: the celiac, superior mesenteric, and inferior mesenteric arteries. These vessels service the foregut, midgut, and hindgut, respectively (see Chapter 12).[112] The lateral branches supply the nephrogenic ridge and its derivatives. At first there are several branches, but retrogression results in four vessels remaining in the mature organism. These vessels are the phrenic, suprarenal, renal, and gonadal arteries.

Umbilical Arteries. By far the largest of the dorsal aortic vessels are the paired umbilical arteries (UAs). These vessels pass through the connecting stalk (umbilical cord) and become continuous with the chorionic vessels in the developing placenta. After delivery the proximal portions of these arteries become the internal iliac and superior vesical arteries. The distal portions are obliterated and become the medial umbilical ligaments.

Veins. There are three sets of paired veins that drain into the heart of the 4-week-old (6 weeks menstrual age) embryo. These are the vitelline veins, which return blood from the yolk sac; the umbilical veins, which bring oxygenated blood from the chorion; and the cardinal veins, which return blood from the body.[173] The increased nuchal translucency that occurs in infants with Down syndrome and other disorders is probably a result of issues with the anterior portion of the secondary heart field and cardiac neural crest cells along with alterations in lymphatic endothelial cell differentiation.[51]

The vitelline veins follow the yolk stalk and ascend on either side of the foregut. They then pass through the septum transversum and enter the sinus venosus of the heart. As the primitive liver grows into the septum transversum, the hepatic sinusoids become linked with the vitelline veins. As the right vitelline vein begins to disintegrate, parts are incorporated into the developing hepatic vessels. The portal vein develops from the vitelline-derived vessels that surround the duodenum.[26,112]

The umbilical veins originate as a pair of vessels; however, the right vein and part of the left degenerate so that only a single vessel remains to return blood from the placenta to the fetus. As these vessels degenerate, the DV develops in the liver and connects the remaining umbilical vein with the inferior vena cava. At birth the umbilical vein and the DV are obliterated with the cutting of the umbilical cord and the modifications in the circulation. The remnants of the vessels are the ligamentum teres and ligamentum venosum, respectively.[26,112]

Very early in the embryonic period, the cardinal vessels are the main drainage system. The anterior and posterior cardinal veins bring blood from the cranial and caudal regions and empty into the heart via a common cardinal vein that enters the sinus venosus on each side. By the eighth week the anterior cardinal veins are connected through an anastomosis that allows for shunting of blood from the left vein to the right. This connection becomes the left brachiocephalic vein. The right anterior and right common cardinal veins form the superior vena cava. The posterior cardinal veins are transitional vessels. These vessels service the mesonephric kidneys and disappear when these transient kidneys degenerate. The subcardinal and supracardinal vessels develop gradually and facilitate perfusion of the mesonephric kidneys. These vessels do not degenerate entirely, as do the posterior cardinal veins, but contribute to the development of the inferior vena cava.[26,112]

The inferior vena cava is the result of a series of changes in the embryonic veins of the trunk. The four main segments of the inferior vena cava are derived from the hepatic vein and hepatic sinusoids (hepatic segment), the right subcardinal vein (prerenal segment), the subcardinal and supracardinal anastomosis (renal segment), and the right supracardinal vein (postrenal segment).[112,173]

Developmental Basis for Common Anomalies

Development of the heart is controlled by a group of cardiac genes and transcription factors that are expressed in a specific sequence. Alterations in these genes or factors or in their sequencing may lead to agenesis or aplasia (failure in development), hypoplasia (incomplete or defective development), dysplasia (abnormal development), malposition, failure of fusion of adjoining parts, abnormal fusion, incomplete reabsorption, persistence of a vessel, or early obliteration of a vessel and thus cardiac defects.[26] Cardiac defects are the most common congenital defect and are seen in 0.8% to 1% of live born infants and 10% of spontaneous abortions.[51,165] About one-fourth of spontaneous abortions with cardiac defects have other noncardiac problems.[26,172] The most common heart defects arise from alterations in septation, valve formation, and patterning of the great vessels.[169]

Currently 57% to 83% of critical cardiac malformations and one-third of all congenital heart defects are detected by prenatal ultrasound.[165] Doppler evaluation of the fetal cardiovascular system includes arterial (evaluation of individual arterial beds such as the uterus, umbilical artery, and cerebral circulation), venous (evaluation of the ductus venosus, inferior vena cava, umbilical vein, and hepatic veins), and intracardiac evaluations. Doppler evaluations are used to evaluate fetal growth restriction and to assess potential complications such as preeclampsia, twin-to-twin transfusion, fetal hydrops, and arrhythmias.[15,16,173]

The major structures of the heart are completed by 8 weeks after fertilization (10 weeks postmenstrual age).[169] The timing of the development of major anomalies is summarized in Table 9-5. Most major defects arise during weeks 4 to 8 of development. However, lesions may continue to evolve during the remainder of gestation. For example, ventricular inflammation; outflow tract obstruction; arch obstruction; or ventricular, aortic, or pulmonary artery hypoplasia may develop or progress. Arterioventricular or semilunar valve regurgitation may compromise fetal circulation. Alterations in rhythms may lead to myocardial disease, or heart failure may develop. Newer imaging techniques and fetal echocardiography have led to a better diagnosis of congenital heart defects before birth and the potential for the development of earlier therapies.[15,16,103,173] These therapies are used to decrease the risk of fetal or early neonatal death or to decrease the risk of a primary anomaly developing into a more severe one.[103] Therapies can be either pharmacologic interventions (see Chapter 7) or procedures such as fetal aortic valvuloplasty done via percutaneous needle insertion in infants with aortic stenosis or hypoplastic left heart syndrome with atrial septum restriction, pulmonary atresia, or pulmonary stenosis.[103]

The brain and heart develop simultaneously and share genes and signaling pathways. Children with alterations in development of the heart have a higher frequency of focal brain injury and white matter injury.[104] This may be because of abnormal cerebral blood flow in early development, especially in infants with hypoplastic left heart syndrome and dextro-transposition of the great vessels, with increased risk of injury.[104]

The etiology of most congenital heart defects is incompletely understood but includes both genetic and environmental factors in most nonsyndrome congenital heart defects.[165] Most congenital heart defects are polygenic with variable penetrance and severity.[20] Defects may arise from mutations in transcription factors and other proteins that guide cardiogenesis, such as alterations in factors involved in formation of structures from the cardiogenic mesoderm (NKx2-5, Tbx5, and GATA-40 can lead to septal defects; alterations in epicardial progenitors have a role in development of hypoplastic left heart syndrome; and alteration in cardiac neural crest cells are seen in DiGeorge syndrome [22g11 deletion]).[20]

In about 8% of children there is a clear genetic cause; most are associated with obvious chromosomal anomalies (e.g.,

Down, cri du chat, trisomy 18, trisomy 13, and Turner syndrome). The incidence of cardiac defects is about 40% in infants with Down syndrome and higher in infants with trisomy 13 and 18.[172] Many of the single-gene and other inherited syndromes, including Marfan, Williams, and DiGeorge syndromes, are associated with heart disease. However, these syndromes account for only a small percentage of all congenital heart defects. Environmental factors may also play a role in congenital cardiac malformations. Fetal exposure to teratogens (see Chapter 7) through maternal ingestion of drugs, such as antiepileptic drugs or warfarin, or alcohol or exposure to viral infections (e.g., rubella or cytomegalovirus) can result in alterations in cardiac development. These variables account for about 2% of known congenital heart disease. Maternal disorders such as diabetes mellitus and phenylketonuria also increase the risk of fetal cardiac defects. For example, the frequency of cardiac defects in infants of women with diabetes mellitus is two to four times higher than normal. Systemic lupus erythematosus is associated with fetal heart block (see Chapter 13).

In the remaining 85% of infants with defects, there is no clear cause. Some are caused by multifactorial inheritance (see Chapter 1), in which there may be a heritable predisposition for cardiac anomalies. This combined with some type of environmental trigger during a vulnerable period results in abnormal development. Implications of selected congenital heart defects are discussed under "Clinical Implications for Neonatal Care."

Functional Development

Functional development of the heart involves maturation of the fetal myocardium, myocardial performance, fetal circulation, control of fetal circulation, oxygenation, and heart rate. Heart rate, fetal acid-base balance, control of heart rate, and fetal responses to hypoxia and asphyxia are discussed in depth in Chapter 6. The fetal heart is characterized by fewer contractile elements; altered titan (a large protein involved in muscle elasticity and compliance) function because of immature isotypes; and decreased calcium release, sympathetic innervation, and β-adrenoceptors.[42]

Fetal Myocardium

Fetal myocytes have a small amount of contractile tissue, which is restricted to the subsarcolemmal region. About 60% of the myocardial tissue consists of noncontractile mass in the fetus (versus 30% in adults).[143,160] The fetal myocardium has fewer myofibrils, which are arranged in a more random fashion rather than in a parallel organization as occurs in adults.[6,45,140] These changes, along with the decreased number of sarcomeres per gram of ventricular muscle and increased water content, limit the amount of force that the fetus can generate per unit of area.[42,141] The sarcoplasmic reticulum in the fetal myocardium is reduced and less organized, reducing calcium sequestration and altering calcium transport and thus contractility.[108] Therefore the fetal heart is more dependent on transsarcolemmal calcium movement with lower

intracellular concentrations. As a result, the fetal myocardium develops less contractile force, with a lower velocity of shortening and reextension.

The fetal myocardium has been thought to be less compliant than that of the adult, although the relationship between muscle length and force is qualitatively similar and some data suggest compliance is increased because of differences in titin (connectin) isotypes.[42] The altered compliance may be partially a result of constraint of the pericardium, lungs, and chest.[82] As extrauterine growth occurs, the compliance of both ventricles increases. Right-side pressures are greater than left-side pressures in the fetus, so blood flows from right to left across the foramen ovale from the right atrium to left atrium or across the ductus arteriosus (DA) from the pulmonary artery to aorta.[6,82,141]

Metabolism is also immature in the fetal myocardium. Lactate is the main energy source in the fetal and neonatal myocardium as opposed to long-chain fatty acids (LCFAs) in adults because of limitations in fatty acid transport from decreased activity of the enzymes needed to transport LCFAs into the mitochondria.[108,143] However, the fetal heart has an increased ability to utilize anaerobic metabolism, which partially compensates for these limitations.

Myocardial Performance

After birth, when circulation flows in series (Figure 9-11, B), the stroke volume of the RV equals that of the LV. However, in the fetus, which is not dependent on the lungs to oxygenate the blood, circulation is arranged in a parallel fashion (Figure 9-11, A). This arrangement allows for mixing of oxygenated blood with deoxygenated blood at the atrial and great vessel levels. Blood from the RV and LV is mixed in the descending aorta below the DA. The modifications in the circulation that allow for this mixing divert blood from the immature lungs to the placenta, where oxygen–carbon dioxide exchange occurs. Stroke volumes of the two fetal ventricles are not equal. The fetus sends 65% of the venous return to the RV and 25% to the LV; therefore RV stroke volume is greater than that in the LV.[45] As a result of these differences, cardiac output in the fetus is defined as the total output of the RV and LV, or the combined cardiac output (CCO).[41,45] The RV pumps up to two-thirds of the combined ventricular output.[129,141] RV stroke volume is greater than that of the LV and plays a major role in maintaining CCO.[120,143] The RV delivers blood to the descending aorta, lower body, and placenta; LV output goes primarily to the cerebral and coronary circulations with little going to the lower body.[120,143] Cerebral blood flow increases with increasing weight and as a percentage of cardiac output.[119]

The fetal resting cardiac output is the highest of any time of life with a CCO of 400 to 450 mL/minute/kg at term.[118] The high fetal cardiac output may be necessary to meet the high fetal oxygen consumption demands. Compared with that of the adult, fetal oxygen consumption is 1.5 to 2 times higher. This may be an adaptive mechanism for the low oxygen tension found in the fetus.[41] The ability to maintain this high

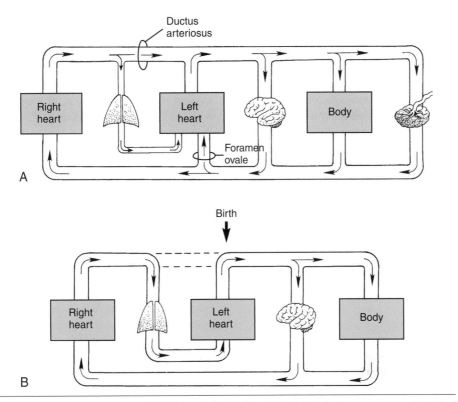

FIGURE 9-11   Comparison of **(A)** fetal (parallel) with **(B)** adult (series) circulatory systems. (Modified from Dawes, G.S. [1968]. *Fetal and neonatal physiology.* Chicago: Year Book, by Bloom, R.S. [2006]. Delivery room resuscitation of the newborn. In R.J. Martin, A.A. Fanaroff, & M.C. Walsh. [Eds.]. *Fanaroff and Martin's neonatal-perinatal medicine: Diseases of the fetus and infant* [8th ed.]. Philadelphia: Mosby.)

output is a result of the elevated heart rate and the cardiac shunts. Changes in fetal cardiac output seem to be directly related to fetal heart rate (FHR) changes, with reduced sensitivity to preload and afterload.[108] A 10% increase in FHR above the resting level is associated with an increase in both right and left ventricular output; a decrease in heart rate results in a decrease in combined ventricular output.

In the fetal heart, the RV and LV have stages of filling that are similar to those in the adult; however, the end-diastolic dimensions of the RV are larger than those of the LV. There also seems to be a difference in the rate of filling between the ventricles. In the fetus, an increase in RV volume or afterload interferes with LV filling. The Frank-Starling relationship is present and is a primary regulator of fetal cardiac output.[6,45,82] However, fetal cardiac function is less responsive to changes in preload and afterload.[99] There may be less functional reserve because the fetal heart functions at the maximum and interventions such as volume infusion do not significantly increase stroke volume and output.[41,143] Heart rate is the most effective way for the fetus to increase ventricular function and cardiac output.[82,99,120]

In terms of afterload, the fetal myocardium shortens more slowly compared with adult tissue. This fetal liability is to be expected given the maturation of the force-generating ability of the myocardium.[41] Arterial pressure is a major component of afterload and has a significant effect on ejection (the higher the pressure, the smaller the stroke volume). This relationship holds throughout development, although neonates seem to be less tolerant of increases in arterial pressure.[8,101]

Changes in inotropy (the strength of myocardial contractions) reflect a change in the ability of the myocardium to contract, and maturational development affects inotropy in the fetus and neonate. These changes are probably related to the availability of calcium and the control of cytosolic calcium. The development of the sarcomeres and their intracellular control mechanisms is integrally tied to this process. The sarcoplasmic reticulum calcium pump is immature and less able to remove calcium, leading to less relaxation of the fetal heart in response to sympathetic stimulation.[99]

Heart rate also affects the strength of contraction in a positive way in the fetus, neonate, and adult. In fetal lambs, however, as heart rate increases, stroke volume decreases. This is most likely because of a decrease in end-diastolic volume that is a natural consequence of the increased heart rate. Conflicting data have been found in studies of human fetuses, although most studies suggest a positive effect of heart rate on ventricular output. This may be related to additional factors that have inotropic effects.[8] Systemic systolic blood pressure is 15 to 20 mm Hg (1.99 to 2.66 kPa) at 16 weeks, rising to 30 to 40 mm Hg (3.99 to 5.32 kPa) at 28 weeks.[82] Diastolic blood pressure is less than 5 mm Hg (0.67 kPa) at 16 to 18 weeks and 5 to 15 mm Hg (0.67 to 1.99 kPa) at 19 to

26 weeks.[82] Umbilical venous pressure increases from 4.5 mm Hg (0.60 kPa) at 18 weeks to 6 mm Hg (0.80 kPa) at term.[82]

Fetal Circulation

The fetal circulation (Figure 9-12) is unique in several aspects: (1) presence of intracardiac (foramen ovale) and extracardiac (DV and DA) shunts; (2) high-resistance pulmonary circuit; and (3) low-resistance systemic circuit.[85] The high pulmonary vascular resistance (PVR) is a result of the collapsed lungs and the thick medial smooth muscle layer of the pulmonary arteries (see Pulmonary Vasculature).[141] As a result of the high PVR and collapsed lungs, blood flow to the lungs is low in the fetus, although some is retained to support lung growth and development (see Pulmonary Vasculature). The high resting tone and PVR in fetuses are believed to be maintained by mechanical factors (compression of small pulmonary arteries by the fluid-filled alveolar spaces), the

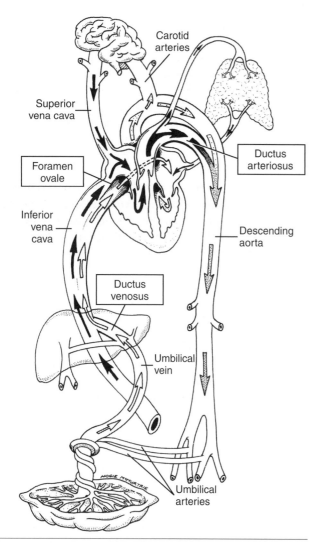

low fetal Po_2, and a balance between vasoconstrictors and vasodilators that favors vasoconstriction. The most important pulmonary vasoconstrictors are probably endothelin, arachidonic acid metabolites, and hypoxia.[17] Po_2 in the fetal pulmonary circuit is 17 to 20 mm Hg (2.26 to 2.66 kPa). Pulmonary vascular resistance, although still high, decreases with increasing gestational age and growth of the pulmonary vascular bed.[85]

The communication between the atria (i.e., foramen ovale), along with the DA, allows for equalization of pressures between the atria and the great vessels. Because these pressures are equal, the ventricular pressures are also equal. The low-resistance systemic circuit is also a result of the passive nature of umbilical and placental blood flow.[126]

As noted previously, blood flow in the fetus is arranged in a parallel fashion (see Figure 9-11, *A*). This arrangement results in mixing of oxygenated and deoxygenated blood at the atrial and great vessel levels. The fetal shunts allow for this mixing, which diverts blood from the immature lungs to the placenta, where oxygen–carbon dioxide exchange takes place. As a result, 30% to 50% of the fetal cardiac output is directed toward the placenta, with 14% to the brain and less than 10% to 12% to the lungs.[41,85,118] The remainder is divided among the gastrointestinal tract, kidneys, and the rest of body. The fetal liver is the first organ to receive maternal substances, followed by the heart and brain.

As the blood returns from the placenta to the fetus via the umbilical vein (UV), it passes either into the portal system's microcirculation to later run off into the inferior vena cava (IVC) or into the DV. The DV is a narrow trumpet-shaped structure that originates from the UV as it turns below the liver.[15,82] The DV is narrowest at the UV end, with a mean diameter of 0.5 mm at midgestation increasing to no more than 2 mm by term.[82] The DV connects, via the umbilical vein–portal sinus, to the IVC just below the diaphragm (see Figure 9-12). The DV is important in nutrient and oxygen partitioning.[15] At 20 weeks, 30% of the blood flow from the UV is shunted across the DV, decreasing to 18% to 20% after 32 weeks.[17,82,97,173] By late pregnancy, 70% to 80% of the oxygenated blood from the placenta goes first to the liver, reflecting an increased priority of the liver needs near term.[82] DV shunting is influenced by its diameter, pressure gradients, and blood viscosity.[97] An increase in the diameter of the DV increases the proportion of DV blood reaching the heart and downregulates the volume of blood going to the left lobe of the liver.[15] With hypovolemia or hypoxemia, more blood is shunted across the DV and thus to the heart.[17,82] Shunting across the DV is also increased in fetal growth restriction, even under stable conditions.[82]

The liver blood supply consists of blood from the UV (80%), portal vein (15%), and hepatic artery (5%).[41,45] UV blood entering the liver flows to both lobes; portal venous blood is directed primarily to the right lobe.[126] Therefore 95% of the blood flow to the left lobe comes from the UV. The right lobe blood supply comes from the UV (40% to 60%), portal vein (30% to 50%), and hepatic artery (10%).[45,60]

FIGURE 9-12   Fetal circulation. (From Goldsmith, J.P. [2015]. Congenital defects of the cardiovascular system. In R.J. Martin, A.A. Fanaroff, & M.C. Walsh. [Eds.]. *Fanaroff and Martin's neonatal-perinatal medicine: Diseases of the fetus and infant* [10th ed.]. Philadelphia: Saunders.)

The DV is a low-resistance channel that allows a portion of relatively well-oxygenated blood to enter the heart directly. Normal flow is phasic and anterograde. Abnormal flow patterns in the DV may indicate fetal stress.[143] The DV is under tonic adrenergic control and dilates in the presence of nitric oxide, prostaglandins (PGs), and hypoxemia.[82] The blood entering the IVC from the UV via the DV joins with the blood that returns from the lower half of the fetal body. The blood that reaches the IVC from the umbilical vein has a greater oxygen content and kinetic energy and so stays in a stream that is separate from the blood returning from the lower body.[15,82] Because of this preferential streaming, DV blood is found along the left dorsal wall of the IVC.[45,91] Altered DV flow in early pregnancy and low-velocity IVC flow are associated with fetal acidemia, aneuploidy, hydrops, arrhythmias, and cardiac defects.[15,97,164]

As the IVC blood enters the right atrium, a tissue flap, the eustachian valve, at the junction of the RA and IVC directs blood from the dorsal portion of the IVC (i.e., where the more highly oxygenated blood from the UV streams) toward the crista dividens and foramen ovale; the lower-velocity blood is directed toward the tricuspid valve.[42,45,173] The foramen ovale is formed by the overlap of the atrial septum secundum over the atrial septum primum (see Figure 9-9). Patency of the foramen ovale is maintained by increased blood flow and pressure in the right versus left atrium.[82] The crista dividens (the free edge of the atrial septum) separates the flow into two streams, with 50% to 60% (which is the blood with the highest oxygen saturation) diverted across the foramen ovale into the left atrium; the remainder flows into the right atrium and right ventricle.[41]

In the left atrium the blood from the IVC mixes with the (minimal) pulmonary venous return and passes through the mitral valve into the LV. Thus most of the blood in the LA and LV is the more oxygenated umbilical vein blood. Left ventricular preload in the fetus is caused primarily by umbilical vein blood return.[85] Upon contraction of the heart, this blood is ejected into the ascending aorta to feed the coronary, left carotid, and subclavian arteries. Only 10% of fetal CO continues across the aortic isthmus into the descending aorta.[84]

The aortic isthmus (between the left subclavian and DA) is the area between the site where blood is ejected from the RV and the site where blood is ejection from the LV. Normally flow is both systolic and diastolic and anterograde across the isthmus, but with fetal stress diastolic flow may become retrograde as a compensatory response to preserve cerebral perfusion.[143]

The blood flowing along the anterior portion of the IVC consists of hepatic and lower body desaturated blood. This blood mixes with blood from the superior vena cava (SVC) and coronary sinus in the right atrium. This blood flow is directed downward across the tricuspid valve and into the RV. Very little of the SVC blood return crosses the foramen ovale to the left atrium. SVC blood is directed by the crista interveniens on the right atrial posterolateral wall toward the tricuspid valve and right ventricle.[41] Venous return to the RA

is about two-thirds blood from the IVC (about one-third of which is blood from the UV and DV), about one-third from the SVC, and about 3% from the coronary sinus.[41,45]

The mixed blood in the right ventricle is then ejected into the pulmonary artery, where increased PVR prevents more than 10% to 12% of the RV blood flow (or about 8% of the CCO) from entering the pulmonary bed. In the second half of pregnancy, less than 40% of the CCO is shunted across the DA to enter the descending aorta and the low-resistance systemic and placental circulations.[82,84] Blood flow to the pulmonary bed increases after 30 weeks to up to 30% of the CCO, perhaps because of growth and thus increased metabolic need of the lungs.[42,45,82,118] Decreased diastolic flow and increased pulsations are associated with placental infection and twin-to-twin transfusion.[143]

The DA is similar in size to the descending aorta and pulmonary artery. The medial layer of the DA consists of longitudinal and spiral layers of smooth muscle surrounded by concentric layers of elastic tissue; the intima consists of thick neointimal cushions made up of smooth muscle and endothelial cells.[55] The DA smooth muscle is the site of oxygen sensors; the endothelium releases vasoactive substances such as PGE_2 and PGI_2 to modulate DA tone.[55]

The low fetal Po_2 and high levels of circulating PGs (especially PGE_1, PGE_2, and PGI_2) maintain patency of the DA in utero.[41] PGs are normally metabolized in the lungs. Because pulmonary blood flow is so low in the fetus, PGs are metabolized more slowly and therefore levels remain high. PGE_2 is the most powerful and interacts with receptors (EP_2, EP_3, EP_4) on the ductal wall. This interaction activates adenylate cyclase, which increases cAMP to decrease sensitivity of the ductus to calcium and help maintain relaxation. Stimulation of EP_3 opens K-ATP channels to hyperpolarize the ductus and reduces tone.[31] Reactivity of the DA increases in the late third trimester, increasing its vulnerability to the constricting effects of prostaglandin synthetase inhibitors such as indomethacin.[82] Blood returns to the placenta via the two UAs, which arise from the internal iliac arteries. The UAs spiral around the umbilical vein in the cord, then anastomose near the placental surface to equalize arterial pressures.[83] The UA wall is relatively thick compared with its lumen size, with several layers of vascular smooth muscle cells but no internal elastic lamina.[83]

Fetal circulation is not significantly altered by increased intrauterine pressure with uterine contractions in a healthy fetal-placental unit. Even with compression of the placental vessels, the vessels are relatively unreactive to short-term changes.[45]

Oxygen Content

The oxygen content in a fetus is lower than that in a neonate, child, or adult. The highest oxygen content is found in the blood returning from the placenta via the umbilical vein, which is 30 to 35 mm Hg (3.99 to 4.65 kPa) and 70% to 80% saturated.[42] This falls to 26 to 28 mm Hg (3.45 to 3.72 kPa) (saturation, 65%) by the time it reaches the left atrium and mixes with blood from the IVC and pulmonary veins and is ejected into the ascending aorta and to the brain.[42,84]

The umbilical return that mixes with the superior vena caval blood (Po_2, 12 to 14 mm Hg [1.59 to 1.86 kPa]; saturation, 40%) is reduced to a PaO_2 of 15 to 25 mm Hg (1.99 to 3.32 kPa).[45,84,141] This blood is destined for the pulmonary arteries, descending aorta (55% saturated), upper torso and brain, and placenta. Therefore the heart delivers blood with the highest oxygen content to the coronary arteries and brain, whereas the blood with the lowest PaO_2 is shunted toward the placenta, where reoxygenation occurs.

Another fetal adaptation to low oxygen tension is the presence of fetal hemoglobin. This specific type of hemoglobin has a high affinity for oxygen even at low oxygen tensions, thereby improving saturation and facilitating transport of oxygen to the tissues. The perfusion rate is greater in a fetus than in an adult, which helps compensate for the lower oxygen saturations and increased oxygen-hemoglobin affinity. The low oxygen tension in the fetus keeps the pulmonary vasculature constricted and, along with PGE_2, the DA dilated. See Chapters 8 and 10 for a further discussion of fetal hemoglobin and oxygenation.

Control of Fetal Circulation

Fetal circulation is controlled by neural inputs and humoral factors, such as catecholamines, vasopressin, angiotensin II, and PGs. Baroreceptors in the aortic arch and carotid arteries are sensitive to changes in systemic arterial pressure. With development, the sensitivity of the arterial baroreflex changes and is reset as blood pressure increases.[41,150] The mechanism involves both peripheral and central resetting. Endogenous nitric oxide, angiotensin II, serotonin, and changes in basal autonomic nerve sensitivity may all modulate this process.[150] Carotid receptor stimulation leads to a mild tachycardia and marked increase in blood pressure, whereas stimulation of aortic chemoreceptors leads to bradycardia and a slight increase in blood pressure.[41,45] Natriuretic peptides are functional by midgestation and have a role in volume and blood pressure regulation.[34] Other regulators of fetal circulation include the renin-angiotensin system (see Chapter 11), vasopressin, natriuretic peptides, PGs, and endothelial-derived factors such as nitric oxide and endothelin.[41]

Sympathetic innervation is immature, with parasympathetic (vagal) dominance. Both vagal and sympathetic tone increase with fetal hypoxia. Parasympathetic stimulation has a primary job in maintaining FHR and beat-to-beat variability. The sympathetic nervous system provides a reserve to improve the heart's pumping ability during intermittent stress. Cholinergic fibers develop early in gestation. α-Adrenergic and β-adrenergic fibers and receptors also appear early (although concentrations of receptors differ from those in adults) and increase with gestation.[41,45] If oxygen content of the fetal blood decreases, blood flow to the brain, myocardium, and adrenals increases; pulmonary blood flow and flow to the lower body decreases.[45] Autonomic control of fetal circulation is discussed further in Chapter 6.

NEONATAL PHYSIOLOGY

The cardiovascular system is designed to deliver adequate oxygen and nutrients to the tissues and remove metabolic byproducts at all stages of development. The coordinated functioning of respiratory, cardiovascular, and endocrine systems is essential to meet the cellular metabolic needs, especially in times of stress. During fetal, neonatal, and adult life, these processes are quite different, and maturational processes continue after birth. Alterations or a delay in transitional circulation processes in the preterm infant can result in low systemic blood flow and hypotension.

Transitional Events

At birth the cardiac output (CO) is redistributed with increased pulmonary blood flow. Pulmonary and systemic pressure change as pulmonary vascular resistance (PVR) decreases and systemic vascular resistance (SVR) increases. The ventricles begin working in series (see Figure 9-11, *B*), which is the adult configuration, rather than in parallel, and the fetal extracardiac and intracardiac shunts close. With birth, oxygenation is moved from the placenta to the lungs, and air ventilation results in increased oxygen availability, with a concomitant rise in Po_2 levels. Cardiovascular transition is influenced by lung aeration, increasing oxygenation, and umbilical cord clamping as well as changes in autonomic reflexes and sympathetic activity with release of catecholamines, thyroid hormones, vasopressin, and changes in the renin-angiotensin system.[67,120,150]

Epinephrine and norepinephrine levels increase during labor and at birth, decreasing to prebirth levels within 4 hours, although the increase in sympathetic outflow is maintained for at least 6 hours.[6,150] The catecholamine surge mediates the increase in systemic blood pressure, metabolic adaptation, and thermoregulatory changes with birth.[67] This surge is influenced by cortisol release, alterations in blood gases with birth, decreased ambient temperature, cord clamping, increased intracranial pressure, or other events during transition.[67,150] Control mechanisms may temporarily override arterial baroreflexes to maintain high sympathetic tone with transition.[150] Epinephrine mediates increased CO and myocardial contractility, which are important for changes in myocardial function with birth and for enhancing contractility with the stresses of transition.[150] These responses may be attenuated in preterm infants.[67,150] As a result, preterm infants tend to have higher catecholamine levels than term infants, because their organ systems are less responsive with higher concentration thresholds and reduced responsiveness.[67]

The changeover from fetal to neonatal circulation is linked with the development and function of the pulmonary vasculature and changes in PVR (see "Pulmonary Vasculature"). At delivery the low-resistance placental circulation is removed, leading to an increase in SVR.[101] The increased SVR results from the increased volume of blood in the arterial system (i.e., blood that no longer has a placenta to return to), which must now be accommodated in the systemic circulation, and to the decreasing PVR. As a result of these changes, systemic blood pressure demonstrates a sustained increase over the first hours to days after birth.[101,107] Left ventricular stroke volume and output increase after birth, peaking at 2 hours then decreasing over the next few hours, probably secondary to changes in ductus arteriosus (DA) flow.[120] After birth cerebral blood flow (CBF) also increases with a transient pressure-passive cerebral circuit (see Cerebral Autoregulation in Chapter 15).[85] Decreases in CBF are noted in term infants during the first minutes after birth and are believed to be a response to increasing PaO_2 and to changes in flow across the patent ductus arteriosus (PDA) from right to left to bidirectional to left to right.[120]

The increased SVR may lead to transient myocardial dysfunction in very-low-birth-weight (VLBW) infants because of the limited capacity of their myocardium and decreased systemic perfusion. Immature compensatory mechanisms may further reduce CBF and brain oxygen delivery, increasing the risks for white matter injury and periventricular hemorrhage (germinal matrix hemorrhage)/intraventricular hemorrhage (PVH/IVH) during the subsequent reperfusion phase.[37,119,120] The immature myocardium (see "Neonatal Myocardium") of VLBW infants may have difficulty pumping blood against the increased SVR at birth, leading to a period of low cardiac output in the first 12 to 24 hours after birth with a transient decrease in systemic blood flow (as measured by superior vena cava flow) and CBF.[118] After this time cardiac output begins to normalize, and CBF may increase rapidly over the next 2 days.[119,120] This increase in CBF increases the risk of PVH/IVH (most hemorrhages occur within the first 2 days after birth).[119] These changes are more pronounced in extremely-low-birth-weight (ELBW) infants who have a more immature myocardium, autonomic nervous system, and baroreflex and chemoreflex responses.[37] As a result ELBW infants may be in a state of compensated shock immediately after birth with low systemic blood flow and brain hypoperfusion. They have a decreased ability to increase stroke volume to increase cardiac output, and are thus more dependent on heart rate, which is also limited because of their immature autonomic nervous system.[37] Use of positive pressure ventilation may further alter hemodynamics. As the cardiac output normalizes over the next 2 to 3 days, CBF increases. This may result in reperfusion injury and PVH/IVH.[120] The transition process is also extended because of delays in the closure of the foramen ovale and DA and persistence of lower pulmonary vascular resistance with increased pulmonary blood flow.[37]

The initiation of air breathing leads to lung expansion, an increase in alveolar oxygen concentration, and vasodilation of the pulmonary vascular bed. As vasodilation occurs, PVR falls rapidly. At birth the PVR falls by almost 80%, resulting in a dramatic increase in pulmonary blood flow and a fall in ductal shunting. Before birth the high PVR and low SVR result in 90% of the right ventricle (RV) output going through the ductus. After delivery, 90% of this flow goes to the pulmonary

arteries.[45] The left ventricle (LV) must now pump the entire CO (approximately 350 mL/kg). This change is mediated by the increase in circulating catecholamines and myocardial β-adrenergic receptors.[84]

Factors decreasing PVR at birth include lung aeration; increasing PO_2; and release of vasodilators such as bradykinin (which increases as PO_2 increases), prostaglandin (PG) E_1, PGE_2, PGI_2 (prostacyclin), nitric oxide, and endothelial-derived releasing factor (EDRF). Lung aeration and PO_2 are the most critical factors. Lung inflation and increasing PO_2 either alone or together (greatest effect) decrease PVR and increase nitric oxide.[17,141] Lung inflation stimulates pulmonary stretch receptors, leading to a reflexive vasodilation and a 4- to 10-fold increase in pulmonary blood flow.[45,141] Currently the major pulmonary vasodilators at birth are believed to be nitric oxide and prostacyclin, whose release may be mediated by gaseous expansion of the lungs. Adenosine, bradykinin, and possibly adrenomedullin may also have important roles.

Nitric oxide, a main component of endothelial-derived relaxing factor, is released by the endothelium and stimulated by oxygen.[17] Studies in fetal lambs suggest that both increased PO_2 and rapid increase in pulmonary blood flow (creating shear stress) induce endothelial nitric oxide synthetase (NOS) and thus increase nitric oxide levels with birth.[141] Increased NOS expression with oxygen stimulation develops late in gestation as the pulmonary vasculature become more sensitive to nitric oxide. Pulmonary vasoconstriction in utero is believed to be mediated by inhibition of nitric oxide production by substances such as endothelins.[41] Prostacyclin increases late in gestation and in the early postbirth period. Its action is believed to be stimulated by rhythmic lung distention rather than increased oxygenation. Oxygen may also mediate dilation by opening oxygen-sensitive potassium channels in the pulmonary smooth muscle.[141]

Umbilical blood flow is reduced within 40 to 60 seconds after birth; diameters of the umbilical vein and arteries decrease significantly within 120 seconds. The exact cause of these changes is not clear but may be related to exposure of the cord to the cooler, more highly oxygenated room temperature, although these are not the only factors; contraction precedes the increase in oxygenation, and cooling leads to transitional, not sustained, constriction as well as local vasoconstrictors.[83]

Closure of the Ductus Venosus

The ductus venosus (DV) is functionally closed within minutes of birth as a result of the cessation of blood flow. Cessation of placental blood flow is mediated by mechanical stimulation with stretching of the umbilical cord and its blood vessels. This enhances initial constriction of the umbilical blood vessels. The rapid increase in PO_2 with initiation of breathing maintains constriction of the umbilical vessels.[45] The DV is obliterated by 1 week in three-fourths of term infants and in most by 10 to 14 days.[47] The DV remains open longer in preterm infants and infants with persistent pulmonary hypertension (PPHN) and cardiac malformations.[82] Closure is probably mediated by endothelin-1 and thromboxane A_2.[99]

Closure of the Foramen Ovale

Alterations at birth lead to pressure changes within the cardiac chambers and the movement from parallel circulation to in-series circulation. The pressure changes result from the rapid drop in systemic venous return via the inferior vena cava (IVC) and the increase in pulmonary venous return. The left atrial pressure rises, exceeding the right atrial pressure, and the foramen ovale's flap valve closes, functionally separating the two atria. The foramen ovale usually closes anatomically by 30 months but may remain patent into childhood or longer.[45,99,126] In 15% to 25% of adults the flaps remain open enough for a probe to be easily passed through them. This opening occurs without significant right-to-left shunting.[39,84,141] A patent foramen ovale in adults is associated with a risk of paradoxical systemic embolism; refractory hypoxemia in individual with myocardial infarction or pulmonary disease; migraine headaches with aura; and neurologic decompression illness in divers, high-altitude pilots, and astronauts.[39]

Closure of the Ductus Arteriosus

The DA begins to close almost immediately after birth but remains patent for several hours to days after delivery. The pulmonary vascular resistance may remain higher than the systemic vascular bed for a short time after the first breath. This allows for a small right-to-left shunt to remain and for desaturated blood to mix with oxygenated blood in the descending aorta. If the PVR remains high or is increased during the first hours or days after delivery, the right-to-left shunt may become clinically significant, as is seen in PPHN.

As the SVR continues to increase and stabilize and the PVR continues to fall, the movement of blood across the DA reverses and becomes left to right. For a time, flow is bidirectional, with both right-to-left and left-to-right flow, before right-to-left flow ceases. During bidirectional flow there is a tendency for left-to-right flow during early systole and left-to-right flow during late systole and diastole (these patterns are related to the timing of pressure waves in the right versus left ventricles).[85] Within the first 10 to 15 hours of extrauterine life in most term infants, the DA achieves functional closure through smooth muscle constriction.[99] By 96 hours of age, the DA is functionally closed in nearly all term infants.[31,47,126] The DA remains open for a longer period in preterm infants (see Patent Ductus Arteriosus in the Preterm Infant). In most healthy preterm infants older than 30 weeks' gestation, the DA has closed functionally by 4 days. Only 11% of these infants have a PDA, versus 65% of infants younger than 30 weeks' gestation with severe respiratory distress.[31]

Anatomic closure takes longer and is usually achieved within 2 to 3 months. During this time, the ductus may be reopened if hypoxia or increased PVR occurs. This may result from prolonged crying or with pathologic problems. Anatomic closure involves neointimal thickening with endothelial

destruction and loss of smooth muscle cells from the inner muscle media, proliferation of subintimal tissue, and formation of connective tissues to form a fibrous strand known as the *ligamentum arteriosus*.[45,75,146] By term the DA has a very thick wall and requires an intramural vasa vasorum to provide nutrients to the outer muscle. Constriction of the DA obliterates the vasa vasorum, and the muscle becomes avascular and hypoxic. This ischemic hypoxia of the ductal wall smooth muscle and epithelial cells inhibits PGE_2 and NO and induces expression of vascular endothelial growth factor (VEGF) and vascular cell adhesion molecule-1 (VCAM-1).[31] VEGF and VCAM-1 mediate monocyte movement and adherence to the epithelium and release of factors that promote migration of smooth muscle into the ductal wall with neointimal formation and eventually occlusion of the ductal lumina.[31,75,146]

Functional closure of the DA at birth is influenced primarily by oxygen and these vasoactive substances rather than primarily hemodynamic changes, as is seen with closure of the foramen ovale and DV.[45,146] Other factors favoring DA dilation include PGE_1, PGE_2, PGI_2, hypoxia, and acidosis, whereas factors favoring DA constriction include PGF_2, prostaglandin synthetase, increased Po_2 and pH, endothelin-1, and bradykinin.[55,74,126,146] Ductal oxygen sensitivity and closure is also facilitated by glucocorticoids.[146]

Although there is a relative hypoxia present at birth (compared with adult oxygen levels), within 10 minutes neonates have a PaO_2 of 50 mm Hg (6.65 kPa). This continues to increase over the first hour to approximately 62 mm Hg (8.24 kPa). Arterial oxygen concentrations stabilize between 75 and 85 mm Hg (9.97 to 11.30 kPa) over the first 2 days, with a concomitant fall in PVR and improved ventilation-perfusion ratios. The fall in PVR continues for the next several weeks; however, the adult circulatory pattern is usually achieved within the first 2 days.[41]

The increased PaO_2 alters the ductal smooth muscle membrane potential, mediated by a cytochrome P450 hemoprotein, which leads to increased calcium influx and contraction, or by altering potassium channels.[146] Potassium channels in the ductus change during gestation to ones that can be inhibited by oxygen.[31] Potassium modulates voltage-gated calcium channels, opening them to increase the influx of calcium.[55] Endothelin-1, which may be induced by the increased PaO_2 after birth, increases intracellular calcium via G-protein coupling.[74,146] The Rho/Rho kinase pathways induce calcium sensitization (via persistent myosin light-chain phosphorylation) and vasoconstriction.[55,74] Platelets may also be involved in DA closure by enhancing sealing of the constricted DA; proinflammatory cytokines inhibit this thrombic sealing.[55]

PGE_2 is believed to be primarily responsible for maintaining the patency of the DA during fetal life. The DA is extremely sensitive to PGE_2, and it is the loss of this reactivity that keeps the ductus closed after birth. Just before birth there is a decrease in circulating PGE_2 concentrations, possibly a result of an increase in pulmonary blood flow that enhances delivery of PGE_2 to the lungs for metabolism. This may prepare for or enhance ductal closure at the time the infant converts to air breathing and active ductal constriction occurs.[41,45,146] PG receptors in the ductal wall also decrease, further reducing PGE$_2$ efficacy. The continued decrease in PGE$_2$ with birth is related to increased pulmonary blood flow and increased lung metabolic activity as well as removal of the placenta, the main source of PGE$_2$ in the fetus.[45,55,106,121]

Neonatal Myocardium

The myocardium undergoes structural and functional changes after birth. The newborn myocardium has less sarcoplasmic reticulum and t-tubule synthesis with shorter, more rounded and disorganized myofibrils.[12,118] The myocardium also contains more fibrous noncontractile tissue than older individuals and has decreased sympathetic innervation.[12] The myocytes become more cylindrical; myofibrils increase and become more organized.[99,121] In the first month, growth occurs because of increases in myocyte numbers; by the second month, increases are caused by changes in cell size.[6] The major physiologic change in the myocardium is the improved ability to generate force and of the myofibrils to shorten. The weeks after birth bring about a change in ventricular mass, with the left increasing more than the right.[140] However, during this process the RV becomes more compliant. As a result, changes in RV volume have a greater effect on LV filling in a fetus and newborn than in an adult.[8,41]

Myocardial compliance increases rapidly during the first few days of extrauterine life. Changes in connective tissue content can be seen during this time and may explain the change in compliance, although additional explanations may lie in collagen, extracellular matrix, or matrix attachment site differences between a fetus and an adult. VLBW infants have a more immature myocardium with fewer contractile elements, fewer mitochondria, immature sarcoplasmic reticulum, and lower energy stores, impairing myocardial function, altered titan (which influences muscle elasticity), and immature sympathetic innervation.[37,42,85,118,120] In these infants the myometrium has a higher water content and less contractile mass; therefore the ventricles are less distensible, generate less force per unit weight, have altered systolic and diastolic function, and have less reserve to compensate for changes in blood volume and PVR.[7,31,85,90,118]

Pulmonary Vasculature

As noted in the previous section, with transition to extrauterine life, blood flow to the lungs increases 8- to 10-fold with the marked decrease in PVR.[156] Failure of PVR to fall at birth can lead to PPHN (see Chapter 10). PPHN is characterized by acute respiratory distress with hypoxemia and acidemia caused by decreased pulmonary blood flow because of elevated PVR. PPHN may represent failure to achieve transition to air breathing or may be secondary to other disorders or lung injury that impedes the normal decreases in PVR after birth.[17,156] The high PVR in a fetus is the result of the thick muscular coat of medial smooth muscle. This muscle involutes rapidly after birth. Toward the periphery the encircling

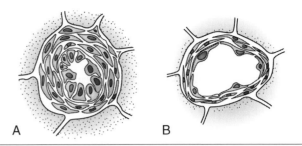

FIGURE 9-13   Changes in the small muscular pulmonary arteries during transition. Muscularized small pulmonary arteries from a near-term fetus **(A)** demonstrate swollen endothelial cells and increased thickness of the muscular layer. Within 24 hours after birth **(B)**, a considerable increase in luminal diameter is noted secondary to flattening of the endothelial cells, spreading of the smooth muscle cell, and an increase in external diameter caused by relaxation of the smooth muscles. These events contribute to the drop in pulmonary vascular resistance after birth. (From Lakshminrushimha, S. & Steinharn, R.H. [1999]. Pulmonary vascular biology during neonatal transition. *Clin Perinatol, 26,* 604.)

smooth muscle is less complete; it is absent in the most peripheral arteries.[17]

Changes in the pulmonary vasculature after birth occur in two phases (Figure 9-13). The first phase is prominent during the first 24 hours after birth, with dilation and recruitment of nonmuscularized and partially muscularized arteries.[132] The second phase involves further involution from 24 hours of age to 6 to 8 weeks. The partially muscularized arteries become nonmuscularized and the completely muscularized vessels become partially muscularized with thinning of the remaining muscle layer.[132] As a result of these changes, the vessel lumen size increases, the ability of the pulmonary arteries to constrict decreases, and PVR continues to fall. By 6 to 8 weeks after birth, PVR reaches adult values and the pulmonary vasculature becomes less sensitive to the effects of Po$_2$ changes.

Metabolic Rate and Oxygen Transport

Metabolic rate is measured as oxygen consumption and is much higher in neonates than in adults. The neonatal metabolic rate is also higher than that of the fetus because of independent extrauterine functioning and growth requirements. The components of oxygen consumption are related to energy expenditure and include basal metabolic rate, growth, heat production, and physical activity. The growth component is approximately 2% to 3% of the total metabolic rate and is higher in preterm infants. Oxygen consumption in neonates increases exponentially with physical activity, placement in a nonneutral thermal environment, therapeutic and diagnostic procedures, and increased work of breathing.[108]

The oxygen availability, which is the product of the CO and the arterial oxygen content, is also elevated in neonates. The estimated delivery of oxygen in a neonate at rest is 75% higher than in an adult. Three major processes impair oxygen availability: ventilation-perfusion mismatching from either intrapulmonary or extrapulmonary sources, reduced oxygen-hemoglobin–binding capacity, and reduced CO. In addition to these processes, a cardiovascular system that is unable to respond to an increased metabolic demand can result in decompensation.[108]

Endocrine, respiratory, and cardiovascular responses to altered oxygenation are similar to those found in adults, the major difference being that the neonate functions close to maximum capacity normally and therefore has little reserve to compensate for further demands. Therefore, when impaired oxygen transport results in increased CO (primarily because of an increased heart rate), the maximum is readily reached. Further oxygen demands are associated with an increase in oxygen extraction and a decrease in oxygen saturation.[73]

Hypoxemia results in a decrease in oxygen consumption, oxygen availability, and SVR and an increase in oxygen extraction by the tissues. Heart rate and CO increase, because the ability to deliver and release oxygen to the myocardium is essential for the myocardium to respond to the hypoxemia and compensate for impaired oxygen transport. Isovolemic anemia results in a significant decrease in arterial and mixed venous oxygen content, mean aortic pressure, and SVR. CO and stroke volume increase regardless of the hemoglobin content; however, heart rate increases are seen only with hemoglobin levels of 6 g/dL (60 g/L) or less. If oxygen affinity is reduced, CO and stroke volume increase to a greater degree. These events, once again, occur only when myocardial function is maintained. Impaired CO results in redistribution of blood flow, with flow directed to the heart and brain preferentially and shunted away from the peripheral organ systems. This is reflected in an increase in vascular resistance in the lower body, with no change in upper body resistance.

Over the first 2 to 4 months of life, there is a fall in hemoglobin concentration, an increase in adult hemoglobin (HbA), and a rightward shift in the oxygen-hemoglobin dissociation curve (see Chapters 8 and 10). This enables more oxygen to be released to the tissues at the same capillary oxygen tension. However, the increased metabolic demands of extrauterine life (including physical activity) must be accompanied by an increase in the P50 to compensate for the total hemoglobin concentration. The pattern of changes during these first 2 to 4 months includes a decline in total hemoglobin (reaching its lowest point at 8 to 12 weeks in term infants); a progressive shift in P50 to the right; and an increase in 2,3-diphosphoglycerate (2,3-DPG) (see Chapter 8). There may also be an increase in CO and an increase in oxygen extraction. The latter is adjusted depending on the oxygen consumption, total hemoglobin, and P50. Once hemoglobin levels fall below a critical point, however, CO is unable to compensate for the reduced oxygen availability, necessitating a redistribution in CO.[73]

Myocardial Performance in the Neonate

Myocardial performance is influenced by ventricular preload, myocardial contractility, heart rate, and ventricular afterload. The adaptation to neonatal life is characterized by an increase in heart rate, end-diastolic volume, and enhanced inotropy because of sympathetic stimulation.[6] Even at rest the neonate is functioning near full capacity with reduced reserve in contractility, preload, and afterload.[12] This functional state is needed to meet the increased vascular loading that occurs with birth. Consequently, the newborn heart has less ability to adapt to additional acute pressure (afterload) or volume (preload) stresses.[6] Because many inotropic agents increase afterload, this may reduce positive inotropic effects.[12] The increased sympathetic stimulation with birth may be one reason that the newborn is less able to significantly increase CO with hypotension.[150] Myocardial performance is altered in VLBW infants because of structural and functional limitations (see "Neonatal Myocardium"); thus the limitations discussed in the following sections are more prominent in immature infants.

Preload

Ventricular preload is a measure of end-diastolic volume (EDV). Myocardial fiber length changes with EDV in a predictable manner as described by the Frank-Starling law. According to this law, up to critical length, increased EDV leads to increased fiber length and improved contractility. This leads to increased stroke volume (SV) and CO.

Ventricular preload in the neonate is influenced by the less-compliant ventricles. The neonatal heart does function under the Frank-Starling law, but under homeostatic conditions it operates at the upper limit of this law. Compared with the adult heart, the neonatal heart requires a higher filling pressure, and this filling pressure is reached at lower volumes. In addition, neonates have a higher CO because of increased metabolism.

The neonatal heart must deal with the increased preload generated by the high volume load at delivery. Moreover, the lower compliance of the LV decreases the preload reserve volume. Heart rates in neonates are already high, especially in VLBW infants, which may limit the ability to increase CO by increasing heart rate.[7,42] Whether infants can augment CO through further increases in heart rate continues to be examined, as does the effectiveness of inotropic support in the neonate without contractility failure. If increases in afterload or preload are associated with decreased contractility, as with sepsis or asphyxia, inotropic support can rapidly improve CO.[6] Compromised early diastolic filling is seen more in preterm infants because of their lower myocardial compliance and fetal titan isotope forms that limit muscle elasticity.[42]

In the fetus and newborn, an increase in RV volume interferes with LV filling.[6] The effects one chamber has on another are also more marked with decreasing compliance. Thus if there are changes in RV diastolic or loading pressures in the fetus, the LV is compromised and stroke volume is reduced.[42] Once the pulmonary vascular resistance (PVR) drops at delivery and throughout the neonatal period, LV filling is enhanced and stroke volume is improved. Therefore neonates are more compromised than are adults by an increase in RV preload (i.e., rapid administration of a large fluid bolus) or afterload with specific pathologic conditions (e.g., pulmonary hypertension).

Contractility

Myocardial contractility relates to the heart's intrinsic pumping ability, which is dependent on calcium influx in the myocardium. Acidosis, hypercarbia, and hypoxia alter cell permeability and the NA-K pump and lead to decreased contractility. As noted, early contractility is further altered in VLBW infants because of their immature myocardium (see "Neonatal Myocardium").

Contractile capabilities are dependent on the force of contraction, shortening velocity (preload), inotropy, and afterload (load carried at the time of contraction). The maximum shortening of muscle is obtained when there is zero load; however, as the afterload increases, the velocity of muscle shortening decreases. If the load is so great that no external shortening is possible, the contraction is considered isometric. Changing the muscle length can alter the force of the contraction; force development is related to the number of cross-bridges (the greater the number, the greater the force).[8]

An increase in contractility and development of force is part of the maturation process of the myocardium. There is no sudden change in force-generating ability with birth, but rather a slow progression over time as the entire cardiac system matures into adulthood. Most of these maturational processes are related to structural changes in the myocardial anatomy. As myofibril content increases, there is an increase in the number of cross-bridge attachments and therefore greater force generation. The increased organization of the myofibrils may also contribute to the ability to generate forceful contractions. Whether changes in the responsiveness of the contractile apparatus to calcium facilitate any of these changes is currently unclear. Maturation of membrane systems and calcium control may also affect muscle contractions.

The maturational increase in the force-generating ability of the myocardium begins to be seen in late gestation and continues until adulthood. Ventricular filling, pressure development, and ejection in a fetus are similar to those in neonates and adults, except that at birth there is a marked increase in combined ventricular output.[45] With birth, RV output increases by one third, whereas LV output triples. An increase in pulmonary venous return, improved inotropy (strength of contraction), increased heart rate, and the diastolic and systolic interactions of the right and left ventricles may contribute to the change in combined ventricular output. LV output increases significantly while the DA is still patent. A PDA increases the volume load of the heart, which may initiate a Frank-Starling response. The doubling of the LV stroke volume seen at birth may be related to release of ventricular constraint (from the chest wall, lungs, and pericardium) with lung aeration and clearance of lung fluid (see Chapter 10), thus increasing ventricular preload.

In the weeks after birth, LV output returns to fetal levels or lower, whereas systolic and end-diastolic pressures continue to rise. Other indicators of the increased birth inotropy also return to fetal baselines. This may have to do with the restoration of reserves after the birth process. Therefore diseases that place an additional demand on the heart to produce more CO in the first days of extrauterine life can result in cardiovascular compromise in neonates.[8]

Myocardial contractility is altered in neonates because of their decreased ventricular compliance and reduced contractile mass. As a result, neonates rely more on heart rate than on stroke volume to increase CO.[42,118] Yet this mechanism is also limited by their parasympathetic domination and immaturity of the sympathetic nervous system. In addition, neonates are vulnerable to metabolic and biochemical alterations that can further compromise contractility. Increasing heart rate may only improve CO slightly in the neonate, because CO is near maximum under homeostatic conditions.

Because myocardial contractility in neonates is high during the first week of life, there is little reserve in contractility.[13] This implies that inotropic drugs will do little to improve the contractile state of a normally functioning neonatal heart. One mechanism for this increased inotropic state and the elevated CO is the high level of adrenergic stimulation that occurs around birth. However, the increased CO that remains for several weeks postnatally cannot be explained by continued catecholamine activity.

Heart Rate

The baseline heart rate is determined by the intrinsic depolarization rate of the sinoatrial node, which is actively inhibited by tonic parasympathetic input. Myocardial sympathetic innervation is incomplete at birth, with decreased norepinephrine levels during the first 3 weeks. As a result, vagal effects predominate, with limited response to catecholamine stimulation of β-adrenergic receptors. As the parasympathetic system matures, the resting heart rate decreases.[41] Tachycardia (more than 160 beats per minute) is usually seen with events that lead to catecholamine release, sympathetic stimulation, or parasympathetic withdrawal. A higher heart rate is also seen in the extremely premature infant, in whom control of cardiac function is dominated by the sympathetic nervous system.

Afterload

Ventricular afterload is the force the myocardium must overcome to pump blood out of the ventricles against resistance from PVR and SVR.[42] Afterload affects contractility. Increased afterload leads to decreased contractility, whereas decreased afterload leads to increased contractility. Although PVR decreases significantly at birth, it remains higher than adult levels for 6 to 8 weeks after birth. During this time, PVR gradually decreases to adult values as the medial muscle layer of pulmonary arterioles is restructured (see "Pulmonary Vasculature"). In addition, neonatal pulmonary vasculature is characterized by increased reactivity of pulmonary arterioles, with a tendency toward vasoconstriction and increased PVR.

The LV end-diastolic volume increases with birth. This probably contributes to the neonatal increase in output via the Frank-Starling relationship. These changes may be related to the circulatory transition that occurs at delivery and the fall in PVR and increased pulmonary venous return. LV filling may be augmented by a decrease in RV afterload. Therefore a fall in pulmonary artery pressure would enhance LV output by decreasing RV afterload, which would improve RV ejection and result in a smaller RV end-diastolic volume. The LV is then able to fill to a larger volume at a comparable filling pressure. This interaction is magnified in the fetus and neonate because of the reduced cardiac compliance.[8]

Newborns have altered afterload because of their lower blood pressures, increased peripheral alpha and decreased beta receptors, and higher PVR.[7] The increased afterload leads to lower CO because of lack of contractile reserve.[13] The newborn, especially preterm infants, are more sensitive to changes in afterload. Delayed umbilical cord clamping (see Chapter 8) results in a gradual increase in afterload at birth (versus the rapid increase in SVR that occurs with early cord clamping) that may reduce stress on the immature myometrium, spikes in CBF, and thus the risk for PVH/IVH (see "Vulnerabilities to Brain Injury in Preterm and Term Infants" in Chapter 15).[120]

Regulation of Fetal and Neonatal Circulation

As in the adult, medullary, hypothalamic, and cerebral cortical activity, along with other hormonal and metabolic mechanisms, influence fetal and neonatal cardiovascular functions. The medullary centers appear to influence cardiovascular responses in a variable fashion in the fetus and the newborn; however, higher cortical or hypothalamic activities are associated with an increase in heart rate and hypertension. This stimulation and response are quite different than the baroreflex, which is a peripheral response by the baroreceptors to hypertension that is itself secondary to increased peripheral resistance. Baroreceptor and chemoreceptor function is reviewed in Box 6-1.

Complex neurohumoral and metabolic responses maintain blood pressure, heart rate, and distribution of blood flow in the fetus and the newborn. These include systemic sensors (stretch receptors and neural and hormonal mediators) as well as local responses that allow an organ to regulate flow. The interaction of the two systems allows the fetus and the newborn to respond to stress events by redistributing blood flow to spare high-priority organs with specific oxygen requirements.

The arterial baroreflex modulates heart rate and peripheral vasodilation by altering autonomic activity and regulating release of substances such as angiotensin II and arginine vasopressin.[150] Baroreceptors that are sensitive to changes in blood pressure are located in the aortic arch and the carotid sinuses (see Figure 6-2). These sensors cause changes in heart rate and, in the fetus, may be responsible for stabilizing fetal blood pressure, with increasing sensitivity as gestational age advances. Baroreceptor activity has been implicated in the decreasing fetal heart rate (FHR) baseline seen in later gestation as blood pressure rises. In late gestation and in the early

postbirth period, the baroreflex is reset toward higher pressures, paralleling the gradual increase in blood pressure.[93,150] Short-term increases in blood pressure do not cause resetting, although this is seen in adults.[150] Chemoreceptors can be found in both the peripheral and central nervous systems and may alter FHR in response to hypoxemia and acidosis (see Chapter 6). Chemoreceptors are present in the latter half of gestation and appear to be responsive to changes in pH and carbon dioxide tension and give rise to bradycardia while CO and umbilical blood flow are preserved. After birth, hypoxia leads to tachycardia and an increase in CO associated with increased respiratory effort.[41]

Sympathetic intervention is present and functional in the fetus and newborn, increasing responsiveness with increasing gestational age. Stimulation results in tachycardia, augmented myocardial contractility, and increased systemic arterial blood pressure. Newborns have limited α-receptors and myocardial sympathetic innervation.[12] Sympathetic nerves may exhibit "denervating hypersensitivity" (maximal stimulation with small amounts of catecholamines).[12] β-adrenoceptors are low in ELBW infants but increase to term and are higher in term infants than at older ages. Responses of α- and β-receptors have a more limited effect on cardiac contractility in the newborn, with fewer β2-receptors (important for vasodilation and bronchodilation) and many active α-receptors (which increase cardiac inotropy, vascular tone, and thus blood pressure and afterload).[12]

Parasympathetic input also increases with advancing gestational age. The major effector is the vagus nerve, which provides an inhibitory effect on FHR. Short-term variability of the FHR is modulated primarily by impulses from the vagus nerve (see Chapter 6). With increasing gestational age the parasympathetic system has a greater role in heart rate regulation, especially after 28 to 30 weeks, and increases more rapidly after 37 to 38 weeks, suggesting a marked increase in vagal tone.[150]

Humoral regulation of the cardiovascular system is related to the effects of catecholamines, vasopressin, renin-angiotensin, and PGs on the heart and vascular bed.[150] Catecholamines are secreted by the adrenal medulla and may be involved in fetal cardiovascular system regulation before the development of the sympathetic nervous system. Fetal myocardium appears to have similar responsiveness to catecholamines compared with that in adults.[41] As noted earlier, catecholamine levels increase markedly with birth, reaching pharmacologic levels.[93]

Arginine vasopressin is produced by the fetal pituitary gland early in gestation. Although usually undetectable, the concentration of vasopressin increases during hypoxia, hypotension, or hypernatremia. This results in vasoconstriction of the vessels in the musculoskeletal system, skin, and gut while increasing flow to the brain and heart. PGs may also play a role in augmenting blood flow to the brain during hypoxic episodes. These mechanisms may play a major role in the redistribution of fetal blood flow that occurs during significant hypoxia (see Chapter 6).[41]

Stimulation of the renin-angiotensin system leads to an increase in FHR, blood pressure, and combined ventricular output. Blood flow to the lungs and myocardium increases; flow to the renal system falls off. Angiotensin II seems to exert a vasotonic effect on the peripheral circulation. These effects may support the fetus during episodes of significant blood loss.[41]

CLINICAL IMPLICATIONS FOR NEONATAL CARE

Neonatal cardiovascular disturbances include congestive heart failure (CHF), cyanosis, murmurs, and arrhythmias. Cardiac malformations occur in 0.8% to 1% of live births and represent about 10% of all congenital malformations. Murmurs that are related to the normal turbulence of transitional circulation (i.e., ductal closure) or physiologic turbulence in the pulmonary artery are considered benign. Gestational age and disease also affect the cardiovascular system and are factors in PDA and bronchopulmonary dysplasia (BPD).

Alterations in development of the cardiovascular system can have long-term implications. For example preterm infants are at increased risk for developing hypertension and cardiovascular disease in later life because of interruption of angiogenesis (leading to decreased microvascular density and altered vascular tone), impaired endothelial function, and decreased arterial dimensions and elasticity.[2] These limitations as well as alterations in renal development (Chapter 11) and metabolic programming (Chapter 16) increase the risk of hypertension, diabetes mellitus, and other disorders.[2,154]

Assessment of Heart Sounds

A newborn's heart rate ranges from 120 to 160 beats per minute, with significant state-related variations. Heart rate increases with birth and remains higher for the first hour, although there is marked variability between individual infants. Because heart rate is the most effective method for the neonate to increase CO, cardiorespiratory illness, sepsis, and metabolic problems are often accompanied by tachycardia.

The heart accounts for 0.75% of a neonate's body weight (versus 0.35% in adults). On chest radiographs, the neonatal heart generally occupies about 40% of the field (versus 35% in adults). Because the heart is positioned more transversely, the apical pulse is felt to the left of the sternal border. A precordial impulse may be visible along the left sternal border for 4 to 6 hours after birth.[61,159]

Heart sounds are of higher pitch, shorter duration, and greater intensity, and functional murmurs, hums, and clicks may be heard. Murmurs are heard in about one-third of healthy infants in the first 24 hours after birth and in two-thirds in the first 48 hours. A systolic DA murmur is heard in about 15% of infants while the ductus is still patent, most often around 5 to 6 hours of age. Sinus arrhythmias are common in infants and children.[159] Atrial premature beats are the most common irregular rhythms heard in newborns and are usually benign and self-limited.[151] The most common

significant arrhythmias in infants are bradycardia and supraventricular tachycardia.[61] Sinus bradycardia may result from the predominant parasympathetic innervation of the sinus node in neonates. Bradycardia may occur because of vagal stimulation or secondary to hypoxemia or acidosis. Bradycardia may not be well tolerated in infants, because heart rate comprises a greater portion of CO than stroke volume. Arrhythmias often do not compromise systemic perfusion or CO as much in neonates as in older individuals. Abnormal sinus rhythms in infancy may indicate underlying cardiac anomalies that alter reflexive mechanisms for heart rate control.[61,151]

Cardiac Shunts

Right-to-left cardiac shunts involve shunting of blood from systemic venous circulation to the arterial circulations without oxygenation. These shunts are usually characterized by obstruction to flow on the right side of the heart distal to an abnormal communication. Right-to-left shunting is characteristic of fetal circulation; that is, placental blood moves from the venous circulation to the arterial circulation, bypassing the lungs via either the foramen ovale or DA. Pathologic examples of right-to-left cardiac shunts include persistent pulmonary hypertension of the newborn (PPHN), in which the foramen ovale or DA or both remain open; pulmonary stenosis or atresia, in which blood is shunted from right to left via a PDA, foramen ovale, or ventricular septal defect (VSD); or transposition of the great vessels.

Left-to-right cardiac shunts are characterized by recirculation of oxygenated blood through the lungs, bypassing the peripheral circulation. Left-to-right shunting at the atrial level increases the amount of blood pumped by the pulmonary ventricle (normally the RV). Left-to-right shunting at the level of the great vessels or ventricles increases the volume load on the systemic ventricle (usually the LV). With a large VSD, there may also be increased stress on the pulmonary ventricle.[87] Examples of left-to-right shunting include a PDA (shunting of blood from the aorta to the pulmonary artery and thus back to the lungs) or a VSD with shunting of oxygenated blood from the LV to the RV and thus back to the lungs. Common clinical manifestations of left-to-right shunts are tachypnea (caused by pulmonary edema), tachycardia (from catecholamine release), diaphoresis in older infants (from catecholamine release), poor weight gain (resulting from increased energy demands of the heart and other systems), and sometimes hepatomegaly (because of altered hemodynamics).[88]

Cyanosis

Cyanosis is a physical sign characterized by blue-gray mucous membranes, nail beds, and skin. Central cyanosis occurs after 5 g/dL (50 g/L) of hemoglobin has been desaturated. Hypoxemia is a state of abnormally low arterial blood oxygen concentration. The degree of hypoxemia may or may not correlate with cyanosis, depending on the blood hemoglobin concentration and the ability of the observer to detect cyanosis. The most common causes of neonatal cyanosis are cardiac disease and pulmonary disease. The ability to distinguish between these two is essential. Therefore when congenital heart disease is suspected, the degree of hypoxemia must be related to the volume of pulmonary blood flow.

In infants with hypoxemia as a result of right-to-left shunting (diversion of blood from the lungs), ventilation and oxygen delivery do not significantly improve oxygenation. This is the basis for the hyperoxia challenge test. With adequate ventilation and 100% oxygen, the PaO_2 should rise above 150 mm Hg (19.95 kPa). If the PaO_2 does not increase above 100 mm Hg (13.30 kPa), cyanotic congenital heart disease is most likely the cause of the cyanosis. Between 100 and 150 mm Hg (13.30 to 19.95 kPa), cardiac disease is possible, but further diagnostic testing needs to be conducted (e.g., echocardiography). Selected congenital anomalies are discussed in the next section to demonstrate these principles.

Patent Ductus Arteriosus in the Preterm Infant

General physiologic characteristics of a PDA in the preterm infant are: (1) increased flow through the lungs with diastolic volume overload; (2) increased flow through the left atrium, LV, and aorta; and (3) left-to-right shunting to the pulmonary circulation. Blood is shunted from the upper and lower aortic circulations with a large ductus and multiorgan effects.

The DA in the preterm infant is thin-walled and less dependent on the vasa vasorum, so it does not develop the ischemia-hypoxia–stimulated remodeling unless there is complete cessation of blood flow.[31] The preterm ductus is also less likely to constrict with birth because of the presence of immature myosin isoforms, potassium channels that are less responsive to oxygen inhibition, altered Rho/Rho kinase pathways, higher circulating PGE_2 levels secondary to decreased clearance by the immature lungs, and especially increased sensitivity to the vasodilating effects of PGE_2 and NO.[31,55,74,106,121] Thus cyclooxygenase inhibitors such as indomethacin and ibuprofen, which inhibit prostaglandin synthetase and thus PG production, can be effective in constricting the ductus.[55,106,121]

Preterm infants have less pulmonary arterial muscle (see Closure of the Ductus Arteriosus) and an immature pulmonary parenchyma. The presence of a PDA is associated with interstitial edema and decreased compliance of the lung because of pulmonary edema. Ductal closure results in an increased compliance and a decreased need for ventilatory support (especially end-expiratory pressure). Prolonged ventilatory support for a PDA increases the risk of bronchopulmonary dysplasia in preterm infants.

Perfusion of peripheral organ systems is dependent on adequate systolic and diastolic flow. With a PDA, blood flow is redistributed, with decreased flow to the skin, bone, and skeletal muscle, followed by the gastrointestinal system and kidneys.[30] Even with limitations in myocardial performance, a preterm infant is able to increase LV output and maintain effective systemic blood flow with a small to moderate PDA

by increasing stroke volume (secondary to a simultaneous decrease in afterload resistance and increase in LV preload).[31] If a large PDA exists, systemic diastolic arterial flow is compromised and may even be reversed in the descending aorta. This can lead to decreased renal perfusion and contribute to the development of volume overload and CHF.

Gastrointestinal effects are also related to a decrease in flow and intestinal ischemia. Preterm infants with intestinal ischemia as a result of a PDA are at risk for developing necrotizing enterocolitis (see Chapter 12).[68] Cerebral ischemia may also occur as blood is diverted from the upper body. Cerebral blood flow changes can also increase the incidence of intraventricular hemorrhage (see Chapter 15).

A large left-to-right shunt through the PDA increases the left atrial and ventricular volume, leading to enlargement of these two chambers. The increased LV size also increases the myocardial wall stress, which could lead to myocardial ischemia in the preterm infant. If LV compromise exists, inotropic support may be needed until PDA closure is achieved. Diagnosis and management of PDA in preterm infants is controversial.[68] Treatments have included supportive management, pharmacologic therapy, and surgical intervention.[55,106,121]

Congenital Heart Defects

Most cardiac defects are compatible with intrauterine life and only become significant at birth. Even defects that significantly alter hemodynamics and flow in the fetal heart are often tolerated well, because the fetal shunts allow for compensation (see Figures 9-11, A, and 9-12). The exceptions to this include defects with atrioventricular valve regurgitation and myocardial dysfunction, which tend to be less well tolerated.[45,126] With any severe defect, birth may result in acute compromise as the fetal shunts close. Closure of the DA can be life-threatening in infants with ductal-dependent pulmonary blood flow (PDA allows left-to-right shunting to send blood to the lungs) or ductal-dependent systemic blood flow (PDA allows right-to-left shunting to send blood to the body).[147] Thus initial management is often directed at maintaining fetal shunts. Table 9-6 classifies congenital cardiac defects by physiologic consequence. Hemodynamic consequences of select disorders with transition to extrauterine life are described in the following sections.

Screening for critical congenital heart defects (CCHD) using pulse oximetry has been added to other newborn assessments in recent years. The goal of early cardiac screening is to identify infants who appear healthy after birth but who have a significant CHD, for which early surgical intervention is needed for survival, before the infant develops life-threatening symptoms and cardiac collapse.[3,23,80] Examples of CCHD include hypoplastic left heart syndrome (HLHS), tetralogy of Fallot, transposition of the great arteries, tricuspid atresia, truncus arteriosus, and total anomalous pulmonary venous return (TAPVR). Screening for CCHD has been reported to be reliable and cost-effective.[23] Each state has developed policies for CCHD screening as part of their newborn screening

BOX 9-2   Recommendations for Clinical Practice Related to the Cardiovascular System in Neonates

Monitor cardiovascular adaptation to extrauterine life (pp. 280-284).

Assess and evaluate the neonate for changes in cardiovascular performance related to transitional changes (pp. 284-286).

Conduct a thorough cardiovascular assessment of any infant presenting with a murmur during the transitional period, especially if associated with cyanosis (pp. 287-288).

Develop an understanding of the embryonic mechanisms that may result in cardiac congenital anomalies (pp. 270-276).

Provide continuous physiologic monitoring for infants suspected of cardiac disease (pp. 287-291).

Monitor infants with cardiac defects for signs of congestive heart failure and shock (pp. 287-291).

Evaluate all preterm infants serially for signs of a patent ductus arteriosus (p. 288).

Monitor infants with a patent ductus arteriosus for signs of increasing respiratory distress and congestive heart failure (p. 288).

Monitor and evaluate cardiovascular function in infants at risk for persistent pulmonary hypertension (pp. 282-283, 287, Chapter 10).

References

1. Abbas, A. E., Lester, S. J., & Connolly, H. (2005). Pregnancy and the cardiovascular system. *Int J Cardiol, 98,* 1.
2. Abitbol, C. L., & Rodriguez, M. M. (2012). The long-term renal and cardiovascular consequences of prematurity. *Nat Rev Nephrol, 8,* 265.
3. American Academy of Pediatrics. *Newborn screening for CCHD.* https://www.aap.org/en-us/advocacy-and-policy/aap-health-initiatives/PEHDIC/Pages/Newborn-Screening-for-CCHD.aspx. Accessed 20.06.16.
4. American College of Obstetricians and Gynecologists Task Force on Hypertension in Pregnancy. (2013). Hypertension in pregnancy. Report of the American College of Obstetricians and Gynecologists' Task Force on Hypertension in Pregnancy. *Obstet Gynecol, 122,* 1122.
5. American College of Obstetricians and Gynecologists. (2015). ACOG Committee Opinion No. 650: Physical Activity and Exercise During Pregnancy and the Postpartum Period. *Obstet Gynecol, 126,* e135.
6. Anderson, P. A. W., et al. (2004). Cardiovascular function during development and the response to hypoxia. In R. A. Polin, W. W. Fox, & S. H. Abman (Eds.), *Fetal and neonatal physiology* (3rd ed.). Philadelphia: Saunders.
7. Armentrout, D. (2014). Not ready for prime time: transitional events in the extremely preterm infant. *J Perinat Neonatal Nurs, 28,* 144.
8. Artman, M., Mahoney, L., & Teitel, D. (2011). *Neonatal cardiology* (2nd ed.). New York: McGraw Hill Medical.
9. Ashwath, R., & Snyder, C. S. (2015). Congenital defects of the cardiovascular system. In R. J. Martin, A. A. Fanaroff, & M. C. Walsh (Eds.), *Fanaroff and Martin's Neonatal-perinatal medicine: Diseases of the fetus and infant* (10th ed.). Philadelphia: Saunders.
10. Aune, D., et al. (2014). Physical activity and the risk of preeclampsia: a systematic review and meta-analysis. *Epidemiology, 25,* 331.
11. Babbar, S., & Shyken, J. (2016). Yoga in pregnancy. *Clin Obstet Gynecol, 59,* 600.
12. Barrington, K. J. (2008). Hypotension and shock in the preterm infant. *Semin Fetal Neonatal Med, 13,* 16.

13. Barrington, K. J. (2013). Common hemodynamic problems in the neonate. *Neonatology, 103,* 335.
14. Barron, D. J., et al. (2009). Hypoplastic left heart syndrome. *Lancet, 374,* 551.
15. Baschat, A. A. (2010). Ductus venosus Doppler for fetal surveillance in high-risk pregnancies. *Clin Obstet Gynecol, 53,* 858.
16. Baschat, A. A. (2011). Examination of the fetal cardiovascular system. *Semin Fetal Neonatal Med, 16,* 2.
17. Belloti, M., et al. (2000). Role of ductus venosus in distribution of umbilical flow in human fetuses during second half of pregnancy. *Am J Physiol, 279,* H1256.
18. Blanchard, D. G., & Daniels, L. B. (2014). Cardiac disease. In R. K. Creasy, et al. (Eds.), *Creasy & Resnik's Maternal-fetal medicine: Principles and practice* (7th ed.). Philadelphia: Saunders.
19. Bø, K., et al. (2016). Exercise and pregnancy in recreational and elite athletes: 2016 evidence summary from the IOC expert group meeting, Lausanne. Part 1-exercise in women planning pregnancy and those who are pregnant. *British journal of sports medicine, 50,* 571.
20. Brade, T., et al. (2013). Embryonic heart progenitors and cardiogenesis. *Cold Spring Harb Perspect Med, 3,* a013847.
21. Bridges, E. J., et al. (2003). Hemodynamic monitoring in high-risk obstetrics patients, I. Expected hemodynamic changes in pregnancy. *Crit Care Nurse, 23,* 53.
22. Brooks, V. L., Dampney, R. A., & Heesch, C. M. (2010). Pregnancy and the endocrine regulation of the baroreceptor reflex. *Am J Physiol Regul Integr Comp Physiol, 299,* R439.
23. Bruno, C. J., & Havranek, T. (2015). Screening for Critical Congenital Heart Disease in Newborns. *Adv Pediatr, 62,* 211.
24. Carbillon, L., et al. (2000). Pregnancy, vascular tone, and maternal hemodynamics: A crucial adaptation. *Obstet Gynecol Surv, 55,* 574.
25. Carlin, A., & Alfirevic, Z. (2008). Physiological changes of pregnancy and monitoring. *Best Pract Res Clin Obstet Gynaecol, 22,* 801.
26. Carlson, B. M. (2013). *Human embryology and developmental biology* (5th ed.). Philadelphia: Saunders.
27. Caulin-Glaser, T., & Setaro, J. F. (2004). Pregnancy and cardiovascular disease.

In G. N. Burrow, T. Duffy, & J. A. Copel (Eds.), *Medical complications during pregnancy* (6th ed.). Philadelphia: Saunders.
28. Clapp, J. F. (1989). Oxygen consumption during treadmill exercise before, during and after pregnancy. *Am J Obstet Gynecol, 161,* 1458.
29. Clapp, J. F. (2000). Exercise during pregnancy. A clinical update. *Clin Sports Med, 19,* 273.
30. Clapp, J. F., 3rd. (2003). The effects of maternal exercise on fetal oxygenation and feto-placental growth. *Eur J Obstet Gynecol Reprod Biol, 110,* S80.
31. Clyman, R. I. (2017). Mechanisms regulating closure of the ductus arteriosus. In R. A. Polin, et al. (Eds.), *Fetal & neonatal physiology* (5th ed.). Philadelphia: Saunders.
32. Corton, M. M., et al. (2014). *Williams obstetrics* (24th ed.). New York: McGraw-Hill.
33. Curry, R., Swan, L., & Steer, P. J. (2009). Cardiac disease in pregnancy. *Curr Opin Obstet Gynecol, 21,* 508.
34. Das, B. B., Raj, S., & Solinger, R. (2009). Natriuretic peptides in cardiovascular diseases of fetus, infants and children. *Cardiovasc Hematol Agents Med Chem, 7,* 43.
35. Davenport, M. H., Skow, R. J., & Steinback, C. D. (2016). Maternal Responses to Aerobic exercises in pregnancy. *Clin Obstet Gynecol, 59,* 541.
36. Dietl, J. (2000). The pathogenesis of pre-eclampsia: New aspects. *J Perinat Med, 28,* 464.
37. du Plessis, A. J. (2012). Hemodynamics and brain injury in the preterm neonate. In C. S. Kleinman & I. Seri (Eds.), *Hemodynamics and cardiology* (2nd ed.). Philadelphia: Saunders.
38. Emmanuel, Y., & Thorne, S. A. (2015). Heart disease in pregnancy. *Best Pract Res Clin Obstet Gynaecol, 29,* 579.
39. Fazio, G., et al. (2010). Patent foramen ovale and thromboembolic complications. *Curr Pharm Des, 16,* 3497.
40. Ferrero, S., Colombo, B. M., & Ragni, N. (2004). Maternal arrhythmias during pregnancy. *Arch Gynecol Obstet, 269,* 244.
41. Fineman, J. R., & Clyman, R. (2014). Fetal cardiovascular physiology. In R. K. Creasy, et al. (Eds.), *Creasy & Resnik's Maternal-fetal medicine: Principles and practice* (7th ed.). Philadelphia: Saunders.

42. Finnemore, A., & Groves, A. (2015). Physiology of the fetal and transitional circulation. *Semin Fetal Neonatal Med, 20*, 210.

43. Fisher, S. J., McMaster, M., & Roberts, J. M. (2015). The placenta in normal pregnancy and preeclampsia. In R. N. Taylor, et al. (Eds.), *Chesley's hypertensive disorders in pregnancy* (4th ed.). New York: Academic Press.

44. Fleming, S., et al. (2011). Normal ranges of heart rate and respiratory rate in children from birth to 18 years of age: a systematic review of observational studies. *Lancet, 377*, 1011.

45. Friedman, A. H., & Fahey, J. T. (1993). The transition from fetal to neonatal circulation: Normal responses and implications for infants with heart disease. *Semin Perinatol, 17*, 106.

46. Fu, Q., & Levine, B. D. (2009). Autonomic circulatory control during pregnancy in humans. *Semin Reprod Med, 27*, 330.

47. Fugelseth, D., et al. (1997). Ultrasonographic study of ductus venosus in healthy neonates. *Arch Dis Child Fetal Neonatal Ed, 77*, F131.

48. Gandhi, M., & Martin, S. R. (2015). Cardiac disease in pregnancy. *Obstet Gynecol Clin North Am, 42*, 315.

49. Gao, Y., & Raj, J. U. (2010). Regulation of the pulmonary circulation in the fetus and newborn. *Physiol Rev, 90*, 1291.

50. Gei, A. F., & Hankins, G. D. (2001). Cardiac disease and pregnancy. *Obstet Gynecol Clin North Am, 28*, 465.

51. Gittenberger-de Groot, A. C., et al. (2013). Embryology of the heart and its impact on understanding fetal and neonatal heart disease. *Semin Fetal Neonatal Med, 18*, 237.

52. Gowda, R. M., et al. (2003). Cardiac arrhythmias in pregnancy: Clinical and therapeutic considerations. *Int J Cardiol, 88*, 129.

53. Gregg, A. R. (2004). Hypertension in pregnancy. *Obstet Gynecol Clin North Am, 31*, 223.

54. Hale, R. W., & Milne, L. (1996). The elite athlete and exercise in pregnancy. *Semin Perinatol, 20*, 277.

55. Hamrick, S. E., & Hansmann, G. (2010). Patent ductus arteriosus of the preterm infant. *Pediatrics, 125*, 1020.

56. Haram, K., Mortensen, J. H., & Nagy, B. (2014). Genetic aspects of preeclampsia and the HELLP syndrome. *J Pregnancy, 2014*, 910751.

57. Harris, I. S., & Black, B. L. (2010). Development of the endocardium. *Pediatr Cardiol, 31*, 391.

58. Harris, I. S. (2011). Management of pregnancy in patients with congenital heart disease. *Prog Cardiovasc Dis, 53*, 305.

59. Hartmann, S., & Bung, P. (1999). Physical exercise during pregnancy—Physiological considerations and recommendations. *J Perinat Med, 27*, 204.

60. Haugen, G., et al. (2004). Portal and umbilical venous blood supply to the liver in the human fetus near term. *Ultrasound Obstet Gynecol, 24*, 599.

61. Hazinski, M. F. (2012). *Nursing care of the critically ill child* (3rd ed.). St. Louis: Mosby.

62. Hegewald, M. J., & Crapo, R. O. (2011). Respiratory physiology in pregnancy. *Clin Chest Med, 32*, 1.

63. Henderson, J. T., et al. (2014). Low-dose aspirin for prevention of morbidity and mortality from preeclampsia: a systematic evidence review for the U.S. Preventive Services Task Force. *Ann Intern Med, 160*, 695.

64. Higgins, J. R., & de Swiet, M. (2001). Blood-pressure measurement and classification in pregnancy. *Lancet, 357*, 131.

65. Hilfiker-Kleiner, D., Sliwa, K., & Drexler, H. (2008). Peripartum cardiomyopathy: Recent insights in its pathophysiology. *Trends Cardiovasc Med, 18*, 173.

66. Hill, C. C., & Pickinpaugh, J. (2008). Physiologic changes in pregnancy. *Surg Clin North Am, 88*, 391.

67. Hooper, S. B., et al. (2015). Cardiovascular transition at birth: a physiological sequence. *Pediatr Res, 77*, 608.

68. Jain, A., & Shah, P. S. (2015). Diagnosis, Evaluation, and Management of Patent Ductus Arteriosus in Preterm Neonates. *JAMA Pediatr, 169*, 863.

69. Jeyabalan, A. (2015). Hypertensive disorder of pregnancy. In R. J. Martin, A. A. Fanaroff, & M. C. Walsh (Eds.), *Fanaroff and Martin's neonatal-perinatal medicine: Diseases of the fetus and infant* (10th ed.). Philadelphia: Saunders.

70. Jim, B., et al. (2010). Hypertension in pregnancy: A comprehensive update. *Cardiol Rev, 18*, 178.

71. Johnson, A. C., & Cipolla, M. J. (2015). The cerebral circulation during pregnancy: adapting to preserve normalcy. *Physiology (Bethesda), 30*, 139.

72. Johnson, T. R. (1978). Changes in the developing cardiovascular system in relation to age. In T. R. Johnson, W. M. Moore, & J. E. Jeffries (Eds.), *Children are different*. Columbus, OH: Ross.

73. Kafer, E. R. (1990). Neonatal gas exchange and oxygen transport. In W. A. Long (Ed.), *Fetal and neonatal cardiology*. Philadelphia: Saunders.

74. Kajimoto, H., et al. (2007). Oxygen activates the Rho/Rho-kinase pathway and induces RhoB and ROCK-1 expression in human and rabbit ductus arteriosus by increasing mitochondria-derived reactive oxygen species: A newly recognized mechanism for sustaining ductal constriction. *Circulation, 115*, 1777.

75. Kajino, H., et al. (2002). Vasa vasorum hypoperfusion is responsible for medial hypoxia and anatomic remodeling in the newborn lamb ductus arteriosus. *Pediatr Res, 51*, 228.

76. Kametas, N. A., et al. (2003). Maternal cardiac function in twin pregnancy. *Obstet Gynecol, 102*, 806.

77. Kametas, N. A., et al. (2004). Maternal cardiac function during pregnancy at high altitude. *BJOG, 111*, 1051.

78. Karumanchi, S. A., & Granger, J. P. (2016). Preeclampsia and pregnancy-related hypertensive disorders. *Hypertension, 67*, 238.

79. Katz, V. L. (2003). Exercise in water during pregnancy. *Clin Obstet Gynecol, 46*, 432.

80. Kemper, A. R., et al. (2011). Strategies for implementing screening for critical congenital heart disease. *Pediatrics, 128*, e1259.

81. Kirkpatrick, C. A. (2010). The HELLP syndrome. *Acta Clin Belg, 65*, 91.

82. Kiserud, T. (2005). Physiology of the fetal circulation. *Semin Fetal Neonatal Med, 10*, 493.

83. Kiserud, T., & Haugen, G. (2017). Umbilical circulation. In R. A. Polin, et al. (Eds.), *Fetal and neonatal physiology* (5th ed.). Philadelphia: Saunders.

84. Kleigman, R. M., et al. (2016). *Nelson's textbook of pediatrics* (20th ed.). Philadelphia: Elsevier.

85. Kluckow, M., & Hooper, S. B. (2015). Using physiology to guide time to cord clamping. *Semin Fetal Neonatal Med, 20*, 225.

86. Knotts, R. J., & Garan, H. (2014). Cardiac arrhythmias in pregnancy. *Semin Perinatol, 38*, 285.

87. Kulik, T. J. (2017). Physiology of congenital heart disease in the neonate. In R. A. Polin, et al. (Eds.), *Fetal & neonatal physiology* (5th ed.). Philadelphia: Saunders.

88. Kung, G. C., & Triedman, J. (2015). Pathophysiology left to right shunts. *UpToDate online*. http:www.uptodateonline.com. Accessed 20.06.16.

89. Lee, W., & Cotton, D. B. (1990). Maternal cardiovascular physiology. In R. D. Eden & F. H. Boehm (Eds.), *Assessment and care of the fetus: Physiological, clinical, and medicolegal principles*. Norwalk, CT: Appleton & Lange.

90. Lewandowski, A. J., et al. (2013). Right ventricular systolic dysfunction in young adults born preterm. *Circulation, 128*, 713.

91. Lincoln, J., Lange, A. W., & Yutzey, K. E. (2006). Hearts and bones: Shared regulatory mechanisms in heart valve, cartilage, tendon, and bone development. *Dev Biol, 294*, 292.

92. Lindheimer, M. D., Taler, S. J., & Cunningham, F. G. (2010). Hypertension in pregnancy. *J Am Soc Hypertens, 4*, 68.

93. Long, W. A., et al. (2004). Autonomic and central neuroregulation of fetal cardiovascular function. In R. A. Polin, W. W. Fox, & S. H. Abman (Eds.), *Fetal and neonatal physiology* (3rd ed.). Philadelphia: Saunders.

94. Lowrey, G. H. (1986). *Growth and development of children*. Chicago: Year Book Medical Publishers.

95. Lyall, F., Robson, S. C., & Bulmer, J. N. (2013). Spiral artery remodeling and trophoblast invasion in preeclampsia and fetal growth restriction: relationship to clinical outcome. *Hypertension, 62*, 1046.

96. Mahendru, A. A., et al. (2014). A longitudinal study of maternal cardiovascular function from preconception to the postpartum period. *J Hypertens, 32*, 849.

97. Maiz, N., & Nicolaides, K. H. (2010). Ductus venosus in the first trimester: Contribution to screening of chromosomal, cardiac defects and monochorionic twin complications. *Fetal Diagn Ther, 28*, 65.

98. Malone, F. D., & D'Alton, M. D. (2014). Multiple gestation: Clinical characteristics and management. In R. K. Creasy, et al. (Eds.), *Creasy & Resnik's Maternal-fetal medicine: Principles and practice* (7th ed.). Philadelphia: Saunders.

99. Mann, D., & Mehta, V. (2004). Cardiovascular embryology. *Int Anesthesiol Clin, 42*, 15.

100. Markham, K. B., & Funai, E. F. (2014). Pregnancy-related hypertension. In R. K. Creasy, et al. (Eds.), *Creasy & Resnik's Maternal-fetal medicine: Principles and practice* (7th ed.). Philadelphia: Saunders.

101. Marsal, K. (2017). Fetal and placental circulation during labor. In R. A. Polin, et al. (Eds.), *Fetal and neonatal physiology* (5th ed.). Philadelphia: Saunders.

102. May, L. E., Allen, J. J., & Gustafson, K. M. (2016). Fetal and maternal cardiac responses to physical activity and exercise during pregnancy. *Early Hum Dev, 94*, 49.

103. McElhinney, D. B., Tworetzky, W., & Lock, J. E. (2010). Current status of fetal cardiac intervention. *Circulation, 121*, 1256.

104. McQuillen, P. S., & Miller, S. P. (2010). Congenital heart disease and brain development. *Ann N Y Acad Sci, 1184*, 68.

105. Melzer, K., et al. (2010). Physical activity and pregnancy: Cardiovascular adaptations, recommendations and pregnancy outcomes. *Sports Med, 40*, 493.

106. Mercanti, I., Boubred, F., & Simeoni, U. (2009). Therapeutic closure of the ductus arteriosus: Benefits and limitations. *J Matern Fetal Neonatal Med, 22*, 14.

107. Mercanti, I., et al. (2011). Blood pressure in newborns with twin-twin transfusion syndrome. *J Perinatol, 31*, 417.

108. Mitchell, A. L., & Snyder, C. S. (2015). Genetic and environmental contributions to congenital heart disease. In R. J. Martin, A. A. Fanaroff, & M. C. Walsh (Eds.), *Fanaroff and Martin's Neonatal-perinatal medicine: Diseases of the fetus and infant* (10th ed.). Philadelphia: Saunders.

109. Mittelmark, R. A., Wiswell, R. A., & Drinkwater, B. L. (1991). Fetal responses to maternal exercise. *Exercise in pregnancy* (2nd ed.). Baltimore: Williams & Wilkins.

110. Mol, B. W., et al. (2016). Pre-eclampsia. *Lancet, 387*, 999.

111. Monga, M., & Mastrobatista, J. M. (2014). Maternal cardiovascular, respiratory and renal adaptation to pregnancy. In R. K. Creasy, et al. (Eds.), *Creasy & Resnik's Maternal-fetal medicine: Principles and practice* (7th ed.). Philadelphia: Saunders.

112. Moore, K. L., Persaud, T. V. N., & Torchia, M. G. (2015). *The developing human: Clinically oriented embryology* (10th ed.). Philadelphia: Saunders.

113. Morris, S. N., & Johnson, N. R. (2005). Exercise during pregnancy: A critical appraisal of the literature. *J Reprod Med, 50*, 181.

114. Muñoz-Chápuli, R., & Pérez-Pomares, J. M. (2010). Cardiogenesis: An embryological perspective. *J Cardiovasc Transl Res, 3*, 37.

115. Myatt, L., & Webster, R. P. (2009). Vascular biology of preeclampsia. *J Thromb Haemost, 7*, 375.

116. Nama, V., et al. (2011). Mid-trimester blood pressure drop in normal pregnancy: Myth or reality? *J Hypertens, 29*, 763.

117. National High Blood Pressure Education Program. (2000). Report of the National High Blood Pressure Education Program Working Group on high blood pressure in pregnancy. *Am J Obstet Gynecol, 183*, 1.

118. Noori, S., et al. (2012). Principles of developmental cardiovascular physiology and pathophysiology. In C. S. Kleinman & I. Seri (Eds.), *Hemodynamics and cardiology* (2nd ed.). Philadelphia: Saunders.

119. Noori, S., et al. (2014). Changes in cardiac function and cerebral blood flow in relation to peri/intraventricular hemorrhage in extremely preterm infants. *J Pediatr, 164*, 264.e1–3.

120. Noori, S., & Seri, I. (2015). Hemodynamic antecedents of peri/intraventricular hemorrhage in very preterm neonates. *Semin Fetal Neonatal Med, 20*, 232.

121. Ohlsson, A., Walia, R., & Shah, S. S. (2015). Ibuprofen for the treatment of patent ductus arteriosus in preterm or low birth weight (or both) infants. *Cochrane Database Syst Rev, 2015*(2), CD003481.

122. O'Connor, M., McDaniel, N., & Brady, W. J. (2008). The pediatric electrocardiogram: part I: Age-related interpretation. *Am J Emerg Med, 26*, 506.

123. O'Toole, M. L. (2003). Physiologic aspects of exercise in pregnancy. *Clin Obstet Gynecol, 46*, 379.

124. Ouzounian, J. G., & Elkayam, U. (2012). Physiologic changes during normal pregnancy and delivery. *Cardiol Clin, 30*, 317.

125. Parsons, M. (1988). Effects of twins: Maternal, fetal, and labor. *Clin Perinatol, 15*, 41.

126. Patel, C. R., et al. (2002). Fetal cardiac physiology and fetal cardiovascular assessment. In A. A. Fanaroff & R. J. Martin (Eds.), *Neonatal-perinatal medicine: Diseases of the fetus and infant* (7th ed.). Philadelphia: Mosby.

127. Patterson, A. J., & Zhang, L. (2010). Hypoxia and fetal heart development. *Curr Mol Med, 10*, 653.

128. Pearce, W. J., & Khorram, O. (2013). Maturation and differentiation of the fetal vasculature. *Clin Obstet Gynecol, 56*, 537.

129. Pelech, A. N. (2004). The physiology of cardiac auscultation. *Pediatr Clin North Am, 51*, 1515.

130. Pivarnik, J. M., Perkins, C. D., & Moyerbrailean, T. (2003). Athletes and pregnancy. *Clin Obstet Gynecol, 46*, 403.

131. Pritchard, J. A., et al. (1972). Blood volume changes in pregnancy and the puerperium. II. Red blood cell loss and changes in apparent blood volume during and following vaginal delivery, cesarean section, and cesarean section plus total hysterectomy. *Am J Obstet Gynecol, 84*, 1271.

132. Rabinovitch, M. (2017). Developmental biology of the pulmonary vasculature. In R. A. Polin, et al. (Eds.), *Fetal and neonatal physiology* (5th ed.). Philadelphia: Saunders.

133. Rana, S., & Karumanchi, S. A. (2017). Pathophysiology of preeclampsia. In R. A. Polin, et al. (Eds.), *Fetal and neonatal physiology* (5th ed.). Philadelphia: Saunders.

134. Redman, C. W., & Sargent, I. L. (2005). Latest advances in understanding preeclampsia. *Science, 308*, 1592.

135. Resnik, R. (2004). The puerperium. In R. K. Creasy, R. Resnik, & J. D. Iams (Eds.), *Maternal-fetal medicine: Principles and practice* (5th ed.). Philadelphia: Saunders Elsevier.

136. Riemann, M. K., et al. (2000). Effects on the foetus of exercise in pregnancy. *Scand J Med Sci Sports, 10*, 12.

137. Roberts, J. M., & Cooper, D. W. (2001). Pathogenesis and genetics of pre-eclampsia. *Lancet, 357*, 53.

138. Roberts, J. M., et al. (2003). National Heart Lung and Blood Institute. Summary of the NHLBI Working Group on Research on Hypertension During Pregnancy. *Hypertension, 41*, 437.

139. Romem, A., et al. (2004). Incidence and characteristics of maternal cardiac arrhythmias during labor. *Am J Cardiol, 93*, 931.

140. Rudolph, A. M. (2000). Myocardial growth before and after birth: Clinical implication. *Acta Paediatr, 89*, 129.

141. Rudolph, A. M. (2003). Fetal circulation and cardiovascular adjustments after birth. In A. M. Rudolph & C. D. Rudolph (Eds.), *Rudolph's pediatrics* (21st ed.). New York: McGraw-Hill.

142. Russo, L. M., et al. (2015). Physical activity interventions in pregnancy and risk of gestational diabetes mellitus: a systematic review and meta-analysis. *Obstet Gynecol, 125*, 576.

143. Rychik, J. (2004). Fetal cardiovascular physiology. *Pediatr Cardiol, 25*, 201.

144. Sanabria-Martínez, G., et al. (2015). Effectiveness of physical activity interventions on preventing gestational diabetes mellitus and excessive maternal weight gain: a meta-analysis. *BJOG, 122*, 1167.

145. Sanghavi, M., & Rutherford, J. D. (2014). Cardiovascular physiology of pregnancy. *Circulation, 130*, 1003.

146. Schneider, D. J. (2012). The patent ductus arteriosus in term infants, children, and adults. *Semin Perinatol, 36*, 146.

147. Scholz, T. D., & Reinking, B. E. (2012). Congenital heart disease. In C. A. Gleason & S. Devaskar (Eds.), *Avery's diseases of the newborn* (9th ed.). Philadelphia: Saunders.

148. Schrier, R. W. (2010). Systemic arterial vasodilation, vasopressin, and vasopressinase in pregnancy. *J Am Soc Nephrol, 21*, 570.

149. Seely, E. W., Tsigas, E., & Rich-Edwards, J. W. (2015). Preeclampsia and future cardiovascular disease in women: How good are the data and how can we manage our patients? *Semin Perinatol, 39*, 276.

150. Segar, J. L., & Giussani D. A. (2017). Neural regulation of blood pressure during fetal and neonatal life. In R. A. Polin, et al. (Eds.), *Fetal & neonatal physiology* (5th ed.). Philadelphia: Saunders.

151. Sekarski, N., et al. (2014). Perinatal arrhythmias. *Eur J Pediatr, 173*, 983.

152. Shenoy, V., Kanasaki, K., & Kalluri, R. (2010). Pre-eclampsia: Connecting angiogenic and metabolic pathways. *Trends Endocrinol Metab, 21*, 529.

153. Silva, L. M., et al. (2008). No midpregnancy fall in diastolic blood pressure in women with a low educational level: the Generation R Study. *Hypertension, 52*, 645.

154. Simeoni, U., et al. (2011). Adverse consequences of accelerated neonatal growth: cardiovascular and renal issues. *Pediatr Nephrol, 26*, 493.

155. Sircar, M., Thadhani, R., & Karumanchi, S. A. (2015). Pathogenesis of preeclampsia. *Curr Opin Nephrol Hypertens, 24*, 131.

156. Steinhorn, R. (2015). Pulmonary vascular development. In R. J. Martin, A. A. Fanaroff, & M. C. Walsh (Eds.), *Fanaroff and Martin's neonatal-perinatal medicine: Diseases of the fetus and infant* (10th ed.). Philadelphia: Saunders.

157. Streuling, I., Beyerlein, A., & von Kries, R. (2010). Can gestational weight gain be modified by increasing physical activity and diet counseling? A meta-analysis of interventional trials. *Am J Clin Nutr, 92*, 678.

158. Szymanski, L. M., & Satin, A. J. (2012). Exercise during pregnancy: fetal responses to current public health guidelines. *Obstet Gynecol, 119*, 603.

159. Tappero, E. P., & Honeyfield, M. E. (2014). *Physical assessment of the newborn: A comprehensive approach to the art of physical examination* (5th ed.). Petaluma, CA: NICU Ink.

160. Teitel, D. F. (2004). Physiologic development of the cardiovascular system in the fetus. In R. A. Polin, W. W. Fox, & S. H. Abman (Eds.), *Fetal and neonatal physiology* (3rd ed.). Philadelphia: Saunders.

161. Thornburg, K. L., et al. (2000). Hemodynamic changes in pregnancy. *Semin Perinatol, 24*, 11.

162. Tranquilli, A. L., et al. (2014). The classification, diagnosis and management of the hypertensive disorders of pregnancy: A revised statement from the ISSHP. *Pregnancy Hypertens, 4*, 97.

163. Tsen, L. C. (2005). Gerard W. Ostheimer "What's new in obstetric anesthesia" lecture. *Anesthesiology, 102*, 672.

164. Turan, O. M., et al. (2011). The duration of persistent abnormal ductus venosus flow and its impact on perinatal outcome in fetal growth restriction. *Ultrasound Obstet Gynecol, 38*, 295.

165. van der Bom, T., et al. (2011). The changing epidemiology of congenital heart disease. *Nat Rev Cardiol, 8*, 50.

166. van Hagen, I. M., & Roos-Hesselink, J. W. (2014). Aorta pathology and pregnancy. *Best Pract Res Clin Obstet Gynaecol, 28*, 537.

167. Volman, M. N., et al. (2007). Haemodynamic changes in the second half of pregnancy: A longitudinal, noninvasive study with thoracic electrical bioimpedance. *BJOG, 114*, 576.

168. Wanga, S., et al. (2016). Pregnancy and thoracic aortic disease: managing the risks. *Can J Cardiol, 32*, 78.

169. Wantanabe, M., & Wikenheiser, J. (2015). Cardiac embryology. In R. J. Martin, A. A. Fanaroff, & M. C. Walsh (Eds.), *Fanaroff and Martin's Neonatal-perinatal medicine: Diseases of the fetus and infant* (10th ed.). Philadelphia: Saunders.

170. Warnes, C. A. (2004). Pregnancy and pulmonary hypertension. *Int J Cardiol, 97*, 11.

171. Warnes, C. A. (2015). Pregnancy and Delivery in Women with Congenital Heart Disease. *Circ J, 79*, 1416.

172. Wolfe, L. A., & Weissgerber, T. L. (2003). Clinical physiology of exercise in pregnancy: A literature review. *J Obstet Gynaecol Can, 25*, 473.

173. Yagel, S., et al. (2010). The fetal venous system, part I: Normal embryology, anatomy, hemodynamics, ultrasound evaluation and Doppler investigation. *Ultrasound Obstet Gynecol, 35*, 741.

Respiratory System

Respiration is the totality of those processes that ultimately result in energy being supplied to the cells. In pregnancy the respiratory system undergoes significant changes. The increased metabolic needs of the pregnant woman, fetus, and placenta require improved maternal respiratory efficiency to ensure adequate oxygenation. The placenta functions as the respiratory system for the fetus, providing nutrients and oxygen (O_2) and removing carbon dioxide (CO_2). This makes the relationship between the mother and fetus not only intimate but also interdependent. At birth, tremendous energy is expended by the neonate to generate sufficient negative pressure to convert to an air-liquid interface in the alveoli and maintain functional residual capacity (FRC). Transitional events continue over the first week of life as the neonate adjusts to the new environment, more alveoli are recruited, and the surfactant system stabilizes. This chapter examines alterations in the respiratory system and acid-base homeostasis during the perinatal period and their implications for the mother, fetus, and neonate. Fetal blood gases and responses to hypoxia are discussed in Chapter 6.

MATERNAL PHYSIOLOGIC ADAPTATIONS

Changes in the respiratory system during pregnancy increase the volume of air and gas exchange with each breath, enhancing oxygen availability to and CO_2 removal from the fetus. These changes are mediated by hormonal and biochemical changes as well as by the enlarging uterus. As the muscles and cartilage in the thoracic region relax, the chest broadens and tidal volume (V_T) is improved with a conversion from abdominal to thoracic breathing. This leads to a 50% increase in air volume per minute. These changes result in a mild respiratory alkalosis.[138] For the fetus, this mild alkalosis enhances gas exchange across the placenta.

Antepartum Period

Pregnancy is associated with major changes in the respiratory system, including changes in lung volumes and ventilation. Both biochemical and mechanical factors interact to increase the delivery of oxygen and the removal of CO_2. Otolaryngeal changes are discussed in Chapter 15.

Factors Influencing Respiratory Function

Mechanical Factors. The gradual enlargement of the uterus leads to changes in abdominal size and shape, shifting the resting position of the diaphragm up to 4 cm above its usual position to accommodate the growing uterus (Figure 10-1).[24,39,81,209] The thoracic circumference increases by 5 to 7 cm and the transverse diameter of the chest by about 2 cm in response to the increased intraabdominal pressure with a flaring of the lower ribs.[39,81,188,209] The subcostal angle progressively increases from 68 to 103 degrees in late gestation.[24,81,188,209] Not all of these changes can be attributed to intraabdominal pressure, in that the increase in the subcostal angle occurs before the increasing mechanical pressure.[209,212] Relaxation of the ligamentous rib attachments increases rib cage elasticity.[188] This change is similar to those seen in the pelvis (see Chapter 15) and is mediated by progesterone and relaxin.

Diaphragmatic movement increases about 1.5 to 2 cm during pregnancy, with the major work of breathing being accomplished by the diaphragm rather than by the costal muscles.[24,39,81,209] These changes in thoracic structures modify the abdominal space, perhaps in preparation for the increase in uterine size, and peak at 37 weeks.[81] The changes in thoracic configuration along with the increasing intraabdominal pressure have a major effect on lung volumes.[209]

Hormonal and Biochemical Factors. Hormones and other biochemical factors are important in stimulating changes in the respiratory system in pregnancy. These substances can act centrally via stimulation of the respiratory center or directly on smooth muscle and other tissues of the lung. The most important influences are mediated by progesterone, in combination with estradiol (which increases progesterone receptors in the hypothalamus) and prostaglandins (PGs).[94]

Serum progesterone levels increase progressively throughout pregnancy and are believed to be a major factor in the changes seen in ventilation.[209,212] Progesterone is a respiratory stimulant. The administration of progesterone to nonpregnant subjects increases minute ventilation and enhances responses to hypercapnia.[81,94] This suggests an increased sensitivity to CO_2 by the respiratory center and that progesterone lowers the CO_2 threshold of the respiratory center.[39,94,212] For example, in a nonpregnant woman, an increase of 1 mm Hg

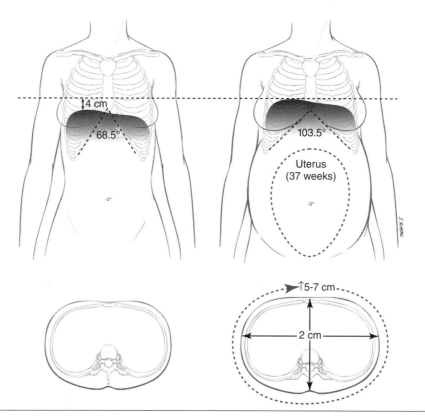

FIGURE 10-1 Chest wall changes that occur during pregnancy. The subcostal angle increases, as do the anterior-posterior and transverse diameters of the chest wall and the chest wall circumference. These changes compensate for the 4-cm elevation of the diaphragm so that the total lung capacity is not significantly reduced. (From Hegewald, M.J. & Crapo, R.O. [2011]. Respiratory physiology in pregnancy. *Clin Chest Med, 32,* 1.)

(0.13 kPa) in the $PaCO_2$ results in a 1.5 L/minute increase in ventilation, whereas during pregnancy the same 1 mm Hg increase in $PaCO_2$ leads to a 6 L/minute increase in ventilation.[209] More than 60% of the increase in CO_2 sensitivity occurs by 20 weeks' gestation.[178]

This increased sensitivity most likely contributes to the sensation of dyspnea that is experienced by many pregnant women and may also lead to some of the hyperventilation that occurs during the second stage of labor after pushing efforts (as CO_2 levels increase during breath holding). Progesterone may also exert a local effect on the lung, causing water retention in the lung that results in decreased diffusion capacity. Therefore hyperventilation is an attempt to maintain normal PO_2 levels.[209]

Progesterone may also play a role in decreasing airway resistance (up to 50%), thereby reducing the work of breathing and facilitating a greater airflow in pregnancy. Relaxation of bronchiole smooth muscle has been attributed to progesterone. This counteracts the expected increase in airway resistance that would be the result of lungs that are less distended.

PGs may also play a role in ventilatory changes by affecting the smooth muscle tissue of the bronchial airways. $PGF_{2\alpha}$ is a bronchial smooth muscle constrictor, whereas PGE_1 and PGE_2 have bronchodilator effects. PGs may balance or counteract the consequences of structural changes in the respiratory system during pregnancy (e.g., decreased lung distension as a result of elevated diaphragm) and modify respiration to meet fetal requirements (maternal respiratory alkalosis promotes CO_2 transfer from the fetus).

Lung Volume

Changes in lung volumes begin in the middle of the second trimester and are progressive to term (Figure 10-2). The most significant change is a 30% to 40% (from 500 to 700 mL) increase in V_T, with a progressive 15% to 20% decrease in expiratory reserve volume (ERV), 20% to 25% decrease in residual volume (RV), and 20% to 30% decrease in FRC.[81,131] The FRC is further decreased in the supine position at term.[81] Along with the change in V_T, there is a concomitant increase in inspiratory capacity (IC) by 5% to 10%, allowing the total lung capacity (TLC) to remain relatively stable, with a slight decrease of up to 5% by term mediated by lower chest wall compliance.[24,81,188] Vital capacity (VC) and inspiratory reserve volume (IRV) are essentially unaltered, although some literature notes a small change in IRV.[188,209,212] Peak expiratory flow rates tend to decrease during pregnancy, possibly because of mechanical changes in the respiratory system. Physiologic dead space is increased by 60 mL.[209]

The decreased RV, in conjunction with an elevated metabolic rate, increases the risk of hypoxia if respiratory depression occurs.[212] However, forced expiratory volume in 1 second

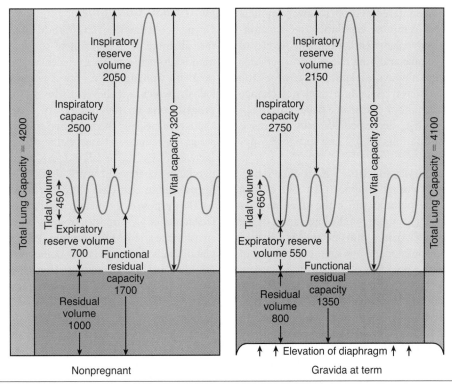

FIGURE 10-2   Lung volume changes in pregnancy (units in milliliters). (From Gardner, M.O. & Doyle, N.M. [2004]. Asthma in pregnancy. *Obstet Gynecol Clin North Am, 31*, 390.)

(FEV$_1$) does not change, nor does the FEV$_1$/VC ratio.[131,188,212] These assessments are used in individuals with asthma and are generally considered reliable in pregnant women.[39,212]

Changes in lung volumes result from the elevation of the diaphragm and the changes in the configuration of the chest. The alteration in RV is also the result of a 35% to 40% decrease in chest wall compliance; lung compliance is unchanged.[39,81,209] The decreased chest wall compliance is caused by hormonal influences as well as changes in abdominal pressure. This reduction in compliance allows for more inward movement of the chest wall and reduces the amount of trapped air (residual trapped volume) that contributes to the RV. Therefore the RV decreases 200 to 300 mL. This, along with an approximately 200 mL decrease in ERV, brings the total deficit in the FRC up to 500 mL (see Figure 10-2). The FRC falls progressively from 20 weeks' gestation for a change of 10% to 24% by term.[212]

Lung Function

Changes in lung function are related to three major factors: ventilation, airflow, and diffusing capacity. Oxygen consumption increases during pregnancy; however, the arterial oxygen pressure (PaO$_2$), though it increases, does not change significantly, even though the arteriovenous oxygen difference decreases. This indicates that there must be a change in ventilation.[209]

Ventilation. Minute ventilation (V$_T$ × respiratory rate [RR]) increases up to 30% to 50% during pregnancy because of the increased V$_T$.[24,138,209] Changes begin by 8 weeks' gestation and result in an increase in minute volume, from 6.5 to 7.5 L/minute

in early pregnancy to 10 to 10.5 L/minute at term.[94] The elevated resting ventilation exceeds the demands in oxygen consumption, indicating that women tend to hyperventilate during pregnancy.[209,212] The greater increase in resting ventilation is believed to result from the stimulatory effects of progesterone on the respiratory center. Progesterone may also increase red blood cell levels of carbonic anhydrase B, which facilitates CO$_2$ transfer and lowering of the PCO$_2$.[209] The hyperventilation of pregnancy and associated respiratory system alterations are also mediated by the interaction of acid-base balance changes, increased breathing drive, increased central chemoreflex sensitivity, increased metabolism, and decreased cerebral blood flow.[95]

The increase in minute ventilation is probably primarily results from the 30% to 40% increase in V$_T$ rather than changes in respiratory rate, which usually is unchanged.[24,39,81,138,209] It is much more efficient to increase alveolar ventilation through an increase in V$_T$ than with a proportionately equal increase in respiratory rate. The increased metabolic rate and CO$_2$ production also influence V$_T$ changes.[212] Maximal inspiratory and expiratory pressures are not altered in pregnancy. The reduced RV further enhances alveolar ventilation. This change in RV decreases the amount of gas mixing that occurs with each tidal exchange in the alveolus, thereby improving gas exchange at the alveolar level. Alveolar ventilation increases by 50% to 70% during pregnancy.[16,209]

Airflow. Airflow is dependent on resistance encountered in the bronchial tree. Two important determining factors for resistance are smooth muscle tone in the bronchi and the degree of congestion encountered in bronchial wall capillaries. Despite the changes in minute ventilation and the concomitant increase in alveolar ventilation, the work of breathing (airway resistance and lung compliance) remains unchanged. In the larger airways, congestion has very little to do with resistance. Airway resistance does not change significantly during pregnancy because of a balance between bronchoconstricting ($PGF_{2\alpha}$, decreased RV, and decreased $PaCO_2$) and bronchodilating (PGE_2 and progesterone) forces.[81]

Assessment of small airway function is most often determined by evaluation of closing volume (CV) and closing capacity (CC). CV is the point at which the small airways close (collapse and cease to ventilate) in the lowest part of the lung. Small airway (smaller than 1 mm) patency is believed to be the result of transpulmonary pressure, compliance of the airway walls, and the presence of sufficient surfactant. Closure in the lung bases normally occurs somewhere between the RV and FRC. CV is usually expressed as a percentage of vital capacity (CV/VC). CC is the term applied to the sum of the CV and RV and is expressed as a percentage of total lung capacity (CC/TLC).[39,212]

Under normal circumstances, airway closure does not occur during tidal breathing. When closure occurs at a higher than normal volume, however, gas exchange may be affected, because ventilation to the lung bases is decreased. In pregnancy, airway closure above the FRC has been reported near term, possibly because of the decrease in ERV. This alteration changes gas distribution and may result in a decrease in oxygen content and PaO_2 in the third trimester.[39,209,212] When airway closure is at or above FRC, there is a possibility of altering PaO_2 through ventilation-perfusion ($\dot{V}/\dot{Q}$) mismatch in the lung bases. If these differences are significant, compensatory maternal physiologic responses such as an increase in respiratory rate may result. However, this is not a usual event in healthy women who compensate by changes in the oxygen-hemoglobin dissociation curve (see "Acid-Base Changes").[26]

Diffusing Capacity. Diffusing capacity refers to the ease with which gas is transferred across the pulmonary membrane. Diffusion capacity of CO_2 may show an increase or no change in early pregnancy, followed by a decrease, reaching a plateau in the second half of pregnancy in many women. These changes are not believed to be clinically significant.[24,81] CO_2 production increases by 30% because of changes in cholesterol and fat metabolism.[212] Oxygen consumption (VO_2) increases 20% to 40% or by 32 to 58 mL/minute.[138,143,209] This change is accounted for by the needs of the fetus (average of 12 mL/minute) and placenta (4 mL/minute) and by increased maternal cardiac output (7 mL/minute), ventilation (2 mL/minute), renal function (7 mL/minute), and extra tissue in the breasts and uterus (5 mL/minute). The increase in CO_2 production exceeds the changes in oxygen consumption, leading to an increase in the respiratory quotient from 0.70 to 0.83 by term.[209] Pregnant women are at higher risk for hypoxia because of decreased O_2 reserves because of the increased O_2 consumption and reduced FRC.[188]

Acid-Base Changes

Oxygen consumption, CO_2 production, and basal metabolic rate all increase as a result of the increased metabolic demands from the mother, placenta, and fetus.[81] The normal pregnant woman is in a state of compensated respiratory alkalosis, which is believed to be the result of the effects of progesterone on the respiratory system and lung volume changes, especially the increased minute volume.[138,209,212] The result is a reduction in arterial and alveolar CO_2 and a slight increase in PaO_2. The fall in PCO_2 begins early in pregnancy, paralleling changes in ventilation.[209] Definitions of common terms used in acid-base physiology are listed in Table 6-1.

The purpose of the maternal respiratory alkalosis seems to be facilitation of CO_2 transfer from the fetus to the mother by increasing the arterial CO_2 pressure ($PaCO_2$) gradient. Hyperventilation leads to average $PaCO_2$ values of 27 to 32 mm Hg (3.6 to 4.3 kPa) and a concomitant decrease in serum bicarbonate levels to between 18 and 21 mEq/L (mmol/L) with a base deficit of −3 to −4 mEq/L (mmol/L) by term.[24,131] The latter is a consequence of increased renal excretion of bicarbonate, reflecting a metabolic compensation for the lower $PaCO_2$.[209] The lower $PaCO_2$ produces a gradient within the intervillous space that enhances fetal offloading of CO_2.[24,138] This may be the primary function of the hyperventilation of pregnancy.[137] $PaCO_2$ values vary with the altitude at which the mother resides; the decrease in $PaCO_2$ is greater at higher altitudes (compensatory hyperventilation to maintain adequate PaO_2).[24,81,209] The pH increases to the high end of normal (7.40 to 7.45) to maintain homeostasis.[131] These changes are stable throughout pregnancy until the onset of labor.[39] The reduction in blood buffer reduces the mother's ability to compensate for a metabolic acidosis that could develop during prolonged labor or other states in which tissue perfusion may be reduced. The decreased bicarbonate buffering capacity increases the risk of ketoacidosis in pregnant insulin-dependent diabetic women.[188]

In contrast, PaO_2 levels increase from those of prepregnancy (95 to 100 mm Hg [12.6 to 13.3 kPa]) because of the increase in alveolar ventilation. During the first trimester, PaO_2 levels range from 104 to 108 mm Hg (13.8 to 14.3 kPa), dropping to 101 to 104 mm Hg (13.4 to 13.8 kPa) by the third trimester.[131,209] Even though the PaO_2 level remains elevated, the alveolar-arterial PO_2 gradient ($AaDO_2$) is unchanged throughout most of pregnancy; it may increase near term as an attempt to offset hyperventilation. Oxygen delivery is maintained within normal limits during pregnancy because of the increased CO_2, which compensates for changes in the respiratory system and the decrease in red blood cells.[209] Supine positioning versus sitting in late pregnancy further decreases PaO_2 levels and increases the $AaDO_2$ gradient.[209] However, these changes are believed to have little clinical significance.

Oxygen-Hemoglobin Dissociation Curve. The oxygen-hemoglobin dissociation curve (Box 10-1) demonstrates that once the plateau of the curve is achieved it takes large changes in oxygen concentration to make small changes in

BOX 10-1   Oxygen-Hemoglobin Dissociation Curve

The oxygen-hemoglobin dissociation curve demonstrates the equilibrium between oxygen and hemoglobin (see Figure 10-3). The curve relates the partial pressure of oxygen to the percentage of hemoglobin that is saturated. There are two aspects of the curve that must be considered: its shape and its position. The shape of the curve is sigmoid, indicating that at higher levels (more than 50 mm Hg [6.65 kPa]) the curve flattens and an increase in PO_2 produces little increase in saturation. This upper region is the PO_2 range in which oxygen binds to hemoglobin in the lungs. At low PO_2 levels the curve is steep, and small changes in PO_2 result in large changes in hemoglobin saturation. In this range, oxygen is released from hemoglobin and cellular activities occur. A small drop in PO_2 here allows a large amount of oxygen to be unloaded to the tissues.

The position of the curve, whether it is shifted to the right or the left, depends on the oxygen affinity for the hemoglobin molecule. The affinity of hemoglobin for oxygen must be sufficient to oxygenate the blood during its movement through the pulmonary circulation. However, it must be weak enough to allow release of oxygen to the tissues. This affinity is expressed as the P_{50}, the oxygen tension at which hemoglobin is half saturated. The higher the affinity, the lower the P_{50}, and vice versa, indicating an inverse relationship. The P_{50} for adult blood at a pH of 7.40 and a temperature of 37° C (98.6° F) is normally 26 mm Hg (3.45 kPa). Numerous factors, both genetic and environmental, can influence the affinity of hemoglobin and shift the oxygen-hemoglobin dissociation curve.

A shift to the right implies a lowered affinity; a shift to the left indicates that oxygen is more tightly bound to hemoglobin. The structure of the hemoglobin molecule regulates the affinity and can be affected by pH, PCO_2, and temperature. Increasing amounts of carbon dioxide reduce hemoglobin affinity for oxygen. This is termed the *Bohr effect*. Because of the Bohr effect, the reciprocal exchange of oxygen for carbon dioxide is facilitated. Elevations in temperature also shift the curve to the right such that saturation is decreased at any given PO_2. The pH increases with release of CO_2, and the curve shifts to the left. The shift indicates an increased affinity for oxygen and favors the uptake of oxygen by hemoglobin.

The "30–60–90" rule can be used to remember general relationships between PaO_2 and saturation: At a PaO_2 of 30 mm Hg (3.99 kPa), the saturation is about 60%; at a PaO_2 of 60 mm Hg (7.98 kPa), saturation is about 90%, and at a PaO_2 of 90 mm Hg (11.97 kPa), saturation is about 95%.

Because of the sigmoid shape of the curve, a shift in position has little effect on the saturation when the PO_2 is within the normal arterial range (95–100 mm Hg [12.63–13.33 kPa]). However, in the venous system, in which the PO_2 range is around 40 mm Hg (5.32 kPa), there is a right shift in the curve, leading to an increased unloading of oxygen to the tissues and improving tissue oxygenation. Figures 10-3 and 10-17 illustrate oxygen-hemoglobin dissociation curves for the pregnant woman and term newborn. Changes in oxygen equilibrium after birth in term and preterm infants are illustrated in Figure 10-18.

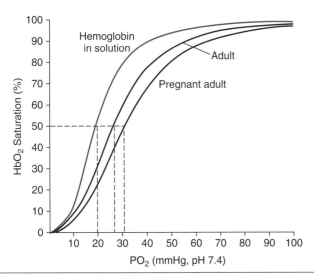

FIGURE 10-3   Oxyhemoglobin dissociation curve under standard conditions for normal blood of pregnant and nonpregnant adults. Also shown is the dissociation curve for hemoglobin in solution. (From McNamara, P.J. & El-Khuffash, A. [2017]. Oxygen transport and delivery. In R.A. Polin, S.H. Abman, D.H. Rowitch, W.E. Benitz & W.W. Fox [Eds.]. *Fetal and neonatal physiology* [5th ed.]. Philadelphia: Saunders.)

Sao_2. The P_{50} increases from 26 to 30 mm Hg (3.5 to 3.9 kPa) by term (Figure 10-3), thus decreasing the affinity of hemoglobin and enhancing transfer of oxygen from mother to fetus.[209,212] These changes are mediated by the increase in 2,3-diphosphoglycerate (2,3-DPG), which is stimulated by

the increase in maternal pH.[1,39] The increased 2,3-DPG shifts the oxygen-hemoglobin dissociation curve to the right to enhance oxygen release to the fetus.

It is unclear whether the small changes seen in PaO_2 levels during pregnancy are significant to the maternal-fetal oxygen gradient and therefore to the fetus. Considering that fetal PaO_2 levels are between 25 and 35 mm Hg (3.32 and 4.65 kPa), this seems unlikely. However, this increase may reflect increased maternal pulmonary circulation, with a greater volume of blood contained within the pulmonary vasculature at any given point in time. This may be significant at higher altitudes (see "Effects of Altitude and Air Travel"). Sao_2 does not change significantly during pregnancy, although saturations below 96% may be seen in women who smoke.

Intrapartum Period

The major effect of labor on the respiratory system is related to the increased muscular work, metabolic rate, and oxygen consumption.[24,209] Consequently, alterations in ventilation and acid-base status can be anticipated. A healthy woman is able to tolerate these changes because oxygen delivery is much greater than needs, but this can become a problem in a compromised woman.[209]

With the onset of labor, there is an increased demand for oxygen; oxygen consumption increases with uterine muscle activity. If there is insufficient time for uterine relaxation and restabilization after a contraction, oxygen content is lower and myometrial hypoxia as well as metabolic acidosis may occur with subsequent contractions. Over time this can lead to inadequate oxygenation, which increases the severity of the pain experienced. Most studies have evaluated respiratory system changes during active and painful labor. There are few studies evaluating the labor process with the use of sporadic analgesia and psychoprophylaxis. The pain experienced during labor is the result of the interaction of a number of factors (see Chapter 15).

Ventilatory alterations related to pain vary significantly from patient to patient; therefore each laboring woman must be evaluated individually. Changes seen during the intrapartum period include an increase in respiratory rate and a change in V_T, with a tendency toward further hyperventilation as minute ventilation increases.[188] Hyperventilation is a natural response to pain and becomes evident as the pain and apprehension of labor increase. Hyperventilation is diminished when pain is alleviated.[34] Maximal inspiratory pressure decreases during strong expulsive efforts, possibly as a result of development of transient diaphragmatic fatigue.

Although pain seems to be the major cause of this hyperventilatory response, anxiety, drugs, and the use of psychoprophylactic breathing exercises can contribute to the elevated respiratory rate. V_T may be further increased during the second stage of labor when hyperventilation after breath holding with expulsive efforts occurs. Potential risks of the Valsalva maneuver are discussed in Chapter 4.

Increases in oxygen uptake and minute ventilation are seen during labor, with a significant increase noted between early latent and active phases. Oxygen consumption increases 40% to 60% during labor with further increases (up to twofold) with contractions.[24,209] This is balanced by an increase in cardiac output. Women with low oxygen delivery may become compromised with inadequate oxygen delivery to both the woman and fetus.[209] The increase in ventilation can lead to a progressive and substantial decline in $PaCO_2$. There are wide variations in values between patients; however, a $PaCO_2$ level around 25 mm Hg is representative of what might be encountered during the first stage of labor. A transient decline in $PaCO_2$ occurs with each contraction until cervical dilation is complete, at which time the decline in $PaCO_2$ may be seen even between contractions.

The changes in $PaCO_2$ are markedly reduced or eliminated when continuous lumbar epidural anesthesia is used during labor. Variables affecting $PaCO_2$ levels that need to be considered include breath holding (which elevates $PaCO_2$ levels), compensatory hyperventilation after breath holding, length of contractions, and frequency of contractions. The timing of analgesia administration as well as the frequency and efficacy of the analgesia may also alter $PaCO_2$ values.[39] The respiratory alkalosis that ensues from hyperventilation is normally associated with a drop in base excess and possibly a decrease in arterial pH, according to some researchers. Others have documented a rise in pH. In either case, the degree of change indicates that labor and hyperventilation are highly significant events that may lead to alterations in physiologic parameters.[34]

Mild maternal acidosis is not uncommon and can be attributed to isometric muscular contractions that reduce the blood flow to working muscles, leading to tissue hypoxia and anaerobic metabolism in the face of a normal PaO_2. The degree of maternal acidosis is dependent on the extent of maternal anxiety and tension, intensity of muscular workload, degree of isometric contractions, and duration of labor.

In the first stage of labor, the maternal and fetal $PaCO_2$ levels parallel each other. This may reflect the respiratory nature of these changes. As labor progresses, this paralleling of values is lost. Fetal $PaCO_2$ levels increase when maternal acidosis occurs, reflecting not only fetal base deficit alterations but also the hypoxia within the uterine muscle. Contractions not only decrease the blood flow to the intervillous space but also reduce the oxygen supply to the uterus. The longer and stronger the contractions, the more pronounced the effects are. The local buildup of $PaCO_2$ decreases the fetal elimination of CO_2, which may lead to a drop in fetal pH. During the second stage of labor, maternal $PaCO_2$ levels may rise during pushing efforts. During this stage, a further increase in blood lactate levels from voluntary muscle activity during bearing down is seen. This is reflected in a further decline in blood pH and a fall in blood buffering capability (base deficit).

Significant changes in acid-base status because of hyperventilation and increased oxygen consumption are potentially hazardous to both the mother and fetus.[34,190] Extremely low $PaCO_2$ levels result in cerebral vasoconstriction and possibly reduce intervillous perfusion and blood flow.[190] The alkalemia that results shifts the oxygen-hemoglobin dissociation curve to the left. This shift impairs the release of oxygen from maternal blood to fetal blood, thereby decreasing the availability of oxygen to the fetus during a time when oxygenation may already be impaired by uterine contractions.[34] Hyperventilation may lead to dizziness and tingling in the mother because of low $PaCO_2$ levels. Interventions can include counting respirations out loud to help the mother slow her respiratory rate, letting her know when the contraction is ending so that she can begin to relax, avoiding the Valsalva maneuver, and promoting deep breathing between contractions to cleanse the system and promote oxygenation and restabilization.

The acid-base changes encountered in the first and second stages of labor quickly reverse in the third stage and postpartum period with compensatory respiratory efforts. These efforts are largely a result of a decrease in respiratory rate. Acid-base levels return to pregnancy values within 24 hours of delivery and to nonpregnant levels by several weeks after delivery. Table 10-1 summarizes the changes in arterial blood gases during the intrapartum period.

Research on the effects of labor on acid-base status has been conducted in conjunction with the delivery of epidural analgesia. Psychoprophylaxis (psychoanalgesia) has been shown to reduce the need for medication, reduce tension and pain by self-report, and engender a positive attitude toward the labor and delivery experience.[33,102] Reduction of pain sensations and perception is achieved through distraction by

TABLE 10-1   Maternal Blood Gas Alterations During the Intrapartum Period

STAGE OF LABOR	PARAMETER	RANGE VALUE	ACID-BASE STATUS
Early	$PaCO_2$	21–26 mm Hg (2.79–3.45 kPa)	Respiratory alkalosis
	Plasma base deficit	−0.9–26.9 mEq/L (mmol/L)	
	Blood pH	7.43–7.49	
End of first stage	$PaCO_2$	21–35 mm Hg (2.79–4.65 kPa)	Mild metabolic acidosis compensated by respiratory alkalosis
	Plasma base deficit	−1.2–29.2 mEq/L (mmol/L)	Mild respiratory acidosis during bearing down
	Blood pH	7.41–7.54	
End of second stage (delivery)	$PaCO_2$	16–24 mm Hg (2.12–3.19 kPa)	Metabolic acidosis uncompensated by respiratory alkalosis
	Plasma base deficit	−2.3 to −12.3 mEq/L (mmol/L)	
	Blood pH	7.37–7.45	

From Burgess, A. (1979). *The nurse's guide to fluid and electrolyte balance.* New York: McGraw-Hill.

using conditional responses such as breathing patterns and other nonpharmacologic measures (see Chapter 15).

Postpartum Period

The respiratory tract rapidly returns to its prepregnant state after delivery. This is a direct result of the separation of the placenta and consequential loss of progesterone production, as well as the immediate reduction in intraabdominal pressure with delivery of the infant that allows increased excursion of the diaphragm. Chest wall compliance changes immediately after delivery because of a decrease in pressure on the diaphragm and reduction in pulmonary blood volume. A 20% to 25% increase in static compliance has been reported after delivery. Changes in rib cage elasticity may persist for months after delivery.[212] V_T and RV return to normal soon after delivery, whereas ERV may remain in an abnormal state for several months. As progesterone levels fall in the first 2 days after delivery, $PaCO_2$ levels rise. Diffusing capacity, which at term is slightly below postpartum levels, increases during the postpartum period. Overall, anatomic changes and ventilation return to prepregnant status by 24 weeks after delivery, although the subcostal angle tends to remain about 20% wider than prepregnancy values.[81]

CLINICAL IMPLICATIONS FOR THE PREGNANT WOMAN AND HER FETUS

The respiratory changes that occur with pregnancy can be annoying as well as limiting in some circumstances. Common complaints and experiences include dyspnea, capillary engorgement of the upper respiratory tract, and altered exercise tolerance. As a result, modifications in activity levels as well as in the activities themselves may need to be considered. Discussions with women regarding their usual activities can help provide sufficient information for determining when change is needed. In addition, changes in the maternal respiratory system can influence the course of disease processes (e.g., asthma in some women), affecting not only the mother but also the fetus. Specific areas addressed in this section include dyspnea of pregnancy, exercise (respiratory effects), upper respiratory capillary engorgement, respiratory infections, asthma, smoking, and anesthesia.

Pregnancy-Related Dyspnea

The sensation of dyspnea is reported by 60% to 70% of pregnant women, usually beginning during the first or second trimester. A maximal incidence is reached between 28 and 31 weeks and remains relatively stable to term.[209,212] Because abdominal girth has not increased significantly at the time of dyspnea onset, intraabdominal pressure cannot be ascribed as the cause.

Pregnancy-related dyspnea is a physiologic dyspnea; that is, it occurs even at rest or with mild exertion.[212] The exact cause remains unclear, but it is believed to be caused by the increased respiratory drive and load, changes in oxygenation, or a combination of these events.[131,212] Increased sensitivity to CO_2 and hypoxia may be important contributing factors, especially in early pregnancy. During late pregnancy, mechanical factors may aggravate these changes.[143] The increased V_T and lower $PaCO_2$ have also been implicated. In addition, the heightened maternal awareness of the normal hyperventilation of pregnancy might result in the sensation of dyspnea. An improvement in symptoms in some women with increasing gestation suggests an adjustment to this normal process.

Dyspnea can be quite uncomfortable and anxiety provoking. The hyperventilation and dyspnea may decrease the ability of some pregnant women to maintain their usual activity levels. Pathologic dyspnea, which may occur with disorders such as pulmonary emboli (a complication sometimes seen in pregnancy), asthma, and cardiac disorders, must be differentiated from physiologic dyspnea during pregnancy.[131] Pathologic dyspnea is characterized by respiratory rates greater than 20 breaths per minute, PCO_2 below 30 mm Hg (3.9 kPa) or greater than 35 mm Hg (4.7 kPa), or abnormal FEV_1.[212]

Upper Respiratory Tract Capillary Engorgement

Hormonal changes (especially the increase in estrogens) along with the increased blood volume, decreased oncotic pressure, hyperemia, edema, glandular hypersecretion, and increased phagocyte activity alter the mucosa of the oropharynx and nasopharynx with capillary engorgement throughout the respiratory tract.[81,86] Progesterone may contribute to engorgement by inducing vascular smooth muscle relaxation, peripheral vasodilation, and nasal vascular pooling.[131] The results of these changes can be uncomfortable to some women and may be exacerbated in women with preeclampsia.[113] With preeclampsia, the airways may be narrower because of soft tissue edema.[141] In some situations these changes can be hazardous. For example, swelling of the airway along with other physiologic changes in pregnancy (e.g., weight gain, changes in the gastrointestinal system, and increased total body water) increase the risk for a pregnant woman who requires intubation for obstetric or nonobstetric problems.[24,54,63,141,169,188] The rate of failed intubations is seven to eight times higher during pregnancy.[24,54]

The nasopharynx, larynx, trachea, and bronchi may become swollen and reddened. For some individuals this may be uncomfortable, but it usually does not pose any unusual difficulties. These symptoms can be markedly aggravated with minor upper respiratory infections and preeclampsia. The swelling can lead to inflammation (noninfective in nature) that causes changes in the voice (e.g., hoarseness), make nose breathing difficult, and increase the incidence of nosebleeds. Abrasions and lacerations of the mucosa may occur, and bleeding may ensue.[34,63,141] The increased mucosal vascularity, edema, estrogens, placental growth hormone (a stimulator of nasal mucosal growth), and progesterone-mediated vasodilation increase the risk of rhinitis and epistaxis.[29] Upper respiratory tract changes may also increase snoring and exacerbate sleep-disordered breathing or increase obstructive sleep apnea.[24,26,165] These changes are discussed further in Chapter 15.

Exercise

The effect of exercise on the respiratory system is related to alveolar ventilation and is dependent on the age, body weight, body composition, and physical condition of the individual. Cardiovascular function, uterine blood flow, respiratory function, blood gases, aerobic capacity, metabolism, temperature, and psychological state are all affected by exercise. Regular exercise during pregnancy has many benefits for the pregnant woman.[81,131] These benefits, changes with exercise during pregnancy, and effects of exercise on the mother and infant are discussed further in Chapter 9.

The usual changes in maternal respiratory function during pregnancy are similar to those with mild to moderate exercise.[95,152] Studies of respiratory rates with exercise in pregnant and nonpregnant women demonstrate that respiratory rates in pregnant women are higher than those in nonpregnant women during mild exercise, but this difference disappears during moderate exercise. V_T and minute volume remain higher in pregnant subjects during all levels of exercise.[152] Ventilation increases 38% and oxygen consumption is 15% greater during exercise in pregnant versus nonpregnant women.[152] The efficiency of gas exchange does not seem to be impaired in most pregnant woman during exercise. During prolonged exercise, however, PaO_2 increases and $PaCO_2$ decreases. This decrease in $PaCO_2$ is most likely a result of the effects of progesterone on the respiratory center. Oxygen consumption also increases with advancing gestational age. Part of this increase is caused by the increased work of carrying the extra weight associated with pregnancy.[131] Exercise-induced changes in acid-base balance are similar in pregnant and nonpregnant women.

Effects of Altitude and Air Travel

With increasing altitude, compensatory decreases in PaO_2 and changes in other parameters can be seen. These are an attempt by the maternal system to maintain higher PaO_2 levels under relatively hypoxic conditions.[127] The change in altitude has a significant effect on oxygen saturation and changes the oxygen-hemoglobin dissociation curve. Pregnant women living at high altitude have a higher minute ventilation, FRC, TLC, forced VC, forced expiratory volume, and diffusion capacity than women at sea level.[24,103] The hyperventilation of pregnancy is also accentuated, and maternal dyspnea may be more prominent; therefore patients need to be given assurance that it is normal.[8] The woman increases her ventilation and oxygen saturation during the first trimester, whereas diffusing capacity decreases to the third trimester, leading to decreased oxygen content by term. These changes are not significant if the woman comes from a family that has lived at that altitude for at least three generations.[24,103] Pregnancy at high altitude is also associated with morphologic differences in placental villi with increased capillary diameter. Women living at high altitude have lower birthweight infants. Birth weight is decreased by an average of 100 g for each 3000 feet (1000 meters) increase in altitude.[24]

Commercial aircraft are usually pressurized to 6000 to 8000 feet (1829 to 2434 meters) above sea level, so flying results in a transient exposure to altitude. During ascent, the pregnant woman may experience transient cardiopulmonary adaptations (increased heart rate and blood pressure; decreased aerobic capacity).[4] The fetal heart rate may also increase transiently during both takeoff and landing but stays within normal limits.[63] Pregnant women who travel by airplane may also experience an increase in dyspnea and respiratory rate as their bodies attempt to compensate for the increased altitude. Fetal hemoglobin (HbF) and the fetal circulation protect the fetus from desaturation during commercial flights.[163] Thus flying in commercial aircraft is generally not a risk in women with uncomplicated pregnancies.[4,63,119] The American College of Obstetricians and Gynecologists states that "in the absence of obstetric or medical complications, pregnant women can observe the same general precautions for air travel as the general population and can fly safely."[4] Most airlines allow travel up to 36 weeks of pregnancy, with travel up to 7 days before the woman's expected due date permitted with a certificate from their health care provider.[4] For international travel the cutoff may be earlier.

Pregnant women may be at greater risk of venous thromboembolism (VTE) during air travel because of changes in hemostasis (see Chapter 8) and hemoconcentration resulting from the low cabin humidity (less than 25%) and should be sure to stretch, perform isometric exercises, and walk around the cabin (an aisle seat facilitates this) at regular intervals.[163] Although air travel is associated with a risk of VTE, data on VTE risk in pregnant women is limited.[28,91] A statistical analysis of air travel risk during pregnancy estimated the risk of VTE in pregnant women in general as 0.03% to 0.1% but may be higher for women with other VTE risk factors (see Chapter 8).[28] Because of the low cabin humidity, the woman should also maintain hydration with frequent intake of nonalcoholic beverages, because hydration is important for placental blood flow.[163]

Pulmonary Disease and Pregnancy

Pulmonary disorders may be aggravated by the changes in the respiratory system during pregnancy. Respiratory infections and asthma are discussed here. Women with pulmonary hypertension (see Chapter 9) and cystic fibrosis (see Chapter 1) are also at increased risk for complications during pregnancy. Outcomes depend on their status at the onset of pregnancy.

Adult respiratory distress syndrome (ARDS) is an acute lung injury involving diffuse interstitial infiltrates, inflammation, decreased lung compliance, hypoxia, and respiratory failure.[54] ARDS is usually triggered by sepsis but may also be triggered by other factors, including disseminated intravascular coagulation (see Chapter 8), preeclampsia, trauma, aspiration, amniotic fluid embolism, abruptio placenta, or fetal demise.[54,131,169,209] Physiologic changes during pregnancy may increase the risk of ARDS after lung injury and increase mortality.[131]

Respiratory Infection

Changes in the immune (see Chapter 13) and pulmonary systems in the pregnant woman, along with upper airway hyperemia and edema, not only make having an upper respiratory infection more uncomfortable but can also potentiate movement of the infection into the lungs. Infections associated with lung involvement can potentially increase airway resistance, thereby increasing the work of breathing, and lead to decreased V_T and RV. This may lead to decreased maternal and subsequently fetal PaO_2 levels. The increased oxygen requirements of pregnancy, elevated diaphragm, decreased FRC, increased lung water, and changes in closing volume may increase the severity of respiratory problems.[39] Avoidance of those situations in which infections might be contracted and avoidance of individuals carrying infections when possible is a good practice. Most upper respiratory infections are only annoyances and do not lead to significant consequences for the mother or fetus.

Pneumonia, although rare, is a leading cause of nonobstetric maternal death in North America.[71,169,209] The prevalence of bacterial pneumonia is similar during pregnancy in nonpregnant, healthy women.[71,209] However, pregnant women are more susceptible to viral pneumonia, and the pneumonia may progress more rapidly during pregnancy.[209] The risk of pneumonia increases with each trimester, and by the third trimester the risk of hospitalization from pneumonia is five times higher in pregnant than nonpregnant women.[71,209]

Pneumonia increases the risk of preterm labor, altered fetal growth, and maternal and perinatal mortality.[71,75,209] The risk of influenza-related morbidity is also increased in pregnant women.[71] As a result, influenza vaccinations are recommended for all pregnant women during flu season, regardless of trimester.[10,75] Pregnancy may also increase the risk of varicella pneumonia.[71,209] Although chronic infections such as tuberculosis (TB) have often been reported to reactivate and worsen with pregnancy, recent evidence suggests that in women with drug-sensitive TB who have received adequate therapy, fetal and maternal outcomes are generally good.[209] Respiratory infections and vaccination during pregnancy are discussed further in Chapter 13.

Asthma

The prevalence of asthma has increased in the general population, leading to an increase in pregnant women with asthma.[143] As a result, asthma is the most common pulmonary problem seen during pregnancy, occurring in approximately 8% (6% to 12%) of pregnant women.[145,169,170] Asthma has been reported to improve (about 23%), worsen (about 30%), or remain unchanged (about 47%) during pregnancy.[49] Predicting an individual's course during pregnancy is extremely difficult. Women with more severe asthma before pregnancy are more likely to have severe asthma, and require hospitalization, during pregnancy, although this is not always the case.[49,209] No change in perinatal mortality has been reported in women with mild to moderate asthma when the asthma was medically managed; women with severe asthma are at high risk for exacerbation and pregnancy complications, including preterm delivery, low birth weight, fetal growth restriction, increased perinatal mortality and morbidity, and preeclampsia.[143,189]

Asthma may lead to maternal hypoxia or hyperventilation with resultant hypocapnia and alkalosis, potentially affecting fetal well-being.[209] Transient hypoxia is not generally as great a concern as chronic hypoxia, which increases the risk of preterm birth, altered fetal growth, and mortality.[209] Acute hypocapnia and alkalosis, however, can contribute to fetal depression by reducing uterine and fetal blood flow secondary to vasoconstriction. Alkalosis also increases maternal hemoglobin affinity for oxygen, thereby reducing availability to the fetus.

The normal alterations of the respiratory system during pregnancy may influence asthma in both positive and negative ways (Box 10-2). The hyperventilation of pregnancy may be more distressful for an asthmatic woman. The increase in circulating cortisol levels may augment cAMP functioning and reduce inflammation through steroid action. Progesterone levels decrease bronchomotor tone (relaxing smooth muscle tissue) and thereby decrease airway resistance. Elevated serum cAMP levels may also promote bronchodilation. Improvement of asthma during pregnancy may be secondary to increased free cortisol, decreased plasma histamine, decreased bronchial smooth muscle tone because of progesterone, and decreased airway resistance because of

---

BOX 10-2 Factors Affecting Asthma in Pregnancy

IMPROVEMENT

Increased progesterone-mediated bronchodilation
β-Adrenergic-stimulated bronchodilation
Decreased plasma histamine levels
Increased free cortisol levels
Increased glucocorticoid-mediated β-adrenergic responsiveness
Increased PGE-mediated bronchodilation
PGI$_2$-mediated bronchial stabilization
Increased half-life of bronchodilators
Decreased protein-binding of bronchodilators

WORSENING

Pulmonary refractoriness to cortisol effects
Increased PGF$_{2\alpha}$-mediated bronchoconstriction
Decreased functional residual capacity, causing airway closure and altered ventilation-perfusion ratios
Increased risk of respiratory infection
Increased risk of viral pneumonia
Increased gastroesophageal reflux
Increased stress

Data from Schatz, M. & Hoffman, C. (1987). Interrelationships between asthma and pregnancy: Clinical and mechanistic considerations. *Clin Rev Allergy, 5,* 301.

---

decreased tone.[143,209] Conversely, asthma may worsen as a result of increased progesterone and mineral steroids that compete for glucocorticoid receptors, increased β2-adrenoreceptor responsiveness, increased viral respiratory infections and thus bronchial inflammation, increased PGF$_{2\alpha}$ and hyperventilation.[143] The increased tendency for gastroesophageal reflux (see Chapter 12) during pregnancy may also exacerbate asthma.[143] Therefore the effect of pregnancy on the course of asthma in an individual woman depends on the balance of these factors in her system.

Pharmacologic treatment and the selection of an appropriate agent are based on the risk-to-benefit ratio of bronchodilator effect and hypoxia avoidance versus possible adverse consequences.[145] Oral corticosteroids in the first trimester have been linked to an increased risk of cleft lip with or without cleft palate and an increase in preeclampsia, preterm delivery, and low birth weight.[49,209] Thus inhaled corticosteroids are generally advocated as a first-line therapy.[49,145,209] Maternal physiologic changes may alter the pharmacokinetics, although most agents seem to be as effective during pregnancy as in nonpregnant women.[209] Women with exacerbations may need stepwise increase in therapies; women who improve may also need changes in treatment.[145] The National Asthma Education and Prevention Program has published guidelines for management of the pregnant asthmatic woman and notes that "it is safer for pregnant women with asthma to be treated with asthma medication than it is for them to have asthma symptoms and exacerbations."[145] Women need to be counseled to use only those medications prescribed and to avoid over-the-counter medications. Prescribed medications should be taken only as directed; maternal and fetal side effects need to be explained clearly and concisely.

Smoking

"Smoking during pregnancy is among the leading preventable causes of adverse maternal and fetal outcomes."[143] Maternal smoking increases perinatal morbidity and mortality. Smoking may also interfere with a woman's ability to conceive.[142] Risks for the pregnant woman include increased rates of spontaneous abortion, abruptio placenta, placenta previa, early or late bleeding, premature rupture of membranes, and preterm labor.[23,142,143,213] The number of women who complete smoking cessation programs during pregnancy is low, with many relapsing postpartum.[168]

"Human and animal data support that nicotine exposure during periods of developmental vulnerability (fetal through adolescent stages) has multiple adverse health consequences, including impaired fetal brain and lung development, and altered development of cerebral cortex and hippocampus in adolescents."[56] Fetal and neonatal risks of maternal smoking include low birth weight (two- to threefold increase), preterm delivery, and fetal growth restriction.[23,142] Infants of women who smoke on average weigh 200 g less at birth than infants of women who do not smoke.[142,195] There is a dose-related effect of the number of cigarettes per day and the decrease in birth weight, especially in women who continue smoking past 32 weeks' gestation.[142,155] The degree of risk for a low birth-weight infant in women who smoke may be influenced by maternal genotype, especially genetic polymorphisms that affect the activity of specific enzymes needed to metabolize the various chemicals in cigarettes. Paternal smoking and secondary smoke exposure are also associated with risks to offspring.[131,142] Levels of nicotine are similar to those in tobacco in electronic cigarettes and are believed to have similar effects on the pregnant woman and her infant, but there is little data to date.[56,213]

The exact mechanism for fetal and neonatal effects is not completely understood but includes indirect effects on uterine blood flow and direct effects from transfer of toxins such as nicotine, which appears to be the toxin causing the most maternal and fetal harm, across the placenta (see Chapter 7).[23,142] Nicotine and its main metabolite, cotinine, are lipid soluble and readily cross the placenta.[142] Fetal levels are generally 90% of maternal levels and may be higher.[143] Nicotine may also compete with nutrients for placental nutrient carriers, reducing nutrient transfer and thus fetal growth. Many of the risks seen with smokers are related to the placental histologic alterations or consequences of altered placental function. This supports an etiology mediated by changes in placental structure and alterations in uteroplacental blood flow and oxygenation. Adverse effects of nicotine may be mediated by oxidative stress, reactive oxygen species, endoplasmic reticulum stress, and inflammation with production of proinflammatory cytokines that may alter placental development.[213]

Children of smokers are at risk for later problems as well, including behavioral difficulties; alterations in long-term learning memory; and mood, conduct, and attention-deficit disorders.[23,56,142] Changes in the central nervous system may result from alterations in expression of neurotransmitters in the fetus, fetal adrenergic activation leading to sympathetic nervous system dysfunction, or alterations in the serotonin system.[95] Nicotine exposure increases the risk of altered cognitive and learning skills; sudden infant death syndrome; altered respiratory function; increased respiratory infections; and the incidence of childhood respiratory disorders, including asthma, pneumonia, and bronchitis.[57,142,143]

Inhalation Anesthesia

The use of inhalation anesthesia in pregnant women usually occurs only during emergencies. The effect on the maternal respiratory system is related to maternal cardiorespiratory status before induction and the type and adequacy of ventilation after induction. Light to moderate anesthesia with adequate oxygen mixing should provide no difficulties to a well-hydrated, stable pregnant woman.[34] Because of the reduced FRC and increased CV during pregnancy, as well as the higher metabolic requirements and alterations in the upper airway (see "Upper Respiratory Tract Capillary Engorgement"), pregnant women are less tolerant of apnea and are at higher risk for a difficult or failed intubation.[24,54,86,156,169] Oxygen partial pressure levels drop rapidly in these situations, leading to hypoxia, hypoxemia, and acidosis. These events not only place the mother at risk, but also jeopardize the status of the fetus. Because of the reduced maternal oxygen reserves and increased risk of hypoxia, preoxygenation is recommended for pregnant women before the use of general anesthesia.[188]

Inhalation agents are dose- and time-dependent compounds that affect the fetus directly through transplacental movement of drugs or indirectly by altering maternal homeostasis or changing uteroplacental blood flow.[34] If fetal depression does occur, it is an indication of impaired placental blood flow, possibly because of decreased maternal cardiac output.[34,39] Most of the time, no serious depression occurs. However, uteroplacental blood flow may be altered through several mechanisms: (1) change in perfusion pressure, (2) modification of vascular resistance, (3) alterations in uterine contractions and basal tone, and (4) interference in fetal cardiovascular function (umbilical circulation). Uterine blood flow varies directly with perfusion pressure across the uterine vascular bed (uterine arterial pressure minus uterine venous pressure) and inversely with uterine vascular resistance. The balance between perfusion pressure and vascular resistance is the primary basis for acute changes in uterine blood flow.[34,117]

Adverse responses or heavy anesthesia can precipitate a hazardous sequence of events. Maternal cardiac output may fall, precipitating a fall in blood pressure and an increased likelihood of maternal acidosis and decreased uterine blood flow. The result is a decreased uteroplacental blood flow with decreased nutrient supply to the fetus. Fetal heart rate and blood pressure may fall as a result of direct fetal cardiovascular depression (drug response) or the indirect effect of decreased uteroplacental perfusion. The decreased cardiac output and low blood pressure culminate in fetal hypoxia and acidosis, as reflected in low oxygen saturations, elevated PCO_2 levels, and falling base excess. Fetal status before induction affects the severity of the response.[34,117] This same sequence of events may occur with severe maternal hyperventilation. Marked reductions in maternal PCO_2 reduce uteroplacental blood flow and maternal cardiac output and can lead to fetal hypoxemia and acidosis.

SUMMARY

The maternal respiratory alterations that occur during pregnancy ensure an adequate supply of oxygen to the developing fetus and its supporting structures. These demands are increased with activity and labor and are usually compensated for without difficulty. However, subjective interpretation of labor and the pain experienced can trigger maternal hyperventilation and alter fetal homeostasis. Adequate education of the mother about the normal physiologic changes and the labor experience is essential to maternal–fetal well-being. Psychoprophylaxis, analgesia, and anesthesia can moderate the experience and can be used safely during the intrapartum period. Careful monitoring with all these methods is important to safeguard the fetus. Clinical implications for the pregnant woman and her fetus are summarized in Box 10-3.

BOX 10-3 Recommendations for Clinical Practice Related to the Respiratory System in the Pregnant Woman and Fetus

Understand the normal respiratory changes that occur during pregnancy (pp. 297-303).

Explain to the pregnant woman the changes that can occur in the respiratory system early in pregnancy and how they can affect daily activities and exercise tolerance (pp. 297-304).

Encourage prelabor preparation to reduce discomfort, hyperventilation, and anxiety during labor (pp. 301-303).

Reduce hyperventilation during labor by counting respirations slowly, discouraging breath holding, and encouraging deep breathing between contractions (pp. 302-305).

Discuss upper airway changes that may lead to nasal congestion and other symptoms (pp. 303-304).

Counsel women regarding respiratory infections during pregnancy (p. 305).

Counsel pregnant women to get an influenza vaccine if they are pregnant during flu season (p. 305).

Discuss usual exercise routines and changes that may be necessary during pregnancy (pp. 304-305 and Chapter 9).

Counsel pregnant women regarding air travel (pp. 304-305).

Counsel asthmatic women who are pregnant to follow their medical regimen as directed, to avoid known precipitating factors, and seek medical intervention when symptoms persist (pp. 305-306).

Encourage and support pregnant women in reducing or eliminating cigarette use during and after pregnancy (p. 306, Chapter 7).

DEVELOPMENT OF THE RESPIRATORY SYSTEM IN THE FETUS

Embryonic development of the lung and the role of lung liquid and fetal breathing movements in development, as well as surfactant synthesis and secretion, set the stage for understanding the changes that occur with transition to extrauterine life. Respiratory system development is stimulated by multiple genes and a complex interplay of regulatory molecules, including growth factors, transcription factors (deoxyribonucleic acid [DNA]–binding proteins), extracellular matrix molecules, integrins, intracellular adhesion molecules, morphogens, and exogenous factors such as retinoic acid and antioxidants.[37,70,203] Lung development is also stimulated by mechanical forces, especially stretch of lung tissue by fetal breathing movements and accumulation of lung liquid.[35] Mechanical forces increase the rate of cell proliferation and differentiation, especially of the alveolar epithelium.[74]

Anatomic Development

Lung growth occurs in five stages: embryonic (3 to 7 weeks' gestation), pseudoglandular (5 to 17 weeks' gestation), canalicular (16 to 26 weeks' gestation), saccular (24 to 36 weeks' gestation), and alveolar (36 weeks' gestation to childhood).[99] These stages and regulating factors are summarized in Table 10-2.

The embryonic stage of lung development lasts from 3 to 7 weeks' gestation. Around day 22, a ventral diverticulum (outpouching) can be seen developing from the foregut, developing into the lung bud by day 26.[99,203] This groove extends downward and is gradually separated from the future esophagus by a septum (see Chapter 12). After 2 to 4 days, the first dichotomous branches can be seen (Figure 10-4). By the end of this stage, three main divisions are evident on the right and two on the left, with 10 rudimentary bronchopulmonary segments on the right and 8 or 9 on the left.[139,193,203] Factors regulating lung bud branching are listed in Table 10-2. Alterations in these factors can lead to pulmonary agenesis, tracheal esophageal fistula, and lobar agenesis.[37,203] By the end of this stage a primitive pulmonary circulation is established.[203]

Between 5 and 16 weeks' gestation, a tree of narrow tubules forms (Figure 10-4, *G*). New airway branches arise through a combination of cell multiplication and necrosis. These tubules have thick epithelial walls made of columnar or cuboidal cells. This morphologic structure, along with the loose mesenchymal tissue surrounding the tree, gives the lungs a glandular appearance (hence the term *pseudoglandular stage*).[99,139,203] The principal pulmonary arteries grow alongside the airways and are in place by 14 weeks.[99] By the end of this stage, branching of the conducting portion of the tracheobronchial tree is established. These preacinar airways can, from this point forward, increase only in length and diameter, not in number. The most peripheral structures are the terminal bronchioles (Figure 10-5, *A*).[203] Between 15 and 20 generations of airways develop (all branches to the level of the alveolar ducts).[99,104]

Epithelial-mesenchymal interaction is critical for early lung and pulmonary vasculature development and branching morphogenesis mediated by fibroblast growth factor (FGF)-10, FGF-7, vascular endothelial growth factor

---

TABLE 10-2 Lung Development in the Fetus

STAGE OF DEVELOPMENT	FETAL AGE (WEEKS)	STRUCTURAL EVENTS	PRIMARY REGULATORS OF LUNG GROWTH AND DIFFERENTIATION	ASSOCIATED ABNORMALITIES
Embryonic	3–7	Lung bud formation, trachea, lobar and segmental bronchi	TTF-1, FGF-10, Gli genes, retinoic acid, HOX genes	Tracheoesophageal fistula, pulmonary agenesis, lobation defects
Pseudoglandular	5–17	Subsegmental bronchi, terminal bronchi, mucous glands, cartilage, smooth muscle, early vasculature and epithelial differentiation, diaphragm formation	TTF-1, FGFs, FOXa1/a2, TGF-β, VEGF	Sequestration, cystic adenomatoid malformation, lymphangiectasias, congenital diaphragmatic hernia
Canalicular	16–26	Respiratory bronchioles, acinar saccules, thinning of capillary-epithelial space, type I and type II epithelial cells	Glucocorticoids, VEGF	Pulmonary hypoplasia, alveolar-capillary dysplasia
Saccular	26–36	Division of acinar saccules, microvascular expansion, increase in gas-exchange surface area	Glucocorticoids, VEGF	Pulmonary hypoplasia, pulmonary hypertension
Alveolar	32 weeks through childhood	Septation of alveoli, maturation of type II cells, surfactant	Elastin, glucocorticoids, retinoic acids, inflammatory mediators	SP-B, SP-C, and ABCA3 transporter deficiencies, pulmonary hypertension

FGF-10, Fibroblast growth factor-10; *FOXa1/a2*, forkhead box a1/a2; *SP*, surfactant protein; *TGF-β*, transforming growth factor-β; *TTF-1*, thyroid-specific transcription factor 1; *VEGF*, vascular endothelial growth factor.
From Jobe, A.H. & Kamath–Rayne, B.D. (2014). Fetal lung development and surfactant. In R.K. Creasy, R. Resnik, J.D. Iams, C.J. Lockwood, T.R. Moore, & M.F. Greene. (Eds.). *Creasy & Resnik's maternal-fetal medicine: Principles and practice* (7th ed.). Philadelphia: Saunders.

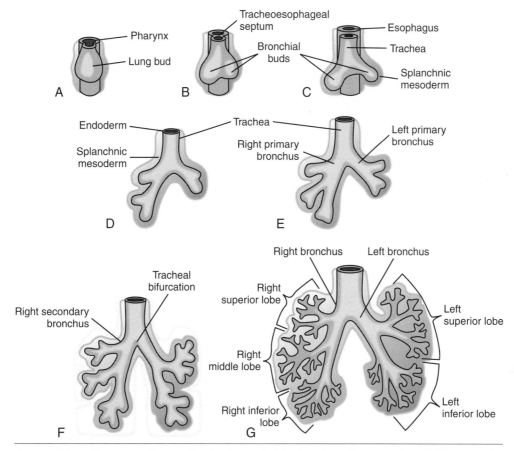

FIGURE 10-4   Successive stages in the development of the bronchi and lungs. (**A** through **C**) Four weeks. (**D** and **E**) Five weeks. (**F**) Six weeks. (**G**) Eight weeks. (Adapted from Moore, K.L., Persaud, T.V.N., & Torchia, M.G. [2015]. *The developing human: Clinically oriented embryology* [10th ed.]. Philadelphia: Saunders.)

(VGEF), and transforming growth factor-α (TGF-α) (see Table 10-2).[74,104] The mesenchymal tissue surrounding the airways has an inductive influence via expression of multiple growth and transcription factors and other signaling molecules. Removal of this tissue interrupts epithelial branching until regeneration occurs. Mesenchyme that surrounds the endodermal tree contributes to the nonepithelial elements of the bronchial tree. Another type of mesenchyme develops into the pleura, subpleural connective tissue, intralobular septa, and cartilage of the bronchi. Toward the end of the pseudoglandular period, rudimentary forms of cartilage, connective tissue, muscle, blood vessels, and lymphatic vessels can be identified. Ciliated cells appear in the upper airway by 10 weeks and in the bronchi by 12 to 13 weeks.[203] Mucus-producing glands appear in the bronchi by 13 weeks, with active mucus production by 14 weeks.[99,203]

Around 16 weeks, the epithelial cells of the distal air spaces (future alveolar lining) begin to flatten (becoming more cuboidal) and increase in glycogen (which serves as a substrate for surfactant synthesis), signaling the beginning of the canalicular stage.[160] This stage is called canalicular because of the vascular capillaries that begin to multiply in the interstitial space.[203] A rich vascular supply begins to proliferate in the interstitial space, and with the changes in

mesenchymal tissue, the capillaries are brought closer to the airway epithelium to form alveolar-capillary respiratory membranes (future gas exchange areas) by 21 weeks (Figure 10-5, *B*).[99] Primitive respiratory bronchioles begin to form during this stage, delineating the acinus (gas-exchanging section of the lung) from the conducting portion of the lung (see Figure 10-5, *B*). Type I and type II alveolar epithelial cells begin to differentiate.[203] Between 20 and 24 weeks, the cuboidal type II cells lining the terminal portions of the airway begin to develop lamellar bodies, indicating the beginning of surfactant production.[99,104,160] The canalicular stage continues until 26 weeks' gestation.

By 24 to 26 weeks, terminal air sacs begin to appear as outpouchings of the terminal bronchioles, marking the beginning of the saccular stage (see Figure 10-5, *C*). During the saccular stage the number of terminal sacs increases, forming multiple pouches off a common chamber (the future alveolar duct). Glucocorticoid receptors on these cells increase with increasing gestation.[74] Type II alveolar cells continue to mature with increases in surfactant phospholipid synthesis, surfactant proteins, and lamellar bodies; type I cells continue to develop and thin.[203] As blood vessels develop, they stretch and thin the epithelium that covers them, bringing the double capillary network (see Pulmonary Vasculature) into closer

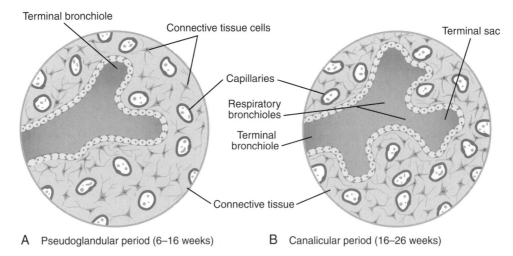

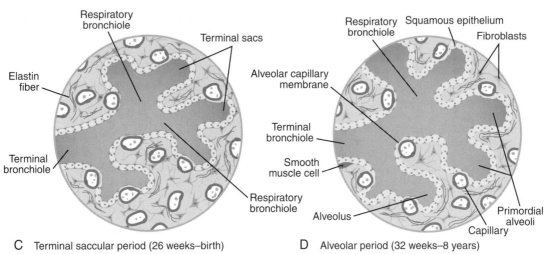

FIGURE 10-5   Sketches of histologic sections illustrating the stages of lung development. **(A** and **B)** Early stages of lung development. **(C** and **D)** The alveolocapillary membrane is thin and some capillaries bulge into the terminal sacs and alveoli. (From Moore, K.L., Persaud, T.V.N., & Torchia, M.G. *The developing human: Clinically oriented embryology* [10th ed.]. Philadelphia: Saunders.)

proximity with the developing air spaces (see Figure 10-5).[139,203] The number of air spaces (initially saccules, then later alveoli) increase from 65,000 at 18 weeks to 240,000 by 24 weeks, 4 million by 32 to 36 weeks, and up to 150 million by term (versus 500 million in adults).[97,99,104]

The alveolar stage begins around 36 weeks' gestation (see Figure 10-5, *D*). Shallow cup-shaped indentations in the saccule walls can be detected. These primitive alveoli consist of smooth-walled transitional ducts and saccules with primitive septa with double capillary loops.[35] These saccules will deepen and multiply via septation postnatally to form true alveoli, markedly increasing the gas exchange surface area.[35,203] Only about 20% of the alveoli are formed by term. Alveolarization also involves thinning of the distal airways and alveolar walls and growth of lung capillary network.[6] These processes are stimulated by growth and can be disrupted by hypoxia or hyperoxia.[104] The alveolar stage is also a time of microvascular maturation with further thinning of the gas exchange membrane and intraalveolar walls and formation of a single

capillary network (see Pulmonary Vasculature).[74] Factors regulating this stage are listed in Table 10-2. Disruption of lung development between 32 weeks and term interferes with alveolarization and can have both short- and long-term effects on lung function.[99]

Lung structures and cells are differentiated to the point that extrauterine life can usually be supported by around 24 to 26 weeks' gestation (late canalicular stage). Although the normal number of air spaces has not developed, the epithelium has thinned enough and the vascular bed has proliferated to the point that oxygen exchange can occur. The 24- to 26-week lung, however, is markedly different than that of a term neonate, just as a term infant's lung is different from that of a child or adult.

The respiratory portion of the lung has a continuous epithelial lining composed mainly of two cell types: type I and type II cells (pneumocytes). Development of these cells is under the influence of multiple signaling processes and a network of transcription factors, including glucocorticoids

TABLE 10-5   Changes in Lung Size With Growth

PARAMETER	30 WEEKS' GESTATION	FULL TERM	ADULT	FOLD INCREASE AFTER BIRTH
Lung volume	25 mL	150–200 mL	5 L	23
Lung weight	20–25 g	50 g	800 g	16
Alveolar number		50 m	300 m	8
Surface area	0.3 m^2	3–4 m^2	75–100 m^2	23
Surface area/kg		0.4 m^2	1 m^2	2.5
Alveolar diameter	32 mm	150 μm	300 μm	22
Number of airways	24	23–24	22–24	0
Tracheal length		26 mm	184 m	7
Main bronchi length		26 mm	254 m	10

From Hodson, W.A. (1998). Normal and abnormal structural development of the lung. In R.A. Polin & W.W. Fox. (Eds.). *Fetal and neonatal physiology* (2nd ed.). Philadelphia: Saunders.

Transitional Events

Transitional events are those activities that must occur within organ systems to achieve appropriate functioning in the extrauterine environment. Transition begins before birth with changes in the hypothalamic-pituitary-adrenal axis and cortisol release (see Chapter 19).[186] The most critical of these activities is the establishment of an air–liquid interface at the alveolar level and the acquisition of sustained rhythmic respirations by the neonate. This must occur within seconds of placental separation, or pulmonary and cardiovascular changes will not occur and resuscitation will be necessary. Respiratory changes at birth are linked with the cardiovascular changes discussed in Chapter 9. Lung aeration triggers an increase in pulmonary blood flow and restores venous return and ventricular preload.[88,90,194] Delaying umbilical cord clamping until after initiation of respiration may enhance early hemodynamic stability (see Chapter 8).[88,90,194]

In most instances, transition to extrauterine life is smooth. Approximately 10% of newborns will require some assistance at birth; less than 1% require extensive resuscitation.[77] When intervention is needed, evidence-based guidelines are available from the International Liaison Committee on Resuscitation (ILCOR), which are incorporated into the Neonatal Resuscitation Program (NRP).[170,202,214]

Establishment of Extrauterine Respiration

At term, the acinar portion of the lung is well established, although "true" alveoli have only begun to develop. The pulmonary blood vessels are narrow; less than 10% to 12% of the cardiac output perfuses the lungs to meet cellular nutrition needs. This low-volume circulation is in part a result of the high pulmonary vascular resistance created by constricted arterioles.

Lung aeration is complete when lung liquid is replaced with an equal volume of air and the functional residual capacity (FRC) is established. A substantial amount of air is retained from the early breaths, and within an hour of birth 80% to 90% of the FRC is created. The retention of air is a result of surfactant and a decrease in surface tension. Surfactant decreases the tendency toward atelectasis; promotes capillary circulation by increasing alveolar size, which indirectly dilates precapillary vessels; improves alveolar fluid clearance; and protects the airway. The blood gas levels that are encountered in the fetal state would result in significant hyperventilation if encountered postnatally. This indicates a diminished responsiveness of the respiratory centers to chemical stimuli in the blood in the prenatal period. Postnatal breathing is responsive to stimuli from arterial and central chemoreceptors (via oxygen and CO_2 tension in the blood); stimuli from the chest wall and lungs, musculoskeletal system, and skin; and environmental and behavioral stimuli. The changes that take place at birth and the increase in aerobic metabolism are not only rapid but irreversible. Within a few hours of birth, a full-term neonate is responsive to hypoxia and hypercapnia in much the same manner as an adult.[70]

During the course of labor, progressive changes are seen in fetal blood gases. The PO_2 slowly decreases, PCO_2 increases, pH decreases, and a base deficit is seen; these usual changes are not significant enough to cause depression at birth.[68] Changes in blood gases with transition are summarized in Figure 10-9. Delivery is an oxidative stress and is associated with upregulation of antioxidant defenses, although these defenses are still immature.[43,122,149] Antioxidant potential (antioxidant enzymes and nonenzymatic antioxidants) is reduced in infants born by cesarean delivery and in preterm infants, increasing the risk of injury from reactive oxygen species.[43,149] Use of room air or low oxygen levels for resuscitation reduces oxidative stress at birth.[36,187,197,214] Resuscitation with low oxygen levels has been associated with less oxidative stress, inflammation, and chronic lung disease in preterm infants.[196] Oxygenation changes gradually with birth, and it may take a healthy term newborn 5 to 15 (median 7.9) minutes to achieve a percutaneous oxygen saturation (SpO_2) of more than 90%.[45,197] Infants born by cesarean delivery and preterm infants take longer.[197] Preductal values are higher than postductal and are representative of brain values.[46,197] A predictive nomogram is available for preductal SpO_2 changes in the first 10 minutes after birth in term and preterm infants (data from infants who did not require medical intervention in the delivery room).[45]

Many factors have been suggested to stimulate the first breath, including stimulation of chemoreceptors, changes in

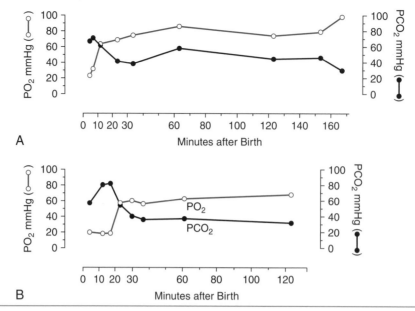

FIGURE 10-9 Changes in PO_2 and PCO_2 during the first minutes after birth in normal infants **(A)** and in asphyxiated infants **(B)** with delayed onset of respiration. (Courtesy of R. Turnell, M.D. From Carlo, W.A. & DiFiore, J.M. [2002]. Assessment of pulmonary function. In A.A. Fanaroff & R.J. Martin. [Eds.]. *Neonatal-perinatal medicine: Diseases of the fetus and infant* [7th ed.]. St. Louis: Mosby.)

PaO_2, hypercapnia, cord clamping, cold, touch, and other sensory stimuli. Establishment of continuous respirations after birth requires resetting of thresholds of both peripheral and central chemoreceptors.[66] Hormonal or chemical mediators may also be critical and perhaps as important as low oxygen or sensory input. Occlusion of the umbilical cord stimulates peripheral and central chemoreceptors, perhaps mediated by adenosine, prostaglandins (PGs), and endorphins.[9,66,68] Before birth placental hormones and factors such as PGs are believed to inhibit continuous fetal breathing; with birth this inhibition is removed.[9]

The actual mechanics of respiratory conversion begins with the passage of the fetus through the birth canal. The thorax is markedly depressed during this passage, and external pressures of 160 to 200 cm H_2O (15.68 to 19.61 kPa) and intrathoracic pressures of 89 cm H_2O (8.72 kPa) or greater are generated.[148] As the face or nares are exposed to atmospheric pressure, a small amount of lung liquid is expelled from the nares and mouth.[89] Recoil of the chest to predelivery proportions allows for passive inspiration of air. This initial step helps reduce forces that must be overcome to establish an air-liquid interface in the alveoli.[143]

The forces that must be overcome in the first breaths include the viscosity of the lung liquid column, tissue resistive forces (compliance), and surface tension forces at the air-liquid interfaces. The viscosity of lung liquid provides resistance to movement of fluid in the airways. The maximal resistance takes place at the beginning of the first breath, and the greatest displacement occurs in the trachea.[148] The dissipation of tracheal fluid during the vaginal squeeze reduces the amount of pressure that must be generated to move the liquid column down the conducting airways.

During movement of lung liquid down the conducting branches, the total surface area of the air-liquid interface increases as the bronchiole number increases and diameter is reduced. The surface tension, however, increases. The surface tension forces are the most difficult forces to overcome during the first breath events. Maximal forces are encountered where the radial curvature of the airways is smallest (terminal bronchioles); and influenced by lung liquid viscous forces.[148,204] In this locality, the intraluminal pressure must be at its peak to prevent closure by tension in the intraluminal walls (Laplace relationship).[204] If these smaller airways were fluid-filled only (no air-liquid interface), the pressures needed would be considerably less; however, this would make alveolar expansion more difficult. Surface tension forces drop again once air enters the terminal air sacs.[204] As the air-liquid interface is established, tubular myelin is formed and spreads over the lining layer.[160] During labor and immediately after birth, alveolar surfactant production increases with secretion of lamellar bodies and formation of tubular myelin.[101] Surfactant biosynthesis and function is described in Box 10-5 on page 314 and in Table 10-3.

Liquid within the terminal air sacs enhances air introduction, possibly by modifying the configuration of the smaller units of the lung. This fluid enlarges the radius of the alveolar ducts and terminal air sacs, thereby facilitating expansion (Laplace relationship). The lung liquid also reduces the possibility of obstruction of the small ducts by cellular debris.

Pulmonary vascular resistance (PVR) falls with lung expansion, endothelial changes, vasodilation, and mediators such as endothelial-derived nitric oxide (NO), prostacyclin (PGI_2), and bradykinin (see Chapter 9). The low PO_2 and pulmonary blood flow in utero suppress NO and PGI_2. The

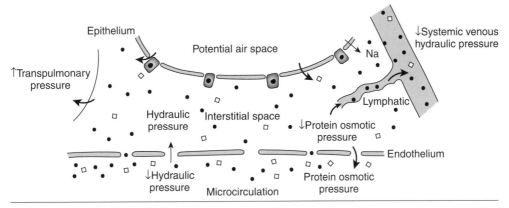

FIGURE 10-10   Schematic diagram of the fluid compartments in the fetal lung showing the forces that affect fluid clearance near birth. *Circles,* Albumin molecules; *squares,* globulin. (From Bland, R.D. [1987]. Pathogenesis of pulmonary edema after preterm birth. *Adv Pediatr, 34,* 175.)

increasing PaO_2 and sheer stress (rapid increase in blood flow to the lungs) with birth increases levels of these vasodilators, facilitating maintenance of pulmonary vasodilation and further enhancing pulmonary blood flow.[41,64,198] Endogenous nitric oxide increases soluble guanylate cyclase, which increases cyclic guanosine monophosphate (cGMP); cGMP causes intracellular calcium to decrease and the pulmonary vascular smooth muscle to relax.[198] PGs increase cyclic adenosine monophosphate (cAMP), which enhances vasodilation by increasing endogenous nitric oxide.[198]

With birth, the lungs must move from secretion to absorption of lung liquid. Because lung liquid production slows in late pregnancy and absorption of lung liquid is believed to begin in early labor, after birth only a portion of the original lung liquid volume needs to be cleared.[99,134,151,160] Ventilation leads to liquid dispersion across the pulmonary epithelium into the pulmonary microcirculation (Figure 10-10). The pulmonary epithelium undergoes a reversible increase in solute permeability, leading to a rapid transfer of lung liquid solutes. The interstitial spaces and lymphatic vessels become distended during the first 4 to 6 hours of life, and an increase in pulmonary lymph flow can be seen.[151]

Three mechanisms have been identified for lung liquid removal: (1) via the trachea (into the mouth and nares) at birth secondary to uterine contractions that increase abdominal and transpulmonary pressures, (2) secondary to actions of catecholamines and epithelial sodium channels (ENaC), and (3) pressure-driven clearance via transepithelial pressure gradients generated during inspiration.[88,89] The latter is thought to be major mechanism of lung liquid removal after birth.[88,89,90]

During inspiration the increase in transpulmonary pressure results in a hydrostatic pressure gradient that moves lung liquid into the interstitial space (ISS).[88,89] Movement of lung liquid from the airways into the ISS occurs within three to five breaths after initiation of respiration.[89] This liquid accumulates in the ISS, increasing ISS tissue pressure, and is gradually removed from the ISS by the capillary and lymphatic systems over 4 to 6 hours in most infants.[88,89]

Movement of lung liquid within the airways into the ISS and prevention of flow of the liquid back into the lungs requires high-pressure gradients or longer inflation times.[88] This is a basis for the proposed use of sustained inflation early in post-birth resuscitation when the lung is filled with liquid. Application of positive end expiratory pressure between inflations maintains sustained lung pressure to prevent movement of lung liquid from the ISS back into the lung.[87,88,108] However, use of sustained inflation with preterm infants in two studies did not demonstrate additional benefits.[116,133]

Epithelial sodium channels (ENaC), Na^+-K^+-ATPase and the catecholamine surge with birth are also involved in lung liquid removal.[31,87,89] ENaC mature late in gestation and thus have less of a role in transition in the preterm infant.[87] Increased catecholamines during labor and the catecholamine surge at birth trigger the switch from lung liquid secretion to reabsorption by activating β-adrenergic receptors, including those in type II alveolar cells, and increasing sodium conductance via ENaC and Na^+ pump activity via increases in Na^+-K^+-ATPase and ENaC expression.[31,64,89,104,106,151] The catecholamine surge also stimulates release of surfactant and enhances lung mechanics and gas exchange.[31] Glucocorticoids, acting in conjunction with thyroid hormones, also help regulate sodium transport by increasing ENaC and the response of the lungs to epinephrine.[31,104] This process is accelerated by the rise in oxygenation with birth.[151] The drop in PVR with lung aeration and the rise in oxygen tension increase the number of alveolar capillaries perfused, resulting in an increase in blood flow and fluid removal capacity.

With the increased lymphatic flow and the dramatic change in the pulmonary blood flow, lung liquid is dispersed within the first few hours after delivery.[31] Loss of lung liquid distention of the lung, along with elastic recoil, results in movement of the lung away from the chest wall. This generates a negative intrapleural pressure that increases as the chest wall becomes less compliant and opposes lung recoil.

Another contributor to lung expansion is the increase in pulmonary blood flow with birth. The increased flow is caused by compression of the placenta during labor and delivery with transfer of blood to the fetus and neonate.[135] Because alveoli are attached to their surrounding capillary network by elastic fibers in the extracellular matrix, expansion of the capillaries would help open the alveoli to allow air entry.[135] The first diaphragmatic inspiration generates large positive intrathoracic pressures (mean, 70 cm H_2O [6.85 kPa]).[186] Air enters as soon as the intrathoracic pressure begins to drop. The large transpulmonary pressure generated by the diaphragm lasts only 0.5 to 1 second, pulling in 10 to 70 mL of air to establish the functional residual capacity (FRC).[89,194]

Establishment of FRC is more difficult in extremely-low-birth-weight (ELBW) infants because of their weaker intercostal and diaphragmatic musculature, greater chest wall compliance, lower lung compliance, reduced inspiratory pressures, less surfactant, and less effective lung liquid clearance.[12] The lack of adequate surfactant (leading to decreased lung compliance, alveolar hypoventilation, and ventilation-perfusion mismatch) and decreased FRC in ELBW infants increases their risk for respiratory distress syndrome (RDS).[12] Constant positive airway pressure (CPAP) has been shown to enhance establishment of FRC in spontaneously breathing ELBW infants.[80] Prophylactic nasal CPAP has been found to reduce the need for mechanical ventilation and surfactant and reduce the incidence of bronchopulmonary dysplasia (BPD).[80,182] Comparison of early CPAP versus early surfactant found no significant differences in the primary outcome of death or BPD, with a decreased intubation rate, use of postnatal corticosteroids, and decreased length of time on mechanical ventilation in the CPAP group.[184]

The alveolar surfactant lining layer becomes established after the first breath. This layer prevents interaction of air and liquid molecules, reducing surface tension and collapsing forces and preventing alveolar collapse at end expiration as the film is compressed.[208] Surfactant secretion is stimulated by lung distention (stretch) and hyperventilation with the initial breaths as well as the increase in catecholamines.[68,99,104] Term infants have an estimated surfactant pool of about 100 mg/kg, whereas infants with RDS have pools of 2 to 10 mg/kg.[99] Pool size increases significantly over the first 3 to 5 days, the timing coinciding with the uncomplicated clinical course of RDS.[49]

The first expiration is also active, establishing a residual volume of air. The magnitude of the expiratory pressure contributes to FRC formation, even distribution of air, and elimination of lung liquid. The second and third breaths are similar to the first but require less pressure, because many small airways are open and surface active forces are diminished.[148] Lung expansion augments surfactant secretion, providing alveolar stability and establishing the FRC. After the first breath, muscle tone helps maintain FRC by providing chest wall stability. Lung compliance increases rapidly in the first day and continues to increase gradually over the first week. Flow resistance also decreases.

Structural and functional changes in the pulmonary circulation occur after birth, with extensive remodeling of the

pulmonary arteries during the first weeks. The fall in PVR with birth described previously and changes in PVR after birth are transitional events mediated by vasoactive agents and their signaling pathways, including endothelial-derived NO, PGI_2, endothelin-1, platelet-activating factor-1, and postnatal remodeling of the pulmonary vasculature.[64] Changes in the pulmonary vasculature and pulmonary vascular resistance after birth are discussed further in Chapter 9. In conjunction with the local vascular changes in the pulmonary bed, there are major organizational changes within the cardiovascular system. The first breath events and cardiovascular events (see Chapter 9) are interdependent and must occur together for transition to be successful.

Control of Respiration

Breathing is controlled by discharge of inspiratory and expiratory neurons in the medulla. Inspiration is active and controlled by an "off switch;" expiration is passive. The inspiratory "off switch" is controlled by pulmonary volume sensors and the pontine pneumotaxic center (for changes in both rate and depth of respiration) and is modulated by peripheral and central chemoreceptors, chest wall proprioceptors, and the cerebral cortex.[210] An overview of the ventilatory control system is in Figure 10-11. The goal of respiration is to meet oxygen and CO_2 metabolic demands through extraction of oxygen from the atmosphere and removal of carbon dioxide produced by the individual. The brain respiratory center is responsible for matching the level of ventilation to the metabolic demand. The assessment of metabolic needs and alteration of ventilation is accomplished by the chemoreceptors.

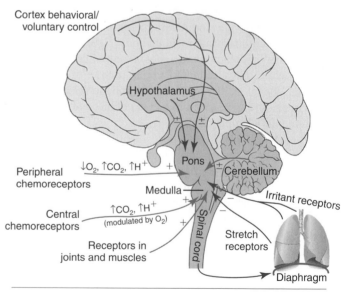

FIGURE 10-11 Overview of the ventilatory control system. Central breathing rhythm is generated in the pons and medulla and modulated by multiple inputs. Symbols: (+) stimulatory, (−) inhibitory, (±) excitatory or inhibitory. Motor output drives diaphragm, upper airway, and other respiratory muscle activity (not shown). (Modified from original drawing by P.J. Lynch and C.C. Jaffe. From Carroll, J.L. & Agarwal, A. [2010]. Development of ventilatory control in infants. *Paediatr Respir Rev, 11,* 199.)

BOX 10-6 Factors Affecting Control of Ventilation in the Spontaneously Breathing Neonate

NEUROLOGIC FACTORS

Maturity of the CNS

Degree of myelination, which largely determines speed of impulse transmission and response time to stimuli affecting ventilation.

Degree of arborization or dendritic interconnections (synapses) between neurons, allowing summation of excitatory potentials coming in from other parts of the CNS and largely setting the neuronal depolarization and response level of the respiratory center.

Sleep State (i.e., REM Sleep vs. Quiet or Non-REM Sleep)

REM sleep is generally associated with irregular respirations (both in depth and in frequency), distortion, and paradoxical motion of the rib cage during inspiration, inhibition of Hering-Breuer and glottic closure reflexes, and blunted responses to CO_2 changes.

Quiet sleep is generally associated with regular respirations, a more stable rib cage, and a directly proportional relationship between PCO_2 and degree of ventilation.

Reflex Responses

Hering-Breuer reflex, whereby inspiratory duration is limited in response to lung inflation (sensed by stretch receptors located in major airways). Not present in adult humans, this reflex is active during quiet sleep of newborns, but absent or weak during REM sleep.

Head's reflex, whereby inspiratory effort is further increased in response to rapid lung inflation. Believed to produce the frequently observed biphasic signs of newborns that may be crucial for promoting and maintaining lung inflation (and thereby breathing regularity) after birth.

Intercostal-phrenic reflex, whereby inspiration is inhibited by proprioception (position-sensing) receptors in intercostal muscles responding to distortion of the lower rib cage during REM sleep.

Trigeminal-cutaneous reflex, whereby tidal volume increases and respiratory rate decreases in response to facial stimulation.

Glottic closure reflex, whereby the glottis is narrowed through reflex constriction of the laryngeal adductor muscles during respiration, thereby breaking exhalation and increasing subglottic pressure (as with expiratory grunting).

CHEMICAL DRIVE FACTORS (CHEMORECEPTORS)

Response to hypoxemia (falling PaO_2) or to decreases in O_2 concentration breathed (mediated by peripheral chemoreceptors in carotid and aortic bodies).

Initially there is increase in depth of breathing (tidal volume), but subsequently if hypoxia persists or worsens, there is depression of reparatory drive, reduction in depth and rate of respiration, and eventual failure of arousal.

For the first week of life at least, these responses are dependent on environmental temperature (i.e., keeping the baby warm).

Hypoxia is associated with an increase in periodic breathing and apnea.

Response to hyperoxia (increase in FiO_2 concentration breathed): enriched O_2 breathing causes a transient respiratory depression, stronger in term than in preterm infants.

Response to hypercapnia (rising $PaCO_2$ or $[H^+]$) or to increase in CO_2 concentration breathed (mediated by central chemoreceptors in the medulla).

Increase in ventilation is directly proportional to inspired CO_2 concentration (or more accurately stated, to alveolar CO_2 tension), as is the case in adults.

Response to CO_2 is in large part dependent on sleep state; in quiet sleep, a rising $PaCO_2$ causes an increase in depth and rate of breathing, whereas during REM sleep, the response is irregular and reduced in depth and rate. The degree of reduction closely parallels the amount of rib cage deformation occurring during REM sleep.

Ventilatory response to CO_2 in newborns is markedly depressed during behavioral activity such as feeding and easily depressed by sedatives and anesthesia.

CNS, Central nervous system; *REM,* rapid eye movement.

From Greenspan, J.S., Shaffer, T.H., Fox, W.W., & Spitzer, A.R. (2004). Assisted ventilation: Implications and complications. In R.A. Polin, W.W. Fox, & S.H. Abman. (Eds.). *Fetal and neonatal physiology* (3rd ed.). Philadelphia: Saunders.

The respiratory control system is immature and unstable in newborns.[149] This physiologic immaturity can be seen in periodic breathing and apnea of prematurity and probably plays a role in sudden infant death syndrome.[3,32] Factors influencing ventilatory control in newborns are summarized in Box 10-6.

Chemoreceptors

Chemoreceptors provide information about the metabolic needs of the infant, and the mechanoreceptors provide information about the status of the respiratory pump. The central respiratory center integrates this information and establishes a ventilatory pattern that efficiently meets the infant's needs. Behavioral influences as well as active sleep states (REM sleep) alter the regularity of breathing.[9] Each respiratory cycle during a stable state (e.g., quiet sleep) is uniform for amplitude, duration, and waveform. The information received from the various receptors helps to determine inspiratory time, expiratory time, lung volume at which the breath should occur (FRC), rate of inspiration, and the braking of the expiration. The recruitment and adjustment of the various respiratory muscle groups result in the predetermined lung volume being achieved.[204]

The information just described is received by the respiratory controller in the brainstem, which is responsible for initiating automatic respiration and adjustments.[204] The respiratory control center is divided into three areas: the apneustic center, the pneumotaxic center, and the medullary center. The pneumotaxic center may be responsible for switching inspiration to expiration. The apneustic center seems to be responsible for cutting off inspiration. Both centers are located in the pons and neither seems to be necessary for rhythmic expiration. The medullary center is believed to be responsible for respiratory rhythm. These centers are connected to the cerebral cortex, thereby allowing voluntary control of respiration. The spinal cord is responsible for the integration and relay of commands to the muscles of the respiratory pump via the phrenic and intercostal nerves. Chemoreceptor responses in the neonate are summarized in Box 10-6.

The peripheral chemoreceptors (carotid and aortic bodies) sense PaO_2 and $PaCO_2$, and the central chemoreceptors (medullary) are sensitive to PCO_2^- [H^+] in the extracellular fluid of the brain. When the PaO_2 falls below the acceptable range, the chemoreceptors increase efferent neural activity to the brain respiratory center, resulting in an increase in ventilation. At birth, the fetal PaO_2 of approximately 25 mm Hg (3.32 kPa) (sufficient for intrauterine growth) increases to 50 to 70 mm Hg (6.65 to 9.31 kPa) within the first few breaths and to 70 mm Hg (9.31 kPa) or more in the first hours.[66] This increase in oxygen tension exceeds the demands for oxygen, yielding a relative neonatal hyperoxia at birth. The change in oxygen tension causes the chemoreceptors to become less responsive to stimuli ("silenced") during the first few days of life.[34] As a result, fluctuations in oxygen tension levels may not lead to an immediate chemoreceptor response during this period, with a gradual increase in the slope of the hypoxic stimulus curve.[65,101] After this lag time, however, the chemoreceptors reset and become increasingly oxygen-sensitive and a major controller of respiration.[3,9,65] This change is a result of increases in the density of K^+ channels, greater increases in intracellular calcium in response to hypoxia, and changes in neurotransmitters.[65] The carotid bodies are the main arterial oxygen sensors. Carotid body oxygen response is low at birth, increasing with increasing postnatal age, with further maturation taking up to 10 weeks.[32] By 2 weeks of age, peripheral chemoreceptor activity is similar to that of adults.[3] Term infants have adultlike central chemoreceptor activity at birth, whereas preterm infants take 4 or more weeks to achieve this level of response.[65,66]

Sustained hyperventilatory efforts during hypoxia cannot be maintained by the neonate. Newborns have a biphasic response with an initial hyperventilatory response (because of stimulation of peripheral chemoreceptors, especially those in the carotid body) followed by a subsequent fall in ventilation (primarily because of a decrease in frequency), to levels below baseline in some preterm infants, and oxygen tension.[2,3,32,38,42] This biphasic response persists for several days in term infants and up to 4 to 6 weeks in preterm infants.[38,66] Preterm infants may not have the initial hyperventilation, only the sustained decrease in ventilation.[66] The reason for this lack of sustained response is unknown but may be a result of a weak chemoreceptor output, a central inhibitory effect of hypoxia on ventilation mediated by the interaction of neurotransmitters or via descending inhibitory pontine tracts, or changes in pulmonary mechanics.[2,38]

The neonate's response to carbon dioxide is also limited in the early neonatal period. Although this is more mature than the response to hypoxia, the neonate can only increase ventilation by three to four times baseline ventilation,

compared with the 10-fold to 20-fold increase that can be achieved by adults. Furthermore, the threshold of tolerance is initially higher, progressively declining over the first month of life.[42,212] This too may be because of the higher $PaCO_2$ levels found in the fetal state (45 to 50 mm Hg [5.98 to 6.65 kPa]) and the need to reset chemoreceptors.[9] Hypercapnic ventilatory responses are weaker in preterm infants. Although with hypercapnia preterm infants develop a sustained increase in tidal volume (V_T), they also have an increase in the expiratory phase that may lead to a net decrease in their respiratory rate.[3]

Modification of ventilatory patterns is dependent on inspiratory muscle strength, rib cage rigidity and compliance, airway resistance, and lung compliance. The status of these parameters at any given time, as well as their integrative functioning, affects the performance of the respiratory pump and is mediated by specific reflex arcs.

Chest Wall Reflexes

Most of the reflexes for the respiratory pump arise from the chest wall via the muscle spindles through local spinal reflex arcs and centrally mediated reflexes. The diaphragm is scantily innervated; however, the intercostal muscles have abundant fibers from which this information is obtained. These stretch-sensitive mechanoreceptors detect chest wall and workload forces.[125]

Excessive stretch is modulated by alpha motor neuron activity altering respiratory muscle activity or recruiting more muscles. Further sensory information is obtained by proprioceptors that sense changes in rib position and tension applied across the joint space. Cutaneous stimulation of the thoracic wall causes a generalized increase in sensory and motor neuron stimulation of the respiratory muscles, augmenting muscle contractions and ventilation.

Chest wall distortion during inspiration stimulates muscle spindles that trigger central reflex arcs, leading to reflex inhibition of intercostal, phrenic, and laryngeal neurons. This is possibly a protective mechanism in the neonate. Termination of distorted inefficient breathing may lead to energy conservation and reduce the possibility of muscle fatigue.

Laryngeal and Pulmonary Reflexes

The mechanoreceptors of the large lung airways include stretch receptors, irritant receptors, and C receptors. The sensory feedback mechanisms for these receptors are along the vagus nerve to the central respiratory center. Laryngeal and pulmonary reflexes in the neonate are summarized in Box 10-6.

The stretch receptors sense lung inflation and deflation, with neural output proportional to lung volume or tension. Lung inflation initiates inhibitory impulses that terminate inspiration and prolong expiratory time. This is termed the *Hering-Breuer reflex*. Once triggered, respiratory frequency slows and may lead to apnea. This reflex is present in fetal life and more active in the neonate.[9] It may be a protective mechanism for the neonate, because inspiratory occlusion results

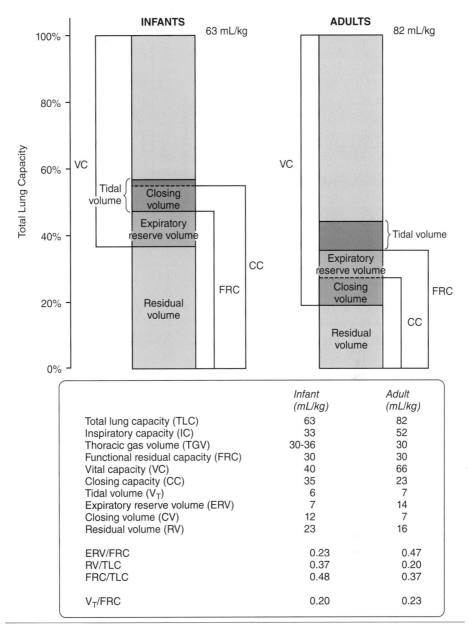

FIGURE 10-13   Lung volumes in the infant and adult. (From Nelson, N.M. [1976]. Respiration and circulation after birth. In C.A. Smith & N.M. Nelson [Eds.]. *The physiology of the newborn infant.* Springfield, IL: Charles C. Thomas.)

main stem bronchus. Bronchiole compliance contributes to these dynamics.

Elastic recoil of the chest wall increases during the first 2 weeks after birth, although it remains considerably less than that of the adult for a longer period. The continued change in recoil pressures is presumed to be the result of progressive ossification, improvement in intercostal muscle tone, and development of a negative pressure on the abdominal side of the diaphragm.[69]

The clinical implications of a highly compliant chest are related to the ease at which lung collapse is possible in the neonate. The low elastic recoil pressure of the neonatal lung and the high compliance of the thorax result in most tidal breathing in the infant occurring near the closing capacity of the lung. This contributes to the possibility of alveolar collapse and affects gas distribution. These characteristics can also alter breathing patterns, with the risk of paradoxical or asynchronous patterns.[72]

The mechanical liabilities of a highly compliant chest wall after delivery include a compromised ability to produce a large V_T, requiring the generation of greater pressures. As a result the infant must perform more work to move the same amount of V_T.[150] This is especially true in preterm infants with lung diseases associated with decreased lung compliance (e.g., RDS). Lung disease causes the respiratory drive (response to stimulus) to increase in an attempt to generate stronger contractions with high inspiratory pressures to expand the stiffer, less compliant lungs.

Increased diaphragmatic force and the pliable chest wall lead to chest distortion.[148] Therefore a portion of the energy and force of the contraction is wasted. Retractions are the clinical signs of these distortions and are indications of the degree of inward rib cage collapse during forceful diaphragmatic contractions. This increase in work of breathing can lead to fatigue and eventually apnea.

The compliance of the chest wall—combined with the compliance of the lungs—affects the closing volume, closing capacity, expiratory reserve volume, and FRC. For the neonate, this means that a high closing volume and high closing capacity combine with a low expiratory reserve volume and FRC, culminating in a propensity toward alveolar collapse.[148]

Mechanical Properties of the Respiratory System

The work of breathing is the cumulative product of the pressure and volume of air moved at each instant. The work is done by the muscles as energy is expended to overcome the elastic and resistive forces (compliance and resistance) of the lung and thorax as well as the frictional resistance to air movement. The respiratory muscles expend about half their energy on inspiration. The rest is stored within the tissues (which have been stretched) as potential energy. As the potential energy is released, expiration occurs passively.

There are two major sources of resistance that the respiratory muscles must overcome during each breath: (1) tissue elastic resistance that is created by displacement of the lung and chest wall from their resting positions (compliance) and (2) resistance presented by gas molecules flowing through the airways. The system is most efficient when the respiratory rate and V_T are set to require the minimum expenditure of work. This can be assessed by evaluating the amount of oxygen used in performing the work.

Lung Compliance

The pressure gradient necessary to overcome the elastic recoil force encountered in the lung depends on V_T and lung compliance. Compliance is the measurement of the elastic properties opposing a change in volume (milliliters) per unit of change in pressure (centimeters of water) (Hooke law). Static compliance reflects the elastic properties of the lung; dynamic compliance reflects both elastic and resistive forces.[204] Compliance can be demonstrated in a pressure-volume curve (Figure 10-14) that relates a change in lung volume to the change in the alveolar-to-intrapleural pressure gradient (i.e., transpulmonary pressure). The slope of the curve indicates the compliance. The flatter the curve, the stiffer the lung.[140,148]

Lung compliance depends on the tissue elastic characteristics of the parenchyma, connective tissue, and blood vessels, as well as the surface tension in the alveoli and the initial lung volume before inflation. When the lung must be inflated from a very low lung volume, the required pressure gradient is greater.

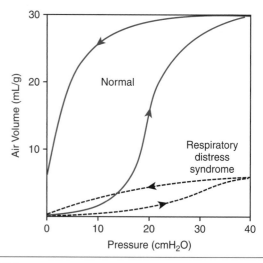

FIGURE 10-14   Air pressure–volume curves of neonatal and abnormal lung. Volume is expressed as milliliters of air per gram of lung. The lung of an infant with respiratory distress syndrome accepts a smaller volume at all pressures. The deflation pressure–volume curve follows very closely the inflation curve for the affected lung. (From Keszler, M., Abubakar, M.K., & Wood, B.R. [2011]. Physiologic principles. In J.P. Goldsmith & E.H. Karotkin. [Eds.]. *Assisted ventilation of the neonate* [5th ed.]. Philadelphia: Saunders.)

Changes in lung compliance are sensed by lung stretch receptors, which, along with muscle spindle fibers from the respiratory muscles, transmit information to the respiratory center to modify the drive necessary to maintain ventilation.[204] Lung compliance decreases (lungs become less elastic) with decreasing gestational age.[109] Lung disease usually leads to a decrease in lung compliance, which translates to a smaller volume change for each pressure change.

The most significant determinant of elastic properties is the alveolar air–liquid interface. When molecules are aligned at an air–liquid interface, they lack opposing molecules on one side; this means that the intermolecular attractive forces are unbalanced and there is a tendency for the molecules to move away from the interface. This reduces the internal surface area of the lung and therefore augments elastic recoil. Surfactant varies surface tension, allowing for high surface tensions at large lung volumes and low tensions at low volumes. Surfactant forms an insoluble surface film upon compression and thereby lowers surface tension. This tends to stabilize air spaces of unequal size and prevents their collapse. Without surfactant, smaller alveoli tend to empty into larger ones, resulting in microatelectasis alternating with hyperaeration (see Figure 10-6).

Alveolar collapse occurs in a number of diseases; probably the most notable is RDS (see "Respiratory Distress Syndrome"). In RDS surfactant deficiency is directly related to gestational age and developmental immaturity of the lungs. Surfactant synthesis, however, is also dependent on normal pH and pulmonary perfusion. Therefore any disease or event that interferes with these processes (e.g., asphyxia, hemorrhagic shock, pulmonary edema) may lead to surfactant deficiencies.[140]

right-to-left shunting through fetal vascular channels—along with atelectatic areas of the lung being perfused—is the source of the admixture. In adults the major component of venous admixture is the maldistribution of ventilation.[150] These differences stabilize as transition progresses, lasting a week or so in full-term infants. The preterm infant, however, is at greater risk for desaturation because of increased chest wall deformation and increased ductal shunting. For a preterm infant it may be several weeks before complete transition and stabilization occur.[148] Hypoxemia may result in ductal opening and shunting during the early transitional period for both term and preterm infants (see Chapter 9). Venous admixture does not fall to adult levels until late infancy and early childhood.

Oxygen-Hemoglobin Dissociation Curve

Because of the low-oxygen environment in which the fetus lives, the need for an increased affinity for oxygen is essential to survival. Fetal hemoglobin (HbF) (see Chapter 8) alters this affinity, and 2,3-diphosphoglycerate (2,3-DPG) regulates it.[130] When 2,3-DPG binds with fetal gamma chains, it does not lower oxygen affinity as it does with binding to adult hemoglobin beta chains. The fetal and neonatal oxygen-hemoglobin dissociation curves therefore lie to the left of the adult curve (see Figure 10-17). This means that in the fetus and neonate the affinity of oxygen for hemoglobin is greater and the release of oxygen to the tissues is somewhat less than in the adult at any given PO_2. The left shift in a very-low-birth-weight infant who has greater HbF may influence SpO_2 measurements.[173]

Oxygen affinity decreases rapidly after birth, changing from a mean P_{50} of 19.4 ± 1.8 mm Hg to adult values of 27 ± 1.1 mm Hg by 4 to 6 months postterm.[130] Changes in the oxygen-hemoglobin dissociation curve in term and preterm infants at different postbirth ages are illustrated in Figure 10-18. The oxygen-hemoglobin dissociation curve is reviewed in Box 10-1 on page 301.

The preterm infant has lower 2,3-DPG and P_{50} and greater HbF, taking around 3 months to reach term oxygen unloading capacity.[130] Changes in oxygen saturation (SpO_2) in the preterm infant "may not reflect concomitant changes in PaO_2 but, rather, may reflect shifting positions of the oxygen-hemoglobin dissociation curve. Sharp increases in pH and decreases in PCO_2 can produce a leftward shift of the curve, raising SpO_2 without changing PaO_2."[192,p. 718] Safe ranges of oxygen saturation and oxygen targeting in ELBW have been investigated in recent years (see "Hypoxia and Hyperoxia").[14,30,121,180]

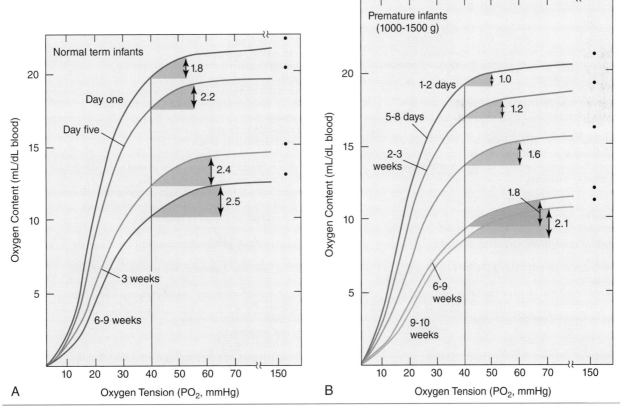

FIGURE 10-18   Oxygen equilibrium curves of blood in term infants **(A)** and preterm infants with birth weight 1000 to 1500 g **(B)** at different postnatal ages. Double arrows represent the oxygen unloading capacity between a given "arterial" and "venous" PO_2. Points corresponding to 150 mm Hg (14.7 kPa) on the abscissa are the O_2 capacities; each curve represents the mean value of the infant studied in each age group. (From McNamara, P.J. & El-Khuffash, A. [2017]. Oxygen transport and delivery. In R.A. Polin, S.H. Abman, D.H. Rowitch, W.E. Benitz, & W.W. Fox. [Eds.]. *Fetal and neonatal physiology* [5th ed.]. Philadelphia: Saunders.)

CLINICAL IMPLICATIONS FOR NEONATAL CARE

Although there are many liabilities within the neonatal respiratory system, a healthy term infant typically achieves transition to the extrauterine environment without any difficulties. However, the developmental stage of the system increases the possibility of respiratory distress and failure above that seen in older individuals. Maturation of both anatomic and functional development are required to achieve adult functioning; therefore both contribute to respiratory vulnerability and the risk of distress. Implications of neonatal respiratory system characteristics are summarized in Table 10-7.

Anatomic risk factors include the incomplete development of the bone and cartilage that make up the thoracic cavity and are a part of the respiratory pump. The increased compliance of the thorax makes it extremely important that the intercostal muscles be able to contract and fixate the chest so that adequate pressure can be generated and inspiration occurs. Although full-term infants appear to compensate well, the intercostal muscles and accessory muscles are still not completely developed. This contributes to diaphragmatic

---

TABLE 10-7   Implications of Alterations in Respiratory Function in Neonates

ALTERATION	IMPLICATION
Immature alveoli; decreased size and number of alveoli	Risk of respiratory insufficiency and pulmonary problems
Thicker alveolar wall; decreased alveolar surface area	Less efficient gas transport and exchange
Continued development of alveoli until childhood	Possible opportunity to reduce effects of discrete lung injury
Decreased lung elastic tissue and recoil	Decreased lung compliance requiring higher pressures and more work to expand; increased risk of atelectasis
Fewer pores and channels for collateral ventilation	Greater distress with airway obstruction Increased risk of air leak and pulmonary edema Increased risk of atelectasis
Compliant boxlike rib cage with almost horizontal insertion of ribs and immature musculature	Difficulty in taking deep breaths Less effective movement of thoracic cage Less effective in generating intrathoracic pressures needed for lung expansion Greater reliance on diaphragmatic and abdominal musculature for respiration Retractions Difficulty maintaining functional residual capacity and increasing tidal volume Risk of atelectasis Increased work of breathing
Reduced diaphragm movement and maximal force potential, with more horizontal position and smaller muscle fiber diameter	Less effective respiratory movement Difficulty generating negative intrathoracic pressures Risk of atelectasis Possible increased risk of muscle fatigue with respiratory insufficiency and failure
Tendency to nose breathe; altered position of larynx and epiglottis	Enhanced ability to synchronize swallowing and breathing Risk of airway obstruction Possibly more difficult to intubate
Small compliant airway passages with higher airway resistance and immature reflexes	Risk of airway obstruction and apnea
Increased pulmonary vascular resistance with sensitive pulmonary arterioles	Risk of ductal shunting and hypoxemia with events such as hypoxia, acidosis, hypothermia, hypoglycemia, and hypercarbia Possible protection against the development of congestive heart failure in first few weeks in infants with a large ventricular septal defect
Increased oxygen consumption	Increased respiratory rate and work of breathing Risk of hypoxia
Increased intrapulmonary right-left shunting	Increased risk of atelectasis with wasted ventilation Lower $PaCO_2$
Immature development of lung capillary basement membrane	More vulnerable to collapse of terminal bronchioles and alveoli
Decreased functional residual capacity	Less oxygen reserves with increased risk of atelectasis and hypoxia Increased work of breathing
Closing volume nearer tidal volume	Areas of airway collapse and atelectasis Risk of hypoxia and hypercarbia Increased work of breathing
Immaturity of pulmonary surfactant system in immature infants	Increased risk of atelectasis and respiratory distress syndrome Increased work of breathing
Immature respiratory control	Irregular respiration with periodic breathing Altered respiratory threshold Instability of respiratory drive Risk of apnea Inability to rapidly alter depth of respiration Difficulty in compensating for hypoxemia and hypercarbia

Adapted from Blackburn, S. (1992). Alterations in the respiratory system in the neonate: Implications for practice. *J Perinat Neonatal Nurs, 6,* 46.

breathing and chest wall instability, which can lead to higher closing volumes and a decreased FRC. In disease states in which increased resistance occurs, the high inspiratory pressures necessary to fill the lungs may result in retractions of the chest wall. The ability to stabilize the chest wall is directly related to increasing gestational age. Therefore preterm infants are highly susceptible to chest wall deformation and atelectasis during tidal breathing. This may result in hypoxemia, hypercarbia, and apnea, necessitating supplemental oxygen or ventilatory support.

Airway resistance is increased because of the smaller nares, shorter airways with multiple bifurcations, and peripheral airway diameter. Therefore upper airway congestion and minor small airway infections may lead to increased resistance and place the infant at risk for respiratory distress, muscle fatigue, and respiratory failure. Edema secondary to trauma or infection of upper airway passages can easily result in obstruction with a marked increase in resistance to airflow. This distress can be seen in nasal flaring, retractions, and tachypnea. Until the age of 5 years, the small peripheral airways contribute 50% of the airway resistance that must be overcome. This is compared with 20% in the adult, who has a much larger cross-sectional area for flow. Bronchi constrict in response to numerous factors, including inhaled irritants, hypoxemia, hypercarbia, and cold. This constriction significantly increases airway resistance and the work of breathing.

The surface area of the lung is also decreased because of the characteristic structure of the chest. The ribs are rounder, giving the typical barrel chest configuration seen initially in the term infant after birth. However, this results in thoracic crowding because of the relative size of the abdominal organs. The surface area of the lung is consequently decreased and lung expansion is reduced.

The lung compliance is decreased. If compounded by disease states that reduce elasticity (e.g., pulmonary congestion, pulmonary fibrosis), the compliance drops even further and the work of breathing must increase to compensate. Oxygen consumption in a newborn infant is twice that of the adult in relation to weight and increases if work of breathing increases.

Cartilaginous support is essential for the stability of the conducting airways. This too is a function of gestational age and development. Cartilage rings continue to increase in number for up to 2 months in age. Weakness secondary to lack of support can result in dynamic compression of the trachea in situations associated with high expiratory flow rates and increased airway resistance. Although bronchiolitis and asthma are common disease entities that cause this, it can also occur during episodes of crying, resulting in reduced saturations.

The gas-exchange portion of the lung in term infants is made up of terminal air sacs and alveoli. Terminal air sacs lack the cupped shape of alveoli and are longer and narrower. They require higher pressures to maintain expansion, and once collapsed, increased pressures must be generated to reopen them. The alveoli that are present are smaller and predisposed to collapse. Preterm infants have only terminal air sacs, because true alveoli have not yet developed.

The surface area available for diffusion is reduced in neonates. During disease states, this may be reduced even further, requiring an increase in minute ventilation. Much of neonatal disease may be related to an alteration in FRC, closing capacity, or both. When the closing capacity is high, the pleural pressure exceeds the intraluminal pressure, resulting in early closure of bronchi, making them unavailable for gas exchange. A reduction in FRC can lead to unstable blood gases between respiratory efforts.

Without collateral ventilation, the neonate cannot divert ventilation to distal airways when obstruction occurs. Although anatomic pathways have not been found on histologic sectioning of neonatal lungs, radiologic evidence suggests that alternative pathways may exist. Without channels for collateral ventilation, there is an increased risk for atelectasis or emphysematous change and ventilation-perfusion mismatching.[150]

Biochemical immaturity of the surfactant system can result in progressive atelectasis. Primary surfactant deficiency is found in premature infants, resulting in RDS. However, surfactant production may be interrupted by numerous events, including cytogenic oxygen toxicity, ischemia of the pulmonary bed, pulmonary edema, and hemorrhagic shock. Synthesis of surfactant is dependent on a normal pH and adequate pulmonary perfusion.

The transition to the extrauterine environment is a move from a relatively hypoxic state to a more hyperoxic one. The is especially of concern in preterm infants who have lower antioxidant defenses and thus may be less able to cope with the oxidative stress of the extrauterine environment.[122,199] Prematurity may result in increased susceptibility to oxygen-induced cytotoxicity. The development and maturation of the antioxidant system parallels the maturation of the surfactant system, both occurring late in gestation. With a diminished ability to detoxify reactive oxygen metabolites, these metabolites are released into the immediate environment, where they can injure normal cells.[39] This may lead to cell death or cause pulmonary edema, surfactant synthesis disruption, and scarring of lung tissues.

Physiologic Basis for Clinical Findings

The presence of increased work of breathing indicates a primary pulmonary disorder. The signs of increased work of breathing are chest wall retractions (subcostal, intercostal, suprasternal) and the use of accessory muscles (alar flare). Infants with respiratory failure have elevated ratios of dead space volume to V_T; this condition results in hypoxia and hypercarbia unless counteracted by an increase in expired minute ventilation.[143]

Respiratory patterns change with increased respiratory work. Tachypnea may be the only sign of abnormalities in lung functioning. Tachypnea is the most efficient way for neonates to increase ventilation and compensate for hypoxia and hypercarbia. Respiratory rates fall as fatigue sets in.

In mild to moderate disease there is tachypnea, slight substernal and intercostal retractions, slight increase in anterior-to-posterior diameter, and intermittent expiratory grunting without cyanosis. Retractions occur because of the increased compliance of the chest wall, the immaturity of the intercostal muscles, and the increased inspiratory pressure generated. As the severity of the disease increases, the retractions become more marked. Deformation of the chest leads to paradoxical breathing (asynchrony of chest and abdominal movements), which is the result of diaphragm fatigue, inability of the intercostal muscles to fixate the chest wall, and increased inspiratory pressures.

Expiratory grunting elevates the end-expiratory pressure and slows the expiratory flow rate. This is accomplished by laryngeal braking through partial closure of the glottis. These maneuvers help maintain expansion and preserve oxygenation between respirations. Grunting is usually not seen in very-low-birth-weight infants. Nasal flaring results from increased inspiratory pressure.

Periodic Breathing and Apnea of Prematurity

Breathing in newborns, especially in preterm infants, tends to be irregular, with marked breath-to-breath variability and episodes of periodic breathing.[9,42] Periodic breathing is defined as "pauses in respiratory movements that last for up to 20 seconds alternating with breathing."[9] Periodic breathing is common in preterm infants and is also seen in term infants, and even adults, at altitude. Periodic breathing is believed to be benign with short respiratory pauses and minimal change in heart rate.[9] Periodic breathing can also be induced by hypoxemia and respiratory depression; respiratory stimulants such as caffeine alleviate periodic breathing.[42] Mechanisms for periodic breathing and apnea are unclear, but they are probably related to alterations in or instability of the respiratory control center. These patterns are more common during REM sleep, possibly because of decreased intercostal muscle tone, diaphragmatic activity, and upper airway adductor muscle tone during REM sleep.[9,39]

Apnea involves longer pauses and changes in heart rate, often to less than 80 beats per minute. Three types of apnea have been described in preterm infants: central (10% to 25% of the episodes), obstructive (10% to 20%), and mixed (50% to 75%).[9,126] Central apnea is characterized by no airflow or breathing effort and obstructive apnea by no airflow with breathing efforts. Mixed apnea begins as central apnea and ends as obstructive.[9,39,162] These patterns are illustrated in Figure 10-19.

Apnea is common in preterm infants and more frequent in infants with chronic lung disease or other respiratory problems. The incidence of central apnea decreases with increasing gestational age, is seen in most infants born at less than 1000 g, and may last until these infants reach 43 to 44 weeks postmenstrual age.[39] Factors involved in the pathogenesis of apnea of prematurity include central mechanisms (decreased central chemosensitivity, ventilatory depression, and upregulation of inhibitory neurotransmitters such as γ-aminobutyric acid [GABA] and adenosine), altered peripheral reflex pathways (altered carotid body activity, laryngeal chemoreflex, increased bradycardic response to hypoxia), and genetic predisposition.[3,39] Physiologic immaturity and depression of the respiratory drive, sleep state, less well-developed ventilatory responses to carbon dioxide, paradoxical responses to hypoxia (that increase baseline chemoreceptor activity and may destabilize breathing), exaggerated inhibitory reflexes, altered responses to sensory input by the upper airway, and a predisposition to pharyngeal collapse may all contribute to apnea of prematurity.[2,9,39,65] Neonatal sepsis with release of proinflammatory cytokines may alter respiratory control via PG-mediated pathways.[3,39]

Methylxanthines (e.g., caffeine, theophylline) have been used to manage apnea in preterm infants. These agents have a central stimulatory effect on brainstem respiratory structures.[3,39,162] Caffeine is the preferred agent because of its efficacy and fewer side effects and potential for improvement in long-term developmental outcomes.[44,82,83,183] Caffeine leads to bronchodilation and may have antiinflammatory effects on the lungs and enhance activity or peripheral chemoreceptors.[1]

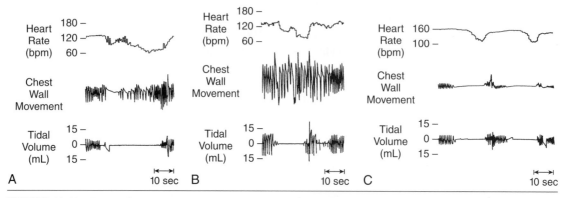

FIGURE 10-19   Types of apnea. **(A)** Mixed apnea. Obstructed breaths precede and follow a central respiratory pause. **(B)** Obstructive apnea. Breathing efforts continue, although no nasal airflow occurs. **(C)** Central apnea. Both nasal airflow and breathing effort cease simultaneously. (From Miller, M. [1986]. Diagnostic methods and clinical disorders in children. In N. Edelman & T. Santiago. [Eds.]. *Breathing disorders of sleep.* New York: Churchill Livingstone.)

Caffeine may improve neurodevelopmental outcome and reduce the risk of motor impairment at least in the early years, although effects are reduced in later follow-up.[53,167] Caffeine may alter neurotransmitters (GABA, adenosine) and providing protection against hypoxia-induced periventricular leukomalacia (PVL) by inhibiting adenosine receptors.[1,3]

Respiratory Outcomes in Preterm Infants

ELBW infants are born in the late canalicular and early saccular stages of lung development (see Table 10-2). The rate at which these preterm infants go through the remaining stages of lung development has not been well studied. The stresses of preterm birth and living in the extrauterine world may accelerate some areas of development, such as development of the surfactant system, probably mediated by corticosteroids that enhance lung development both before and after birth. However, being born early also leads to vulnerabilities in lung development. The later lung problems in children who had been born prematurely can arise because of damage to the lungs from respiratory disorders and/or altered development or function. Even preterm infants without neonatal respiratory disease may have alterations in subsequent lung growth and development (including subtle changes, wheezing, increased risk of respiratory infections or asthma, or other limitations).[19,25,125] Children with a history of BPD have altered pulmonary function at least into late childhood and may be at risk for adult pulmonary alterations.[93]

Many factors influence these issues. For example, it may be the early transition from the relatively hypoxic intrauterine environment to the comparably hyperoxic (for a fetus) extrauterine environment (even 21% oxygen may be "hyperoxic" to an extremely immature infant).[199] Another factor may be the role of proinflammatory cytokines and the inflation of the lungs (i.e., initiation of breathing) before the stage of lung development when that would normally happen. The combination of these vulnerabilities with postbirth damage from respiratory disorders increases the risk of later problems. This vulnerability for lung problems in preterm infants is seen across gestational ages, so although the more immature the lungs the more vulnerable they are to lung injury, late preterm (34–36 week) infants are at risk as well.[25] Given that alveoli continue developing well into childhood, the gas exchange areas of the lungs even in term babies and young infants, though still mature compared with those of preterm infants, are still relatively immature (compared with adults) and therefore vulnerable.

Hypoxia and Hyperoxia

Hypoxia involves a decreased oxygen level of the tissues, whereas hypoxemia involves a decreased oxygen content of the blood. When hypoxia occurs, aerobic metabolism is impaired and there is a subsequent depletion in the supply of adenosine triphosphate (ATP). Therefore those processes that require energy will not occur and free radicals will accumulate, damaging the cell (Figure 10-20 and Chapter 6). If the hypoxic event is not too severe or too long, cellular activities may be disrupted only for a short period, and damage may be reversible. Hypoxia can affect lung development by decreasing alveoli development, altering gas exchange, increasing airway smooth muscle thickness, reducing sodium transport in the alveolar epithelium, and altering lung angiogenesis and may lead to airway inflammation.[199] Neonates, especially preterm infants, are at risk for arterial hypoxemia because of lower PaO_2 levels, decreased oxygen reserves during apnea, an FRC near closing volume, and increased oxygen demands and increased oxygen consumption because of greater metabolic needs.[192] Fetal hypoxia and its consequences are discussed in Chapter 6; perinatal asphyxia and neonatal neuroprotection are discussed in Chapter 15. Definitions of common terms used are in Table 6-1.

Abnormal functioning of organ systems is a result of the energy-dependent cellular activities. In the brain, aerobic metabolism is necessary to maintain the sodium-potassium pump, which allows for nerve impulse transmission and synthesis of synaptic chemicals. Multiple factors affect the availability of oxygen to the cells. Hypoxia may occur when tissue oxygenation is inadequate because the PaO_2 is reduced and hemoglobin is only partially saturated. This situation may be the result of decreased inspired oxygen (altitude), impaired pulmonary diffusion (pulmonary edema), altered perfusion of the lung (persistent pulmonary hypertension), or some combination of these events.[128] Hypoxia may also develop if the hemoglobin available to transport oxygen is reduced even though hemoglobin is completely saturated. PaO_2 levels are usually normal in this situation. Anemia may be the result of excessive loss or destruction of red blood cells or impaired production of hemoglobin or red blood cells. Physiologic compensation for anemia includes an increased heart rate and cardiac output. Hypoxia results in vasodilation and decreased blood viscosity, thereby increasing blood flow in an attempt to maintain normal tissue oxygenation.[128]

When tissue oxygenation is decreased because of inadequate blood flow (as with hyperviscosity syndrome), the infant is also at risk for hypoxia. The oxygen content of the blood may be normal, but the blood flow to the tissues is reduced; consequently oxygen availability is also reduced. Reduced oxygen uptake capacity of cells or the reduced oxygen utilization of the cells can also lead to hypoxia. Blood flow and oxygen tensions are usually not disturbed. Some toxins (e.g., cyanide, arsenic, and some barbiturates) may interfere with oxidative phosphorylation. Deficiencies in thyroid hormone or niacin also can impair cellular energy production and oxygen use, thereby potentiating cellular hypoxia and altered cellular activity levels.[128]

Oxygen can be a toxic agent when too much is available. Prolonged exposure to high concentrations (during resuscitation or ventilatory support) or increased oxygen pressure (e.g., deep sea diving) can lead to oxygen toxicity. In either situation, time is a critical factor. If the hyperoxia is not reversed, tissue injury may result. Hyperoxia can affect lung development by decreasing alveoli development; altering gas exchange; increasing airway smooth muscle thickness and proliferation; and

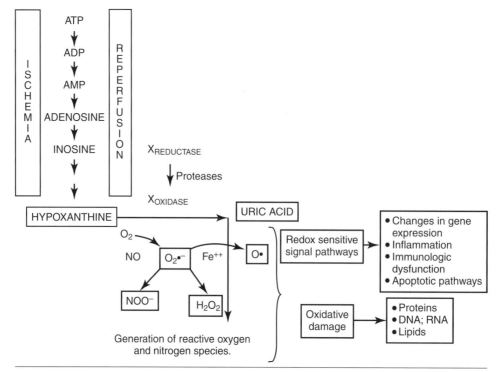

FIGURE 10-20 Events during hypoxia. During hypoxia, adenosine triphosphate *(ATP)* is exhausted, and complete rebuilding is not achieved. Purine derivatives (e.g., hypoxanthine) accumulate. During reoxygenation, specific proteases transform xanthine reductase $(X_{REDUCTASE})$, which uses oxygen as a substrate generating a burst of reactive oxygen species such as superoxide anion $(O_2^{\bullet-})$, hydrogen peroxide (H_2O_2), and hydroxyl radical $(O^\bullet)$ In the presence of ferrous iron (Fe^{++}), large amounts of superoxide anion are generated. Superoxide anion easily combines with abundant nitric oxide *(NO)* generating peroxynitrite $(NOO^\bullet)$, an aggressive nitrogen free radical. Free radicals are capable of damaging nearby molecules and organelles, but also act as signaling molecules, causing changes in gene expression, promoting inflammation, altering immune responses, and inducing apoptosis. *ADP,* Adenosine diphosphate; *AMP,* adenosine monophosphate; *DNA,* deoxyribonucleic acid; *RNA,* ribonucleic acid; $X_{OXIDASE}$, xanthine oxidase. (From Goldsmith, J.P. [2011]. Delivery room resuscitation of the newborn: Overview and initial management. In R.J. Martin, A.A. Fanaroff, & M.C. Walsh. [Eds.]. *Fanaroff and Martin's neonatal-perinatal medicine: Diseases of the fetus and infant* [9th ed.]. Philadelphia: Mosby.)

increasing interstitial fibrosis, edema, macrophage and neutrophil infiltration, and epithelial cell death.[199]

For a premature infant, hyperoxia is a relative term and must be evaluated in light of the PaO_2 levels that are normally encountered in utero. Therefore small increases in PO_2 may represent a hyperoxic state and place the infant at risk for oxygen injury. The pulmonary system, central nervous system, and retina have been identified as being particularly susceptible to oxygen injury. These systems and organs recognize different levels of oxygen as damaging.[120]

Hyperoxia results in excessive production of highly reactive metabolites of oxygen called *free radicals.* These metabolites are normally produced during oxidation-reduction reactions within the cells and are detoxified by the antioxidant system. In hyperoxic states, this system is overwhelmed and unable to keep up with the generation of free radicals. This can result in cellular damage.

In the eye, high concentrations of PaO_2 cause reversible vasoconstriction. In premature infants, this constriction of blood vessels leads to obliteration of the immature vessels

and retinal hypoxia (retinopathy of prematurity [ROP]). ROP is a multifactorial disorder of which oxygen plays a role.[158] Capillary development is stimulated but is abnormal. There is a lack of organization, and the blood vessels may extend beyond the retinal surface into the vitreous body. Often there is resolution with normal retinal development, although there is an increased risk for myopia and other vision problems. However, in severe cases, retinal hemorrhages can occur and fibrous scar tissue forms, causing buckling of the retina, leading to detachment and blindness if untreated. ROP generally progresses in two phases. "The first phase is characterized by an arrest of inner retinal vessel growth associated with microvascular degeneration in both the retinal and choroidal vascular plexus, caused by a relatively high postnatal atmospheric oxygen concentration to the premature infant. The second phase is initiated in the ischemic avascular retina, where the progressive metabolic demand triggers the expression of growth factors involved in the developing of pathologic angiogenesis that may lead to severe visual impairment and/or blindness."[158] Treatment options to prevent permanent damage include laser photocoagulation and previously cryotherapy; more recently pharmacologic interventions have been evaluated.[20,171]

The safest ranges of oxygen saturation and oxygen targeting in ELBW have been of considerable debate and concern in recent years with studies evaluating use of lower target saturations.[14,30,121,180] A recent review of these trials concluded: "In trials conducted in a developed world setting with continuous SpO_2 monitoring and protocols for screening for and treating ROP, targeting SpO_2 below 90% in extremely preterm infants increased mortality and did not reduce the risk of blindness or other disabilities and cannot be recommended."[180]

Transient Tachypnea of the Newborn

Transient tachypnea of the newborn (TTNB) is a disorder characterized by inadequate or delayed clearance of lung liquid leading to a transient pulmonary edema.[39] The population most likely to experience TTNB are term infants born by cesarean section before labor onset or who have experienced a perinatal hypoxic stress event.[89,106] Term infants born by cesarean section before labor onset have reduced liquid clearance during the intrapartum period and a larger volume of lung liquid that must be cleared after birth. Because more fluid must be accommodated in the ISS, ISS tissue pressure is increased, and fluid may move back into the lungs and need to be cleared again.[89] The liquid in the lungs increases inspiratory activity, respiration rate, and grunting. Immaturity or decreased expression of ENaC slows lung liquid removal.[106] Genetic variations in β-adrenergic receptor expression in the alveoli may also alter lung liquid clearance.[106] The net result of transient tachypnea is a delayed respiratory transition, with an increase in diffusion distance, a decrease in V_T, and an increased risk of $\dot{V}/\dot{Q}$ mismatching.[89] TTNB is uncommon in preterm infants born by cesarean, perhaps because of their increased interstitial tissue and smaller gas exchange areas that reduce movement of lung liquid from the ISS back into the airway.[89]

The most common clinical sign is tachypnea. Mild to moderate retractions and grunting may be exhibited. Cyanosis is usually not a prominent finding; if oxygen supplementation is necessary, it rarely needs to be greater than 40%. Air exchange is good; breath sounds may initially be moist but clear quickly. Symptoms usually clear within 48 to 72 hours.[39] Treatment modalities are supportive in nature and based on symptoms exhibited. Sepsis must be ruled out.

Respiratory Distress Syndrome

RDS is a developmental deficiency in surfactant synthesis accompanied by lung immaturity and hypoperfusion. The incidence of RDS is inversely related to gestational age. RDS is the most common cause of respiratory failure in preterm infants and is exacerbated by asphyxia. The pathophysiology of RDS is summarized in Figure 10-21.

RDS is characterized by alterations in surface tension, in which increased pressure is required to keep the immature

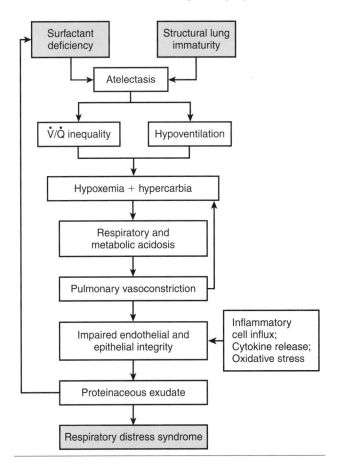

FIGURE 10-21   The complex series of acute and chronic events that lead to neonatal respiratory distress syndrome. (Adapted from Wambach, J.A. & Hamvas, A. [2015]. Respiratory distress syndrome in the neonate. In R.J. Martin, A.A. Fanaroff, & M.C. Walsh. [Eds.]. *Fanaroff and Martin's neonatal-perinatal medicine: Diseases of the fetus and infant* [10th ed.]. Philadelphia: Saunders.)

alveoli open. Pressures in adjacent alveoli are unequal; therefore time constants are changed, with some alveoli taking longer to fill and others filling normally. This leads to overdistention of the normal alveoli. As the alveoli reach their elastic limit, the infant must generate greater transpulmonary pressure to inspire the same amount of volume. The loss of elasticity and the progressive collapse of smaller alveoli reduces lung compliance and results in uneven $\dot{V}/\dot{Q}$ ratios, with concomitant hypoventilation, decreased FRC, and increased closing capacity. When the closing volume exceeds the FRC, some segments of the lung are closed during a portion of tidal breathing. The $\dot{V}/\dot{Q}$ ratio falls and hypoxemia and hypercarbia ensue. The hypoxemia and carbon dioxide retention are usually progressive, culminating in metabolic and respiratory acidosis, which further affect the ability of the type II cells to produce surfactant.[101,200]

If the closing volume exceeds both the FRC and V_T, lung segments are closed during inspiration and expiration. This represents complete atelectasis and is characterized as a "white-out" on chest radiographs. The use of continuous positive airway pressure (CPAP) and positive end-expiratory pressure (PEEP) prevents alveolar collapse during expiration and increases FRC above closing capacity.

Atelectatic areas of the lung contribute to the dead space within the entire lung. This changes the dead space–to–V_T ratio and leads to hypoxia and hypercarbia unless there is a concomitant increase in expired minute ventilation. An increase in respiratory rate reflects the infant's attempt to compensate. If dead space has increased to the point that alveolar ventilation is compromised, respiratory failure may be the result. Dead space may increase up to 70% in severe RDS.[150]

As hypoxemia and hypercarbia become more severe, pulmonary artery vasoconstriction occurs. Pulmonary perfusion is compromised, and right-to-left shunting occurs through the foramen ovale and ductus arteriosus. Hypoperfusion and hypoxemia compound local ischemia, leading to continued alveolar and capillary epithelial damage.[200]

The increased subatmospheric intrapleural pressure created by the infant in an attempt to maintain adequate airflow, along with the low serum protein that is common in preterm infants, causes the shift of alveolar and interstitial fluid toward the alveolar space. Combined with the increased alveolar surface tension, pulmonary edema and alveolar flooding ensue. Fibrinogen in the exudate is converted to fibrin. Fibrin lines the alveoli; it binds blood products and cellular debris found in the alveoli, resulting in formation of hyaline membranes.

The excess alveolar fluid and membrane formation result in an increased diffusing distance and reduced lung surface area. Gas exchange is hampered, and ventilation-perfusion mismatching is compounded. Further hypoxemia and hypercarbia are the end result. This becomes a vicious circle that may increase in severity over the first days of life. Recovery is characterized by regeneration of alveolar tissue and concomitant increase in surfactant activity.

RDS is characterized by impaired or delayed surfactant synthesis (see Box 10-5 on p. 314 and Figure 10-21). The surfactant synthesis rate and surfactant pool size are lower in infants with RDS, and tubular myelin is decreased. Preterm infants have a decreased number of type II alveolar epithelial cells secondary to lung immaturity. Surfactant must not only be present at the time of delivery, but also must be regenerated at a rate consonant with its use. Thus type II cells must be present, viable, and intact to maintain normal surface tension. Inadequate amounts of surfactant at birth may result from a variety of problems. These include extreme immaturity of the alveolar lining cells, diminished or impaired production rates resulting from transient fetal or neonatal stress, impaired release mechanisms from within the cell, and damage to type II cells. Extreme alveolar immaturity and impaired release mechanisms probably explain the inability of the very early fetus to survive.

The surfactant pool is lower in preterm infants and increases more slowly after birth with slower clearance.[104] The half-life of surfactant is 3 to 5 days in preterm infants versus 12 hours in adults.[104] Surfactant components are

also altered in immature infants. Surfactant produced by these infants has a decreased surfactant protein-to-lipid ratio, is less effective in improving lung compliance, and is more susceptible to inactivation by proteinaceous pulmonary edema.[101,208]

Lung hypoperfusion with extrapulmonary and intrapulmonary shunting is another component of RDS pathogenesis. An ischemic injury that occurs either in utero or at the time of delivery results in hypoperfusion of the lung. The more immature the lung and smaller the capillary bed, the greater the ease with which the nutritional blood supply to the developing lung can be compromised. At 35 weeks, the type II cells are presumably differentiated to the point that the pathway for PC synthesis is more resistant to fetal stress and the nutritional blood supply is more abundant and therefore more difficult to compromise.

Oxidative stress may also have a role. Preterm infants are more vulnerable to this stress as a result of decreased levels of antioxidant enzymes (e.g., catalase, glutathione peroxidase) and endogenous free-radical scavengers (e.g., α-tocopherol) and decreased binding proteins (e.g., transferrin, ceruloplasmin).[66]

Clinical Manifestations

Clinically the infant attempts to compensate for the progressive respiratory and metabolic acidosis by increasing both inspiratory pressures and respiratory rate. Grunting may occur in term or more mature preterm infants in an attempt to slow expiratory flow rates and maintain a higher FRC. All of the clinical signs appear early and usually increase in severity over the first 72 hours. The infant may also present with pitting edema, cyanosis, and diminished breath sounds.

Cyanosis is a result of an excessive concentration of deoxygenated hemoglobin in the capillaries, although hypoxia can occur without cyanosis. Factors contributing to cyanosis include alveolar hypoventilation, impaired diffusion across the alveolar–capillary membrane, and right-to-left shunting through fetal channels or through areas of atelectatic lung. Hypoxia and cyanosis are usually progressive, requiring increasing concentrations of oxygen.

Grunting is forced expiration against a partially closed glottis so that end-expiratory pressure is increased and expiratory flow is retarded. This maintains the lung at a slightly higher volume for a longer period, thereby increasing gas exchange time. There is usually a very short expiratory phase; this reduces the time in which the lung can become airless before the next inspiratory effort. The tachypnea and grunting help maintain a more normal FRC. Grunting is uncommon in very-low-birth-weight infants.

Retractions are indicative of the increased inspiratory pressure, decreased lung compliance, and increased chest wall compliance. They can be quite marked in RDS, with substernal retractions pulling to the backbone. This dysfunctional respiratory effort results in cephalocaudal expansion only (paradoxical breathing), with increased negative pressures being generated in the bases. Therefore hyperinflation occurs in the bases and atelectasis in the apices. Marked abnormalities in $\dot{V}/\dot{Q}$ ratios are the result.

Treatment

Interventions are supportive as well as active in nature. Adequate, effective resuscitation with maintenance of body temperature is essential for reducing the incidence and severity of the disease. Therapy is aimed at maintaining oxygenation, adequate ventilation, normal pH, and adequate perfusion and tissue oxygenation. Hydration is important, but overhydration increases the risk of congestive heart failure. A systolic murmur, bounding pulses, active precordium, tachycardia, tachypnea, apnea, and carbon dioxide retention, as well as worsening ventilatory requirements, are indications of patent ductus arteriosus (see Chapter 9) and congestive heart failure. Active interventions include administration of exogenous surfactant and the use of CPAP in an attempt to keep FRC above closing capacity. Many of the effects of surfactant therapy can be achieved by using CPAP to prevent end alveolar collapse, decrease work of breathing, and decrease ventilation-perfusion mismatch.[85] Infants can be stabilized with CPAP at delivery and treated with surfactant as needed to avoid mechanical ventilation and decrease their risk for BPD.[59,80,98,112,164,181,184,200] Bubble CPAP and flow-driven CPAP are both effective.[77] Bubble CPAP may reduce volutrauma and the accompanying vibrations may mimic those generated by high-frequency ventilation.[69,77,196] Newer ventilators and ventilatory strategies have improved management and outcomes of premature infants with respiratory failure. More aggressive ventilatory support is needed if the infant is unable to compensate for hypoxemia, hypercarbia, and acidosis by generating sufficient negative pressure and increasing minute ventilation.[85,200] Inhaled nitric oxide (iNO) use with preterm infants to prevent BPD has had mixed results.[17,20,50,110,177] A metaanalysis on the efficacy of iNO to prevent or treat respiratory failure in preterm infants found a 7% decrease in the composite outcome of death or BPD at 36 weeks but not in the individual variables and concluded that currently there was no evidence to support use outside of trials.[50] A Cochrane review concluded that "iNO does not appear to be effective as rescue therapy for the very ill preterm infant. Early routine use of iNO in preterm infants with respiratory disease does not prevent serious brain injury or improve survival without BPD. Later use of iNO to prevent BPD could be effective, but current 95% confidence intervals include no effect . . . and requires further study."[17]

Exogenous surfactant therapy stabilizes the lung until postnatal surfactant synthesis matures. Surfactant therapy became generally available in 1990 after a series of successful clinical trials. "Surfactant therapy has been the single most important factor in reducing overall neonatal mortality rates."[40] Surfactant therapy reduces the risk of RDS and the severity of RDS in those with established disease.[99] Surfactant therapy has been associated with a 30% reduction in mortality and a decrease in pneumothorax, oxygen requirements, and ventilator requirements.[100,185] Effects on bronchopulmonary dysplasia, intraventricular hemorrhage, and patent ductus arteriosus have been inconsistent.[185] The combined use of antenatal corticosteroids (see "Antenatal Corticosteroids") and surfactant therapy has additional beneficial effects.[99,200] Long-term outcome studies have not demonstrated adverse effects related to surfactant therapy.[185] What is currently known and still unknown regarding surfactant therapy for RDS is summarized below in Box 10-8.

Types of surfactant include animal-derived (natural), synthetic without protein components, and synthetic with synthetic phospholipids and hydrophobic surfactant protein analogs (including SP-B and/or SP-C).[166] Surfactant phospholipids and proteins are recycled with little catabolism; lipids in surfactant have a slow catabolic rate so are not rapidly degraded.[104] Surfactant therapy does not inhibit endogenous surfactant production. Surfactant therapy increases the infant's alveolar

---

BOX 10-8   Surfactant Therapy for Respiratory Distress Syndrome

RESOLVED

Improved mortality from respiratory distress syndrome (RDS)

Greatest benefit when antenatal corticosteroids are also employed

Exogenous surfactant does not inhibit endogenous surfactant synthesis

Retreatment may be required in severe RDS

Major component for lowering surface tension: phosphatidylcholine

Endotracheal intubation required for administration of fluid suspension

Improvement in oxygenation, functional residual capacity, and lung compliance

Protein-containing preparations show a faster therapeutic response

Decreased incidence of air leaks

Early use preferable in infants with extremely low birth weight (less than 28 weeks' gestation)

Efficacy of surfactant therapy, early extubation, nasal continuous positive airway pressure (CPAP) strategy

UNRESOLVED

Role of surfactant in the cause and treatment of pulmonary hemorrhage

Optimal ventilator strategy to maximize surfactant response

Effect on incidence and severity of bronchopulmonary dysplasia

Role of surfactant as a modulator of the immune system and inflammatory response

Role for recombinant surfactant protein–based preparations

Role for aerosolized surfactant preparations

Endotracheal administration via a narrow-bore catheter as an alternative to endotracheal intubation

Efficacy of synthetic peptide surfactant preparations

Adapted from Wambach, J.A. & Hamvas, A. (2015). Respiratory distress syndrome in the neonate. In R.J. Martin, A.A. Fanaroff, & M.C. Walsh. (Eds.). *Fanaroff and Martin's neonatal-perinatal medicine: Diseases of the fetus and infant* (10th ed.). Philadelphia: Saunders.

and tissue pools of surfactant as it is taken up into the type II alveolar cell and recycled. As part of the recycling the surfactant is transformed into a better form of surfactant.[104] Exogenous surfactant mixes with the infant's own surfactant. This mixture appears to enhance the function of endogenous surfactant, making it less sensitive to inactivation.[101] Efficacy of different types of surfactant and patterns of use have been analyzed in various metaanalyses.[11,159,166,175,200]

Exogenous surfactant was initially given shortly after birth in at-risk infants (prophylactic) or once the infant began to show signs of RDS (treatment) to reduce the severity of RDS and mortality. However a metaanalysis concluded: "Although the early trials of prophylactic surfactant administration to infants judged to be at risk of developing RDS compared with selective use of surfactant in infants with established RDS demonstrated a decreased risk of air leak and mortality, recent large trials that reflect current practice (including greater utilization of maternal steroids and routine postdelivery stabilization on CPAP) do not support these differences and demonstrate less risk of chronic lung disease or death when using early stabilization on CPAP with selective surfactant administration to infants requiring intubation."[159] Currently surfactant therapy requires that the infant be intubated, although nasopharyngeal instillation and other modes of delivery have been investigated in the past and are currently being reevaluated.[166] Multiple doses are often needed to overcome inactivation of surfactant by soluble proteins in the small airways and alveoli.[185] Surfactant therapy has also been used for other disorders, including adult RDS (ARDS), bronchiolitis, pneumonia, pulmonary hemorrhage, and meconium aspiration.[40,55,58,185]

Bronchopulmonary Dysplasia

Although the incidence of BPD has not changed significantly, the pattern of the disorder has changed since the introduction of surfactant therapy (Table 10-8).[98] There is a slower,

subtler onset, with the gradual development of lung abnormalities that persist after 20 to 30 days of life.[16] Birth weight and gestational age are the best predictors of BPD.[98] BPD is seen primarily in infants weighing less than 1000 g at birth or who are younger than 30 weeks' gestation.[98] Chronic lung disease (CLD), or the "new" (postsurfactant) BPD, is characterized by oxygen requirements after 28 days of age or at 36 weeks' postconceptional age, but without the characteristic sequence of BPD radiographic changes.[174] Infants with this disorder have disruption of alveolar and microvascular development with reduced alveolarization, including alveolar hypoplasia and variable saccule wall fibrosis.[174] Most preterm infants who develop BPD require mechanical ventilation and oxygen therapy; very immature infants without significant lung disease are also at risk.[111]

BPD is the result of lung injury, probably mediated by an inflammatory reaction with cytokine release and oxidative damage (Figure 10-22). These responses can be caused by many factors, including structural lung immaturity, oxidative stress and oxidant injury, pulmonary vascular damage, chorioamnionitis, nosocomial infection, inflammation, volutrauma/barotrauma, edema, and undernutrition.[16,47] "BPD represents the response of the lung during a critical period of lung growth, usually during the canalicular period (17 to 26 weeks), which is a time during which airspace septation and vascular development increases dramatically."[179] BPD also involves disruption of vasculogenesis as well as alterations in alveolar structure with alterations in alveolar and pulmonary vasculature development.[47,136] Characteristics of BPD include alveolar fibroproliferation, vascular smooth muscle hypertrophy, narrowing of the vascular lumens, increased pulmonary vascular resistance, decreased compliance, and inhibition of distal lung formation with decreased alveolarization.[6,179] Alterations in the pulmonary vasculature include a decreased number of arteries, medial hypertrophy, abnormal vasoreactivity, and altered muscularization in distal arteries leading to pulmonary hypertension.[64]

Treatment for BPD has been multifaceted. Some modalities are centered on primary prevention; others are employed after the disease process is diagnosed. Primary prevention includes (1) reducing the incidence of premature births through patient education and recognition of early labor, (2) using drugs to delay preterm birth and using antenatal steroids to mature surfactant synthesis pathways and enhance lung development, (3) identifying and treating chorioamnionitis, (4) providing effective resuscitation, (5) avoiding hyperventilation and hyperoxia, and (6) providing exogenous surfactant.[16,172] Secondary treatment modalities include (1) providing ventilatory support using various techniques and modalities, including reducing volutrauma via use of targeted ventilatory strategies such as volume-generated ventilation and bubble CPAP; (2) supplying adequate nutrition for growth and healing; (3) facilitating closure of the ductus arteriosus through pharmacologic or surgical treatment; and (4) using bronchodilators, antiinflammatory agents, and other pharmacologic agents to decrease resistance to airflow

TABLE 10-8	Differences in Pathologic Features of "New" and "Old" Bronchopulmonary Dysplasia	
PRESURFACTANT ("OLD")	**POSTSURFACTANT ("NEW")**
Alternating atelectasis with hyperinflation	Less regional heterogeneity of lung disease
Severe airway epithelial lesions (e.g., hyperplasia, squamous metaplasia)	Rare airway epithelial lesions
Marked airway smooth muscle hyperplasia	Mild airway smooth muscle thickening
Extensive, diffuse fibroproliferation	Rare fibroproliferative changes
Hypertensive remodeling of pulmonary arteries	Fewer arteries, but "dysmorphic"
Decreased alveolarization and surface area	Fewer, larger, and simplified alveoli

From Kinsella, J.P., Greenough, A., & Abman, S.H. (2006). Bronchopulmonary dysplasia. *Lancet, 367,* 1422.

References

1. Abdel-Hady, H., et al. (2015). Caffeine therapy in preterm infants. *World J Clin Pediatr*, *4*, 81.
2. Abu-Shaweesh, J. M. (2004). Maturation of respiratory reflex responses in the fetus and neonate. *Semin Neonatol*, *9*, 169.
3. Abu-Shaweesh, J. M., & Martin, R. J. (2008). Neonatal apnea: What's new? *Pediatr Pulmonol*, *43*, 937.
4. ACOG (American College of Obstetricians and Gynecologists) Committee on Obstetric Practice. (2009, October). Committee opinion: Number 443. Air travel during pregnancy. *Obstet Gynecol*, *114*, 954.
5. ACOG (American College of Obstetricians and Gynecologists) Committee on Obstetric Practice. (2011). ACOG Committee Opinion: Number 475. Antenatal corticosteroid therapy for fetal lung maturation. *Obstet Gynecol*, *117*, 422.
6. Ad Hoc Statement Committee, American Thoracic Society. (2004). Mechanisms and limits of induced postnatal lung growth. *Am J Respir Crit Care Med*, *170*, 319.
7. Aguilar, A. M., & Vain, N. E. (2011). The suctioning in the delivery room debate. *Early Hum Dev*, *87*, S13.
8. Ahanya, S. N., et al. (2005). Meconium passage in utero: Mechanisms, consequences, and management. *Obstet Gynecol Surv*, *60*, 45.
9. Alvaro, R. E., & Rigatto, H. (2017). Control of breathing in fetal life and onset and control of breathing in the newborn. In R. A. Polin, et al. (Eds.), *Fetal and neonatal physiology* (5th ed.). Philadelphia: Saunders.
10. American College of Obstetricians and Gynecologists Committee on Obstetric Practice. (2014). ACOG Committee Opinion No. 608: Influenza vaccination during pregnancy. *Obstet Gynecol*, *124*, 1648.
11. Ardell, S., et al. (2015). Animal derived surfactant extract versus protein free synthetic surfactant for the prevention and treatment of respiratory distress syndrome. *Cochrane Database Syst Rev*, *2015*(8), CD000144.
12. Armentrout, D. (2014). Not ready for prime time: transitional events in the extremely preterm infant. *J Perinat Neonatal Nurs*, *28*, 144.
13. Asikainen, T. M., & White, C. W. C. (2005). Antioxidant defenses in the preterm lung: Role for hypoxia-inducible factors in BPD? *Toxicol Appl Pharmacol*, *203*, 177.
14. Askie, L. M., et al. (2017). Effects of targeting higher versus lower arterial oxygen saturations on death or disability in preterm infants. *Cochrane Database Syst Rev*, *2017*(4), CD011190.
15. Asztalos, E. V., et al. (2010). Multiple courses of antenatal corticosteroids for preterm birth study: 2-year outcomes. *Pediatrics*, *126*, e1045.
16. Bancalari, E., & Walsh, M. (2015). Bronchopulmonary dysplasia. In R. J. Martin, A. A. Fanaroff, & M. C. Walsh (Eds.), *Fanaroff and Martin's Neonatal-perinatal medicine: Diseases of the fetus and infant* (10th ed.). Philadelphia: Saunders.
17. Barrington, K. J., et al. (2017). Inhaled nitric oxide for respiratory failure in preterm infants. *Cochrane Database Syst Rev*, *2017*(1), CD000509.
18. Baud, O., et al. (2016). Effect of early low-dose hydrocortisone on survival without bronchopulmonary dysplasia in extremely preterm infants (PREMILOC): A double-blind, placebo-controlled, multicentre, randomised trial. *Lancet*, *387*, 1827.
19. Been, J. V., et al. (2014). Preterm birth and childhood wheezing disorders: a systematic review and meta-analysis. *PLoS Med*, *11*, e1001596.
20. Beharry, K. D., et al. (2016). Pharmacologic interventions for the prevention and treatment of retinopathy of prematurity. *Semin Perinatol*, *40*, 189.
21. Bernhard, W. (2017). Regulation of surfactant-associated phospholipid synthesis and secretion. In R. A. Polin, et al. (Eds.), *Fetal and neonatal physiology* (5th ed.). Philadelphia: Saunders.
22. Bevilacqua, E., Brunelli, R., & Anceschi, M. M. (2010). Review and meta-analysis: Benefits and risks of multiple courses of antenatal corticosteroids. *J Matern Fetal Neonatal Med*, *23*, 244.
23. Blood-Siegfried, J., & Rende, E. K. (2010). The long-term effects of prenatal nicotine exposure on neurologic development. *J Midwifery Womens Health*, *55*, 143.
24. Bobrowski, R. A. (2010). Pulmonary physiology in pregnancy. *Clin Obstet Gynecol*, *53*, 285.
25. Bolton, C. E., et al. (2015). Lung consequences in adults born prematurely. *Thorax*, *70*, 574.
26. Bourjeily, G., Ankner, G., & Mohsenin, V. (2011). Sleep-disordered breathing in pregnancy. *Clin Chest Med*, *32*, 175.
27. Brownfoot, F. C., et al. (2013). Different corticosteroids and regimens for accelerating fetal lung maturation for women at risk of preterm birth. *Cochrane Database Syst Rev*, *2013*(8), CD006764.
28. Cannegieter, S. C., & Rosendaal, F. R. (2013). Pregnancy and travel-related thromboembolism. *Thromb Res*, *131*, S55.
29. Caparroz, F. A., et al. (2016). Rhinitis and pregnancy: literature review. *Braz J Otorhinolaryngol*, *82*, 105.
30. Carlo, W. A., et al. (2010). Target ranges of oxygen saturation in extremely preterm infants. *N Engl J Med*, *362*, 1959.
31. Carlton, D. P. (2017). Regulation of liquid secretion and absorption by the fetal and neonatal lung. In R. A. Polin, et al. (Eds.), *Fetal and neonatal physiology* (5th ed.). Philadelphia: Saunders.
32. Carroll, J. L., & Agarwal, A. (2010). Development of ventilatory control in infants. *Paediatr Respir Rev*, *11*, 199.
33. Chaillet, N., et al. (2014). Nonpharmacologic approaches for pain management during labor compared with usual care: a meta-analysis. *Birth*, *41*, 122.
34. Chestnut, D. H., et al. (2014). *Chestnut's obstetric anesthesia: principles and practice* (5th ed.). Philadelphia: Saunders.
35. Copland, I., & Post, M. (2004). Lung development and fetal lung growth. *Paediatr Respir Rev*, *5*, S259.
36. Corff, K. E., & McCann, D. L. (2005). Room air resuscitation versus oxygen resuscitation in the delivery room. *J Perinat Neonatal Nurs*, *19*, 379.
37. Correia-Pinto, J., et al. (2010). Congenital lung lesions—underlying molecular mechanisms. *Semin Pediatr Surg*, *19*, 171.
38. Crowley, M. A. (2015). Neonatal respiratory disorders. In R. J. Martin, A. A. Fanaroff, & M. C. Walsh (Eds.), *Fanaroff and Martin's Neonatal-perinatal medicine: diseases of the fetus and infant* (10th ed.). Philadelphia: Saunders.
39. Cunningham, F. G., et al. (2014). *Williams obstetrics* (24th ed.). New York: McGraw-Hill.
40. Curley, A. E., & Halliday, H. L. (2001). The present status of exogenous surfactant for the newborn. *Early Hum Dev*, *61*, 67.
41. Dakshinamurti, S. (2005). Pathophysiologic mechanisms of persistent pulmonary hypertension of the newborn. *Pediatr Pulmonol*, *39*, 492.
42. Darnall, R. A. (2010). The role of CO(2) and central chemoreception in the control of breathing in the fetus and the neonate. *Respir Physiol Neurobiol*, *173*, 201.
43. Davis, J. M., & Auten, R. L. (2010). Maturation of the antioxidant system and the effects on preterm birth. *Semin Fetal Neonatal Med*, *15*, 191.
44. Davis, P. G., et al. (2010). Caffeine for Apnea of Prematurity trial: benefits may vary in subgroups. *J Pediatr*, *156*, 382.
45. Dawson, J. A., et al. (2010). Defining the reference range for oxygen saturation for infants after birth. *Pediatrics*, *125*, e1340.
46. Dawson, J. A., & Morley, C. J. (2010). Monitoring oxygen saturation and heart rate in the early neonatal period. *Semin Fetal Neonatal Med*, *15*, 203.
47. Day, C. L., & Ryan, R. M. (2017). Bronchopulmonary dysplasia: new becomes old again! *Pediatr Res*, *81*, 210.
48. DiBlasi, R. M., Richardson, C. P., & Hansen, T. N. (2012). Pulmonary physiology of the newborn. In C. A. Gleason & S. Devaskar (Eds.), *Avery's diseases of the newborn* (9th ed.). Philadelphia: Saunders.
49. Dombrowski, M. P., & Schatz, M. (2010). Asthma in pregnancy. *Clin Obstet Gynecol*, *53*, 301.
50. Donohue, P. K., et al. (2011). Inhaled nitric oxide in preterm infants: A systematic review. *Pediatrics*, *127*, e414.
51. Doyle, L. W., et al. (2005). Impact of postnatal systemic corticosteroids on mortality and cerebral palsy in preterm infants: effect modification by risk for chronic lung disease. *Pediatrics*, *115*, 655.
52. Doyle, L. W., et al. (2006). Low-dose dexamethasone facilitates extubation among chronically ventilator-dependent infants: a multicenter, international, randomized, controlled trial. *Pediatrics*, *117*, 75.
53. Doyle, L. W., et al. (2014). Reduction in developmental coordination disorder with neonatal caffeine therapy. *J Pediatr*, *165*, 356.e2.
54. Duarte, A. G. (2014). ARDS in pregnancy. *Clin Obstet Gynecol*, *57*, 862.
55. El Shahed, A. I., et al. (2014). Surfactant for meconium aspiration syndrome in term and late preterm infants. *Cochrane Database Syst Rev*, *2014*(12), CD002054.
56. England, L. J., et al. (2015). Nicotine and the developing human: a neglected element in

the electronic cigarette debate. *Am J Prev Med, 49*, 286.

57. Falck, A. J., et al. (2016). Adverse exposures to the fetus. In R. J. Martin, A. A. Fanaroff, & M. C. Walsh (Eds.), *Fanaroff and Martin's Neonatal-perinatal medicine: diseases of the fetus and infant* (10th ed.). Philadelphia: Saunders.

58. Finer, N. N. (2004). Surfactant use for neonatal lung injury: Beyond respiratory distress syndrome. *Paediatr Respir Rev, 5*, S289.

59. Finer, N. N., et al. (2010). Early CPAP versus surfactant in extremely preterm infants. *N Engl J Med, 362*, 1970. Erratum in: N Engl J Med. 2010 Jun 10;362(23), 2235.

60. Fleming, S., et al. (2011). Normal ranges of heart rate and respiratory rate in children from birth to 18 years of age: A systematic review of observational studies. *Lancet, 377*, 1011.

61. Fraga, M. V., & Guttentag, S. (2012). Lung development: embryology, growth, maturation, and developmental biology. In C. A. Gleason & S. Devaskar (Eds.), *Avery's diseases of the newborn* (9th ed.). Philadelphia: Saunders.

62. Frappell, P. B., & MacFarlane, P. M. (2005). Development of mechanics and pulmonary reflexes. *Respir Physiol Neurobiol, 149*, 143.

63. Freeman, M., et al. (2004). Does air travel affect pregnancy outcome? *Arch Gynecol Obstet, 269*, 274.

64. Gao, Y., & Raj, J. U. (2010). Regulation of the pulmonary circulation in the fetus and newborn. *Physiol Rev, 90*, 1291.

65. Gauda, E. B., et al. (2004). Maturation of peripheral arterial chemoreceptors in relation to neonatal apnoea. *Semin Neonatol, 9*, 181.

66. Gauda, E. B., & Martin, R. J. (2012). Control of breathing. In C. A. Gleason & S. Devaskar (Eds.), *Avery's diseases of the newborn* (9th ed.). Philadelphia: Saunders.

67. Gerber, A. N. (2015). Glucocorticoids and the Lung. *Adv Exp Med Biol, 872*, 279.

68. Goldsmith, J. P. (2015). Overview and initial management of delivery room resuscitation. In R. J. Martin, A. A. Fanaroff, & M. C. Walsh (Eds.), *Fanaroff and Martin's Neonatal-perinatal medicine: diseases of the fetus and infant* (10th ed.). Philadelphia: Saunders.

69. Goldsmith, J. P., et al. (2017). *Assisted ventilation of the neonate: evidence based approach to newborn respiratory care* (6th ed.). Philadelphia: Elsevier.

70. Gosche, J. R., Islam, S., & Boulanger, S. C. (2005). Congenital diaphragmatic hernia: Searching for answers. *Am J Surg, 190*, 324.

71. Graves, C. R. (2010). Pneumonia in pregnancy. *Clin Obstet Gynecol, 53*, 329.

72. Greenspan, J. S., Miller, T. L., & Shaffer, T. H. (2005). The neonatal respiratory pump: A developmental challenge with physiologic limitations. *Neonatal Netw, 24*, 15.

73. Grenache, D. G., & Gronowski, A. M. (2006). Fetal lung maturity. *Clin Biochem, 39*, 1.

74. Groenman, F., Unger, S., & Post, M. (2005). The molecular basis for abnormal human lung development. *Biol Neonate, 87*, 164.

75. Grohskopf, L. A., et al. (2015). Prevention and control of influenza with vaccines: recommendations of the Advisory Committee on Immunization Practices, United States, 2015-2016 influenza season. *MMWR Morb Mortal Wkly Rep, 64*, 818.

76. Gross, I., & Ballard, P. L. (2017). Hormonal therapy for prevention of respiratory distress syndrome. In R. A. Polin, et al. (Eds.), *Fetal and neonatal physiology* (5th ed.). Philadelphia: Saunders.

77. Gupta, S., et al. (2009). A randomized controlled trial of post-extubation bubble continuous positive airway pressure versus Infant Flow Driver continuous positive airway pressure in preterm infants with respiratory distress syndrome. *J Pediatr, 154*, 645.

78. Gyamfi-Bannerman, C., et al. (2016). Antenatal betamethasone for women at risk for late preterm delivery. *N Engl J Med, 374*, 1311.

79. Haram, K., et al. (2017). Antenatal corticosteroid treatment: factors other than lung maturation. *J Matern Fetal Neonatal Med, 30*, 1437.

80. Hascoet, J. M., Espagne, S., & Hamon, I. (2008). CPAP and the preterm: lessons from the COIN trial and other studies. *Early Hum Dev, 84*, 791.

81. Hegewald, M. J., & Crapo, R. O. (2011). Respiratory physiology in pregnancy. *Clin Chest Med, 32*, 1.

82. Henderson-Smart, D. J., & De Paoli, A. G. (2010). Methylxanthine treatment for apnoea in preterm infants. *Cochrane Database Syst Rev, 2010*(12), CD000140.

83. Henderson-Smart, D. J., & Steer, P. A. (2010). Caffeine versus theophylline for apnea in preterm infants. *Cochrane Database Syst Rev, 2010*(1), CD000273.

84. Hislop, A. A. (2002). Airway and blood vessel interaction during lung development. *J Anat, 201*, 325.

85. Ho, J. J., et al. (2015). Continuous distending pressure for respiratory distress syndrome in preterm infants. *Cochrane Database Syst Rev, 2015*(7), CD002271.

86. Hoefnagel, A., Yu, A., & Kaminski, A. (2016). Anesthetic Complications in Pregnancy. *Crit Care Clin, 32*, 1.

87. Hooper, S. B., et al. (2013). Establishing functional residual capacity in the non-breathing infant. *Semin Fetal Neonatal Med, 18*, 336.

88. Hooper, S. B., Polglase, G. R., & Roehr, C. C. (2015). Cardiopulmonary changes with aeration of the newborn lung. *Paediatr Respir Rev, 16*, 147.

89. Hooper, S. B., Te Pas, A. B., & Kitchen, M. J. (2016). Respiratory transition in the newborn: a three-phase process. *Arch Dis Child Fetal Neonatal Ed, 101*, F266.

90. Hooper, S. B., et al. (2016). The timing of umbilical cord clamping at birth: physiological considerations. *Matern Health Neonatol Perinatol, 2*, 4.

91. Izadi, M., et al. (2015). Do pregnant women have a higher risk for venous thromboembolism following air travel? *Adv Biomed Res, 23*, 60.

92. Jadcherla, S. R., Hogan, W. J., & Shaker, R. (2010). Physiology and pathophysiology of glottic reflexes and pulmonary aspiration: from neonates to adults. *Semin Respir Crit Care Med, 31*, 554.

93. Jain, A., & McNamara, P. J. (2015). Persistent pulmonary hypertension of the newborn: Advances in diagnosis and treatment. *Semin Fetal Neonatal Med, 20*, 262.

94. Jensen, D., et al. (2005). Effects of human pregnancy on the ventilatory chemoreflex response to carbon dioxide. *Am J Physiol Regul Integr Comp Physiol, 288*, R1369.

95. Jensen, D., & O'Donnell, D. E. (2011). The impact of human pregnancy on perceptual responses to chemoreflex vs. exercise stimulation of ventilation: a retrospective analysis. *Respir Physiol Neurobiol, 175*, 55.

96. Jensen, E. A., Foglia, E. E., & Schmidt, B. (2015). Evidence-based pharmacologic therapies for prevention of bronchopulmonary dysplasia: application of the grading of recommendations assessment, development, and evaluation methodology. *Clin Perinatol, 42*, 755.

97. Jobe, A. H. (2010). "Miracle" extremely low birth weight neonates: Examples of developmental plasticity. *Obstet Gynecol, 116*, 1184.

98. Jobe, A. H. (2011). The new bronchopulmonary dysplasia. *Curr Opin Pediatr, 23*, 167.

99. Jobe, A. H., & Kamath–Rayne, B. D. (2014). Fetal lung development and surfactant. In R. K. Creasy, et al. (Eds.), *Creasy & Resnik's Maternal-fetal medicine: principles and practice* (7th ed.). Philadelphia: Saunders.

100. Jobe, A. H., & Kallapur, S. (2017). Surfactant treatment. In R. A. Polin, et al. (Eds.), *Fetal and neonatal physiology* (5th ed.). Philadelphia: Saunders.

101. Jobe, A. H., & Ikegami, M. (2017). Pathophysiology of respiratory distress syndrome. In R. A. Polin, et al. (Eds.), *Fetal and neonatal physiology* (5th ed.). Philadelphia: Saunders.

102. Jones, L., et al. (2012). Pain management for women in labour: an overview of systematic reviews. *Cochrane Database Syst Rev, 2012*(3), CD009234.

103. Julian, C. G. (2011). High altitude during pregnancy. *Clin Chest Med, 32*, 21.

104. Kallapur, S. G., & Jobe, A. J. (2015). Lung development and maturation. In R. J. Martin, A. A. Fanaroff, & M. C. Walsh (Eds.), *Fanaroff and Martin's Neonatal-perinatal medicine: diseases of the fetus and infant* (10th ed.). Philadelphia: Saunders.

105. Kamath-Rayne, B. D., et al. (2016). Antenatal corticosteroids beyond 34 weeks gestation: What do we do now? *Am J Obstet Gynecol, 215*, 423.

106. Katz, C., Bentur, L., & Elias, N. (2011). Clinical implication of lung liquid balance in the perinatal period. *J Perinatol, 31*, 230.

107. Keens, D. H., & Ianuzzo, C. D. (1979). Development of fatigue-resistant muscle fibers in human ventilatory musculature. *Am Rev Respir Dis, 119*, 139.

108. Keszler, M. (2015). Sustained inflation during neonatal resuscitation. *Curr Opin Pediatr, 27*, 145.

109. Keszler, M., & Abubakar, M. K. (2017). Physiologic principles. In J. P. Goldsmith, et al. (Eds.), *Assisted ventilation of the neonate* (6th ed.). Philadelphia: Saunders.

110. Kinsella, J. P., et al. (2006). Early inhaled nitric oxide in premature newborns with respiratory failure. *N Engl J Med, 355*, 354.

111. Kinsella, J. P., Greenough, A., & Abman, S. H. (2006). Bronchopulmonary dysplasia. *Lancet, 367*, 1421.

112. Kribs, A., et al. (2010). Surfactant without intubation in preterm infants with respiratory distress: First multicenter data. *Klin Padiatr, 222*, 13.

113. Kumar, R., Hayhurst, K. L., & Robson, A. K. (2011). Ear, nose, and throat manifestations during pregnancy. *Otolaryngol Head Neck Surg, 145*, 188.

114. Laughon, M., et al. (2009). Patterns of respiratory disease during the first 2 postnatal weeks in extremely premature infants. *Pediatrics, 123*, 1124.

115. Lindenskov, P. H., et al. (2015). Meconium aspiration syndrome: possible pathophysiological mechanisms and future potential therapies. *Neonatology, 107*, 225.

116. Lista, G., et al. (2015). Sustained lung inflation at birth for preterm infants: a randomized clinical trial. *Pediatrics, 135*, e457.

117. Littleford, J. (2004). Effects on the fetus and newborn of maternal analgesia and anesthesia: A review. *Can J Anaesth, 51*, 586.

118. Macklem, P. T. (1971). Airway obstruction and collateral ventilation. *Physiol Rev, 51*, 368.

119. Magann, E. F., et al. (2010). Air travel and pregnancy outcomes: a review of pregnancy regulations and outcomes for passengers, flight attendants, and aviators. *Obstet Gynecol Surv, 65*, 396.

120. Maltepe, E., & Saugstad, O. D. (2009). Oxygen in health and disease: regulation of oxygen homeostasis—clinical implications. *Pediatr Res, 65*, 261.

121. Manja, V., Lakshminrusimha, S., & Cook, D. J. (2015). Oxygen saturation target range for extremely preterm infants: a systematic review and meta-analysis. *JAMA Pediatr, 169*, 332.

122. Mankouski, A., & Auten, R. L., Jr. (2017). Mechanisms of neonatal lung injury. In R. A. Polin, et al. (Eds.), *Fetal and neonatal physiology* (5th ed.). Philadelphia: Saunders.

123. Mantilla, C. B., et al. (2017). Functional development of respiratory muscles. In R. A. Polin, et al. (Eds.), *Fetal and neonatal physiology* (5th ed.). Philadelphia: Saunders.

124. Maritz, G. S., Morley, C. J., & Harding, R. (2005). Early developmental origins of impaired lung structure and function. *Early Hum Dev, 81*, 763.

125. Martin, R. J., et al. (2017). Regulation of lower airway function. In R. A. Polin, et al. (Eds.), *Fetal and neonatal physiology* (5th ed.). Philadelphia: Saunders.

126. Martin, R. J. (2017). Pathophysiology of apnea of prematurity. In R. A. Polin, et al. (Eds.), *Fetal and neonatal physiology* (5th ed.). Philadelphia: Saunders.

127. McAuliffe, F., et al. (2004). Respiratory function in pregnancy at sea level and at high altitude. *BJOG, 111*, 311.

128. McCance, K. L., & Huether, S. L. (2014). *Pathophysiology: the biological basis for disease in adults and children* (7th ed.). St. Louis: Mosby.

129. McKinlay, C. J., et al. (2012). Repeat antenatal glucocorticoids for women at risk of preterm birth: a Cochrane systematic review. *Am J Obstet Gynecol, 206*, 187.

130. McNamara, P. J., & El-Khuffash, A. (2017). Oxygen transport and delivery. In R. A. Polin, et al. (Eds.), *Fetal and neonatal physiology* (5th ed.). Philadelphia: Saunders.

131. Mehta, N., et al. (2015). Respiratory disease in pregnancy. *Best Pract Res Clin Obstet Gynaecol, 29*, 598.

132. Melo, M. F. (2004). Clinical respiratory physiology of the neonate and infant with congenital heart disease. *Int Anesthesiol Clin, 42*, 29.

133. Mercadante, D., et al. (2016). Sustained lung inflation in late preterm infants: a randomized controlled trial. *J Perinatol, 36*, 443.

134. Mercer, B. D. (2014). Assessment and induction of fetal pulmonary maturity. In R. K. Creasy, et al. (Eds.), *Creasy & Resnik's Maternal-fetal medicine: Principles and practice* (7th ed.). Philadelphia: Saunders.

135. Mercer, J., & Skovgaard., R. L. (2002). Neonatal transitional physiology: a new paradigm. *J Perinat Neonat Nurs, 15*, 56.

136. Merritt, T. A., Deming, D. D., & Boynton, B. R. (2009). The 'new' bronchopulmonary dysplasia: challenges and commentary. *Semin Fetal Neonatal Med, 14*, 345.

137. Meschia, G. (2011). Fetal oxygenation and maternal ventilation. *Clin Chest Med, 32*, 15.

138. Monga, M., & Mastrobatista, J. M. (2014). Maternal cardiovascular, respiratory and renal adaptation to pregnancy. In R. K. Creasy, et al. (Eds.), *Creasy & Resnik's Maternal-fetal medicine: Principles and practice* (7th ed.). Philadelphia: Saunders.

139. Moore, K. L., Persaud, T. V. N., & Torchia, M. G. (2015). *The developing human: clinically oriented embryology* (10th ed.). Philadelphia: Saunders.

140. Mortola, J. P. (2017). Mechanics of breathing. In R. A. Polin, et al. (Eds.), *Fetal and neonatal physiology* (5th ed.). Philadelphia: Saunders.

141. Munnur, U., de Boisblanc, B., & Suresh, M. S. (2005). Airway problems in pregnancy. *Crit Care Med, 33*, S259.

142. Murin, S., Rafii, R., & Bilello, K. (2011). Smoking and smoking cessation in pregnancy. *Clin Chest Med, 32*, 75.

143. Murphy, V. E., & Gibson, P. G. (2011). Asthma in pregnancy. *Clin Chest Med, 32*, 93.

144. Myatt, L., & Cui, X. (2004). Oxidative stress in the placenta. *Histochem Cell Biol, 122*, 369.

145. National Asthma Education and Prevention Program (NAEPP). (2005). Managing asthma during pregnancy: recommendations for pharmacological treatment. *J Allergy Clin Immunol, 115*, 34.

146. National Institutes of Health Consensus. (1995). Consensus Developmental Conference on the Effects of Corticosteroids for Fetal Maturation on Perinatal Outcomes. *JAMA, 273*, 413.

147. National Institutes of Health. (2000). Antenatal corticosteroids revisited: repeated courses. *NIH Consensus Statement, 17*, 1.

148. Nelson, N. M. (1976). Respiration and circulation after birth. In C. A. Smith & N. M. Nelson (Eds.), *The physiology of the newborn infant*. Springfield, IL: Charles C Thomas.

149. Neumann, R. P., & von Ungern-Sternberg, B. S. (2014). The neonatal lung—physiology and ventilation. *Paediatr Anaesth, 24*, 10.

150. Nichols, D. G., & Rogers, M. C. (1987). Developmental physiology of the respiratory system. In M. C. Rogers (Ed.), *Textbook of pediatric intensive care* (Vol. 1). Baltimore: Williams & Wilkins.

151. Olver, R. E., Walters, D. V. M., & Wilson, S. (2004). Developmental regulation of lung liquid transport. *Annu Rev Physiol, 66*, 77.

152. O'Tolle, M. L. (2003). Physiologic aspects of exercise in pregnancy. *Clin Obstet Gynecol, 46*, 379.

153. Parker, T. A., & Kinsella, J. P. (2012). Respiratory failure in the term infant. In C. A. Gleason & S. Devaskar (Eds.), *Avery's diseases of the newborn* (9th ed.). Philadelphia: Saunders.

154. Peltoniemi, O. M., Kari, M. A., & Hallman, M. (2011). Repeated antenatal corticosteroid treatment: A systematic review and meta-analysis. *Acta Obstet Gynecol Scand, 90*, 719.

155. Polakowski, L. L., Akinbami, L. J., & Mendola, P. (2009). Prenatal smoking cessation and the risk of delivering preterm and small-for-gestational-age newborns. *Obstet Gynecol, 114*, 318.

156. Quinn, A. C., et al. (2013). Failed tracheal intubation in obstetric anaesthesia: 2 yr national case-control study in the UK. *Br J Anaesth, 110*, 74.

157. Richardson, B. S., et al. (2014). Behavioral states in the fetus: relationship to fetal health and development. In R. K. Creasy, et al. (Eds.), *Maternal-fetal medicine: Principles and practice* (7th ed.). Philadelphia: Saunders.

158. Rivera, J. C., et al. (2016). Review of the mechanisms and therapeutic avenues for retinal and choroidal vascular dysfunctions in retinopathy of prematurity. *Acta Paediatr, 105*, 1421.

159. Rojas-Reyes, M. X., et al. (2012). Prophylactic versus selective use of surfactant in preventing morbidity and mortality in preterm infants. *Cochrane Database Syst Rev, 2012*(3), CD000510.

160. Rozycki, H. J., et al. (2017). Structure and development of alveolar epithelial cells and the surface layer during development. In R. A. Polin, et al. (Eds.), *Fetal and neonatal physiology* (5th ed.). Philadelphia: Saunders.

161. Saccone, G., & Berghella, V. (2016). Antenatal corticosteroids for maturity of term or near term fetuses: systematic review and meta-analysis of randomized controlled trials. *BMJ, 355*, i5044.

162. Sale, S. M. (2010). Neonatal apnoea. *Best Pract Res Clin Anaesthiol, 24*, 323.

163. Samuel, B. U., & Barry, M. (1998). The pregnant traveler. *Infect Dis Clin North Am, 12*, 325.

164. Sandri, F., et al. (2010). Prophylactic or early selective surfactant combined with nCPAP in very preterm infants. *Pediatrics, 125*, e1402.

165. Sarberg, M., et al. (2014). Snoring during pregnancy and its relation to sleepiness and pregnancy outcome – a prospective study. *BMC Pregnancy Childbirth, 14*, 15.

166. Sardesai, S., et al. (2017). Evolution of surfactant therapy for respiratory distress syndrome: past, present, and future. *Pediatr Res, 81*, 240.

167. Schmidt, B., et al. (2012). Survival without disability to age 5 years after neonatal caffeine therapy for apnea of prematurity. *JAMA, 307*, 275.

168. Schneider, S., et al. (2010). Smoking cessation during pregnancy: a systematic literature review. *Drug Alcohol Rev, 29*, 81.

169. Schwaiberger, D., et al. (2016). Respiratory failure and mechanical ventilation in the pregnant patient. *Crit Care Clin, 32*, 85.

170. Shaffer, T. H., et al. (2017). Upper airway: structure, function, regulation and development. In R. A. Polin, et al. (Eds.), *Fetal and neonatal physiology* (5th ed.). Philadelphia: Saunders.

171. Shah, P. K., et al. (2016). Retinopathy of prematurity: past, present and future. *World J Clin Pediatr, 5*, 35.

172. Shah, P. S. (2003). Current perspectives on the prevention and management of chronic lung disease in preterm infants. *Paediatr Drugs, 5*, 463.

173. Shiao, S. Y. (2005). Effects of fetal hemoglobin on accurate measurements of oxygen saturation in neonates. *J Perinat Neonatal Nurs, 19*, 348.

174. Simpson, S. J., Hall, G. L., & Wilson, A. C. (2015). Lung function following very preterm birth in the era of 'new' bronchopulmonary dysplasia. *Respirology, 20*, 535.

175. Singh, N., et al. (2015). Comparison of animal-derived surfactants for the prevention and treatment of respiratory distress syndrome in preterm infants. *Cochrane Database Syst Rev, 2015*(12), CD010249.

176. Sluiter, I., et al. (2011). Vascular abnormalities in human newborns with pulmonary hypertension. *Expert Rev Respir Med, 5*, 245.

177. Sokol, G. M., Konduri, G. G., & Van Meurs, K. P. (2016). Inhaled nitric oxide therapy for pulmonary disorders of the term and preterm infant. *Semin Perinatol, 40*, 356.

178. Soliz, J., & Joseph, V. (2005). Perinatal steroid exposure and respiratory control during early postnatal life. *Respir Physiol Neurobiol, 149*, 111.

179. Stenmark, K. R., & Abman, S. H. (2005). Lung vascular development: Implications for the pathogenesis of bronchopulmonary dysplasia. *Annu Rev Physiol, 67*, 623.

180. Stenson, B. J. (2016). Oxygen saturation targets for extremely preterm infants after the NeOProM Trials. *Neonatology, 109*, 352.

181. Stevens, T. P., et al. (2007). Early surfactant administration with brief ventilation vs. selective surfactant and continued mechanical ventilation for preterm infants with or at risk for respiratory distress syndrome. *Cochrane Database Syst Rev, 2007*(4), CD003063.

182. Subramaniam, P., Ho, J. J., & Davis, P. G. (2016). Prophylactic nasal continuous positive airway pressure for preventing morbidity and mortality in very preterm infants. *Cochrane Database Syst Rev, 2016*(6), CD001243.

183. Supcun, S., et al. (2010). Caffeine increases cerebral cortical activity in preterm infants. *J Pediatr, 156*, 490.

184. SUPPORT Study Group of the Eunice Kennedy Shriver NICHD Neonatal Research Network. (2010). Early CPAP versus surfactant in extremely preterm infants. *N Engl J Med, 362*, 1970.

185. Suresh, G. K., et al. (2017). Pharmacological therapies I: surfactants. In J. P. Goldsmith, et al. (Eds.), *Assisted ventilation of the newborn* (6th ed.). Philadelphia: Elsevier.

186. Swanson, J. R., & Sinkin, R. A. (2015). Transition from fetus to newborn. *Pediatr Clin North Am, 62*, 329.

187. Tan, A., et al. (2005). Air versus oxygen for resuscitation of infants at birth. *Cochrane Database Syst Rev, 2005*(2), CD002273.

188. Tan, E. K., & Tan, E. L. (2013). Alterations in physiology and anatomy during pregnancy. *Best Pract Res Clin Obstet Gynaecol, 27*, 791.

189. Tegethoff, M., et al. (2013). Asthma during pregnancy and clinical outcomes in offspring: a national cohort study. *Pediatrics, 132*, 483.

190. Tomimatsu, T., et al. (2013). Maternal carbon dioxide level during labor and its possible effect on fetal cerebral oxygenation: mini review. *J Obstet Gynaecol Res, 39*, 1.

191. Trabalon, M., & Schaal, B. (2012). It takes a mouth to eat and a nose to breathe: abnormal oral respiration affects neonates' oral competence and systemic adaptation. *Int J Pediatr, 2012*, 207605. Epub 2012 July 3.

192. Truog, W. E., & Kinsella, J. P. (2017). Pulmonary gas exchange in the developing lung. In R. A. Polin, et al. (Eds.), *Fetal and neonatal physiology* (5th ed.). Philadelphia: Saunders.

193. Turner, B. S., Bradshaw, W., & Brandon, D. (2005). Neonatal lung remodeling: Structural, inflammatory, and ventilator-induced injury. *J Perinat Neonatal Nurs, 19*, 362.

194. van Vonderen, J. J., et al. (2014). Measuring physiological changes during the transition to life after birth. *Neonatology, 105*, 230.

195. Vardavas, C. I., et al. (2010). Smoking and smoking cessation during early pregnancy and its effect on adverse pregnancy outcomes and fetal growth. *Eur J Pediatr, 169*, 741.

196. Vento, M., et al. (2009). Preterm resuscitation with low oxygen causes less oxidative stress, inflammation, and chronic lung disease. *Pediatrics, 124*, 439.

197. Vento, M., & Saugstad, O. D. (2011). Oxygen supplementation in the delivery room: Updated information. *J Pediatr, 158*, e5.

198. Verklan, M. T. (2006). Persistent pulmonary hypertension of the newborn: not a honeymoon anymore. *J Perinat Neonatal Nurs, 20*, 108.

199. Vogel, E. R., et al. (2015). Perinatal oxygen in the developing lung. *Can J Physiol Pharmacol, 93*, 119.

200. Wambach, J. A., & Hamvas, A. (2015). Respiratory distress syndrome in the neonate. In R. J. Martin, A. A. Fanaroff, & M. C. Walsh (Eds.), *Fanaroff and Martin's Neonatal-perinatal medicine: Diseases of the fetus and infant* (10th ed.). Philadelphia: Saunders.

201. Watterberg, K. L., & American Academy of Pediatrics Committee on Fetus and Newborn. (2010). Policy Statement: Postnatal corticosteroids to prevent or treat bronchopulmonary dysplasia. *Pediatrics, 126*, 800.

202. Weiner, G. M., et al. (2016). *Textbook of neonatal resuscitation* (7th ed.). Elk Grove Village, IL: American Academy of Pediatrics.

203. Wert, S. E. (2017). Normal and abnormal structural development of the lung. In R. A. Polin, et al. (Eds.), *Fetal and neonatal physiology* (5th ed.). Philadelphia: Saunders.

204. West, J. B., & Luks, A. M. (2017). *West's pulmonary pathophysiology: the essentials* (9th ed.). Philadelphia: Wolters Kluwar.

205. Whitelaw, A., & Thoresen, M. (2000). Antenatal steroids and the developing brain. *Arch Dis Child Fetal Neonatal Ed, 83*, F154.

206. Whitsett, J. A. (2010). Review: the intersection of surfactant homeostasis and innate host defense of the lung: Lessons from newborn infants. *Innate Immun, 16*, 138.

207. Whitsett, J. A., Wert, S. E., & Weaver, T. E. (2010). Alveolar surfactant homeostasis and the pathogenesis of pulmonary disease. *Annu Rev Med, 61*, 105.

208. Whitsett, J. A. (2017). Surfactant homeostasis: composition and function of pulmonary surfactant lipids and proteins. In R. A. Polin, et al. (Eds.), *Fetal and neonatal physiology* (5th ed.). Philadelphia: Saunders.

209. Whitty, J. E., & Dombrowski, M. P. (2014). Respiratory diseases in pregnancy. In R. K. Creasy, et al. (Eds.), *Creasy & Resnik's Maternal-fetal medicine: Principles and practice* (7th ed.). Philadelphia: Saunders.

210. Widmaier, E., et al. (2016). *Vander's Human physiology: The mechanism of body function* (14th ed.). New York: McGraw-Hill Education.

211. Wilson-Costello, D., et al. (2009). Impact of postnatal corticosteroid use on neurodevelopment at 18 to 22 months' adjusted age: Effects of dose, timing, and risk of bronchopulmonary dysplasia in extremely low birth weight infants. *Pediatrics, 123*, e430.

212. Wise, R. A., Polito, A. J., & Krishnan, V. (2006). Respiratory physiologic changes in pregnancy. *Immunol Allergy Clin North Am, 26*, 1.

213. Wong, M. K., et al. (2015). Adverse effects of perinatal nicotine exposure on reproductive outcomes. *Reproduction, 150*, R185.

214. Wyckoff, M. H., et al. (2015). Part 13: Neonatal resuscitation: 2015 American Heart Association guidelines update for cardiopulmonary resuscitation and emergency cardiovascular care. *Circulation, 132*, S543.

215. Yarbrough, M. L., Grenache, D. G., & Gronowski, A. M. (2014). Fetal lung maturity testing: the end of an era. *Biomark Med, 8*, 509.

Renal System and Fluid and Electrolyte Homeostasis

The kidneys are critical organs in maintaining body homeostasis by regulation of water and electrolyte balance, excretion of metabolic waste products and foreign substances, regulation of vitamin D activity and erythrocyte production (via erythropoietin), and gluconeogenesis.[150] The kidneys also have an important role in control of arterial blood pressure through the renin-angiotensin system and regulation of sodium balance. This chapter examines the alterations in basic renal processes and regulation of fluids and electrolytes observed in the pregnant woman, fetus, and neonate and discusses the implications of these changes for clinical practice. Basic renal processes include glomerular filtration, tubular secretion and tubular reabsorption. These process are summarized in Figure 11-1.

MATERNAL PHYSIOLOGIC ADAPTATIONS

The renal system undergoes a variety of structural and functional changes during pregnancy, with many of the structural changes persisting well into the postpartum period. Pregnancy is characterized by sodium retention and increased extracellular volume, which are mediated by alterations in renal function. Many parameters normally used to evaluate renal function and fluid and electrolyte homeostasis are altered in pregnancy, and subclinical renal problems may not be easily recognized.

Antepartum Period

The renal system must handle the effects of increased maternal intravascular and extracellular volume and metabolic waste products and serve as the primary excretory organ for fetal wastes. Changes in the renal system are related to hormonal effects (particularly the influence of progesterone on smooth muscle), pressure from the enlarging uterus, effects of position and activity, and alterations in the cardiovascular system and vasoactive substances. Cardiovascular system changes that interact with alterations in renal hemodynamics include increased cardiac output, increased blood and plasma volume, and alterations in the venous system and plasma proteins (see Chapters 8 and 9). The predominant structural change in the renal system during pregnancy is dilation of the renal pelvis and ureters; functional changes include alterations in hemodynamics, glomerular filtration, and tubular handling of certain substances. Changes in fluid and electrolyte homeostasis result from changes in renal handling of water and sodium and alterations in the renin-angiotensin system. Table 11-1 summarizes changes in the renal system during pregnancy and their clinical implications. Even with these changes, renal reserve is maintained during pregnancy, so that the pregnant woman has the capacity for further vasodilation and filtration above baseline if needed.

Structural Changes

Pregnancy is characterized by physiologic hydroureter and hydronephrosis. Significant dilation of the renal calyces, pelvis, and ureters beginning as early as the seventh week is seen in up to 80% of women.[14,41,66,92,105] The mean kidney length increases by approximately 1 cm because of the increased renal blood flow (RBF), renal vascular volume, and renal hypertrophy.[18,54,92] Renal volume increases by 30%.[66,92] The diameter of the ureteral lumen increases, with hypertonicity and hypomotility of the ureteral musculature seen in more than 80% of pregnant women.[92] Hypomotility and reduced peristaltic movements of the ureters may be mediated by prostaglandin E_2 (PGE_2).[14,42]

The ureters elongate and become more tortuous, especially during the last half of pregnancy as they are laterally displaced by the growing uterus.[14] These changes are seen within the renal pelvis and the upper portion of the ureters to the pelvic brim. The portion of the ureters below the pelvic brim (linea terminalis) is usually not enlarged. The ureters may contain as much as 300 mL of urine by the third trimester.[18,42] This reservoir of urine leads to stasis and can interfere with evaluation of the glomerular filtration rate (GFR) and tubular function and can influence the accuracy of 24-hour urine collections.[92,105] The stasis increases the risk of ascending urinary tract infection (UTI), nephrolithiasis, and pyelonephrosis.[41,55,57,92,105]

The etiology of physiologic hydroureter is unclear. Dilation begins before the uterus reaches the pelvic brim, so initial changes are probably hormonally mediated. Hormonal influences, particularly progesterone, may induce hypertrophy of the longitudinal smooth muscles surrounding distal portions of the ureters and hyperplasia of periurethral connective tissue.[14,42,92]

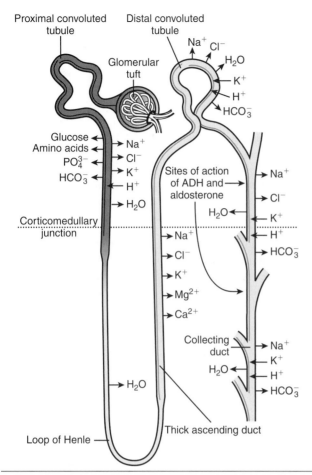

FIGURE 11-1   The nephron. Substances enter the tubule from the blood via glomerular filtration or tubular secretion and are reabsorbed back into the blood by tubular reabsorption. Any substances that are not reabsorbed are lost in the urine. Water is reabsorbed in the proximal tubule together with glucose, amino acids, phosphate, sodium, and bicarbonate and from the distal tubule under the influence of arginine vasopressin and the hypertonic medulla. In the distal tubule, sodium is reabsorbed under the influence of aldosterone with associated tubular secretion of potassium and hydrogen ions. (From Modi, N. [2005]. Fluid and electrolyte balance. In J.M. Rennie. [Ed.]. *Roberton's textbook of neonatology* [4th ed.]. Edinburgh: Churchill Livingstone, as adapted from Cumming, A.D. & Swanson, C.P. [1995]. Disturbances in water, electrolyte and acid-base balance. In C.R.W. Edwards, I.A.D. Bouchier, C. Haslett, & E.R. Chilvers. [Eds.]. *Davidson's principles and practices of medicine.* Edinburgh: Churchill Livingstone.)

This may lead to a temporary stenosis and mild dilation of the upper portion of the ureters. These findings are similar to those seen in women taking oral contraceptives and in postmenopausal women taking estrogen and progesterone.[42]

A major contributing factor to hydronephrosis in later pregnancy is probably external compression of the ureters at the pelvic brim. As pregnancy progresses, the ureters are compressed at the pelvic brim by the iliac arteries, enlarging ovarian vein complexes, and the growing uterus, leading to further marked dilation and urinary stasis.[18,40] Dilation is more prominent in a primipara, whose firmer

abdominal wall may increase resistance and pressure on the ureters.[14]

In most women, the right ureter is dilated to a greater extent than the left.[40,66,92] These differences become more prominent after midgestation.[40] The right ureter makes a right-angle turn as it crosses the iliac and ovarian veins at the pelvic brim; the turn of the left ureter is less acute, and it parallels rather than crosses the left ovarian vein.[18,61] The iliac vessels are more rigid on the right than on the left, thus further compressing the ureter. Compression is maximal by around 30 weeks' gestation, with no further significant changes to term. The sigmoid colon contributes to dextroversion of the uterus and may increase ureteral compression on the contralateral side during the last trimester.[14,42,66,92] The position of the fetus does not seem to influence ureteral dilation. The site of placental attachment may increase venous flow on that side with subsequent compression of the ureter by the dilated vessels.[42]

Bladder tone has been shown to decrease in most studies as a result of the effects of progesterone on smooth muscle.[92] Bladder capacity doubles by term. The bladder becomes displaced anteriorly and superiorly by the end of the second trimester.[43] Under the influence of estrogen, the trigone undergoes hyperplasia with hypertrophy of the bladder musculature. The bladder mucosa becomes hyperemic with increased size and tortuosity of the blood vessels. The mucosa becomes more edematous and vulnerable to trauma or infection after engagement of the presenting part.[42]

The baseline intravesical pressure doubles because of the enlarged uterus.[86] The decreased bladder tone and flaccidity may lead to incompetence of the vesicoureteral valve and reflux of urine. Vesicoureteral reflux is seen in up to 3.5% of pregnant women, especially in the third trimester.[86] Predisposing factors for this reflux include hypertrophy and hyperplasia of the ureteral wall, increased elasticity of the ureters, increased bladder pressure, and decreased peristalsis in the distal ureter.[86] Alterations in bladder placement by the growing uterus stretch the trigone and displace the intravesical portion of the ureters laterally. This shortens the terminal ureter, decreasing intravesical pressure. If intravesical pressure subsequently increases with micturition, urine regurgitates into the ureters.[42]

Urodynamic Changes

Urine output increases from a mean of 1475 to 1919 mL per 24 hours, primarily because of changes in sodium excretion; polyuria (more than 3 L/day), however, is rare.[18,86] Mean flow rate decreases in the second and third trimesters with an increase in flow time and time to maximal flow throughout pregnancy.[86] The number of voids per day and mean daily urine output increase throughout gestation.[143] Studies of changes in bladder capacity during pregnancy have reported variable findings. Some have found a mean bladder capacity similar to that of the nonpregnant state in the first two trimesters, but decreased capacity in the third trimester because of elevation of the trigone and the size of the presenting part.[110] Another study reported that the pregnant woman's bladder has a larger capacity with a lower pressure per volume.[119] In nonpregnant women

TABLE 11-1   Changes in the Renal System During Pregnancy

PARAMETER	ALTERATION	SIGNIFICANCE
Renal calyces, pelvis, and ureters	Dilation (more prominent on right)	Increased risk of urinary tract infection in pregnancy and postpartum
	Elongation, decreased motility, and hypertonicity of ureter	Altered accuracy of 24-hour urine collections
	May last up to 3 months postpartum	Increased risk of urinary tract infection in pregnancy
		Increased risk of urinary tract infection postpartum
Bladder	Decreased tone, increased capacity	Increased risk of urinary tract infection
		Urinary frequency and incontinence
		Alteration in accuracy of 24-hour urine collections
	Displaced in late pregnancy	Urinary frequency
	Mucosa edematous and hyperemic	Risk of trauma and infection
	Incompetence of vesicoureteral valve	Risk of reflux and infection
		Alteration in accuracy of 24-hour urine collections
Renal blood flow	Increases up to 60%–80% by mid–second trimester, then decreases to term	Increased glomerular filtration rate
		Increased solutes delivered to kidney
Glomerular filtration rate	Increases 40%–60%	Increased filtration and excretion of water and solutes
		Increased urine flow and volume
		Decreased serum blood urea nitrogen, creatinine, uric acid
		Altered renal excretion of drugs with risk of subtherapeutic blood and tissue levels
Renal tubular function	Increased reabsorption of solutes (may not always match increase in filtered load)	Maintenance of homeostasis
		Avoidance of pathologic solute or fluid loss
	Increased renal excretion of glucose, protein, amino acids, urea, uric acid, water-soluble vitamins, calcium, hydrogen ions, phosphorus, bicarbonate	Tendency for glycosuria, proteinuria
		Compensation for respiratory alkalosis
		Increased nutritional needs (i.e., calcium, water-soluble vitamins)
		Decreased serum bicarbonate levels
	Net retention of sodium and water	Accumulation of sodium and water to meet maternal and fetal needs
Renin-angiotensin-aldosterone system	Increase in all components	Maintenance of homeostasis with expanded extracellular volume
		Retention of water and sodium
	Resistance to pressor effects of angiotensin II	Balance forces favoring sodium excretion
		Maintenance of normal blood pressure
Arginine vasopressin and regulation of osmolarity	Osmostat reset at lower baseline osmolarity	Expansion of plasma volume and other extracellular volume
		Maintenance of volume homeostasis despite reduction in plasma osmolarity

the first urge to void was at a bladder capacity of 150 to 200 mL and maximum at 450 to 550 mL, with an intravesicular pressure of 20 cm H_2O (1.96 kPa); in pregnant women the first urge to void was at a bladder capacity of 250 to 400 mL (intravesical pressure of 4 to 8 cm H_2O [0.39 to 0.78 kPa]) and often did not reach maximum until 1000 to 1200 mL (intravesicular pressure of 12 to 15 cm H_2O [1.17 to 1.47 kPa]).[119]

Changes in Renal Hemodynamics

Significant hemodynamic changes occur within the kidneys beginning early in pregnancy in conjunction with systemic vasodilation (see Chapter 9). RBF and GFR increase. Increases in these parameters, although not to the degree seen in pregnancy, also occur during the luteal phase of the menstrual cycle, when progesterone peaks.[61,66]

RBF increases by up to 60% to 80% by the mid–second trimester and then slowly decreases to term.[92] Higher values are seen in the left lateral recumbent position (time of maximal venous return).[20] This change is accompanied by increased GFR, decreased renal vascular resistance (RVR), and activation of the renin-angiotensin-aldosterone (RAA) system. Renal hemodynamic changes begin before significant expansion of plasma volume and are thought to be primarily related to the decrease in systemic vascular resistance (SVR), which may stimulate decreased RVR leading to increased RBF and GFR, and by sodium retention.[21] These changes may be mediated by nitric oxide (NO), prostacyclin (PGI_2), atrial natriuretic factor (ANF), progesterone, endothelin B, vascular endothelial growth factor (VEGF), and relaxin (initially produced by the corpus luteum), possibly via their effects on GFR. Increased flow is enhanced by vasodilation of preglomerular and postglomerular capillaries.[18,20,61,66,92,105] Another measure of renal hemodynamics is the effective renal plasma flow (ERPF), which increases 80% by midpregnancy.[27,92,142] ERPF then gradually decreases during the third trimester to values 50% greater than nonpregnant values.[54,92] Attenuation of angiotensin II vasoconstrictor action occurs in both systemic and renal circulations. Progesterone and VEGF increase angiotensin II refractiveness.[21,61]

Changes in Glomerular Filtration

The GFR increases 40% to 60% (average around 50%) during pregnancy.[18,22,54,77,92] The rise begins as early as 6 weeks and precedes plasma volume expansion and changes in cardiac output (see Chapter 9).[77] Changes in GFR are detectable 3 to 4 weeks after conception, with 25% of the increase occurring by 2 weeks postconception; peak in the first trimester; and then remain relatively stable to near term.[92] Values for GFR in pregnancy, as measured by creatinine clearance, average 110 to 150 mL/minute.[92] Differences in reported values for RBF and GFR during pregnancy vary with the method of measurement. The increased GFR is related to the increased glomerular blood flow (and glomerular capillary hydrostatic pressure) and decreased colloid osmotic (plasma oncotic) pressure (because of a reduction in the concentration of plasma proteins).[18,58,61,77] Failure of the GFR to increase early in pregnancy has been associated with pregnancy loss.[151]

The increases in RPF and GFR parallel each other, although RPF changes are slightly greater than GFR changes. This alters the filtration fraction (GFR/RPF), the portion of the RBF that is filtered.[57,61,66,92] The filtration fraction is decreased in the first half of gestation and increased in late gestation as ERPF decreases, but GFR remains elevated.[61,66,77] As a result, renal excretion of amino acids, glucose, protein, electrolytes, and vitamins increases, whereas serum urea, creatinine, blood urea nitrogen (BUN), and uric acid levels decrease (Table 11-2).

The causes of the increased GFR during pregnancy are still not completely clear, but the primary factor is the increased RPF and decreased afferent and efferent RVR.[21,77] These changes are stimulated by relaxin (which upregulates vascular gelatinase activity and leads to activation of endothelin receptors, causing vasodilation), increased GFR, and relaxation of the small renal arteries. This process is mediated by NO, which is a potent renal vasodilator.[28,77] Other factors that may play a role are prostacyclin, ANF, human chorionic somatomammotropin (also called *human placental lactogen*), and human chorionic gonadotropin, which stimulates relaxin secretion.[20,28]

During pregnancy, 24-hour urine volumes are higher because of the increased GFR. The degree to which renal handling of substances is altered during pregnancy depends on the renal processes involved (see Figure 11-1). For example, because urea and creatinine are processed only by glomerular filtration, the increased GFR leads to a significant decrease in serum urea and creatinine levels.[77,92]

The increased RBF and GFR alter renal excretion of drugs (see Chapter 7).[72,137] In addition, activity of renal drug transporters, such as p-glycoprotein, organic cation transporter, and organic anion transporter is increased during pregnancy and may also alter renal clearance of drugs and dosing for some drugs.[137]

Alterations in Tubular Function

The elevated GFR increases the concentration of solutes and volume of fluid within the tubular lumen by 50% to 100%. Tubular reabsorption increases to prevent rapid depletion from the body of sodium, chloride, glucose, potassium, and water. There is actually a net retention of most of these substances during pregnancy. Conversely, tubular reabsorption rates cannot always accommodate the increased filtered load. This results in increased excretion of substances such as glucose and amino acids. Alterations in GFR and tubular function result in altered plasma values of many substances during pregnancy (see Table 11-2).

Renal glucose excretion increases soon after conception and remains high to term. Urinary glucose values may be 10- to 100-fold greater than the nonpregnant values of 20 to 100 mg per 24 hours because of alterations in reabsorption of glucose in the loop of Henle and collecting ducts.[27,92] Glycosuria is more common during pregnancy and can vary from day to day and within any 24-hour period. Glycosuria is discussed in Evaluation of Renal Function During Pregnancy.

Excretion of amino acids, urea, and protein increases in pregnancy. Protein excretion rises from less than 100 mg per 24 hours to up to 250 to 300 mg per 24 hours, with marked day-to-day variation.[27,54] The primary amino acids that have increased excretion throughout pregnancy are alanine, glycine, histidine, serine, and threonine; excretion of cysteine, leucine, lysine, phenylalanine, taurine, and tyrosine increases in early pregnancy but decreases later.[92] Increased urea clearance leads to decreased plasma urea nitrogen levels by 8 to 10 weeks.[27] Plasma urea levels may be only 63% of nonpregnant values by the third trimester.

Proteinuria is more common during pregnancy, with increases in both total protein and urinary albumin.[18,66] The

TABLE 11-2 Changes in Laboratory Values Associated With Renal Function During Pregnancy

VARIABLE	NONPREGNANT VALUES	VALUES DURING PREGNANCY	VALUES REQUIRING FURTHER INVESTIGATION
Creatinine clearance	85–120 mL/min	110–150 mL/min	
Plasma creatinine	0.65 ± 0.14 mg/dL	0.46 ± 0.13 mg/dL	>0.80 mg/dL
Blood urea nitrogen	13 ± 3 mg/dL	8.7 ± 1.5 mg/dL	>14 mg/dL
Urinary protein	<100–150 mg/24 hours	<250–300 mg/24 hours	>300 mg/24 hours
Urinary glucose	20–100 mg/24 hours	>100 mg/24 hours (up to 10 g/24 hours)	
Plasma urate	4–6 mg/dL	2.5–4 mg/dL	>5.8 mg/dL
Urinary amino acids		Up to 2 g/24 hours	>2 g/24 hours

filtered load of amino acids during pregnancy may exceed tubular reabsorptive capacity with small amounts of protein lost in the urine. Values of 1+ protein on dipsticks are common and do not necessarily indicate the presence of glomerular pathology or preeclampsia.[3] Urinary protein excretion during pregnancy is not considered abnormal until values exceed 300 mg per 24 hours (which is twice the normal limit in nonpregnant women).[55,66,92,105] Protein excretion does not correlate with the severity of renal disease, and increased protein excretion in a pregnant woman with known renal disease does not necessarily indicate progression of the disease.[27] However, proteinuria associated with hypertension in pregnant women is associated with a greater risk of an adverse pregnancy outcome.[55,140]

Uric acid is normally handled by filtration, secretion, and reabsorption (see Figure 11-1), so less than 10% of the filtered load appears in urine. During pregnancy, filtration of uric acid increases up to 30% in the first 16 weeks, and net reabsorption is decreased and secretion enhanced.[151] As a result, serum uric acid levels decrease up to 25% to 35%, beginning as early as 8 weeks, to a nadir of 2 to 3 mg/dL by 24 weeks.[18,66,92] Levels gradually increase toward nonpregnant values after that point as tubular reabsorption of uric acid increases.[18] This increase may also be a result of the rise in RPF that alters the filtration fraction at this stage of gestation.[27,92] In women with preeclampsia, uric acid clearance is reduced with higher serum levels.[66]

Potassium excretion is stable with changes in tubular reabsorption reflecting alterations in the filtered load.[18] Retention of an additional 300 to 350 mEq is believed to be related to increased proximal tubular reabsorption.[77,92] Serum potassium levels do not rise, because the additional potassium is used for maternal tissues and by the fetus. The mechanisms for potassium retention in pregnancy are not well documented. These changes occur despite the increase in aldosterone that normally would increase urinary potassium loss. Therefore the altered potassium excretion may be a result of antagonistic action of progesterone on renal tubular actions of aldosterone.[18,77]

Renal acid-base balance is altered to compensate for the respiratory alkalosis that develops secondary to an increased loss of carbon dioxide from changes in ventilation during pregnancy (see Chapter 10). The respiratory alkalosis is compensated for by increased renal loss of bicarbonate. This is accomplished by renal retention of H^+ ions and a decrease in serum bicarbonate. As a result, serum bicarbonate levels fall 4 to 5 mEq/L (mmol/L) during the first trimester to 20 to 22 mEq/L (mmol/L).[54,105] This change may limit buffering capacity in the pregnant woman.[66]

Urinary calcium excretion is increased, possibly because of the increased GFR, and serum calcium and phosphorus levels decrease. This calcium loss is balanced by increased intestinal absorption of calcium, so serum ionic calcium levels remain stable (see Chapter 17).[92] To maintain homeostasis and meet fetal demands, women need 1200 mg of calcium per day in their diet. Excretion of water-soluble vitamins also increases, so maternal diet must be evaluated to ensure adequate supplies of vitamins B_1, B_2, B_6, and C; folate; and niacin (see Chapter 12).

Fluid and Electrolyte Homeostasis

Pregnant women must retain additional fluid and electrolytes to meet their needs and those of the growing fetus. To do this, renal excretory responses are modified and a new balance achieved. Because fluid and electrolyte balance is mediated predominantly by sodium and water homeostasis, pregnancy changes primarily involve alterations in these substances. The hormonal systems involved in regulation of sodium and water homeostasis, such as the arginine vasopressin (AVP) and RAA systems, must also be altered to react appropriately to the new equilibrium.

Sodium Homeostasis. The filtered load of sodium increases up to 50% as a result of the increased GFR. A nonpregnant woman filters approximately 20,000 mEq of sodium per day; a pregnant woman filters 30,000.[28,92] To prevent excessive urinary sodium loss, tubular reabsorption of sodium also increases so that 99% of the filtered sodium is reabsorbed. As a result, there is a net retention of 900 to 950 mEq (2 to 6 mEq/day) of sodium during pregnancy.[27,28,66,92] Sodium retention occurs gradually, with an increase in late pregnancy.[28] Much of the sodium is used by the fetus and placenta; the rest is distributed in maternal blood and extracellular fluid (ECF) (Table 11-3).[151] Decreases in maternal serum sodium are thought to be a result of vasodilation, arteriole underfilling, release of arginine vasopressin (stimulated by relaxin), and increased β-human chorionic gonadotropin.[18]

Despite these alterations, the pregnant woman remains in sodium balance and responds normally to changes in both sodium and water balance. The specific mechanisms for sodium retention during pregnancy are unclear. The maintenance of sodium balance during pregnancy is multifactorial and related to a balance (Figure 11-2) between natriuretic factors favoring sodium excretion (increased GFR, decreased RVR, decreased plasma oncotic pressure, decreased serum albumin, vasodilating prostaglandins, increased ANF, and the diureticlike and aldosterone-antagonistic actions of progesterone) and antinatriuretic factors favoring sodium conservation (increased renin, aldosterone, deoxycorticosterone, human chorionic somatomammotropin, and estrogen).[18,21,92,150,151] ANF is released by the atrial

TABLE 11-3	Storage of Sodium During Pregnancy
STORAGE SITE	**SODIUM (MEQ [MMOL/L])**
Fetus	290
Edema fluid	240
Plasma	140
Amniotic fluid	100
Uterus	80
Placenta	57
Breasts	35
Red cells	5
Total	947

From Sullivan, C.A. & Martin, J.N. (1994). Sodium and pregnancy. *Clin Obstet Gynecol, 37,* 558.

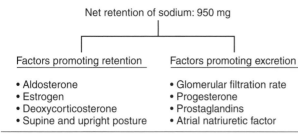

Net retention of sodium: 950 mg

Factors promoting retention	Factors promoting excretion
• Aldosterone	• Glomerular filtration rate
• Estrogen	• Progesterone
• Deoxycorticosterone	• Prostaglandins
• Supine and upright posture	• Atrial natriuretic factor

FIGURE 11-2   Factors influencing the regulation of sodium excretion in pregnancy. (From Monga, M. [2014]. Maternal cardiovascular and renal adaptation to pregnancy. In R.K. Creasy, R. Resnik, J.D. Iams, C.J. Lockwood, T.R. Moore, & M.F. Greene. [Eds.]. *Maternal-fetal medicine* [5th ed.]. Philadelphia: Saunders.)

endothelial lining and increases early in pregnancy. ANF opposes the action of progesterone and inhibits the RAA system, thus stimulating sodium loss. Relaxin also mediates sodium balance during pregnancy. Relaxin is associated with osmoregulatory changes, vasodilation, and increased GFR.[20,105] As a result of these changes, sodium retention in pregnancy is proportional to water accumulation, and the woman remains in homeostatic balance.

Renin-Angiotensin-Aldosterone System

The RAA system is important in fluid and electrolyte homeostasis and maintaining arterial blood pressure (Figure 11-3 and Box 11-1) and is markedly altered during pregnancy.

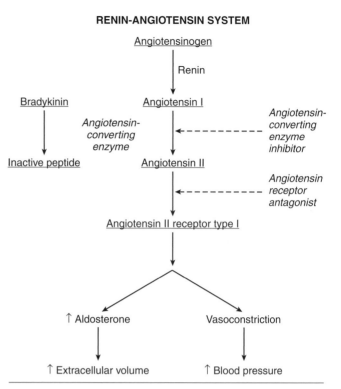

RENIN-ANGIOTENSIN SYSTEM

FIGURE 11-3   Renin-angiotensin-aldosterone system. (From Quan, A. [2006]. Fetopathy associated with exposure to angiotensin-converting enzyme inhibitors and angiotensin receptor antagonists. *Early Hum Dev, 82,* 23.)

BOX 11-1   Renin-Angiotensin-Aldosterone System

The renin-angiotensin-aldosterone system has key roles in blood pressure regulation and fluid and electrolyte homeostasis. Angiotensinogen (plasma renin substrate) is produced in the liver and is always present in the blood. Renin is a proteolytic enzyme found in blood in active and inactive forms. Renin is secreted and stored primarily in the juxtaglomerular cells surrounding afferent arterioles of cortical nephron glomeruli. Renin is also synthesized in extrarenal sites such as the brain, vascular smooth muscle, the genital tract, and the fetoplacental unit. Stretch receptors in the juxtaglomerular cells sense changes in renal perfusion and afferent arteriole pressures and increase renin release.

Renin release is also influenced by the sympathetic nervous system and concentrations of circulating potassium, angiotensin II, and possibly sodium. Renin acts on angiotensinogen to form angiotensin I, whose actions include stimulating catecholamine release, facilitating norepinephrine release from peripheral sympathetic veins, and reducing renal blood flow in the cortex and the medulla. A measure of the capacity of plasma renin to generate angiotensin I is plasma renin activity (PRA). Angiotensin I is broken down by angiotensin-converting enzyme (ACE) to angiotensin II in the pulmonary circulation. Angiotensin II is a potent vasoconstrictor that stimulates adrenal production and release of aldosterone and constriction of the renal vasculature to reduce glomerular filtration rate (GFR) and the effective renal plasma flow (ERPF). Angiotensin II helps to maintain the arterial blood pressure and peripheral perfusion. Atrial natriuretic factor (ANF) also influences blood pressure and

stimulates urinary sodium excretion. Other angiotensin peptides (III, IV, 1–9, 1–7) are also found, each with various roles; angiotensin II is the most potent.[63,81]

Angiotensin 1 receptors (AT$_1$R) are found on vascular smooth muscle, adrenal gland, and other tissues. Simulation of AT$_1$ receptors by angiotensin II increases intracellular calcium leading to increased vasoconstriction, sympathetic activity, and aldosterone synthesis and release.[64,81] AT$_1$R are also involved in angiogenesis and cell proliferation.[81] Binding of angiotensin II to AT$_1$R leads to G protein activation, increased intracellular Ca++, and vasoconstriction.[63] AT$_2$R receptors are found in the fetal kidney and mediate vasodilation and apoptosis.[81] Binding of angiotensin II to AT$_2$R leads to vasodilation. Stimulation of angiotensin II receptors enhances fetal renal development.[64]

Aldosterone is a mineralocorticoid secreted by the outer zona glomerulosa cells of the adrenal cortex. The two major activities of aldosterone are regulation of extracellular fluid (ECF) balance by altering sodium retention and excretion and regulation of potassium. Aldosterone regulates fluid volume via a direct effect on renal distal tubular transport of sodium to increase sodium reabsorption and decrease potassium reabsorption. As sodium is reabsorbed, potassium and hydrogen ions are secreted into the tubular lumen. Increased reabsorption of sodium results in increased water retention, because water is passively reabsorbed along with the sodium, thus increasing body ECF volume. Aldosterone is regulated via feedback mechanisms involving potassium and ECF volume.[64,136,150]

Changes in this system in the ovary, placenta, and decidua are also seen during pregnancy and are important in ovulation, implantation, placentation, and uteroplacental circulation.[81] Pregnancy is characterized by increases in components of the RAA system and decreased sensitivity to the pressor effects of angiotensin II.[6,146] Changes in most of these components peak at 30 to 32 weeks. The changes are mediated by estrogens, progesterone, prostaglandins, and alterations in the renal processing of sodium.[52] Although the RAA system is altered during pregnancy, this system responds normally, but at a new set point, to interventions that alter volume such as salt restriction, diuretics, and positional changes.[76]

Action of the RAA system depends on available renin and angiotensinogen.[81] During pregnancy, major sites for renin production include the uterus, placenta, and fetus as well as the kidneys.[18] Renin peaks at levels two to three times or more higher than normal during the first trimester and remains elevated, with a tendency to reach a plateau by about 32 weeks.[81] The increase in renin is primarily a result of increased inactive renin; however, both active renin and plasma renin activity (PRA) (a measure of the capacity of plasma to generate angiotensin I) also increase.[52,81,136] PRA increases 4- to 10-fold during the first trimester, peaking at 12 weeks, and then remaining high to term, with a possible decrease in the third trimester noted by some investigators.[136]

Renin release is stimulated by estrogens (which also increase concentrations of angiotensinogen), decreased blood pressure, increased levels of plasma and urinary PGE, and the aldosterone-antagonizing effects of progesterone.[6,136] Increases in plasma renin are also seen during the latter part of the secretory phase of the menstrual cycle, peaking at twice normal levels with the luteinizing hormone surge and persisting until midway into the luteal phase. These changes coincide with progesterone release.

Angiotensinogen (plasma renin substrate) levels double by 8 to 10 weeks, increase twofold to threefold by 20 weeks, and peak at 30 to 32 weeks.[6,81] This increase is a result of the effects of estrogen on the liver, which synthesizes this substrate. Low angiotensinogen levels are associated with spontaneous abortion and may reflect reduced placental estrogen production.

Angiotensin-converting enzyme (ACE) levels may be similar or slightly lower than nonpregnant values, although increases after 30 weeks have been reported. ACE levels are also high in the uterus and placenta.[6] Angiotensin II increases early in pregnancy, stimulated by estrogen-induced increases in angiotensinogen levels, and peaks at two to three times nonpregnant levels by 30 weeks.[81] Angiotensin II levels may fall in the third trimester but are still above nonpregnant values. Increased angiotensin II during pregnancy is important in maintaining circulating blood volume, systemic blood pressure and uteroplacental blood flow by interacting with angiotensin II receptors and by alterations in these receptors.[81] Increased systemic angiotensin II increases renal angiotensin II and aldosterone leading to increased sodium reabsorption and plasma volume expansion.[81] Another angiotensin form, angiotensin (1-7) is also elevated during pregnancy. This vasodilating peptide downregulates angiotensin I receptor (AT_1R) activity and upregulates angiotensin II receptor, VEGF, and NO activity.[81]

Plasma aldosterone levels are significantly increased by 8 weeks and reach levels four to six times higher than those in nonpregnant women by the third trimester.[28,54,84,136] Aldosterone increases again late in gestation, peaking at about 36 weeks at levels 8 to 10 times higher than nonpregnant values. The increased aldosterone opposes the sodium-losing effects of progesterone and allows a progressive accumulation of sodium in maternal and fetal tissues.

Despite these changes, the pregnant woman remains responsive to both sodium depletion and loading, suggesting that a new equilibrium has been established.[28,136] The expanded intravascular and ECF compartments are sensed as "normal" by the woman's vascular and renal volume-regulating mechanisms. The elevated levels of aldosterone may be necessary to maintain the expanded extracellular volume. This new equilibrium is protected against further increases or depletion in a manner similar to that in nonpregnant individuals.[54]

Angiotensin II is a potent vasopressor. Yet despite markedly elevated levels during pregnancy, the blood pressure does not rise and in fact actually decreases as does the peripheral vascular resistance (see Chapter 9).[6] The basis for resistance of the pregnant woman to the pressor effects of angiotensin II and other vasoactive substances is unclear. This refractoriness may be a result of decreased vascular smooth muscle responsiveness to angiotensin II, perhaps mediated by local action of vasodilating prostaglandins, such as PGI_2, and progesterone.[65,141] Other mechanisms include downregulation of AT_1R vasoconstrictive receptors, with alterations in AT_1R structure so that they are monomeric rather than heterodimeric, and the effects of endothelial-derived relaxing factors such as NO.[18,141] The result is an estimated 60% decrease in sensitivity of the systemic vasculature to the pressor effects of angiotensin II during pregnancy. Diurnal variations in PRA, angiotensin II, aldosterone, and angiotensin sensitivity during pregnancy have been reported.[32]

Preeclampsia is associated with a suppression of the RAA system (see Hypertension and the Renal System).[64,65] The increases in renin, aldosterone, and angiotensin II are smaller in women with preeclampsia than in normotensive women with loss of angiotensin II desensitization, alteration in AT_1Rs, and the presence of AT_1R autoantibodies.[18] Thus preeclamptic women are highly sensitive to the vasopressor effects of angiotensin II. The AT_1R agonistic autoantibodies may play a role in the pathogenesis of preeclampsia (see Chapter 9).[18,64,65]

Volume Homeostasis and Regulation of Osmolarity

Because ECF volume is determined by sodium, the accumulation of sodium in pregnancy is accompanied by accumulation of water. Both extracellular and intravascular volumes

TABLE 11-4 Estimates (in mL) of Average Accumulated Extracellular and Intracellular Water at the End of Pregnancy

	TOTAL WATER	EXTRACELLULAR	INTRACELLULAR
Fetus[a]	2414	1400	1014
Placenta[b]	540	260	280
Amniotic fluid[c]	792	792	0
Uterus[d]	800	528	272
Mammary gland	304	148	156
Plasma	920	920	0
Red cells	163	0	163
Total	5933	4048	1885

For the purposes of the listed estimates, the following assumptions have been made:
[a]Extracellular space = 41.2% of body weight.
[b]48% is extracellular water.
[c]99% is water.
[d]66% of water is extracellular.
From Davison, J.M. (1997). Edema in pregnancy. *Kidney Int Suppl*, 59, S90.

expand during pregnancy. The largest portion of this expansion is in the vascular component, favoring placental perfusion. The amount of water filtered by the kidneys increases 50% or more during pregnancy because of the increased GFR. Pregnant women accumulate up to 6 to 7 L of water (Table 11-4) to meet their needs and those of the fetoplacental unit.[76,92] About 70% to 75% of maternal weight gain is a result of increased body water in the extracellular spaces. Interstitial fluid volume increases 2 to 3 L beginning at 6 weeks and peaks at 24 to 30 weeks, with the greatest accumulation during the second half of pregnancy.[28,151] Accumulation of greater than 1.5 L of interstitial fluid is associated with edema. Alterations in blood volume are discussed in Chapters 8 and 9.

The exact mechanisms for water retention in pregnancy are still unclear, especially regarding the significance of these volume changes during pregnancy and how pregnant women "sense" these changes.[76,77] Lindheimer noted: "All agree that normal pregnancy is characterized by an absolute increment in both extracellular and intravascular volume (by some 6–7 L, at that), but investigators disagree on the meaning of these changes. For some ('underfill' theory) it is an incomplete response to both the systemic vasodilation and markedly increased arterial global compliance characteristic of normal pregnancy, and indeed, the lower blood pressure and markedly stimulated RAS and aldosterone levels that persist during normal pregnancy are consistent with this paradigm. For others, this is an absolute hypervolemia perhaps due to the higher levels of salt-retaining steroids that accompany gestation ('overfill' theory), and to still others, there is a constant resetting of the 'volumestat' as pregnancy progresses ('normal-fill' theory), the gravida always acting as if her current volume status were 'normal'." [76,p. 1712]

The increase in plasma volume occurs despite decreases in plasma osmolality and colloid osmotic pressure, changes that

would normally stimulate decreases in intravascular volume. Estrogen and progesterone may play a role through dilation of the venous capacitance vessels so that they can accommodate additional volume without stimulation of atrial baroreceptors to alter AVP and aldosterone release.[27]

Plasma osmolality decreases from conception, reaching 8 to 10 mOsm/kg below nonpregnant values of 290 mOsm/kg by 10 weeks' gestation and remaining low to term.[28,54,66,92,105,121,141] This change is associated with changes in sodium, urea, and other ions and may arise from the decrease in PCO_2 and subsequent compensatory adjustments in renal ion excretion. A decrease in plasma osmolality of this magnitude in a nonpregnant person would significantly reduce the osmotic threshold for thirst, suppress AVP release, and lead to a massive water diuresis (as occurs in diabetes insipidus). However, the pregnant woman senses this change in osmolality as normal. At this new baseline, she responds to water loading and deprivation and concentrates and dilutes urine in a manner similar to that in nonpregnant individuals.[92] Because of these changes, the urine of pregnant women is concentrated at levels below nonpregnant values.

Arginine Vasopressin. AVP (also known as *antidiuretic hormone*) secretion and its effect on renal reabsorption of water are similar in pregnant and nonpregnant women, as is AVP secretion in response to changes in baseline plasma osmolarity.[151] During pregnancy, the osmostat for AVP is reset, so the threshold at which the osmoreceptors signal the need for increased release is reduced from 280 to 270 mOsm/kg.[18,28,54,105] The thirst threshold (usually 10 mOsm/L [mmol/L] above the osmostat) is also reset during pregnancy, falling from 290 to 280 mOsm/L (mmol/L).[18,54,121]

AVP metabolites increase in pregnancy, probably because of placental metabolism, but maternal circulating AVP levels do not change significantly. The threefold to fourfold increase in plasma AVP clearance, which peaks at 22 to 24 weeks, is secondary to placental vasopressinases.[18,54,141] The posterior pituitary responds to this increased clearance by releasing more AVP to maintain normal plasma levels.[54] These changes in osmoregulation parallel the progressive increase in vasopressin metabolism and placental vasopressinases. The increased plasma vasopressinase in multiple pregnancies may be a basis for polyuria in these women.[121]

Nonosmotic factors regulating AVP secretion in pregnancy are not completely understood. In nonpregnant individuals a decrease in arterial blood pressure stimulates AVP secretion. In pregnancy the fall in plasma osmolality occurs weeks before the decline in blood pressure, and the lowered osmolality is still sensed as normal at term when the blood pressure has returned to nonpregnant values. AVP release is also influenced by plasma volume (decreased plasma volume increases AVP release and increased plasma volume decreases AVP release). During pregnancy the threshold for the release of AVP is reset to accommodate the increase in extracellular volume at a lower baseline plasma osmolality.[27,54] Human chorionic gonadotropin may also have a role in resetting the thirst and osmostat receptors during pregnancy.[54,92] The lowering of the osmotic threshold is probably a result of the systemic arterial vasodilation leading to vasopressin simulation and upregulation of aquaporin 2 water channels in the collecting ducts.[121]

Intrapartum Period

The renin-angiotensin systems of both the fetus and the mother are further altered during labor and delivery. At delivery, maternal renin, PRA, and angiotensinogen, as well as fetal renin and angiotensinogen levels, are elevated. These changes may be important in control of uteroplacental blood flow during the intrapartum and immediate postbirth periods.

Because the changes in renal function may also affect handling and excretion of drugs, drug doses and responses must be carefully monitored (see Chapter 7). General anesthesia decreases GFR, RPF, and sodium excretion and is associated with renal vasoconstriction, which may be magnified by the effects of stress with catecholamine release. Thus monitoring of fluid and electrolyte status is especially important after the use of general anesthesia for cesarean birth or with nonobstetric surgery during pregnancy.

Some pregnant women are also at risk for iatrogenic water intoxication during late pregnancy and the intrapartum period. This risk may result from the loss of electrolytes by use of saluretics, forcing fluids in a woman with preeclampsia and compromised renal function, or oxytocin infusion during labor (because the antidiuretic action of oxytocin reduces water excretion).

Some bladder and urethral trauma probably occurs in most women during the intrapartum period.[86] With contractions, intravesicular pressure increases by about 5 cm H_2O (0.49 kPa); however, bearing down increases pressure by up to 50 cm H_2O (4.90 kPa). Therefore prolonged straining during the second stage of labor may be more important in causing injury to the bladder than are contractions.[86]

Postpartum Period

RPF decreases markedly in the first 5 days after delivery.[111] GFR remains elevated (by about 40%) during the first day postpartum and then decreases over the next 2 weeks but remains about 20% elevated.[58] RPF, GFR, plasma creatinine, creatinine clearance, and BUN return to nonpregnant levels by 2 to 3 months postpartum.[111] Urinary excretion of calcium, phosphate, vitamins, and other solutes generally returns to normal by the end of the first week, but hyperfiltration may be maintained for up to 4 weeks because of decreased glomerular oncotic pressure.[136] Immediately after delivery, the creatinine clearance increases, but by 6 days postpartum it is similar to nonpregnant levels.[27] PRA and angiotensin II concentrations fall to nonpregnant values immediately after delivery and then rise again and remain elevated for up to 14 days.[136] These changes may reflect the loss of renin from the fetoplacental unit, with subsequent "overshooting" by the maternal system.[136] Urinary glucose excretion returns to nonpregnant patterns by 1 week postpartum.[14,27] In women without pregnancy-related glycosuria, efficient renal glucose reabsorption is seen by 8 to 12 weeks; however, in women

with glycosuria during pregnancy, some impairment in glucose reabsorption continues to be seen, although glycosuria is not present.[18] Pregnancy-associated proteinuria is resolved by 6 weeks.[14,27] Plasma osmolality returns to nonpregnant levels by 2 weeks.[141]

The postpartum period is characterized by rapid and sustained natriuresis and diuresis, especially prominent on days 2 to 5, as the sodium and water retention of pregnancy is reversed.[27] Fluid and electrolyte balance is generally restored to nonpregnant homeostasis by 21 days postpartum and often earlier. Persistence of more than a trace of edema after this time is indicative of sodium retention or a protein-losing state.

The decrease in oxytocin contributes to diuresis because oxytocin acts similarly to AVP in promoting reabsorption of free water. As oxytocin levels decrease, the diuresis becomes more pronounced, with up to 3000 mL of urine excreted per 24 hours on the second through fifth days after delivery.[26,54,83] A normal voiding for a postpartum woman may be 500 to 1000 mL, several times greater than a nonpostpartum individual. Water may also be lost via night sweats.

Women with preeclampsia may become hypervolemic during the postpartum period as water accumulated in the interstitial space returns to the vascular compartment. If the woman's renal function remains impaired, the normal diuresis may be delayed. She may be unable to rapidly excrete this increased fluid volume and in rare cases may develop congestive heart failure or pulmonary edema.

The alterations in tone of the ureters and bladder during pregnancy do not permanently impair function of these structures in most women unless damage from infection has incurred.[14,84,92] Morphologic changes in the urinary tract may last 3 to 4 months and up to 6 months in some women.[18,54,92] In many women the dilation of the bladder, ureters, and renal pelvis has decreased significantly by the end of the first week, although the potential for distensibility of these structures may persist for several months. In most women these structures return to their nonpregnant state by 6 to 8 weeks; in some women these changes may persist for 12 to 16 weeks or longer.[27,54] In up to 10% of women, the anatomic changes in the ureters and bladder persist.[111]

The decreased tone, edema, and mucosal hyperemia of the bladder can be aggravated immediately postpartum by prolonged labor, instrumentation use, analgesia, or anesthesia.[14] These events may also lead to submucosal hemorrhages. Pressure of the fetal head on the bladder during labor can result in trauma and transient loss of bladder sensation in the first few days or weeks postpartum. This can lead to overdistention of the bladder, with incomplete emptying (in about 20%) and an inability to void.[111] Stress incontinence is also seen postpartum, although it usually develops before delivery.[143] Altered sphincter tone may increase the frequency of incontinence with events such as coughing.

Decreased urine flow rates are seen after vaginal delivery, with an increased voided volume, total flow time, and time to peak flow on the first day postpartum returning to nonpregnant levels by 2 to 3 days.[109] Urinary retention is reported in

1.7% to 17.9% of women and is more common after the first vaginal delivery, epidural anesthesia, and catheterization before delivery.[119] Retention is a result of the continuing bladder hypotonia after delivery without the weight of the pregnant uterus to limit its capacity.[119]

CLINICAL IMPLICATIONS FOR THE PREGNANT WOMAN AND HER FETUS

Changes in the renal system and fluid and electrolyte homeostasis during pregnancy are associated with events such as urinary frequency, nocturia, dependent edema, and an inability to void postpartum that are experienced by many pregnant women. These events are usually not pathologic but can be annoying and are often amenable to nursing interventions. However, renal changes are also associated with an increased risk of pathologic events such as UTI and pyelonephritis and can interfere with the recognition and evaluation of renal disease during pregnancy. In addition, renal system changes interact with or are aggravated by preeclampsia and other renal and hypertensive disorders.

Urinary Frequency, Incontinence, and Nocturia

Urinary frequency (more than 7 daytime voidings) occurs in about 80% of pregnant women.[176] Urinary frequency is progressive and maximum at term.[143] Frequency begins in the first trimester before the uterus is large enough to put significant pressure on the bladder.[143] Throughout most of pregnancy, urinary frequency is primarily caused by the effects of hormonal changes, hypervolemia, and the increased RBF and GFR.[41,143] Pressure of the pregnant uterus probably influences urinary frequency during the third trimester. Alterations in bladder sensation postpartum can lead to overdistention with incomplete emptying and overflow incontinence.[14]

During pregnancy, 30% to 50% of women (versus about 8% of nonpregnant women) experience incontinence.[86] Urinary incontinence can begin in any trimester, but once it begins, an increase in severity until delivery is noted.[86,143] An increase is seen in both stress incontinence and urge incontinence.[41,118] Stress incontinence is reported in up to 41% of pregnant women, urge incontinence in 3% to 15%.[41,44] Urinary incontinence regresses after delivery in the majority of women but often returns in subsequent pregnancies.[86] Onset of stress incontinence after delivery is associated with continued symptoms at 1 year postpartum in 24% of women.[44] Women with urinary incontinence during pregnancy are at increased risk of urinary incontinence after delivery.[74] Pregnancy is a major risk factor for the development of stress urinary incontinence in young women, probably because of the pressure of the growing uterus and fetus on the pelvic floor muscles and hormonal effects reducing the strength of these muscles. This results in bladder neck and urethral mobility and urinary sphincter incompetence with urine leakage.[74,110] Pelvic floor (Kegel) exercises can reduce the incidence of stress urinary incontinence.[107,118]

Nocturia results from increased sodium excretion, with an obligatory, concomitant loss of water. During the day, water and sodium are trapped in the lower extremities because of venous stasis and pressure of the uterus on the iliac vein and inferior vena cava. At night, when the pregnant woman lies down, pressure on the iliac vein and inferior vena cava is reduced, promoting increased venous return, cardiac output, RBF, and glomerular filtration with subsequent increase in urine output. However, because pregnant women excrete large amounts of sodium at night, diurnal differences in sodium, and therefore water, excretion may be the primary cause of nocturia.[41,86] Nursing interventions and recommendations for women experiencing urinary frequency and nocturia are summarized in Table 11-5.

TABLE 11-5	Nursing Interventions and Recommendations for Common Problems During Pregnancy Related to the Renal System
PROBLEM	**NURSING INTERVENTIONS**
Urinary frequency	Restrict fluids in evening.
	Ensure adequate intake over 24-hour period.
	Encourage to void when there is sensation to reduce accumulation of urine.
	Limit intake of natural diuretics (e.g., coffee, tea, and cola with caffeine).
	Teach the mother signs of urinary tract infection.
Nocturia	Use the left lateral recumbent position in the evening to promote diuresis.
	Reduce fluid intake in evening.
	Ensure adequate fluid intake over 24-hour period.
	Avoid coffee, tea, and cola with caffeine in the evening.
Dependent edema	Avoid the supine position.
	Avoid the upright position for extended periods.
	Rest in the left lateral recumbent position with legs slightly elevated.
	Elevate the legs and feet at regular intervals and when sitting.
	Use water immersion.
	Use support hose or elastic stockings.
	Avoid tight clothing on lower extremities (e.g., tight pants, socks, girdles, garter belts, knee-high stockings).
	Engage in regular exercise.
	Restrict intake of high-salt foods and beverages.
	Assess for signs of preeclampsia (e.g., increased blood pressure, proteinuria, generalized edema).
Inability to void postpartum	Assess for bladder distention and urine retention.
	Promote adequate hydration.
	Promote early ambulation.
	Provide privacy.
	Administer analgesic before voiding attempt.
	Place ice on perineum to reduce swelling and pain.
	Pour warm water over perineum.
	Turn on the water in the bathroom.
	Provide fluid during the voiding attempt.
Risk of urinary tract infection	Screen urine culture on initial prenatal visit.
	Encourage use of the left lateral position to maximize renal output and urine flow.
	Teach perineal hygiene.
	Encourage adequate fluid intake.

Dependent Edema

Dependent edema is seen in up to 70% of pregnant women and is more common as pregnancy progresses.[28] Edema is more common in obese women and is associated with larger babies.[28] The forces resulting in the movement of fluid out of the vascular space include capillary hydrostatic pressure and colloid osmotic (plasma oncotic) pressure, which is generated primarily by albumin.[28] Compression of the iliac vein and inferior vena cava by the growing uterus increases capillary hydrostatic pressure below the uterus, with filtration of fluid into the interstitial spaces of the lower extremities. The net reduction in plasma albumin during pregnancy reduces plasma colloid osmotic pressure, interfering with return of fluid to the vascular compartment. However, Theunissen and Parer suggest that the increased interstitial fluid is not caused by the decreased plasma oncotic pressure, because interstitial oncotic pressure is reduced to an even greater degree by increased flow of protein into the lymphatic system to maintain the transcapillary osmotic gradient.[141] They suggest the basis of the edema is alterations in capillary permeability and changes in interstitial ground substance. These changes reduce the margin of safety against edema but increase the margin of safety for vascular engorgement and provide a transcapillary pool of fluid that can be mobilized with delivery.[141]

Dependent edema is more likely to develop in women who are in supine or upright positions for prolonged periods. The development of edema in pregnancy is associated with the amount of water accumulation in maternal tissues. Women with no visible edema have an accumulation of approximately 1.5 L. Pedal edema is associated with an accumulation of 2 L or more; women with generalized edema have accumulated 4 to 5 L or more of water. Edema in the lower legs increases the risk of varicosities and thromboembolic complications (see Chapter 8). Nursing interventions and recommendations for women experiencing dependent edema are summarized in Table 11-5 and include leg elevation, increased fluids, activity changes, and water immersion.[28] Leg elevation uses gravity to decrease capillary hydrostatic pressure and thus reabsorption of interstitial fluid into the vascular space.[28] Water immersion also changes hydrostatic pressure to help move water back into the vascular space. Increased urine flow and diuresis are noted after immersion.

Effects of Position on Renal Function

Position can markedly alter renal function during pregnancy, especially during the third trimester. These postural effects are magnified in women with preeclampsia and hypertension. As pregnancy progresses, there is pooling of blood in the pelvis and lower extremities while sitting, lying supine, or standing. The pooling of blood leads to a relative hypovolemia and decreased cardiac output. To compensate and maintain adequate perfusion of vital organs such as the heart and brain, blood vessels supplying less vital organs such as the kidneys are constricted. Renal plasma flow is maximal in the left lateral position.[92]

During the second half of pregnancy, the supine and upright positions are associated with a reduction in GFR and in urine output.[92] As a result, pregnant women excrete water poorly and have a reduced urine volume when lying supine and, to a lesser extent, when upright.[92] For example, renal excretion of a water load while in the supine position may be decreased by 40% in late pregnancy. Water excretion is enhanced by the lateral recumbent position. However, this position interferes with the ability of the woman to concentrate urine, possibly because of mobilization of fluid from the lower extremities with increased intravascular volume and subsequent suppression of AVP.

Renal handling of sodium is also affected by postural changes. Moving from a lateral recumbent to a supine or sitting position is associated with sodium retention and, in some cases, with an increase in plasma renin and aldosterone levels.[151] Sodium excretion may be decreased in the supine and upright positions. This sodium retention is associated with weight gain and occasional ankle swelling that comes and goes rapidly depending on the woman's activity patterns and position and does not necessarily indicate pathology. Therefore in evaluating sudden weight gain and edema in the extremities during pregnancy, data regarding recent activity patterns are essential.

Inability to Void Postpartum

Postpartum urinary retention, defined as "the inability to void spontaneously within 6 hours after a vaginal delivery or 6 hours after removal of an indwelling bladder catheter after cesarean section" is seen in approximately 5% of postpartum women.[155] An additional 10% of woman may have covert urinary retention (i.e., a bladder volume of 150 mL or more after spontaneous voiding).[155] An increased risk of urinary retention is seen after first labors, instrument delivery, cesarean birth, epidurals, labor longer than 13 to 14 hours, and perineal lacerations.[41] Immediately after delivery, the woman has a hypertonic bladder with an increased capacity and decreased sensation, leading to incomplete emptying. Women should void within 6 to 8 hours of delivery. An inability to void after delivery is related to the following factors: (1) trauma to the bladder from pressure of the presenting part during labor, with transient loss of bladder sensation; (2) edema of the urethra, vulva, and meatus and spasm of the sphincter from the forces of delivery; (3) decreased intraabdominal pressure immediately postpartum because of continuing distention of the abdominal wall; (4) decreased sensation of the bladder because of regional anesthesia and catheter use; and (5) hematomas of the genital tract.[83,94] Nursing interventions and recommendations are summarized in Table 11-5.

Risk of Urinary Tract Infection

UTI (including asymptomatic bacteriuria [ASB], pyelonephritis, and cystitis) occurs with increased frequency during pregnancy and is related to anatomic changes in the renal system. ASB occurs in 2% to 10% of pregnant women, which is similar to rates in sexually active nonpregnant women.[86,140] However, during pregnancy, up to 30% of women with untreated ASB develop pyelonephritis.[43,140]

Dilation of the urinary tract, along with partial obstruction of the ureters from ureteral compression at the pelvic brim, results in urinary stasis. Large volumes of urine may be sequestered in the ureters and hypotonic bladder during pregnancy. These static pools increase the risk of ASB, especially because the urine may contain glucose, protein, and amino acids, which provide additional substrates for bacterial growth. Edema and hyperemia of the bladder mucosa also increase susceptibility to infection. The static column of urine in the hypoactive ureters also facilitates ascending bacterial migration, increasing the risk of pyelonephritis.[86] UTI has been associated with preterm labor (see Chapters 4 and 13).[43,140]

UTIs are also more common during the postpartum period. Factors that increase the risk of UTIs postpartum include pregnancy-induced changes in the bladder (hypotonia, edema, and mucosal hyperemia) that may be aggravated by the trauma of labor and delivery. Decreased bladder sensation from pressure of the fetal head during labor may lead to incomplete emptying and urinary stasis, further predisposing the woman to UTI for the first few postpartum weeks. Recommendations to reduce the risk of UTI during pregnancy and the postpartum period are summarized in Table 11-5.

Fluid Needs in Labor

Fluid needs of women in labor are becoming less restrictive with the routine use of intravenous (IV) infusions being questioned and discontinued in some practices.[67,144] Before the use of general anesthesia for delivery, food and fluid intake was maintained during labor. With introduction of general anesthesia, food and fluid were prohibited and IV administration of fluids and glucose became routine to provide fluid and calories to prevent dehydration and ketosis.[123,144] Routine IV use has continued in many settings even with the decline in use of general anesthesia and increased use of regional anesthesia. There is little documentation supporting either the benefits of this therapy or the risk of oral intake for most women.[4,30,70,73,123,127,131,144] A Cochrane review of 19 studies (n = 3130) found no benefit or harm of oral fluids in labor and concluded that "there is no justification for the restriction of fluids and food in labor for women at low risk for complications."[127] Allowing mothers to self-select oral intake during labor was not found to be detrimental, especially when nurses encouraged mothers to maintain hydration with oral fluids.[4,30,70] Professional guidelines support oral intake during labor in low-risk women.[4,5]

IV infusions may be needed for anesthesia or medication administration and must be carefully monitored. However, there is little evidence to support routine use of IV infusions in otherwise healthy women not receiving these agents. O'Sullivan notes the following: "Intravenous therapy is seldom necessary during the first 12 hours of labor, irrespective of the finding of ketonuria; when it is prescribed, the indication for its use should be clearly documented and fluid balance charts should be meticulously maintained. In fact, the judicious use of oral fluids should mitigate the need for intravenous fluids in many patients."[103,p. 39] In addition, it may be harder for the woman to change her position during IV therapy, leading to increased use of the supine position. IV therapy is also linked to increased use of medications because there is an accessible line.[67] Volume loading with colloids before or during can blunt the hemodynamic alterations with spinal anesthesia in pregnant women.[124] Crystalloids administered 20 to 30 minutes before spinal anesthesia have been found to have no advantage over administration during the procedure.[25,139] Complications such as infection, phlebitis, hyponatremia, and fluid overload can occur with IV therapy.[73,97]

Acute hydration can lead to hypervolemia, with a greater risk in pregnant women who already have expanded body water and plasma volume. The use of hypertonic glucose infusions can lead to elevations in maternal blood glucose, which can in turn result in fetal hyperglycemia and hyperinsulinemia and eventually neonatal hypoglycemia (see Chapter 16).[67,90,97,101,144] Lower cord blood sodium values and increased neonatal weight loss in the first 48 hours have been reported after the administration of 5% dextrose solutions to laboring women.[26,30]

Although rare, pregnant women are at increased risk for water intoxication.[91] Oxytocin infusions have been associated with water intoxication and maternal and fetal hyponatremia.[73,91] The risk of water intoxication is increased when oxytocin is administered with large volumes of hypertonic dextrose solution.[73,91] The hypertonic solution pulls fluid into the vascular compartment from the interstitial space, resulting in hemodilution. However, the additional fluid cannot be readily excreted because of the antidiuretic effects of oxytocin. Water intoxication results in electrolyte imbalances such as hyponatremia, which can affect both mother and fetus and in severe cases can lead to seizures and hypoxia.[73,101] Thus not only must oxytocin infusions be carefully monitored, but maternal electrolyte and fluid status and urine output must also be carefully evaluated for any woman receiving this type of infusion.

Maternal-Fetal Fluid and Electrolyte Homeostasis

Fetal fluid and electrolyte balance is dependent on maternal homeostasis and placental function. Because serum osmolarity is similar in the fetus and the mother, changes in maternal or fetal osmolarity will lead to transfer of water from the opposite compartment to achieve homeostasis. Water is continuously exchanged between mother and fetus, with a net flux in favor of the fetus, placenta, and amniotic fluid. Factors that influence the rate and direction of water exchange between the mother and the fetus include maternal and fetal blood flow to and from the placenta, osmotic and hydrostatic pressure gradients across the placenta, and the availability of cellular transport mechanisms.[77]

Fetal balance is affected by any maternal or fetal conditions that alter the supply, demand, and transfer of water. Maternal events such as altered nutrition, electrolyte imbalance, diabetes, hypertension, or the excessive use of diuretics are associated with alterations in fetal fluid and electrolyte status, amniotic fluid volume, and fetal growth.[69] For example, fetal urine flow can be increased by volume loading of maternal blood or administration of diuretics, because acute changes in maternal plasma osmolarity induce parallel changes in the fetus through the transplacental movement of fluid, with decreased urine flow and increased AVP.[69] In addition, because fetal free water is derived from the mother, net movement of water to the fetus is decreased when maternal osmolarity increases; this leads to decreased fetal urine flow and increased tubular reabsorption of water. The fluid and electrolyte status of the infant reflects maternal balance during labor.[141] A reduction in fetal plasma volume with increased fetal osmolarity occurs in most infants during labor. These changes are more pronounced after prolonged labor, with administration of hyperosmolar glucose solutions to the mother, or during fetal hypoxia, because fluid is redistributed from the extracellular fluid (ECF) to intracellular fluid (ICF) compartments. Maternal electrolyte imbalances result in similar alterations in the fetus. Administration of hypotonic fluid to the mother can, by increasing the maternal ECF volume, lead to decreases in fetal osmotic pressure and serum sodium and has resulted in maternal and neonatal hyponatremia and an increased risk of neonatal complications.[39] If this therapy is used, the fluid and electrolyte status of both the mother and newborn must be carefully monitored.

Evaluation of Renal Function During Pregnancy

The marked increase in GFR during pregnancy significantly reduces serum blood urea nitrogen (BUN), plasma urea, uric acid, and creatinine by the end of the first trimester. As a result, values that are normal for nonpregnant individuals may actually be elevations for a pregnant woman and reflect pathologic alterations in renal function. Thus it is critical for health care providers to know the normal values for these parameters during pregnancy (see Table 11-2) so that early signs of renal impairment are not missed. In a pregnant woman, serum creatinine decreases in each trimester to an average of 0.5 mg/dL (44.2 μmol/L) versus nonpregnant values of 0.80 mg/dL (70.7 μmol/L).[66] Serum creatinine levels greater than 0.80 mg per 100 mL, plasma urea nitrogen levels greater than 14 mg per 100 mL (6 mmol/L), or plasma BUN and creatinine levels that do not decrease to expected values by midgestation may indicate a significant reduction in renal function and require further investigation.[27,54,140,151]

GFR is best measured by endogenous creatinine clearance (C_{cr}) during pregnancy, because other measures have been demonstrated to underestimate GFR.[55,129] The 24-hour C_{cr} is generally a good index of GFR in both pregnant and nonpregnant women but is less valid in women with severe renal impairment or diminished urine production.[77] In the latter case,

the amount of creatinine secreted by the proximal tubule can markedly alter urinary creatinine values.[27] The C_{cr} rises approximately 45% by 4 weeks postconception and remains elevated to or near term, when it may begin to fall.[27,77]

Dilation of the urinary tract with stasis and retention of large volumes of urine can lead to collection errors. Accuracy of clearance measures in pregnancy can be improved by using 24-hour collections to avoid "washout" from diurnal changes in urine flow, ensuring that the woman is well hydrated to ensure a high urine flow rate, discarding the first morning specimen, and having the woman assume a lateral recumbent position for 1 hour before the start and 1 hour before the end of the collection. Dietary intake must be evaluated in the timing of blood samples during a clearance period; recent ingestion of cooked meat can increase plasma creatinine levels up to 0.18 mg per 100 mL (1.59 μmol/L). Plasma creatinine levels, used to estimate GFR, are influenced by age, height, weight, and gender. In the pregnant woman, body size and weight may not accurately reflect kidney size.[27]

Interpretation of diagnostic studies such as ultrasound or IV pyelography in the pregnant woman must be done in light of the normal structural changes.[140] Because structural changes in the urinary system may persist for several months after delivery, these alterations also need to be considered when evaluating postpartum renal function. Evaluation of renal function is considered if the GFR during the postpartum period decreases more than 25% to 30% from predelivery values or if the serum creatinine rises above nonpregnant levels.[12]

Glycosuria

Chemically detectable glycosuria is found in more than 50% of pregnant women.[3,17,151] Glucose excretion may be 10 to 100 times greater than the nonpregnant levels of 20 to 100 mg per 24 hours.[92] About 70% of pregnant women excrete more than 100 mg of glucose per 24 hours; in up to 50%, glucose excretion is greater than 150 mg per 24 hours.[12,27,151] Large day-to-day variation in glucose excretion is reported, with little correlation between excretion rate, plasma glucose levels, and the stage of pregnancy.[27,151] Few women with glycosuria have abnormal glucose tolerance test results. Thus glycosuria in pregnancy does not reflect alterations in carbohydrate metabolism but rather alterations in renal function.[92,151]

The basis for glycosuria in pregnancy is secondary to the increases in GFR and tubular flow rate that exceeds the maximal tubular reabsorptive capacity for glucose (200 to 240 mg/dL).[3,66,92] As the GFR increases during pregnancy, renal reabsorptive capacity for glucose also increases, but not to the same extent. Thus as the filtered load of glucose increases, more glucose is excreted, leading to glycosuria at normal plasma glucose levels.[18,151] When glucose excretion increases, alterations in reabsorption seem to occur primarily in that portion of the glucose load that escapes reabsorption in the proximal tubules (usually 5% of the filtered glucose) and is normally reabsorbed in the loops of Henle and collecting duct.[27,66,92]

Glycosuria during pregnancy has not been associated with alterations in perinatal mortality or morbidity or with subsequent development of diabetes or renal disorders.[3,17] However, Davison suggests that women with greater than the usual degree of glycosuria during pregnancy may have sustained renal tubular damage from earlier untreated UTIs.[27] How this alters renal handling of glucose is unclear. Infection is known to cause a temporary impairment of distal tubular function. In some women, sites for glucose reabsorption may not be completely healed and thus are unable to deal with the stresses imposed by the increased filtered load of glucose during pregnancy.

Because of the high incidence of glycosuria in normal pregnant women, glycosuria is not useful in screening for pregnancy-related glucose intolerance.[66] In addition, urinary glucose may not be a reliable indicator of plasma glucose control in pregnant diabetics, thus decreasing the usefulness of urinary glucose concentrations for monitoring these women.[27] In the pregnant diabetic, any elevation of blood glucose results in a greater urinary loss of glucose than in the nonpregnant state. Because water and electrolytes are normally lost along with glucose, volume depletion and polydipsia occur sooner in pregnant than in nonpregnant diabetic women (see Chapter 16).

Hypertension and the Renal System

The kidneys play a critical role in the regulation of blood pressure; therefore alterations in renal function often lead to hypertension. During the perinatal period, renal disorders associated with hypertension often have a poorer outcome for both mother and infant. Preeclampsia involves specific lesions and functional alterations in the renal system (see Table 9-4). The renal lesion usually seen in preeclampsia is glomerular capillary endotheliosis, which decreases the diameter of the glomerular capillary lumina, resulting in decreased (although still higher than in nonpregnant women) GFR, RPF, and ERPF.[7,21,55] The RAA system is altered in preeclampsia (see p. 357), with smaller increases in renin, aldosterone, and angiotensin II in women with preeclampsia accompanied by loss of angiotensin II desensitization, alteration in AT_1Rs, and the presence of AT_1R autoantibodies believed to suppress circulating renin and aldosterone.[18,61,146] Thus the preeclamptic woman is highly sensitive to the vasopressor effects of angiotensin II.[18,64,77] The exaggerated response to angiotensin II has been reported before the onset of clinically detectable hypertension in women who develop preeclampsia.[7,136] Sodium excretion is reduced in these women because of the decreased GFR, increased vascular resistance, decreased RPF (with decreased perfusion of the peritubular capillaries), alterations in plasma and blood volume, and possibly inadequate tubular reabsorptive mechanisms.[55,64,65] Soluble fms-like tyrosine kinase (inhibits VEGF and angiogenesis) is higher in preeclampsia, decreasing VEGF.[7] Further discussion of vascular changes associated with pregnancy, preeclampsia, and the impact of preeclampsia and chronic hypertension can be found in Chapter 9.

Renal Disease and Pregnancy

Regardless of the specific disorder, as the severity of renal disease and reduction in renal function increase, the ability to conceive and sustain a pregnancy also decreases.[27,29,105,140] In general, normotensive women with minimal proteinuria and mild renal disease before pregnancy do well during pregnancy, although the risk of preeclampsia, preterm birth, and fetal growth restriction increases, and their renal prognosis is not significantly altered by pregnancy.[105,129] Women with moderate to severe disease have a greater risk of worsening renal function, hypertension, preeclampsia, preterm birth, or other pregnancy complications.[105,129,140,145] A normal pregnancy is rare if, before conception, the woman has a plasma creatinine greater than 2.5 mg/dL (220 μmol/L) or a urea nitrogen above 30 mg/dL (10.72 mmol/L).[105] The effects of pregnancy on specific chronic renal problems are described in various resources.[140,145] Management of women with chronic renal problems includes careful monitoring of maternal functional status and signs of increasing severity of the disease and fetal assessment.

Pregnancy After Renal Transplantation

Having a transplant improves fertility within 1 to 12 months for women who have been on dialysis.[105,140] Many women have conceived after renal transplantation. Overall 71% to 76% of documented pregnancies result in a live birth.[23] Of those women who carried the pregnancy beyond the first trimester, more than 90% have had a successful pregnancy outcome, although pregnancy complications such as hypertension, preterm birth, preeclampsia, and fetal growth restriction were increased.[23,105,140,110,112] The transplanted kidney undergoes the usual renal changes seen in pregnancy. Renal hemodynamics often improve with pregnancy, but some women have impairment of renal function during pregnancy that may persist.[23,54] However, a review did not find any negative effects of pregnancy on either maternal survival or the transplanted kidney.[112] Pregnancy is generally not recommended for at least 1 year after transplantation in stable women to ensure that the transplant is successful and able to function under the increased demands of pregnancy.[104] Optimal immunosuppressant therapy during pregnancy is unknown, but the woman may need to be switched to safer drugs, because some agents have been found to be associated with an increased risk of fetal anomalies.[105,140] Long-term follow-up data are still sparse, especially for the newer drugs.[140]

SUMMARY

The renal system is critical to maintenance of fluid and electrolyte homeostasis within the body. Relatively small changes in renal function can significantly alter this homeostasis, leading to a variety of volume and electrolyte disorders. Renal

---

BOX 11-2 Recommendations for Clinical Practice Related to Changes in the Renal System and Fluid and Electrolyte Homeostasis in Pregnant Women

Recognize the usual changes in the renal system during pregnancy and postpartum (pp. 351-360 and Table 11-1).

Recognize the usual values for renal function tests and patterns of change during pregnancy and postpartum (pp. 352-360, 363 and Table 11-2).

Recognize that individual laboratory values must be evaluated in light of clinical findings and previous values (pp. 362-360, 363).

Teach women to recognize and reduce the risk of urinary tract infection during pregnancy and postpartum (pp. 361-362).

Recognize the effects of altered renal function on pharmacokinetics of drug elimination by glomerular filtration (pp. 354, 359 and Chapter 7).

Monitor and evaluate maternal responses to drugs for evidence of subtherapeutic doses (pp. 354, 359 and Chapter 7).

Assess maternal nutritional status in relation to calcium and water-soluble vitamins and provide nutritional counseling (p. 355 and Chapters 12 and 17).

Know the influences of position on renal function (p. 361).

Counsel women regarding appropriate positions and activity patterns (p. 361).

Assess activity patterns and position in evaluating changes in weight gain and edema (p. 361).

Monitor fluid and electrolyte status and renal function after the use of general anesthetics (pp. 359, 362).

Monitor oxytocin and intravenous infusions during labor and delivery to avoid overload (pp. 359, 362-363).

Use fluids, ice chips, and other alternatives to the use of intravenous infusions with women with uncomplicated labors (p. 362).

Know the benefits and risks for the mother, fetus, and neonate of different types of intravenous fluids (pp. 362-363).

Avoid use of hypertonic solutions during labor (pp. 362-363).

Know indications for intrapartum intravenous therapy (pp. 362-363).

Monitor maternal fluid and electrolyte status and urine output (especially in women receiving an oxytocin infusion or with preeclampsia or compromised renal function) during labor for development of water intoxication (pp. 363-364).

Teach women the common experiences associated with changes in the renal system (urinary frequency, dependent edema, nocturia) and implement appropriate interventions (pp. 360-362 and Table 11-5).

Monitor women with dependent edema for varicosities and thromboembolism (p. 361 and Chapter 8).

Know the usual values and monitor for glycosuria and proteinuria in the pregnant woman (pp. 354-355, 363-364).

Monitor fluid and electrolyte status of women with preeclampsia, chronic hypertension, and diabetes, recognizing that alterations may occur more rapidly than in other pregnant women (pp. 362-364).

Monitor fluid and electrolyte status, renal function, amniotic fluid volume, and fetal growth in women on diuretics (p. 364).

Counsel women with renal disorders regarding the impact of their disorder on pregnancy and of pregnancy on their disorder (p. 364).

Monitor women with chronic renal problems for signs of initiation of preterm labor, fetal growth restriction, hypertension, and alterations in maternal renal function (p. 364).

Evaluate bladder function and voiding postpartum (pp. 359, 361).

Implement interventions to encourage postpartum voiding (p. 361, Table 11-5).

Observe for signs of pulmonary edema and congestive heart failure after delivery in women with preeclampsia and impaired renal function (p. 359).

Recognize that structural changes in the urinary system may persist for 6 months or more after delivery (p. 359).

---

function and many related laboratory parameters are altered significantly during pregnancy to levels that would be of concern in a nonpregnant individual. In most cases the pregnant woman readily adapts to these changes and establishes a new equilibrium for volume and electrolyte homeostasis. At this new equilibrium, she responds to alterations in fluid and electrolyte intake in a manner similar to that of a nonpregnant individual. Pathophysiologic conditions that alter renal function or volume homeostasis affect the health of both the pregnant woman and her infant. Monitoring and health counseling related to fluid and electrolyte status are essential during pregnancy. Clinical recommendations for nurses working with pregnant women based on alterations in the renal system and fluid and electrolyte balance are summarized in Box 11-2.

DEVELOPMENT OF THE RENAL SYSTEM IN THE FETUS

Although functionally different, the renal and genital systems (see Chapter 1) are closely linked embryonically and anatomically. Both develop from a common ridge of mesodermal tissue and end in the cloaca. Anatomic development of the kidneys begins early in gestation, with formation of the adult number of nephrons by around 34 to 35 weeks. Urine formation begins by 9 to 10 weeks; during the second half of gestation, urine production by the fetus is a major component of amniotic fluid. Renal function does not reach levels comparable to adults until about 2 years of age.

Renal development is under the control of many genes, including *PAX-2, WTI, EYA1, FLK 1,* and *FLK2,* and their protein products. These genes are differentially expressed to form transcription factors and other proteins that encode for extracellular matrix, cell adhesion, growth factors, and cell receptor proteins (e.g., angiotensin II receptors).[85] Factors influencing nephrogenesis include glial-derived neurotrophic factor, bone morphogenetic proteins, FOXcl, Cxal, roundabout-2, fibroblast growth factors, transforming growth factor-β, insulin-like growth factors, platelet-derived growth factor, protein phosphatases, and the renin-angiotensin system.[84,85,133] The ureteric bud arises in response to signals from transcriptional factors, growth factors, and regulatory genes.[117] The renin-angiotensin-aldosterone (RAA) system is involved in renal angiogenesis via angiotensin II and angiotensin 1 receptor (AT_1R) interaction.[81]

Anatomic Development

Development of the Kidneys

The kidneys arise from a ridge of mesodermal tissue (called the *nephrogenic cord*) that runs along the posterior wall of the abdominal cavity on either side of the primitive aorta. The kidney develops through three successive, overlapping stages. The initial steps involve formation of transient nonfunctional structures (called the *pronephros* and *mesonephros*) on either side of midline, from which the metanephros, or permanent kidney, develops. The pronephros arises in the cervical region in the third week, extends in a cranial-to-caudal direction, and then degenerates beginning in the fourth week. Each pronephros consists of 7 to 10 solid cell groups. The pronephric ducts are incorporated into the mesonephric kidneys.

The mesonephros appears late in the fourth week, forming a large ovoid organ on either side of midline next to the developing gonads in the thoracic and lumbar regions (Figure 11-4). The mesonephros and gonad form the urogenital ridge. The mesonephros consists of S-shaped tubules with glomeruli and collecting ducts that enter a common large duct. This mesonephric duct persists in the male as the wolffian duct and gives rise to the male genital ducts (see Chapter 1). The rest of the mesonephros regresses by 8 to 10 weeks as the metanephros begins to function.[93,154]

The permanent kidneys (metanephros) arise during the fifth week from the ureteric bud at the caudal end of the mesonephric duct. Formation of the permanent kidney involves two separate, interrelated processes. The ureteric bud grows out into the surrounding mesoderm (metanephric blastema), dilates, and branches to form the ureters, renal pelvis, and collecting ducts (see Figure 11-4). Failure of this bud to arise results in renal agenesis. The number of ureteric bud branches determines the eventual number of nephrons. Usually 15 branch generations are formed, the first 9 by 15 weeks' gestational age and the reminder by 20 to 22 weeks.[84,115,117] These branches induce formation of the nephrons, with formation of four to seven nephrons around each terminal collecting duct branch. The growth of the ureteric bud into the surrounding metanephric mesoderm induces formation of small vesicles that elongate to form primitive renal tubules (nephrons). The proximal ends of these tubules form the Bowman capsule. The distal end comes into contact with the blind ends of the collecting ducts and fuses.[93,116,154] Nephron formation begins at about 8 weeks in the juxtamedullary area and progresses toward the cortex. Induction of nephron formation involves the release of a cascade of gene transcription factors and signaling molecules.[84] Nephron formation is illustrated in Figure 11-5.

By 20 to 22 weeks, branching of the collecting ducts is complete and one third of the nephrons have been formed. Nephrons continue to develop until 34 to 35 weeks, when adult numbers of nephrons are reached.[1,115,148] Nephron development continues in the preterm infant born before 35 weeks' gestation until the infant reaches 34 to 35 weeks' postconceptional age. Maturation and hypertrophy of the nephrons continue into infancy with growth of glomeruli and tubules.[68,93] Renal vascularization parallels nephrogenesis. A primitive glomerulus appears at 9 to 10 weeks.[117]

Initially the kidneys are in the pelvic area. With straightening of the embryo and growth of the sacral and lumbar areas, the kidneys undergo a series of positional changes and

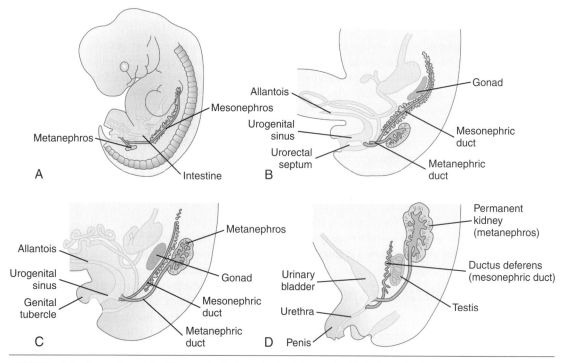

FIGURE 11-4   Formation of the kidneys. **A,** At 6 weeks. **B,** At 7 weeks; **C,** At 8 weeks. **D,** At 3 months (male). (From Carlson, B.M. [2013]. *Human embryology and developmental biology* [5th ed.]. Philadelphia: Saunders)

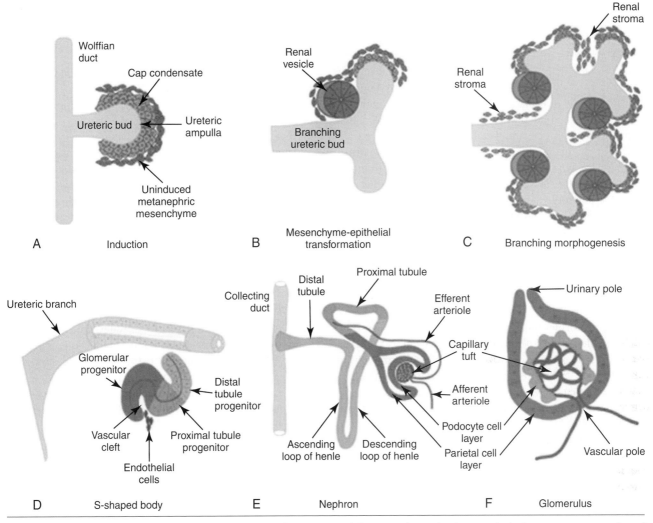

FIGURE 11-5   Stages of kidney formation. **A,** Induction of the metanephric mesenchyme by the ureteric bud promotes aggregation of mesonephric cells around the tip of the ureteric bud. **B,** Polarized renal vesicles are formed next. **C,** Stromal cells secrete factors that influence nephrogenesis and branching morphogenesis. **D,** Formation of S-shaped body involves the formation of a proximal cleft that is invaded by angioblasts. **E,** Complete nephron joined to collecting duct. **F,** Glomerulus demonstrating organization of the capillary tuft, podocytes, and parietal cells. (From Rosenblum, N.D. [2008]. Developmental biology of the human kidney. *Semin Fetal Neonatal Med, 13,* 125.)

migrate upward. During this process, the kidneys rotate 90 degrees so that the renal pelvises face midline.[154] Failure of the kidneys to ascend leads to pelvic kidneys. Abnormal ascent and rotation can result in configurations such as horseshoe-shaped kidneys (in which the caudal ends of the kidneys are pushed together and fuse).

Development of the Urinary System

The urinary system develops after division of the cloaca. The cloaca is the dilated end of the hindgut and is involved in the development of the terminal portions of the genital (see Chapter 1), urinary, and gastrointestinal (see Chapter 12) systems. Downward growth of the urorectal septum at 5 to 6 weeks divides the cloaca into the posterior anorectal canal and anterior primitive urogenital sinus (see Figure 11-4, *C*). The upper and largest part of the urogenital sinus becomes the bladder and is initially continuous with the allantois. The

allantois eventually becomes a thick fibrous cord (the urachus, or median umbilical ligament). The ureters are incorporated into the bladder wall. The urethra develops from the lower urogenital sinus along with portions of the external genitalia.[93,154] Bladder capacity increases from 10 mL at 32 weeks to 40 mL by term.[47]

Developmental Basis for Common Anomalies

Alterations in renal function in adults may be a result of altered programming during renal development by poor maternal nutrition, decreased placental blood flow, and epigenetic changes.[149] Fetal or neonatal insults can also alter nephrogenesis and programming of the kidney.[36,68,82,114] Preterm infants and infants with fetal growth restriction have fewer glomeruli and smaller kidneys at birth with impaired growth into early childhood and an increased risk of later hypertension and renal disease.[31,68,114] These changes may be a result of poor maternal nutrition, chronic fetal hypoxemia, increased maternal glucocorticoids, altered intrauterine nutrient availability (which suppresses the RAA system and alters sodium transport), or endothelial dysfunction.[113,117] Other factors that may alter renal development include maternal hyperglycemia, alterations in the RAA system, decreased vitamin A availability, and pharmacologic agents.[117] Alterations in fetal renal development can lead to decreased numbers of nephrons and renal dysfunction with an increased risk of adult cardiovascular and renal disorders.[36,82,113,117] For example, altered programming or numbers of nephrons alter GFR, increase the risk of glomerular and tubular hypertrophy, and decrease the capacity of the renal blood vessel for vasodilation with an increased risk of chronic renal insufficiency and later hypertension.[113,117] Upregulation or downregulation of RAA system receptors can also lead to later renal dysfunction. In addition, rapid weight gain after either prenatal or postnatal growth restriction has been associated with increased risk of later hypertension and cardiovascular disease.[31]

Major malformations of the renal system and urinary tract can be divided into three broad categories: agenesis-dysplasia of the renal system, polycystic kidneys, and malformations of the lower urinary tract. Several events are critical for the normal development of the kidneys. If the ureteric bud does not arise from the end of the mesonephric duct or if the ureteric bud does not induce formation of the renal cortex and nephrons, unilateral or bilateral renal agenesis, aplasia, or hypoplasia results. If the ureteric bud splits early or if two buds arise on one side, there may be duplication of the kidneys or ureters. Renal agenesis and hypoplasia are often associated with oligohydramnios. The marked decrease in amniotic fluid with bilateral renal agenesis, as occurs in Potter sequence, is believed to result in adverse effects on extrarenal fetal development (see Chapter 3).[39] Renal anomalies can be isolated or components of a syndrome; more than 50% of syndromes that have been described include renal or urinary anomalies.[149]

Increased use of routine fetal ultrasound has resulted in more fetuses being identified with hydronephrosis.[11,149] The significance of this finding and its predictive value for long-term outcomes are not well understood.[11] Mild unilateral dilation of the renal pelvis, without any renal or urinary tract abnormalities, is usually transient and secondary to a larger renal pelvic area and an increased urine flow rate.[11,35] Between 30% and 80% of these infants have a normal postnatal renal appearance.

Polycystic kidneys are a heterogeneous group of disorders that arise from environmental and genetic causes. The specific embryologic basis for these defects is unknown. Theories that have been proposed include (1) failure of the collecting ducts to develop, with subsequent cystic degeneration; (2) failure of the developing nephrons to unite with the collecting tubules; (3) persistence of remnants of early rudimentary nephrons, which normally degenerate but instead remain and form cysts; and (4) secondary to a

concomitant urinary tract obstruction with urine retention leading to cyst formation in the nephrogenic area.[93] The latter theory has been proposed as a possible cause of adult-onset polycystic kidneys.

Malformations of the lower urinary tract include obstructive uropathy and exstrophy. Obstructive uropathy arises from obstructions at the ureteropelvic junction because of adhesions, aberrant blood vessels, or strictures, or in the urethra from posterior urethral valves. Severe forms result in fetal renal damage from hydronephrosis. Anomalies of other systems may occur secondary to oligohydramnios (see Chapter 3). Percutaneous placement of a diverting shunt into the fetal bladder to drain urine into amniotic fluid has been used to promote drainage of the urinary tract and prevent irreversible renal damage before birth.[84] Exstrophy of the bladder arises from incomplete midline closure of the inferior part of the anterior abdominal wall, with concurrent abnormalities in the mesoderm of the bladder wall.[93]

Functional Development

The fetus is composed primarily of water, much of which is contained in the extracellular compartment. As gestation increases, total body water and extracellular fluid slowly decrease and intracellular volume increases (Figure 11-6).[99,106] Maintenance of this high water content may also be mediated by prolactin, which increases the water-binding capacity of fetal cells.

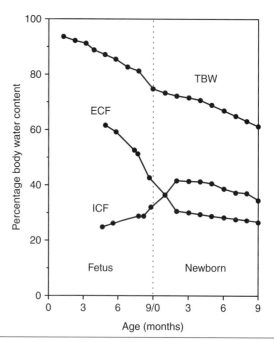

FIGURE 11-6 Total body water *(TBW)* content and fluid distribution between intracellular fluid *(ICF)* and extracellular fluid *(ECF)* compartments in humans during the fetal and neonatal periods and during the first 9 months after birth. (From Kim, C.-R., Katheria, A.C., Mercer, J.S., & Stonestreet, B.S. [2017]. Fluid distribution in the fetus and neonate. In R.A. Polin, S.H. Abman, D.H. Rowitch, W.E. Benitz, & W.W. Fox. [Eds.]. *Fetal and neonatal physiology* [5th ed.]. Philadelphia: Saunders.)

Urine production and glomerular filtration in the fetus begin at 9 to 10 weeks; the loop of Henle functions by 14 weeks, and tubular function begins by 9 to 12 weeks.[45,85] Renal blood flow (RBF) and the glomerular filtration rate (GFR) are low throughout gestation because of the high renal vascular resistance (RVR) and low systemic blood pressure but increase between 20 and 35 weeks and then level off to birth.[85,45,46,117] This increase is concurrent with increases in numbers and growth of nephrons. In adults, 20% to 25% of the cardiac output goes to the kidneys. In the fetus, 40% to 50% of the combined ventricular output goes to the placenta and only 2% to 7% to the kidneys.[38,79] Fetal fluid and electrolyte balance is therefore maintained primarily by the placenta and influenced by maternal balance.

Although fetal RBF and GFR are low, this does not lead to low fetal urine output.[39] Fetal urine is an important component for amniotic fluid production and the primary component of amniotic fluid after 18 weeks.[148] Fetal urine output and amniotic fluid production both increase with gestation. Urine flow rates in the fetus at term are significantly higher than in the newborn.[11] Mean hourly flow rates of urine are about 5 mL at 10 weeks, 10 mL at 30 weeks, and 30 mL at 40 weeks.[47] Urine flow rates are decreased in infants with fetal growth restriction.[12,63] Alterations in urine production or excretion can significantly alter both amniotic fluid volume and development of other systems (see Chapter 3).

Fetal ability to concentrate urine and conserve sodium is limited, with a concentrating ability about 20% to 30% of adult values because of low sensitivity of the collecting duct to arginine vasopressin (AVP), an immature loop of Henle, and lower expression of aquaporin 2 (AQ2) water channels.[63] The placenta maintains electrolyte balance in utero, so fetal urine is hypotonic (100 to 200 mOsm/kg) because of the greater tubular reabsorption of solute than water.[47,85,95,117] Fetal urine becomes less hypotonic with increasing gestation.[148] The major solute in fetal urine is sodium, decreasing from 120 mEq/L (mmol/L) at 16 weeks to 50 mEq/L (mmol/L) from 24 to 40 weeks. Sodium is primarily reabsorbed in the distal tubule.[117] The fetus is not dependent on the kidneys for sodium conservation; sodium is readily transported across the placenta. The expanded extracellular fluid (ECF) compartment of the fetus may stimulate decreased tubular reabsorption of sodium and water. Renal excretion of potassium is low, increasing to term as glomerular and tubular surface area increases and the tubule becomes more sensitive to aldosterone.[117] During the third trimester, fetal urine may become isotonic with plasma during severe stress.[69] The fetal kidney is less sensitive to AVP, which is present by 12 weeks, possibly as a result of immaturity of AVP receptors or presence of antagonists such as prostaglandins.[46,63,148,154] AVP may also help regulate amniotic fluid volume.[46,63] Osmoreceptors and volume receptors in the fetus stimulate prolonged secretion of AVP from about 26 weeks' gestation.

The renin-angiotensin system (see Figure 11-3 and Box 11-1 on p. 356) is upregulated in the fetus, with increased renal and extrarenal production of all components. The RAA system helps maintain RBF and renal perfusion in the fetus.[117] Maintenance of tubular function is influenced by the RAA system, prostaglandins, atrial natriuretic peptide and cortisol.[117] Thus an intact renin-angiotensin system is necessary for normal development and fetoplacental circulation.[56,64] As noted previously, alterations in the RAA system during gestation can alter fetal programming and increase the risk of adult cardiovascular disease.[63] Angiotensin II acts as a growth modulator and renal growth factor.[85,64,117] Angiotensin type 2 (AT$_2$) receptors are denser early in development; later in gestation, both AT$_2$ and angiotensin type 1 (AT$_1$) receptors increase in the fetus. Both types of receptors are also found in the placenta. After birth the density of AT$_2$ (but not AT$_1$) receptors decreases.[56,64] Therefore it is believed that AT$_2$ receptors regulate morphogenesis, whereas AT$_1$ may be important in later neurovascular development.[56,64,128] Blocking of AT receptors in developing animals leads to congenital anomalies of the kidneys and urinary tract.[130] Exposure to angiotensin-converting enzyme (ACE) inhibitors is associated with altered renal hemodynamics and development.[136]

Angiotensinogen is produced in the yolk sac and found in the immature renal tubule by 30 days. Renin is found by 4 to 6 weeks in the mesonephros and by 8 weeks in the metanephros.[56] Renin concentration and activity are both elevated in the fetus, decreasing to term but still higher than adult levels. The juxtamedullary cells produce increasing amounts of renin from the third month of gestation. Renal responsiveness to aldosterone is decreased in the fetus, which may lead to increased sodium loss. Endothelial cells lining the villous capillaries and the cells of the trophoblast are rich in ACE; the fetal membranes and amniotic fluid contain large amounts of renin. ACE is found by 30 days, primarily in the proximal tubules. The chorion also produces renin and angiotensinogen.[136] Placental circulation is a major site for conversion of angiotensin I to angiotensin II (similar to processes in the pulmonary circulation after birth), which is involved in control of placental blood flow in the fetus. The increased angiotensin II appears important in modulating fetal blood pressure and renal hemodynamics, especially at birth.[63,130]

During the last 20 weeks of gestation, the weight of the kidney increases in a linear relationship to gestational age, body weight, and body surface area. Before 5 months, renal growth occurs primarily in the inner medullary area, which contains mostly collecting ducts. From 5 to 9 months, major growth is in the cortex and outer medullary areas. After birth, nephron growth occurs primarily in the tubules and the loop of Henle. At birth, approximately 20% of the infant's loops of Henle are too short to reach into the medulla, which can lead to problems in concentrating urine. The rate of tubular growth after birth is reflected in changes in glomerular-to-tubular surface area. This ratio is 27:1 at birth, 8:1 by 6 months, and 3:1 in adults.

NEONATAL PHYSIOLOGY

The newborn's kidney differs from that of the older child and adult in glomerular and tubular function. The adult number of nephrons is achieved by 34 to 35 weeks, but the nephrons are shorter and less functionally mature. Alterations in renal function and fluid and electrolyte balance are heightened in preterm infants who have not yet achieved their full complement of nephrons. When evaluating postnatal renal function, both gestational age and postbirth age must be considered, because postnatal renal maturation is more a function of postbirth than gestational age; that is, a preterm infant who is several weeks old may have more mature renal function than a newborn term infant. In addition, the immature renal function in the neonate alters renal excretion of drugs (see Chapter 7). Basic renal processes are summarized in Figure 11-1 on page 352. Alterations in neonatal renal function and their implications are summarized in Table 11-6.

Transitional Events

During intrauterine life, the placenta is the major organ of excretion, handling many functions that are normally performed by the lungs and kidney. With birth, the kidneys must rapidly take over control of fluid and electrolyte balance, excretion of metabolic wastes, and other renal functions. Activity of arginine vasopressin (AVP) and the renin-angiotensin system increases with birth, perhaps stimulated by catecholamines, prostaglandins, hypercarbia, and the renin-angiotensin, kinin-kallikrein, and other systems. As a result,

blood pressure increases, with peripheral vasoconstriction and redistribution of blood flow to the vital organs (see Chapter 9). Tubular sodium reabsorption decreases during the intrapartum period, so the first urine has a higher fractional sodium excretion.[148] Renal blood flow (RBF) may not increase immediately at birth but does increase significantly by 24 hours as renal vascular resistance (RVR) falls.[48] Activity of the renin-angiotensin system increases further during the first few days after birth. Transient increases in glomerular filtration rate (GFR) may occur during the first 2 hours after birth. These changes are variable, decreasing to previous levels by 4 hours.[12]

Body Composition

Body composition changes with gestational age and is influenced by maternal fluid and electrolyte balance. Newborns have higher total body and extracellular water and less intracellular water than older individuals. With advancing gestation, total body water content and extracellular water decrease, whereas intracellular water increases as cells proliferate and organs mature.[69] The fetus is 83% water at 32 weeks' gestation and 78% at term.[100] Higher total body water is seen in small-for-gestational-age infants because of their decreased levels of body solids and reduced fat deposition.[135] Extracellular fluid (ECF) decreases from 60% to 70% at 23 to 27 weeks' gestation, to 50% to 60% at 28 to 32 weeks' gestation, and 40% to 44% at 36 to 40 weeks; intracellular water increases from 27% to 34% (see Figure 11-6).[12,34,64,89,99] The relative interstitial volume of the newborn is three times greater than that of the adult.[96] This increases the risk of periorbital, peripheral, and pulmonary edema.[96] Pulmonary edema can interfere with gas exchange; in the brain germinal matrix edema may increase the risk of germinal matrix and intraventricular hemorrhage (see Chapter 15).[96]

Electrolyte composition also changes with gestational age. Because the electrolyte composition of extracellular water is primarily Na^+ and Cl^-, preterm infants (with more extracellular water) have more Na^+ and Cl^- and fewer intracellular ions (K^+, Mg^{2+}, PO_4) per unit weight. Protein, fat, and carbohydrate composition of the body also increases with age. Infants who are small for gestational age (SGA) have more water and less fat, whereas infants who are large for gestational age (LGA) have more fat and less water.

Before the onset of labor, the infant's arterial blood pressure rises because of increases in catecholamines, atrial natriuretic factor (ANF), cortisol, and movement of additional blood from the placenta into the fetus.[106] These changes plus alterations in the acid-base status of the fetus during labor lead to increased capillary permeability with a shift in fluid from the intravascular to the interstitial space. This results in up to a 25% decrease in fetal plasma volume and 14% decrease in fetal blood volume during the intrapartum period.[69,88] With birth, ECF volume increases further, primarily because of placental transfusion (see Chapter 8). With increased oxygenation and changes in vasoactive hormones after birth, capillary integrity is gradually restored and fluid

---

TABLE 11-6   Implications of Alterations in Renal Function in Neonates

ALTERATION	IMPLICATIONS
Decreased glomerular filtration rate	Difficulty excreting water loads with risk of overhydration and water intoxication
	Narrow margin of safety for fluid management
	Tendency for water retention and edema (especially pulmonary edema)
	Increased half-lives of drugs such as antibiotics, barbiturates, and diuretics
	Altered drug doses and dosing intervals
	Risk of hyperglycemia in very-low-birth-weight (VLBW) infants
Altered tubular function: sodium	Increased sodium loss in urine, especially in VLBW infants
	Alterations in other electrolytes with risk of acidosis, hyperkalemia, hypocalcemia, and hypoglycemia
	Limited ability to excrete excess sodium
Altered tubular function: glucose	Less able to handle exogenous glucose
	Risk of glycosuria
	Load with risk of hyperglycemia
	Risk of hyponatremia and dehydration
	Less able to compensate for acid-base abnormalities with risk of acidosis, especially in VLBW infants
Decreased concentrating ability	Risk of dehydration

From Blackburn, S. (1994). Renal function in the neonate. *J Perinat Neonatal Nurs, 8*, 37.

begins to move from the interstitial space back into the vascular space.[106]

The increase in ECF volume is followed by a diuresis as fluid in the interstitial space is mobilized and eliminated and the extracellular space contracts.[34,53,79,100] The postbirth fluid decrease in ECF volume is believed to be related to increases in GFR (with removal of excess sodium and water via the kidney); increased levels of epithelial transport proteins, which enhance tubular function; and primarily to decreases in ANF, which is elevated in the fetus and for the first week after birth.[87,99,106,135] These changes are primarily a result of decreased pulmonary vascular resistance and not renal maturation.[88] The decreased pulmonary vascular resistance after birth increases pulmonary blood flow and left atrial return. This stretches the atrial wall with release of ANF.[87,99] The fluid shifts are greater in extremely low-birth-weight (ELBW) infants.[10] In the first 72 hours, an ELBW infant may have a water loss of up to 10 mL/kg or more because of immature renal function, high transepidermal insensible water loss (IWL), and changes in the extracellular space.[10] Loss of fluid from the interstitial space may lead to hypernatremia, hyperglycemia, and hyperkalemia.[10]

Average losses of 5% to 7% of birth weight (up to 10% to 15% in many preterm infants) is a transitional physiologic process seen during the first week after birth as a result of the changes in body water compartments.[12,34,69,79,100,106] Contraction of the extracellular space increases with decreasing gestational age at birth.[69,78] Postnatal weight loss is usually less in SGA infants because of their lower total body water volume.[100] Losses are also higher in preterm infants because they produce a more dilute urine and have greater urine sodium (and therefore additional obligatory water) loss. Fluid therapy during the first week must account for these changes; otherwise fluid overload, which is associated with increased morbidity including a risk of congestive heart failure, necrotizing enterocolitis (NEC), and symptomatic patent ductus arteriosus (PDA), may occur.[34,79]

Bladder

The neonate's bladder is almost entirely in the abdominal cavity and is cigar shaped (as opposed to the pyramidal shape in adults); therefore the ureters are short. As a result, distention of the bladder compresses the abdomen and increases pressure on the diaphragm. As the pelvic cavity increases in size during infancy and early childhood, the bladder gradually sinks into the pelvis and the ureters lengthen. Bladder capacity is about 13 mL at 32 weeks, 20 mL by 36 weeks, and 40 mL by term.[47,125]

Urine Output and Micturition

Urine output varies with fluid and solute intake, renal concentrating ability, perinatal events, and gestational age. Generally, term infants excrete 15 to 60 mL/kg of urine per day and preterm infants 1 to 3 mL/kg/hour (24 to 48 mL/kg/day) during the first few days. Urine output less than 0.5 mL/kg/hour after 24 hours is considered oliguria. Output increases over the first month to 250 to 400 mL/day. In the first 2 days after birth, frequency of micturition is two to six times per hour; subsequently, micturition occurs one or more times with each feeding.[148] Preterm infants less than 32 weeks' gestational age tend to void once per hour, have more interrupted voids (two to three small voids within 10 minutes), and have smaller voids with residuals.[125] These differences may be because of immaturity of the detrusor sphincter complex.

The initial voiding after birth usually occurs within 24 hours but may be delayed. Approximately 13% to 21% of newborns void in the delivery room, more than 95% by 24 hours, and all (unless there are problems) by 48 hours.[19] If infants urinate for the first time in the delivery room, this event may be missed or not recorded. The force and direction of the urine stream are as important in assessing the urinary system as is the time of first voiding. A delay in spontaneous voiding, in the absence of renal anomalies, is usually a result of inadequate perfusion with contraction of the intravascular compartment and temporary expansion of interstitial fluid volume. Delayed voiding may occur in infants whose mothers received magnesium sulfate before delivery. Side effects of magnesium sulfate in the newborn include neuromuscular blockade with hypotonia and urine retention.

Renal Blood Flow and Glomerular Filtration

RBF at birth in both term and preterm infants is lower than in adults, primarily because the RVR is high in infants, but also because of decreased glomerulus and systemic blood pressures and smaller vessel sizes.[130] RVR is inverse to gestational age and falls after birth, but it is still higher than in adults.[48] RVR is high in the fetus because renal function is primarily needed in utero only for amniotic fluid production, increased renin-angiotensin-aldosterone (RAA) system activity, and increased sensitivity to vasoconstrictive catecholamines.[130] Only a small percentage of the fetal cardiac output perfuses the kidney. During the first 12 hours after birth, 4% to 6% of the cardiac output perfuses the kidneys, increasing to 8% to 10% (versus 25% in adults) over the next few days.[12] RVR falls as RBF and GFR increase.[47] The increasing RBF with increasing age is believed to be a result of the decrease in vasoconstrictive influences and changes in vasodilation.[130] A similar pattern is seen in preterm infants greater than 34 to 35 weeks' gestational age, but the decrease in RVR is more gradual, with a slower increase in GFR. The higher RVR and low blood flow to the outer cortex of the kidney in preterm infants may be a result of the predominance of sympathetic tone in these infants.

Effective renal plasma flow (ERPF) increases with postconceptional age. ERPF is 20 mL/minute per 1.73 m² at 30 weeks, increasing to 45 at 35 weeks and 83 at term, versus about 300 mL/minute per 1.73 m² at 3 months and 650 by 12 to 24 months (1.73 m² is a correction factor for differences in surface area that allows comparison of values between persons of different sizes).[130,133] Changes in RBF after birth are related to the formation of new glomeruli; vascular remodeling; decreased RVR; and vasoactive substances such as

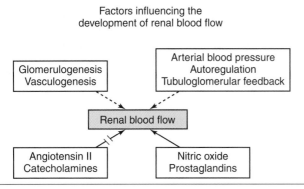

Factors influencing the
development of renal blood flow

FIGURE 11-7   Factors that influence the development of renal blood flow include anatomic factors (glomerulogenesis and vasculogenesis), physical factors (arterial blood pressure, myogenic autoregulatory response), and vasoactive factors (autoregulation, tubuloglomerular feedback, nitric oxide, and prostaglandins). Other vasoactive agents can regulate renal blood flow, although renal vascular resistance regulation in the newborn is probably the result of a balance between the vasoconstrictor influences of angiotensin II and catecholamines or renal nerves and the vasodilatory influences of nitric oxide and prostaglandins. (From Solhaug, M.J. & Jose, P.A. [2017]. Development and maturation of renal blood flow in the neonate. In R.A. Polin, S.H. Abman, D.H. Rowitch, W.E. Benitz, & W.W. Fox. [Eds.]. *Fetal and neonatal physiology* [5th ed.]. Philadelphia: Saunders.)

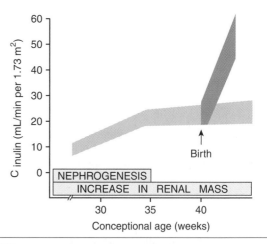

FIGURE 11-8   Maturation of glomerular filtration rate in relation to conceptional age. (From Guignard, J.P. [1981]. The neonatal stressed kidney. In A.B. Gruskin & M.E. Norman. [Eds.]. *Pediatric nephrology.* The Hague: Martinus Nijhoff.)

adenosine, endothelin, angiotensin II, prostaglandins (especially PGE_2 and PGI_2), ANF, nitric oxide (NO), and the renin-angiotensin and kinin-kallikrein systems.[47,48,130] Because the newborn has a higher RVR and sensitivity to vasoconstrictors than older individuals, the increase in RBF in early infancy is related to decreases in vasoconstrictor influences (Figure 11-7).[130] In newborns, the juxtamedullary nephrons are more mature than the outer cortical nephrons, and a greater proportion of the blood perfuses the inner cortical and medullary nephrons versus the outer cortical nephrons. After birth, perfusion of the outer cortex increases rapidly, perhaps in response to catecholamines and redistribution of placental blood flow.

A major difference in renal function between newborns and adults is the lower GFR in newborns, which is even lower when infants' smaller size and surface area are considered. The GFR is approximately 20 to 25 mL/minute per 1.73 m^2 at term or after 35 weeks, 10 to 13 mL/minute per 1.73 m^2 in infants less than 28 weeks' gestational age, and as low as 2 mL/minute per 1.73 m^2 at 25 weeks.[53,60,95] GFR (Figure 11-8) and RBF increase rapidly after birth, doubling by 2 weeks of age.[45] The pattern of maturation is similar in preterm infants over 34 to 35 weeks' gestation and term infants, although preterm infants may exhibit a slower increase, especially during the first week. The GFR is lower in preterm infants less than 34 to 35 weeks' gestational age and remains low until their full complement of nephrons has developed. After this point, maturation of RBF and GFR increases rapidly (up to fivefold) and eventually becomes similar to that of term infants.[95] The decreased initial GFR in very low–birth weight (VLBW) infants may limit their ability to respond to physiologic

stress, such as hypoxia and apnea, or to nephrotoxic drugs, such as indomethacin, that impair renal perfusion.[37]

Although the preterm infant continues to develop nephrons after birth, nephrogenesis may be altered with both accelerated maturation and an earlier cessation of this process leading to decreased numbers of glomeruli, abnormal glomeruli, smaller kidneys, and altered distal tubular function.[45,75,98,117,120] This alteration in development is particularly apparent in infants born at less than 1000 g birth weight.[15,45,98,117] This can lead to long-term impairment in renal function in some infants.[45,68,98] Preterm infants may have a lifelong reduction in the number of nephrons, and up to 13% of their nephrons have been found to have morphologic abnormalities (see pp. 367-368).[134] In addition, altered postbirth nutrition with extrauterine growth restriction may also alter nephron formation in these infants.[31,120] Factors that may alter renal development in preterm infants include fetal and extrauterine growth restriction; maternal glucocorticoids and medications such as aminoglycosides, indomethacin, ibuprofen; and hyperoxia (compared with what the infant experiences in utero).[45] These infants are at increased risk for hypertension and renal disease in adulthood.[1,36,82,113,117,126]

The increase in GFR after birth (see Figure 11-8) is a result of redistribution of placental blood flow with increased RBF and perfusion pressure, decreased RVR, and increased systemic blood pressure, which increases glomerular capillary hydrostatic pressure, along with increasing glomerular surface area (initially glomerular surface area is about 10% that of an adult) and increased permeability of the glomerular membrane.[48] Increased angiotensin II may help maintain the GFR in the face of a low mean arterial pressure. GFR correlates with gestational age in infants before 35 weeks, so after the postbirth increase in GFR, GFR increases with postmenstrual age.[48,51] After 35 weeks, GFR is more closely related to weight, length, and postbirth age. Maturation of GFR and other aspects of renal function may occur at varying rates in preterm infants, so infants must be evaluated individually to determine dosages of many pharmacologic agents (see Chapter 7).

Tubular Function

Tubular function is also altered in neonates. The decreased RBF and GFR reduce the volume of solutes per unit time that the tubules must handle. However, the neonate has a smaller tubular reabsorptive surface area, fewer solute transporters, decreased Na^+-K^+-ATPase activity, and altered control of H^+ transport.[59] Tubular thresholds for reabsorption of many solutes are also reduced, and neonates are more likely to lose sodium, glucose, and other solutes in urine, with the ability to excrete a sodium load blunted.[9] Although tubular function is quite adequate for a healthy infant, immature infants or compromised infants are at risk for fluid and electrolyte problems. Infants treated with antenatal steroids, which increase Na^+-K^+-ATPase activity, have more mature renal function at birth.[89]

Sodium

Immediately after birth, both term and preterm infants are in negative sodium balance because of the physiologic natriuresis stimulated by ANF changes with birth.[37,51] This rapidly changes to a positive sodium balance in term infants. Rapidly growing infants are in positive sodium balance (sodium intake greater than output). Excretion of sodium in neonates is reduced compared with adults, possibly because of increased plasma renin activity (PRA) and aldosterone levels, decreased Na^+-K^+-ATPase activity (especially in infants less than 34 weeks' gestation), and incorporation of sodium into the new tissue.[9,39,51] Renal tubular handling of sodium undergoes rapid changes after birth as the reabsorptive capacity for sodium and other solutes increases.[9] Maturation of sodium transport results from changes in both paracellular and transcellular mechanisms, including increases in the number of sodium transporters and changes in transporter isoforms, especially those involved in Na^+-H^+ exchange.[9]

Term newborns readily conserve sodium, with increased responsiveness of the distal tubule to aldosterone and a rapid increase in Na^+-K^+-ATPase activity after birth.[51,89,148] Tubular chloride permeability is low in neonates, with little passive transfer thus influencing sodium chloride transfer in the proximal tubule.[9]

The pattern for renal reabsorption of sodium is different in the infant than in an older child or adult, primarily because of the altered distribution of blood flow and changes in reabsorption in the proximal versus distal tubules. In infants, a greater portion of RBF is to juxtamedullary nephrons, whereas in the adult most RBF is to the cortical area and only about 10% goes to the medullary area. Because the juxtamedullary nephrons tend to be more involved in conservation than excretion of sodium, an infant's ability to excrete a sodium load is limited. This limitation increases the tendency toward sodium retention, with increased ECF volume and edema formation if excess sodium is given.[12,95] Increased urinary sodium loss is seen with hypoxia; respiratory distress syndrome; hyperbilirubinemia; acute tubular necrosis; and with use of pharmacologic agents such as diuretics, dopamine, and beta blockers.[34]

In addition, loop of Henle and proximal tubule reabsorption of sodium in infants is decreased; distal tubule reabsorption is relatively increased, perhaps as a compensatory mechanism to reduce renal sodium loss.[47,51,148] The increased distal tubule reabsorption is enhanced by elevated levels of aldosterone. Tubular reabsorption of sodium is greater in term infants than in preterm infants, who have increased urinary sodium losses and lower plasma sodium levels. Factors that influence natriuresis are summarized in Table 11-7.

TABLE 11-7   Factors Affecting Natriuresis and Urine Output in Fetuses and Newborn Infants

FACTOR	EFFECT ON NATRIURESIS	EFFECT ON URINE OUTPUT
Low renal blood flow (e.g., PDA)	↓	↓
Indomethacin for PDA	Variable	↓
Limited GFR: prerenal failure	↓	
Intrinsic or postrenal failure	↑	↑ or ↓
Tubular function: low tubular Na^+-K^+-ATPase	↑	
Prenatal glucocorticoid administration (upregulates transcription)	↓	
High cord levels of DLIF (inhibit Na^+-K^+-ATPase)	↑	
Dysfunction: aminoglycosides, amphotericin	↑	↑
Dopamine (note that receptor is probably not present in ELBW infants)	↑	↑
Renin-angiotensin-aldosterone system/high PRA and angiotensin activity:*		
Aldosterone (low level at birth later stimulated by sodium depletion)	↓	
Progesterone (limits tubule sensitivity to aldosterone)	↑	
High circulating level of atrial natriuretic factors	↑	
High concentration of AVP	May ↑	↓
Prostaglandins (limit effect of AVP)		↑
Osmotic diuresis caused by hyperglycemia	↑	↑
Diuretics	↑	↑

*Increased natriuresis caused by extracellular fluid expansion mediated by adrenocorticotropic hormone; decreased natriuresis if sodium depletion.
AVP, Arginine vasopressin; *DLIF,* circulating endogenous digoxin-like immunoreactive factors; *ELBW,* extremely low birth weight; *GFR,* glomerular filtration rate; *Na*-K-ATPase, sodium potassium adeno-sine triphosphatase; *PDA,* patent ductus arteriosus; *PRA,* plasma renin activity.
From Brion, L.P., Bernstein, J., & Spitzer, A. (1997). Kidney and urinary tract. In A.A. Fanaroff & R.J. Martin. (Eds.). *Fanaroff & Martin's neonatal-perinatal medicine: Diseases of the fetus and infant* (6th ed.). St. Louis: Mosby.

Sodium Balance in Preterm Infants. Preterm infants are more likely to be in negative sodium balance (sodium intake less than output) and have difficulty conserving sodium during the first few weeks after birth.[9,33,34] A VLBW infant may excrete up to 5% to 10% of the filtered sodium load (versus 0.1% to 0.2% in term infants).[9] Negative sodium balance has been observed initially in most infants less than 30 weeks' gestation, 70% at 30 to 32 weeks, and 40% between 33 and 35 weeks.[9,95,148] Factors leading to the negative sodium balance in these infants include decreased Na^+-K^+-ATPase, high ECF volume, reduced tubular aldosterone sensitivity (with a lack of epithelial sodium channels in the distal tubule that normally increase in response to aldosterone), and other factors listed in Table 11-7.[9,95,148] Even though the GFR is lower in preterm infants (so the kidneys have less sodium to handle at any given time), the altered tubular reabsorption with decreased proximal tubular reabsorption (where 80% to 90% of sodium is reabsorbed in adults), decreased loop of Henle reabsorption (only 20% of adult capacity), and increased distal tubule load results in increased fractional sodium excretion.[9,89] Antenatal steroids may decrease the alterations in sodium and water balance in preterm infants by decreasing insensible water loss and hypernatremia.[34] These infants tend to have an earlier diuresis and natriuresis after birth, possibly because of earlier maturation of epithelial transport systems in the kidney.[34]

Decreased proximal tubule reabsorption of sodium in preterm infants may be a result of the shorter length of the tubules and immature transport mechanisms. As a result, greater amounts of fluid and electrolytes such as Na^+ remain in the lumen and are sent to the distal tubule. The distal tubule is unable to increase its reabsorptive capacity to handle the additional sodium load despite elevated PRA and aldosterone levels, so more sodium is lost in the urine. The ability of the distal tubule to respond to aldosterone may be reduced or the distal tubule may already be under maximal aldosterone stimulation and thus may be unable to further increase its reabsorptive capacity.[148]

Thus preterm infants have a limited ability to both excrete and retain sodium.[51] The result is a narrow margin for sodium homeostasis in the VLBW infant. These infants lose excess sodium in their urine because of the limitations in sodium conservation described previously. In addition, these infants cannot readily excrete a sodium load. If fluid intake is inadequate, they are at risk of sodium retention and hypernatremia, especially in the first week after birth.[87] As noted previously, antenatal steroid therapy to stimulate lung maturation is associated with a lower incidence of hypernatremia in VLBW infants, as well as decreased insensible water loss and an earlier diuresis and natriuresis.[34]

The fractional sodium excretion (FE_{Na}) is the amount of urinary sodium excretion as a percent of the filtered sodium.[9] FE_{Na} is highest in the first 10 days after birth and by 1 month is less than 0.4% to 1%. There is an inverse relationship between (FE_{Na}) and gestational age.[45] For example, there is a greater than 10-fold increase in FE_{Na} between 23 and 31 weeks' gestation.[33] In a larger preterm infant, FE_{Na} is 1% to 5%, versus more than 5% in VLBW infants and 0.5% to 1% in term infants.[34,85,117] Adult values of less than 0.5% are reached by 2 to 3 weeks' postbirth age in most infants.[85,117] The high FE_{NA} in preterm infants is in part a result of resistance to the effects of aldosterone on tubular sodium transport.[108] FE_{Na} is a measure of tubular function (as GFR is a measure of glomerular function) and is calculated as follows:

$$FE_{Na} = \frac{\text{Urine sodium}}{\text{Serum sodium}} \times \frac{\text{Serum creatinine}}{\text{Urine creatinine}} \times 100$$

Tubular reabsorption of sodium (T_{Na}) can be estimated by the formula $T_{Na} = 100\% - FE_{Na}$. The greater the FE_{Na}, the more sodium is lost in the urine. To determine whether FE_{Na} is excessive, sodium and fluid intake must be considered.[9,39] By several weeks of age, most preterm infants are in positive sodium balance as tubular function matures. Maturation takes longer in VLBW infants, who are at risk for fluid and electrolyte disturbances for a longer period.[148]

Glucose

The ability of the tubules to reabsorb glucose and the transport maximum (T_m) for glucose are decreased in the preterm infant but similar to or exceed those of adults in term infants.[9,53,148] The lower T_m in the preterm infant, and the increased risk of glycosuria, is a result of low levels of sodium-glucose transporters in the proximal tubule.[108,148] Even at term, the renal threshold for glucose (corrected for surface area) is lower in the infant. Even with this lower threshold, most normoglycemic infants (unless very immature) are not glycosuric. This is probably because the glucose T_m-to-GFR ratio is high.[148] Although the glomerulotubular balance for glucose filtration and reabsorption can be demonstrated as early as 25 weeks' gestation, low renal thresholds for glucose (less than 100 to 150 mg/dL [less than 5.55 to 8.32 mmol/L]) and increased fractional excretion of glucose are seen in some VLBW infants less than 28 weeks' gestation.[59,95] Urinary glucose levels are increased in preterm infants, with higher fractional glucose excretion, less reabsorption of glucose, and a tendency toward glycosuria.[12] VLBW infants are also at risk for hyperglycemia, because they are unable to readily excrete a glucose load. Because renal handling of glucose is interrelated with that of water, Na^+, K^+, and other solutes, attempts to excrete a glucose load may lead to hyponatremia, dehydration, and other abnormalities. Therefore VLBW infants receiving intravenous glucose must be monitored for hyperglycemia, glycosuria, and fluid and electrolyte status. Glucose metabolism is discussed in Chapter 16.

Renal Handling of Other Solutes

In general, renal excretion of solutes increases with both gestational and postnatal age. Potassium excretion is low during gestation, and the newborn is less able to excrete a potassium load. With the lower GFR, less sodium is delivered to and reabsorbed by the tubules. Because K^+ is exchanged for Na^+ in the distal tubule, less K^+ is secreted and subsequently excreted.[12] Healthy term and growing preterm infants are in positive potassium balance; stressed or ill infants may have a negative balance. Transient hyperkalemia occurs in some VLBW infants (especially those less than 27 to 28 weeks' gestational age), probably because of their low GFR, decreased tubular response to aldosterone, decreased expression of potassium channels in the collecting duct, and decreased Na^+-K^+-ATPase activity.[40,78,108,117] The turnover of potassium is related to that of energy needs and nitrogen. Stressed infants have greater energy needs. After other energy sources (i.e., carbohydrate and fat stores) have been used, protein will be catabolized for energy, with release of nitrogen. This leads to a negative nitrogen balance and increase in K^+ secretion and excretion. A negative potassium balance is also associated with the use of diuretics and parenteral fluid therapy.

Uric acid levels are higher in preterm than term infants (averaging 7.7 versus 5.2 mL/dL [457.99 versus 309.20 μmol/L]) and decrease with gestation. Serum levels are higher in infants because of increased production of uric acid as a byproduct of nucleotide breakdown.[154] Serum uric acid levels may also be elevated in hypoxic infants or after asphyxia. Uric acid crystals may occasionally be seen as reddish staining of the diaper in normal newborns and can be misinterpreted as blood. Urea excretion is usually decreased in the neonate, because they are using nitrogen for growth. Urinary protein excretion is greater at birth, gradually decreasing over the first few weeks. Transient proteinuria may occur during the first 5 days.[148]

The fractional renal reabsorption of amino acids is greater than 98% for all but histidine. Newborns may have a mild but not usually clinically significant aminoacidemia because of immaturity of proximal tubule transporters for glycine, taurine, and proline.[53] Amino acid excretion is increased in preterm infants, especially for taurine.[53]

Renal excretion of phosphorus, calcium, and magnesium is interrelated with sodium reabsorption and excretion. During the first week, calcium excretion varies inversely with gestational age and directly with urine flow and sodium excretion, thus increasing the risk for hypocalcemia in VLBW infants.[12] Alterations in sodium intake and excretion alter renal handling of these solutes in ill infants, so liberal sodium supplementation may lead to development or exacerbation of hypocalcemia.[13] Phosphorus excretion is higher during the first weeks after birth and is related to gestational age and type of oral feeding. Calcium and phosphorus metabolism are discussed in Chapter 17.

VLBW infants are at higher risk for nephrocalcinosis, with an incidence of 16% to 64%.[147] Contributory factors are the high urinary calcium excretion, low serum phosphorus, metabolic acidosis, and elevated urinary oxalate and urate excretion.[147] Urinary calcium and phosphorus excretion are increased with

use of furosemide. Nephrocalcinosis increases the risk of osteopenia and rickets.

Acid-Base Homeostasis

Serum bicarbonate levels and plasma pH are lower in neonates because of a lower renal threshold for and reduced capacity to reabsorb bicarbonate. The lower threshold (serum level at which bicarbonaturia occurs) might be the result of altered transport capacity for bicarbonate (because of weak expression of enzymes and transporters needed for bicarbonate reabsorption) and immature epithelial cell structure and function or may be related to expansion of ECF volume.[12,31,47,154] The more immature the infant, the lower the bicarbonate levels. Initially, serum bicarbonate levels may be 14 to 16 mEq/L (mmol/L) or lower in VLBW, 16 to 20 mEq/L (mmol/L) in low-birth-weight (LBW), and 19 to 22 mEq/L (mmol/L) in term infants (versus 24 to 28 mEq/L in adults).[47] Serum bicarbonate levels in preterm infants increase to values greater than 20 mEq/L within the first 1 to 2 weeks. Urinary pH is 6 to 7 initially, with minimum values (4.5 to 5.3) reached by 1 to 2 weeks. The occurrence of alkaline urine along with a metabolic acidosis suggests renal tubular acidosis.

Term and preterm infants are able to excrete an acid load, although the ability of the kidneys to respond to an acid load increases with gestational and postnatal age.[47,148,153] The decreased response to an acid load in a VLBW infant may result from immaturity of the hydrogen ion–secreting mechanism, decreased excretion of urinary buffers, or unresponsiveness of the distal tubule to aldosterone, as well as the lower GFR.[53,95] Normally most newborns are probably secreting near to their maximal ability, with little reserve to cope with any disorders that produce acidosis. Thus any event that increases the potential for acidosis, such as cold stress, hypoxemia, or malnutrition, is more likely to produce alterations in acid-base status in the newborn.

Water Balance

Regulation of water balance by newborns is similar to that of adults, but it occurs within a narrower range. The ability of newborns to dilute urine is similar to that of adults, whereas their ability to concentrate urine is limited. The ability to dilute is defined as the minimum amount of solute (electrolytes, protein) that can be excreted in a volume of urine; that is, there is an obligatory amount of solute that the body must lose to excrete water in urine. Because diluting segments of the distal tubule and ascending loop of Henle develop early, term newborns and preterm infants of more than 35 weeks' gestation can dilute their urine to an osmolarity of 50 mOsm/L (mmol/L) (similar to adult values) or lower; preterm infants of less than 35 weeks' gestation can dilute to 70 mOsm/L (mmol/L).[34] However, neither term nor preterm infants can handle large or rapidly administered water loads because of their low GFR.[63,95] Therefore neonates are at risk for overhydration, water retention, and fluid overload. The decreased ability to excrete a water load is related primarily to a lower GFR and perhaps decreased sensitivity of the tubules to AVP. The ability to excrete a water load increases after 3 to 4 days in term infants and preterm infants born at 35 weeks' gestation or more.[154]

The ability to concentrate urine relates to the maximum amount of solute that can be excreted within a volume of urine (i.e., the ability to excrete a solute load without becoming dehydrated). To excrete more solute, the body would have to increase the amount of water in the urine. The ability to concentrate urine is mediated by vasopressin and occurs via aquaporins (water channel proteins).[63] The concentration of solutes in urine depends on a complex interaction of events called the *countercurrent multiplier system* (Box 11-3). Generally the newborn can maximally concentrate urine to approximately half of adult levels (600 to 700 mOsm/L [mmol/L] versus 1200 to 1400 mOsm/L [mmol/L]). This ability is further decreased in preterm infants, with maximum urinary concentration of 245 to 450 mOsm/kg/L in 1300- to 1500-g infants at 1 to 3 weeks of age and even lower levels in more immature infants. By 4 to 6 weeks after birth, preterm infants can concentrate similarly to term infants.[148] The immature concentrating ability is why normal saline is not used as a routine intravenous fluid in the neonatal intensive care unit; it will be hypertonic compared with the infant's urine and increase the risk of hypernatremia.[16] The limitation in concentrating ability is related to several factors:

1. Decreased medullary osmotic gradient related to decreased accumulation of urea and other solutes and increased medullary blood flow.
2. Lower concentrations of blood urea. Urea is a solute that sets up the concentration gradient. Because urea is an end-product of nitrogen metabolism, growing infants—who use nitrogen to make protein and new tissue—metabolize less nitrogen and produce less urea.
3. Decreased solute levels for the concentration gradients in the interstitial space because of decreased reabsorption and increased excretion of Na^+, Cl^-, glucose, and urea, possibly mediated by increased prostaglandin production.
4. Decreased length of loops of Henle and collecting ducts and immature tubular function.
5. Decreased response to circulating AVP and immaturity of AVP-signal transducer pathways; decreased transcription and expression of aquaporin 2 (AQP2) water channels in the collecting ducts.
6. Interference of prostaglandins with the hypoosmotic action of AVP.[34,46,63,88,95,148,154]

Hormonal Regulation

Renin-Angiotensin-Aldosterone System

RAA system activity (see Figure 11-3 and Box 11-1 on p. 356) is inversely related to gestational age.[125,130] Values in the newborn are higher than in adults and decrease gradually over the first months.[95,125,128,130] Angiotensinogen and PRA are particularly high.[9,95,128] PRA is inversely related to gestational age and three to five times higher in infants than adults.[95] PRA remains high for the first 2 to 3 weeks in all newborns and then begins to slowly decrease.[133] Circulating angiotensin II is also high at birth, and the decrease parallels the decrease in PRA.[128] The high angiotensin II levels may be mediated by decreased end organ responsiveness in the newborn.[95,128] Hyperfunction of this system may be related to the low systemic blood pressure and RBF, sodium wasting, and normal decrease in ECF volume after birth.[154] The increased renin and aldosterone concentrations may be also mediated by prostaglandins, which are elevated at birth.[12] By increasing sodium reabsorption by the distal tubules, or by influencing vasoconstriction, aldosterone modulates changes in GFR to protect the renal tubules from overload with loss of electrolytes and other solutes in the urine.

In VLBW infants, adrenal production of aldosterone is decreased compared with that in term infants, and the distal tubule is less responsive to aldosterone.[12,148] These changes increase the risk of hyponatremia and dehydration. Hypertension in the newborn is usually related to factors that activate the renin-angiotensin system to stimulate angiotensin II production (e.g., renal vein thrombosis, coarctation of the aorta, bronchopulmonary dysplasia, and glucocorticoid administration).[128] The basis for the decreased response to

---

BOX 11-3   Countercurrent Multiplier System

The ability to concentrate urine is the maximum amount of solute that can be excreted within a volume of urine. Adults concentrate to a maximum of 1200–1400 mOsm/L (mmol/L); term newborns to 600–700 mOsm/L (mmol/L). To excrete more solute, the amount of urine water would have to be increased. Concentration of solutes in urine depends on the countercurrent system, which involves movement of Na^+, water, and other solutes between the tubular lumen, collecting ducts, and surrounding interstitial fluid.

This system can be summarized as follows: Fluid entering the descending limb of the loop of Henle is hypoosmotic because of movement of solutes out of the proximal tubule (see Figure 11-1). Because water but not Na^+ is reabsorbed in the descending limb, the fluid in the loop of Henle becomes hyperosmotic. As the filtrate moves through the ascending limb, Na^+ and Cl^- (but not water) move out of the lumen, so that the filtrate again becomes hypoosmotic and the surrounding interstitial fluid becomes hyperosmotic. The longer the loops of Henle, the more concentrated the urine. As the filtrate passes through the distal tubule and collecting duct, Na^+ reabsorption is mediated by aldosterone, and Na^+ is exchanged for secreted H^+ and K^+. There is little water movement in the distal tubule. In the collecting duct, arginine vasopressin (AVP) controls water reabsorption. When AVP is present, water reabsorption increases, resulting in a hypertonic urine.

Adapted from Ramanathan, S. & Turndorf, H. (1988). Renal disease. In F.M. James, A.S. Wheeler, & D.M. Dewan. (Eds.). *Obstetric anesthesia: The complicated patient.* Philadelphia: F.A. Davis.

aldosterone is uncertain but may relate to lack of receptors, the presence of an undetermined antagonist, or the deficiency of intracellular transport system enzymes. At the same time, inhibition of aldosterone release is decreased, which increases the risk of sodium overload if too much supplemental sodium is given.[51]

Arginine Vasopressin

Although the distal tubule and the collecting ducts of the infant respond to AVP (also called anti-diuretic hormone), the responses of the collecting ducts to AVP are immature at birth, possibly because of low expression of AQP2 water channels.[46] Aquaporins are vasopressin-sensitive water channels that are needed for water reabsorption. AVP works by inserting aquaporins (water channels) into the apical membranes of collecting duct cells. These proteins are decreased in immature infants.[88] AQP2 is the main target of AVP in regulating collecting duct permeability and the ability to concentrate urine.[62] Urinary AQP2 excretion is low for the first 1 to 4 days after birth, then stabilizes over the next month, increasing from 4 to 6 weeks.[46] AVP binds to arginine-vasopressin V2 receptors that stimulate signaling pathways to promote movement of preformed vesicles containing AQP2 channels to the membrane surface, making the collecting duct membrane more permeable to water.[34]

AVP increases at birth, especially in infants born vaginally (possibly stimulated by head compression).[46,95,106] Sensitivity of volume receptors and osmoreceptors in neonates is similar to that in adults. However, tubular response to circulating AVP is decreased in preterm infants with resistance of the immature kidney to AVP because of immature transcription of AQP2.[62,95,106,108,148] Plasma and urinary AVP are increased after hypoxic-ischemic events (possibly mediated by catecholamines) and in infants with intracranial hemorrhage, respiratory distress syndrome (RDS), meconium aspiration syndrome, and pneumothorax. These findings may be a result of decreased osmolarity in the medullary interstitium (from decreased tubular function and decreased reabsorption of solutes) or inhibition of AVP by increased levels of prostaglandin E$_2$ (PGE$_2$).[39,63,106] The increase in AVP at birth may enhance extrauterine adaptation by increasing blood pressure and peripheral vasoconstriction and enhancing postnatal fluid homeostasis.

Factors regulating AVP secretion in neonates are not fully understood. Increased AVP and water retention may be important in the development of later hyponatremia in VLBW infants.[148] Chronically increased sodium excretion with contraction of the ECF compartment may stimulate the RAA system and AVP secretion. AVP increases renal water reabsorption to restore ECF volume but may also decrease plasma sodium. As noted previously, AVP is increased with stressful events such as birth, surgery, intraventricular hemorrhage, and other complications.[51] The result is increased water and subsequently sodium loss with a risk of hyponatremia and other electrolyte alterations.[51,87]

Other Regulating Factors

Renal function and hemodynamics are influenced by other substances in addition to the RAA system and AVP. The kallikrein-kinin system is activated at birth and modulates RBF and handling of sodium and water by stimulating formation of bradykinins and prostaglandins and by acting as an antagonist to the RAA system and AVP.[130] The kidneys produce dopamine (precursor to norepinephrine and epinephrine) in the proximal tubules of superficial nephrons.[106] Dopamine inhibits renal sodium absorption (thus increasing sodium excretion), increases water excretion by inhibiting AVP release from the pituitary, and alters water transport in the collecting ducts.[106] Prostaglandins also mediate RBF and may be important in regulating RBF during stress; they may also balance the increased RAA system activity.[128,130]

ANF is released by the atrial myocardium in response to atrial stretch. ANF has natriuretic and diuretic actions. ANF increases at birth, peaking at 48 to 72 hours, the time of maximal postbirth diuresis.[12] Birth results in decreased pulmonary vascular resistance, increased pulmonary blood flow, and thus increased blood return to the left atrium. This stretches the left atrium and stimulates ANF release. The ANF response is blunted in preterm infants, perhaps because of decreased cyclic guanosine monophosphate, more rapid clearance of ANF, and altered renal hemodynamics.[95]

CLINICAL IMPLICATIONS FOR NEONATAL CARE

Newborns are able to regulate sodium and water balance, but within a much narrower range than seen in older children and adults. As a result, the neonate is much more likely to develop fluid and electrolyte disturbances within a shorter period of time, with a small margin between homeostasis and overload or underload. Careful calculation and monitoring of needs are essential to maintain homeostasis. Immaturity of renal function limits the ability of the infant, especially if preterm or ill, to cope with additional stress and increases the risk of renal dysfunction after pathophysiologic events such as hypoxia, ischemia, or RDS. Alterations in renal function affect excretion of drugs and influence serum levels and drug half-life values, increasing the risks of side effects and toxicity.[75,120] In addition, drug therapy can alter renal development after birth, especially in preterm infants.

Fluid and Electrolyte Balance

Birth represents a major change in the infant's fluid and electrolyte status, which in fetal life is maintained by the placenta and mother. During the transitional period, infants undergo a physiologic diuresis and natriuresis (see Transitional Events), resulting in an isotonic contraction of the extracellular space and a transient negative sodium and water balance. If caregivers do not allow this normal transition, the infant is at risk of fluid retention, including accumulations of pulmonary interstitial fluid.[87] Lorenz notes that, in light of these changes after birth, "the goal is not to maintain fluid and electrolyte status after birth but rather to allow these changes to occur appropriately."[78] Early volume expansion of VLBW infants without cardiovascular compromise has not been documented to improve outcomes.[102] Fluid restriction has sometimes been suggested for early management of infants at risk for bronchopulmonary dysplasia. However, a recent Cochrane review concluded that there was no evidence to support this practice in infants with early or established bronchopulmonary dysplasia.[8]

Calculation of fluid needs for any infant involves consideration of maintenance needs, replacement of losses, and provision of allowances for growth. Maintenance needs include consideration of endogenous water produced by oxidative metabolism plus insensible water loss (IWL) and loss of water in urine and stool. Usual values for these parameters are known and can be used to calculate fluid needs. In healthy term or large preterm infants, individual variations from these values, unless major, are probably not crucial; the infant's kidneys will adjust to ensure fluid and electrolyte homeostasis.[34] However, ill or VLBW infants may not be able to adjust if their renal function is inefficient or compromised by illness. In addition, these infants are more likely to be in environments (e.g., incubator, radiant warmer, or phototherapy) that can markedly alter IWL.[34]

Stool water loss is estimated at 5 to 10 mL/kg/day under basal conditions but can increase markedly with diarrhea. Stool water losses are considered to be minimal during the first few days after birth and thus are not included in calculation of initial fluid needs. Approximately 5 to 10 mL/kg/day of endogenous water is produced by oxidation. This water is often ignored in calculation of fluid requirements, because it offsets fecal losses.[12] Water for growth varies with body water composition. For example, if an infant is assumed to have water content of 70%, water needed for growth would be 0.70 mL per gram of weight gain. Because body water composition is not static, water for growth is generally estimated at 10 to 20 mL/kg/day, with the higher values used for more immature infants who have a larger proportion of body water.[34] In the first week after birth, during the period of physiologic weight loss, calculation of maintenance fluid needs does not include replacement of water for growth but is based primarily on calculation of IWL and urine water loss.

Insensible Water Loss

IWL is water loss from the skin (70%) and respiratory tract (30%). IWL generally consists of about 32% of the total water requirement, unless IWL is markedly increased.[12] Basal levels of IWL in the neonate are 20 mL/kg/day or 0.7 to 1.6 mL/kg/hour.[12] IWL is markedly increased in preterm infants. In ELBW infants with thin, gelatinous skin, these losses are particularly high (see Chapter 14).[10] Skin water loss is proportional to surface area, and these infants have greater ratios of surface area to weight. Preterm infants also have greater IWL because of increased permeability of their epidermis to water, greater

BOX 11-4   Factors Influencing Insensible Water Loss in Neonates

INCREASE INSENSIBLE WATER LOSS

Immaturity (50%–300%)
Radiant warmer (50%–200%)
Forced convection incubator (30%–50%)
Phototherapy (40%–100%)
Respiratory distress
Elevated body or ambient temperature*
Skin breakdown or injury
Congenital defects (omphalocele, gastroschisis, neural tube defect)
Motor activity, crying (up to 70%)
Other factors that increase metabolic rate

DECREASE INSENSIBLE WATER LOSS

Plastic heat shields (30%–50%)
Double-wall incubator or heat shield (30%–50%)
Plastic blanket under radiant warmer (30%–50%)
High humidity (50%–100%)
Transport thermal blanket (70%)
Assisted ventilation with warmed and humidified air (20%–30%)
Increasing postnatal age
Semipermeable dressing or topical agents (50%)

Compiled from references 10, 12, 34, 78, 89, 148.
*A 1° increase in body temperature is equal to a 30% increase in insensible water loss.

percentage of body water, and increased skin blood flow in relation to metabolic rate.[12,34,106] IWL can be significantly altered by conditions that increase the basal metabolic rate and by therapeutic modalities such as phototherapy, radiant warmers, heat shields, humidity, and incubators (see Chapter 20).[10,12] Lower ambient humidity or higher ambient temperature increase IWL; higher ambient humidity or humidified oxygen lower IWL.[34] For example, water loss increases 100% in infants older than 26 weeks' gestational age if the ambient humidity is decreased from 60% to 20%.[2] Factors that increase or decrease IWL in neonates are summarized in Box 11-4.

Urine Water Loss

Urine water loss generally accounts for about 56% of total body water requirements (generally about 50 to 100 mL/kg/day).[12] The amount of water the infant must excrete in urine, the maximum urine concentrating ability (urine osmolarity), and the renal solute load are all interrelated and can be calculated using the following formula:

$$\text{Urine volume (mL/kg)} = \frac{\text{Solute load (mOsm/kg)}}{\text{Urine osmolarity (mOsm/L[mmol/L])}} \times 1000$$

Variations in renal solute load can markedly alter obligatory urinary water losses. For example, a nongrowing infant who could concentrate to a maximum of 300 mOsm/L would have to excrete about 25 mL/urine/kg to get rid of a solute load of 7.5 mOsm/kg; the same infant would be obligated to lose 50 mL/urine/kg if receiving a solute load of 15 mOsm/kg (7.5/300 × 1000 = 25 mL/kg urine versus 15/300 × 1000 = 50 mL/kg urine) and would be at greater risk for dehydration. The renal solute load is the amount of solutes from metabolic end-products (especially nitrogenous compounds and electrolytes) and exogenous sources that must be excreted by the kidneys. Endogenous solutes are produced from catabolism of tissues when caloric and protein intake is inadequate. Exogenous solutes are derived from parenteral solutions and enteral intake. The solute load from exogenous sources can be calculated from the following formula:

$$\text{Solute load (mOsm/L [mmol/L])} =$$
$$4 \text{ (g protein per dL)} + 1 (Na^+ + k^+ + Cl^-)$$

Renal solute load varies with the type of oral intake and whether the infant is receiving an intravenous solution with additional electrolytes and other solutes.

Renal solute load is lowest for growing infants fed human milk and highest for infants who are starved or receiving high osmolar parenteral fluids or a high-protein formula. Renal solute loads for commercial formulas can be found in the manufacturer's formula handbook. Renal solute loads for parenteral fluids average 10 to 20 mOsm of solute per 100 kcal expended (in infants less than 10 kg, mL/kcal = mL/kg). For example, an intravenous line with a 10% glucose solution would average 10 mOsm/kg/day, and a maintenance IV with 3 mEq NaCl and 2 mEq KCl would yield an additional 10 mOsm/L (mmol/L) of solute from these electrolytes (i.e., 3 from Na, plus 3 from Cl, plus 2 from K, plus 2 from Cl).[12]

Various factors can modify renal solute load and urine water excretion. In a growing preterm infant who is incorporating protein and other solutes into new tissue, each gram of weight gain decreases the renal solute load by about 1 mOsm. The decrease in solute load is reflected in decreased obligatory urine water loss. Urine water volume and thus fluid needs may be increased with glycosuria or furosemide therapy and decreased in infants on positive-pressure ventilation or with the syndrome of inappropriate secretion of antidiuretic hormone (SIADH [ADH is the former term for AVP]) or acute renal tubular necrosis.[12]

Estimating Fluid and Electrolyte Needs

During the first few days after birth, maintenance fluid requirements are based on IWL and urine water loss. With increasing postbirth age, fluid requirements increase because of increased stool water losses and growth. There are many variations in specific recommendations for fluid and electrolyte needs. Fluid needs for the first few days are generally calculated to account for the normal physiologic weight loss of birth weight. If IWL is increased (see Box 11-4), fluid needs are also increased. On the other hand, fluid needs are reduced in infants with acute renal failure or congestive heart failure. Fluid needs are higher in infants weighing less than 1000 g because of markedly increased IWL and decreased renal concentrating ability (which increases obligatory urine water loss). Current recommendations for fluid and electrolyte management of term and preterm neonates are available.[12,34,106,138]

Sodium Requirements of Preterm Infants

There are differing viewpoints on the management of fluid and electrolyte status in preterm infants. Sodium intake is usually calculated at 1 to 3 mEq/kg/day. Sodium supplementation is usually lower for the first few days because of the relatively volume-expanded state of most infants.[34] Preterm infants, particularly those less than 30 to 32 weeks' gestation, may be unable to maintain sodium balance on the standard sodium intake because of increased urinary sodium loss, and may require higher sodium intakes.[9,34,37] Dell recommends 1 to 2 mEq/kg/day for the first 3 to 7 days, then 2 to 3 after that, perhaps increasing to 4 to 5 in VLBW infants due to increased urinary sodium losses in the first few weeks.[34]

Early administration of sodium can also increase the risk of hypernatremia and respiratory problems by interfering with the normal extracellular water loss after birth.[39,49,50,88] Hartnoll and colleagues studied early (day of life 1) versus late (once infant had lost 6% of birth weight) administration of 4 mEq/kg of supplemental sodium.[49,50] Infants with early sodium intake had less of a decrease in extracellular water and increase in respiratory problems both at 1 week and 28 days. The investigators believed that the increased respiratory problems were a result of persistent extracellular volume expansion with increased pulmonary interstitial fluid.[49] Restriction of sodium intake in the first 5 days decreased the incidence of hypernatremia, whereas fluid restriction led to hyponatremia.[24] Modi notes that, if given liberal fluid intake with sodium supplementation, infants will not have the usual initial postbirth weight loss. However, eventually most infants will experience the typical postbirth changes in fluid compartments.[89] "The diuresis that accompanies improving respiratory function in babies with RDS is in fact a natriuresis and is an example of delayed postnatal maturation."[89]

All infants have a reduction in ECF volume in the first few days associated with increased excretion of fluid and sodium. This in part accounts for the increased sodium losses in the first week. Thus correcting the high sodium excretion by increasing sodium intake in the first week may impede the normal postbirth adjustments in body fluid compartment values.[89,148] However, after these adjustments have occurred, sodium balance in the VLBW infant must be carefully evaluated and monitored. Most clinicians agree that sodium supplementation is necessary in VLBW infants after the initial decrease in extracellular volume.[12,148] The more immature the infant, the less able he or she is to adapt to a low sodium intake.[148] Various protocols have been recommended for management of fluids and electrolytes in VLBW infants.[12,34,106,138] Sodium acetate or sodium bicarbonate may be used to help compensate for the respiratory acidosis from respiratory immaturity and problems and from metabolic acidosis caused by renal tubular immaturity.[12] Some formulas as well as human milk may not contain adequate sodium for the VLBW infant with immature renal function. These infants may require sodium supplementation until sodium balance is positive.

Risk of Overhydration and Dehydration

Although infants can dilute urine to osmolarities of 50 to 70 mOsm/L (mmol/L), the usual diuretic response to a water load often diminishes before the entire load can be excreted.[79] This decreased ability to excrete a water load makes the infant more susceptible to fluid overload. Term and larger preterm infants are more vulnerable to overhydration in the first 5 days after birth, because maximal dilution is not achieved until after that time.[34] GFR remains low in preterm infants until a gestational age greater than 34 to 35 weeks is reached; thus these infants are at risk for volume overload for a longer period. Fluid overload in preterm infants has been associated with an increased risk of PDA.[132] The expanded extracellular volume secondary to fluid overload may stimulate production of PGE_2, which maintains a patent ductus. In infants with PDA and a large shunt, blood flow to the intestines is reduced, which may result in hypoperfusion, ischemia, and increased risk of necrotizing enterocolitis (see Chapter 12).

Because of decreased concentrating ability, neonates (especially preterm infants) are at risk for dehydration, particularly if fluid intake is inadequate or extrarenal losses are elevated, as with transepidermal loss in VLBW infants. In evaluating dehydration in the first week, the usual postbirth weight loss must be considered so that infants do not become overhydrated.[34]

Electrolyte Imbalances

Limitations in renal function in preterm and ill neonates increase the risk of electrolyte disturbances from physiologic or iatrogenic causes. Electrolyte imbalances can also arise from pathophysiologic problems, but these are not considered here.

Hyponatremia

Hyponatremia in preterm or sick infants can occur secondary to alterations in fluid (dilutional hyponatremia) or in sodium balance. Dilutional hyponatremia can arise from excess transfer of free water across the placenta because of rapid or excessive administration of fluids to the woman in labor. Excessive administration of a hypotonic solution overwhelms the limited fetal or neonatal renal capacity to deal with a water overload. This may occur if maintenance fluid requirements for the first week after birth do not allow for the physiologic weight loss, especially in VLBW infants. These events lead to rapid expansion of extracellular volume and reduced serum sodium and are associated with an increased incidence of PDA, congestive heart failure, NEC, intracranial hemorrhage, and bronchopulmonary dysplasia.[16,135]

Dilutional hyponatremia can also occur subsequent to water retention associated with SIADH. This syndrome is seen with a variety of pathophysiologic problems such as asphyxia, respiratory distress, sepsis, and central nervous system problems and after PDA ligation and other stressful situations. SIADH involves excessive secretion of AVP with normal fluid intake, serum hyponatremia and hypoosmolality, increased urine osmolality and renal sodium excretion, absence of volume depletion and dehydration, and normal renal and adrenal function.[106]

Hyponatremia can also arise from negative sodium balance and excessive loss of sodium by the immature kidneys of VLBW infants. In these infants the greater sodium loss increases water loss (renal excretion of sodium must be accompanied by excretion of water), leading to decreased ECF volume and hyponatremia.[106] Urinary sodium loss and subsequent hyponatremia in VLBW infants interfere with renal concentrating ability by changing the osmotic gradient and impairing AVP response. This further reduces water reabsorption and increases sodium loss and risk of hyponatremia.[9] Dilutional hyponatremia is an ever-present risk for VLBW infants in the early postnatal period. This risk may be reduced by increasing sodium intake in VLBW infants during the first few weeks and careful monitoring of intake, output, electrolytes, weight, and fluid status.[12] A late hyponatremia may be seen at 4 to 6 weeks of age in rapidly growing VLBW infants.[37]

Hypernatremia

Hypernatremia related to immaturity of renal function may arise from dehydration caused by excessive sodium intake or increased IWL. The dehydration may be aggravated by limited concentrating ability of the immature kidney.[63] Hypernatremia can also follow intravenous administration of sodium bicarbonate; the infant may not be able to rapidly excrete this sodium load.[135] Hypernatremia in VLBW infants is usually secondary to high transepidermal water losses in the first week.[40] Hypernatremia is associated with an increased risk of intracranial bleeding in both term and preterm infants.[16,135]

Hyperkalemia in Preterm Infants

VLBW infants are also at risk for both oliguric and nonoliguric hyperkalemia because of alterations in renal function and changes in fluid dynamics after birth.[16] Up to 30% to 50% of infants weighing less than 1000 g at birth have been reported to have nonoliguric hyperkalemia in the first 48 to 72 hours after birth; the incidence has decreased with antenatal steroid use and early initiation of parenteral and enteral nutrition.[9,152] Nonoliguric hyperkalemia may result from shifts in potassium from the intracellular to extracellular space or immaturity of renal tubular K^+ secretion mechanisms.[9,108,117,152] As a result, potassium needs must be carefully monitored, and routine replacement may need to be decreased in the first few days.[10,78] Some infants less than 26 to 27 weeks of age have signs of dehydration at 24 to

48 hours, with elevated sodium, potassium, and glucose without oliguria, acidosis, or shock. This may result from excessive evaporative losses (up to 100 to 200 mL/kg/day) because of the immature skin and greater surface area–to–body mass ratio, aldosterone insensitivity, and immaturity of renal Na^+-K^+-ATPase activity or a shift in potassium from the intracellular to extracellular space.[9,78,108,117] This is rare today with current management strategies and the use of humidity.

Measurement of Renal Function and Hydration Status

Parameters used to assess hydration status in neonates include weight, fluid intake, urine specific gravity (1.002 to 1.010) and osmolarity (60 to 300 mOsm), urine output (minimum 1 to 3 mL/kg/hour) and electrolytes, and serum electrolytes and osmolarity. Findings indicative of adequate renal function in a newborn include urine volume greater than 1 to 3 mL/hour, FE_{Na} less than 3%, and urine specific gravity of 1.008 to 1.012.[34] Changes in urine specific gravity are often an early response to alterations in hydration. Urine for this measurement can be obtained reliably either from collecting bags or by aspirating several drops from the diaper. Urine output can be assessed by weighing the diaper before and after use and noting the difference (1 g = 1 mL urine). Because urine rapidly evaporates from diapers of infants under radiant warmers, this assessment must be done soon after the infant voids.

Serum osmolarity can be estimated by doubling the serum sodium value (because sodium and its anions are the major components of ECF), or more precisely by the following formula:

$$\text{Serum osmolality (mOSm/L [mmol/L])} = \frac{\text{BUN (mg/dL)}}{2.8} + \frac{\text{Blood glucose (mg/dL)}}{18}$$

The 2.8 and 18 represent molecular weights divided by 10. Measurement of renal function also involves assessment of GFR.

Plasma creatinine levels at birth reflect maternal values and increase shortly after birth (possibly because of a shift in ECF), followed by a decrease and stabilization at about 0.35 to 0.40 mg/dL (30.94 to 35.96 μmol/L) (range, 0.14 to 0.70 mg/dL [12.37 to 61.88 μmol/L]) by 1 to 2 weeks in term infants and up to 3 weeks in most preterm infants.[37,48,122] The elevated creatinine levels may be a result of immature tubular function with "leaky" tubular membranes. Plasma creatinine levels are higher at birth in VLBW infants and inversely related to gestational age.[108] In VLBW infants, there is a transient increase at birth, peaking at 3 to 4 days followed by a decrease that stabilizes at 3 to 4 weeks.[37,48] Because GFR increases more slowly after birth in these infants, the decrease in plasma creatinine is slower. Therefore plasma creatinine levels are a poorer predictor of renal function in VLBW infants.[37,78]

This measure is also limited in infants and children in general because of the progressive changes in GFR and muscle mass.[122]

Creatinine clearance generally approximates GFR in term infants (as in adults) but is considerably more variable in preterm infants.[133] At lower GFR values, creatinine clearance tends to overestimate GFR; at high GFR, creatinine clearance tends to underestimate GFR.[48,122] Creatinine clearance correlates with birth weight, length, and gestational age. Plasma creatinine and creatinine clearance are useful measurements in stable infants but are less accurate in infants with renal failure or preterm infants whose renal function is rapidly changing with maturation.[122] The formula GFR (mL/minute per 1.73 m^2) = KL/P_{cr} (L = length in cm; P_{cr} = plasma creatinine; K = estimate of muscle mass) is a better estimate of GFR than plasma creatinine alone, because it accounts for percentage of muscle mass. In this formula, K = 0.27 for VLBW, 0.33 for preterm infants with weight appropriate for gestational age (AGA), 0.31 for SGA preterm infants, 0.45 for AGA term infants, and 0.33 for SGA term infants younger than 1 year.[48,122] This formula can be used after the first week in term infants and until 1 year of age for preterm infants after 34 to 35 weeks' gestational age. The accuracy of this formula has been questioned, however, especially because variations in hydration status and various pathophysiologic states can alter the results and because of a lack of adequate validation data.[9,48]

Renal Function During Neonatal Illness

Immaturity in renal function in infants, especially preterm infants, limits their ability to cope with additional stresses and can lead to significant alterations of renal function in association with specific pathologic problems such as RDS, perinatal asphyxia, congestive heart failure, bronchopulmonary dysplasia, and PDA. These disorders can also interfere with maturation of renal hemodynamics and tubular function (Figure 11-9).[148]

During hypoxic-ischemic events, severe RDS, or other hypoxemic events, vascular resistance is increased, GFR is decreased, and the RAA system is activated, further magnifying alterations that usually occur in healthy newborns. In addition, cardiac output is redistributed, with increased blood flow to vital organs (heart, brain, and adrenal glands) and reduced flow to less essential areas such as the renal and gastrointestinal systems. The percentage of decrease in flow to these nonessential systems is greater in immature animals and perhaps in human preterm infants as well.[34] The decreased blood flow increases the risk of renal and intestinal ischemia and disorders such as acute tubular necrosis and NEC. After hypoxic-ischemic events, infants are at risk for SIADH, reduced urine output, impaired electrolyte reabsorption, hyperkalemia, and hyponatremia.[148] These infants require careful calculation and titration of fluid intake. Oliguria or anuria is most likely to develop within the first 24 hours. Initial fluid

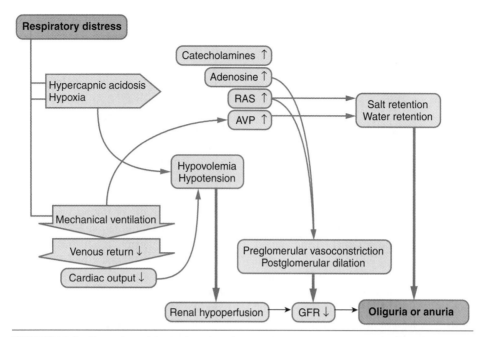

FIGURE 11-9   The main pathways of renal dysfunction in respiratory distress. Mechanical ventilation and the hypoxemia-induced activation of vasoactive factors contribute to the development of systemic hypotension and hypovolemia. *AVP,* Arginine vasopressin; *GFR,* glomerular filtration rate; *RAS,* renin-angiotensin system. (From Tóth-Heyn, P., Drukker, A., & Guignard, J.P. [2000]. The stressed neonatal kidney: From pathophysiology to clinical management of neonatal vasomotor neuropathy. *Pediatr Nephrol, 14,* 230.)

intake is limited to replacement of insensible and urinary water losses.

Infants with RDS and hypoxemia have marked changes in renal function with impairment of renal perfusion and reduced urine output by hypoxemia. Oliguria is associated with renal tubular necrosis, decreased renal perfusion, and impaired diluting ability. These impairments can lead to a decreased ability to excrete water, water retention, and edema. The reduction in perfusion is a result of vasoconstriction with increased RVR possibly mediated by elevated activity of the renin-angiotensin system. The decreased urine output is related to increased AVP and altered renal hemodynamics with a decreased GFR. In hypoxemic infants, an increase in urine output may occur before improvement in the alveolar-arterial oxygen gradient, suggesting that the improvement in respiratory function may be secondary to renal excretion of fluid sequestered in the lungs. Renal tubular function is also altered in these infants, with increased renal loss of protein, glucose, and sodium, decreased concentrating ability, and impairment of the ability to excrete acid (increasing the risk of renal tubular acidosis).

Positive-pressure ventilation further alters renal function by decreasing cardiac output and renal perfusion, redistributing blood flow, and increasing intrathoracic and inferior vena caval pressure. Positive-pressure ventilation and constant positive airway pressure alter renal function by decreasing GFR. Adequate hydration and careful monitoring of fluid and electrolyte status are especially critical for infants with respiratory problems and those on assisted ventilation.

MATURATIONAL CHANGES DURING INFANCY AND CHILDHOOD

Renal function undergoes rapid maturation during the first 2 years. Thus the first 1 to 2 years are a time of increased risk of fluid and electrolyte problems in infants. Function comparable to that of adults is achieved by around 2 years. Effective renal plasma flow increases rapidly from birth to 3 months and then more slowly reaches adult values by 12 to 24 months.[9,71,130,133] Increases are associated with increased flow to the outer cortical region.[133] GFR also increases rapidly during the first 3 months, reaching 60 mL/minute per 1.73 m² by 3 months, 80 mL/minute per 1.73 m² by 6 months, 100 mL/minute per 1.73 m² by 12 months, and adult values (120 mL/minute per 1.73 m²) by 2 years.[53,133,148] Values may remain lower in preterm infants, with a lag in reaching values seen in term infants, and may not reach adult values until childhood.[133] Creatinine output per unit of body weight increases throughout childhood as muscle mass increases.[56] Plasma creatinine values are stable at values averaging 0.35 to 0.40 mg/dL (30.94 to 35.36 μmol/L) until 2 years of age, when they increase further until adolescence.[122]

By 2 months of age, the infant is able to maximally excrete a water load; concentrating ability reaches adult levels of 1400 mOsm until 6 to 12 months and maximal adult values by 2 years.[63,108,133] The ability to concentrate urine is probably related to increasing protein content in the diet, which increases urea levels in serum and tubular filtrate. This increase is important in creating the necessary gradient essential for maximizing renal concentrating mechanisms. Maturation of sodium and water reabsorption in the tubules can take up to 18 months; before this time the kidneys have a limited capacity to regulate salt and water excretion.[68]

PRA decreases significantly from 1 to 6 weeks and then more slowly. Adult values for PRA and aldosterone levels are reached by 6 to 9 years, possibly earlier.[128,133] The decrease in angiotensin II parallels the decrease in PRA.[128]

Glomerular development continues after birth, involving primarily hypertrophy.[84] Glomerular size is similar to adult values by 3 years.[117] Further maturation and growth of nephrons continues to about 2 years of age.[128] There is a 10-fold increase in proximal tubule length and diameter in the first year.[117] Anatomically the lobulation seen in the newborn kidney disappears and the glomerulus and tubules approach adult relationships by about 6 months.[12] The cuboidal epithelium of the newborn's glomerulus is gradually replaced by thin epithelium by 1 year of age.

Total body water decreases to 60% to 65% by 12 months. ECF volume decreases to 30% by 3 to 6 months and then gradually to adult values of 20% by adolescence.[133] Urine output increases to 500 to 600 mL per 24 hours by 1 year of age. The bladder remains a cigar-shaped abdominal organ until early childhood, with achievement of the adult pelvic position and pyramidal shape by about 6 years of age.[80]

SUMMARY

The neonate is vulnerable to significant alterations in volume homeostasis and electrolyte balance because of immaturity of renal function. This vulnerability is especially marked in preterm infants, in whom there is very little margin for errors in management of fluid and electrolyte status. These infants can rapidly become overhydrated or dehydrated or develop hyponatremia, hypernatremia, and other electrolyte disorders. By careful assessment and observation, the nurse can prevent or minimize the effects of many of these disorders. Recommendations for clinical practices related to alterations in the renal system and fluid and electrolyte balance are summarized in Box 11-5. By providing care to minimize these alterations, neonatal health can be enhanced, with a reduction in the risks associated with pathophysiologic complications.

BOX 11-5   **Recommendations for Clinical Practice Related to Changes in the Renal System and Fluid and Electrolyte Homeostasis in Neonates**

Recognize the usual changes in the renal system in the fetus and neonate (pp. 368-377 and Table 11-6).

Monitor fluid and electrolyte status of infants of mothers who received large volumes or rapidly administered intravenous fluids during labor or hypertonic intravenous solutions (pp. 362-363, 380).

Know the normal values for parameters used to assess renal function and fluid and electrolyte status and recognize abnormalities (pp. 371-377, 381).

Know expected patterns of weight loss after birth and monitor status (p. 371).

Carefully calculate fluid and electrolyte requirements (pp. 377-381).

Record fluid intake and output and maintain within calculated limits (pp. 377-381).

Use an infusion device to administer intravenous fluids, calculate intake hourly, and adjust as needed (pp. 375-376, 377-381).

Assess the hydration status of infants using weight, intake and output, urine specific gravity and osmolality, serum osmolality, and electrolytes (pp. 377-381).

Observe for signs of overhydration, water retention, vascular overload, and dehydration (pp. 375-376, 380).

Know and monitor complications associated with excess fluid (pp. 375-378, 380).

Record the time and character of the first voiding (p. 371).

Monitor voiding and fluid and electrolyte status in infants with hypoxic-ischemic events and after maternal magnesium sulfate administration (pp. 371, 379-382).

Monitor infants receiving intravenous glucose for glycosuria, hyperglycemia, and fluid and electrolyte status (p. 374 and Chapter 16).

Monitor potassium levels in very-low-birth-weight (VLBW) infants and in infants with increased energy needs, in infants who are stressed, or in infants on diuretics or volume expanders (pp. 374-375, 380-381).

Monitor calcium and magnesium levels in VLBW infants or those on sodium supplementation or with increased sodium excretion (pp. 373-375, 379-380).

Monitor blood and urine pH values in low-birth-weight (LBW) or ill infants (p. 375).

Know the risk factors for acidosis and observe for acid-base alterations in infants with cold stress, altered nutrition, and fluid and electrolyte alterations (p. 375).

Observe for renal sodium loss and hyponatremia, especially in VLBW infants (pp. 373-375, 379-380).

Know the effects of illness on renal function and monitor ill or stressed infants for problems such as hyponatremia and dehydration (pp. 381-382 and Figure 11-9).

Recognize and monitor for drug side effects related to immature renal function (pp. 371-372, 377 and Chapter 7).

Know the components (e.g., maintenance, replacement of loss, provision for growth) of usual fluid and electrolyte needs for infants and how these needs vary at different gestational ages (pp. 377-381).

Calculate infant fluid and electrolyte needs and renal solute load (pp. 377-381).

Avoid the use of high–solute load formulas, especially in LBW infants (pp. 375-376, 378-379).

Recognize factors that influence insensible water loss and act to minimize the effects of these losses (p. 378 and Box 11-4).

Recognize and monitor for effects of neonatal pathophysiologic problems on renal function (pp. 381-382).

Recognize factors that place an infant at risk for overhydration, dehydration, and electrolyte imbalances, and monitor infants for these problems (pp. 380-381).

Recognize parameters associated with the syndrome of inappropriate secretion of antidiuretic hormone (SIADH) (pp. 379, 380).

References

1. Abitbol, C. L., & Rodriguez, M. M. (2012). The long-term renal and cardiovascular consequences of prematurity. *Nat Rev Nephrol, 8,* 265.
2. Agren, J., Sjörs, G., & Sedin, G. (1998). Transepidermal water loss in infants born at 24 and 25 weeks of gestation. *Acta Paediatr, 87,* 1185.
3. Alto, W. A. (2005). No need for glycosuria/proteinuria screen in pregnant women. *J Fam Pract, 54,* 978.
4. American College of Nurse-Midwives. (2016). Providing oral nutrition to women in labor. *J Midwifery Womens Health, 61,* 528.
5. American Society of Anesthesiologists Task Force on Obstetric Anesthesia. (2016). Practice guidelines for obstetric anesthesia: an updated report by the American Society of Anesthesiologists Task Force on Obstetric Anesthesia and the Society for Obstetric Anesthesia and Perinatology. *Anesthesiology, 124,* 270.
6. Anton, L., & Brosnihan, K. B. (2008). Systemic and uteroplacental renin–angiotensin system in normal and pre-eclamptic pregnancies. *Ther Adv Cardiovasc Dis, 2,* 349.
7. August, P. (2013). Preeclampsia: a "nephrocentric" view. *Adv Chronic Kidney Dis, 20,* 280.
8. Barrington, K. J., et al. (2017). Fluid restriction of preterm infants with chronic lung disease. *Cochrane database Sys Rev, 2017*(2), CD005389.
9. Baum, M. (2017). Renal transport of sodium during early development. In R. A. Polin, et al. (Eds.), *Fetal and neonatal physiology* (5th ed.). Philadelphia: Saunders.
10. Baumgardt, S., & Costarino, A. T. (2000). Water and electrolyte metabolism of the micro-premie. *Clin Perinatol, 27,* 131.
11. Becker, A., & Baum, M. (2006). Obstructive uropathy. *Early Hum Dev, 82,* 15.
12. Bell, E. F., et al. (2016). Fluid and electrolyte management. In M. G. MacDonald & M. M. K. Seshia (Eds.), *Avery's neonatology: Pathophysiology and management of the newborn* (7th ed.). Philadelphia: Wolters Kluwer.
13. Bert, S., Gouyon, J. B., & Semama, D. S. (2004). Calcium, sodium and potassium urinary excretion during the first five days of life in very preterm infants. *Biol Neonate, 85,* 37.
14. Beydoun, S. N. (1985). Morphologic changes in the renal tract in pregnancy. *Clin Obstet Gynecol, 28,* 249.
15. Black, M. J., et al. (2013). When birth comes early: effects on nephrogenesis. *Nephrology (Carlton), 18,* 180.
16. Bockenhauer, D., & Zieg, J. (2014). Electrolyte disorders. *Clin Perinatol, 41,* 575.
17. Buhling, K. J., et al. (2004). The usefulness of glycosuria and the influence of maternal blood pressure in screening for gestational diabetes. *Eur J Obstet Gynecol Reprod Biol, 113,* 145.
18. Cheung, K. L., & Lafayette, R. A. (2013). Renal physiology of pregnancy. *Adv Chronic Kidney Dis, 20,* 209.
19. Clark, D. A. (1977). Time of first void and first stool in 500 newborns. *Pediatrics, 60,* 457.
20. Conrad, K. P. (2011). Emerging role of relaxin in the maternal adaptations to normal pregnancy: Implications for preeclampsia. *Semin Nephrol, 31,* 15.
21. Conrad, K. P., & Davison, J. M. (2014). The renal circulation in normal pregnancy and preeclampsia: is there a place for relaxin? *Am J Physiol Renal Physiol, 306,* F1121.
22. Cornelis, T., et al. (2011). The kidney in normal pregnancy and preeclampsia. *Semin Nephrol, 31,* 4.
23. Coscia, L. A., et al. (2010). Report from the National Transplantation Pregnancy Registry (NTPR): Outcomes of pregnancy after transplantation. *Clin Transpl, 24,* 65.
24. Costarino, A. T., et al. (1992). Sodium restriction versus daily maintenance replacement in low birth weight premature neonates: A randomized, blind therapeutic trial. *J Pediatr, 120,* 999.
25. Cyna, A. M., et al. (2006). Techniques for preventing hypotension during spinal anaesthesia for caesarean section. *Cochrane Database Syst Rev, 2006*(4), CD002251.
26. Dahlenburg, G. W., Burnell, R. H., & Braybrook, R. (1980). The relation between cord se-rum sodium levels in newborn infants and maternal intravenous therapy during labour. *Br J Obstet Gynaecol, 87,* 519.
27. Davison, J. M. (1987). Overview: Kidney function in pregnant women. *Am J Kidney Dis, 9,* 248.
28. Davison, J. M. (1997). Edema in pregnancy. *Kidney Int Suppl, 59,* S90.
29. Davison, J. M., & Lindheimer, M. D. (2011). Pregnancy and chronic kidney disease. *Semin Nephrol, 31,* 86.
30. Dawood, F., Dowswell, T., & Quenby, S. (2013). Intravenous fluids for reducing the du-ration of labour in low risk nulliparous women. *Cochrane Database of Syst Rev, 2013*(6), CD007715.
31. De Curtis, M., & Rigo, J. (2012). Nutrition and kidney in preterm infant. *J Matern Fetal Neonatal Med, 25,* S55.
32. Delemarre, F. M., et al. (1996). Diurnal variation in angiotensin sensitivity in pregnancy. *Am J Obstet Gynecol, 174,* 259.
33. Delgado, M. M., et al. (2003). Sodium and potassium clearances by the maturing kidney: Clinical-molecular correlates. *Pediatr Nephrol, 18,* 759.
34. Dell, K. M. (2015). Fluids, electrolytes and acid-base homeostasis. In R. J. Martin, A. A. Fanaroff, & M. C. Walsh (Eds.), *Fanaroff and Martin's Neonatal-perinatal medicine: Diseases of the fetus and infant* (10th ed.). Philadelphia: Saunders.
35. Dighe, M., et al. (2011). Fetal genitourinary anomalies—a pictorial review with postnatal correlation. *Ultrasound Q, 27,* 7.
36. Dötsch, J., Plank, C., & Amann, K. (2012). Fetal programming of renal function. *Pediatr Nephrol, 27,* 513.
37. Drukker, A., & Guignard, J. P. (2002). Renal aspects of the term and preterm infant: A selective update. *Curr Opin Pediatr, 14,* 175.
38. Ellis, D. (2011). Regulation of fluids and electrolytes in infants and children. In P. J. Davis, F. P. Cladis, & E. K. Motoyama (Eds.), *Smith's anesthesia for infants and children* (8th ed.). Philadelphia: Mosby.
39. Engle, W. D. (1986). Development of fetal and neonatal renal function. *Semin Perinatol, 10,* 113.
40. Faúndes, A., et al. (1998). Dilatation of the urinary tract during pregnancy: Proposal of a curve of maximal caliceal diameter by gestational age. *Am J Obstet Gynecol, 178,* 1082.
41. Fiadjoe, P., Kannan, K., & Rane, A. (2010). Maternal urological problems in pregnancy. *Eur J Obstet Gynecol Reprod Biol, 152,* 13.
42. Freed, S. Z. (1981). Hydronephrosis of pregnancy. In S. Z. Freed & N. Herzig (Eds.), Urology in pregnancy. Baltimore: Williams & Wilkins.
43. Glaser, A. P., & Schaeffer, A. J. (2015). Urinary tract infection and bacteriuria in pregnancy. *Urol Clin North Am, 42,* 547.
44. Granese, R., & Adile, B. (2008). Urinary incontinence in pregnancy and in puerperium: 3 months follow-up after delivery. *Minerva Ginecol, 60,* 15.
45. Gubhaju, L., Sutherland, M. R., & Black, M. J. (2011). Preterm birth and the kidney: Implications for long-term renal health. *Reprod Sci, 18,* 322.
46. Guignard, J. P., & Gouyon, J.-B. (2012). Glomerular filtration rate in neonates. In W. Oh, et al. (Eds.), *Nephrology and fluid/electrolyte physiology* (2nd ed.). Philadelphia: Saunders.
47. Guignard, J. P., & Sulyok, E. (2012). Renal morphogenesis and development of renal function. In C. A. Gleason & S. Devaskar (Eds.), *Avery's diseases of the newborn* (9th ed.). Philadelphia: Saunders.
48. Guignard, J. P. (2017). Postnatal development of glomerular filtration rate in neonates. In R. A. Polin, et al. (Eds.), *Fetal and neonatal physiology* (5th ed.). Philadelphia: Saunders.
49. Hartnoll, G., Bétrémieux, P., & Modi, N. (2000). Randomized controlled trial of postnatal sodium supplementation on body composition in 25 to 30 week gestational age infants. *Arch Dis Child Fetal Neonatal Ed, 82,* F24.
50. Hartnoll, G., Bétrémieux, P., & Modi, N. (2001). Randomised controlled trial of postnatal sodium supplementation in infants of 25-30 weeks gestational age: effects on cardiopulmonary adaptation. *Arch Dis Child Fetal Neonatal Ed, 85,* F29.
51. Hartnoll, G. (2003). Basic principles and practical steps in the management of fluid balance in the newborn. *Semin Neonatol, 8,* 307.
52. Hassan, E., et al. (2000). Clinical implications of the ovarian/endometrial renin-angiotensin-aldosterone system. *Ann N Y Acad Sci, 900,* 107.
53. Haycock, G. (2005). Renal function and renal disease in the newborn. In J. M. Rennie (Ed.), *Roberton's textbook of neonatology* (4th ed.). Edinburgh: Churchill Livingstone.
54. Hayslett, J. P. (2004). Renal disease in pregnancy. In G. N. Burrow, T. P. Duffy, & J. A. Copel (Eds.), *Medical complications during pregnancy* (6th ed.). Philadelphia: Saunders.
55. Hennessy, A., & Makris, A. (2011). Preeclamptic nephropathy. *Nephrology, 16,* 134.
56. Hilgers, K. F., et al. (1997). Angiotensin's role in renal development. *Semin Nephrol, 17,* 492.

57. Hill, C. C., & Pickinpaugh, J. (2008). Physiologic changes in pregnancy. *Surg Clin North Am, 88*, 391.

58. Hladunewich, M. A., et al. (2004). The dynamics of glomerular filtration in the puerperium. *Am J Physiol Renal Physiol, 286*, F496.

59. Holtbäck, U., & Aperia, A. C. (2003). Molecular determinants of sodium and water balance during early human development. *Semin Neonatol, 8*, 291.

60. Hoseini, R., et al. (2012). Glomerular function in neonates. *Iran J Kidney Dis, 6*, 166.

61. Hussein, W., & Lafayette, R. A. (2014). Renal function in normal and disordered pregnancy. *Curr Opin Nephrol Hypertens, 23*, 46.

62. Iacobelli, S., et al. (2010). Aquaporin-2 urinary excretion in preterm infants: Relationship to diuresis and vasopressin. *Acta Physiol (Oxf), 200*, 339.

63. Iacobelli, S., et al. (2017). Concentration and dilution of the urine. In R. A. Polin, et al. (Eds.), *Fetal and neonatal physiology* (5th ed.). Philadelphia: Saunders.

64. Irani, R. A., et al. (2010). Autoantibody mediated angiotensin receptor activation contributes to preeclampsia through tumor necrosis factor-alpha signaling. *Hypertension, 55*, 1246.

65. Irani, R. A., & Xia, Y. (2011). Renin angiotensin signaling in normal pregnancy and preeclampsia. *Semin Nephrol, 31*, 47.

66. Jeyabalan, A., & Lain, K. Y. (2007). Anatomic and functional changes of the upper urinary tract during pregnancy. *Urol Clin North Am, 34*, 1.

67. Keppler, A. B. (1988). The use of intravenous fluids during labor. *Birth, 15*, 75.

68. Kett, M. M., & Denton, K. M. (2011). Renal programming: Cause for concern? *Am J Physiol Regul Integr Comp Physiol, 300*, R791.

69. Kim, C.-R., et al. (2017). Fluid distribution in the fetus and neonate. In R. A. Polin, et al. (Eds.), *Fetal and neonatal physiology* (5th ed.). Philadelphia: Saunders.

70. King, T. L., & Pinger, W. (2014). Evidence-based practice for intrapartum care: the Pearls of Midwifery. *J Midwifery Womens Health, 59*, 572.

71. Knobel, R. B., & Smith, J. M. (2014). Laboratory blood tests useful in monitoring renal function in neonates. *Neonatal Netw, 33*, 35.

72. Koren, G. (2011). Pharmacokinetics in pregnancy: Clinical significance. *J Popul Ther Clin Pharmacol, 18*, e523.

73. Lamp, J. M., & Macke, J. K. (2010). Relationships among intrapartum maternal fluid intake, birth type, neonatal output, and neonatal weight loss during the first 48 hours after birth. *J Obstet Gynecol Neonatal Nurs, 39*, 169.

74. Liang, C. C., et al. (2013). Clinical impact of and contributing factors to urinary incontinence in women 5 years after first delivery. *Int Urogynecol J, 24*, 99.

75. Ligi, I., et al. (2013). The neonatal kidney: implications for drug metabolism and elimination. *Curr Drug Metab, 14*, 174.

76. Lindheimer, M. D., & August, P. (2009). Aldosterone, maternal volume status and healthy pregnancies: A cycle of differing views. *Nephrol Dial Transplant, 24*, 1712.

77. Lindheimer, M. D., et al. (2012). Renal physiology and disease in pregnancy. In R. J. Alpern, et al. (Eds.), *Seldin and Giebisch's The kidney: Physiology and pathophysiology* (5th ed.). San Diego: Academic Press.

78. Lorenz, J. M. (1997). Assessing fluid and electrolyte status in the newborn. National Academy of Clinical Biochemistry. *Clin Chem, 43*, 205.

79. Lorenz, J. M. (2012). Fetal and neonatal body water compartment values with reference to growth and development. In R. A. Polin, W. W. Fox, & S. H. Abman (Eds.), *Fetal and neonatal physiology* (4th ed.). Philadelphia: Saunders.

80. Lowrey, G. H. (1986). *Growth and development of children*. Chicago: YearBook Medical.

81. Lumbers, E. R., & Pringle, K. G. (2014). Roles of the circulating renin-angiotensin-aldosterone system in human pregnancy. *Am J Physiol Regul Integr Comp Physiol, 306*, R91.

82. Luyckx, V. A., et al. (2013). Effect of fetal and child health on kidney development and long-term risk of hypertension and kidney disease. *Lancet, 382*, 273.

83. Malinowski, J. (1978). Bladder assessment in the postpartum patient. *J Obstet Gynecol Neonatal Nurs, 7*, 14.

84. Mann, S., Johnson, M. P., & Wilson, R. D. (2010). Fetal thoracic and bladder shunts. *Semin Fetal Neonatal Med, 15*, 28.

85. Matsell, D. J., & Hiatt, M. J. (2017). Functional development of the kidney in utero. In R. A. Polin, et al. (Eds.), *Fetal and neonatal physiology* (5th ed.). Philadelphia: Saunders.

86. Mikhail, M. S., & Anyaegbunam, A. (1995). Lower urinary tract dysfunction in pregnancy: A review. *Obstet Gynecol Surv, 50*, 675.

87. Modi, N. (2003). Clinical implications of postnatal alterations in body water distribution. *Semin Neonatol, 8*, 301.

88. Modi, N. (2004). Management of fluid balance in the very immature neonate. *Arch Dis Child Fetal Neonatal Ed, 89*, F108.

89. Modi, N. (2005). Fluid and electrolyte balance. In J. M. Rennie (Ed.), *Roberton's textbook of neonatology* (4th ed.). Edinburgh: Churchill Livingstone.

90. Moen, V., et al. (2009). Hyponatremia complicating labour: Rare or unrecognised? A prospective observational study. *Br J Obstet Gynaecol, 116*, 552.

91. Moen, V., & Irestedt, L. (2009). Water intoxication following labour and surgery: Blaming oxytocin—the easy way out? *Acta Anaesthesiol Scand, 53*, 1226.

92. Monga, M. (2014). Maternal cardiovascular, respiratory, and renal adaptation to pregnancy. In R. K. Creasy, et al. (Eds.), *Creasy & Resnik's Maternal-fetal medicine: Principles and practice* (7th ed.). Philadelphia: Saunders.

93. Moore, K. L., Persaud, T. V. N., & Torchia, M. G. (2015). *The developing human: Clinically oriented embryology* (10th ed.). Philadelphia: Saunders.

94. Mulder, F., et al. (2012). Risk factors for postpartum urinary retention: a systematic re-view and meta-analysis. *BJOG, 119*, 1440.

95. Nafday, S. M., et al. (2016). Renal disease. In M. G. MacDonald & M. M. K. Seshia (Eds.), *Avery's neonatology, pathophysiology and management of the newborn* (7th ed.). Philadelphia: Wolters Kluwer.

96. Nakayama, D. K. (2010). Management of the surgical newborn: Physiological foundations and practical considerations. *J Pediatr Urol, 6*, 232.

97. Newton, N., Newton, M., & Broach, J. (1988). Psychologic, physical, nutritional and technologic aspects of intravenous infusion during labor. *Birth, 15*, 67.

98. Nuyt, A. M., & Alexander, B. T. (2009). Developmental programming and hypertension. *Curr Opin Nephrol Hypertens, 18*, 144.

99. O'Brien, F., & Walker, I. A. (2014). Fluid homeostasis in the neonate. *Paediatr Anaesth, 24*, 49.

100. Oh, W. (2012). Body water changes in the fetus and newborn: normal transition after birth and the effects on intrauterine growth aberration. In W. Oh, et al. (Eds.), *Nephrology and fluid/electrolyte physiology* (2nd ed.). Philadelphia: Saunders.

101. Ophir, E., et al. (2007). Water intoxication—a dangerous condition in labor and delivery rooms. *Obstet Gynecol Surv, 62*, 731.

102. Osborn, D. A., & Evans, N. (2004). Early volume expansion for prevention of morbidity and mortality in very preterm infants. *Cochrane Database Syst Rev, 2004*(2), CD002055.

103. O'Sullivan, G. (1994). The stomach—fact and fantasy: eating and drinking during labor. *Int Anesthesiol Clin, 32*, 31.

104. Palma-Reis, I., et al. (2013). Renal disease and hypertension in pregnancy. *Clin Med (Lond), 13*, 57.

105. Podymow, T., August, P., & Akbari, A. (2010). Management of renal disease in pregnancy. *Obstet Gynecol Clin North Am, 37*, 195.

106. Posencheg, M. A., & Evans, J. R. (2012). Acid-base, fluid and electrolyte management. In C. A. Gleason & S. Devaskar (Eds.), *Avery's diseases of the newborn* (9th ed.). Philadelphia: Saunders.

107. Price, N., Dawood, R., & Jackson, S. R. (2010). Pelvic floor exercise for urinary incontinence: a systematic literature review. *Maturitas, 67*, 309.

108. Quigley, R. (2012). Developmental changes in renal function. *Curr Opin Pediatr, 24*, 184.

109. Ramsay, I. N., et al. (1993). Uroflowmetry in the puerperium. *Neurourol Urodyn, 12*, 33.

110. Rao, S., et al. (2016). Long-term functional recovery, quality of life, and pregnancy after solid organ transplantation. *Med Clin North Am, 100*, 613.

111. Resnik, R. (2004). The puerperium. In R. K. Creasy, R. Resnik, & J. D. Iams (Eds.), *Creasy & Resnik's Maternal-fetal medicine: principles and practice* (5th ed.). Philadelphia: Saunders.

112. Richman, K., & Gohh, R. (2012). Pregnancy after renal transplantation: a review of registry and single-centre practices and outcomes. *Nephrol Dial Transplant, 27*, 3428.

113. Richter, V. F., et al. (2016). The role of maternal nutrition, metabolic function and the placenta in developmental programming of renal dysfunction. *Clin Exp Pharmacol Physiol, 43*, 135.

114. Ritz, E., et al. (2011). Prenatal programming—effects on blood pressure and renal function. *Nat Rev Nephrol, 7*, 137.

115. Rosenblum, N. D. (2008). Developmental biology of the human kidney. *Semin Fetal Neo-natal Med, 13*, 125.

116. Sadler, T. W. (2015). *Langman's Medical embryology* (13th ed.). Philadelphia: Wolters Kluwer.

117. Saint-Faust, M., Boubred, F., & Simeoni, U. (2014). Renal development and neonatal adaptation. *Am J Perinatol, 31*, 773.

118. Sangsawang, B., & Sangsawang, N. (2013). Stress urinary incontinence in pregnant women: a review of prevalence, pathophysiology, and treatment. *Int Urogynecol J, 24*, 901.

119. Saultz, J. W., et al. (1991). Postpartum urinary retention. *J Am Board Fam Pract, 4*, 341.

120. Schreuder, M. F., Bueters, R. R., & Allegaert, K. (2014). The interplay between drugs and the kidney in premature neonates. *Pediatr Nephrol, 29*, 2083.

121. Schrier, R. W. (2010). Systemic arterial vasodilation, vasopressin, and vasopressinase in pregnancy. *J Am Soc Nephrol, 21*, 570.

122. Schwartz, G. J., Brion, L. P., & Spitzer, A. (1987). The use of plasma creatinine for estimating glomerular filtration rate in infants, children, and adolescents. *Pediatr Clin North Am, 34*, 571.

123. Sharts-Hopko, N. (2010). Oral intake during labor: a review of the evidence. *MCN Am J Matern Child Nurs, 35*, 197.

124. Siddik-Sayyid, S. M., et al. (2009). A randomized trial comparing colloid preload to co-load during spinal anesthesia for elective cesarean delivery. *Anesth Analg, 109*, 1219.

125. Sillén, U., et al. (2000). The voiding patterns of healthy preterm neonates. *J Urol, 163*, 278.

126. Simeoni, U., et al. (2011). Adverse consequences of accelerated neonatal growth: cardio-vascular and renal issues. *Pediatr Nephrol, 26*, 493.

127. Singata, M., et al. (2013). Restricting oral fluid and food intake during labour. *Cochrane Database Syst Rev, 2013*(8), CD003930.

128. Smith, F. G. (2017). Development of the renin-angiotensin system. In R. A. Polin, et al. (Eds.), *Fetal and neonatal physiology* (5th ed.). Philadelphia: Saunders.

129. Smith, M. C., et al. (2008). Assessment of glomerular filtration rate during pregnancy using the MDRD formula. *BJOG, 115*, 109.

130. Solhaug, M. J., & Jose, P. A. (2017). Development and Regulation of Renal Blood Flow in the Neonate. In R. A. Polin, et al. (Eds.), *Fetal and neonatal physiology* (5th ed.). Philadelphia: Saunders.

131. Sperling, J. D., Dahlke, J. D., & Sibai, B. M. (2016). Restriction of oral intake during labor: whither are we bound? *AJOG, 214*, 592.

132. Stephens, B. E., et al. (2008). Fluid regimens in the first week of life may increase risk of patent ductus arteriosus in extremely low birth weight infants. *J Perinatol, 28*, 123.

133. Sulemanji, M., & Vakili, K. (2013). Neonatal renal physiology. *Semin Pediatr Surg, 22*, 195.

134. Sutherland, M. R., et al. (2011). Accelerated maturation and abnormal morphology in the preterm neonatal kidney. *J Am Soc Nephrol, 22*, 1365.

135. Suylok, E. (2012). Renal aspects of sodium metabolism in the fetus and neonate. In W. Oh, et al. (Eds.), *Nephrology and fluid/ electrolyte physiology* (2nd ed.). Philadelphia: Saunders.

136. Symonds, E. M. (1988). Renin and reproduction. *Am J Obstet Gynecol, 158*, 754.

137. Tasnif, Y., Morado, J., & Hebert, M. F. (2016). Pregnancy–related pharmacokinetic changes. *Clin Pharmacol Ther, 100*, 53.

138. Taylor, S. N., et al. (2010). Fluid, electrolytes, and nutrition: minutes matter. *Adv Neonatal Care, 10*, 248.

139. Teoh, W. H., & Sia, A. T. (2009). Colloid preload versus coload for spinal anesthesia for cesarean delivery: The effects on maternal cardiac output. *Anesth Analg, 108*, 1592.

140. Thadhani, R. I., et al. (2014). Renal disorders. In R. K. Creasy, et al. (Eds.), *Creasy & Resnik's Maternal-fetal medicine: Principles and practice* (7th ed.). Philadelphia: Saunders.

141. Theunissen, I. M., & Parer, J. T. (1994). Fluid and electrolytes in pregnancy. *Clin Obstet Gynecol, 37*, 3.

142. Thornburg, K. L., et al. (2000). Hemodynamic changes in pregnancy. *Semin Perinatol, 24*, 11.

143. Thorp, J. M., et al. (1999). Urinary incontinence in pregnancy and the puerperium: A prospective study. *Am J Obstet Gynecol, 181*, 266.

144. Tourangeau, A., et al. (1999). Intravenous therapy for women in labor: Implementation of a practice change. *Birth, 26*, 31.

145. Vellanki, K. (2013). Pregnancy in chronic kidney disease. *Adv Chronic Kidney Dis, 20*, 223.

146. Verdonk, K., et al. (2014). The renin-angiotensin-aldosterone system in preeclampsia: the delicate balance between good and bad. *Clin Sci (Lond), 126*, 537.

147. Verhulst, A., et al. (2005). Preconditioning of the distal tubular epithelium of the human kidney precedes nephrocalcinosis. *Kidney Int, 68*, 1643.

148. Vogt, B. A., & Dell, K. M. (2015). The kidney and urinary tract of the neonate. In R. J. Martin, A. A. Fanaroff, & M. C. Walsh (Eds.), *Fanaroff and Martin's Neonatal-perinatal medicine: Diseases of the fetus and infant* (10th ed.). Philadelphia: Saunders.

149. Weber, S. (2012). Novel genetic aspects of congenital anomalies of kidney and urinary tract. *Curr Opin Pediatr, 24*, 212.

150. Widemaier, E., et al. (2015). Vander's Human physiology: The mechanisms of body function (13th ed.). New York: McGraw-Hill.

151. Winston, J., & Levitt, M. F. (1985). Renal function, renal disease and pregnancy. In S. H. Cherry, R. L. Berkowitz, & N. G. Kase (Eds.), *Rovinsky and Guttmacher's Medical, surgical and gynecologic complications of pregnancy*. Baltimore: Williams & Wilkins.

152. Wolf, M. T., et al. (2017). Potassium homeostasis in the fetus and neonate. In R. A. Polin, et al. (Eds.), *Fetal and neonatal physiology* (5th ed.). Philadelphia: Saunders.

153. Wong, A. M., et al. (2017). Urinary acidification. In R. A. Polin, et al. (Eds.), *Fetal and neonatal physiology* (5th ed.). Philadelphia: Saunders.

154. Yared, A., Barakat, A. Y., & Ichikawa, I. (1990). Fetal nephrology. In R. D. Eden & F. H. Boehm (Eds.), *Assessment and care of the fetus*. Norwalk, CT: Appleton & Lange.

155. Yip, S. K., et al. (1997). Urinary retention in the post-partum period. The relationship be-tween obstetric factors and the post-partum post-void residual bladder volume. *Acta Obstet Gynecol Scand, 76*, 667.

Gastrointestinal and Hepatic Systems and Perinatal Nutrition

Georgia R. Ditzenberger

The gastrointestinal (GI) system consists of processes involved in intake, digestion, and absorption of nutrients and elimination of byproducts in bile and stool.[274] Utilization of nutrients for production of energy and other vital functions is discussed in Chapters 16 and 17. This chapter focuses on the processes involved in preparing nutrients for absorption across the intestinal villi.

Maternal nutrition is one of the most important factors affecting pregnancy outcome. The maternal GI tract must digest and absorb nutrients needed for fetal and placental growth and development and to meet the altered demands of maternal metabolism, as well as eliminate unneeded byproducts and waste materials from both the woman and the fetus. Structural and physiologic immaturity of the neonate's GI tract can result in alterations in neonatal nutritional status and increase the risk of malabsorption and dehydration. This chapter reviews GI and hepatic function in the pregnant woman, fetus, and neonate and implications for clinical practice. Hepatic function related to drug metabolism is discussed in Chapter 7.

MATERNAL PHYSIOLOGIC ADAPTATIONS

In pregnant woman, the gastrointestinal (GI) and hepatic systems are characterized by marked anatomic and physiologic alterations that are essential in supporting maternal and fetal nutrition. These changes are related to mechanical forces such as the pressure of the growing uterus and hormonal influences such as effects of progesterone on GI smooth muscle and effects of estrogen on liver metabolism.

Antepartum Period

The antepartum period is characterized by anatomic and physiologic changes in all the organs of the GI system. These changes and their implications are summarized in Table 12-1. Pregnancy is associated with increased appetite; increased consumption of food; and alterations in the types of food desired, including cravings, avoidance of certain foods, and, rarely, pica (craving for nonnutrient substances). Specific changes in food consumption and the types of foods craved or avoided are strongly influenced by cultural and economic factors. Food consumption has been reported to increase

15% to 20% beginning in early pregnancy, peaking at midgestation and decreasing near term.[225] Alterations in food intake and appetite create a positive energy balance during pregnancy to meet the needs of the pregnant woman and fetus and to prepare for lactation (see Chapter 16).[141,207] Changes in maternal caloric intake do not parallel changes in basal metabolism or fetal growth.

The basis for changes in patterns of food intake is unclear but may be a response to the movement of glucose and other nutrients to the fetus, alterations in taste threshold and acuity, and hormonal changes. Estrogen acts as an appetite suppressant and progesterone as an appetite stimulant. Influences of estrogen and progesterone on patterns of food intake are supported by similar changes during the menstrual cycle. Decreased appetite and food intake have been reported during the follicular phase of the menstrual cycle (when estrogen peaks), and with increased appetite during the luteal phase (when progesterone peaks).[207,274] During pregnancy, alterations in insulin and glucagon combine with estrogen and progesterone to influence food intake.[274] Leptin serum levels parallel changes in body mass index (BMI) during pregnancy and may also mediate maternal appetite changes. The increased food intake with increased leptin levels suggests the development of leptin insensitivity or resistance, which is mediated by human chorionic somatomammotropin.[141,207]

Mouth and Pharynx

Contrary to the old wives' tale regarding the loss of a tooth per baby, pregnancy does not result in demineralization of the woman's teeth. Fetal calcium needs are drawn from maternal body stores, not from the teeth (see Chapter 17). The major component of tooth enamel (hydroxyapatite crystals) is not reduced by the biochemical or hormonal changes of pregnancy.[169,231] As a result of gingival alterations, however, the pregnant woman may become more aware of preexisting or newly developed dental caries. Changes in saliva and the nausea and vomiting of pregnancy may increase the risk of caries during pregnancy, although this has not been well studied. Dental plaque, calculus, and debris deposits increase during pregnancy and are associated with gingivitis.[231,292] In addition, there may be a transient increase in tooth mobility.[236]

TABLE 12-1 Alterations in the Gastrointestinal System During Pregnancy

ORGAN	ALTERATION	SIGNIFICANCE
Mouth and pharynx	Gingivitis	Friable gum tissue with bleeding and discomfort with chewing
		Increased periodontal disease
	Epulis formation	Bleeding and interference with chewing
	Increased saliva production	Annoyance
Esophagus	Decreased lower esophageal sphincter pressure and tone	Increased risk of heartburn
	Widening of hiatus with decreased tone	Increased risk of hiatal hernia
Stomach	Decreased tone and motility with delayed gastric emptying time	Increased risk of gastroesophageal reflux and vomiting
		Increased risk of vomiting and aspiration with use of sedatives or anesthetics
	Incompetence of pyloric sphincter	Reflux of alkaline biliary material into stomach
	Decreased gastric acidity and histamine output	Improvement of peptic ulcer symptoms
Small and large intestines	Decreased intestinal tone and motility with increased transit time	Facilitated absorption of nutrients such as iron and calcium
		Increased water absorption in large intestine with tendency toward constipation
		Increased flatulence
	Increased height of duodenal villi	Increased absorption of calcium, amino acids, and other substances
	Altered enzymatic transport across villi; increased activity of brush border enzymes	Increased absorption of specific vitamins and other nutrients; increased sodium and water absorption
	Displacement of the cecum and appendix by the uterus	Complicates diagnosis of appendicitis
Gallbladder	Decreased tone and motility	Alteration in measures of gallbladder function
		Increased risk of gallstones
Liver	Altered position	May mask mild to moderate hepatomegaly
	Altered production of liver enzymes, plasma proteins, bilirubin, and serum lipids	Some liver function tests less useful in evaluating liver disorders
		May cause early signs of liver dysfunction to be missed
		Altered early recognition of liver dysfunction
	Presence of spider angiomata and palmar erythema	Discomfort because of itching

Pregnancy may exacerbate existing periodontal disease with an increase in periodontal pocket depth during gestation.[292] Periodontal disease has also been associated with intrauterine infection and an increased risk of preterm birth and low-birth-weight risk in some but not all studies.[4,91,104,198,273,294] The mechanism is unclear but may be related to either alterations in maternal and fetal immune responses or translocation of oral bacteria into the uterus with colonization and inflammation of the placenta.[105,292] Increased prostaglandin (PG) synthesis mediated by proinflammatory cytokines from inflamed gingival tissues or via release of bacterial endotoxins might then initiate labor onset (see Chapter 4).[198,292,294] These studies lack consistent definitions of periodontal disease, with lack of control for confounding variables such as socioeconomic status and smoking in some studies.[104] Several meta-analyses concluded that oral prophylaxis and treatment of periodontal disease may reduce preterm and low-birth-weight rates and that further evaluation is needed; another analysis did not find an association.[91,273]

Gingivitis occurs in 30% to nearly 100% of pregnant women in varying severity, generally beginning around the second month, peaking in the middle of the third trimester, and decreasing around 3 months postpartum.[103,169,231,292] Gingivitis in pregnancy ranges in severity depending on prepregnancy dental health. Chronic dental plaque-induced gingivitis increases the severity of the inflammatory response to oral bacteria. Pregnancy-associated gingivitis is characterized by gingival swelling and increased tendency of bleeding.[103] Gingival tissue contains both estrogen and progesterone receptors.[292] Estrogen increases blood flow to the oral cavity and accelerates turnover of gum epithelial lining cells. The gums become highly vascularized (with proliferation of small blood vessels and connective tissue), hyperplastic, and edematous.[103,169,292] Progesterone and estradiol may stimulate local inflammation via production of PGs and decreased levels of inflammatory inhibitors.[292] Development of gingivitis may be related to these alterations in the inflammatory process during pregnancy (see Chapter 13), with increased intensity of localized irritation, or to changes in connective tissue metabolism.[155] These changes, along with the decreased thickness of the gingival epithelial surface, result in friable gum tissues that may bleed easily or cause discomfort with chewing. Bleeding with brushing occurs more frequently during pregnancy. The incidence of gingivitis is higher with increasing maternal age and parity, preexisting periodontal disease, and poor dentition.[103,169]

In up to 5% of pregnant women, a specific angiogranuloma known as an epulis or pregnancy tumor develops.[228,231,274] Epulis formation generally occurs between the second and third month but can occur later.[228] Epulis may gradually increase in size but rarely is larger than 2 cm in diameter. The etiology is unknown but is believed to relate to hormonal changes (epulis tissue has estrogen and progesterone receptors) and inflammation. Epulis formation is characterized by gingivitis that is advanced and severe. There is a hyperplastic outgrowth that is generally found along the maxillary gingiva and often appears between the upper anterior maxillary teeth. This mass is purplish red to dark purple, very friable, bleeds easily, and often interferes with chewing. Epulis is usually painless but may ulcerate and become painful in some women.[228] Epulis usually regresses spontaneously after delivery but may recur in the same locations with subsequent pregnancies. Occasionally these growths may need to be excised during pregnancy because of bleeding, interference with chewing, or increasing periodontal disease.[169,228,231]

Saliva becomes more acidic during pregnancy, with alterations in electrolyte content and microorganism load, but it usually does not increase in volume.[257] Some women may experience a sense of increased saliva production because of difficulty in swallowing saliva during the period of nausea and vomiting in early pregnancy.[169,257] A few women do experience excessive salivation (ptyalism). This uncommon disorder begins as early as 2 to 3 weeks and ceases with delivery. The excessive salivation seems to occur primarily during the day.[257] The pathogenesis of ptyalism is unknown, but it is believed to be a result of increased saliva production, alterations in swallowing because of nausea, or activation of the esophagosalivary reflex during gastroesophageal reflux (GER).[231,257]

Esophagus

Lower esophageal sphincter (LES) tone decreases. This decrease is believed to be primarily because of the smooth muscle relaxant activity of progesterone.[59,131,154,242] The LES is a pressure barrier between the stomach and the esophagus, acting as a protective mechanism to prevent or minimize GER. Resting LES pressure decreases during pregnancy with decreased responsiveness to hormonal and physiologic stimuli.[59,131,154,242] At the beginning of the second trimester, basal LES tone is unchanged, although a marked decrease in the normal rise in LES pressure in response to stimulation with a protein meal has been reported.[61,276] This suggests an inhibitory effect and may signal the loss of an important protective response, which is the ability to modify LES pressure in response to increased intragastric pressure so that reflux is prevented.[61] LES pressure gradually falls by 33% to 50%, with most of the decrease occurring in the third trimester and reaching a nadir at about 36 weeks.[276]

Changes in the LES in pregnancy are similar to changes seen during the ovarian cycle and in women taking oral contraceptives, supporting the theory of a hormonal cause for this alteration. An increased incidence of acid reflux with heartburn, which is associated with decreased LES pressure, is seen in nonpregnant women during the luteal phase of the ovarian cycle, when progesterone levels are highest.[274,276] After delivery or discontinuance of oral contraceptives, LES function returns to normal.[61,81,274] Alterations in LES tone and pressure are etiologic factors in the development of heartburn during pregnancy.

Other changes in the esophagus during pregnancy include an increase in secondary peristalsis and nonpropulsive peristalsis and increased incidence of hiatal hernia. Flattening of the hemidiaphragm causes a loss of the normal acute esophageal-gastric angle, which may also lead to reflux.[61,160]

Stomach

The stomach of the pregnant woman tends to be hypotonic, with decreased motility resulting from the actions of progesterone. GI motility is decreased, with prolonged small intestinal transit time. Incompetence of the pyloric sphincter may result in alkaline reflux of duodenal contents into the stomach.[131,160,276] Gastric emptying time is believed to be unchanged.[59,81,231,251,276,291]

The effect of pregnancy on gastric acid secretion is unclear. In several studies, gastric volume was not increased, nor was gastric pH decreased during early pregnancy.[131,214,268] Others have reported a decrease in acidity during the first and second trimesters along with normal gastrin levels, with an increase in acidity to greater than nonpregnant values during the third trimester, accompanied by an increase in gastrin.[113,231] In general there seems to be a tendency for decreased gastric acidity in pregnancy, especially during the first and second trimesters, with an increase in the third along with small but statistically significant decreases in both basal and histamine-stimulated acid output.[61,214] Women with peptic ulcers tend to have fewer symptoms during pregnancy, partly because of these changes (see Pregnancy in Women With Peptic Ulcer Disease).[131,214]

Secretion of pepsin parallels changes in gastric acid output.[59] Decreased gastric acidity is believed to result from hormonal influences (particularly estrogen) and increased levels of placental histaminase.[61,160] Placental histaminase is believed to mediate acid and pepsin secretion by reducing parietal cell responsiveness to endogenous histamine.[61] Gastrin levels are normal during most of pregnancy, with marked increases late in the third trimester, at delivery, and immediately after delivery. The additional gastrin is probably of placental origin.

Small and Large Intestines

The action of progesterone on smooth muscles decreases intestinal tone and motility. The decreased motility observed in pregnancy may not necessarily be a direct effect of progesterone, however, but rather a result of inhibition by plasma motilin.[154,251] Decreased GI tone leads to prolonged intestinal transit time, especially during the second and third trimesters. Alterations in transit time increase with advancing gestation, paralleling the increase in progesterone.

Intestinal transit times during stages of pregnancy have been compared with phases of the ovarian cycle in nonpregnant women. Intestinal motility is altered and transit time prolonged during late pregnancy and the luteal phase of the ovarian cycle when progesterone secretion is elevated. The prolonged transit time in late pregnancy is a result of an increase in small bowel transit secondary to inhibition of smooth muscle contraction and not to delayed gastric emptying time. The woman may experience a sense of "bloating" and abdominal distention secondary to the delay in intestinal transit times.[154,231,242]

The height of the duodenal villi increases (hypertrophies) during pregnancy, which in turn increases absorptive capacity.[131] This change, along with the influences of progesterone on intestinal transit time and increased activity of brush border enzymes, increases the absorptive capacity for substances such as calcium, lysine, valine, glycine, proline, glucose, sodium, chloride, and water.[131,274] Progesterone also increases lactase and maltase activity. Absorption of other nutrients (including niacin, riboflavin, and vitamin B_6) is reduced, perhaps because of the influence of progesterone on enzymatic transport mechanisms.[131,231,242,274] Duodenal absorption of iron increases nearly twofold by late pregnancy, probably in response to a reduction of maternal circulating iron stores resulting from uptake by the placenta and fetus.[207,231] As a result of the decreased intestinal motility, nutrients and fluids tend to remain in the intestinal lumen for longer periods of time. This may facilitate absorption of nutrients such as iron and calcium. The amount and efficiency of intestinal calcium absorption increase, mediated primarily by increased 1,25-dihydroxyvitamin D (see Chapter 17).

Progesterone may also enhance absorption of calcium, sodium, and water and increase net secretion of potassium.[207,231,274] The reduced motility and increased transit time in the large intestine increase water and sodium absorption in the colon.[131,154,207] Stools are smaller with lower water content, which contributes to development of constipation during pregnancy. Increased flatulence may also occur as a result of decreased motility along with compression of the bowel by the growing uterus. The appendix and cecum are displaced superiorly by the growing uterus, so by term the appendix tends to be located along the right costal margin.

Pancreas

The pancreas contains estrogen receptors, which in the rich estrogen environment of pregnancy may increase the risk of pancreatitis.[274] Serum amylase and lipase decrease during the first trimester. The significance of this change is unclear. Changes in the islet cells and the increased production and secretion of insulin are discussed in Chapter 16.

Gallbladder

Muscle tone and motility of the gallbladder decrease during pregnancy, probably because of the effects of progesterone on smooth muscle. As a result, gallbladder volume is increased and emptying rate decreased, especially in the second and third timesters.[59,64,231,246] Most measures of gallbladder function are altered during pregnancy, especially after 14 weeks. Some studies have reported that fasting and residual volumes increase to about 20 weeks' gestation, then remain high to term, paralleling the increase in progesterone.[64,81,246] The residual gallbladder volume after fasting and emptying is nearly twice as large in pregnant women as in nonpregnant women who are not taking oral contraceptives. The increased fasting volume may also be a result of decreased water absorption by the mucosa of the gallbladder. This change occurs because of reduced activity of the sodium pump in the mucosal epithelium secondary to estrogens. Consequently, bile is more dilute, with a decreased ability to solubilize cholesterol. The sequestered cholesterol may precipitate to form crystals and stones, increasing the tendency to form cholesterol-based gallstones in the second and third trimesters.[59,64,81,152,246] In the third trimester, bile is supersaturated with lithogenic cholesterol, which, in conjunction with biliary stasis and sludging, increases the risk of gallstones (see Cholelithiasis and Pregnancy).[64,81,152,246] Alterations in gallbladder tone also lead to a tendency to retain bile salts, which can lead to pruritus. There may also be an association between vitamin D deficiency and risk of gallbladder stasis and sludging, as indicated in a study by Singla et al.[246]

Liver

During pregnancy the enlarging uterus displaces the liver superiorly, posteriorly, and anteriorly. Hepatic blood flow per se is not significantly altered despite marked changes in total blood volume and cardiac output. This is because much of the increased cardiac output is sent to the uteroplacental circulation. As a result, the proportion of cardiac output delivered to the liver remains constant at 25% to 35%.[132] Histologically, only minor nonspecific changes in the liver such as increased fat and glycogen storage and variations in cell size have been reported. The size of the liver does not increase.[290]

Liver production of plasma proteins, bilirubin, serum enzymes, and serum lipids is altered. These changes arise primarily from estrogen, which increases the rough endoplasmic reticulum and liver protein synthesis, and in some cases from hemodilution. Progesterone increases proliferation of the smooth endoplasmic reticulum and cytochrome P450 isoenzymes.[290] Changes in liver products during pregnancy and their significance are summarized in Table 12-2.

Although liver function is not impaired during pregnancy, most of the changes in liver function tests are in the same direction as seen in individuals with liver disorders. Some liver function tests are less useful in evaluating liver disorders during pregnancy; other tests such as aspartate aminotransferase (AST, or serum glutamic-oxaloacetic transaminase

hemodilution rather than to greater fetal and maternal demands.[207,225] With the exception of vitamin D (see Chapter 17) and iron (see Chapter 8), little is known about the effects of pregnancy on metabolism of most vitamins and minerals. Recommended dietary reference intakes (DRIs) for childbearing-age, pregnant, and lactating women are available from the Food and Nutrition Board of the National Academy of Science's Institute of Medicine.[118-122,253]

During pregnancy, recommended dietary reference intakes for many vitamins are increased by 20% to 100%, including vitamin E, vitamin C, thiamin, riboflavin, niacin, vitamin B_6, and vitamin B_{12}.[4,119,120,206] Vitamin E is essential during pregnancy for tissue growth and integrity of cell and red blood cell membranes. Vitamin C increases iron absorption and is needed for collagen formation and tissue formation and integrity. Thiamin, niacin, riboflavin, and vitamins B_6 and B_{12} serve as coenzymes for protein and energy metabolism, which are increased in the pregnant woman.[258] Zinc supplementation has been reported to increase birth weight in undernourished women with low serum zinc levels and decrease the risk of fetal growth restriction.[9] Requirements for minerals and other vitamins are discussed in Chapter 8 (iron and folate), Chapter 17 (calcium, phosphorus, magnesium, and vitamin D), and Chapter 19 (iodine). Absorption of some minerals, including calcium, iron, zinc, and selenium, increases during pregnancy.[9,132] Excessive intake or marked deficiency of specific vitamins and minerals has been reported to be associated with adverse pregnancy outcome, although the number of observations is limited. Excessive vitamin A (retinol) is associated with an increase in birth defects.[9,173,206] The reader is referred to texts on nutrition during pregnancy for further discussion of nutritional assessment and requirements.[117,225,258]

The benefits of routine multivitamin supplementation other than for specific supplements such as folic acid and iron have not been clearly documented. The IOM recommendations indicate that pregnant women with balanced diets do not need routine multivitamin and mineral supplementation, except iron, and even routine iron supplementation is not without controversy (see Chapter 8).[46,117] Folic acid supplementation is recommended for all women of childbearing age to reduce the incidence of neural tube defects (see Chapter 15).[68,138] Additional multivitamin and mineral supplementation or supplementation of specific nutrients may be needed by women whose diet is inadequate (which may apply to women both below and above the poverty level) or who have a multiple pregnancy, smoke, or are alcohol or drug abusers. Micronutrient supplementation during pregnancy has been reported to decrease the risk for low birth weight but not to affect preterm birth rates or perinatal or neonatal mortality.[46,52]

Fetal Nutritional Needs

The fetus is dependent on the mother and placenta for transfer of nutrients essential for normal fetal growth and development. (Fetal growth and alterations are discussed in Development of the Gastrointestinal and Hepatic Systems in the Fetus.)

Maternal nutrition during pregnancy, whether adequate, inadequate, or excessive, leads to "programming" of fetal tissues and may have long-term consequences for neurobehavioral outcomes and later health of offspring, including risks of hypertension, obesity, and cardiovascular disease (see p. 410 and Chapter 19).[156]

Nutritional needs of the fetus are met by three mechanisms depending on the stage of development. Before implantation, the blastocyst absorbs nutrients from its surrounding tissues and from fluids within the fallopian tube and uterus. Between implantation and placental development, nutrients are absorbed via a sinusoidal space between maternal and fetal tissues. With formation of the placenta, nutrients are transferred across this structure from mother to fetus via a variety of mechanisms (see Chapter 3). The energy needs of the fetus near term are met through carbohydrates (80%) and amino acids (20%).[207,225,253] Fats are not used as a primary energy source by the fetus because of the immaturity of fat metabolism. The major fetal energy source is glucose from the mother; free fatty acids are used as an alternative energy source and a substrate for lipid formation (see Chapter 16). Amino acids are actively transported from mother to fetus, and imbalances in maternal plasma amino acid concentrations can result in excessive fetal concentrations; subsequent damage as can occur in women with phenylketonuria (see Chapter 1).

Fetal needs for most vitamins and minerals can be met if maternal intake follows recommended DRIs.[46,117,138,253] Lipid-soluble vitamins (A, D, E, and K) cross the placenta more readily than water-soluble vitamins and with increasing ease with advancing gestation. The vitamins most likely to be associated with deficiencies during pregnancy are folate and B_6 (see Chapter 8).

Calcium and phosphorus are actively transported across the placenta, which allows accumulation of calcium and calcification of the fetal skeleton (see Chapter 17). The fetus needs micronutrients such as zinc, copper, chromium, iodine, magnesium, and manganese. Maternal dietary intake of these elements is usually sufficient. Iron supplementation is recommended to enhance maternal iron stores (see Chapter 8).

Heartburn and Gastroesophageal Reflux

Heartburn (reflux esophagitis with retrosternal burning) arises from reflux of gastric acids into the lower esophagus. Heartburn has been reported in up to 80% of women at some point during pregnancy, with an increased frequency seen in the third trimester.[131,160,231,251,276] Heartburn usually begins during the second trimester, although about 25% experience heartburn in the first trimester. Heartburn intensifies with advancing gestation and disappears after delivery.[276] Interventions are summarized in Table 12-5.

The pathogenesis of heartburn during pregnancy is multifactorial. The major etiologic factor is relaxation of the LES along with alterations in pressure gradients across the sphincter. In nonpregnant women, LES tone increases in response

TABLE 12-5   Recommendations for Common Problems During Pregnancy Related to the Gastrointestinal System

PROBLEM	NURSING RECOMMENDATIONS
Heartburn	Eat small, frequent meals
	Eat bland foods
	Avoid fatty or spicy foods, tomatoes, and highly acidic citrus products
	Avoid late night or large meals
	Avoid foods that reduce lower esophageal sphincter pressure (e.g., alcohol, chocolate, caffeine)
	Avoid lying down for 1–3 hours after meals
	Chew gum
	Sleep with the torso elevated
	Avoid lying flat or bending
	Use antacids (calcium-magnesium based) after meals and at bedtime
	Avoid the use of antacids containing phosphorus (alters calcium-phosphorus balance, leading to leg cramps), sodium (increases water retention), or high-dose aluminum (accumulates in woman and fetus; causes constipation)
	Monitor for side effects of chronic antacid use (alteration in muscle tone and deep tendon reflexes, electrolyte imbalance)
	Recognize potential effects of chronic antacid use on malabsorption of potassium, phosphorus, calcium, and drugs such as anticoagulants, salicylates, vitamin E
Constipation	Drink fluids
	Drink hot or cold liquids (especially on an empty stomach)
	Eat high-fiber/bulk laxative foods such as fruits and raw vegetables
	Eat high-fiber bran and wheat foods
	Participate in regular light exercise during pregnancy
	Ambulate early postpartum
	Use stool softeners
	Use bulk-forming fiber-containing agents (which are not absorbed and are therefore safest)
	Use stimulant laxatives with caution and avoid long-term use
	Avoid use of mineral oil in pregnancy (absorbs fat-soluble vitamins including vitamin K)
	Monitor for side effects if laxatives are prescribed (fluid accumulation, sodium retention and edema, cramping)
	Monitor for drug interactions if laxatives are prescribed (decreased serum K with diuretics, decreased effectiveness of anticoagulants and salicylates)
Hemorrhoids	Use a sitz bath
	Use astringents such as witch hazel (Tucks), lemon juice, or vinegar
	Eat bulk foods
	Prevent constipation and straining (see previous entries)
Nausea and vomiting	Eat small, frequent, high-carbohydrate, low-fat meals and snacks
	Avoid strong odors, fatty or spicy foods, and cold liquids
	Consume dry crackers or toast before arising
	Consume ginger (e.g., soda, tea, cookies, supplement)
	Suck on hard candy
	Try elastic wrist bands (SeaBands)
	Lie down when first experiencing symptoms
	Practice relaxation techniques
	Avoid factors and situations that precipitate symptoms
	Monitor for side effects of pharmacologic agents (see Chapter 7)

to elevations in intragastric pressure as a protective mechanism to prevent or minimize reflux. Alterations in LES tone during pregnancy eliminate or significantly reduce this protective mechanism.[59,131,251] Pregnant women without heartburn tend to have LES pressures sufficient to maintain the normal pressure gradient across the gastroesophageal junction, whereas women with heartburn do not demonstrate this compensatory mechanism.[251] Pregnant women (regardless of whether they experience heartburn) have increased nonpropulsive esophageal motor activity with decreased wave amplitude and slower spread of peristaltic waves, with a reduction in secondary peristalsis. These findings are suggestive of reflux and are more prominent in women who experience symptoms of heartburn during pregnancy.[160,214,276]

Pressure from the growing uterus increases intragastric pressure and, along with flattening of the hemidiaphragm, causes anatomic distortion of the stomach and decreases the acuteness of the angle at the gastroesophageal junction.[61,131] Elevations in intragastric and intraabdominal pressure are intensified by multiple pregnancy, hydramnios, obesity, lithotomy position, bending over, or application of fundal pressure.[251] The tendency toward reflux is increased by the decreased GI tone and relaxation of the cardiac sphincter.[61,271] As a result of gastric stasis and pyloric incompetence, the refluxed material may be alkaline or acidic. Prolonged reflux of normal pH or alkaline duodenal material can lead to esophagitis.[61] If pharmacologic therapy is needed, histamine₂-receptor antagonists are usually recommended, with cimetidine and ranitidine having the greatest use.[251] For more severe GER, proton pump inhibitors are increasingly used.[214] Data on use of these agents during pregnancy are limited, but several studies have reported that use of omeprazole was not associated with major teratogenic risks, especially with use after the first trimester.[189]

The frequency of hiatal hernia is also increased, occurring in 15% to 20% of pregnant women primarily after 7 to 8 months' gestation. This disorder arises from alterations in muscle tone and pressure with widening of the hiatus. Interventions are similar to those for heartburn (see Table 12-5).

Constipation

Constipation occurs in 10% to 30% of women and tends to be worse in the first and third trimesters.[154,231,242,251,271] Constipation probably arises primarily from alterations in water transport and reabsorption in the large intestine. The smooth muscle relaxant effects of progesterone decrease intestinal motility and prolong transit time, which increases electrolyte and subsequently water absorption in the large intestine. Progesterone may also inhibit motilin (a stimulating GI hormone) release.[251] Other predisposing factors are compression of the rectosigmoid area by the enlarging uterus and changes in dietary habits and activity and exercise patterns. Interventions for women with constipation are summarized in Table 12-5.

Hemorrhoids

Hemorrhoids are more common during pregnancy and are aggravated by constipation. Factors that contribute to hemorrhoid formation during pregnancy include poor support for hemorrhoidal veins in the anorectal area; lack of valves in these vessels, leading to reversal in the direction of blood flow and stasis; gravity; pressure of the expanding uterus; increased venous pressure in the pelvic veins; venous congestion and engorgement; and enlargement of the hemorrhoidal veins.[18] Interventions for women with hemorrhoids are summarized in Table 12-5.

Nausea and Vomiting

Nausea with or without vomiting is a self-limiting event experienced by up to 70% to 90% of pregnant women.[33,48,63,76,149,202] Nausea and vomiting in pregnancy (NVP) generally begins between 4 and 6 weeks, but may occur as early as 2 to 3 weeks after the last menstrual period, and peaks at 8 to 12 weeks..[76,202,251] NVP usually resolves by 10 to 12 weeks, although a few women (less than 10%) may experience symptoms to term.[76,251,278] NVP incidence and severity are often linked to dietary cravings and aversions.[48,55,202] The most common food aversions are to meat, fish, poultry, and eggs.[48,87] NVP is often thought to occur most prominently before rising in the morning and ingestion of food (hence the term morning sickness), but many women experience symptoms in the afternoon, evening, or throughout the day.[63,131] Although NVP usually disappears by 10 to 12 weeks, it persists to 14 weeks in 40% of women, 16 weeks in less than 20%, and 20 weeks in less than 10%.[202,231]

The exact cause and function of nausea and vomiting is unknown. Many theories have been proposed, focusing on mechanical, endocrinologic, allergic, metabolic, genetic, and psychosomatic etiologies, but none has substantial research support.[76,98,114,149,231,251] An adaptive and protective mechanism for NVP has also been postulated.[48,87,114,202] NVP likely results from a combination of metabolic and endocrine factors, many of them placental in origin, mediated by other factors.[76,149,202]

The most common hormonal theories are related to rapidly increasing and high levels of estrogen, human chorionic gonadotropin (hCG), and possibly thyroxine. Support for a hormonal basis comes from studies documenting nausea in women taking estrogen medications or combined oral contraceptive pills, the high correlation between women who experience nausea with both oral contraceptive use and pregnancy, and parallels between hCG patterns and the timing of symptom appearance and disappearance in NVP.[48,76,114,149,202] However, studies examining the correlation of hCG levels with symptom appearance and intensity in individual women have produced inconsistent results. Increased NVP is seen in women with multiple and molar pregnancies, both of which are characterized by increased hCG.[48,98,149,202] Perhaps a combination of endocrine factors leads to NVP, and individual women may have different sensitivities to these substances. The prevalence of specific hCG isoforms or alterations in hCG receptors may account for differences in NVP prevalence among various populations.[48,76,149] NVP has been associated with favorable pregnancy outcomes such as decreased miscarriage rates, low birth weight, and perinatal mortality, although some researchers have found no differences in perinatal mortality and low birth weight.[55,76,87,114,131] Few studies have been done to document a psychogenic basis to NVP, and many available reports are case studies of women in psychotherapy. Studies that have been done on more representative populations present conflicting findings.

Another hypothesis is that NVP may have an adaptive function to protect the embryo from potentially toxic substances in foods, such as animal products that might contain parasites and other pathogens if not handled correctly, caffeinated beverages, and alcohol.[76,114,202] A study of 20 societies in which women experience NVP and 7 in which NVP is uncommon found that the societies in which NVP was uncommon were more likely to have plants (corn) as the primary staple rather than animal products.[87]

Decreased energy intake in early pregnancy is correlated with increased placental weight in animal and human studies.[87] Huxley suggests that hCG activates the thyroid, thus increasing thyroxine secretion, which stimulates placental growth. As noted previously, hCG (and thyroxine) levels correlate with severity and onset of NVP in some but not all studies. Huxley postulates that NVP reduces maternal energy intake. Maternal levels of anabolic hormones, insulin, and insulin-like growth factor I (IGF-I) are lowered, as is maternal tissue synthesis, favoring early placental growth and development and later fetal growth.[76,114] Underweight women tend to experience less severe NVP than women with normal preconceptional BMI.[114]

Interventions for women experiencing NVP are summarized in Table 12-5. Pharmacologic treatment may occasionally be required because of severity of symptoms or interference with the woman's responsibilities. Use of pharmacologic agents is fraught with potential problems, in that NVP and thus the administration of any drugs occur during the period of embryonic organogenesis. Until the early 1980s, Bendectin (which combined an antihistamine and pyridoxine) was commonly used to treat NVP. Litigation over the relationship of Bendectin and congenital defects resulted in removal of this drug from the market, although a causal relationship has never been documented.[283] Alternative therapies have been investigated.[112,165,166,283] Ginger has been reported to be effective in reducing nausea in most studies, although there continue to be concerns about high doses.[33,278,283] Ginger may work by increasing gastric tone and peristalsis via anticholinergic and antiserotonin actions.[278] Vitamin B_6 and doxylamine have also been shown to reduce NVP.[76,112] However, studies on the use of acupuncture for NVP have had equivocal findings.[76,112,165,166]

Hyperemesis gravidarum, an uncommon disorder seen in 0.3% to 1% of pregnant women, is intractable vomiting associated with alterations in nutritional status, dehydration, electrolyte imbalance, significant weight loss (greater than 5%), ketosis, and acetonuria.[59,76,131,251,278] These women often require hospitalization. Risk factors include primiparas, multiple gestation, family history, or hyperemesis in previous pregnancies.[83,131,149] Hyperemesis has been linked to alterations in thyroid hormones (see Chapter 19) and endocrine changes (especially progesterone and human chorionic gonadotropin), immunologic changes, and metabolic alterations and is associated with Helicobacter pylori.[59,149,251,278] Hyperemesis usually begins by 4 to 10 weeks and resolves by 20 weeks but persists to delivery in about 10%.[278]

Food and Fluid Intake in Labor

For many years most hospitals in the United States did not allow women in active labor to eat or consume beverages other than ice chips or clear liquids. These prohibitions developed during the period when general anesthesia was commonly used during the second stage of labor; accordingly, there were concerns regarding the risk of aspiration should the anesthetized woman vomit. These constraints have been questioned, with many practitioners advocating more liberal food and fluid policies during labor.[133,245] Potential benefits include meeting maternal energy needs and reducing maternal stress and the risks of ketosis, hyponatremia, and vomiting.[240] There is little documentation supporting either the benefits of this therapy or the risk of oral intake for most women (see Chapter 11).[245] Most studies have not reported adverse effects of oral intake during labor in low-risk women (studies of high-risk women are lacking).[159,194,240,245] O'Sullivan and associates compared a light diet versus water during labor and found no differences in labor duration, cesarean section rate, incidence of vomiting, or outcomes.[194] A Cochrane review examined oral fluid or food intake during labor and concluded that there was no evidence to support restrictions for low-risk women.[245] Current guidelines from professional groups also support oral intake during labor in low-risk women.[13,14,133,245]

Individuals opposed to a more liberal food and fluid policy in labor argue that, although rare, aspiration has devastating consequences and can still occur with an endotracheal tube in place or use of regional anesthesia. Pregnant women are at particular risk for pulmonary aspiration because of delayed gastric emptying time in late pregnancy, increased levels of gastrin (resulting in increased gastric volume), and decreased LES tone (which allows stomach contents in an unconscious woman to passively move into the pharynx and into the lungs). Those advocating relaxation of restrictions note that (1) general anesthesia has been replaced by regional anesthesia; (2) the incidence of maternal mortality from aspiration of stomach contents in normal labor is rare; (3) gastric emptying may not be significantly altered in healthy women who have not received narcotics; (4) use of intravenous fluid administration is increased; and (5) prolonged fasting during labor has physiologic and psychological effects.[38,39] Sharts-Hopko noted that maternal aspiration "is so rare that a randomized control trial to see if oral intake related to maternal mortality is not even feasible."[240, p. 198] General anesthesia, if used, is safer than in the past as the result of changes in anesthetic agents and administrative techniques, such as the use of endotracheal tubes that prevent aspiration of vomitus. Potential physiologic effects of fasting include increased ketones and fatty acids with decreased alanine, glucose, and insulin. Psychological effects include increased anxiety and stress.[39] Use of intravenous fluids has been associated with maternal and infant fluid and electrolyte problems (see Chapter 11). Low-risk women who deliver at home or in alternative settings and women in other cultures often consume food and beverages during labor with few complications.

Effects of Altered Maternal Nutrition

Adequate nutrition during pregnancy is essential for optimal fetal growth and development. Most studies demonstrate a correlation between maternal weight gain and birth weight even when other variables that influence birth weight (gestational age, maternal height, and birth order) are held constant. The relationship between weight gain during pregnancy and perinatal mortality varies with maternal prepregnancy weight and pregnancy weight gain (see Figure 12-2). Alterations in maternal nutrition can influence both fetal growth and later outcomes of offspring. For example, undernourished women, especially those with low prepregnancy BMI and low weight gain during pregnancy, have an increased risk of SGA and fetal-growth-restricted infants. These infants are at risk for later developing obesity and type 2 diabetes.[90,141,151] Infants born to obese women are at later risk of developing obesity, type 2 diabetes, and cardiovascular disease.[90,223,250] Specific effects of altered maternal nutrition are listed in Table 12-6. Effects of maternal nutrition on the fetus are discussed further in Fetal Growth.

TABLE 12-6	Potential Consequences of Inadequate Nutrition in Women During a Reproductive Cycle	
PREPREGNANCY	**PREGNANCY**	**POSTPREGNANCY**
DEFICIENT NUTRITION		
Short stature	Small placenta	Body weight
Low body weight	Reduced duration of	deficiency
Low adiposity	pregnancy	Poor lactation
Low lean body	Risk of low birth weight	performance
mass	and fetal growth	Prolonged
Delayed menarche	restriction	amenorrhea
Low nutrient re-	Inadequate weight gain	Longer birth
serves (includ-	Low deposition of fat	interval
ing Ca, Fe, I,	Inadequate volume	Nutrient deficien-
Zn, vitamin A)	expansion	cies (Fe, Ca,
Low discretionary	Inadequate hormonal	Zn, vitamin A,
activity	response	and so on)
	Nutrient deficiencies	Low discretionary
	(including Fe, I, Zn,	activity
	vitamin A, folate,	Poorer prepreg-
	vitamin D)	nancy nutrition
	Perinatal complications	
	Lower discretionary	
	activity	
RELATIVE EXCESS OF ENERGY (OBESITY)		
Poor health	Increased adiposity	Worsening of
(higher preva-	Risk of macrosomic	diabetes and
lence of hyper-	baby	health conse-
tension, type 2	Perinatal complications	quences
diabetes)	Risk of preeclampsia	Low discretionary
Low discretionary	and gestational	activity
activity	diabetes	

IUGR, Intrauterine growth restriction.
Adapted from Viteri, F.E., Schumacher, L., & Silliman, K. (1989). Maternal malnutrition and the fetus. *Semin Perinatol, 13,* 236.

Undernutrition and Pregnancy

Women who are underweight have a higher incidence of pregnancy loss and SGA infants. These women may fail to gain adequate weight during pregnancy, further increasing the risk of fetal growth restriction and maternal nutritional anemia and malnutrition. Maternal undernutrition can also alter fetal metabolic programming, increasing the risk of later disorders (see Fetal Growth).[45,86]

Kristal and Rush and others have reviewed studies examining the effects of maternal undernutrition on fetal growth and concluded the following: (1) limitations in the overall amount of maternal food intake from either starvation or iatrogenic limitations lead to a consistent depression in birth weight (up to 550 g); (2) relief of acute undernutrition up to the beginning of the third trimester is associated with return of birth weight to previous levels; (3) results of supplementation studies with pregnant women at risk nutritionally (in resource-rich and resource-constrained countries) are consistent, with increases in birth weight of 40 to 60 g; (4) there seems to be a limit in the amount of supplementation a given individual can tolerate and to the effect of these supplements; and (5) a consistent depression in birth weight is seen with

use of high-density protein supplements in which more than 20% of calories supplied are protein.[137,140] High-density protein diets have also been associated with an increased incidence of SGA infants and possibly increased neonatal morbidity in some populations.[137] Both caloric and protein deprivation affect the fetus, although it is controversial as to which is most detrimental to fetal growth and development. Providing undernourished women with balanced protein energy supplementation reduces the risk of fetal growth restriction.[116,253] Studies of supplementation with micronutrients of undernourished women have been sparse (and tend to focus on a single nutrient), although some have reported improvements in maternal and fetal weight.[52]

Maternal Obesity and Pregnancy

Maternal obesity is one of the most common risk factors in pregnant women.[141,262] Maternal obesity is associated with an increased incidence of macrosomia, LGA infants, delivery complications, and perinatal mortality.[56,135,232,249] These LGA infants are usually larger than expected in weight but not length because of increased deposition of adipose tissue.[56,90,135,232] The woman's excess adipose tissue reserves may be supplying some of the fuel needed for fetal growth. Because obese women tend to have LGA infants even when pregnancy weight gain is inadequate, it may be difficult to determine whether their infants are growth restricted.

Many of the metabolic changes seen in pregnancy (e.g., increased circulating insulin, insulin resistance) are similar to those seen in obese women. Obese women tend to have more problems during delivery related to increased fetal growth and macrosomia. The incidence of preeclampsia and chronic hypertension, thrombophlebitis, varicose veins, and type 2 diabetes mellitus is increased in obese women.[27,151,193] These women may gain excess weight during pregnancy, which can be difficult to lose later.[53,161,190,193,281,289] Maternal obesity also has been reported to be a risk factor for neural tube defects.[193]

Dietary and physical activity interventions during pregnancy can prevent excessive gestational weight gain and improve outcomes.[262] Caloric restriction during pregnancy is generally not recommended because of potential adverse effects on the fetus. Severe caloric restriction can significantly reduce the availability of glucose (the major fetal energy substrate) and increase maternal serum amino acid and ketone levels. Maternal ketosis has been associated with poor neurologic development in offspring, although some studies have not confirmed this finding.[101] However, caloric restriction may be indicated in obese pregnant women to maintain a weight associated with an improved pregnancy outcome.[94,107,295]

Pregnancy and Gastrointestinal Disorders

The physiologic and anatomic changes of the GI tract during pregnancy have varying effects on disorders of this system. The course of some disorders is minimally affected by pregnancy. Approximately 1 in 500 to 735 pregnant women require nonobstetric surgery. Appendicitis and cholelithiasis are the most common reasons for nonobstetric surgery during pregnancy.[80,248]

Pregnancy and Acute Appendicitis

Appendicitis is not more common during pregnancy, but it may be more severe because of delayed diagnosis.[80,88,131] Diagnosis of appendicitis during pregnancy is complicated by anatomic and physiologic changes of pregnancy. Because the appendix is displaced upward and laterally to the right, the point of maximal tenderness may be as high as the right costal margin. By the second trimester, the appendix lies above the iliac crest. As a result, radiated pain associated with suppuration or perforation tends to be felt at the point where the appendix abuts the peritoneum, which becomes higher and more lateral as gestation progresses.[88,248,255] Guarding and rebound tenderness are often milder and less well localized because the uterus is between the appendix and the parietal peritoneum.[251] Nausea is common in the first trimester, and changes in white blood cell counts associated with appendicitis are similar to changes in pregnancy. Suidan and Young suggest that one way to differentiate uterine from appendiceal pain is to turn the woman onto her left side while pressing the point of maximal tenderness. If the pain decreases or ceases, the pain is probably uterine in origin; if not, appendicitis should be suspected.[255] Appendicitis increases the risk of spontaneous abortion and preterm labor, especially if accompanied by perforation and peritonitis.[131,251] The risk of perforation is greatest in the third trimester.[251]

Pregnancy in Women With Inflammatory Bowel Disease

One of the more common GI disorders occurring in the childbearing population is inflammatory bowel disease (IBD), which includes ulcerative colitis and Crohn's disease. Most recent studies report that fertility rates in women with IBD are similar to the general population; however, fertility is reduced after surgical intervention.[26] If these disorders are quiescent at the time of pregnancy the outcome for both mother and fetus is usually good, although these women have an increased risk of preterm delivery (most ≥ 35 weeks or later), low birth weight, cesarean delivery, and spontaneous abortion.[26,34,131,158,177,251] If the disorder is active at the time of conception, there is a greater risk of these complications.[26,34,131,158,177,251] The risk of exacerbation during pregnancy is similar to the risk in nonpregnant women. Risk of exacerbation is highest during the first trimester and postpartum. Long-term detrimental effects of pregnancy on the course of IBD have not been reported.[26,34]

Pregnancy in Women With Peptic Ulcer Disease

PUD in women is more common after menopause and is uncommon during the childbearing years. The risk of PUD is greatest with use of nonsteroidal antiinflammatory agents in combination with colonization with Helicobacter pylori.[251] In women of childbearing age, estrogen may protect the gastric lining from ulcer formation, perhaps by increasing gastric and duodenal mucous secretion.[274] Pregnancy has a further protective effect on the development and progression of PUD.[131,226] Up to 80% of women with PUD improve during pregnancy, although 50% experience recurrence of symptoms by 3 months postpartum and almost all by 2 years after delivery.[61,226] Women with persistent symptoms during pregnancy usually have other problems such as hyperemesis gravidarum and albuminuria.[226]

The basis for improvement during pregnancy may be related to the normal GI changes that accompany pregnancy, including decreased gastric acidity and motility and increased mucous secretion.[59] Production of hydrochloric acid (both basal and in response to histamine) decreases in pregnancy, with a tendency to return to normal or increased levels of acidity in the third trimester.[251] Decreased gastric acidity, increased plasma histaminase (thought to mediate acid and pepsin secretion by reducing parietal cell responsiveness to endogenous histamine), increased prostaglandins (protective of gastric mucosa), and increased mucous secretion (which protects the gastric mucosa from the effects of acid) may all contribute to improvement in peptic ulcer symptoms.[61,200,231] Gastrin levels are normal during most of pregnancy, with marked increases late in the third trimester, at delivery, and immediately after delivery. Thus by late pregnancy, gastric pH and pepsin output have returned to nonpregnant levels. It is at this time that peptic ulcer symptoms tend to recur.[61,226]

Cholelithiasis and Pregnancy

The incidence of cholelithiasis, which is more common in women, is increased further during pregnancy and in women taking oral contraceptive agents.[64,152,196,290] Cholelithiasis is the second most common nonobstetric surgical problem (acute appendicitis being the most common) during pregnancy. A hormonal basis for the risk of gallstones in women has been suggested because the increased risk is seen primarily between menarche and menopause. Elevated estrogen and progesterone levels during pregnancy may further aggravate the tendency toward cholelithiasis, as does the increased bile stasis and sludging during pregnancy.[64,152,290]

There are three forms of gallstones: cholesterol, pigment, and mixed (composed primarily of calcium bilirubinate). The increased incidence of gallstones associated with females and pregnancy is seen primarily with cholesterol gallstones. The process of gallstone development involves (1) production of bile supersaturated with cholesterol; (2) nucleation and crystallization of cholesterol, which initiates stone formation; and (3) growth of the stone.[222] Supersaturation of bile with cholesterol occurs when cholesterol secretion is high or bile acid secretion is low (concentrated bile is more likely to hold cholesterol in solution). Cholesterol production increases during pregnancy. In addition, estrogens and progesterone increase biliary cholesterol saturation, and estrogen decreases the proportion of chenodeoxycholic acid. This acid is a component of the bile acid pool that dissolves gallstones by decreasing biliary cholesterol secretion. Altered gallbladder tone during pregnancy, with incomplete emptying and increased fasting and residual volumes, may also increase the risk of gallstone formation by sequestering cholesterol crystals.[81,152,222] Cholelithiasis during pregnancy may increase the risk of chronic gallbladder disease.[152,196]

Pregnancy and Liver Disease

Liver disease in pregnancy can be divided into two categories: (1) disorders seen only in pregnancy and associated with jaundice and abnormal liver tests (intrahepatic cholestasis, preeclampsia, and fatty liver of pregnancy) and (2) liver diseases that may occur during and are affected by pregnancy.[197] Fetal fatty acid oxidation defects may increase the risk of maternal liver disease, especially acute fatty liver of pregnancy and HELLP syndrome, which includes hemolysis (H); elevated serum levels of liver enzymes, especially AST and ALT (EL); and low platelets (LP).[35,42,284] The reason for this risk is postulated to be accumulation and deposition of fetal 3-hydroxy fatty acid acylcarnitine intermediary metabolites.[42]

The most common liver disease seen in pregnant women is viral hepatitis.[197] Major effects of pregnancy on liver disorders are potential difficulties with diagnosis, increased fetal risk, and, especially with hepatitis B, transmission to the fetus. Alterations in some liver function tests during pregnancy (see Table 12-2) can make diagnosis of liver disorders more difficult, although jaundice is always abnormal. Jaundice and liver disorders during pregnancy are discussed in Chapter 18.

Severe pruritus and jaundice characterize intrahepatic cholestasis (see Table 14-2). The risk of postpartum hemorrhage, gallstones, fetal distress, stillbirth, and prematurity is increased.[64] The basis for this disorder is unclear, although it may have a genetic basis or hormonal origin because a similar syndrome occurs with oral contraceptive use. Fatty liver of pregnancy is a rare disorder of unknown cause that usually appears during the third trimester, often in association with preeclampsia, with high fetal and maternal mortality rates. Delivery of the infant results in rapid improvement.[196,222]

Liver function and histologic changes are associated with preeclampsia (see Table 9-4), with alterations in liver function tests (AST, ALT, GGT, and bilirubin) reported in some women. The degree of liver abnormality tends to parallel the severity of preeclampsia. The most significant involvement is in women who develop HELLP syndrome (see Chapter 9).[222,284,290]

SUMMARY

Pregnant women experience changes in GI and hepatic function that enhance absorption of nutrients for herself and her fetus. These changes are associated with common experiences and discomforts of pregnancy such as heartburn, constipation, nausea, and vomiting. A major component of interconceptional and prenatal care is nutritional assessment and counseling. Maternal nutrition before and during pregnancy is critical for optimal growth and development of the fetus and prevention of maternal, fetal, and neonatal disorders. Box 12-1 summarizes recommendations for clinical practice related to the GI system and perinatal nutrition.

BOX 12-1 Recommendations for Clinical Practice Related to Changes in the Gastrointestinal System in Pregnant Women

Counsel women regarding changes in appetite, food preferences, and intake during pregnancy (p. 387).

Counsel women regarding gingival changes during pregnancy and the need for dental hygiene (pp. 387-389).

Counsel women regarding common problems (heartburn, nausea and vomiting, constipation, hemorrhoids) associated with the gastrointestinal (GI) system (pp. 395-398 and Table 12-1).

Implement interventions to reduce or relieve heartburn, nausea and vomiting, constipation, and hemorrhoids (pp. 395-398 and Table 12-5).

Counsel women regarding the presence of spider angiomas and palmar erythema (p. 392 and Chapter 14).

Recognize the usual parameters for liver function tests and patterns of change during pregnancy and the postpartum period (pp. 390-392 and Table 12-2).

Know the expected parameters for weight gain during pregnancy and monitor maternal patterns (pp. 392-393 and Table 12-3).

Know the recommended nutritional requirements during pregnancy (pp. 394-395 and Table 12-4).

Assess maternal nutritional status and provide nutritional counseling (pp. 394-395 and Table 12-4).

Recognize potential maternal and fetal/neonatal complications associated with undernutrition and obesity during pregnancy (pp. 398-399, 409-410 and Table 12-6).

Monitor fluid, food, and caloric intake during labor and the early postpartum period (p. 398 and Chapter 11).

Counsel women regarding weight loss patterns after delivery (p. 393).

Recommend postpartum exercises to enhance weight loss and return of abdominal and perineal tone (p. 393).

Evaluate GI function postpartum (pp. 393-394).

Recognize factors that increase the risk of gallstone formation and recognize signs of cholelithiasis (pp. 390, 400-401).

Counsel women with GI and liver problems regarding the effect of their disorder on pregnancy and of pregnancy on the disorder (pp. 390, 400-401).

Recognize signs of appendicitis during pregnancy (p. 400).

Recognize signs of liver disorders that are unique to pregnancy (pp. 390, 401 and Chapters 14 and 18).

Counsel women with phenylketonuria and other metabolic disorders regarding risks to their infant and need for dietary restrictions (p. 395, Chapter 1).

Know fetal nutritional requirements and counsel women regarding fetal needs and growth patterns (pp. 395, 409-410).

Know factors that can alter fetal growth and monitor fetal growth patterns (pp. 398-399, 409-410 and Table 12-6).

Counsel women regarding changes in GI function with use of oral contraceptive agents (pp. 388-390).

DEVELOPMENT OF THE GASTROINTESTINAL AND HEPATIC SYSTEMS IN THE FETUS

The development of the gastrointestinal (GI) system can be divided into three phases. During early gestation, anatomic development gives rise to the organs and other structures of this system (Figure 12-3). During middle to late gestation, functional components such as hormones, enzymes, and reflexes develop (Figure 12-4). Finally, after birth, coordinated function develops with interaction of hormones and enzymes in the digestion of food substances along with maturation of suck-swallow coordination.

The enteric nervous system (ENS) consists of neurons in the wall of the GI tract that modulate motility, microcirculation, secretion, and immune responses. The ENS develops from neural crest cells that colonize the gut by 13 weeks. Failure of migration and colonization can lead to disorders such as Hirschsprung's disease.[42] Characteristics and timing of other common GI anomalies are described in the next section and are summarized in Table 12-7. GI anomalies may occur as isolated malformations or in association with malformations of other systems, most commonly the skeletal, cardiovascular, or urogenital systems.[260] Fetal growth restriction is seen in approximately one third of infants with GI malformations.[260]

Anatomic Development

Anatomic development of the GI system begins during the fourth week with partitioning of the yolk sac into intraembryonic and extraembryonic portions. Initially the cranial portion of the GI system develops concurrently with the respiratory system (see Chapter 10). The epithelium of the trachea, the bronchi, and the lungs and digestive tract arise from the primitive gut, a derivation of the yolk sac. The GI system develops in a cranial-to-caudal direction. The yolk sac arises at 8 days and by the fourth week has divided into two parts. The extraembryonic or secondary yolk sac provides for nutrition of the embryo, before development of the mature placenta,

WEEKS OF GESTATION

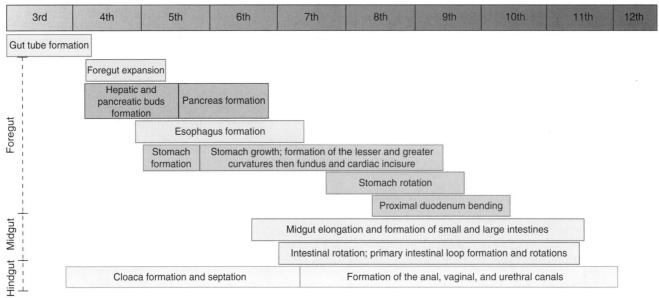

FIGURE 12-3   Gastrointestinal tract organogenesis timeline. The organogenesis of the gut tube starts around the third week of gestation to approximately the twelfth week of gestation. The specific segments and organs of the digestive tract are derived from the endoderm and the primary gut tube (derived from the secondary yolk sac). (From Mahe, M.M., Helmrath, M.A., & Shroyer, N.F., et al. [2017]. Organogenesis of the gastrointestinal tract. In R.A. Polin, W.W., et al. [Eds.]. *Fetal and neonatal physiology* [5th ed.]. Philadelphia: Saunders.)

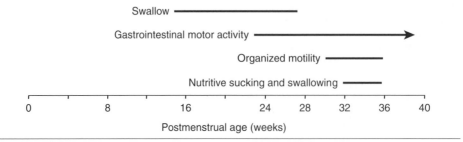

FIGURE 12-4   Timetable of gastrointestinal functional development. (From Newell, S.J. [1996]. Gastrointestinal function and its ontogeny: How should we feed the preterm infants? *Semin Neonatol, 1,* 60.)

TABLE 12-7   Incidence, Time of Occurrence, and Associated Defects of Various Gastrointestinal Anomalies

ANOMALY	INCIDENCE (PER LIVE BIRTHS)	FETAL AGE AT WHICH DEFECT OCCURS	PRESENCE OF HYDRAMNIOS	OTHER CONCURRENT DEFECTS
Diaphragmatic hernia	1:4000	8th–10th week of fetal life	>75%	Lung hypoplasia, malrotation of bowel, PDA, coarctation of aorta, and neurologic malformations
Tracheoesophageal fistula and esophageal atresias	1:3000 1:4000	4th–5th week of fetal life	>60%	Seen in more than 50% of patients and include GI, skeletal, and cardiac defects
Duodenal atresia	1:10,000–1:40,000	8th–10th week of fetal life	~50%	Down syndrome, GI malformations, and congenital heart disease
Jejunoileal atresia	1:330–1:1500	During fetal life after embryogenesis (after 12 weeks' gestation)	35% jejunal 10%–15% ileal	Infrequent, but volvulus, malrotation, and meconium peritonitis may occur
Colonic atresia	1:5000–1:20,000	Vascular accidents in gestation	Rare	Other defects in 30%–40%, typically associated with abdominal wall defects, vesicointestinal fistulas, and jejunal atresias
Anorectal anomalies	1:5000–1:15,000	5th–8th week of fetal life	Rare	May be familial-associated anomalies in 30%–70%, anomalies including cardiac, GI, and vertebral anomalies
Omphalocele	1:3000–1:10,000	8th–11th week of fetal life	Common, but incidence unknown	Other defects in 60%; cardiac defects 15%–20%; tetralogy of Fallot, and specific syndromes; Beckwith and trisomy D, E, and F
Gastroschisis	1:6000	9th–11th week of fetal life	Incidence unknown	Foreshortened gut and intestinal atresias (15%); cardiac defects (<10%)
Duplications of GI tract	1:1000–1:4000	4th–6th week of fetal life	Unknown	Most common in ileum and esophagus
Meckel's diverticulum	1:50–1:100	5th–7th week of fetal life	Rare	Usually occurs as isolated defect

GI, Gastrointestinal; *PDA,* patent ductus arteriosus.
From Sunshine, P. (1990). Fetal gastrointestinal physiology. In R.D. Eden & F.H. Boehm. (Eds.). *Assessment and care of the fetus.* Norwalk, CT: Appleton & Lange.

and then is assimilated into the umbilical cord by 3 to 4 months. The intraembryonic portion is incorporated into the embryo as the primitive gut (Figure 12-5).

The primitive gut is initially closed at both ends by membranes. The cranial (oropharyngeal, also called the buccopharyngeal) membrane is reabsorbed during the third week, forming the stomodeum (future site of the mouth); the caudal (cloacal) membrane is absorbed during the ninth week. The midgut remains temporarily connected to the yolk sac by the vitelline duct. Development of the primitive gut and its derivatives can be divided into four sections: pharyngeal gut, foregut, midgut, and hindgut.[173]

Development of the Pharyngeal Gut

The pharyngeal gut extends from the oropharyngeal membrane (which becomes the stomodeum) to the tracheobronchial diverticulum, forming the pharynx and its derivative, lower respiratory tract, and upper esophagus (Figure 12-6). The pharyngeal area develops from bands of mesenchymal tissue (branchial or pharyngeal arches) separated by deep clefts (branchial or pharyngeal clefts) on the exterior of the embryo. A series of indentations (pharyngeal pouches) appear on the lateral walls of the pharyngeal gut and penetrate into the surrounding mesenchyme but do not communicate with the external clefts. The pharyngeal arches form the muscular and skeletal components of the pharyngeal area, aortic arch, and nerve networks; the mandible; the dorsal portion of the maxillary process; the hyoid bone; the thyroid bone; the laryngeal cartilage; and

associated vascular and nerve supplies. The pharyngeal pouches form the eustachian tubes, tonsils, thymus, parathyroid, and part of the thyroid.[173,227]

Development of the Foregut and Common Anomalies

The foregut extends from the tracheobronchial diverticulum to the upper part of the duodenum. Structures formed from the foregut (lower esophagus, stomach, liver, upper portion of the duodenum to the entry of the common bile duct, liver, biliary tree, and pancreas) are all supplied by the celiac artery.[173]

Esophagus. During the fourth week the tracheobronchial diverticulum appears along the ventral wall of the foregut, dividing the foregut into the ventral respiratory primordium and dorsal esophagus. The esophagus is initially short but quickly elongates with ascent of the pharynx and cranial growth. The rapidly growing endothelium temporarily obliterates the esophageal lumen, with recanalization of the lumen by 8 weeks.[173]

Incomplete division of the foregut into respiratory and digestive portions at 4 to 5 weeks leads to tracheoesophageal fistula with or without esophageal atresia (Figure 12-7; also see Table 12-7). This malformation probably arises from posterior deviation or unequal development of the septum between the primitive trachea and esophagus because of genetic and environmental factors.[65,84] The lumen of the esophagus becomes obliterated by rapidly growing epithelium.

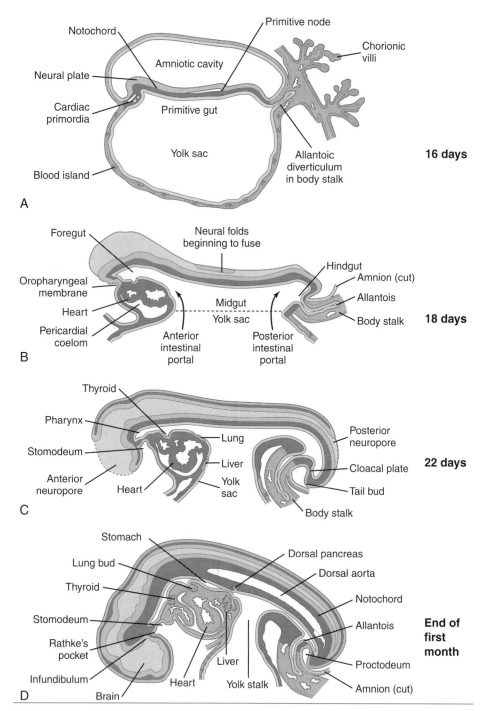

FIGURE 12-5 Sagittal section through human embryos showing the early establishment of the digestive system. **A,** At 16 days. **B,** At 18 days. **C,** At 22 days. **D,** At the end of the first month. (Adapted from Carlson, B.M. [2013]. *Human embryology and developmental biology* [5th ed.]. Philadelphia: Saunders.)

Failure of the lumen to recanalize during the eighth week leads to esophageal stenosis or atresia.

Stomach, Duodenum, and Pancreas. The stomach arises during the fourth week as a spindle-shaped dilation in the caudal area of the foregut (see Figure 12-6), and its structure is well established by 6 weeks. The stomach dilates and enlarges, rotating around a longitudinal and an anteroposterior axis. During the longitudinal rotation, the stomach rotates 90 degrees clockwise, ending with the left side facing anteriorly and the right posteriorly. The subsequent greater growth of the posterior wall in comparison with the anterior wall leads to the lesser and greater curvatures of the stomach. Initially the cephalic and caudal ends of the stomach are in midline. During the anteroposterior rotation of the stomach,

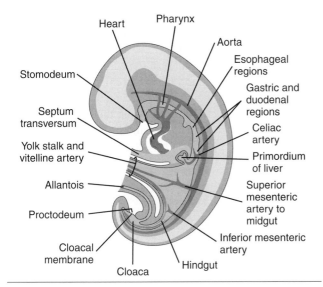

FIGURE 12-6   Early development of the digestive system and its blood supply. (Adapted from Moore, K.L., Persaud, T.V.N., & Torchia, M.G. [2015]. *The developing human: Clinically oriented embryology* [10th ed.]. Philadelphia: Saunders.)

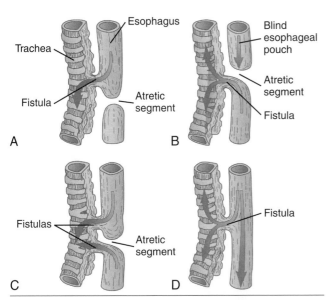

FIGURE 12-7   Varieties of tracheoesophageal fistulas. **A,** Fistula above the atretic esophageal segment. **B,** Fistula below the atretic esophageal segment. **C,** Fistulas above and below the atretic esophageal segment. **D,** Fistulas between the patent esophagus and the trachea. (Adapted from Carlson, B.M. [2013]. *Human embryology and developmental biology* [5th ed.]. Philadelphia: Saunders.)

the caudal (pyloric) portion moves right and upward, and the cephalic (cardiac) portion moves left and slightly downward.[173,227] Embryonic anomalies of the stomach are rare, probably because stomach development is relatively simple. The most common stomach anomaly is pyloric stenosis, which is believed to be genetic in origin.

The duodenum arises from both the foregut and midgut. As the stomach rotates, the duodenum takes on a C-shaped form and rotates to the right. The lumen of the duodenum

becomes obliterated by rapidly growing epithelium, with later recanalization beginning at 6 or 7 weeks.[173] Failure to recanalize leads to duodenal atresia or stenosis.

The pancreas appears at about 5 weeks as dorsal and ventral buds in the duodenal area. As the duodenum rotates to the right and becomes C-shaped, the ventral pancreatic bud migrates toward the lower end of the common bile duct. The two pancreatic buds meet and fuse to form the final pancreas by 7 weeks. In individuals with an annular pancreas, the ventral bud encircles the duodenum and may cause obstruction.[227] All pancreatic cell types are seen by 9 to 10 weeks.

Liver and Gallbladder. The liver appears during the third week as a ventral thickening (liver bud or hepatic diverticulum) consisting of rapidly proliferating strands of cells at the distal end of the foregut (see Figure 12-6). The hepatic diverticulum divides into a large cranial portion, which forms the hepatic parenchyma and main bile duct, and a smaller caudal portion, from which the gallbladder arises.[227] The liver initially grows into the septum transversum, a thick mesodermal plate separating the yolk sac and the thoracic cavity. The liver grows rapidly, eventually bulging into the caudal part of the abdominal cavity and stretching the mesoderm of the septum transversum until it becomes a thin membrane. The ventral portion of this membrane forms the falciform ligament; the dorsal portion forms the lesser omentum. The cranial portion of the septum transversum forms part of the diaphragm. Further growth of the liver promotes closure of the pleuroperitoneal canals (two large openings on either side of the foregut). Hepatocytes develop as long cords 3 to 5 cells thick, inserting into the liver stroma.[25]

The lumina of the gallbladder and the intrahepatic and extrahepatic bile ducts are initially open, becoming temporarily obliterated by proliferating epithelium and later recanalizing. Biliary atresia can arise from failure of recanalization. With complete failure, the ducts are narrow nonfunctional fibrous cords. Failure of part of a bile duct to recanalize results in partial obstruction or atresia of that duct, with distention of the gallbladder and hepatic duct proximal to the atretic area.[173,227]

Development of the Midgut and Common Anomalies

Development of the midgut is characterized by rapid elongation of the gut and associated mesentery. The midgut begins caudal to the liver and gives rise to the small intestine (except for the upper duodenum), cecum, appendix, ascending colon, and proximal portion of the transverse colon. These structures are supplied by the superior mesenteric artery.[173] The intestines increase in length 1000-fold during gestation, doubling in length in the last 15 weeks (mean length is 275 cm at term).[183]

Initially midgut growth parallels the neural tube; however, the rapid growth of the midgut quickly exceeds that of the rest of the body, including the abdominal cavity. This occurs at a time when the liver and kidneys are relatively large, occupying much of the available space in the abdominal cavity.

As a result, the midgut herniates into the extraembryonic coelom of the proximal umbilical cord. This physiologic herniation begins in the sixth week, with return of the midgut to the abdominal cavity during the tenth week.[173]

Development of the midgut involves four steps: herniation, rotation, retraction, and fixation (Figure 12-8).[173,227] The midgut initially elongates and forms a U-shaped loop, which projects (herniates) into the proximal umbilical cord (see Figure 12-8, *A*). The cranial limb of this loop grows rapidly,

forming coils characteristic of the small intestine with little change in the caudal portion except for appearance of the cecal bud (see Figure 12-8, *B*).

The midgut rotates a total of 270 degrees in a counterclockwise direction around an axis formed by the superior mesenteric artery. Midgut rotation occurs in two stages. The initial 90-degree rotation occurs while the midgut is in the umbilical cord (see Figure 12-8, *A* and *B*); the second rotation (180 degrees) takes place as the gut returns to the abdomen

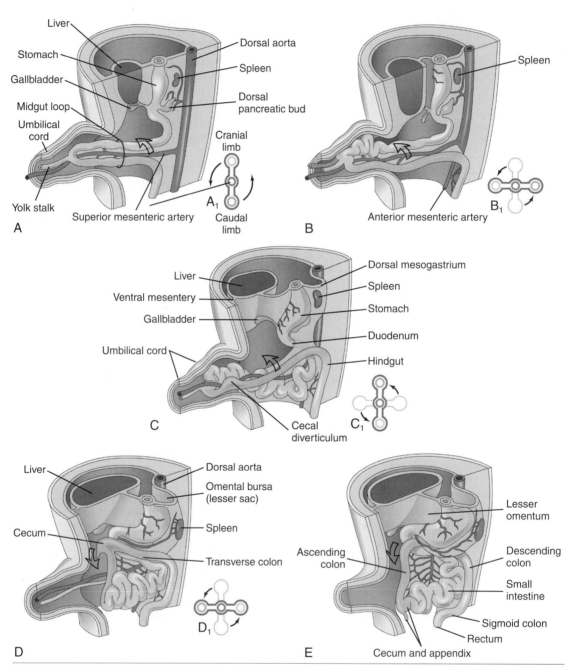

FIGURE 12-8 Development of the midgut (see p. 405). **A,** Midgut loop in proximal umbilical cord at 6 weeks. **A₁,** Transverse section through midgut, showing initial relationships of limbs of midgut loop to artery. **B,** Beginning midgut rotation. **B₁,** 90-degree counterclockwise rotation. **C,** Return of intestines to abdomen at 10 weeks. **C₁,** Additional 90-degree rotation. **D,** After return to abdomen. **D₁,** Final 90-degree rotation (for a total of 270 degrees). **E,** Late fetal period, with cecum rotated to normal position. (From Moore, K.L., Persaud, T.V.N., & Torchia, M.G. [1998]. *Before we are born: Essentials of human embryology and birth defects* [5th ed.]. Philadelphia: Saunders.)

at 10 weeks (see Figure 12-8, *B* and *C*). The initial 90-degree rotation is in a counterclockwise direction. As a result, the cranial limb moves to the right and down and the caudal limb moves to the left and up (see Figure 12-8, *B*). The lumen of the intestines becomes temporarily obliterated by rapid epithelial growth, with later recanalization.[173]

Retraction or return of the midgut to the abdominal cavity occurs rapidly during the tenth week. The stimulus for this return is unknown, but it occurs as the rate of liver growth slows, the relative size of the kidney decreases, and the abdominal cavity enlarges. As the midgut reenters the abdominal cavity, the gut rotates 180 degrees counterclockwise. The jejunum returns first and the area of the cecal bud last; the cecum and appendix end up near the liver in the right upper quadrant (see Figure 12-8, *D*).[227]

The final step in development of the midgut is fixation (see Figure 12-8, *E*). The cecum and appendix descend into the lower right quadrant. The proximal colon lengthens, becoming the ascending colon. The mesenteries are pressed against the posterior abdominal wall and fuse with the wall. In some regions of the midgut, the mesenteries also fuse with the parietal peritoneum so that the ascending colon is rectoperitoneal.[173,227]

Common Anomalies of the Midgut. Congenital anomalies of the midgut include omphalocele, gastroschisis, umbilical hernia, intestinal stenosis and atresia, and malrotation (see Table 12-7). Omphalocele arises at 8 to 11 weeks' gestation from a developmental arrest at the stage of herniation of the midgut into the umbilical cord with failure of all or part of the gut to return to the abdominal cavity (results in bowel-containing omphalocele). There is often an associated defect in development of the abdominal musculature at the junction of the umbilical cord (results in liver-containing omphalocele). This defect results from a primary failure in the formation of the lateral folds, which along with the cephalic and caudal folds form the abdominal wall.[173] The size of the defect influences the size of the omphalocele, which can range from a single loop of intestine to a mass containing most of the intestines and parts of the liver, bladder, and other organs. The omphalocele is covered by a thin, avascular membrane (derived from amnion) that may be intact or ruptured. The umbilical cord generally inserts into the apex of the omphalocele sac. Omphalocele is associated with Beckwith-Wiedemann syndrome, congenital heart disease, trisomy 13, trisomy 18, and urinary tract problems.[82]

Gastroschisis, which is an extrusion of the intestines, results from a defect in the anterior abdominal wall that probably arises between 9 and 11 weeks but may occur as early as 5 to 6 weeks. This defect is usually to the right of, and not necessarily continuous with, the umbilical ring. Because there is usually no hernial sac present, the intestines extrude into the amniotic cavity and are embedded in a gelatinous mass. Gastroschisis arises secondary to a paraumbilical abdominal wall defect that may be a result of (1) failure of differentiation of the lateral fold somatopleure after the bowel has returned to the peritoneal cavity and the umbilical ring

has formed; (2) failure in formation of the umbilical coelom with rupture of the amniotic membrane at the base of the umbilical cord; (3) intrauterine rupture of an incarcerated hernia into the cord; or (4) weakness in the abdominal wall arising from alterations in the normal involution of the second umbilical vein or ischemic damage.[102]

An umbilical hernia is associated with an enlarged umbilical ring and failure of the rectus muscles to come together in midline. The protruding viscera are covered with normal skin.

Intestinal stenoses and atresias can arise as primary or secondary defects. Primary stenosis or atresia arises at 8 to 10 weeks, and perhaps as early as 6 to 7 weeks, as a result of partial or complete failure of the intestinal lumen to recanalize. Secondary stenosis or atresia is (1) a result of fetal vascular accidents or infarction (with interruption of blood supply to part of the intestines) or (2) secondary to twisting or inflammatory changes.[99] Vascular accidents and infarction are common causes of jejunal and ileal atresias and probably occur after 12 weeks (see Table 12-7).

Alterations in midgut development can also lead to malrotation. Three of the more common forms are nonrotation, mixed malrotation, and reverse rotation. With nonrotation, the midgut rotates 90 degrees instead of 270 degrees, without the 180-degree rotation that normally occurs upon reentry of the gut into the abdominal cavity. As a result, the colon enters the abdomen first instead of last so that the colon ends up on the left and the small intestine on the right. This form of malrotation is sometimes referred to as left-sided colon. In mixed malrotation, the midgut rotates only 180 degrees, so that the terminal ileum reenters first. The cecum is subpyloric and fixed to the abdominal wall, which may compress the duodenum. In reverse rotation, the initial 90-degree rotation is clockwise instead of counterclockwise, resulting in placement of the transverse colon behind the duodenum. Malrotation increases the risk of volvulus, with twisting of the intestinal loops and abnormal fixation of the mesenteries, resulting in excessive mobility of the bowel. This can lead to kinking of the bowel and blood vessels and necrosis.[173,227]

Development of the Hindgut and Common Anomalies

Development of the hindgut and urogenital systems is interrelated. The cloaca is the expanded terminal end of the gut; the hindgut ends at the cloacal membrane (Figure 12-9). The hindgut gives rise to the distal transverse colon, descending and sigmoid colons, rectum, upper anal canal, bladder, and urethra, which are supplied by the inferior mesenteric artery.[173]

At 5 to 7 weeks, the cloaca is divided into two parts by the urorectal septum, a wedge of downward-growing mesenchymal tissue. During weeks 6 to 7, the urorectal septum reaches and fuses with the cloacal membrane, forming the perineum. The area of fusion is the perineal body. This fusion divides the cloacal membrane into two parts. The ventral urogenital membrane is incorporated in the terminal portion of the

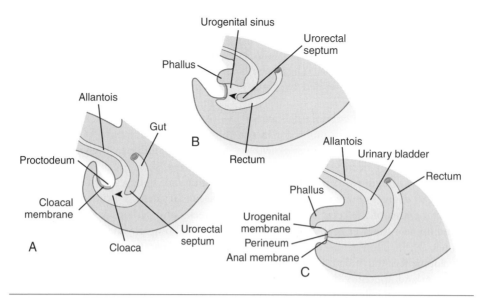

FIGURE 12-9   Stages in the subdivision of the common cloaca by the urogenital septum. **A,** In the fifth week. **B,** In the sixth week. **C,** In the eighth week. The *arrowheads* indicate the direction of growth of the urorectal septum. (Adapted from Carlson, B.M. [2013]. *Human embryology and developmental biology* [5th ed.]. Philadelphia: Saunders.)

urogenital system (see Chapters 1 and 11); the dorsal part becomes the anal membrane. A pit that develops in the anal membrane ruptures at 8 to 9 weeks, resulting in an open communication between the rectum and the body exterior. The lower portion of the anal canal develops from ectodermal tissue around the site of the anal pit.[227]

Imperforate anus and associated malformations arise from abnormal development of the urorectal septum. In the simplest form of imperforate anus, the anal membrane fails to rupture and the anal canal ends at the membrane. In more complex forms, there may be a layer of connective tissue between the end of the rectum and the body surface. Failure of the anal pit to develop or atresia of the end of the rectum can result in these forms. If the descent of the urorectal septum is arrested, the cloaca may remain, with abnormalities of the urogenital and lower GI systems.

Functional Development

Anatomically the fetal GI tract develops to the stage seen in the newborn by about 20 weeks.[134,146,173] Functional development begins during fetal life with development of digestive and liver enzyme systems and the absorptive surfaces of the intestine and continues into the postbirth period. Most of the processes needed for adequate enteral nutrition are in place by 33 to 34 weeks' gestation.[134] Although the placenta takes care of the nutrient needs of the fetus (see Fetal Nutritional Needs on p. 395), function of the fetal GI tract is important in amniotic fluid homeostasis (see Chapter 3). Amniotic fluid in turn contains nutrients, hormones, and growth factors that stimulate secretion of hormones and regulatory peptides and enhance growth and maturation of the gut.[71,134,275]

The major gut-regulating polypeptides, including gastrin, motilin, and somatostatin, are all present by the end of the first trimester and act as local inducing agents regulating growth and development of the gut.[19,187,275] Initially, cells that produce these substances are more widely distributed than in the adult, but they reach adult distribution by 24 weeks. Gastric epidermal growth factor (EGF) receptors appear by 18 weeks. EGF enhances growth and development of the gut and may protect the stomach from hydrochloric acid. Transport of amino acids begins by 14 weeks, glucose transport by 18 weeks, and fatty acid transport by 24 weeks.[144]

The intestinal villi begin to develop around 7 weeks and are present throughout the small intestine by 14 to 16 weeks, with well-developed villi and crypts seen by 19 weeks.[183,200] Intestinal motility and peristalsis develop gradually and mature during the third trimester.[200] Meconium is first found at 10 to 12 weeks and moves into the colon by 16 weeks. Small amounts of meconium may enter the amniotic fluid in the second trimester before development of anal sphincter function at 20 to 22 weeks' gestation.[8]

By 13 to 15 weeks, fetuses respond to oral stimulation with tongue protrusion, rooting, and sucking.[110] Older fetuses have been noted on ultrasound to suck reflexively on their fingers. Nonnutritive sucking begins by 20 weeks.[71] Swallowing begins at 10 to 14 weeks, and by 16 weeks the fetus swallows 2 to 6 mL of amniotic fluid per day, increasing to 200 to 600 mL/day (average, 450 mL/day) by term. About 20% of the fluid swallowed by the fetus is lung fluid, not amniotic fluid. Swallowing is important for amniotic fluid homeostasis, regulation of amniotic fluid volume, GI development, and somatic growth. Swallowing may also be important in fetal thirst and appetite programming. About 10% of fetal protein intake comes from swallowed amniotic fluid.[77] Failure of the fetus to swallow amniotic fluid is associated with GI obstruction and polyhydramnios (see Chapter 3).

Most of the metabolic functions of the fetal liver are handled by the maternal liver. The fetal liver is primarily a hematopoietic organ until the latter part of gestation, when bone marrow erythropoiesis and liver metabolic activity increase. Many liver enzyme systems are still immature at birth. Fetal hepatic metabolism of drugs is discussed in Chapter 7.

GI enzymes involved in protein digestion and absorption develop early in gestation and may be important in fetal life to prevent bowel obstruction by cellular debris.[216] Glucose from the mother is the major source of fetal energy (see Chapter 16). Disaccharidase enzymes are present by 9 to 10 weeks, increase rapidly after 20 weeks, and become very active after 27 to 28 weeks (except for lactase, which does not reach mature levels until 36 to 40 weeks).[82,145] Pancreatic amylase activity is minimal in the fetus.[74] Salivary amylase is present by 16 to 18 weeks in amniotic fluid and by 20 weeks in the fetus, but remains low.[74,187] Pancreatic lipase develops by 32 weeks, but remains low; lingual and gastric lipase are present by 26 weeks and increase to term. Proteolytic enzymes are found by 20 to 25 weeks.[74] Trypsin achieves 90% of childhood values by term.[74] Enterokinase activity appears at 26 weeks. Bile acids can be detected in the liver and gallbladder by 14 to 16 weeks and in the intestines by 22 weeks; however, the bile acid pool remains low even at term. The fetal jejunum and liver have decreased capacity for reabsorbing bile acids and poorer enterohepatic recirculation of taurine-conjugated bile acids, the major bile acid at birth.[102,134] Lipase is present by 10 to 12 weeks.[187]

Fetal Growth

Fetal growth is dependent on factors such as genetic determinants, general maternal health and nutrition, availability of growth substrates, presence of fetal growth–promoting hormones, and vascular support via changes in plasma volume during pregnancy and the maternal blood supply to the placenta.[49,95] Availability of growth substrates depends on perfusion of the intervillous spaces and availability of glucose, amino acids, and fats in maternal blood (see Chapter 16). Fetal growth does not seem to be greatly dependent on hormones such as growth hormone, thyroid hormones, glucocorticoids, and sex steroids that are critical for postnatal growth. Hormones and peptide growth factors believed to be necessary for fetal growth include insulin, human chorionic somatomammotropin, insulin-like growth factors I and II (IGF-I and IGF-II), epidermal growth factor, platelet-derived growth factor, leptin, and transforming growth factor–β.[92,237] Insulin, IGF-I, and IGF-II are critical in regulating fetal growth, although insulin probably has a permissive rather than a direct effect on fetal growth by stimulating nutrient uptake and utilization.[92,179] Growth factors appear early in gestation, beginning at the four- to eight-cell stage. "Disruption of the IGF1, IGF2, or IGF1R [receptor] gene retards fetal growth, whereas disruption of IGF2R or overexpressing IGF2 [genes] enhances fetal growth."[92]

Many of the genes involved in growth regulation are imprinted (see Box 1-1 on p. 11), including IGF-II (paternally imprinted) and its receptor (maternally imprinted).[7,95,171] Loss of paternal imprinting with reactivation of the maternal allele (gene form) is seen in infants with Beckwith-Wiedemann syndrome, which is characterized by abnormal fetal and postnatal growth.[171]

Early in gestation, placental and embryonic growth are regulated primarily by IGF-II. IGF-II is unaffected by nutrient availability and enhances placental growth and nutrient transfer.[7,92,179] Thus embryo and placental growth are maintained even if maternal energy intake is decreased, as often occurs with nausea and vomiting of pregnancy.[114] During the second and third trimesters, fetal growth becomes dependent on IGF-I, which is sensitive to nutrient status.[95,114,179] Another factor that is believed to have a role in fetal growth is placental leptin, which is secreted into both maternal and fetal circulations. Leptin (see Chapter 16) is thought to act on the hypothalamus to regulate food intake and satiety. During pregnancy, placental leptin may signal satiety to the maternal hypothalamus, thus resulting in reduced food intake and energy intake, which stimulates placental growth.[37,73,114] Leptin can be found in cord blood by 18 weeks' gestation.[195] Dysregulation of leptin is seen with fetal growth restriction. Donnelly et al[73] reported that early-pregnancy maternal leptin levels were associated with neonatal abdominal circumference and scapular skinfold thickness, and late pregnancy maternal leptin levels were associated with neonatal triceps skinfold thickness. There was also a significant positive correlation between fetal cord blood levels and neonatal birth weight and adiposity.[73] The correlation between fetal cord blood leptin levels and birthweight has been demonstrated in several studies.[37,73]

Growth is slow during the first 2 months (period of organ formation), and then accelerates rapidly. Maximum growth rate is achieved from the fourth to eighth months, when the fetus grows at the rate of 5% to 9% per week. Most of the fetal weight is gained from 20 weeks to term, increasing from about 5 g/day at 15 weeks, to 15 to 20 g/day at 20 weeks, and 30 to 35 g/day after 32 to 34 weeks.[171,221] At the cellular level, growth occurs through hypertrophy (increased cell size) or hyperplasia (increased cell numbers). The human fetus undergoes primarily hyperplastic growth from conception to 20 weeks (similar increases in deoxyribonucleic acid [DNA] and organ protein content), followed by a period of simultaneous hyperplasia and hypertrophy from 20 to 28 weeks. From 28 weeks on, growth is predominantly hypertrophic with rapid increases in cell size and accumulation of fat, muscle, and connective tissue.[171]

Fetal growth is altered in approximately 15% of pregnancies, with either fetal undergrowth or overgrowth. Fetal overgrowth and macrosomia are discussed in Chapter 16; fetal undergrowth is discussed in the next section. The effects of maternal nutrient restriction or excess depend on the stage of pregnancy, length of restriction, and type of restriction. For example, if maternal nutrients are restricted throughout pregnancy, fetal growth restriction develops. If the restriction is only during the first trimester, infant birth weights tend to be within normal limits, with increased placental weight. Increased food intake in early gestation tends to be associated with infants with lower birth and placental weights. High carbohydrate intake in early pregnancy is associated with lower placental and birth weights. Restricted protein intake (and thus restricted intake of essential amino acids) in early pregnancy has a detrimental effect on both fetal and placental development.[114]

The "developmental origins of health and disease" hypothesis proposes an association between an abnormal fetal environment and later disorders.[21,22,36,45,90,96,223] Developmental programming in utero is mediated by nutrients and hormones. Fetal or developmental programming refers to effects of the fetal environment on susceptibility to later disorders. The nutritional and hormonal status during fetal and early postbirth life can alter organ development, including the hypothalamus and other endocrine structures (see Chapter 19). The mechanisms by which the fetal environment influences later status are not well understood, but are believed to be related to placental adaptive responses to the intrauterine environment. After birth these adaptations may no longer be appropriate for the extrauterine environment and increase the risk for adult onset disorders such as insulin resistance and type 2 diabetes (because of altered endocrine programming or changes in glucose–insulin metabolism); obesity (because of altered leptin and endocrine programming), hypertensive disorders, coronary artery disease (because of alterations in vascular development and lipid metabolism), and osteoporosis (because of alterations in leptin and bone development).[21,22,45,69,75,86,96,97,237]

In infants with fetal growth restriction and "placental insufficiency," nutritional delivery is decreased because of both decreased blood flow and a smaller placental size, as well as down-regulation of nutrient transporters.[127,237] Conversely, with fetal overgrowth, as occurs with maternal diabetes, placental nutritional transporters are upregulated.[127,233] Altered programming can influence later metabolic control, and these changes may be mediated in part by adipocytokines (hormones secreted by white adipose tissue that modulate metabolism, energy homeostasis, and growth).[36,75,86,233] Adipocytokines are secreted by placental and fetal tissues and include dentin, adiponectin, resistin, vistatin, and apelin, all of which exert effects on fat, muscle, and liver cells in early life.[36] Underprovision or overprovision of nutrients in utero can program adipose tissue function and amount.[36,96] As noted previously, adverse in utero nutrition may have long-term effects on infants, with an increased risk of altered neurologic development, increased childhood mortality rates, and a predisposition to chronic diseases such as hypertension, coronary artery disease, and type 1 (with a history of excess fetal growth) or 2 (with fetal undernutrition) diabetes in adult life.[75,86,95,97,141,151,171,237,258]

Fetal Growth Restriction

Fetal growth restriction is the failure of a fetus to achieve its genetic growth potential in utero.[171] In practice this is stated as measures of absolute (i.e., low-birth-weight [LBW]) and relative (i.e., small-for-gestational-age [SGA]) size. Factors that cause alterations in growth, such as malnutrition during the period of hyperplasia, can decrease the rate of cell division and result in organs or a fetus that is smaller in size with fewer cells. This symmetric form of growth alteration is not reversible after the time when hyperplastic cell growth would normally have ceased. Malnutrition during the period of hypertrophy results in organs or a fetus that is smaller in size (because of reduction in cell size) but has a normal number of cells. This is asymmetric growth restriction, which is seen in about 75% of infants with fetal growth restriction.[171] Hypertrophic growth alterations may be reversible with adequate nutrition. Because fetal tissues are undergoing hyperplastic growth throughout gestation, the fetus is especially vulnerable to irreversible changes at the cellular level.[274]

Factors altering fetal growth can be intrinsic or extrinsic.[171,234] Intrinsic factors are those within the fetus arising from chromosomal or genetic abnormalities, infectious agents, or other teratogens that alter the normal process of cell division and usually result in symmetric growth restriction. Extrinsic factors include maternal preeclampsia, placental alterations or insufficiency, and fetal malnutrition. Pathologic changes characteristic of reduction in placental blood flow are seen in placentas of growth-restricted infants.[277] Placental insufficiency because of maternal, fetal, or placental factors often results in caloric restriction to the fetus (inadequate glucose transported to meet fetal growth needs) and tends to occur later in gestation. Caloric restriction usually leads to an asymmetric growth failure in which brain growth is spared. Fetal malnutrition caused by maternal protein restriction (arising from maternal malnutrition or significantly protein-reduced diets) generally results in symmetric fetal growth failure in which brain growth is not necessarily spared.[274] Management of fetal growth restriction varies with the underlying cause. Strategies range from fetal therapies to prepregnancy counseling and preventive interventions such as cessation of smoking and alcohol use, promotion of adequate nutrition, and early identification of and interventions for pathologic problems such as preeclampsia. Growth-restricted fetuses and neonates are at risk for hypoxic-ischemic events, meconium aspiration, hypoglycemia, and other problems (Table 12-8) and later development of type 2 diabetes, obesity, and cardiovascular disease (see previous section).[21,22,45,69,127,172,233,263,287]

NEONATAL PHYSIOLOGY

GI function in the neonate is characterized by functional, anatomic, and physiologic limitations, which are increased in the preterm infant. Provision of adequate nutritional support for growth and development is an ongoing challenge for nurses and other health care providers. As a result of the limitations in GI function, infants are at risk for dehydration, reflux, malabsorption, and electrolyte imbalance.

Gastric acid secretion increases within 24 hours of birth and doubles by 2 months, with varying findings in different studies.[187,212] Pepsinogen production is low (corrected for weight) for the first few months and is even lower in preterm infants.[146,187] The elevated pH reduces pepsin activity and gastric peptic hydrolysis in both term and preterm infants.[125,146,187,200] Although circulating levels of gastrin (which normally stimulates secretion of gastric acid and pepsin) are elevated, receptors for this hormone may be immature.[144,146] The decreased gastric acidity and pepsinogen levels may enhance development of gut host defense mechanisms by promoting activity of immunoglobulins and antigen recognition by the GI tract.[146]

Term and preterm infants have near adult levels of trypsin, but activity of trypsin and the other pancreatic proteolytic hormones is reduced. Chymotrypsin and carboxypeptidase B activity are 10% to 60% and enterokinase activity is 10% of adult values in preterm infants, increasing to 25% by term.[183] Because enterokinase catabolizes the conversion of trypsinogen to trypsin, which in turn activates the other pancreatic proteolytic enzymes, the level of enterokinase is the rate-limiting step for intestinal protein digestion.[146] This limitation does not seem to have a major effect on infants over 26 to 28 weeks' gestation, who are usually able to digest and absorb 85% of the dietary protein in human milk and most formulas.[200] Intestinal brush border peptidase and cytosolic peptidase activity, along with the ability to transport and absorb amino acids, is well developed and efficient in term and preterm infants.[66,71] The newborn's intestine absorbs more intact proteins and macromolecules, which may increase the risk for development of allergies (see Chapter 13) and NEC in infants fed formula.[146] In breastfed infants, absorption of macromolecules from breast milk enhances passive immunity.[181,187]

Digestion and Absorption of Carbohydrates

Carbohydrate digestion in adults is dependent on salivary and pancreatic amylase and disaccharidases. Salivary amylase activity at birth is one third that of adults. Levels increase after 3 to 6 months of age and may be related to the addition of starch (solid foods) to the infant's diet.[145] Salivary amylase retains some activity in the infant's stomach and is effective in digestion of glucose polymers.[187,275]

Pancreatic amylase activity is decreased in term and preterm infants to 0.2% to 5% of adult values. Adequate levels are achieved after 4 to 6 months.[82] Cholecystokinin and secretin have little effect on pancreatic amylase secretion before 1 month. Amylase activity increases significantly after this time.

Mammary amylase in human milk compensates for the decreased pancreatic amylase. Mammary amylase is highest in colostrum, gradually decreasing after 6 weeks. Buffers in human milk and the higher gastric pH in the neonate help maintain mammary amylase activity.[145]

Term newborns have adequate levels of α-glucosidases such as sucrase, maltase, isomaltase, and glucoamylase. Sucrase and maltase attain maximal activity by 32 to 34 weeks' gestation or earlier. Glucoamylase is an intestinal brush border enzyme that digests glucose polymers found in many formulas.[145,200] Levels of glucoamylase are 50% to 100% of adult values and increase rapidly after birth.[146,275] Glucoamylase is less susceptible than disaccharidases to intestinal mucosal injury. This enzyme is evenly distributed along the small intestine, which, along with the prolonged transit time seen in infants, contributes to more efficient hydrolysis and mucosal uptake.[144,145] Digestion of glucose polymers depends on salivary amylase, glucoamylase, and human milk amylase. Neonates can effectively hydrolyze and absorb glucose polymers, especially those of short- to medium-chain length.

The major carbohydrate in human and cow's milk is lactose. Lactase activity increases rapidly in late gestation and is adequate after 36 weeks' gestation. At term, lactase levels are two to four times higher than in older infants. Lactase activity at 28 to 34 weeks' gestation is only 30% of term values but increases after birth with exposure to lactose.[82,146,183] Despite low lactase activity, most preterm infants digest lactose adequately, especially lactose in human milk.[71,82,181,187] Lactose that is not absorbed in the small intestines is conserved by colonic salvage.

Colonic salvage involves bacterial fermentation of carbohydrates to hydrogen gas and short-chain fatty acids, which are absorbed by the colon, minimizing carbohydrate loss in stools (Figure 12-10).[71,82,183,187] These fatty acids are a source

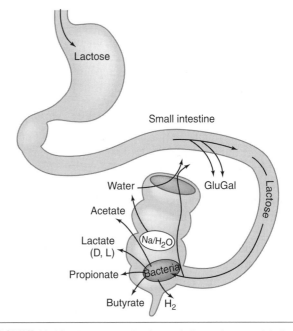

FIGURE 12-10 The two major fates of dietary lactose: (1) digestion in the small intestine with absorption of glucose *(Glu)* and galactose *(Gal)*, or (2) fermentation in the colon to various gases such as H_2; lactate; and short-chain fatty acids including acetate, propionate, and butyrate. The absorption of short-chain fatty acids stimulates sodium and water absorption in the colon. Unfermented lactose may exert an osmotic stimulus causing fecal excretion of water. (From Kien, C.L. [1996]. Digestion, absorption, and fermentation of carbohydrates in the newborn. *Clin Perinatol, 23,* 213.)

of calories, enhance fluid and electrolyte absorption by the colon, and promote cell replication in the gut.[82] In preterm infants, two thirds of the ingested lactose may reach the colon. Changes in colonic bacterial flora after antibiotic use or surgery may alter the infant's ability to conserve energy via colonic salvage. Lactase deficiency generally resolves when the preterm infant reaches a postmenstrual age of 36 to 40 weeks.[145] Infants need some lactose intake, because lactose enhances calcium absorption.

Mechanisms for glucose, galactose, and fructose absorption develop early in gestation and are relatively mature. The capacity for mucosal glucose uptake at term is 50% to 60% of adult values. Absorption of glucose is slower in preterm infants, with further reductions in SGA infants, suggesting that growth restriction may delay maturation of these processes. Infants seem to absorb glucose as well as adults at low glucose concentrations but have a maximal absorptive capacity about 20% that of the adult. Glucose transport increases by 2 to 3 weeks of age.[145] Hypoxia and ischemia decrease intestinal perfusion, altering the ultrastructure of intestinal cells, which decreases active transport and uptake of glucose.

Digestion and Absorption of Fats

Fat digestion in the adult relies on pancreatic lipase to break down triglycerides and bile acids to emulsify fat droplets before and during lipolysis. These processes are decreased in term and especially in preterm infants.[146,187,213] Lipase activity at term is 10% to 20% of that seen in older children, partly because of minimal responsiveness by pancreatic acinar cells to secretin and cholecystokinin during the first month. Term infants fail to absorb 10% to 15% and preterm infants 30% or more of ingested fat.[71,216] Lipase activity increases up to fourfold during the first week postbirth in healthy preterm infants.[187]

Bile acid synthesis is low because of lower bile synthesis and ileal absorption.[183] Bile acid pool size is one half of adult values in term infants, and one sixth of adult and one third of term infant values in preterm infants.[125,146,213,275] Because hepatic conjugation of bile acids in infants is taurine-dependent (versus glycine-dependent in the adult), adequate intake of taurine is essential in infancy.[146] The decreased bile acid pools are a result of reduced hepatic synthesis and poorer recirculation and conservation of bile salts through enterohepatic shunting as a result of immaturity of liver and intestinal active transport processes.[146,200]

In preterm infants, concentrations of bile acids in the duodenal lumen may be below critical levels necessary for micelle formation (water-soluble aggregates of lipids and lipid-soluble substances).[200] Decreased micelle formation results in poor absorption of long-chain triglycerides (LCT), which are dependent on micelle formation for solubilization and subsequent hydrolysis. Infants are better able to absorb medium-chain triglycerides (MCT) and short-chain triglycerides (SCT), which are not dependent on micelle formation. SCTs and MCTs are absorbed directly into the portal venous system, whereas LCTs must first be reesterified to form chylomicrons before entering the lymphatics.[183]

Alternative pathways to compensate for the decreased levels of pancreatic lipase and bile acids include human milk bile salt–stimulated lipase (also called mammary lipase or milk digestive lipase), lingual lipase, and gastric lipase. Both gastric and lingual lipase have high activity at birth.[71,187] Gastric and lingual lipase activity is present by at least 26 weeks' gestation.[71] Lingual and gastric lipases hydrolyze 50% and mammary lipase 20% to 40% of dietary fat in infants.[216] Intragastric lipolysis by these extrapancreatic lipases breaks down triglycerides in the milk fat globule. As a result, the fat globule is a better substrate for the available pancreatic lipase and enhances action of bile salts. Hydrolysis of fat in the stomach can be documented in preterm infants as young as 26 to 32 weeks' gestation.

Mammary lipase is present in the milk of term and preterm mothers. This enzyme is stable at low pH (and not inactivated in the stomach) and hydrolyzes triglycerides at low concentrations of bile salts.[187] Mammary lipase works in the duodenum, and its activity is stimulated by bile salts at concentrations below those required for micelle formation, such as are found in many preterm infants. Temperatures above 55° C (131° F) inactivate this enzyme; freezing does not seem to affect its activity. This lipase also produces monolauryl, a substance with antibacterial, antiviral, and antifungal activity.

Absorption of Other Substances

Alterations in fat absorption affect absorption of fat-soluble vitamins, especially in preterm infants who may need supplementation with water-soluble analogs. Absorptive capacity for folate is also lower. Lower gastric secretion of intrinsic factor may interfere with absorption of vitamin B_{12}.[146] Neonates are less able to adapt to changes in osmotic load in the large intestine, increasing the risk of diarrhea and electrolyte imbalance.

Mechanisms for absorption of iron are relatively well developed in term and preterm infants, with a high rate of iron absorption for the first 10 weeks postbirth.[146] Iron in human milk is absorbed better than iron in formula, with absorption of up to 50% of the iron in human milk, even in preterm infants.[146,275] For the first few months, however, preterm infants may not absorb large quantities of iron because of saturation of transferrin with iron from turnover of red blood cells (see Chapter 8).

Calcium absorption is influenced by vitamin D, calcium, and phosphorus concentrations (see Chapter 17); fatty acids; and lactose. The complex relationship between calcium and lipid intake makes determining calcium concentrations for formulas difficult. A high calcium intake alters absorption and retention of fatty acids; a high lipid intake can decrease calcium absorption.[146] Calcium absorption is lower in infants than in adults when calcium concentrations are low, but it is more efficient at higher levels.[146] Zinc and copper are well absorbed in term infants but not in preterm infants, who may be in negative zinc or copper balance.[146,268] Mechanisms for absorption of many nutrients have not been well studied in human neonates.

Liver Function in the Neonate

Portal blood flow is lower in fetuses, with shunting of a portion of the blood away from the portal sinuses and liver parenchyma and into the inferior vena cava via the ductus venosus. Many excretory and detoxification functions of the fetal liver are assumed by the placenta and maternal liver. With removal of the placenta, blood flow through the ductus venosus ceases, with anatomic closure by proliferation of connective tissue by approximately 2 weeks in most term infants (see Chapter 9).

The newborn liver accounts for about 5% of the infant's weight. This physiologic enlargement is a result of the following factors: (1) increased labile connective tissue (possibly in response to hypoxic stress with the abrupt shift in the oxygenation of blood supplying the liver at birth [i.e., from blood from the placenta to systemic venous blood]); (2) active liver hematopoiesis, which decreases by 6 weeks as liver metabolic functions increase; (3) increased liver glycogen; and (4) hepatic congestion because of changes in blood flow with removal of the placenta.[25,102]

Infants have a unique pathologic response to liver dysfunction, with active fibroblastic proliferation and early bile stasis that can alter the presentation of liver disorders. Decreased bile flow (cholestasis)—often in association with a direct (conjugated) hyperbilirubinemia—is seen with many liver disorders in infants. The cholestasis is a result of disruption of the canalicular membrane, poor development of bile acid secretory mechanisms, and immaturity of bile acid synthesis.[102,134]

Birth results in induction of many liver enzyme systems; however, enzyme systems necessary for metabolism of some drugs are depressed in newborns.[25] In the mature liver, oxidation and conjugation result in formation of water-soluble metabolites that are more readily excreted into bile. In the fetus, depression of these processes is an advantage, in that lipid-soluble metabolites are more readily transferred across the placenta, where they can be handled by the maternal system. The liver's smooth endoplasmic reticulum (SER) is the location of many hepatic microsomal enzymes. The neonatal liver has little SER, and activities of microsomal enzymes are reduced or undetectable at birth, interfering with drug metabolism.[121] Hepatic metabolism of drugs is discussed in Chapter 7.

CLINICAL IMPLICATIONS FOR NEONATAL CARE

Food and warmth are "two of the most important controllable factors in determining survival and normal development."[204] Limitations of GI function in term and preterm neonates have major implications for the infant's nutritional needs and the composition and method of feedings. The feeding of sick and preterm infants is associated with many controversies, including when, what, and how to feed. Decisions regarding feeding can lead to other problems such as an increased risk of NEC and metabolic or nutritional alterations. This section reviews nutritional requirements of infants and implications of GI limitations for the selection of method and composition of feedings. Problems related to neonatal physiologic limitations such as reflux, dehydration, and NEC are also examined.

Infant Growth

Growth is controlled by complex hormonal, growth factor, and nutrient interactions.[296] Major regulating factors are growth hormone (somatostatin) and IGF-I. Thyroid hormones, insulin, glucocorticoids, leptin, and local growth factors also have important roles, especially in regulation of intermediary metabolism.[150,296] Pituitary growth hormone (GH) stimulates IGF-I (primarily from the liver, but also found in many other organs), which in conjunction with other growth factors stimulates cell differentiation and function. Growth hormone resistance (characterized by increased GH and low IGF-I) has been reported in ELBW infants.[296]

Growth rates during the neonatal period are more rapid than at any other time. The method for growth assessment of term infants generally involves use of standardized charts from the National Center for Health and Statistics (http://www.cdc.gov/growthcharts). These charts have been revised to include a broader population base as well as more breast-fed infants. Expected patterns and assessment of growth for preterm infants in the immediate postbirth period are controversial, especially regarding whether these infants should be expected to follow intrauterine or extrauterine patterns. Both intrauterine and extrauterine growth standards are available.[54,85,192,280]

Generally recommendations have been that postnatal growth of preterm infants follow the pattern for intrauterine growth of a fetus of the same gestation, although it is unclear whether intrauterine rates are appropriate or realistic for these infants.[11,57,205,264] VLBW infants often do not grow at intrauterine rates and are at risk for postnatal growth restriction.[110,205,264,266] ELBW infants may not regain their birth weight for 2 to 3 weeks and are especially vulnerable for extrauterine growth restriction. Lower than optimal nutritional intake during the first week may result in a significant energy and protein deficit, which increases over the early weeks. Calculation of infant nutritional needs may need to take into account requirements for catch-up growth as well as the usual requirements for maintenance and growth.[57]

A variety of intrauterine growth charts are available, all of which have limitations in that they were developed from measurements of preterm infants at various gestations and thus may not represent a normal fetal population. Recently new postnatal growth curves were published using data from Canada, the United States, and the World Health Organization (WHO).[54,85,192,280] The revised growth curves are more reflective of newborns universally; there are also growth curves for gender and breastfeeding/formula-fed infants.[136,280]

TABLE 12-11 Approximate Daily Weight Gain for Infants

AGE	WEIGHT
GESTATIONAL AGE	
24–28 weeks	15–20 g/kg/day
29–32 weeks	17–21 g/kg/day
33–36 weeks	14–15 g/kg/day
37–40 weeks	7–9 g/kg/day
CORRECTED AGE	
40 weeks–3 months	30 g/day
3–6 months	12 g/day
6–9 months	15 g/day
9–12 months	10 g/day
12–24 months	6 g/day

From Kalhan, S.C. & Price, P.T. (1999). Nutrition and selected disorders of the gastrointestinal tract. I: Nutrition for the high risk infant. In M.H. Klaus & A.A. Fanaroff. (Eds.). *Care of the high risk neonate* (5th ed.). Philadelphia: Saunders.

TABLE 12-12 Estimated Energy Requirements for Low-Birth-Weight Infants

EXPENDITURE	AVERAGE ESTIMATE (kcal/kg/day)
Energy expended	40–60
Resting metabolic rate*	40–50
Activity*	0–5
Thermoregulation*	0–5
Synthesis	15[†]
Energy stored	20–30[†]
Energy excreted	15
Energy intake	90–120

*Energy for maintenance.
[†]Energy cost of growth.
From Adamkin D.H., Radmacher, P.G., & Lewis, S. (2013). Nutrition and selected disorders of the gastrointestinal tract. I: Nutrition for the high risk infant. In A.A. Fanaroff & J.M. Fanaroff. (Eds.). *Klaus & Fanaroff's care of the high risk neonate* (6th ed.). Philadelphia: Saunders.

General parameters for daily weight gain are in Table 12-11. Postnatal growth grids for LBW and VLBW infants for the first 3 years (using gestation-adjusted ages) have been developed for postdischarge care.

Nutritional Requirements of Term and Preterm Infants

Nutritional requirements of infants vary with gestational age and health status. Requirements for healthy term infants are assumed to be those found in human milk. For infants who are not breastfed, commercial formulas are alternatives for meeting nutritional needs. Nutritional requirements for preterm infants have been less clear. One problem has been the lack of knowledge and agreement regarding the optimal growth rate for the preterm infant and how closely this rate should parallel that of the fetus. Nutritional requirements for preterm infants are often estimated by assaying the body composition of fetuses at different gestational ages and examining fetal accretion of different nutrients. Water, energy, and caloric requirements are higher for preterm infants because of greater insensible water loss (see Chapter 11), increased exposure to stressors, and increased expectations for growth. Recommended nutritional requirements for preterm infants are available.[11,136,270]

Protein and energy are critical for growth and neurodevelopment.[17,252] Energy needs vary depending on the infant's age, thermal environment, activity, maturation, growth rate, and health status. Maintenance caloric requirements are calculated based on resting energy expenditure, activity, thermoregulation, and losses (Table 12-12). Growth requires additional calories (approximately 45 kcal for each 1-g weight gain).[82] The caloric (energy) maintenance and growth requirement for breastfed term newborns averages 85 to 100 kcal/kg/day; the requirement is 100 to 110 kcal/kg/day for formula-fed newborns.[216]

Preterm infants weighing less than 1000 g have maintenance requirements of approximately 50 to 70 kcal/kg/day, although this may be higher for some infants, depending on the infant's basal metabolic rate (increased with health problems), activity level (decreased in infants on morphine or fentanyl), cold stress (increases metabolic rate), specific dynamic action (efficiency of nutrient absorption), and fecal losses. For growth these infants need an additional 45 to 70 kcal/kg/day.[67,82] Increasing the growth allowance above this level will increase weight gain, but not exponentially because the energy cost of weight gain also increases.[82] Most stable preterm infants achieve satisfactory growth on approximately 120 kcal/kg/day.[67,268] Caloric requirements for infants on parenteral feedings tend to be lower, averaging 80 to 110 kcal/day, because activity level and fecal losses are lower.[71,82,216]

Fetal protein accretion is 3 to 4 g/kg/day. The type of dietary protein affects daily protein requirements. Postnatal inadequate protein leads to alterations in cardiorespiratory, liver, and renal function; decreased immunocompetence; altered brain growth; and poor weight gain and somatic growth. Term infants need 1.5 to 2.5 g/kg/day, whereas up to 4.5 g/kg/day has been used for preterm infants.[28,41,67,108,122,264] Preterm infants need protein intake early, beginning on days 1 or 2 of extrauterine life, to minimize loss of body stores and enhance growth.[67,264,296] Inadequate protein can alter IGF-I and other growth factors, increasing the risk of postnatal growth restriction in preterm infants. Serum IGF-I levels correlate with protein intake and nitrogen retention.[296] Current practices have moved toward earlier introduction of protein and use of minimal enteral feedings using colostrum or breast milk.[296] Excessive protein intake (greater than 5 g/kg/day) results in a metabolic overload with irritability and can lead to late metabolic acidosis, azotemia, edema, fever, lethargy, diarrhea, elevated blood urea nitrogen, and poorer developmental outcome.[28,102,209]

A major energy source in human milk and most formulas is fat, which accounts for 30% to 50% of the total calories.[11,208] Specific requirements include those for the essential fatty acids linoleic and α-linolenic acid (an omega-3 fatty acid), which are important for synthesis of other fatty acids and for growth and development, especially brain and vision development. Approximately 3% (300 mg linoleic acid per 100 kcal) of the infant's energy intake should be essential fatty acids.[11,28,138] Inadequate fats or lack of essential fatty acids can lead to metabolic problems, skin disorders, and poor growth; excessive fats can lead to ketosis.

Carbohydrates make up 40% to 50% of the caloric content.[100] Inadequate carbohydrate intake can lead to hypoglycemia; excessive carbohydrate intake can lead to diarrhea. Infants, especially preterm infants who have poor stores and a higher growth rate, have increased needs for calcium, phosphorus, and vitamins to support growth and bone mineralization. Nutrient requirements for enteral and parenteral nutrition are available in neonatal texts.

Composition of Feedings

To maximize growth and reduce stress, the limitations of the neonate's GI, renal, and metabolic systems must be considered in selecting substances for feeding. This can be accomplished through analysis of the composition of human milk and commercial formulas and consideration of the advantages and disadvantages of each for that individual infant. This section discusses considerations in selecting feedings for term and preterm infants.

Protein

Milk protein consists of casein and whey proteins. Whey forms soft, flocculent curds. Casein forms tougher, more rubbery curds; it requires greater energy expenditure to digest and is more likely to be incompletely digested. Human milk has a whey-to-casein ratio around 70:30; by comparison, the whey-to-casein ratio in cow's milk is 20:80. Whey is easier to digest in the presence of low levels of trypsin and pepsin and is associated with fewer imbalances in plasma amino acids in preterm infants.[229] Whey protein contains a different mixture of amino acids than casein, with increased levels of cystine and decreased methionine. Human milk contains less protein than cow's milk but has higher levels of nonprotein nitrogen with an amino acid composition that is easy for the infant to use.[208] The major whey protein in human milk is α-lactalbumin, which is high in amino acids that are essential for the infant. Other human milk proteins include lactoferrin, lysozyme, and secretory immunoglobulin A.

The amino acid composition of feedings is critical for optimal neonatal growth and development. Some amino acids that are essential in neonates are not essential for adults because of the decreased ability of infants to synthesize these amino acids.[82] For example, taurine is essential for central nervous system (CNS) growth, maintaining optimal retinal integrity and function, and bile acid synthesis. Intermediary metabolic pathways for synthesis of some amino acids are immature. The last enzyme in transsulfuration is absent in the fetus and develops slowly in preterm infants. These infants cannot synthesize cystine and have limited tolerance for methionine (which is normally converted to cystine). Similar limitations exist in the ability of infants to oxidize tyrosine and phenylalanine. Transamination pathways are also not well developed, so histidine is an essential amino acid in neonates but not in adults.[146] Thus infants need a feeding that contains lower levels of methionine, phenylalanine, and tyrosine and adequate cystine, taurine, and histidine.[82] Glutamine is another important component in that it acts as a nitrogen transporter and enhances gut maturation, fat metabolism, and gut immune function in addition to producing glutamate, a neurotransmitter needed for CNS development (see Chapter 15).[100,182,208] Glutamine is a component of human milk. Glutamine supplementation of preterm infants has not proved to be of significant benefit in most studies.[170] Other amino acids such as threonine, aspartate, and proline may also be important in gut function and maturation.[43]

Carbohydrate

Immaturity of lactase activity in preterm infants may interfere with their ability to optimally use lactose-based formulas, although most infants have little difficulty digesting lactose. For example, preterm infants can absorb up to 90% of the lactose in human milk.[208,229] Carbohydrates other than lactose are often included in feedings if greater carbohydrate absorption is needed or if lactose is poorly tolerated. Use of low-lactose feedings reduces the risk of overwhelming the infant's available lactase. Infants require some lactose for calcium and magnesium absorption. In addition, feedings containing lactose, especially breast milk, help stimulate lactase activity and lactose utilization.[208]

Glucose polymers are often used as an alternative carbohydrate substrate in formulas. Preterm infants hydrolyze and absorb glucose polymers in a manner similar to that with lactose in term infants.[146] Glucose polymers have several advantages: (1) ready availability from natural sources, including corn syrup solids; (2) high caloric density without significantly increasing the renal solute load (see Chapter 11); (3) incorporation into feedings without significantly increasing the osmotic load and risk of increased water loss and diarrhea; (4) more rapid emptying from the stomach of young infants than lactose or glucose; (5) independence from lactase and amylase; and (6) digestion by glucoamylase, which is present in adequate quantities in preterm infants and whose secretion is less likely to be altered by mucosal injury.[145,146]

Oligosaccharides are glucose polymers that prevent bacterial attachment to the intestinal mucosa, thus providing protection against infection. Oligosaccharides function as prebiotics and may play a role in gut host defense mechanisms. Oligosaccharides are a major component of human milk (see Chapter 5).[229] These substances are only partially digested in the small intestine, and when they reach the colon stimulate development of bifidogenic flora.[58]

Fat

Fats are the primary source of energy in human milk and many formulas. Fats provide a higher caloric density without significantly increasing osmotic load. Limitations in neonatal fat digestion and absorption can reduce the usefulness of this energy source. High-caloric-density formulas tend to be retained in the stomach for longer periods, thus delaying gastric emptying.

Infants need both saturated and unsaturated fatty acids in their diet. Human milk and vegetable oils (corn, coconut, and soy) are absorbed better than saturated fat (cow's milk or butter fat). Human milk fat is contained in fat globules that consist of fatty acids such as linoleic, linolenic, oleic, palmitic, arachidonic, and docosahexaenoic acids. The latter two acids are long-chain polyunsaturated fatty acids (PUFAs) that are sources of omega-6 fatty acids and are found in human milk. These PUFAs are precursors for prostaglandins and phospholipids and are important in neurologic and vision development.[163,208,229] Milk fat globules are more easily absorbed than other forms of fat in the presence of a reduced bile acid pool.[229] Human milk also contains long-chain polyunsaturates that are well absorbed and may enhance nervous system development.[82,163] Carnitine (synthesized from methionine and lysine) is important for fatty acid oxidation.[26,208] In formulas, unsaturated fats in vegetable oils are a source of the essential fatty acid linoleic acid. Short- and medium-chain fatty acids (MCFAs) can be absorbed intact across the gastric and intestinal mucosa. These triglycerides are not dependent on the reduced bile acid pools for emulsification and do not require carnitine, often low in preterm infants, for transfer into the mitochondria.[82] MCFAs are associated with more rapid gastric emptying and enhanced calcium and magnesium absorption.[20,208] About 10% to 50% of the fat in preterm formulas is in the form of MCFAs to enhance fat absorption. Infants need some long-chain fatty acids for integrity of cell membranes and brain development.[163,272] Excessive fat intake from MCFAs has been associated with a risk of essential fatty acid deficiency.[208]

Vitamins, Minerals, and Micronutrients

Infants need adequate amounts of essential vitamins, minerals, and micronutrients in their diet to support normal growth and development. Immature infants have decreased stores of most of these substances, because stores accumulate late in gestation, and dietary supplementation may be needed. Specific requirements for many vitamins and micronutrients in preterm infants are unknown. Increased quantities of fat-soluble vitamins (A, D, E, K) and their water-soluble analogs compensate for the inadequate bile acid pools and poorer absorption of fat, especially in preterm infants. Requirements for B vitamins (coenzymes for metabolic processes and energy production) and folic acid (a cofactor for DNA synthesis) may also be increased because of the infant's greater growth rate and decreased intestinal absorption. Vitamin K is discussed in Chapter 8. Recommended daily intakes of minerals, vitamins, and micronutrients are available.[3,270]

Vitamin A. Vitamin A is needed for development of retina rod cells, light perception, tissue integrity, and repair and growth of epithelial tissue. Higher levels are needed in preterm infants because of poorer absorption and stores. Decreased vitamin A has been reported in infants with chronic lung disease (CLD).[3,216] This may be related to lowered intake or consumption of vitamin A in the repair of damaged lung epithelial tissue. Vitamin A levels should be monitored in infants on parenteral alimentation. Vitamin A in parenteral solutions decreases over 24 hours as a result of adherence of the vitamin to intravenous tubing and photodegradation.

Vitamin C. Vitamin C is water soluble, readily absorbed, and not stored in significant amounts. It is important in amino acid metabolism (needed for growth) and intestinal iron absorption. Deficiencies are associated with scurvy (rare) and transient hypertyrosinemia.[3,11,268]

Vitamin D. Vitamin D facilitates intestinal calcium and phosphorus absorption, bone mineralization, and calcium reabsorption from bone (see Chapter 17). Preterm infants have lower serum concentrations of vitamin D and increased needs because of more rapid growth and immaturity of enzymes involved in metabolism of dietary vitamin D to active substrates. These infants are at greater risk of osteopenia and, less often, rickets (see Chapter 17).[3,11,268]

Vitamin E. An important consideration related to both the fat and vitamin composition of feeding is the ratio of polyunsaturated fatty acid (especially linoleic acid) to vitamin E. The fat content of the red blood cell membrane is determined by dietary fat. Diets that contain high levels of PUFA or iron necessitate increased levels of vitamin E to protect red blood cells from oxidative injury and hemolysis. Recommended concentrations of vitamin E (α-tocopherol) to PUFA are 0.9 international unit vitamin E per gram of linoleic acid.[3,11,28] Preterm infants have lower vitamin E stores, poor absorption, and increased needs to protect cell membranes from peroxidative damage and prevent hemolytic anemia. Elevated serum vitamin E levels have been associated with NEC and cerebral hemorrhage, so high doses must be avoided.

Folate. Folate deficiency, which can lead to anemia, poor growth, and delayed CNS maturation, is seen more often in preterm infants. Folate needs are increased in VLBW infants, who have decreased stores and absorption and more rapid growth.[71] Supplementation has been recommended for preterm infants during the first 2 to 3 months, when intake is limited.[3,82,268]

Calcium, Phosphorus, and Magnesium. Calcium, phosphorus, and magnesium are essential in neonates for bone mineralization and growth. A newborn with lower levels of parathyroid hormone (PTH) is less able to remove calcium from the bone, increasing the risk of hypocalcemia (see Chapter 17). Calcium levels in feedings may be increased to allow for calcium storage and to support bone mineralization and growth. If calcium levels are altered, phosphorus intake also needs to be adjusted to maintain a homeostatic calcium-phosphorus balance. Vitamin D and magnesium are also needed for adequate bone mineralization and to prevent osteopenia and rickets.

Iron. Term and preterm infants develop a physiologic anemia during the first weeks after birth because of postnatal suppression of erythropoiesis (see Chapter 8). During this period, iron from destroyed red blood cells is stored for use when erythropoiesis resumes. Once the stored iron is used up, the infant's hemoglobin will again fall if adequate iron is not available from dietary sources or supplementation. Iron supplementation is usually started before the point of depletion to maintain and build up stores. Intestinal iron transport is lower in neonates because of the inability to regulate iron absorption from the gut and upregulate transport in response to low dietary intakes and downregulate with high intakes.[139] Supplementation is started earlier in preterm infants, because their iron stores are lower at birth and often further depleted by iatrogenic blood losses. Recommendations regarding iron supplementation are discussed in Chapter 8.

Micronutrients and Other Substances. Stores of micronutrients such as zinc, copper, iodine, chromium, selenium, and molybdenum are accumulated late in gestation. Requirements for micronutrients are often increased in preterm infants because of poor stores and increased growth rates. Specific requirements and absorptive mechanisms for many of these elements are unknown. Concentrations in human milk are generally adequate, and commercial formulas are supplemented.[20] Parenteral alimentation solutions are also supplemented with these elements so the infant does not become deficient. Other substances found in human milk are inositol, choline, and nucleotides and many antiinfective substances (see Chapters 5 and 13). Inositol is a lipotrophic growth factor that may enhance surfactant function and reduce cell damage by free radicals. Nucleotides enhance growth and development, GI function, and host defenses. Choline, a component of phospholipids and acetylcholine precursor, may enhance neural development and function. Antiinfective substances in human milk are summarized in Table 5-3.

Zinc. Zinc is an essential cofactor for more than 70 enzymes needed for protein and nucleic acid synthesis. Zinc also is needed for neonatal immune system maturation and function.[62] Zinc deficiencies, usually characterized by an erythematous skin rash, inhibit uptake of fat-soluble vitamins and protein synthesis and can lead to growth restriction.[208] Deficiencies have been reported in preterm infants fed human milk and infants on parenteral nutrition with inadequate supplementation.[238] Excessive losses may occur in infants with ostomies or chronic diarrhea.[6,204]

Copper. Copper is also an enzyme cofactor and is essential for hemoglobin synthesis, myelinization, and formation of antioxidant enzymes and collagen. Copper deficiency (failure to thrive, iron-resistant anemia, osteopenia, neutropenia, pallor, edema, seborrheic dermatitis, and hypotonia) has been reported in preterm infants fed formulas with low levels of copper and in infants with ostomies or chronic diarrhea.[6,208,238,272]

Electrolytes. Levels of potassium and sodium may be increased in preterm formulas to compensate for increased intestinal potassium and renal sodium losses and to support growth (sodium is coprecipitated in the bone during periods of active bone growth). Concentrations of specific electrolytes are also determined by fluid composition and levels of other electrolytes. Electrolytes are discussed in Chapter 11.

Calories and Renal Solute Load

The caloric level of the feeding should reflect the infant's energy needs, but at an osmolality that the infant's kidneys and other systems can handle without stress (see Chapter 11). Caloric content of human milk is generally around 19 kcal/oz but may vary considerably.[20,41,178] Preterm human milk has a slightly higher caloric density, but it also varies.[178] Standard formulas contain 19 kcal/oz and preterm formulas 24 kcal/oz.[41] Higher calorie formulas are cautiously used to enhance growth for preterm and failure-to-thrive infants, monitoring closely for potential problems with osmotic and solute load. Osmolalities should be similar to those of physiologic fluids (250 to 300 mOsm per kg of water).

Human Milk

Human milk is an ideal, nutritionally adequate feeding for term and most preterm infants that meets the infant's unique nutritional needs and provides more than 45 other enzymes, growth factors, and bioactive substances to enhance growth and development, protect the infant from infection, and enhance gut maturation.[12,20,93,148,178,182,230,261] Human milk also contains substances such as human milk bile salt–stimulated (mammary) lipase and mammary amylase and has a low renal solute load (see Chapter 11), an amino acid composition ideal for the newborn, and lipids in a form that can be easily digested and absorbed. These and other characteristics of human milk compensate for the neonate's physiologic limitations. Preterm infants fed human milk have a lower incidence of NEC and infection, enhanced fat absorption, and more rapid gastric emptying.[93,148,182,261] Benefits of human milk for preterm infants also include a decreased rate of rehospitalization for illness after discharge and improved long-term sensorimotor and neurologic development.[20,93] Composition of human milk is described further in Chapter 5. The nutrient content of human milk can vary depending on methods of expression and storage, portion of the milk used (i.e., foremilk versus hindmilk), and use of feeding tubes.[20,229,247]

Milk from mothers of preterm infants is different initially from that of term mothers and more closely approximates what are believed to be the nutritional needs of these infants (see Chapter 5).[93,178] The composition of this milk changes gradually over the first month after birth and by 1 month is similar to term milk. Preterm human milk is low (in terms of the preterm infant's nutrient requirements) in protein, calcium, phosphorus, iron, vitamins, and sodium, although nutrients such as protein, iron, and calcium are in forms that are more readily absorbed by the infant. For example, it has been estimated that preterm infants fed human milk retain calcium and phosphorus equivalent to 15% to 20% of the calcium and 30% to 35% of the phosphorus accumulated by the fetus in utero. Most preterm infants fed their own mother's milk gain at rates similar to intrauterine rates or those of infants fed whey formulas.[82,93,178] VLBW infants fed human milk may need supplementation to promote growth and prevent deficiencies.

Human milk fortification is used to "increase the concentration of nutrients to such levels that at the customary feeding volumes infants receive amounts of all nutrients that meet the requirements."[17, p. 234] Human milk fortifiers contain protein, carbohydrate, calcium, phosphate, vitamins, sodium, and other substances.[17,208,229,298] Use of these fortifiers results in short-term increases in weight gain, length, and head circumference.[40] However, standard fortification of human milk can lead to slower weight gain (than with formula feeding) in some preterm infants because of low protein intake (related to variable protein content of the breast milk for mothers of preterm infants and the decrease in protein content over the duration of lactation).[16,17,109,111,298] As a result individual fortification either via adjustable (protein intake is adjusted based on infant metabolic responses evaluated by periodic blood urea nitrogen levels) or targeted (periodic analysis of the protein content of the milk) fortification has been recommended.[17,72,298] The effect of fortification on antiinfective and other nonnutrient milk components has also been a concern.[208,229,298]

Parenteral Nutrition Solutions

Parenteral nutrition is the intravenous administration of a hypertonic solution containing amino acids, carbohydrates, fats, electrolytes, vitamins, minerals, and micronutrients to maintain positive nitrogen balance. Partial parenteral nutrition involves infusion of amino acids and carbohydrates with or without fats to supplement enteral feedings.[268] Infants generally cannot tolerate glucose loads over 6 to 8 mg/kg/minute in the first 1 to 2 weeks. The usual range in solutions is 4 to 8 mg/kg/minute, although some infants may need higher amounts given gradually based on evaluation of energy needs and laboratory values.[130] Parenteral alimentation has been associated with nitrogen retention and weight gain in LBW infants.[82,282] Nutritional requirements of infants on parenteral feedings differ from those of infants on enteral feedings in that these solutions are infused directly into the blood rather than the immature gut.

Pediatric and neonatal mixtures are constituted for neonates with immature liver function and intermediary metabolic pathways for synthesis of some amino acids. These solutions, which contain higher levels of taurine, cytosine, and tyrosine and branched-chain amino acids, with reduced methionine and phenylalanine, improve nitrogen retention and normalize plasma values and approximate the amino acid pattern of human milk.[82,216] Early parenteral amino acid administration (within the first 1 to 2 days) seems to be well tolerated by most infants and is associated with greater nitrogen retention and a positive nitrogen balance.[28,216,209,265,266,282]

Lipid emulsions are isotonic with a high caloric density and can be used to provide adequate caloric intake through a peripheral infusion.[213,244,282] These emulsions are started within the first few days and gradually increased as tolerated. Lipid emulsions can lead to hyperlipidemia and hyperglycemia (reasons for alteration in glucose metabolism are unclear), especially with rates greater than 0.2 to 0.25 g/kg/hour (equivalent to 6 g/kg/day) or with use in VLBW and SGA infants with little adipose tissue.[28,216,265,266] The 20% emulsions are used, because 10% emulsions have a higher phospholipid content, which slows triglyceride clearance.[216,265] The 20% solutions also provide more calories without increasing fluid. Excess free fatty acids may compete with and displace bilirubin from albumin (see Chapter 18).[216] Although fats have been associated with decreased oxygenation and increased pulmonary vascular tone, these effects may be minimized by prolonging the infusion period and using rates less than 0.2 g/kg/hour.[82,265]

Issues in Infants With Various Health Problems

Immature infants generally tolerate feeding with preterm breast milk or preterm formulas better than standard formulas. Considerations discussed in the following sections for selecting feedings for preterm infants are also important in planning nutritional support for infants with specific health problems. These infants have individualized nutritional needs that may require the use of specialized formulas or feeding methods. For example, critically ill infants may need to be fed via total or partial parenteral nutrition because of their inability to digest and absorb enteral feedings or the risk of complications. Nutrient needs of preterm and term infants with specific problems are summarized in Table 12-13.

TABLE 12-13   Effect of Disease on Selected Nutrient Requirements in Preterm and Term Infants

	Preterm Infants			Term Infants			Both
NUTRIENT	RDS	CLD	NEC/SBS	CYANOTIC CHD	CHF	SEPSIS	IUGR
Free water	↓	↓	↑	↔	↓	↑	↑
Energy	↑	↑↑	↑↑	↑↑	↑↑	↑↑	↑
Fat	↔	↑	↑↑a	↑	↑	↔	↑
Carbohydrate	↑	↓	↑	↑	↑	↑	↑
Protein	↔	↑	↑	↑	↑	↑↑	↑
Calcium	↔	↑b,c	↑a	↑d	↑c,d	↔	↑
Iron	↔	↑b	↑	↑	↔	↓	↑

aParticularly with loss of terminal ileum.
bIn preterm infants less than 1500 g.
cParticularly with calciuric diuretics such as furosemide.
dParticularly if postoperative.

CHD, Congenital heart disease; CHF, congestive heart failure; CLD, chronic lung disease; IUGR, intrauterine growth restriction; NEC, necrotizing enterocolitis; RDS, respiratory distress syndrome; SBS, short bowel syndrome.

Adapted from Brown, L.D., Hendrickson, K., Evans, R., Davis, J., Anderson, M.S., & Hay, W.W., Jr. (2016). Enteral nutrition. In S.L. Gardner, et al. (Eds.). *Merenstein & Gardner's handbook of neonatal intensive care* (8th ed.). St. Louis: Mosby.

Very-Low-Birth-Weight Infants

The considerations in selecting feedings are even more critical in planning for nutritional support of VLBW infants, whose body systems are even more immature. These infants are at risk for postnatal growth restriction.[110,266] Unique nutritional problems of these infants include the following:

1. Limited protein and energy reserves (e.g., a 1000-g preterm infant has only 10 g of stored fat, versus 400 g in a term neonate). Energy needs may be increased by intermittent cold stress, infection, or stresses of the neonatal intensive care unit environment.
2. High ratio of surface area to body weight.
3. Small gastric capacity, which limits intake.
4. High water requirements because of increased insensible water losses and immature renal function. These factors limit the ability of the infant to tolerate high-caloric-density formulas because of risks associated with hyperosmolar solutions.
5. Immature digestive and absorptive capacities for fats, carbohydrates, vitamins, and micronutrients.
6. Immature brain and liver, which are vulnerable to damage from elevated plasma concentrations of amino acids such as tyrosine, methionine, and phenylalanine.[5]

Infants With Respiratory Problems

Infants with respiratory distress, including infants with bronchopulmonary dysplasia (BPD), may be unable to feed by breast or bottle because of rapid respiratory rates, fatigue, and inability to coordinate sucking, swallowing, and breathing. These infants need to be fed by other enteral (intragastric) or parenteral methods. Fluid and caloric requirements are often increased because of the increased metabolic demands, respiratory workload, oxygen consumption, and insensible water losses. Energy needs may increase up to 20% to 40% above baseline in infants with BPD. Oxygen consumption, energy expenditure, and workload are higher for infants with respiratory problems who are breathing spontaneously than for those on assisted ventilation. Intestinal disaccharidases may be diminished in infants after shock or ischemia, with a temporary carbohydrate intolerance.[102] Infants recovering from respiratory distress syndrome have been reported to have decreased functional residual capacity, with increases in respiratory rate and minute ventilation during nasogastric feedings.[102]

Infants With Cardiac Problems

Infants with cardiac problems often grow poorly because of increased metabolic demands and difficulty with feeding. Caloric requirements are increased because of hypermetabolism (higher metabolic rate and oxygen consumption secondary to increased cardiac and respiratory workload), tissue hypoxia, protein loss, increased frequency of infection, and poorer nutrient absorption as a result of decreased splanchnic blood flow. Infants with cardiac problems may be fluid and sodium restricted. Feeding problems may limit intake because the infant may become fatigued, tachypneic, and stressed with feeding. Intervention strategies include use of higher-caloric-density and low-sodium formulas, frequent smaller feedings, feeding on demand and in an upright position, avoidance of feeding immediately after prolonged crying or when the infant is exhausted, and administration of oxygen with feeding as needed. Infants with renal problems may also need to be on low-sodium or low–solute-load formulas.

Infants With Short-Bowel Syndrome

Infants with reduction in the length of their small intestine, which usually results from surgical resection because of a congenital anomaly or NEC, are at very high risk for nutritional and growth problems because of reduction in intestinal absorptive surface area. In addition, the remaining sections of bowel may have been ischemic with villous atrophy. Loss of intestinal surface area results in loss of brush border enzymes such as the disaccharidases, resulting in carbohydrate intolerance and a pool of unabsorbed sugars that act as a rich substrate for bacterial growth. Infants who have less than 25 cm of residual small intestine (normal small intestinal length is 250 to 270 cm at term) if the ileocecal valve is intact or more than 40 cm without this valve are likely to eventually be able to tolerate enteral-only feedings.[15,130,275] During resection, particular efforts are made to preserve the ileum (because of its critical role in bile acid and vitamin B_{12} absorption) and cecal valve. Ileocecal resection is associated with gastric hypersecretion and hypersecretion of regulatory peptides (including motilin, enteroglucagon, and peptide YY) for several weeks.[275] Other problems in digestion and absorption of nutrients resulting from small bowel resection include disaccharide intolerance; decreased pancreatic and biliary secretions; impaired vitamin (especially folate and vitamin B_{12}), calcium, iron, zinc, and magnesium absorption; protein malabsorption; and bile salt depletion.[15,102]

With adequate enteral nutrition, the remaining bowel usually undergoes villous hyperplasia with increased cell proliferation and migration. This response is similar to maturational responses seen in the newborn after initiation of enteral feedings and is related to exposure of the gut to enteral feedings and to the trophic effect of GI hormones. Most infants receive parenteral nutrition immediately after surgery, but initiation of minimal enteral feedings—using an elemental lactose-free feeding as soon as the bowel has recovered—is important in enhancing villous hyperplasia.[15,146] Vitamin, mineral, and trace element supplementation is needed because of increased intestinal loss.

Considerations Related to Feeding Method

A healthy term infant is fed by breast or bottle depending on the parent's choice. The choice of feeding method for preterm or ill infants also depends on the parent's choice of breast milk or formula, as well as maturity, health status, growth pattern, and individual responses to specific methods. These infants can be fed by enteral or parenteral methods, each of which has specific advantages and disadvantages (Table 12-14). Factors related to oral feeding readiness in preterm infants have been reviewed.[10,153,167,180,199,267]

TABLE 12-14   Advantages and Risks of Various Feeding Methods

METHOD	ADVANTAGES	DISADVANTAGES
Peripheral venous nutrition	Not dependent on GI function No danger of aspiration Low infection risk	Repeated thermal and physiologic stress with replacement Effort to start and maintain Risk of tissue injury with extravasation Lack of nutrients into gut to promote intestinal growth and maturation
Central venous nutrition: percutaneous line	High concentration of infused glucose Not dependent on GI function No danger of aspiration Low risk of NEC No need of general anesthesia Lower risk of thrombosis than surgical line	Infection Lack of nutrients into gut to promote intestinal growth and maturation Perforation of vessel or heart
Central venous nutrition: surgical line	High concentration of glucose Possible when other methods fail Not dependent on GI function No danger of aspiration Low risk of NEC Avoids risk of peripheral vein	General anesthesia Vena cava thrombosis Infection Perforation of vessel or heart Lack of nutrients into gut to promote intestinal growth and maturation
Intermittent intragastric feeding	Promotes intestinal growth, gut hormone secretion, and bile flow Reliable nutrient delivery	Bypasses salivary and lingual enzymes
Continuous intragastric feeding	Larger volumes may be tolerated	Bypasses salivary and lingual enzymes Feeding components may be separated in tube
Transpyloric feeding	Does not rely on gastric emptying	Difficult tube placement Decreased fat absorption Possible increased mortality

GI, Gastrointestinal; *NEC*, necrotizing enterocolitis.
Adapted from Bell, E.F. (2011). Nutritional support. In J.P. Goldsmith & E.H. Karotkin. (Eds.). *Assisted ventilation of the neonate* (5th ed.). Philadelphia: Saunders.

Clinically stable preterm infants can be breastfed. Infants as young as 32 weeks' gestation (approximately 1200 g) have been reported to have an organized sucking pattern at the breast, with 2 to 3 sucks per burst followed by a pause and stable transcutaneous oxygen pressures. Infants who have not developed adequate suck-swallow, who fatigue easily, or for whom oral feeding is contraindicated because of health status require an alternative feeding method. With preterm infants this method is usually gavage (intragastric), given either as a bolus or in a continuous drip and using either breast milk or formula.

Intragastric gavage permits normal digestive processes and hormonal responses to occur. Tube insertion is generally easy, because most infants who require gavage do not have a well-developed gag reflex. Infants who are fed intragastrically are generally able to tolerate higher osmotic loads than those fed transpylorically, with less distention, vomiting, and diarrhea. Risks of intragastric gavage such as regurgitation, aspiration, and gastric distention—which may compromise respiratory function—are reduced with transpyloric feedings. Transpyloric feeding tubes are harder to insert, and this feeding method is associated with complications such as impaired fat absorption, intestinal perforation, and ileus (see Table 12-14). Routine use of transpyloric feedings is not recommended because of the increased mortality risk.[168,210]

The benefits of continuous versus intermittent bolus feedings are not clear. The enteral feeding–induced surge of gut hormones after birth may be enhanced by bolus methods, although others have reported that continuous feeding may enhance intestinal motility and GI tolerance.[19,29] No significant differences have been reported in growth, length of stay, or NEC incidence in VLBW infants fed by continuous nasogastric versus intermittent bolus feedings.[210] Bolus feedings stimulate cyclic responses in the secretion of gut hormones, insulin, and glucagon that are not seen in infants fed by continuous drip, although which response is best at this age is unknown.[19] Use of syringe pump infusion systems to deliver human milk by continuous infusion has been associated with loss of milk fat, decreased fat concentrations (especially at low infusion rates), and terminal delivery of a large fat load if fat in the tubing is recovered using an air infusion. Lesser amounts of fat are lost during intermittent and bolus feeds as a result of adhesion to the nasogastric tube, as well.[218] The method and type of feeding will influence gastric emptying. Increasing caloric density decreases gastric emptying.

Parenteral solutions may be given via central or peripheral lines, which have advantages and risks (see Table 12-14). Infants on parenteral nutrition require careful monitoring because they are at greater risk for metabolic derangements, electrolyte imbalances, sepsis, anemia, and thromboembolic complications.

Regurgitation and Reflux

Newborns are more susceptible to regurgitation, vomiting, and gastroesophageal reflux (GER) because of the anatomic and functional immaturity of their GI system. Regurgitation peaks at 3 months of age; 40% to 50% of infants regurgitate more than once a day. Regurgitation is common in infants as a result of LES immaturity, transient LES relaxation, alterations in esophageal and gastric motility, delayed gastric emptying, entry of air into the stomach with swallowing, a less acute esophageal-stomach angle, more time spent lying in a supine position, increased esophageal peristalsis, and a tendency toward reverse peristalsis.[124] These limitations and the frequency of regurgitation are more marked in preterm infants. Interventions to reduce regurgitation include frequent burping; feeding slowly in a semiupright position to reduce air swallowing and passage of swallowed air into the duodenum; using small, frequent feedings; and placing the infant in a right lateral position after feeding to enhance gastric emptying.

Regurgitation does not mean that an infant has gastroesophageal reflux disease (GERD), although GERD is also seen more frequently in infants, particularly in preterm and ill neonates. GERD is the retrograde flow of gastric contents into the esophagus often accompanied by regurgitation, but it may occur in the absence of regurgitation.[102] Although this is a temporary phenomenon that generally resolves by 8 to 12 months, probably because of maturation of the GI system and introduction of solid food, GER can be severe enough to result in aspiration, esophagitis, and dysphagia.[124] Infants with reflux may present with choking, gagging, or other respiratory symptoms.

Reflux in preterm infants is related to immaturity: decreased LES tone, pressure, and size; intrathoracic LES position; delayed gastric emptying; and impaired intestinal motility, with abdominal distention and higher pressure. Transient LES relaxation (because of esophageal or gastric distention) is the most common cause of GER in neonates.[124] Altered esophageal motility and peristalsis lead to poor clearance of refluxed material and increased risk of aspiration.[166,200] Most infants with reflux respond to interventions such as positioning; small, frequent, or thickened feedings; or drugs that enhance gastric emptying or reduce acid secretion. Rarely, some infants may require surgical correction.[30]

Necrotizing Enterocolitis

NEC is a multifactorial disorder seen primarily in preterm infants, although the incidence is also increased in growth restricted infants secondary to altered placental function.[175,239] The incidence of NEC in preterm infants ranges from 5% (younger than 32 weeks) to 10% (younger than 28 weeks).[239,254] Although the entire gut can be involved, NEC is most prominent in the jejunum, ileum, and colon. Clinical manifestations range from signs of feeding intolerance (abdominal distention, residuals, gross or occult blood in the stools, vomiting) or general systemic signs (lethargy, apnea, respiratory distress, thermal instability) to sepsis, shock, and peritonitis, with intestinal perforation in about 30% of these infants.[82,130,216,239,297]

The cause of NEC is unclear, with no single etiologic factor found in all infants. "NEC appears to represent an overreaction of the immune system to some type of insult (for example, ischemia, infectious, related to introduction of enteric feeds, or response to translocation of normal enteric bacteria). This insult leads to disruption of intestinal epithelium, bacterial translocation, and overreaction of immature intestinal epithelial cells. There is activation of stress pathways and suppression of inhibitory pathways which lead to inappropriate mobilization of the host immune system and cytokine release. The result is an unfettered inflammatory response which has diffuse, harmful effects."[29, pp. 145-146] An immature GI tract with immature immune and barrier function (including decreased mesenteric blood flow, increased local metabolic activity, reduced intercellular junction integrity with increased permeability, decreased mucous production, altered repair capacity and mobility, and altered antioxidant defenses), and luminal stasis that can lead to exaggerated inflammation and tissue injury also play a role in the pathogenesis of NEC.[47,130,175,184,239,297] These factors increase the risk of bowel ischemia, colonization with pathogenic organisms, and stimulation of cytokines and other proinflammatory mediators.[297] Genetic polymorphisms in toll-like receptors (TLRs) and abnormal TLR signaling and release of excessive proinflammatory cytokines such as interleukin-8, along with decreased or altered microbial colonization with altered species, may also contribute to NEC (see Chapter 13).[176,184,241] An association has been reported between packed red blood cell transfusion and NEC in preterm infants in some, but not all, studies.[31,50,186,203] The interaction of NEC and transfusion may be a result of a transfusion-related acute reaction in the intestines, impaired blood flow to the intestines (and thus intestinal injury) from an anemia that led to the need for transfusion, or injuries to stored RBCs used for the transfusion that could increase the risk of vasoconstriction and ischemia in the intestinal microcirculation.[31,50,203]

Enteral feeding may be a key trigger for development of NEC because it leads to "increased metabolic demands, alteration of mucosal integrity, disturbance of optimal microbiological ecological balance (infection or overcolonization with pathogenic bacteria) and an exaggerated inflammatory response."[175, p. 184] Early feeding per se does not necessarily predispose to an increased incidence of NEC. Although most infants have had enteral feedings before the development of symptoms, significant mortality from NEC has been reported in VLBW infants before the first feeding.[28,47,186,215]

With initiation of enteral intake, feedings remain in the intestinal lumen for extended periods (due to mucosal damage and limitations in absorptive function in immature infants) and serve as a substrate for further bacterial growth and intramural gas formation. The source of this gas is uncertain, but it may arise from bacterial fermentation of carbohydrates.[82,186,216,239] Rapid advances in feeding (especially increases of greater than 20 cal/kg/day) along with impaired absorptive function secondary to immaturity or ischemia may result in intraluminal accumulation of fermentation products and bacteria-derived peptides that lead to mucosal inflammation.[47,124,186,215] A large volume might further stress the mucosa (already injured from ischemia) and further impede blood flow by distention. This may lead to a local hypoxemia, vascular insufficiency, and accumulation of fermentation products because of impaired absorption.[186,215,275] Finally, hyperosmolar feedings may overwhelm the immature or damaged mucosa.

Human milk feedings have been demonstrated to reduce the risk of NEC although current data are still insufficient to determine the feeding strategies that are most effective in preventing NEC.[32,89,174,175,184,215,256] Small enteral feedings (see Minimal Enteral Feedings) of human milk may protect the bowel from NEC by stimulating gut maturation, promoting mucosal integrity, providing substrate for intestinal enzymes, reducing pathogenic bacterial colonization, promoting growth of nonpathogenic microflora, reducing ileus, increasing perfusion, and ameliorating the proinflammatory response.[32,89,124,175,215] Use of probiotics (nonpathogenic lactobacilli and bifidobacteria) has been reported to decrease the incidence of NEC, but concerns remain because of the methodological limitations of current studies and about safety, particularly the risk of sepsis.[70,185,259]

MATURATIONAL CHANGES DURING INFANCY AND CHILDHOOD

Digestive and absorptive capabilities gradually mature over the first 6 months to 2 years following birth. An important aspect of intestinal maturation is development of gut defense mechanisms and maturation of the gut mucosa, which provides protection against the transport of macromolecules across the intestinal mucosa, reducing the risk of infection and allergy development (see pp. 460-461). The LES lengthens from 1 cm at birth to 2.5 cm by 6 months, with most of the increased length in the portion of the esophagus below the diaphragm.[121] LES basal tone increases after 6 months and is associated with resolution of reflux in most infants.[200] The esophagus, which is 10 cm (range, 7 to 14 cm) in length at term, grows about 0.65 cm per year, reaching an adult length of 25 cm in childhood.[134]

Pepsinogen levels reach adult levels by 3 months. Gastric acid production and pepsin activity do not reach adult levels until 2 years, limiting gastric proteolysis in infants. Levels of trypsin reach adult levels by 1 month.[146]

Pancreatic enzymes are minimal for the first 4 to 6 months; thus the infant is dependent on salivary and mammary amylase for initial digestion of carbohydrate. Pancreatic amylase activity increases after 4 to 6 months at about the time that starch (cereal) is introduced into the diet. Cereal is not efficiently digested before this time. Because hydrolysis of amylopectin (starch) is incomplete up to about 6 months, some neonates given formula thickened with cereal may develop diarrhea.[146]

Activity of maltase, isomaltase, and sucrase remains high into adulthood, with some decrease seen in older adults. Retention of lactase activity is variable and genetically controlled. Lactase activity usually decreases after 3 to 5 years to very low levels.[181] Significant lactase activity is retained primarily in individuals of northern European descent. Mucosal glucose transport is reduced until about 12 months.

Fat absorption does not approach adult efficiency until about 6 months. Lipase reaches adult levels by 2 years, so infants are dependent on lingual-gastric and mammary lipase. Lipolysis and micelle activity are minimal until 4 to 6 months; liver uptake of bile acids is decreased until 6 months.

Liver hematopoietic tissue generally disappears by 6 months.[25] Full expression of liver signaling pathways and amino acid transport pathways occurs by 2 years.[25] Development of enzyme systems needed for drug metabolism is described in Chapter 7.

Introduction of Solid Foods

Maturation of the intestinal system in infancy may be stimulated by weaning and the introduction of solid foods in a manner somewhat similar to changes induced by enteral feedings after birth.[2,146] Timing for introduction of solids should be based on development of neuromuscular processes involved in the ability of the infant to handle solids. The infant's ability to handle foods can be divided into three physiologic stages: (1) nursing (birth to 6 months), when the infant has excellent suck-swallow coordination and does best if fed human milk or formula; (2) transitional (4 to 8 months), when neuromuscular processes needed to swallow pureed solids develop; and (3) modified adult (6 to 12 months), when chopped foods can be swallowed without choking.[162]

There are no particular advantages, and some disadvantages, to introducing solid foods before 3 to 4 months in formula-fed or before 5 to 6 months in breastfed infants. Before 3 to 4 months, an extrusion reflex is present (extrusion of material placed on the anterior tongue) and GER may still be present. Contrary to what many parents and professionals believe, feeding cereal before bedtime in young infants has not been demonstrated to reduce the incidence of night awakenings and may contribute to dental caries and obesity.[157]

Introduction of solid foods is generally recommended at 4 to 6 months for formula-fed infants and after 6 months for breastfed infants. Infants fed foreign proteins before 6 months may actually be at lower risk for developing food allergies than at higher risk as had been previously believed, although data from controlled studies are limited (see p. 466).[2] Cereal is usually the initial solid food given to infants. Rice and barley cereals are of low antigenicity and contain iron in a relatively easy to digest form. Early introduction of high-caloric-density foods is associated with an increased risk of obesity.

SUMMARY

Supporting nutritional needs and promoting nutritional status of infants are a challenge, but one that is critical for optimal outcome. Management of nutritional needs must be based on understanding of the anatomic and physiologic limitations of the GI system and the effect of these alterations on the infant's ability to consume, digest, and absorb various nutrients. Recommendations for clinical practice related to the GI system and perinatal nutrition are summarized in Box 12-3.

BOX 12-3   Recommendations for Clinical Practice Related to the Gastrointestinal System and Perinatal Nutrition in Neonates

Assess feeding reflexes, suck-swallow coordination, cardiorespiratory and gastrointestinal (GI) function before initiating oral feedings (pp. 413-414).

Observe for regurgitation and GI reflux (pp. 426-427).

Observe respiratory status after feeding (p. 425).

Evaluate for signs of dehydration and electrolyte imbalance (pp. 410, 415, and Chapter 11).

Monitor stools for reducing substance, blood, and consistency (pp. 427-428).

Record timing and appearance of first meconium stool (p. 413).

Know parameters used to measure growth and factors that alter accuracy of these parameters (pp. 419-420).

Monitor growth parameters using appropriate curves (pp. 419-420).

Counsel women regarding nutritional advantages of breastfeeding (pp. 423-424 and Chapter 5).

Support breastfeeding in mothers of term and preterm infants (pp. 423-424 and Chapter 5).

Initiate early enteral feeding as appropriate (pp. 411-413).

Promote early breastfeeding and colostrum intake (pp. 411-413 and Chapter 5).

Know limitations of gastrointestinal function in term and preterm infants (pp. 411-419 and Table 12-10).

Know the effects of health problems or surgery on digestion and absorption (p. 425).

Evaluate composition of feedings (formula or human milk) in relationship to an individual infant's GI system limitations (pp. 411-413, 420-424).

Avoid use of high-solute-load and high-caloric-density formulas in immature infants (pp. 423-424 and Chapter 11).

Evaluate renal function and fluid and electrolyte status in infants on high-solute-load or high-caloric-density feedings (pp. 423, 425 and Chapter 11).

Recognize signs of liver dysfunction in infants (p. 424).

Know nutritional requirements for preterm and term infants (pp. 420-424).

Monitor nutritional intake to ensure that nutritional requirements are met (pp. 420-424).

Know energy requirements and factors that alter these requirements (pp. 420-421 and Table 12-12).

Monitor the caloric intake of infants (pp. 420-421).

Monitor neonates for signs of excessive or inadequate protein, carbohydrate, and fat intake (pp. 420-424).

Monitor intake and ratio of vitamin E and linoleic acid (p. 422).

Ensure that term and preterm infants receive iron at the recommended times (pp. 422-423 and Chapter 8).

Monitor intake of vitamins, minerals, and trace minerals (pp. 422-423).

Provide dietary supplementation (e.g., vitamins, minerals, trace elements, calories) as required (pp. 422-423).

Monitor infants for signs of vitamin, mineral, and micronutrient deficiencies (pp. 422-423).

Monitor preterm infants for signs of hypocalcemia (p. 422 and Chapter 17).

Monitor very-low-birth-weight infants for alterations in serum sodium and potassium (pp. 423-424 and Chapter 11).

Recognize the advantages and limitations of the use of human milk with preterm infants (pp. 420-424).

Assist mothers of preterm and ill infants in providing breast milk for their infants (pp. 420-424, 428 and Chapter 5).

Recognize and monitor for signs of complications associated with parenteral nutrition (p. 424).

Recognize potential problems of infants with fetal growth restriction and the basis for these problems (pp. 409-410, 420 and Table 12-8).

Know the effects of specific health problems on nutritional intake, feeding method, and gastrointestinal function (pp. 424-425 and Table 12-13).

Use feeding techniques that promote adequate intake and reduce stress in infants with cardiorespiratory problems (p. 425).

Monitor infants after intestinal resection or with ostomies for adequacy of nutritional intake and excessive loss of nutrients (p. 425).

Know the advantages and disadvantages of different feeding methods and monitor infants for potential complications (pp. 425-426 and Table 12-14).

Select feedings and feeding methods appropriate for an individual infant's maturity, age, and health status (pp. 425-426 and Table 12-14).

Identify infants at risk for necrotizing enterocolitis and monitor for signs (pp. 427-428).

Counsel parents regarding the introduction of solids (p. 428).

References

1. Abebe, D. S., et al. (2015). Developmental trajectories of postpartum weight 3 years after birth: Norwegian mother and child cohort study. *Matern Child Health J, 19*, 917.

2. Abram, E. M., & Becker, A. B. (2013). Introducing solid foods. *Can Fam Phys, 59*, 721.

3. Abrams, S. A., et al. (2014). Micronutrient requirements of high-risk infants. *Clin Perinatol, 41*, 347.

4. Abu-Saad, K., & Fraser, D. (2010). Maternal nutrition and birth outcomes. *Epidemiol Rev, 32*, 5.

5. Adamkin, D. H. (1986). Nutrition in very low birth weight infants. *Clin Perinatol, 13*, 419.

6. Aggett, P. J. (2000). Trace elements of the micropremie. *Clin Perinatol, 27*, 119.

7. Agrogiannis, G. D., et al. (2014). Insulin-like growth factors in embryonic and fetal growth and skeletal development (review). *Mol Med Rep, 10*, 579.

8. Ahanya, S. N., et al. (2005). Meconium passage in utero: Mechanisms, consequences, and management. *Obstet Gynecol Surv, 60*, 45.

9. Allen, L. H. (2005). Multiple micronutrients in pregnancy and lactation: An overview. *Am J Clin Nutr, 81*, 1206S.

10. Amaizu, N., et al. (2008). Maturation of oral feeding skills in preterm infants. *Acta Paediatr, 97*, 61.

11. American Academy of Pediatrics Committee on Nutrition. (2013). *Pediatric nutrition handbook* (7th ed.). Elk Grove Village, IL: American Academy of Pediatrics.

12. American Academy of Pediatrics Section on Breastfeeding. (2012). Breastfeeding and the use of human milk. *Pediatrics, 129*(3), 827–841.

13. American College of Nurse-Midwives. (2016). Providing oral nutrition to women in labor. *J Midwifery Womens Health, 61*, 258.

14. American Society of Anesthesiologists Task Force on Obstetric Anesthesia. (2016). Practice guidelines for obstetric anesthesia: an updated report by the American Society of Anesthesiologists Task Force on Obstetric Anesthesia and the Society for Obstetric Anesthesia and Perinatology. *Anesthesiology, 124*, 270.

15. Amin, S. C., et al. (2013). Short bowel syndrome in the NICU. *Clin Perinatol, 40*, 53.

16. Arslanoglu, S., Moro, G. E., & Ziegler, E. E. (2009). Preterm infants fed fortified human milk receive less protein than they need. *J Perinatol, 29*, 489.

17. Arslanoglu, S., Moro, G. E., & Ziegler, E. E. (2010). Optimization of human milk fortification for preterm infants: New concepts and recommendations. The WAPM Working Group on Nutrition. *J Perinat Med, 38*, 233.

18. Avsar, A. F., & Keskin, H. L. (2010). Haemorrhoids during pregnancy. *J Obstet Gynaecol, 30*, 231.

19. Aynsley-Green, A., et al. (1990). Gut hormones and regulatory peptides in relation to enteral feeding, gastroenteritis, and necrotizing enterocolitis in infancy. *J Pediatr, 117*, S24.

20. Ballard, O., & Morrow, A. (2013). Human milk composition: nutrients and bioactive factors. *Pediatr Clin North Am, 60*, 49.

21. Barker, D. J. (2004). The developmental origins of adult disease. *J Am Coll Nutr, 23*, 588S.

22. Barker, D. J. (2005). The developmental origins of insulin resistance. *Horm Res, 64*, 2.

23. Barlow, S. M. (2009). Oral and respiratory control for preterm feeding. *Curr Opin Otolaryngol Head Neck Surg, 17*, 179.

24. Beard, M. P., & Millington, G. W. (2012). Recent developments in the specific dermatoses of pregnancy. *Clin Exp Dermatol, 37*, 1.

25. Beath, S. V. (2003). Hepatic function and physiology in the newborn. *Semin Neonatal, 8*, 337.

26. Beaulieu, D. B., & Kane, S. (2011). Inflammatory bowel disease in pregnancy. *Gastroenterol Clin North Am, 40*, 399.

27. Begum, K. S., Sachchithanantham, K., & De Somsubhra, S. (2011). Maternal obesity and pregnancy outcome. *Clin Exp Obstet Gynecol, 38*, 14.

28. Bell, E. F. (2011). Nutritional support. In J. P. Goldsmith & E. H. Karotkin (Eds.), *Assisted ventilation of the neonate* (5th ed.). Philadelphia: Saunders.

29. Berman, L., & Moss, R. I. (2011). Necrotizing enterocolitis: an update. *Semin Fetal Neonatal Med, 16*, 145.

30. Birch, J. L., & Newell, S. J. (2009). Gastrooesophageal reflux disease in preterm infants: Current management and diagnostic dilemmas. *Arch Dis Child Fetal Neonatal Ed, 94*, F379.

31. Blau, J., et al. (2011). Transfusion-related acute gut injury: Necrotizing enterocolitis in very low birth weight neonates after packed red blood cell transfusion. *J Pediatr, 158*, 403.

32. Bombell, S., & McGuire, W. (2013). Early trophic feeding versus enteral feeding for very preterm or very low birth weight infants. *Cochrane Database Syst Rev, 2013*(3), CD000504.

33. Boone, S. A., & Shields, K. M. (2005). Treating pregnancy-related nausea and vomiting with ginger. *Ann Pharmacother, 39*, 1710.

34. Boyd, H. A., et al. (2015). Inflammatory bowel disease and risk of adverse pregnancy outcomes. *PLoS ONE, 10*, e129567.

35. Brawarsky, P., et al. (2006). Fetal fatty acid oxidation defects and maternal liver disease in pregnancy. *Obstet Gynecol, 107*, 15.

36. Briana, D. D., & Malamitsi-Puchner, A. (2010). The role of adipocytokines in fetal growth. *Ann N Y Acad Sci, 1205*, 82.

37. Briffia, J. F., et al. (2015). Leptin in pregnancy and development: a contributor to adulthood disease? *Am J Physiol Endocrinol Metab, 308*, 335.

38. Broach, J., & Newton, N. (1988). Food and beverages in labor. Part I: Cross-cultural and historical practices. *Birth, 15*, 81.

39. Broach, J., & Newton, N. (1988). Food and beverages in labor. Part II: The effects of cessation of oral intake during labor. *Birth, 15*, 88.

40. Brown, J. V., et al. (2016). Multicomponent fortified human milk for promoting growth in preterm infants. *Cochrane Database Syst Rev, 2016*(5), CD000343.

41. Brown, L. D., et al. (2014). High-protein formulas: evidence for use in preterm infants. *Clin Perinatol, 41*, 383.

42. Browning, M. F. (2006). Fetal fatty acid oxidation defects and maternal liver disease in pregnancy. *Obstet Gynecol, 107*, 115.

43. Burrin, D. (2017). Trophic factors and regulation of gastrointestinal tract and liver development. In R. A. Polin, et al. (Eds.), *Fetal and neonatal physiology* (5th ed.). Philadelphia: Elsevier.

44. Caicedo, R. A., et al. (2005). The developing intestinal ecosystem: Implications for the neonate. *Pediatr Res, 58*, 625.

45. Calkins, K., & Devaskar, S. U. (2011). Fetal origins of adult disease. *Curr Probl Pediatr Adolesc Health Care, 41*, 158.

46. Cao, C., & O-Brien, K. O. (2013). Pregnancy and iron homeostasis: an update. *Nutr Rev, 71*, 35.

47. Caplan, M. S. (2017). Pathophysiology of neonatal necrotizing enterocolitis. In R. A. Polin, et al. (Eds.), *Fetal and neonatal physiology* (5th ed.). Philadelphia: Elsevier.

48. Cardwell, M. S. (2012). Pregnancy sickness: a biopsychological perspective. *Obstet Gynecol Surv, 67*, 645.

49. Cetin, I., Alvino, G., & Cardellicchio, M. (2009). Long chain fatty acids and dietary fats in fetal nutrition. *J Physiol, 587*, 3441.

50. Chen, A., et al. (2015). Gestational weight gain trend and population attributable risks of adverse fetal growth outcomes in Ohio. *Paediatric and Perinatal Epidemiology, 29*, 346.

51. Christensen, R. D. (2011). Association between red blood cell transfusions and necrotizing enterocolitis. *J Pediatr, 158*, 349.

52. Christian, P. (2010). Micronutrients, birth weight, and survival. *Annu Rev Nutr, 30*, 83.

53. Chu, S. Y., et al. (2009). Gestational weight gain by body mass index among US women delivering live birth, 2004-2005: fueling future obesity. *Am J Obstet Gynecol, 200*, e1.

54. Clark, R. H., Olsen, I. E., & Spitzer, A. R. (2014). Assessment of neonatal growth in prematurely born infants. *Clin Perinatol, 41*, 295.

55. Coad, J., Al-Rasasi, B., & Morgan, J. (2002). Nutrient insult in early pregnancy. *Proc Nutr Soc, 61*, 51.

56. Committee on Obstetric Practice. (2015). Weight gain in pregnancy. The American College of Obstetricians and Gynecologists Committee Opinion Number 548. (Original 2013; reaffirmed 2015).

57. Cooke, R. (2005). Postnatal growth in preterm infants: Have we got it right? *J Perinatol, 25*, 312.

58. Coppa, G. V., et al. (2004). The first prebiotics in humans: Human milk oligosaccharides. *J Clin Gastroenterol, 38*, S80.

59. Corton, M. M., et al. (2014). *Williams obstetrics* (24th ed.). New York: McGraw-Hill.

60. Crowell, D. T. (1995). Weight change in the postpartum period. A review of the literature. *J Nurse Midwifery, 40*, 418.

61. Cunniham, J. T. (1998). Upper gastrointestinal tract disease. Small and large bowel disease. In N. Gleicher (Ed.), *Principles and practice of medical therapy in pregnancy* (3rd ed.). Stamford, CT: Appleton & Lange.

62. Cunningham-Rundles, S., et al. (2009). Role of nutrients in the development of neonatal immune response. *Nutr Rev, 67*, S152.

63. Davis, M. (2004). Nausea and vomiting of pregnancy: An evidence-based review. *J Perinat Neonatal Nurs, 18*, 312.

64. de Bari, O., et al. (2014). Cholesterol cholelithiasis in pregnant women: pathogenesis, prevention and treatment. *Ann Hepatol, 13*, 728.

65. de Jong, E. M., et al. (2010). Etiology of esophageal atresia and tracheoesophageal fistula: "Mind the gap." *Curr Gastroenterol Rep, 12*, 215.

66. Delma, L., et al. (2017). Development of the enteric nervous system. In R. A. Polin, et al. (Eds.), *Fetal and neonatal physiology* (5th ed.). Philadelphia: Elsevier.

67. Denne, S. C. (2001). Protein and energy requirements in preterm infants. *Semin Neonatol, 6*, 377.

68. De-Regil, L. M., et al. (2015). Effects and safety of periconceptional oral folate supplementation for preventing birth defects. *Cochrane Database Syst Rev, 2015*(12), CD007950.

69. Desai, M., & Ross, M. G. (2011). Fetal programming of adipose tissue: Effects of intrauterine growth restriction and maternal obesity/high-fat diet. *Semin Reprod Med, 29*, 237.

70. Deshpande, G., et al. (2010). Updated meta-analysis of probiotics for preventing necrotizing enterocolitis in preterm neonates. *Pediatrics, 125*, 921.

71. Dimmitt, R., & Sibley, E. O. (2012). Developmental anatomy and physiology of the gastrointestinal tract. In C. A. Gleason & S. Devaskar (Eds.), *Avery's diseases of the newborn* (9th ed.). Philadelphia: Saunders.

72. Di Natale, C., et al. (2011). Fortification of maternal milk for preterm infants. *J Matern Fetal Neonatal Med, 24*, 41.

73. Donnelly, J. M., et al. (2015). Fetal metabolic influences of neonatal anthropometry and adiposity. *BMC Pediatr, 15*, 175.

74. Drozdowski, L. A., Clandinin, T., & Thomson, A. B. (2010). Ontogeny, growth and development of the small intestine: Understanding pediatric gastroenterology. *World J Gastroenterol, 16*, 787.

75. Dyer, J. S., & Rosenfeld, C. R. (2011). Metabolic imprinting by prenatal, perinatal and postnatal overnutrition: A review. *Semin Reprod Med, 29*, 266.

76. Einarson, A., et al. (2007). Treatment of nausea and vomiting in pregnancy. *Can Fam Phys, 53*, 2109.

77. El-Haddad, M. A., et al. (2004). In utero development of fetal thirst and appetite: Potential for programming. *J Soc Gynecol Investig, 11*, 123.

78. Ellington, S. R., et al. (2015). Recent trends in hepatic diseases during pregnancy in the United States, 2002-2010. *Am J Obstet Gynecol, 212*, 524e.1.

79. Endres, L. K., et al. (2015). Postpartum weight retention risk factors and relationship to obesity at one year. *Obstet Gynecol, 125*, 144.

80. Erekson, E. A., et al. (2012). Maternal post-operative complications after nonobstetric antenatal surgery. *J Matern Fetal Neonat Med*, 25, 2639.

81. Everson, G. T. (1992). Gastrointestinal motility in pregnancy. *Gastroenterol Clin North Am*, 21, 751.

82. Fanaroff, A. A., & Fanaroff, J. M. (2013). *Care of the high risk infant* (6th ed.). Philadelphia: Saunders.

83. Fejzo, M. S., et al. (2008). High prevalence of severe nausea and vomiting of pregnancy and hyperemesis gravidarum among relatives of affected individuals. *Eur J Obstet Gyncecol Reprod Bio*, 14, 13.

84. Felix, J. F., et al. (2009). Genetic and environmental factors in the etiology of esophageal atresia and/or tracheoesophageal fistula: An overview of the current concepts. *Birth Defects Res A Clin Mol Teratol*, 85, 747.

85. Fenton, T. R., & Kim, J. H. (2013). A systematic review and meta-analysis to revise the Fenton growth chart for preterm infants. *BMC Pediatr*, 13, 59.

86. Fernandez-Twinn, D. S., & Ozanne, S. E. (2010). Early life nutrition and metabolic programming. *Ann N Y Acad Sci*, 1212, 78.

87. Flaxman, S. M., & Sherman, P. W. (2000). Morning sickness: A mechanism for protecting mother and embryo. *Q Rev Biol*, 75, 113.

88. Franca-Neto, A. H., Amorim, M. M., & Nobrega, B. M. (2015). Acute appendicitis in pregnancy: literature review. *Rev Assoc Med Bras*, 61, 170.

89. Fremont, R. D., & Rice, T. W. (2014). How soon should we start interventional feeding in the ICU? *Curr Opin Gastroenterol*, 30, 178.

90. Gaillard, R. (2015). Maternal obesity during pregnancy and cardiovascular development and disease in the offspring. *Eur J Epidemiol*, 30, 1141.

91. George, A., et al. (2011). Periodontal treatment during pregnancy and birth outcomes: A meta-analysis of randomised trials. *Int J Evid Based Healthc*, 9, 122.

92. Gicquel, C., & LeBouc, Y. (2006). Hormonal regulation of fetal growth. *Horm Res*, 65, 28.

93. Gidrewicz, D. A., & Fenton, T. R. (2014). A systematic review and met-analysis of the nutrient content of preterm and term breast milk. *BMC Pediatr*, 14, 216.

94. Gilmore, L. A., & Redman, L. M. (2016). Weight gain in pregnancy and application of the 2009 IOM guidelines: toward a uniform approach. *Obesity (Silver Spring)*, 23, 507.

95. Gluckman, P. D., & Hanson, M. A. (2004). Maternal constraint of fetal growth and its consequences. *Semin Fetal Neonatal Med*, 9, 419.

96. Gluckman, P. D., Hanson, M. A., & Pinal, C. (2005). The developmental origins of adult disease. *Matern Child Nutr*, 1, 1301.

97. Godfrey, K. M., Inskip, H. M., & Hanson, M. A. (2011). The long term effects of prenatal development on growth and metabolism. *Semin Reprod Med*, 29, 257.

98. Goodwin, T. (2002). Nausea and vomiting of pregnancy: An obstetric syndrome. *Am J Obstet Gynecol*, 186, S184.

99. Gosche, J. R., et al. (2006). Midgut abnormalities. *Surg Clin North Am*, 86, 285.

100. Gregory, K. (2005). Update on nutrition for preterm and full-term infants. *J Obstet Gynecol Neonatal Nurs*, 34, 98.

101. Gross, T. L., & Kazzi, G. M. (1998). Maternal malnutrition and obesity. In N. Gleicher (Ed.), *Principles and practice of medical therapy in pregnancy* (3rd ed.). Stamford, CT: Appleton & Lange.

102. Gryboski, J. D., & Walker, W. A. (1983). *Gastrointestinal problems in the infant* (2nd ed.). Philadelphia: Saunders.

103. Gursoy, M., et al. (2014). Pregnancy-induced gingivitis and OMICS in dentistry: in silico modeling and in vivo prospective validation of estradiol-modulated inflammatory biomarkers. *Journal of Integrative Biology*, 18, 582.

104. Haierian-Ardakani, A., et al. (2013). Relationship between maternal periodontal disease and low birth weight babies. *Iran J Reprod Med*, 8, 625.

105. Han, Y. W. (2011). Oral health and adverse pregnancy outcomes—what's next? *J Dent Res*, 90, 289.

106. Han, Z., et al. (2011). Maternal underweight and the risk of preterm birth and low birth weight: a systematic review and meta-analyses. *International Journal of Epidemiology*, 40, 65.

107. Harper, L. M., Tita, A., & Biggio, J. R. (2015). The Institute of Medicine guidelines for gestational weight gain after a diagnosis of gestational diabetes and pregnancy. *Am J Perinatol*, 32, 239.

108. Hay, W. W., & Thureen, P. (2010). Protein for preterm infants: How much is needed? How much is enough? How much is too much? *Pediatr Neonatol*, 51, 198.

109. Hay, W. W., Jr. (2009). Optimal protein intake in preterm infants. *J Perinatol*, 29, 465.

110. Heird, W. C. (2001). Determination of nutritional requirements in preterm infants, with special reference to "catch-up" growth. *Semin Neonatol*, 6, 365.

111. Henriksen, C., et al. (2009). Growth and nutrient intake among very-low-birth-weight infants fed fortified human milk during hospitalization. *Br J Nutr*, 102, 1179.

112. Herrell, H. E. (2014). Nausea and vomiting of pregnancy. *Am Fam Phys*, 89, 965.

113. Hong, J. Y., Park, J. W., & Oh, J. I. (2005). Comparison of preoperative gastric contents and serum gastrin concentrations in pregnant and nonpregnant women. *Journal of Clinical Anesthesia*, 17, 451.

114. Huxley, R. R. (2000). Nausea and vomiting in early pregnancy: Its role in placental development. *Obstet Gynecol*, 95, 779.

115. Hytten, F. E., & Chamberlain, G. (1980). *Clinical physiology in obstetrics*. Oxford: Blackwell Scientific.

116. Imdad, A., & Bhutta, Z. A. (2011). Effect of balanced protein energy supplementation during pregnancy on birth outcomes. *BMC Public Health*, 11, S17.

117. Institute of Medicine. (1990). *Nutrition during pregnancy*. Washington, DC: National Academy Press.

118. Institute of Medicine. (1997). *Dietary reference intakes for calcium, phosphorus, magnesium, vitamin D, and fluoride 1997*. Washington, DC: National Academy Press.

119. Institute of Medicine. (1998). *Dietary reference intakes for thiamin, riboflavin, niacin, vitamin B$_6$, folate, vitamin B$_{12}$, pantothenic acid, biotin, and choline 1998*. Washington, DC: National Academy Press.

120. Institute of Medicine. (2000). *Dietary reference intakes for vitamin C, vitamin E, selenium, and carotenoids 2000*. Washington, DC: National Academy Press.

121. Institute of Medicine. (2001). *Dietary reference intakes for vitamin A, vitamin K, arsenic, boron, chromium, copper, iodine, iron, manganese, molybdenum, nickel, silicon, vanadium, and zinc 2001*. Washington, DC: National Academy Press.

122. Institute of Medicine. (2002). *Dietary reference intakes for energy, carbohydrates, fiber, fat, protein, and amino acids (macronutrients) 2002*. Washington, DC: National Academy Press.

123. Institute of Medicine. (2009). *Weight gain during pregnancy: reexamining the guidelines*. www.iomedu/pregnancyweightgain.

124. Jadcherla, S. R. (2017). Pathophysiology of gastroesophageal reflux. In R. A. Polin, et al. (Eds.), *Fetal and neonatal physiology* (5th ed.). Philadelphia: Elsevier.

125. James, L. P. (2002). Pharmacology for the gastrointestinal tract. *Clin Perinatol*, 29, 115.

126. Jamjute, P., et al. (2009). Liver function test and pregnancy. *J Matern Fetal Neonatal Med*, 22, 274.

127. Jansson, T., Myatt, L., & Powell, T. L. (2009). The role of trophoblast nutrient and ion transporters in the development of pregnancy complications and adult disease. *Curr Vasc Pharmacol*, 7, 521.

128. Jarlenski, M. P., et al. (2014). Effects of breastfeeding on postpartum weight loss among U.S. women. *Prev Med*, 69, 146.

129. Kaiser, L. (2008). Position of the American Dietetic Association: Nutrition and lifestyle for a healthy pregnancy outcome. *J Am Diet Assoc*, 108, 553.

130. Kastenberg, Z. J., & Sylvester, K. G. (2013). The surgical management of necrotizing enterocolitis. *Clin Perinatol*, 40, 135.

131. Kelly, T. F., & Savides, T. J. (2014). Gastrointestinal disease in pregnancy. In R. K. Creasy, et al. (Eds.), *Creasy & Resnik's Maternal-fetal medicine: Principles and practice* (7th ed.). Philadelphia: Saunders.

132. King, J. C. (2001). Effect of reproduction on the bioavailability of calcium, zinc and selenium. *J Nutr*, 13, 1355S.

133. King, R., et al. (2011). Oral nutrition in labour: "Whose choice is it anyway?" A review of the literature. *Midwifery*, 27, 674.

134. Kleinman, R., et al. (2008). *Walkers' pediatric gastrointestinal disease* (5th ed.). Hamilton, Ontario: B.C. Decker.

135. Knight-Agarwal, C. R., et al. (2016). Association of BMI and interpregnancy BMI change with birth outcomes in an Australian obstetric population: a retrospective cohort study. *BMJ Open*, 6, e1.

136. Koletzco, B., Poindexter, B., & Uauy, R. (2014). *Nutritional care of premature infants: scientific basis and practical guidelines*. New York: Karger Publishing.

137. Kramer, M. S., & Kakuma, R. (2003). Energy and protein intake in pregnancy. *Cochrane Database Syst Rev, 2003*(4), CD000032.

138. Krawinkel, M. B., et al. (2014). Revised D-A-CH intake recommendations for folate: how much is needed? *Euro J Clin Nutr, 68*, 719.

139. Krebs, N. F., Domellof, M., & Ziegler, E. (2015). Balancing benefits and risks of iron fortification in resource-rich countries. *J Pediatr, 167*, S20.

140. Kristal, A. R., & Rush, D. (1984). Maternal nutrition and duration of gestation: A review. *Clin Obstet Gynecol, 27*, 553.

141. Ladyman, S. R., Augustine, R. A., & Grattan, D. R. (2010). Hormone interactions regulating energy balance during pregnancy. *J Neuroendocrinol, 22*, 805.

142. Lai, A. K., & Kominiarek, M. A. (2015). Weight gain in twin gestations: are the Institute of Medicine guidelines optimal for neonatal outcomes? *J Perinatol, 36*, 405.

143. Lau, C., Smith, E. O., & Schanler, R. J. (2003). Coordination of suck-swallow and swallow respiration in preterm infants. *Acta Paediatr, 92*, 721.

144. Lebenthal, A., & Lebenthal, E. (1999). The ontology of the small intestinal epithelium. *J Parenter Enteral Nutr, 23*, S3.

145. Lebenthal, E., & Tucker, N. T. (1986). Carbohydrate digestion: Development in early infancy. *Clin Perinatol, 13*, 37.

146. Lebenthal, E., & Leung, Y. K. (1988). Feeding the premature and compromised infant: Gastrointestinal considerations. *Pediatr Clin North Am, 35*, 215.

147. Lebenthal, E. (1995). Gastrointestinal maturation and motility patterns as indicators for feeding the premature infant. *Pediatrics, 95*, 207.

148. Le Huërou-Luron, I., Blat, S., & Boudry, G. (2010). Breast- v. formula-feeding: Impacts on the digestive tract and immediate and long-term health effects. *Nutr Res Rev, 23*, 23.

149. Lee, N. M., & Saha, S. (2011). Nausea and vomiting of pregnancy. *Gastroenterol Clin North Am, 40*, 309.

150. Lee, Y. K., & Styne, D. M. (2017). Endocrine factors affecting neonatal growth. In R. A. Polin, et al. (Eds.), *Fetal and neonatal physiology* (5th ed.). Philadelphia: Elsevier.

151. Levin, B. E. (2006). Metabolic imprinting: critical impact of the perinatal environment on the regulation of energy homeostasis. *Philos Trans R Soc Lond B Biol Sci, 361*, 1107.

152. Lindseth, G., & Bird-Baker, M. Y. (2004). Risk factors for cholelithiasis in pregnancy. *Res Nurs Health, 27*, 382.

153. Liu, Y., et al. (2013). Early oral-motor management on feeding performance in premature neonates. *J Formosan Med Assoc, 112*, 161.

154. Longo, S. A., et al. (2010). Gastrointestinal conditions during pregnancy. *Clinics in Colon and Rectal Surgery, 23*, 80.

155. Lopez-Jornet, P., & Bermejo-Fenoll, A. (2005). Gingival lesions as a first symptom of pemphigus vulgaris in pregnancy. *Br Dent J, 199*, 91.

156. Lucas, A. (2005). Long-term programming effects of early nutrition—implications for the preterm infant. *J Perinatol, 25*, S2.

157. Mackin, M. L. (1990). Infant sleep and bedtime cereal. *Am J Dis Child, 143*, 1066.

158. Mahadevan, U., et al. (2011). The London Position Statement of the World Congress of Gastroenterology on Biological Therapy for IBD with the European Crohn's and Colitis Organisation: Pregnancy and pediatrics. *Am J Gastroenterol, 106*, 214.

159. Maharaj, D. (2009). Eating and drinking in labor: Should it be allowed? *Eur J Obstet Gynecol Reprod Biol, 146*, 3.

160. Malfertheiner, S. F., et al. (2012). A prospective longitudinal cohort study: evolution of GERD symptoms during the course of pregnancy. *Gastroenterology, 12*, 131.

161. Mannan, M., Doi, S. A. R., & Mamun, A. A. (2013). Association between weight gain during pregnancy and postpartum weight retention and obesity: a bias-adjusted meta-analysis. *Nutrition Reviews, 71*, 343.

162. Margolis, K. G., & Picorar, J. A. (2017). Development of gastrointestinal motility. In R. A. Polin, et al. (Eds.), *Fetal and neonatal physiology* (5th ed.). Philadelphia: Elsevier.

163. Martin, C. R. (2014). Fatty acid requirements in preterm infants and their role in health and disease. *C Clin Perinatol, 41*, 363.

164. Martin, J., et al. (2015). Reducing postpartum weight retention and improving breastfeeding outcomes in overweight women: a pilot randomized controlled trial. *Nutrients, 7*, 1464.

165. Matthews, A., et al. (2015). Interventions for nausea and vomiting in early pregnancy. *Cochrane Database Syst Rev, 2015*(9), CD007575.

166. Mazzotta, P., & Magee, L. A. (2000). A risk-benefit analysis of pharmacological and nonpharmacological treatments for nausea and vomiting of pregnancy. *Drugs, 59*, 781.

167. McGrath, J. M., & Braescu, A. V. (2004). State of the science: Feeding readiness in the preterm infant. *J Perinat Neonatal Nurs, 18*, 353.

168. McGuire, W., & McEwan, P. (2004). Systematic review of transpyloric versus gastric tube feeding for preterm infants. *Arch Dis Child Fetal Neonatal Ed, 89*, F245.

169. Mishkin, D. J., et al. (1998). Dental diseases. In N. Gleicher (Ed.), *Principles and practice of medical therapy in pregnancy* (3rd ed.). Stamford, CT: Appleton & Lange.

170. Moe-Bryne, T., et al. (2016). Glutamine supplementation to prevent morbidity and mortality in preterm infants. *Cochrane Database Syst Rev, 2016*(4), CD001457.

171. Monk, D., & Moore, G. E. (2004). Intrauterine growth restriction—genetic causes and consequences. *Semin Fetal Neonatal Med, 9*, 371.

172. Mook-Kanamori, D. O., et al. (2010). Risk factors and outcomes associated with first-trimester fetal growth restriction. *JAMA, 303*, 527.

173. Moore, K. L., Persaud, T. V. N., & Torchia, M. G. (2015). *The developing human: Clinically oriented embryology* (10th ed.). Philadelphia: Saunders.

174. Morgan, J., Young, L., & McGuire, W. (2015). Slow advancement of enteral feed volumes to prevent necrotising enterocolitis in very low birth weight infants. *Cochrane Database Syst Rev, 2015*(10), CD001241.

175. Morgan, J. A., Young, L., & McGuire, W. (2011). Pathogenesis and prevention of necrotizing enterocolitis. *Curr Opin Infect Dis, 24*, 183.

176. Morowitz, M. J., et al. (2010). Redefining the role of intestinal microbes in the pathogenesis of necrotizing enterocolitis. *Pediatrics, 125*, 777.

177. Moscandrew, M., & Kane, S. (2009). Inflammatory bowel diseases and management considerations: Fertility and pregnancy. *Curr Gastroenterol Rep, 11*, 395.

178. Narang, A. P. S., et al. (2006). Serial composition of human milk in preterm and term mothers. *Ind J Clin Biochem, 21*, 89.

179. Nawathe, A. R., et al. (2016). Insulin-like growth factor axis in pregnancies affected by fetal growth disorders. *Clin Epigen, 8*, 11.

180. Neiva, F. C., et al. (2014). Non-nutritive sucking evaluation in preterm newborns and the start of oral feeding: a multicenter study. *Clinics, 69*, 393.

181. Neu, J. (1996). Nutrient absorption in the preterm neonate. *Clin Perinatol, 23*, 229.

182. Neu, J., & Bernstein, H. (2002). Update on host defense and immunomicronutrients. *Clin Perinatol, 29*, 41.

183. Neu, J. (2007). Gastrointestinal maturation and implications for infant feeding. *Early Hum Dev, 83*, 767.

184. Neu, J., & Walker, W. A. (2011). Necrotizing enterocolitis. *N Engl J Med, 364*, 255.

185. Neu, J. (2011). Routine probiotics for premature infants: Let's be careful! *J Pediatr, 158*, 672.

186. Neu, J. (2015). Preterm infant nutrition, gut bacteria, and necrotizing enterocolitis. *Curr Opin Clin Nutri Metab Care, 18*, 285.

187. Neu, J. (2017). Digestion-absorption functions in fetuses, infants and children. In R. A. Polin, et al. (Eds.), *Fetal and neonatal physiology* (5th ed.). Philadelphia: Elsevier.

188. Ng, S., et al. (2014). Socioeconomic disparities in prepregnancy BMI and impact on maternal and neonatal outcomes and postpartum weight retention: the EFHL longitudinal birth cohort study. *BMC Pregnancy and Childbirth, 14*, 314.

189. Nikfar, S., et al. (2002). Use of proton pump inhibitors during pregnancy and rates of major malformations: A meta-1—I analysis. *Dig Dis Sci, 47*, 1526.

190. Nohr, E. A., et al. (2007). Obesity, gestational weight gain and preterm birth: A study within the Danish National Birth Cohort. *Paediatr Perinat Epidemiol, 21*, 5.

191. O'Brien, C. M., Grivell, R. M., & Dodd, J. M. (2016). Systematic review of antenatal dietary and lifestyle interventions in women with a normal body mass index. *Acta Obstetricia et Gynecologica Scandinavica, 95*, 259.

192. Olsen, I. E., et al. (2010). New intrauterine growth curves based on United States data. *Pediatrics, 125*, 214.

193. Olson, G., & Blackwell, S. C. (2011). Optimization of gestational weight gain in the obese gravida: A review. *Obstet Gynecol Clin North Am, 38*, 397.

194. O'Sullivan, G., et al. (2009). Effect of food intake during labour on obstetric outcome: Randomised controlled trial. *BMJ, 338*, b784.

195. Ozkan, S., et al. (2005). Serum leptin levels in hypertensive disorder of pregnancy. *Eur J Obstet Gynecol Reprod Biol, 120*, 158.

196. Ozkan, S., et al. (2015). Review of a challenging clinical issue: intrahepatic cholestasis of pregnancy. *World Journal of Gastroenterology, 21*, 7134.

197. Pan, C., & Perumalswami, P. V. (2011). Pregnancy-related liver diseases. *Clin Liver Dis, 15*, 199.

198. Papapanou, I. M. (2013). Epidemiology of association between maternal periodontal disease and adverse pregnancy outcomes—systematic review. *J Periodontol, 84*(Suppl. 4), S181.

199. Park, J., et al. (2015). Factors associated with feeding progression in extremely preterm infants. *Nurs Res, 64*, 159.

200. Parry, R. L. (2015). Development of the neonatal gastrointestinal tract. In R. J. Martin, A. A. Fanaroff, & M. C. Walsh (Eds.), *Fanaroff and Martin's Neonatal-perinatal medicine: Diseases of the fetus and infant* (10th ed.). Philadelphia: Saunders.

201. Patel, R. M., & Denning, P. W. (2015). Intestinal microbiota and its relationship with necrotizing enterocolitis. *Pediatr Res, 78*, 232.

202. Patil, C. L., & Abrams, E. T. (2012). Appetite sensations and nausea and vomiting in pregnancy: an overview of the explanations. *Ecol Food and Nutr, 51*, 394.

203. Paul, D. A., et al. (2011). Increased odds of necrotizing enterocolitis after transfusion of red blood cells in premature infants. *Pediatrics, 127*, 635.

204. Pereira, G. R., & Zucker, A. (1986). Nutritional deficiencies in the neonate. *Clin Perinatol, 13*, 175.

205. Pereira-da-Silva, L., & Virella, D. (2014). Is intrauterine growth appropriate to monitor postnatal growth of preterm neonates? *BMC Ped, 14*, 14.

206. Picciano, M. F. (2003). Pregnancy and lactation: Physiological adjustments, nutritional requirements and the role of dietary supplements. *J Nutr, 133*, 1997S.

207. Plecas, D., Plesinac, S., & Kontifá Vucinifá, O. (2014). Nutrition in pregnancy: basic principles and recommendations. *Srp Arh Celok Lek, 142*, 125.

208. Poindexter, B. B., & Schanler, R. J. (2012). Enteral nutrition for the high-risk neonate. In C. A. Gleason & S. Devaskar (Eds.), *Avery's diseases of the newborn* (9th ed.). Philadelphia: Saunders.

209. Premji, S., Fenton, T., & Sauve, R. (2006). Does amount of protein in formula matter for low-birthweight infants? A Cochrane systematic review. *J Parenter Enteral Nutr, 30*, 507.

210. Premji, S., & Chessell, L. (2011). Continuous nasogastric milk feeding versus intermittent bolus milk feeding for premature infants less than 1500 grams. *Cochrane Database Syst Rev, 2011*(11), CD001819.

211. Premji, S. S., & Paes, B. (2000). Gastrointestinal function and growth in premature infants: Is non-nutritive sucking vital? *J Perinatol, 20*, 46.

212. Prozialeck, J. D., & Wershil, B. K. (2017). Development of gastric secretory function. In R. A. Polin, et al. (Eds.), *Fetal and neonatal physiology* (5th ed.). Philadelphia: Elsevier.

213. Putet, G. (2000). Lipid metabolism of the micropremie. *Clin Perinatol, 27*, 57.

214. Quartarone, G. (2013). Gastroesophageal reflux in pregnancy: a systematic review on the benefit of raft forming agents. *Minerva Ginecol, 65*, 541.

215. Ramani, M., & Ambalavana, N. (2013). Feeding practices and necrotizing enterocolitis. *Clin Perinatol, 40*, 1.

216. Ramel, S. E., & Georgieff, M. K. (2016). Nutrition. In M. G. MacDonald & M. M. K. Seshia (Eds.), *Avery's Neonatology, pathophysiology and management of the newborn* (7th ed.). Philadelphia: Wolters Kluwer.

217. Rasmussen, K. M., et al. (2010). Recommendations for weight gain during pregnancy in the context of the obesity epidemic. *Obstet Gynecol, 116*, 1191.

218. Rayyan, M., Rommel, N., & Allegaert, K. (2015). The fate of fat: pre-exposure fat losses during nasogastric tube feeding in preterm newborns. *Nutrients, 7*, 6213.

219. Reber, K. M., Nankervis, C. A., & Nowicki, P. T. (2002). Newborn intestinal circulation. Physiology and pathophysiology. *Clin Perinatal, 29*, 23.

220. Resnik, R. (2004). The puerperium. In R. K. Creasy, R. Resnik, & J. D. Iams (Eds.), *Maternal-fetal medicine: Principles and practice* (5th ed.). Philadelphia: Saunders.

221. Resnik, R., & Creasy, R. K. (2014). Intrauterine growth restriction. In R. K. Creasy, et al. (Eds.), *Creasy & Resnik's Maternal-fetal medicine: Principles and practice* (7th ed.). Philadelphia: Saunders.

222. Riely, C. A., & Fallon, H. J. (2004). Liver diseases. In G. N. Burrow, T. P. Duffy, & J. A. Copel (Eds.), *Medical complications during pregnancy* (6th ed.). Philadelphia: Saunders.

223. Roberts, V. H. J., Frias, A. E., & Grove, K. L. (2015). Impact of maternal obesity on fetal programming of cardiovascular disease. *Physiol (Bethesda), 30*, 224.

224. Rodríguez, J. M., et al. (2015). The composition of the gut microbiota throughout life, with an emphasis on early life. *Microb Ecol Health Dis, 26*, 1.

225. Rosso, P. (1990). *Nutrition and metabolism in pregnancy*. New York: Oxford University Press.

226. Rubin, P. H., & Janowitz, H. D. (1991). The digestive tract and pregnancy. In S. H. Cherry & I. R. Merkatz (Eds.), *Complications of pregnancy: Medical, surgical, gynecological, psychosocial, and perinatal* (4th ed.). Baltimore: Williams & Wilkins.

227. Sadler, T. W. (2015). *Langman's medical embryology* (13th ed.) Philadelphia: Wolters Kluwar.

228. Saravanan, T., Shakila, K. R., & Shanthini, K. (2012). Pregnancy Epulis. *Indian Journal of Multidisciplinary Dentistry, 2*, 514.

229. Schanler, R. J. (2005). Human milk supplementation for preterm infants. *Acta Paediatr Suppl, 94*, 64.

230. Schanler, R. J. (2011). Outcomes of human milk-fed premature infants. *Semin Perinatol, 35*, 29.

231. Schneider, R. E., et al. (2000). Dental complications. In W. R. Cohen, S. H. Cherry, & I. R. Merkatz (Eds.), *Cherry & Merkatz's Complications of pregnancy* (5th ed.). Baltimore: Williams & Wilkins.

232. Scott-Pillai, R., et al. (2013). The impact of body mass index on maternal and neonatal outcomes: a retrospective study in a UK obstetric population, 2004-2011. *BJOG, 120*, 932.

233. Sebert, J. M., et al. (2015). Maternal body weight and gestational diabetes differentially influence placental and pregnancy outcomes. *J Clin Endocrinol Metab, 101*, 59.

234. Sehested, L., & Pedersen, P. (2014). Prognosis and risk factors for intrauterine growth retardation. *Dan Med J, 61*, A4826.

235. Senterre, T. (2014). Practice of enteral nutrition in very low birth weight and extremely low birth weight infants. *World Rev Nutr Diet, 110*, 201.

236. Seraphim, A. P, et al. (2016). Relationship among periodontal disease, insulin resistance, salivary cortisol, and stress levels during pregnancy. *Brazilian Dental Journal, 27*, 123.

237. Sferruzzi-Perri, A. N., et al. (2013). Hormonal and nutritional drivers of intrauterine growth. *Curr Opin Clin Nutri Met Care, 16*, 298.

238. Shah, M. D., & Shah, S. R. (2009). Nutrient deficiencies in the premature infant. *Pediatr Clin North Am, 56*, 1069.

239. Sharma, R., & Hudak, M. L. (2013). A clinical perspective of necrotizing enterocolitis. *Clin Perinatol, 40*, 27.

240. Sharts-Hopko, N. C. (2010). Oral intake during labor: A review of the evidence. *MCN Am J Matern Child Nurs, 35*, 197.

241. Sherman, M. P. (2010). New concepts of microbial translocation in the neonatal intestine: mechanisms and prevention. *Clin Perinatol, 37*, 565.

242. Shin, G. H., Toto, E. L., & Schey, R. (2015). Pregnancy and postpartum bowel changes: constipation and fecal incontinence. *Am J Gastroenterol, 110*, 521.

243. Siega-Riz, A. M., Deierlein, A., & Stuebe, A. (2010). Implementation of the new Institute of Medicine gestational weight gain guidelines. *J Midwifery Women's Health, 55*, 512.

244. Simmer, K., & Rao, S. C. (2005). Early introduction of lipids to parenterally-fed preterm infants. *Cochrane Database Syst Rev, 2005*(2), CD005256.

245. Singata, M., Tranmer, J., & Gyte, G. M. (2013). Restricting oral fluid and food intake during labour. *Cochrane Database Syst Rev, 2013*(8), CD003930.

246. Singla, R., et al. (2015). Vitamin-D deficiency is associated with gallbladder stasis among pregnant women. *Dig Dis Sci, 60*, 2793.

247. Slutzah, M., et al. (2010). Refrigerator storage of expressed human milk in the neonatal intensive care unit. *J Pediatr, 156*, 26.

248. Smoleniec, J. S., & James, D. K. (1993). Gastrointestinal crises during pregnancy. *Dig Dis, 11*, 313.

249. SOGC Clinical Practice Guidelines. (2010). Obesity in pregnancy. *International Journal of Gynecology and Obstetrics, 110*, 167.

250. Starling, A. P., et al. (2015). Associations of maternal BMI and gestational weight gain with neonatal adiposity in the Healthy Start study. *Am J Clin Nutr, 101,* 302.

251. Steinlauf, A. F., Chang, P. K., & Traube, M. (2004). Gastrointestinal complications. In G. N. Burrow, T. P. Duffy, & J. A. Copel (Eds.), *Medical complications during pregnancy* (6th ed.). Philadelphia: Saunders.

252. Stephens, B. E., & Vohr, B. R. (2014). Protein intake and neurodevelopmental outcomes. *Clin Perinatol, 41,* 323.

253. Stephens, T. V., et al. (2015). Protein requirements of healthy pregnant women during early and late gestation are higher than current recommendations. *J Nutr, 145,* 73.

254. Stoll, B. J., et al. (2010). Neonatal outcomes of extremely preterm infants from the NICHD Neonatal Research Network. *Pediatrics, 126,* 443.

255. Suidan, J. S., & Young, B. K. (1986). The acute abdomen in pregnancy. In V. K. Rustgi & J. N. Cooper (Eds.), *Gastrointestinal and hepatic complications in pregnancy.* New York: John Wiley & Sons.

256. Sullivan, S., et al. (2010). An exclusively human milk-based diet is associated with a lower rate of necrotizing enterocolitis than a diet of human milk and bovine milk-based products. *J Pediatr, 156,* 562.

257. Suzuki, S., et al. (2009). Ptyalism gravidarum. *N AM J Med Sci, 1,* 303.

258. Symonds, M. E., & Ramsay, M. M. (2010). *Maternal-fetal nutrition during pregnancy and lactation.* Cambridge: Cambridge University Press.

259. Szajewska, H. (2010). Probiotics and prebiotics in preterm infants: Where are we? Where are we going? *Early Hum Dev, 86,* 81.

260. Tarnok, A., & Mehes, K. (2002). Gastrointestinal malformations, associated congenital abnormalities, and intrauterine growth. *J Pediatr Gastroenterol Nutr, 34,* 406.

261. Taylor, S. N., et al. (2009). Intestinal permeability in preterm infants by feeding type: Mother's milk versus formula. *Breastfeed Med, 4,* 11.

262. Thangaratinam, S., et al. (2012). Interventions to reduce or prevent obesity in pregnant women: a systematic review. *Health Technology Assessment, 16,* 1.

263. Thorn, S. R., et al. (2011). The intrauterine growth restriction phenotype: Fetal adaptations and potential implications for later life insulin resistance and diabetes. *Semin Reprod Med, 29,* 225.

264. Thureen, P., & Heird, W. C. (2005). Protein and energy requirements of the preterm/low birthweight (LBW) infant. *Pediatr Res, 57,* 95R.

265. Thureen, P. J., & Hay, W. W. (2000). Intravenous nutrition and postnatal growth of the micropremie. *Clin Perinatol, 27,* 197.

266. Thureen, P. J., & Hay W. W., Jr. (2001). Early aggressive nutrition in preterm infants. *Semin Neonatol, 6,* 403.

267. Tian, X., et al. (2015). Oral motor intervention improved the oral feeding in preterm infants. *Medicine, 94,* e1.

268. Trahms, C. M. (2001). *Nutrition for the preterm and low-birth-weight infant. In Nutrition in infancy and childhood* (7th ed.). New York: McGraw-Hill.

269. Truong, Y. N., et al. (2015). Weight gain in pregnancy: does the Institute of Medicine have it right? *Am J Obstet Gynecol, 212,* 362.e1.

270. Tsang, R. C., et al. (2005). *Nutrition of the preterm infant. Scientific basis and practical guidelines.* Cincinnati, OH: Digital Educational Publishing, Inc.

271. Tytgat, G. N., et al. (2003). Contemporary understanding and management of reflux and constipation in the general population and pregnancy: A consensus meeting. *Aliment Pharmacol Ther, 18,* 291.

272. Uauy, R., et al. (2000). Essential fatty acid metabolism in the micro premie. *Clin Perinatol, 27,* 71.

273. Uppal, A., et al. (2010). The effectiveness of periodontal disease treatment during pregnancy in reducing the risk of experiencing preterm birth and low birth weight: A meta-analysis. *J Am Dent Assoc, 141,* 1423.

274. Van Thiel, D. H., & Schade, R. R. (1986). Pregnancy: Its physiologic course, nutrient cost, and effects on gastrointestinal function. In V. K. Rustgi & J. N. Cooper (Eds.), *Gastrointestinal and hepatic complications in pregnancy.* New York: John Wiley & Sons.

275. Vanderhoof, J. A., & Paykey-Hunter, R. J. (2016). Gastrointestinal disease. In M. G. MacDonald & M. M. K. Seshia (Eds.), *Avery's Neonatology, pathophysiology and management of the newborn* (7th ed.). Philadelphia: Wolters Kluwer.

276. Vasquez, J. C. (2015). Heartburn in pregnancy. *Clinical Evidence, 9,* 1.

277. Vedmedovska, N., et al. (2011). Placental pathology in fetal growth restriction. *Eur J Obstet Gynecol Reprod Biol, 155,* 36.

278. Verberg, M. E., et al. (2005). Hyperemesis gravidarum, a literature review. *Hum Reprod Update, 1,* 527.

279. Vidakovic, A. J., et al. (2015). Body mass index, gestational weight gain and fatty acid concentrations during pregnancy: the generation R study. *Eur J Epidemiol, 30,* 1175.

280. Villar, J., et al. (2016). INTERGROWTH-21st: very preterm size at birth reference charts. *Lancet, 387,* 844.

281. Vinter, C. A., et al. (2014). Postpartum weight retention and breastfeeding among obese women from the randomized controlled lifestyle in pregnancy (LiP) trial. *Acta Obstetricia et Gynecologica Scandinavica, 93,* 794.

282. Vlaardingerbroek, H., et al. (2013). Safety and efficacy of early parenteral lipid and high-dose amino acid administration to very low birth weight infants. *J Pediatr, 163,* 638.

283. Vutyavanich, T., et al. (2001). Ginger for nausea and vomiting in pregnancy: Randomized, double-masked, placebo-controlled trial. *Obstet Gynecol, 97,* 577.

284. Walker, I., Chappell, L. C., & Williamson, C. (2013). Abnormal liver function tests in pregnancy. *BMJ, 347,* f6055.

285. Walker, W. A. (2000). Role of nutrients and bacterial colonization in the development of intestinal host defense. *J Pediatr Gastroenterol Nutr, 30,* S2.

286. Weaver, L. T. (1993). Development of bowel habit in preterm infants. *Arch Dis Child, 68,* 317.

287. Wells, J. C. (2011). The thrifty phenotype: An adaptation in growth or metabolism? *Am J Hum Biol, 23,* 65.

288. Widen, E. M., & Gallagher, D. (2014). Body composition changes in pregnancy: measurement, predictors and outcomes. *Eur J Clin Nutri, 68,* 643.

289. William, C. B., Mackenzie, K. C., & Gahagan, S. (2014). The effect of maternal obesity on the offspring. *Clin Obstet Gynecol, 57,* 508.

290. Williamson, C., et al. (2014). Diseases of the liver, biliary system, and pancreas. In R. K. Creasy, et al. (Eds.), *Creasy & Resnik's Maternal-fetal medicine: Principles and practice* (7th ed.). Philadelphia: Saunders.

291. Wong, C. A., et al. (2007). Gastric emptying of water in obese pregnant women at term. *Anesth Analg, 105,* 751.

292. Wu, M., Chen, S.W., & Jiang, S.Y. (2015). Relationship between gingival inflammation and pregnancy. Hindawi Publishing Corporation: *Mediators of Inflammation, 2015,* 623427. Epub 2015 Mar 22.

293. Xiao, R. S., et al. (2014). The impact of sleep, stress, and depression on postpartum weight retention: a systematic review (2014). *J Psychosom Res, 77,* 351.

294. Xiong, X., et al. (2011). Optimal timing of periodontal disease treatment for prevention of adverse pregnancy outcomes before or during pregnancy? *Am J Obstet Gynecol, 205,* e1–6.

295. Yan, S., et al. (2015). Pre-pregnancy body mass index, gestational weight gain, and birth weight: a cohort study in China. *J PLoS ONE, 10,* e1.

296. Yeung, M. Y., & Smyth, J. P. (2003). Nutritionally regulated hormonal factors in prolonged postnatal growth retardation and its associated adverse neurodevelopmental outcome in extreme prematurity. *Biol Neonate, 84,* 1.

297. Yost, C. C. (2005). Neonatal necrotizing enterocolitis: Diagnosis, management, and pathogenesis. *J Infus Nurs, 28,* 130.

298. Ziegler, E. E. (2014). Human milk and human milk fortifiers. *World Rev Nutr Diet, 110,* 215.

Immune System and Host Defense Mechanisms

"Remarkable adaptations . . . allow a genetically and antigenically disparate conceptus to develop in direct contact with a fully competent maternal immune system."[99] Why doesn't the mother reject the fetus and placenta? Knowledge of maternal, fetal, and neonatal immune physiology and understanding of the immune relationship between a mother and her fetus are still evolving. Current theories regarding this question—along with alterations in host defense mechanisms in the mother and neonate and implications for clinical practice—are examined in this chapter.

The immune system is made up of organs and specialized cells whose primary purpose is to defend the body from foreign substances (antigens) that may cause tissue injury or disease. These defense mechanisms consist of nonspecific and specific factors. Nonspecific factors include physical and biochemical barriers including skin and mucosal barriers; bone marrow; lymphoid tissue; digestive enzymes; pH; temperature; proteins; and enzymes such as lysozyme, transferrin, and interferon. Specific factors include cellular and humoral components that respond to foreign substances. In addition, individual genetic susceptibilities affect both nonspecific factors and specific factors. Nonspecific and specific factors make up two arms of the immune response—the innate (also known as *natural* or *native immunity*) and the adaptive (also known as *specific* or *acquired immunity*). Mechanisms of innate and adaptive immunity work cooperatively through complex interactions to prevent, control, and eradicate foreign antigens in the body without doing harm to the host. Host immune mechanisms and terminology are summarized in Box 13-1.

MATERNAL PHYSIOLOGIC ADAPTATIONS

During pregnancy the maternal immune system is adapted to protect both the mother and fetus.[116,133] Within adaptive responses, the cell-mediated (T helper 1, or Th1) response is reduced, the antibody-mediated (T helper 2, or Th2) response is enhanced, and the relation between the two is dysregulated. These alterations, which help prevent the mother's immune system from rejecting the semiallogenic fetus, increase her risk of developing certain infections and influence the course of chronic disorders such as autoimmune diseases. Because changes in both innate and adaptive immune responses occur, pregnancy is not a state of immunosuppression, but rather a "modulated immunologic condition."[80] In general, immune function in pregnant women is similar to immune function in nonpregnant women. The most significant changes in the immune system during pregnancy occur at the maternal-fetal interface.[153] The maternal and fetal-placental immune systems work together to provide support and protection for the fetus.[80] "The uniqueness of the immune system during pregnancy is the interaction between the maternal immune system (characterized by a reinforced network of recognition, communication, trafficking, and repair) and the presence of a developing active fetal immune system that can modify maternal response to the environment."[146]

Antepartum Period

During pregnancy, especially in the second and third trimesters, activity of monocytes, phagocytes, dendritic cells (DC), and polymorphonuclear neutrophils (PMN) increases, as do levels of α-defensins and regulatory T (Treg) cells, while activity of CD4$^+$, CD8$^+$, natural killer (NK) cells, NK cytotoxicity, and possibly B cells decreases.[80] Four stages of maternal immunologic adaptation have been described: (1) initiation (during implantation, placentation, and the first and early second trimesters), (2) tolerance (second and third trimesters), (3) activation (later third trimester and parturition), and (4) restoration (postpartum).[105,146] Figure 13-1 illustrates and describes these stages. The first and third stages are predominately proinflammatory stages (influenced by Th1 responses). During stage 1 the embryo is implanting, followed by movement of fetal trophoblast cells into the endometrium to remodel maternal spiral arteries (see Chapter 3); parturition occurs in stage 3, and inflammatory changes are needed for myometrial contraction (see Chapter 4).[105] Stage 2 is predominately antiinflammatory (influenced by Th2 responses).[105] Immunologic changes during pregnancy are protective rather than suppressive and mediated by factors such as progesterone, estradiol, cytokines, and chemokines.[80,146,148] The immune changes that occur systemically in the maternal innate and adaptive systems and those that occur at the site of the fetal-maternal interface are described in this section.

BOX 13-1   Definitions of Terms

Active immunity: Response after exposure to foreign antigens (bacteria, viruses, attenuated, or inactivated or killed viruses).

Adaptive (acquired) immunity: The result of active immunity with establishment of memory cells and antibodies that provide immunity during subsequent exposures to a specific antigen.

Antibody: Proteins (immunoglobulins) that react with specific antigens. Five classes of antibodies are IgA, IgD, IgE, IgG, and IgM.

Antibody (humoral)-mediated immunity: Adaptive immune mechanism mediated by B cells, which produces antibodies and protects the body from extracellular antigens.

Antigen: Substances perceived by one's host defense mechanisms as "foreign" (may include bacteria, viruses, pollutants, dust, certain foods, for example).

Antigen presenting cell (APC): Cells displaying MHC antigen complexes on the surface of the cell that can activate immune system cells. DCs, PMN, NK, B lymphocytes, endothelial, mucosal epithelia cells can act as APCs. APCs process antigens and present them to T cells to initiate adaptive immune responses.

Cell-mediated immunity: Adaptive immune mechanism provided by immune cells. T-helper, T-cytotoxic, and T-regulatory cells provide protection against certain organisms, regulate B-cell function, defend against cancer, and mediate graft rejection.

Chemokines: A subtype of cytokines that induce chemotaxis in surrounding cells.

Chemotaxis: Movement of neutrophils and other phagocytes in an organized fashion toward a site of antigenic invasion.

Complement: Thirty discrete plasma proteins that function in a cascade of reactions that form membrane attack complexes that lyse cells, opsonize antigen, increase vascular permeability, and stimulate chemotaxis to aid phagocytosis. The complement cascade can proceed via the classical pathway or alternate pathway.

Cytokines: Glycoproteins such as lymphokines, ILs, IFN, and TNF that are produced by immune system components, especially T cells and macrophages. Cytokines function as autocrine or paracrine agents to activate different arms of the immune response. Proinflammatory cytokines include TNF, IL-1, IL-6, IL-8, IL-12, and IFN-γ. Antiinflammatory cytokines include IL-10, IL-4, and IL-11.

Cytotoxic/killer T cell: Type of T lymphocyte that acts directly on specific antigens or target cells that exhibit a specific antigen and induces cell lysis.

Dendritic cell (DC): Antigen processing and presenting cells involved in initiating adaptive immunity and development of tolerance and immunologic memory. The myeloid or conventional DC (mDC) is proinflammatory cytokine; the plasmacytoid DC (pDC) is involved in immune tolerance and antiviral activities.

Fibronectin: Nonspecific opsonin, inhibitor of bacterial adherence to epithelial cells, and clot-stabilizing protein found in plasma and endothelial tissue.

Human leukocyte antigen (HLA): The major forms of specific tissue antigens found on tissue surfaces that are unique to each person (includes HLA-A, HLA-B, HLA-C, HLA-D, and in the placenta HLA-G).

Immunoglobulin: Antibodies produced by B lymphocytes, including IgA, IgD, IgE, IgG, and IgM.

Innate immunity: Initial physical and nonspecific responses that eliminate foreign substances or antigen and stimulation of the adaptive immune response. Primary effectors are polymorphonuclear neutrophils (PMNs), macrophages, monocytes, mast cells, NK cells, and complement.

Interleukin: A polypeptide cytokine (produced by T cells, APCs, NK cells, and macrophages) that regulates and facilitates immune responses.

Interferon: Glycoprotein cytokine whose primary role is in fighting viral infections.

Lymphokine: Subclass of cytokines. Mediators released by activated T cells that facilitate or act as costimulatory agents for immune reaction.

Memory cell: Lymphocyte sensitized to specific antigens that can produce specific antibodies with subsequent stimulation by the specific antigen.

Major histocompatibility complex (MHC): Specific antigens found on tissue surfaces divided into two groups: MHC I (HLA-A, HLA-B, and HLA-C, which are found on most cells) and MHC II (found on the surface of immune cells such as T and B lymphocytes).

Natural killer (NK) cells: Type of lymphocytes that are a first line of defense (innate immunity) against cells infected with a virus and cancerous cells. NK cells have receptors that recognize MHC I antigens and can attack without prior sensitization. NKs secrete cytokines that provide costimulation for T and B cells. NK subsets include endometrial NK cells, seen during the menstrual cycle, and decidual NK cells (dNK), which are seen during pregnancy and are critical for pregnancy maintenance.

Opsonization: Processing and marking or altering the cell surface of an antigen by actions of immunoglobulin or complement; substances acting in this manner are called opsonins. This process is critical in allowing phagocytosis of organisms with capsular polysaccharide coats such as group B streptococci.

Pattern recognition receptors (PRR): Initiate intracellular signaling, leading to innate responses and priming of adaptive immunity. PRRs such as TLRs are found on cell surfaces, in intracellular vesicles, or in cytoplasm. PRRs recognize damaging molecular patterns such as cytokines, intracellular proteins, and substances released by damaged cells; pathogen-associated molecular patterns (PAMPS) and danger-associated molecular patterns (DAMPS) are produced by infected or injured cells.[64,173]

Passive immunity: Transfer of antibodies from an actively immunized to a nonimmunized person.

Plasma cell: Form of B lymphocyte able to secrete immunoglobulins.

Regulatory T cell (Treg): A subset of T cells important for immunotolerance and limiting excessive immune responses; may help slow or terminate immune response once antigens are destroyed. Treg cells are also involved in inhibiting the immune response in the placenta at the fetal-maternal interface.

T helper cell: A type of T lymphocyte that proliferates when in contact with an APC that exhibits MHC II/antigen complexes (B cells, DCs). TCD4$^+$ cells differentiate into Th1 or Th2 cells based on the cytokines produced. Th1 cells participate in cell-mediated immunity; Th2 cells participate in antibody-mediated immunity. These cells thus enhance the activity of B lymphocytes, other T cells, and macrophages via secretion of cytokines. Th17 is a T helper subset that acts primarily at mucosal barriers.

T suppressor cells: T lymphocytes that express CD8$^+$ cells and function to suppress the cellular immune response.

Th1 cells: A subset of T-helper cells that facilitates cell-mediated immunity via secretion of IL-12, TNF-β, and IFN-γ. The result is stimulation of macrophages and inflammation.

Th2 cells: A subset of TCD4$^+$ (T-helper cells) that facilitates antibody-mediated immunity via secretion of IL-4, IL-5, IL-12, and IL-13. The result is stimulation of B cells and production of antibodies.

Toll-like receptors (TLRs): Molecules on the surface of phagocytes and other cells that recognize the patterns of microbial products and generate signals to activate an innate immune response.

DC, Dendritic cells; *IFN,* interferon; *IL,* interleukin; *MHC,* major histocompatibility complex; *PMN,* polymorphonuclear neutrophils; *NK,* natural killer; *TLR,* toll-like receptor; *TNF-β,* tumor necrosis factor-β.

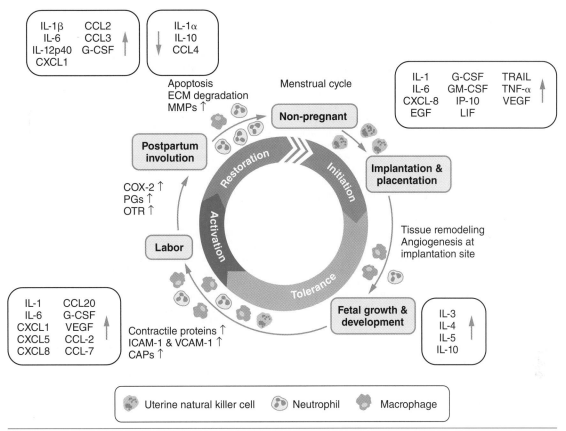

FIGURE 13-1   Gestational transformation of the maternal immune system. Phase 1 ("initiation") includes implantation, placentation, and the first and early second trimester of pregnancy, which resembles "an open wound" that requires a strong proinflammatory response. Cytokines released mainly by trophoblasts and uterine natural killer cells govern tissue remodeling and angiogenesis at the implantation site. Phase 2 ("tolerance") is a period of rapid fetal growth and development. The mother, placenta, and fetus are symbiotic; the predominant immunologic feature is antiinflammatory. During this phase of pregnancy, progesterone maintains uterine quiescence. Phase 3 ("activation") is characterized by an influx of immune cells into the myometrium to trigger the reactivation of an inflammatory cascade. Myometrial cytokines activate the endothelial adhesion molecules for leukocyte infiltration. Uterine contractility is enhanced through the action of oxytocin and the increased production of prostaglandins via cyclooxygenase 2 (COX-2). The last phase is postpartum uterine involution ("restoration"), which completes the reproductive cycle after pregnancy and labor. It is considered a proinflammatory phase and characterized by massive infiltration of immune cells, mostly neutrophils. (From Shynlova, O., Lee, Y.L., Srikhajon, K., & Lye, S.J. [2013]. Physiologic uterine inflammation: integration of endocrine and mechanical signals. *Reprod Sci, 20,* 154.)

Alterations in Innate Immunity

Mediators of the innate response are altered during pregnancy (innate immunity is summarized in Box 13-2). Chemotaxis (see the definition in Box 13-1) is decreased during pregnancy, which may delay initial maternal responses to infection.[105] In addition, production of interferon-γ (IFN—γ) is decreased.[153] Functionally, monocyte and granulocyte activity is enhanced, which results in faster and more efficient phagocytosis. This may help protect the mother so she does not mount a cell-mediated immune response to trophoblastic and fetal cells that appear in the maternal circulation.[153] NK cell activity is altered in a more complex manner. Systemic NK activity is downregulated during pregnancy, secondary to the effects of progesterone, with a shift toward NK2 cells (which produce type 2 cytokines).[39,153] Systemic NK cytolytic activity is normal in the first trimester but lower during the second and third trimesters and immediately after delivery.[105,153]

Total white blood cell (WBC) volume increases slightly beginning in the second month and levels off during the second and third trimesters. The total WBC count in pregnancy varies among individual women, ranging from 5000 to 12,000 per mm³, with values as high as 15,000 per mm³ reported (see Chapter 8).[130] The increase is primarily related to increased numbers of PMNs, nonclassic monocytes (which tend to be more proinflammatory), and granulocytes.[130,153] Classic monocytes, NK cells, and Treg cells in maternal circulation are decreased, possibly because of enhancement and increases of these cells at the maternal-fetal interface (see Immune Function at the Fetal-Maternal Interface).[153] A slight shift to the left may occur, with occasional myelocytes and metamyelocytes seen on the peripheral

BOX 13-2   Overview of Innate Immunity

The innate immune response, which includes inflammation, lysis of an antigen's cell membrane, and phagocytosis, is the first-line defense mechanism that comes into play after exposure to a foreign antigen.[1,105] The innate immune response also has a crucial role in the activation of adaptive immune responses. Innate immunity involves nonspecific inborn responses to a foreign antigen that are activated the first time the antigen is encountered. These defense mechanisms occur rapidly in response to microbes.[1] Important characteristics of innate immunity include the following: (1) prior exposure to the antigen is not required for a response to occur; (2) repeated exposures to an antigen over time will not alter the host's innate immune response (i.e., immune responses do not become more vigorous); and (3) the immune system is able to recognize molecular patterns shared by groups of microbes, but unable to recognize fine distinctions between the microbes.[1] Innate immunity involves physical (e.g., epithelia, mucous membranes, secretions) and biochemical barriers.

Primary effector cells of an innate immune response are polymorphonuclear neutrophils (PMN), macrophages, monocytes, mast cells, and natural killer (NK) cells.[105] Pattern recognition receptors (PRR) on cell surfaces (responsible for recognizing the molecular patterns of microbial products), endothelial cells, circulating factors (e.g., complement and acute-phase proteins such as C-reactive protein), along with cytokines and chemokines, which are secreted by macrophages and other cells, are actively involved in mediating the innate immune response and engaging the adaptive immune response.[1,105] Cytokines and other factors can generate either proinflammatory or antiinflammatory environments.

PRRs include toll-like receptors (TLRs) and nucleotide-binding oligomerization domain (NOD) proteins. TLRs and NODs are used by monocytes, macrophages, PMNs, and dendritic cells (DCs) to recognize one's own self from microbes and other foreign substances and induce expression of cytokines and chemokines to activate defensive cells.[64,110] PRRs are found on cell surfaces, in intracellular vesicles, or in the cytoplasm. PRRs can recognize damaging molecular patterns such as cytokines, intracellular proteins, and substances released by damaged cells; pathogen-associated molecular patterns (PAMPS) and danger-associated molecular patterns (DAMPS) are produced by infected or injured cells.[64,173] Pathogens bind to TLR and other receptors on monocytes and macrophages, initiating a complement cascade with release of prostaglandins (which mediate fever with bacterial pathogens). The transcription factor nuclear factor-κ-B (NF-κB) is released, which stimulates synthesis and release of both proinflammatory (such as IL-1B, IL-6, and TNF-α) and antiinflammatory cytokines (such as IL-1 and IL-10).[151] DCs link innate and adaptive immunity.[12] DCs, macrophages, and B lymphocytes act as antigen presenting cells (APC) to process antigens for T lymphocytes.

IL, Interleukin; *TNF,* tumor necrosis factor.

---

smear. Changes in other WBC forms are minimal (see Chapter 8).

Alterations in PMN function have been reported with increased production of oxygen radicals and phagocytic activity.[153] PMN attachment, ingestion, and digestion of *Candida albicans* have been found to be increased, possibly secondary to the effects of human chorionic gonadotropin (hCG). Even so, pregnant women have higher rates of fungal infection, which may be secondary to the effects of estrogen on nutrient availability for fungal growth in the reproductive tract.[130] Estrogens may alter local mucosal barrier function, allowing adherence of pathogenic organisms and increasing the risk of colonization. Conversely, improved PMN antibody expression during pregnancy may enhance phagocyte recognition and destruction of antigen-antibody complexes.

DCs are antigen presenting cells (APCs) that link innate and adaptive systems. DCs decrease during pregnancy but show increased tolerance–associated molecules.[153] The mDC type is proinflammatory, whereas pDCs are involved in maintaining tolerance and antiviral protection. The main decidual DCs are mDC and are believed to regulate Th1/Th2 balance to maintain an increased Th2 influence.[26] Toll-like receptors (TLR) and other pattern recognition receptors (PRR) such as nodlike receptors (NLR) are essential for the innate recognition of microorganisms and endogenous signals from tissue breakdown products, such as fetal fibronectin, hyaluronan, matrix proteins, and biglycans.[29,105] Both TLRs and NLRs are involved in regulating innate responses of the trophoblast to infections and tissue damage signals.[105,153] Changes in the cervix and fetal membranes with tissue remodeling near parturition may release these endogenous signals as part of the cascade leading to labor onset (Chapter 4).[29]

Alterations in the Complement System

The complement system has a role in both innate and adaptive responses. Pregnancy stimulates an overall activation of the complement system.[132] Alterations in the function of the complement system during pregnancy begin at 11 weeks' gestation with an increase (because of greater hepatic synthesis) in both total serum complement and specific proteins of the complement system, including C2, C3, and C3 split products.[94,132] These components enhance chemotaxis and actions of immunoglobulins through opsonization, thereby augmenting maternal defenses against bacterial infection. Other protein fragments of the complement system, such as C1, C1a, B, and D, are decreased.[132] C1q (involved in activation of the classic complement pathway, immune cell modification, cell processes, and maintenance of immune tolerance) is synthesized and secreted by decidual epithelial cells during pregnancy and is believed to have a role in changes in decidual blood vessels (see Chapter 3) and mediation of cell-to-cell interaction between decidual and trophoblast cells.[116]

Alterations in Adaptive Immunity

Pregnancy is characterized by changes in the balance of Th1 and Th2 cell subsets that result in enhanced Th2 function. This change is probably mediated by progesterone, which stimulates production of Th2 cytokines (e.g., IL-3, IL-4, IL-6, and IL-10)

not significantly affected at the systemic level.[39] Failure of Th2 responses to increase or of Th1 responses to decrease is associated with an increased risk of recurrent abortion.[21]

Maternal and Placental Microbiome

The maternal microbiome changes during pregnancy, with changes in the microbial composition and number in the gut, vagina, oral cavity, and placenta.[117] Less diversity is seen in both the vaginal and intestinal/fecal microbiomes.[57,79,109] With increasing gestation gut microbes change with a decrease in proinflammatory and an increase in antiinflammatory species.[79] The changes in gut microbiota during gestation have been shown in animal studies to increase energy uptake.[79,109] Transfer of these organisms to the fetus with birth (see Intestinal Colonization on pp. 454-455), and possibly prior to birth, may enhance energy stores immediately after birth.[109] Vaginal lactobacilli with its antiinfective metabolic products also increases during gestation. This increase may limit diversity of bacteria and help protect the fetus from ascending infections.[109]

The maternal microbiome is an important source of signals for development of the fetal and neonatal immune system and later health outcomes.[57,65,79] Recently, a placental microbiome has been described. Aerobic and anaerobic organisms are found in the placenta, which had been thought to be sterile except for pathogenic infections.[117] The source of these organisms is probably the material gut, vagina, and oral cavity. The roles of the placental microbiome and interactions with maternal and fetal systems are not well understood. Alterations have been reported with pregnancy complications such as preterm birth, chorioamnionitis, preeclampsia, and gestational diabetes.[117]

Transplacental Passage of Maternal Antibodies

Both protective and potentially damaging maternal antibodies cross the placenta. Maternal IgG antibodies are the only ones to cross in significant amounts. IgG has a specific carrier that facilitates active placental transport. Maternal antibody has multiple functions in the fetus and neonate, including passive immunity against pathogens, epigenetic inheritance of immunologic memory, immunologic imprinting, suppression of immunoglobulin E (IgE) responsiveness, and suppression of tumor development.[91]

Fetal levels of IgG are low until 20 to 22 weeks' gestation, when passive and active transfer of IgG across the placenta increases.[37,161] Fetal IgG is 5% to 10% of maternal levels at 17 to 22 weeks, increasing to 50% at 28 to 32 weeks.[122] Most transfer occurs during the last 4 weeks of gestation, with fetal values exceeding maternal values by term.[32,37,78,122] All four IgG subclasses cross, although the IgG_1 and IgG_3 subclasses predominate and are transferred more efficiently.[37,161] A carrier attached to a syncytiotrophoblast surface receptor (called neonatal FC receptor or FcRn) that is specific for the Fc fragments of IgG (and does not bind to other immunoglobulins that lack Fc) mediates active transfer of IgG across

the placenta.[15,37,62,161] FcRn expression increases in the third trimester, reducing transfer in very-low-birth-weight infants born in the late second or early third trimester.[122] FcRn has the greatest affinity for IgG_1 and IgG_3, followed by IgG_4 with low affinity for IgG_2; the receptor has no affinity for IgM or IgA.[46,84,122] Active transfer allows for movement of IgG to the fetus even when maternal levels are low.[15] IgG is transferred by endocytosis through the syncytiotrophoblast (IgG binds to FcRn in the endosome for transport, which protects the IgG from degradation by lysosomal enzymes, and is released on the fetal side).[47,122]

IgG_1 crosses as early as 13 weeks and is the primary immunoglobulin transferred before 28 weeks.[47,122] IgG_3 crosses later and does not reach maternal levels until after 32 to 33 weeks.[84] IgG_2 levels remain below maternal levels.[37] IgG levels are lower in preterm infants as well as in low-birth-weight term infants, who have decreased transfer efficiency in all IgG subclasses and impaired transfer of IgG_1 and IgG2.[122] IgG transfer is also impaired in infants of mothers with malaria and human immunodeficiency virus (HIV).[47,122] Depending on maternal antibody complement, the newborn may have passive immunity against tetanus, diphtheria, polio, measles, mumps, group B streptococcus (GBS), *Escherichia coli*, hepatitis B virus (HBV), *Salmonella enterica*, and other pathogens.

Protection of the Fetus From Infection

Most pathogenic viruses and many bacteria are capable of being transferred across the placenta, although relatively few are.[15] Immune factors that promote maternal tolerance of the fetus also protect the placenta from infectious agents.[2,77,153] Innate immune system cells at the fetal-maternal interface express TLR, NOD, and other receptors that assist the trophoblast in recognizing microorganisms, as well as signals from the mother, so a localized immune response can be initiated.[26,77,105]

All known TLRs found in humans are expressed in the placenta, primarily in the trophoblast.[105] The TLR and NOD expression and function vary with gestational age.[77,105,134] Each TLR is specific for the molecular pattern of certain organisms. For example, TLR-4 has a receptor for gram-negative bacterial lipopolysaccharide; TLR-3 binds double-stranded viral deoxyribonucleic acid (DNA). TLR-3, TLR-7, and TLR-8 have roles in responses to viruses; TLR-5 senses bacterial flagellin, TLR-2 responds to gram-negative bacteria, and TLR-9 to HSV.[77] TLRs help the trophoblast to recognize microorganisms. TLR simulation initiates an inflammatory response with upregulation of cytokines, interferon, antimicrobial proteins, and peptides.[173] The trophoblast also secretes various antimicrobial factors to inhibit infectivity, recruit monocytes and macrophages, and prevent transmission to the fetus.[105]

Aggressive microorganism invasion may overcome these defenses and lead to fetal infection and preterm labor.[105] Ascending infection can result in a maternal immune response, production of PMNs in the amniotic fluid, and a fetal inflammatory response (FIRS).[58,76,173] FIRS is associated with release of proinflammatory cytokines affecting the cardiovascular and central nervous systems with an increased risk of later neurologic, and possibly allergic, disorders.[105] Altered TLR signal transduction is seen with preterm labor, preeclampsia, and intrauterine growth restriction.[76,105,134]

Occasionally organisms may reach the fetus by directly infecting placental tissue. Once the organism avoids cytokines at the maternal-placental interface, it must interact with trophoblast receptors to pass through the placental stroma and enter fetal blood. The primary placental defense is the Hofbauer (macrophage) cells. The placenta also contains phagocytes and lymphocytes and produces cytokines such as interferon.[39] The organisms most commonly transferred across the placenta are *Listeria monocytogenes, Treponema pallidum,* HIV, parvovirus B19, rubella, *Toxoplasma gondii,* and cytomegalovirus (CMV).[113]

Amniotic fluid contains antibacterial and other protective substances similar to many of those found in human milk. These substances include transferrin, beta-lysin, peroxidase, fatty acids, IgG, IgA, and lysozyme.[71,105] The antibacterial capacity of amniotic fluid improves with advancing gestation. Additionally, the fetal membranes provide barrier protection against ascending infection, although some organisms can penetrate intact membranes. Pathogenic organisms may enter the fetus via the respiratory tract, where surfactant protein (SP)-A and SP-D, alveolar macrophages, and PMNs provide additional defenses.[167,173,174]

Intrapartum Period

Initiation of labor, cervical ripening, membrane rupture, and myometrial contractility involve an inflammatory process (see Chapter 4).[29] Innate immune cells such as macrophages, dendritic cells, NK cells, and mast cells have roles in the onset of labor.[82] During labor and in the early postpartum period, the WBC count increases to values of up to 25,000 to 30,000 per mm[3]. This increase is primarily a result of an increase in neutrophils and may represent a normal response to physiologic stress.[33] Impairment in the functional activity of peripheral blood lymphocytes and a decrease in the absolute number of total CD4[+] and CD8[+] lymphocytes may be observed immediately after birth. Cytokines also have a role in the initiation of labor (see Chapter 4) and in reversing the pregnancy-induced reduction of maternal immune responsiveness at the decidual-trophoblast barrier during labor and birth.[51] For example, IL-1 and IL-6 also increase with the onset of labor. TNF-α may assist in the initiation of contractions. IFN-γ may play a role in placental separation via activation of NK cells.[51]

Labor also has an effect on the fetal immune system. Labor alters neonatal neutrophil responses (see Neonatal Physiology). For example, newborns born vaginally exhibit leukocytosis, elevation of neutrophil count, and delayed apoptosis compared with infants born by cesarean section. These changes may be immunologically beneficial to the fetus.[103]

Postpartum Period

It is unclear how quickly the immune system returns to prepregnant function after delivery, with various studies reporting timelines from a few weeks to 3 to 9 months because of differences in measurement techniques.[152] The WBC count, which increases in labor and immediately after birth, gradually returns to normal values by 4 to 7 days. Progenitor cells from the fetus can be found in maternal tissue for many years postpartum.[110]

Immunologic Properties of Human Milk

The newborn is immunologically immature and therefore vulnerable to infection. Human milk contains many immunologic components, including leukocytes, immunoglobulins, oligosaccharides, monoglycerides, fatty acids, and other peptides and proteins (see Table 5-3) that inhibit inflammation and enhance production of adaptive immune responses.[70] Immunologic benefits for the breastfeeding infant include lowered risk of developing asthma, cow's milk allergy, food allergy, gastrointestinal (GI) and respiratory infections, necrotizing enterocolitis, diabetes mellitus, and some immune disorders such as Crohn's disease, celiac disease, and multiple sclerosis.[48,91]

The leukocytes in human milk are primarily monocytic macrophages (85% to 90%) and lymphocytes (10% to 15%), with some neutrophils and epithelial cells.[48,70] Breast milk immune cells contain PRRs such as TLR-2 and TLR-4 that help with recognition of bacteria and viruses.[11] Lower TLR-2 at birth may facilitate establishment of normal intestinal microbiota.[11] Monocytic macrophages in human milk synthesize complement, lysozyme, and lactoferrin; transport immunoglobulin; and protect against necrotizing enterocolitis. These cells also have phagocytic activity against *Staphylococcus aureus, E. coli,* and *C. albicans* and may help regulate T cell function.[70]

Similar concentrations of B and T lymphocytes are found in breast milk. B lymphocytes in human milk produce IgA, IgG, and IgM. IgM levels are highest in colostrum, decrease after 5 days, and then remain constant for at least 180 days.[15] Levels of secretory IgG in human milk are also consistent for at least the first 180 days. T cells produce interferon, macrophage migration-inhibiting factor (MIF), and other cytokines. Because the neonate's own T cells are functionally immature, human milk may provide significant protection against gram-negative organisms. Human milk often contains antibodies against the O and K antigens of several *E. coli* serotypes, including K1, which has been associated with neonatal meningitis.

The immunoglobulin found in highest concentrations (90%) in colostrum and human milk is secretory IgA (sIgA).[11] sIGA has antimicrobial, antiinflammatory, and immunoregulatory roles.[70] Levels of sIgA are highest in colostrum, fall gradually until 12 weeks, and then remain stable for the next 2 years of lactation.[11,57,70] The secretory component attached to the IgA monomer protects the IgA molecule from proteolytic digestion in the GI tract. sIgA does not enter the circulation from the gut but provides localized barrier protection by attaching to the mucosal epithelium and preventing attachment and invasion by specific infectious agents.[57,70] sIgA also neutralizes certain viruses and bacterial enterotoxins and inhibits intestinal absorption of proteins and other macromolecules found in foods.[57,70] The latter function may provide protection against the development of allergies. sIgA actions are enhanced by complement.

Human milk contains C3 and C4 and produces complement by the alternative pathway, which can be activated by factors such as bacterial products and circulating proteins. Most of the immunoglobulins in human milk are produced by sensitized antibody cells in the breast that have been transported to that site from gut-associated (i.e., maternal intestinal) lymphatic tissue and bronchotracheal-associated lymphatic tissue. Thus sIgA that is specific for a wide variety of respiratory and enteric bacterial and viral organisms can be found in human milk.[15] Depending on the mother's immunologic experience, the immunoglobulins in human milk may provide the infant with protection against pathogens such as diphtheria, pertussis, *Shigella, Salmonella,* poliovirus, and echoviruses.

Human milk contains other nonspecific protective factors that act synergistically with each other and sIgA to provide immunity to the newborn.[15,87,173] Lactoferrin, α-lactalbumin, and sIgA form the major whey proteins in human milk and constitute 60% to 80% of total human milk protein. Lactoferrin is an iron-binding protein that restricts the availability of iron needed for growth by certain fungi and bacteria such as *S. aureus* and *E. coli.*[12] Folic acid and vitamin B_{12}–binding protein restrict available folate and vitamin B_{12} for bacterial and fungal growth.

Lysozyme is a bactericidal enzyme that lyses the cell walls of many bacteria and enhances *Lactobacillus* growth. Levels of lysozyme in human milk are several hundred times higher than in cow's milk. Lactoperoxidase inhibits bacterial growth and bifidus factor, a nitrogen-containing polysaccharide, and promotes growth of anaerobic lactobacilli that compete with invasive gram-negative organisms. This factor also limits growth of *Shigella* and *Salmonella.* Lysozyme also acts with other substances to destroy *E. coli* and some strains of *Salmonella.* Factors in human milk that promote lactobacilli growth include lactose, low pH, and buffers.

Human milk oligosaccharides are complex carbohydrates that prevent attachment of bacteria and other antigens to gut epithelial receptors. Oligosaccharides are the third largest component of human milk and act as prebiotics and immune modulators, enhance growth of beneficial intestinal bacteria, and protect the gut from colonization by pathogenic organisms.[11,87] Other immune components of human milk include MIF, antiviral and antistaphylococcal factors, interferon (which prevents viral replication), and lipase (which increases levels of free fatty acids and monoglycerides that may act against certain viruses).[87] Human milk acetic and lactic acid are two byproducts of breast milk digestion in the gut. These acids decrease stool pH and inhibit growth of *Shigella*

and *E. coli.* In addition, human milk can induce the production of immune factors such as sIgA by the infant. Maternal T cells in breast milk stimulate development of immune cells in the newborn thymus; thus the thymus gland of a breastfed infant is larger than the thymus in an infant receiving formula.[48]

In preterm infants, human milk may have a critical role in providing protection against infection and the development of allergies. The preterm infant's gastrointestinal tract lacks many intrinsic local host defense factors, including sIgA, lysozyme, and gastric acid. In addition, the intestinal mucosal barrier function is more immature (see Gut Host Defense Mechanisms).[70] As a result, the preterm infant is at higher risk for bacterial penetration through the intestines and development of sepsis and necrotizing enterocolitis compared with term infants. The lack of sIgA and immaturity of the intestinal mucosa increase the likelihood of foreign macromolecules entering the circulation, which may increase the risk of allergies in genetically susceptible infants.[70] Human milk may enhance maturation of the intestinal mucosal barrier, thereby reducing the risk of both infections and allergies. Increased levels of sIgA, lactoferrin, and lysozyme have been found in milk from mothers of preterm infants.[70] Thus mothers of preterm infants may have an important immune adaptation that provides additional protection for their infants.

CLINICAL IMPLICATIONS FOR THE PREGNANT WOMAN AND HER FETUS

Disruption and dysfunction of the immune system can result in disease processes (e.g., type 1 diabetes mellitus, rheumatoid arthritis, systemic lupus erythematosus [SLE], and Graves' disease), the course of which can be influenced by pregnancy. In addition, immune dysfunction during pregnancy can be manifest in several ways that can adversely affect the outcome for the mother and her infant. For example, conditions such as infertility, spontaneous abortion, preeclampsia, and blood incompatibilities can be linked to immune dysfunction in the pregnant woman and fetus/neonate. Changes in maternal immune function during pregnancy can alter the course of preexisting disorders of the immune system and facilitate the development of some complications of pregnancy. Implications of these changes are reviewed in this section along with issues related to maternal-fetal interactions and immunization during pregnancy.

Spontaneous Abortion

There are multiple causes for spontaneous abortion. Immunologic factors include activation of an immune response secondary to microbial infection (e.g., chlamydia, listeriosis, parvovirus B19, or toxoplasmosis), an exaggerated maternal immune response to trophoblastic invasion (e.g., predominance of Th1 reactivity), a cytokine-induced failure of the ovary to produce sufficient progesterone, and the presence of autoimmune antibodies such as antiphospholipid antibodies that interfere with placentation.[137,169] Increased Th17 levels and decreased Treg cells in the decidua are also associated with unexplained recurrent abortion (Th17 promotes inflammation, transplant rejection, and autoimmunity).[85] Decreased expression of HLA-G on the extravillous trophoblast is seen in some women with recurrent abortion and is associated with altered conversion of the spiral arteries.[135,169] Decreased sHLA-G is also seen with spontaneous abortion.[134] Spontaneous abortion is also associated with decreased IL-10 (which normally reduces uNK cytotoxicity).[85] Some spontaneous abortions before 3 months in primiparous women may be secondary to a defect in active maternal tolerance of the fetus, whereas loss after the third month or in women who have had a prior pregnancy may be a result of excess rejection-type responses with increased levels of Th1 inflammatory cytokines such as IFN-γ, TNF-α, and TNF-β.[23,85,164]

Women who experience recurrent pregnancy loss (e.g., three or more consecutive spontaneous abortions) often exhibit dNK cell activity that is similar to the activity of NK cells in peripheral circulation and a shift toward exaggerated Th1 immune responses instead of the usual pregnancy-exaggerated Th2 responses.[4,85] It is unclear whether the altered NK cells are the result of the Th1 predominance or whether the Th1 response is the result of a different population of dNK cells that cause spontaneous abortion instead of trophoblast expansion.

Risk of Maternal Infection

The host defense mechanism and the immune system in pregnant women are highly active, so even with alterations in host defense mechanisms, most women are not significantly immunocompromised during pregnancy, nor do they experience a significant increase in the severity of most bacterial infections during pregnancy.[105,133,146,153] However, reduction of maternal Th1 cell–mediated immunity may increase maternal susceptibility to, but not necessarily severity of, certain infections, especially viruses and certain opportunistic pathogens, such as *C. albicans, T. gondii, L. monocytogenes, Streptococcus pneumoniae, Neisseria gonorrhoeae, Mycobacterium tuberculosis,* malaria, influenza, varicella, CMV, and herpes simplex virus (HSV).[47,80,143,148] Increased severity has been reported for influenza, hepatitis E, HSV, malaria, and *L. monocytogenes* infections.[80,143] Susceptibility and severity vary over the course of gestation and the stages of immune system adaptations (see Figure 13-1). For example, increased severity of maternal malaria in early pregnancy "may reflect dominant local proinflammatory Th1 and Th17 immune responses."[47] The greater "severity of influenza A and *L. monocytogenes* in the second trimester may reflect diminished systemic and local Th1 immunity."[47]

Genetic polymorphisms in the genes that encode modulators of innate mucosal immunity, such as IL-6, IL-8, and TNF-α, may increase the risk of altered vaginal microflora.[55] Alterations in neutrophil chemotaxis and function also contribute to the persistence of infections during pregnancy.[130] Other factors also cause changes in the frequency of infections during pregnancy. For example, the increased incidence of urinary tract infections and pyelonephritis during pregnancy is primarily a result of anatomic alterations in the urinary tract that result in urinary stasis (see Chapter 11); the risk of severe illness and pneumonia from influenza may also be influenced by cardiovascular and respiratory system changes during pregnancy (see Chapters 9 and 10).[80]

Viral infections are more common during the second and third trimesters and tend to be more severe. For example, in pregnant women, primary varicella is more likely to result in pneumonia and increased morbidity and the risk of complications with influenza is increased (see Chapter 10).[80,148] Susceptibility to HIV infection during pregnancy is influenced by hormonal changes, respiratory tract mucosa, and morphologic changes.[148] Most studies of HIV infection find that pregnancy does not appear to significantly increase the risk of death or disease progression.[80] Antiviral therapies during pregnancy have significantly reduced perinatal transmission and improved outcomes for HIV-infected women and their infants.[40,103]

Fungal infections are also more common during pregnancy with an increase in symptomatic vulvovaginitis during the third trimester. The increased incidence of fungal infections is related to increased adherence of *Candida* to vaginal mucous membranes, increased glycogen in the vagina, enhanced proliferation of *Candida* under the influence of estrogen, and alterations in cell-mediated immunity.[40] The incidence of infection with protozoa (e.g., malaria, amebiasis) and helminthic (intestinal parasites) organisms is increased in countries where these organisms are prevalent. During pregnancy, malaria is more common and more severe, with an increased risk of sequelae.[80] The malaria parasite has an affinity for placental tissue, leading to stillbirth and preterm birth. In addition, malaria is a major cause of low birth weight in endemic areas.[51]

Inflammation, Infection, and Preterm Labor

Inflammation (decidual, chorioamnionic, or systemic) and infection are significant etiologic factors in preterm labor (see Chapter 4 and Figure 4-6).[24,130] Approximately 80% of preterm deliveries before 30 weeks demonstrate evidence of inflammation or infection.[106] "Preterm labor is a syndrome initiated by multiple mechanisms including intrauterine infection, uteroplacental ischemia or hemorrhage, uterine over-distention, cervical disease, stress, endocrine disorders, and other immunologically mediated processes."[29] Many of these processes lead to inflammation at the maternal-fetal interface. Onset of labor involves inflammatory processes and mediators, which these events can trigger.[26,146]

Both acute and chronic maternal infections, including urinary tract infections (see Chapter 11), are associated with preterm labor. Intrauterine infection leads to activation of the innate immune system. Recognition of microorganisms by TLRs results in release of inflammatory chemokines and cytokines. Proinflammatory cytokines (especially IL-1β, TNF-α, Il-6) and chemokines (such as IL-8 and monocyte and macrophage chemoattractant proteins) in combination with microbial endotoxins increase prostaglandin production and release of matrix metalloproteases and other substances that can lead to early cervical ripening, fetal membrane rupture, and increased myometrial contractility.[24,26,29]

Although high levels of IgG and sIgA in maternal cervical mucus may provide protection against infection from vaginal pathogens, vaginal and cervical organisms have been linked with the initiation of preterm labor and premature rupture of membranes.[24,133] Both these events are probably mediated via inflammatory cytokines that stimulate prostaglandin $E_{2}\alpha$ production.[24]

Maternal fever can lead to maternal dehydration, resulting in increased uterine activity, which, along with elaboration of prostaglandins, may result in initiation of labor. In women with acute infections, high temperature alone may lead to the release of catecholamines and corticotropin-releasing hormone and increase uterine irritability. Preterm labor is discussed further in Chapter 4.

Infections and Neurodevelopmental Disorders in Offspring

Infections during gestation can alter brain structural and functional development.[31] Intrauterine infections associated with abnormal fetal brain development and altered outcomes include CMV, influenza, Zika virus, enterovirus varicella zoster, toxoplasmosis, syphilis, HSV, HIV, and rubella.[31] Altered neurodevelopmental outcomes include an increased risk of cerebral palsy, schizophrenia, autism spectrum disorders, and other neurodevelopmental disorders, possibly via inducing high levels of proinflammatory cytokines in the brain.[31,133]

Chorioamnionitis or inflammation of the placental membranes increases the risk that the fetus will develop cerebral palsy, periventricular leukomalacia, or other abnormal neurodevelopmental outcomes.[30,31,171] Although the exact mechanism has not been completely determined, several processes may contribute to the underlying pathophysiology. Elevated levels of fetal cytokines produced in response to maternal infection may directly injure the fetal brain or cause damage indirectly by increasing the permeability of the blood-brain barrier and facilitating passage of cytokines and microbial products into the brain. The presence of microbial products may induce an inflammatory process that damages the fetal brain and induces periventricular leukomalacia. Inflammation of the placental membranes may contribute to cerebral palsy by interfering with gas exchange and inducing a hypoxic-ischemic injury in the fetus (see Figure 6-4). Maternal fever may raise the core temperature of the fetus, which could be harmful to the fetal brain. Finally, maternal infection could cause direct infection of the fetal brain with subsequent alterations in development and tissue damage. Although the fetus is more susceptible to adverse effects of maternal infection early in gestation, the placenta is a poorer barrier against some pathogens late in gestation. Consequently, although adverse fetal effects of maternal infection are more likely at early gestational ages, the incidence of fetal infection is more likely late in pregnancy.[171]

Immunization and the Pregnant Woman

Alterations in the immune system during pregnancy do not significantly alter the woman's responses to immunization.[43,51] "Maternal vaccination generates active innate, humoral and cell-mediated immune protection in the mother to increase resistance against infections and reduce the chance of vertical transmission of infections to the fetus. In addition, maternal vaccination elicits systemic immunoglobulin G (IgG) antibodies that can be transferred to the fetus via the placenta in humans and mucosal IgG, IgA and IgM antibodies that are secreted into the colostrum and milk and ingested by the newborn during breastfeeding to confer immune protection."[47, p. 121] Potential risks associated with immunization during pregnancy include fetal viremia, teratogenesis, interference with development of the infant's response to immunizations during childhood, and maternal side effects that might compromise uteroplacental function.[47]

Ideally, immunization of women of childbearing age should occur at least 3 months before conception (or immediately after delivery) to reduce the risk of infection and adverse fetal effects.[8,43] Immunity can be achieved by either passive or active means. At times, passive immunizations may be recommended during pregnancy after accidental or potential exposure to an organism associated with significant maternal or fetal risks.[8] Passive immunity involves transfer of antibodies from an actively immunized to a nonimmunized person and confers short-term protection until the antibodies are catabolized by the nonimmunized person's system. The physiologic transfer of antibodies from mother to fetus and injection of γ-globulin are both examples of passive immunity.

Active immunity involves exposure to some form of the antigen (attenuated or live organisms rendered noninfectious, inactivated or killed organisms, inactivated exotoxins or toxoids) that stimulates the production of antibodies and memory cells against that antigen by the nonimmunized person. Active immunization induces long-lasting or permanent immune responses.[43]

Immunization of pregnant women with live attenuated viruses or bacteria is not recommended (unless there is a high risk of exposure putting the mother or fetus at risk) because there is a small risk of transfer of the antigen to the fetus.[43,47] Immunization with measles (rubeola), mumps, and rubella vaccines is avoided because of potential adverse fetal consequences. However, if a woman is accidentally vaccinated for rubella early in pregnancy, the risk of adverse fetal effects appears to be low, and therapeutic abortion is not recommended.[43] Inactive (i.e., dead) viruses (e.g., pneumococcal, influenza, diphtheria, tetanus, hepatitis B) are considered safe for use in pregnancy.[8,9,43,47] Influenza and TDaP (tetanus, diphtheria, acellular pertussis) vaccination is recommended for all women of reproductive age before, during, or after pregnancy by the World Health Organization and the Advisory Committee on Immunization Practices (ACIP) of the Centers for Disease Control and Prevention.[27,46,47,115] Because the risk of influenza-related morbidity is increased during pregnancy, influenza vaccinations are recommended for all pregnant women during flu season, regardless of trimester.[10,43] Administration of immunization for rubella during the first few days after birth is often recommended. A woman who receives the rubella vaccine should be counseled to use methods to prevent conception for at least 4 weeks afterward.[8]

Blood and blood products given within 14 days of active immunization may interfere with the effectiveness of the vaccine, because blood may contain antibodies against the antigens in the vaccine and therefore interfere with the woman's own immune response.[166] Although there is a small theoretic risk of transfer of antigens through breast milk or nasopharyngeal secretions from a recently immunized woman to her infant, this is a rare event without significant reported morbidity.[166] Recommendations regarding specific immunizations during pregnancy can be found in several reviews.[8,115]

The Pregnant Woman With an Autoimmune Disease

The effect of pregnancy on autoimmune disorders is varied; individual women experience improvement, exacerbation, or no change depending on the disorder. These differences may be related to the immune mechanism involved in the specific disorder; that is, whether the disorder involves alteration in Th1/Th17 responses (which tend to decrease during pregnancy and exacerbate postpartum) or Th2 responses (which tend to increase).[85,153] Autoimmune disorders are thought to impair T suppressor cell activity, resulting in hyperactive B lymphocyte response and production of autoantibodies that form immune (antibody-antigen) complexes with their target antigens.[123] Autoantibodies damage tissue either by directly reacting with antigens on the surface of cells or by combining with antigens to form immune complexes.[120,123] The immune complexes activate the complement cascade, which in turn stimulates phagocytosis, inflammatory responses, and tissue damage.

Because the usual changes in the immune system during pregnancy are the exact opposite of these events, some women with autoimmune disorders may experience an improvement in their symptoms.[35,120,123] For example, in a prospective study, 48% of women with rheumatoid arthritis experienced improvement during pregnancy (this disorder is associated with increased Th1 mediators, which are decreased in pregnancy), followed by a relapse within the first 3 months postpartum.[35] Other studies have found improvement in up to 75% of women with this disorder.[94,110,121,153,177] Other changes during pregnancy that might lead to this amelioration include changes in plasma levels of maternal humoral factors, depression of cell-mediated immunity, and suppression of inflammatory reactions.[94,98,110,123,177]

Pregnancy is unlikely to alter the natural history of SLE unless the woman has nephritis or is experiencing a flare at the time of conception.[94,98] However, SLE can adversely affect the course of pregnancy. Women with mild disease that is under control for 6 to 12 months before and during pregnancy usually experience no exacerbation of SLE during pregnancy, and some may improve. Exacerbation, when it occurs, has been reported to be more frequent in early pregnancy and during the first 6 to 8 weeks after birth.[177] Postpartum exacerbation may represent a rebound phenomenon as suppression of cell-mediated activity is terminated.[123]

SLE involves production of autoantibodies of the IgG class and increases in Th2 mediators, which are normally increased in pregnancy.[123] Women with SLE who have anticardiolipin antibodies or lupus anticoagulant antibodies have an increased risk of thrombosis, spontaneous abortion, thrombocytopenia, preeclampsia, fetal growth restriction, and preterm birth.[94,98,121] Lupus anticoagulant factor is an immunoglobulin that binds to prothrombin-activating complexes and predisposes the woman to recurrent thrombosis in the spiral arteries and placental infarction. Some women with SLE who have anti-Ro/SS-A or anti-LA/SS-B will have a fetus with neonatal lupus syndrome.[94,121,122] These infants may have congenital heart block, cutaneous lupus rashes, cytopenia, and possibly other systemic manifestations. This syndrome is usually transient and resolves after birth, although complete heart block may not be transient.[20,94] Fetal heart block occurs because the anti-Ro/SS-A or anti-LA/SS-B antibodies lodge in the fetal cardiac conducting system and interfere with conduction pathways.[121,122]

Fetal and Neonatal Complications Associated With Transplacental Passage of Maternal Antibodies

Potentially damaging IgM class antibodies, such as the ABO antigens, and allergy-producing IgE antibodies generally do not cross the placenta. Smaller, potentially damaging maternal IgG antibodies may cross the placenta as a result of Rh incompatibility (see next section) or one of several maternal chronic diseases, leading to transient disorders in some neonates. Neonatal effects from the passage of these IgG antibodies range from mild to severe. In general, if the disorder is not fatal during the perinatal period, manifestations are transient and regress as maternal antibody is catabolized.

Maternal Graves' disease may involve transplacental passage of a thyroid-stimulating immunoglobulin resulting in transient neonatal hyperthyroidism (in approximately 1% of offspring) that can persist for up to 2 to 6 months.[88,129] Myasthenia gravis is associated with passage of maternal IgG against acetylcholine receptors, resulting in transient myasthenia gravis in 10% to 20% of offspring. Symptoms can last from a few hours to up to 3 months.[151] Because symptoms usually develop after 12 hours of age, infants who appear healthy at birth may later develop respiratory failure.[14] The delay in symptom onset may be caused by transfer of anticholinesterase drugs from the mother or elevated AFP.[151]

Maternal alloimmune thrombocytopenia (AIT) involves maternal alloimmunization against fetal human platelet alloantigens (HPA) and can be life-threatening to the fetus and neonate because of the risk of thrombocytopenia, bleeding, and intracranial hemorrhage.[73] With AIT the mother develops specific IgG antibodies against fetal platelet antigens that then cross the placenta and destroy fetal platelets leading to fetal and neonatal alloimmune thrombocytopenia (FAIT).[138] The incidence of FAIT is 1 in 1000 live births.[34] Work is in progress to develop prophylaxis similar to that for Rho(D) alloimmunization.[73] Risk to infants from antibody passage in women with SLE is described in the previous section.

Rho(D) Alloimmunization and ABO Incompatibility

Rho(D) alloimmunization (formerly called isoimmunization) can be used as a model to examine the application of immunologic principles and to illustrate how the interaction of maternal and fetal host defense mechanisms can result in pathophysiologic processes during the perinatal period. *Isoimmune or alloimmune hemolytic disease, hemolytic disease of the newborn (HDN),* and *erythroblastosis fetalis* are all terms for a disorder caused by transplacental passage of maternal IgG antibody that reacts with antigens on the fetal red blood cell (RBC) and leads to cell lysis. The fetal-neonatal effects include an increased risk of neonatal hyperbilirubinemia and, in severely affected infants, can include severe anemia, congestive heart failure, and death. Because maternal antibody remains in the infant's circulation, the hemolytic process continues after birth.

The Rh system involves a group of at least 45 different RBC surface antigens controlled by genes encoding Rh proteins (DCE). The Rh locus is on the short arm of chromosome 1.[102] A related protein, Rh glycoprotein, is essential for expression of the Rh antigen. Antigens of the D group are the ones usually involved in incompatibility between mother and fetus. Rho(D) alloimmunization occurs when an Rho(D)-negative mother carrying an Rho(D)-positive fetus produces antibody against the D antigen on the fetal RBC. Isoimmunization can also occur with other RBC antigens such as Kell, Duffy, Kidd, MNS, and the ABO system.

Rho(D) alloimmunization is of particular clinical importance because the D antigen is a potent antigen, is present in large amounts on the fetal RBC, appears as early as 5 to 6 weeks' gestational age, and stimulates formation of IgG-type antibody and memory cells in the mother.[61] The amount of antigen necessary to trigger an immune response in the mother varies for each person, as does the intensity of the response by the mother's immune system. The incidence of Rho(D) alloimmunization is relatively low, ranging from 10% to 14% if Rho(D) immune globulin (RhIG) is not given after birth or less than 2% if RhIG is given.[19,60] The R_2 phenotype (cDE) expresses the most D antigen and increases the risk of maternal sensitization.[159] Rho(D)-negative women are unlikely to have antibodies against the D antigen unless they have been immunized during a previous pregnancy or from a mismatched blood transfusion. As a result, alloimmunization is rare in first pregnancies. Normally during pregnancy the small amounts of fetal blood (less than 0.05 mL) that cross the placenta and enter the maternal circulation are too small to trigger production of antibodies by the mother's

immune system. In a few women, however, as little as 0.01 mL of fetal blood has been reported to cause maternal immunization (sensitization).[19] Detectable fetal blood cells can be found in approximately 3% of pregnant women in the first trimester, 12% in the second trimester, and 45% in the third trimester.[61,159] Approximately 1% to 2% of Rho(D)-negative women develop anti-D antibodies during their first pregnancy.[19] This number can be reduced by prophylactic administration of RhIG during pregnancy.

At birth or with a large fetomaternal hemorrhage during pregnancy, larger quantities of fetal blood (0.5 mL or more) may enter the maternal circulation. This amount of fetal blood (if the fetus is Rho[D] positive) is sufficient to stimulate formation of both anti-D antibody and memory cells in many women (Figure 13-3, *A*). Formation of memory cells results in permanent immunization. During subsequent pregnancies, even a very small amount of blood from an Rho(D)-positive fetus entering the mother's system may be enough to trigger memory cells to become plasma B cells that produce antibodies against the D antigen on the fetal RBC (the D antigen is expressed on fetal RBC by 38 days after conception).[102] The antibodies that are produced in this secondary response are predominantly of the IgG_1 and IgG_3 subclasses and are thus actively transported across the placenta (see Transplacental Passage of Maternal Antibodies) to the fetal circulation where they hemolyze fetal RBCs (Figure 13-3, *B*). With development of RhIG (a human γ-globulin concentrate of anti-D), initial active immunization of most Rh-negative women can be prevented. RhIG is given prophylactically at 28 weeks to prevent immunization during pregnancy; in the first 72 hours after birth if the newborn is Rh-positive; or after any potentially immunizing events such as an abortion, ectopic pregnancy, amniocentesis, chorionic villus sampling, or significant antepartal bleeding. A dose of RhIG at 28 weeks provides protection for approximately 12 weeks (i.e., until term).[61,102] The incidence of immunization during pregnancy is 1.6% to 2%, decreasing by 96% with administration of both antenatal and postpartum RhIG.[61,102,159] RhIG does not cause hemolysis in the fetus even though the majority of the antibodies are transported across the placenta.[60,159]

RhIG destroys fetal RBCs in the mother's system before the foreign D antigen on these cells can be recognized by her immune system and trigger formation of antibodies and, more importantly, memory cells (Figure 13-3, *C*). However, the exact mechanism by which RhIG acts to prevent alloimmunization is unclear.[102] Three potential mechanisms have been suggested for the action of RhIG: (1) clearance of antigen from the mother's system; (2) antigen blocking (B cell inhibition) by attaching to antigenic sites on the fetal cells, thereby preventing interaction with maternal lymphocytes; or (3) antigen binding, preventing B cell receptors from recognition and thus inhibiting antibody production.[19,22,61,73,159]

The standard dose (300 μg or 1500 IU) provides protection for up to 15 mL of fetal RBCs (or 300 mL of whole blood).[102] Because development of an adequate antibody response to a specific antigen can take days or weeks in persons not previously sensitized, RhIG can probably be given up 28 days after delivery if omitted earlier for some reason.[102] After antenatal administration of RhIG, some women may develop a low (1:4 or less) anti-D serum antibody titer. This positive titer reflects a passive immunity from the RhIG. The

infant of a mother who received RhIG prophylaxis within 12 weeks may have a weakly positive direct Coombs test because of placental transfer of RhIG antibodies. Neither of these responses indicates maternal immunization, and postpartum RhIG administration is indicated.[19,61] When RhIG is given prenatally the fetal blood type is not usually known. Some countries now use cell-free fetal DNA found in maternal serum (see Chapter 2) to determine fetal blood type and only give RhIG prenatally to Rh− women with Rh+ fetuses.[73]

ABO Incompatibility

The potential for alloimmunization also exists with ABO incompatibility. Severe hemolytic disease in the fetus and newborn is rare even though ABO incompatibility is three times as common as Rho(D) incompatibility. Previous exposure and immunization are not necessary with ABO incompatibility because the mother already has naturally occurring antibodies against fetal RBC antigens. The most common situation in which ABO incompatibility occurs is with a type O mother and a type A (Figure 13-4, *A*) or, less commonly, type B infant. The A antigen seems to be more antigenic than the B antigen. The type O mother has naturally occurring anti-A and anti-B antibodies in her serum that can react against the

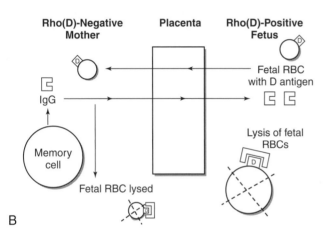

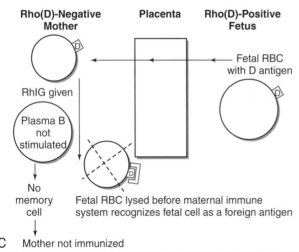

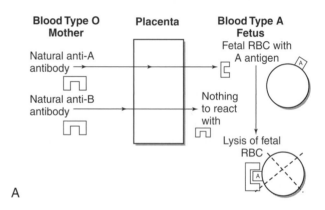

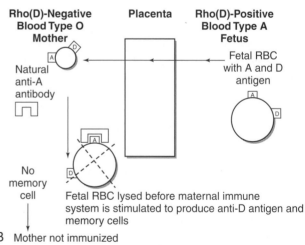

FIGURE 13-3   Rh isoimmunization. **A,** Process of immunization if Rho(D) immune globulin *(RhIG)* is not given to a previously nonimmunized woman. **B,** Action of maternal immune system in subsequent pregnancies once the mother has been immunized. **C,** Role of RhIG in prevention of maternal immunization. *IgG,* Immunoglobulin G; *RBC,* red blood cell.

FIGURE 13-4   ABO incompatibility. **A,** Mechanisms of ABO incompatibility. **B,** Mechanism by which ABO and Rh incompatibility—occurring simultaneously—reduce the severity of Rh incompatibility. *RBC,* Red blood cell.

A or B antigens on the fetal RBCs. ABO incompatibility could also occur with a type AB infant but never with a type O infant (type O RBCs have neither A nor B antigens for maternal anti-A or anti-B antibodies to identify and react against).

Why is ABO incompatibility a relatively mild disorder compared with Rho(D) alloimmunization? The primary reason is that the antibodies of the ABO system are primarily IgM, which does not cross the placenta. However, rarely these antibodies may be of the IgG type. IgG antibodies of the ABO system are more common in persons with type O blood; hence ABO alloimmunization occurs most between mothers who are type O and their type A or type B infants. Because A and B antigens also appear on somatic cells and are secreted into body fluids in most people, there is a large quantity of antigen to compete with the fetal RBCs for any maternal antibody. In addition, the fetus may have its own anti-A or anti-B antibodies that can neutralize maternal antibody. There are fewer A and B antigens than D antigens on the fetal RBCs, and these antigens are relatively weak, resulting in only a weakly positive Coombs test. ABO alloimmunization and probably Rho(D) alloimmunization do not occur in the opposite direction (i.e., from baby to mother), because fetal antibodies tend to be in a macroglobulin form that cannot cross the placenta.

The simultaneous occurrence of Rho(D) and ABO alloimmunization has a protective effect that reduces the likelihood of maternal Rho(D) sensitization. This is illustrated in Figure 13-4, *B*, with an Rho(D)-negative, type O (naturally occurring anti-A and anti-B serum antibodies) woman who is carrying a fetus who is Rho(D)-positive and type A (with A and D RBC antigens). The naturally occurring maternal anti-A antibody destroys fetal cells entering maternal circulation (during pregnancy or at delivery) before they can trigger the mother's immune system to produce anti-D antibodies and memory cells. If anti-D antibodies and memory cells are not formed, the woman remains unimmunized.[19,159]

SUMMARY

Alterations in maternal host defense mechanisms are critical for maintenance of the pregnancy, ensuring that the mother tolerates and protects the fetus. Yet these mechanisms may increase the risk of infection and other immune system disorders in the pregnant woman. Transplacental passage of maternal immunoglobulins provides protection against specific pathogens but can also lead to fetal disease. Concerns related to organisms that colonize the maternal genital tract (e.g., GBS) and sexually transmitted diseases such as HSV, HBV, and HIV have increased interest in host defense mechanisms and maternal-fetal interrelationships and altered clinical practice in recent years. Recommendations for clinical practice based on changes in host defense mechanisms are summarized in Box 13-4. By recognizing the changes in maternal host defense mechanisms, health care providers can

---

BOX 13-4 Recommendations for Clinical Practice Related to Changes in Host Defense Mechanisms: Pregnant Woman

Recognize normal parameters for immune system components and patterns of change during pregnancy and the postpartum period (pp. 435, 437-440).

Obtain and evaluate a complete history for possible exposure to infectious organisms, current illness, or presence of autoimmune disorders (pp. 445-447).

Recognize risk factors for development of specific infections (p. 446).

Monitor and counsel women regarding early signs and symptoms of infection (pp. 446-447).

Recognize clinical and laboratory changes during labor and delivery and postpartum that may mask signs of infection (pp. 444-445 and Chapter 8).

Assess women with infections during the second and third trimesters for signs of preterm labor (pp. 446-447 and Chapter 4).

Teach women methods to prevent or reduce the risk of infection while pregnant (pp. 445-447).

Counsel woman regarding the immunologic advantages of human milk and its potential role in preventing gastrointestinal infections and allergies (pp. 444-445, Table 5-3, and Chapter 12).

Monitor iron intake and serum ferritin levels in women with a history of malaria (p. 446).

Counsel women regarding risks of immunizations with live attenuated or killed vaccine during pregnancy and to avoid pregnancy for 3 months after immunization (pp. 447-448).

Avoid giving immunizations within 14 days of administration of blood or blood products (except Rh immune globulin [RhIG]) (p. 448).

Give RhIG to unsensitized Rho(D)-negative women prophylactically at 24–30 weeks' gestation and after potentially immunizing events (pp. 449-450).

Recognize that women who have received antenatal RhIG may have low antibody titers for approximately 13 weeks yet may still need RhIG postpartum if the newborn is RH positive (pp. 449-450).

Understand the implications of a weakly positive direct Coombs' test in some infants of women who have received RhIG during the prenatal period and the need for RhIG postpartum (p. 450).

Give RhIG postpartum to unsensitized Rho(D)-positive women with a Rho(D)-positive newborn in the first 72 hours after birth (pp. 449-450).

Counsel women with autoimmune disorders about potential effects of pregnancy on the course of their disease (p. 448).

Use Standard Precautions for blood and body fluids during the perinatal period (pp. 446, 463).

Counsel women with hepatitis B virus (HBV), herpes simplex virus (HSV), human immunodeficiency virus (HIV), and other viral infections regarding long-term effects on infants (including shedding of virus) and use of precautions to prevent spread of the infection (p. 446).

Counsel women with chronic disorders associated with transplacental passage of antibodies regarding the potential effects on their fetus and neonate (pp. 448-449).

identify women and infants at risk and initiate appropriate interventions and counseling.

DEVELOPMENT OF HOST DEFENSE MECHANISMS IN THE FETUS

Cellular components of the immune system develop from precursor cells within blood islands of the yolk sac (see Chapter 8). Multipotential stem cells arise in these islands and migrate into the liver and spleen and later to the bone marrow and thymus. The mucosal immune system is developed by 28 weeks' gestation but not activated until after birth, unless the infant is exposed to an intrauterine infection.[56] Box 13-1 includes definitions of selected immune terminology.

B and T lymphocytes arise from common lymphoid stem cells. Development of lymphocytes is regulated by cytokines, stromal cells, transcription factors, and other immune system components.[12] Exposures to allergens or infections before birth or alterations in maternal nutrition or health status may alter immune system development and maturation.[12] Pre–B cells are seen in the liver by 7 to 8 weeks; immature B lymphocytes with surface IgM receptors and complement are found in the fetal liver by 10 weeks.[15,78] By 12 weeks, B lymphocytes that have IgG and IgA cell surface receptors are seen in peripheral blood, bone marrow, liver, and spleen; numbers reach adult values by 15 weeks.[113,168] Fetal synthesis of immunoglobulins begins by 10 to 14 weeks; however, levels of immunoglobulins produced by the fetus normally remain low throughout gestation.[63,168] Fetal serum IgG levels rise in the second and third trimesters primarily because of increased transplacental passage from the mother (see Transplacental Passage of Maternal Antibodies on p. 443). IgA increases slowly during gestation, but levels at term are still significantly below maternal levels.[37] Secretory IgA is not produced until after birth. Elevated IgM levels in cord blood (greater than 20 mg/dL [0.20 g/L]) suggest intrauterine infection and may be seen in newborns with congenital cytomegalovirus (CMV), rubella, or toxoplasmosis. This IgM is of fetal origin, because IgM does not cross from the mother.

Differentiation of the thymus begins at 6 to 7 weeks.[104] The thymus develops as an outgrowth of the third and fourth pharyngeal pouches. The rudimentary thymus on each side of the body grows toward the midline. These structures fuse by 8 weeks and then gradually descend into the chest.[45] Stem cells from the liver and spleen migrate to the thymus to form thymocytes. T lymphocytes appear in the thymus by 7 weeks and in the blood by 12 weeks.[12,168] Dendritic-like cells are found in the thymus, liver, and mesenteric lymph nodes around 12 weeks and in tonsils and the skin by around 23 weeks.[12] Mature αβ T cells (conventional T cells) are found by 14 weeks and differentiate their receptors in the second and third trimesters; regulatory T (Treg) cells develop concurrently.[78] T cells are found in the intestine as early as 11 weeks and form Peyer's patches with B cells by 16 weeks.[13] Toll-like receptors (TLR) 2 and 4 are active in the fetal gut by 18 to 21 weeks.[13] Fetal T cells are naive in both phenotype

and function with an abundance of Treg cells.[96] Naive fetal T cells differentiate into T17 or Treg cells depending on the local cytokine milieu.[12]

Differentiation of CD4+ and CD8+ surface antigens begins around 10 weeks.[15] Mature CD4+ and CD8+ T lymphocytes are detected in the liver and spleen by 14 weeks and in the fetal circulation by 15 to 16 weeks' gestation.[63,113] By midgestation, T cells are capable of secreting interleukin (IL)-2; tumor necrosis factor (TNF)-α; TNF-β; and, to a lesser extent, interferon (IFN)-γ, IL-3, IL-4, IL-5, and IL-6.[113] TNF, IL-1B, and IL-6 are found in amniotic fluid and increase to term; elevation of IL-6 is seen with intrauterine infection.[150,173] Surfactant protein (SP)-A and SP-D are elevated in amniotic fluid and may also have an immunoregulatory function.[167,174] Fetal Th1 responses tend to be inhibited by IL-10 from the placenta.[97] Innate responses are characterized by IL-23–directed immunity, which promotes development of T helper (Th)17 CD4+ and enhances defenses against extracellular pathogens.[169] Production of IL-12, which induces IFN-γ production by CD4+ T cells and NK cells, and differentiation of Th1 cells, is decreased.[169] Transplantation responses develop relatively early. Antigen recognition can be demonstrated by 12 weeks, and graft-versus-host reactions by 13 weeks' gestation. The fetus can increase production of proinflammatory cytokines with intrauterine infections and mount an inflammatory response.[150] However, this may increase the risk of brain injury, especially white matter damage, and cerebral palsy (see Infections and Neurodevelopmental Disorders in Offspring on p. 447 and Chapter 15).

The fetal immune system is dominated by Th2 to "avoid proinflammatory Th1 type alloimmune responses to maternal tissue that may trigger preterm birth or spontaneous abortion."[127] IL-6, IL-10, and IL-23 and Th17-mediated immune responses are all upregulated with increased production in response to bacterial lipopolysaccharide-binding protein.[169] TNF-α, IL-1B, and Th1-mediated immune responses are downregulated in the fetus and amniotic fluid. This decreases the extent and duration of proinflammatory immune responses that can lead to preterm birth.[169] An exaggerated fetal immune response has been linked to periventricular leukomalacia and cerebral palsy in addition to preterm labor onset (see pp. 443 and 447).[105,169,173]

White blood cells arise initially from yolk-sac stem cells (see Chapter 8); however, granulocytopoiesis occurs primarily in the fetal bone marrow.[15] Neutrophils and macrophages arise from colony-forming unit–granulocyte-macrophage progenitor stem cells.[15] Myelopoiesis is 10 times more active in fetuses than in adults and increases fourfold by the second trimester.[74] Granulocytic cells from which neutrophils arise can be found in fetal blood by 6 to 8 weeks and mature neutrophils by 14 to 30 weeks.[78,113] After 5 months, neutrophils are produced primarily in the bone marrow. Few granulocytes are found in peripheral blood during the first half of gestation, then gradually increase by 22 to 23 weeks' gestation; by term the number of granulocytes is similar to those observed in adults.[15] Fetal blood has 10- to 50-fold more

concentrations of C3 and thus opsonic activity are proportional to gestational age, further increasing the risk of sepsis in preterm infants.[15] In addition, neonatal γδ-T cells (which are early responders to infection) have fewer cell surface receptors and weaker cytolytic activity.[12,32]

The inability to localize infection results in clinical manifestations of infection that are different in newborns compared with adults, and this can make the diagnosis of sepsis in neonates difficult. Specifically, early signs of sepsis in a neonate are often subtle and nonspecific, involving changes in activity, tone, color, or feeding. In addition, neonates have a poor hypothalamic response to pyrogens; therefore fever is not a reliable indicator of infection in a neonate. Alterations in innate immunity in the neonate are summarized in Table 13-1.

TABLE 13-1 Alterations in Host Defense Mechanisms in the Neonate

ALTERATION	RESULT	IMPLICATION
INNATE IMMUNITY		
Structural alterations of PMNs	Altered movement kinetics and orientation of PMNs	Delayed initial response to invasion by pathogenic organisms
Altered PMN chemotaxis, adherence, and L-selectin expression	Slower movement to site of antigenic invasion	Decreased ability to localize infection
	Poorer PMN aggregation and adherence	Increased risk of generalized sepsis
Decreased NSP	Decreased ability to increase PMN production with sepsis	Neutropenia and more immature PMNs
		Increased risk of generalized sepsis
Altered APCs and TLCs	Delayed initial response to infection	Decreased ability to localize infection
		Increased risk of generalized sepsis
Decreased NK activity and function	Decreased opsonization and lysis	Decreased ability to localize infection
	Delayed initial response to infection	Increased risk of generalized sepsis
Poor hypothalamic response to pyrogens	Fever is not a reliable sign of sepsis	Signs of sepsis often subtle and nonspecific
Altered respiratory "burst" and bactericidal activity in stressed and VLBW neonates	Decreases ability to destroy pathogens	Increased risk of severe infection
COMPLEMENT		
Decreased complement proteins C1, C3, C4, C7, and C9 and receptors	Decreased opsonization	Decreased ability to localize infection
Deficient activity of compliment pathways	Decreased chemotaxis	Decreased opsonization and ability to eliminate organisms with capsular polysaccharide coats such as GBS
	Decreased cell lysis	Increased risk and severity of bacterial sepsis
ADAPTIVE IMMUNITY: CELL-MEDIATED IMMUNITY		
Altered T cell function (reduced cytokine production, cytotoxic activity)	Reduced defenses against viral and fungal infections	Increased risk of severe infection and generalized septicemia
	Alteration in B-lymphocyte function	
Downregulation of Th1 responses	Decreased cell-mediated helper functions	Increased risk and severity of infection from herpes, CMV, and other TORCH organisms
Reduced levels of IL-4, IL-8, IL-12, and IFN-γ	Altered cell-mediated responses, immunoglobulin production, and innate responses	Increased risk of severe or overwhelming infection
		Decreased ability to localize infection
		Increased risk of generalized sepsis
Primary (naive) T cells, few memory cells	Delayed responses to specific pathogenic organisms	Increased risk of viral and fungal infections
ADAPTIVE RESPONSES: ANTIBODY-MEDIATED IMMUNITY		
Decreased IgG in a preterm infant because of lack of maternal transfer	Reduction in maternal antibodies that provide passive immunity against selected organism	Reduced defense against many pathogens
Decreased IgG$_2$ isotype	Decreased opsonization of organisms with capsular polysaccharide coats	Increased risk of bacterial sepsis, especially from gram-positive cocci (GBS)
Decreased IgA and absent sIgA	Reduced defense against GI and respiratory infections	Increased risk of respiratory and GI infections
Decreased IgM with less specificity	Reduced defense against viral and gram-negative organisms	Increased risk of *Escherichia coli* sepsis and rubella, syphilis, toxoplasmosis, CMV, and other viral infections
Altered B cell function due to altered T cell support and cytokine production	Slower switch from IgM to IgA and IgG production	Increased risk of severe infection and generalized septicemia
Lack of previous exposure of B cells to many organisms, with few memory cells	Delayed specific responses to pathogenic organisms	Increased risk of severe or overwhelming infection

APCs, Antigen presenting cells; CMV, cytomegalovirus; GBS, group B streptococci; GI, gastrointestinal; IFN, interferon; Ig, immunoglobulin; IL, interleukin; NK, natural killer cells; NSP, neutrophil storage pool; PMN, polymorphonuclear neutrophils; Th1, T helper 1; Th2, T helper 2; TLRs, toll-like receptors; VLBW, very low birth weight.

Alterations in the Complement System

Newborns have decreased serum levels of both classic and alternative pathway components, defective complement activation, and a decrease in complement receptors.[14,16,64,168,173] Components of the classic system in a term neonate are slightly reduced or comparable to adult values, whereas levels of these factors are significantly reduced in preterm infants and correlate with gestational age (Table 13-2).[15] Lower levels of complement proteins result in decreased opsonization, decreased chemotaxic activity, and decreased cell lysis.[14,15] Neonatal B cells have lower levels of complement receptor 2, leading to inadequate responses to bacteria with polysaccharide coatings such as GBS.[122]

Alterations in Adaptive Immunity

Cell-mediated and antibody-mediated (humoral) immunity is developmentally immature in both preterm and term neonates. The response of neonates' adaptive system to APCs is less efficient than that in adults.[173] Neonatal B and T lymphocytes are naive and have differences from adult lymphocytes. "Neonates exhibit an increased susceptibility to infections because of immaturity in their lymphocytes including a high frequency of naive recent thymic emigrants, low numbers of effector-memory T-cells, impaired Th1 cytokine secretion and reduced strength of B-cell receptor signaling."[12] Box 13-3 on page 439 provides an overview of adaptive immunity.

Alterations in Cell-Mediated Immunity

Absolute numbers of T lymphocytes in are higher in newborns than in adults, but the functional ability of newborn T cells is altered, as is the diversity of specific T cell receptors, which results in a delay in the response to specific

TABLE 13-2   Ranges of Complement Levels in Neonates

COMPLEMENT COMPONENT	Mean % of Adult Levels (Number of Studies)	
	TERM NEONATE	PRETERM NEONATE
CH50	56–90 (5)	45–71 (4)
AP50	49–65 (4)	40–55 (3)
C1q	61–90 (4)	27–58 (3)
C4	60–100 (5)	42–91 (4)
C2	76–100 (3)	67–96 (2)
C3	60–100 (5)	39–78 (4)
C5	73–75 (2)	67 (1)
C6	47–56 (2)	36 (1)
C7	67–92 (2)	72 (1)
C8	20–36 (2)	29 (1)
C9	<20–52 (3)	<20–41 (2)
B	35–64 (4)	36–50 (4)
9	33–71 (6)	16–65 (3)
H	61 (1)	—
C3bi	55 (1)	—

From Lewis, D.B. & Wilson, C.B. (2001). Developmental immunology and role of host defenses in fetal and neonatal susceptibility to infection. In J.S. Remington & J.O. Klein. (Eds.). *Infectious diseases of the fetus and newborn infant* (5th ed.). Philadelphia: Saunders.

organisms.[12,64] Cytotoxic activity of neonatal T cells is lower than in adults, production of some cytokines reduced, and neonatal T cells are less able to produce multiple cytokines simultaneously.[12,122]

The predominant T cells in newborns are regulatory T (Treg) and Th2 cells with greater IL-4 and lower levels of Th1 cytokines such as IFN-γ, TNF-α, and IL-2.[12,47,122] These cells provide poorer defenses against intracellular pathogens.[47] Treg cells are found in high levels in cord blood.[127] These cells suppress T-cell proliferation in response to cytokines and Th1 cytokine (especial IFN-γ) production, thus limiting adaptive responses. This is an advantage in limiting autoimmunity but also limits responses to infection and vaccines.[127] Treg cells are higher in preterm than term infants.[15] Neonatal T cell responses during APC interaction are characterized by decreased TLC-mediated activity and Th2 responses.[12] CD4+ T cells have a decreased capacity to generate memory cells.[122] Although Th2 responses are the dominant response in neonates, T helper cells provide relatively poor support of B cells.[144] For example, neonatal T cells do not induce neonatal B cells to produce some of the immunoglobulins that adult B cells would produce (see Alterations in Antibody-Mediated [Humoral] Immunity).[64]

At birth most of the T lymphocytes are primary (naive) T cells (most are recent thymic emigrants), with few secondary memory T cells.[45] Primary T cells release less cytokine and have a diminished response to antigens.[24,113] The most prevalent T cell phenotype in the neonate is the CD45RA+ cell. CD45RA+ cells are "naive" because of lack of exposure to foreign antigens by the fetus. When exposed to a foreign antigen presented by a B lymphocyte or DC, the neonatal CD45RA+ cells differentiate into CD45RO+ (memory) cells.[45] The neonatal CD45RO+ cell is capable of producing significant amounts of cytokines (e.g., IFN-γ, TNF-α, GM-CSF) and acting as a helper cell for B cell function.[15,24,113,144] However, because the newborn's T cells have no previous experience with most antigens until exposed and sensitized after birth, it probably takes 4 to 6 weeks for the newborn to achieve minimal adaptive immune protection.[14,45]

Alterations in cytokine production alters cell-mediated immunity, immunoglobulin production, and innate responses.[44,95] Although some cytokine production by neonatal T cells is altered, IL-1, IL-2, and IL-6 levels are normal or slightly reduced. However, levels of IL-4, IL-8, IL-12, and IFN-γ are reduced.[44,78] The decrease in IL-4 and IFN-γ is consistent with the naive state of CD45RA+ cells.[12,45,97] Genomic polymorphisms in gene encoding for production of cytokines may help explain individual differences in neonatal susceptibility to sepsis.

As noted previously, neonates have downregulation of Th1 responses, with a decreased capacity to produce cytokines thus promoting Th1 (cell-mediated) responses with a blunted response to activation by IFN-γ, possibly because of decreased signal transduction.[15,45,78,97] This may increase susceptibility to oropharyngeal candidiasis in both term and preterm infants.[44] Neonatal T cells are able to increase cytokine production when stimulated.[15] For example, CD8[+] cytotoxic T cells can be stimulated and reach near adult levels of function in some cases with cytomegalovirus (CMV) exposure.[64,97] However, neonatal T cells require greater stimulation as well as stimulation from additional factors (e.g., accessory cells and signaling molecules) than adult cells to achieve full activity.[15,144] Cell-mediated immunity is further depressed in small-for-gestational-age (SGA) infants. These infants have a smaller proportion of T lymphocytes and altered lymphocyte function than appropriate-for-gestational-age (AGA) infants, perhaps secondary to alterations in thymic activity. The thymus of SGA infants is smaller in weight and volume and demonstrates histologic alterations and decreased activity of thymic inductive factors, which may contribute to immune dysfunction in these neonates.

Alterations in Antibody-Mediated (Humoral) Immunity

The fetal and neonatal differences in antibody-mediated immunity are primarily related to the alterations in T cell activity, immature cytokine function, and the effects of passive immunization from immunoglobulins acquired transplacentally and/or through breastfeeding. Activity of B cells requires signaling from the interaction of surface antigen and T helper cells to amplify the immune response.[15] Because T cell activity and cytokines are needed to enhance B cell function, there is a reduction in fetal and neonatal production of immunoglobulins (Ig).[63,78] T cell–dependent B responses have a delayed onset, peak at lower levels, are of shorter duration, and show different IgG isotypes than in adults.[15,97,122] T cell–independent B responses are also deficient, especially in response to antigens with capsular polysaccharide coats such as group B streptococcus.[97,147] Neonatal B cells have fewer IL-5 receptors, decreased activation by IL-10, and poorer responses to Th2 antigens.[83,147] Many neonatal B cells have CD5[+] surface antigens (B1a cells). B1a cells are not dependent on T cell help for activation as are conventional B cells (B2).[83,113] However, neonatal T cells do not stimulate B cells to readily switch production of immunoglobulins from IgM to IgG or IgA because of alterations in nuclear signaling pathways.[12] As a result, neonates produce primarily IgM and little IgG and IgA, even when exposed to bacteria with polysaccharide capsules.[83,144] In response to vaccine antigens neonatal B cells tend to differentiate into memory B cells rather than antibody-producing plasma B cells.

The total amount of immunoglobulin at birth is 55% to 80% of adult values and primarily consists of IgG from the mother.[78] Levels of serum immunoglobulins after birth are illustrated in Figure 13-5. Neonatal IgG values reflect the IgG acquired from the mother either transplacentally or via breast milk.[64] The newborn can produce IgG$_1$ in a manner similar to that of an adult; however, IgG$_2$ production is reduced until about 2 years of age. IgG$_2$ is important for defense against

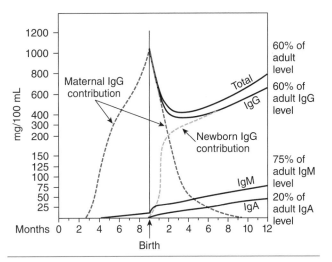

FIGURE 13-5 Immunoglobulin (Ig) levels in the fetus, newborn, and infant. (From Stiehm, E.R. [1989]. *Immunologic disorders in infants and children* [3rd ed.]. Philadelphia: Saunders.)

polysaccharide antigens such as are seen with GBS, K1 forms of *E. coli, Haemophilus influenzae,* pneumococcus, and meningococcus.[78] Development of antibody responses is primarily dependent on postbirth age rather than postmenstrual age.[32] Decreased antibody production in neonates is a result of B cell immaturity from lack of antigenic exposure, incomplete development of Ig surface receptors, and reduced B cell receptor signaling (a result of altered expression of surface molecules and lower proliferation rates).[12]

IgG is important for immunity to bacteria, especially gram-negative organisms, bacterial toxins, and viruses.[15,168] Neonatal values depend on gestational age, because placental transfer of IgG increases during the third trimester. Thus preterm infants may have inadequate protection. For example, cord blood values of IgG are minimal in infants born at 24 to 25 weeks' gestation and average 400 mg/dL (4.0 g/L) at 32 weeks and 1500 mg/dL (15 g/L) at term.[113,168,173] Term IgG levels are 90% to 95% of adult values and 5% to 10% higher than maternal values.[15,141] Levels of IgG are lower in SGA infants, possibly because of impaired placental transport of maternal IgG.[64] After birth, levels fall gradually as maternal IgG is catabolized. Because significant production of IgG by the infant does not occur until after 6 months, all infants experience a transient "physiologic hypogammaglobulinemia" (see Physiologic Hypogammaglobulinemia) in the first 6 months. However, as a result of IgG transfer in breast milk, the neonate continues to get antibodies against infectious agents for which the mother has circulating antibodies because of previous exposure or immunization.

IgA is important for localized immunity in the GI and respiratory tracts. IgA does not cross the placenta in significant amounts.[37] Neonatal (term and preterm) values are less than 2% of adult values. Elevated IgA is found in cord blood after maternal-fetal transfusion and occasionally with intrauterine infection, although IgM is seen more commonly after fetal infection.[113] Although sIgA is not found in neonates at birth, it can be detected in saliva, tears, and intestinal mucosa by 2 weeks to 2 months.[78] A polypeptide chain (secretory component) provides resistance to pH changes and protects the IgA molecule from proteolytic digestion in the GI tract.

IgM, which does not cross the placenta, is important for protection against blood-borne infections and can trigger multiple effector functions of the classical complement cascade.[168] IgM is the major immunoglobulin synthesized in the first month of life.[63,123] IgM levels increase rapidly by 2 to 4 days after birth, probably secondary to stimulation from environmental antigens, although neonatal values are low (5 to 15 mg/dL [0.05 to 0.15 g/L]), with means of 6 mg/dL (0.06 g/L) at 28 weeks' gestation and 11 mg/dL (0.11 g/L) at term, which is approximately 10% of adult values.[15,64] The fetus is capable of producing significant IgM in response to exposure to certain antigens, such as the TORCH organisms, after 19 to 20 weeks' gestation, which may be a result of activation of the fetal B1a cells.[113] However, neonatal IgM has less specificity than adult IgM in responding to specific antigens, which may hinder the initial recognition of pathogenic organisms. IgE and IgD do not cross the placenta in significant amounts, and newborn values are less than 10% of adult values.[63]

Few B cells that have differentiated into immunoglobulin-secreting cells (IgSCs) are seen in the first 5 days after birth, and those that are found are mostly IgM-secreting cells. By a month of age, two thirds of neonates have IgSCs, most of which are IgA-secreting cells. Increased IgSCs are more common in both term and preterm infants with intrauterine infection. Low serum concentrations of IgG in preterm infants may also be a result of a decreased ability of their B cell to switch immunoglobulin isotype forms.[168]

Gut Host Defense Mechanisms

Maturation of the mucosal immune system occurs rapidly after birth in response to antigenic exposure and is well developed by 1 year of age in both preterm and term infants.[56] Host defense mechanisms in the gut involve both nonimmune (gastric acidity, intestinal motility, intraluminal proteolysis, mucosal surface, microvillous membrane) and immune factors (sIGA, gut associated lymphatic tissue, cell mediated immunity) as well as the developing neonatal microbiome.[13,50,56,95,124,172] Many of these factors are initially immature in the neonate, which reduces the effectiveness of the gut mucosal barrier and increases the risk of GI disorders. Neonatal GI mucosal immaturity includes (1) increased permeability to macromolecules (potential antigens), (2) altered immune tolerance, (3) decreased sIgA, and (4) decreased cytokine production. This allows entry of pathogenic organisms into systemic circulation and may increase the risk of development of allergic disorders. As defense mechanisms mature, GI barriers become more impermeable, offering greater protection against uptake of antigenic substances.[28,95]

The gut microbiome (see pp. 454-455) is important in regulating intestinal immune function, maintaining homeostasis, cytoprotection, regulating mucosal barrier function, and secretion of antimicrobial peptides.[13,124] The gut microbiome mediates tolerance of their presence in the gut by regulating TLR, downregulating proinflammatory transcription factors such as nuclear factor-κ-B (NF-κB), and influencing development and function of T cell subsets in the gut mucosa.[13,124] "Immune development, including the capacity to synthesize the key Th1 cytokine, interferon γ (IFNγ), appears to be shaped by microbial exposure. Microbes are thought to influence the process of immune maturation through repeated stimulation via pathogen-associated molecular patterns (PAMPs) that are recognized by pattern recognition receptors such as TLRs found on cells of the innate immune system. Simultaneous TLR stimulation with multiple ligands, mimicking exposure in microbe-rich environments, appears to induce neonatal dendritic cells to mature, primarily through the production of the Th1-polarizing cytokine, IL12. This suggests that environments with high microbial content may induce early life T cell responses toward the Th1 phenotype and boost baseline airway Treg activity."[67, p. 66] Disorders such as necrotizing enterocolitis (see Chapter 12) are associated with alterations in the protective bacterial population, TLC responses, and pathogenic organisms.[3,124]

The development of gut defense mechanisms is also influenced by ingestion of food, beginning with colostrum, which enhances maturation of the intestinal lining via introduction of factors such as thyroxine, TGF, insulin-like growth factors, neurotensin, cortisol, lactoferrin, bombesin, and epidermal growth factor.[95] Gut maturation is delayed in preterm and SGA infants. Nonimmune factors that stimulate gut maturation include maturation of gastric acid production, intestinal motility and peristalsis, intraluminal proteolytic activity, and the mechanical barrier properties of the gut mucosal surface. Development of the gut mucosal barrier is influenced by the intestinal microbiota and microbiota-epithelium interactions.[13,109] Bacterial colonization may modify gut barrier tight junctions to enhance structural integrity and prevent bacterial translocation.[13]

Examples of specific immune factors that affect gut maturation are sIgA and cell-mediated immunity. Fermentation of the prebiotic oligosaccharides contained in breast milk results in production of probiotic ("good") bacteria such as bifidobacteria and lactobacilli. These probiotics stimulate synthesis and secretion of sIgA and help produce a balanced Th1/Th2 response. sIgA also coats the mucosa to protect against bacterial invasion.[50]

DCs and epithelial cells, which express TLR-2 and TLR-4, detect and respond to pathogen-associated molecular patterns to prevent infection.[13] Neonatal cell-mediated immunity, especially a localized depression of T lymphocyte suppressor activity, and the decreased IgA hinder an effective response to antigens that can cross the intestinal barrier. The mature immune response to the presence of antigens in the gut is immune tolerance. With immune tolerance, the absorbed antigen elicits a localized IgA response that destroys most of the antigen. As a result, there are fewer antigens available to enter the systemic system. Immune tolerance appears to be enhanced by the presence of partially digested polypeptide fragments. These fragments may not be formed in the neonate secondary to immature proteolysis. With decreased IgA, greater amounts of antigen are absorbed. The presence of antigens also triggers T suppressor cell activity, which interferes with and inhibits systemic responses to these antigens.[95] Decreased T suppressor response can alter systemic immune responses and lead to inflammatory or allergic responses.

CLINICAL IMPLICATIONS FOR NEONATAL CARE

Neonates are more likely than adults to develop specific bacterial, viral, and fungal infections and septicemia or meningitis if infection occurs. Immunodeficiency diseases are rarely manifested in newborns, because maternally acquired IgG and sIgA in breast milk usually mask the effects of these disorders. However, immature neonatal immune responses are associated with the pathophysiology of several disorders. For example, the inflammatory response and cytokines play a role in tissue damage seen in bronchopulmonary dysplasia. Infection that causes cytokine-mediated injury to oligodendrocytes has been proposed as having a role in the pathogenesis of periventricular leukomalacia and brain injury after cerebral hypoxic-ischemic insults, which can lead to cerebral palsy (see Infections and Neurodevelopmental Disorders in Offspring on p. 447 and Chapter 15).[119,142] Programming of the immune system in the fetal and neonatal period has long-term influences on immune system function and can increase or decrease the risk for later development of allergies and autoimmune disorders.[93,149]

Neonatal Vulnerability to Infection

Neonates are at increased risk of infection primarily because of their small NSP, reduced chemotaxis, decreased complement activity, decreased protective responses against capsular polysaccharide antigens, and large numbers of naive T cells, which reduce cell-mediated responses.[78,97,144] The chance of developing sepsis from exposure to gram-negative rods is increased because protection against these organisms is provided by IgM, IgA (against enteropathic *E. coli*), and T lymphocytes, all of which are present at decreased levels or have inefficient activity in neonates. Similarly, markedly low values of IgA and the lack of sIgA increase vulnerability to respiratory and GI infections, whereas low IgM levels increase vulnerability to rubella, toxoplasmosis, CMV, and syphilis. The risk of GI infections is increased because of immaturity of the intestinal mucosal barrier and lack of gut maturation.

Decreased complement activity, particularly the alternative pathway, leads to less opsonic activity. This may be a critical deficiency if the infant also lacks type-specific antibodies for organisms with a capsular polysaccharide coating, such as GBS or K1 *E. coli*. Altered activity of T lymphocytes

along with their lack of antigen exposure increases the vulnerability to infection from herpes simplex virus (HSV), CMV, and *Candida*. Decreased production of IFN-γ (which inhibits viral replication) by the lymphocytes also increases the risk of viral infection. In addition, IFN-γ is an important macrophage-activating factor that has an important role in destruction of intracellular pathogens such as *T. gondii* and *L. monocytogenes*.

Limitations in Immune Responses to Bacterial Infections

The pathophysiologic processes that lead to early-onset neonatal sepsis described here provide an example of how limitations in immune responses affect bacterial infections in neonates. GBS and *E. coli* are common pathogens seen with neonatal sepsis.

GBS is a β-hemolytic gram-positive cocci found in the vaginal and intestinal tracts of 15% to 30% of healthy individuals.[78] Newborns may acquire GBS via vertical transmission before or during birth. Although approximately 1 in 10 newborns born to maternal carriers will be colonized at birth, passively acquired immunity derived from maternal antibodies protects the majority of healthy newborns from developing infection.[78] At birth, 1% to 2% of newborns born to colonized women will develop early-onset neonatal sepsis.[136] Skin and mucosal barriers undergo changes with birth and initially may be less effective barriers.[78] Postnatal skin and gut colonization provide additional protections (see Neonatal Microbiome).

GBS type III in particular adheres to neonatal epithelium and is more likely to cross mucosal and blood barriers (increasing the risk of meningitis), partially because of increased expression of hypervirulent GBS adhesin (a GBS surface protein that may promote central nervous system entry) that enhances movement of GBS across the intestinal wall and blood-brain barrier.[78] GBS sepsis is more likely to occur in infants deficient in type-specific IgG antibody. Neonates will lack these antibodies if their mother does not have the type-specific antibody to transfer to her infant, or if the infant is born prematurely before adequate maternal antibody has been transferred to the fetus. Maternal antibiotic prophylaxis given during the intrapartum period to women who are colonized with GBS reduces the risk of neonatal GBS sepsis.[162,163]

Once infected, the neonate may be unable to mount an appropriate response to GBS, including reduced plasma levels of complement, alterations in APCs, and impaired deployment of neutrophils and other APCs.[78] When exposed to GBS, the B lymphocytes of most neonates do not produce adequate quantities of type-specific high-quality antibody critical for opsonization and phagocytosis.[64,78] Lower levels of complement in newborns, especially in preterm infants, further reduce opsonization of GBS and interfere with the phagocytic ability of the PMNs. In addition, optimal destruction of GBS depends on type-specific antibody, complement, and functional phagocytes. In neonates circulating macrophages have a decreased capacity to produce TNF-α, IL-1β, and other inflammatory cytokines, and tissue-based macrophages are less efficient phagocytes.[78]

In infected neonates who do not have type-specific antibody, an increase in the time required for neutrophil migration to the invading organisms has been noted, along with a delay of 4 to 6 hours between the onset of infection and release of neutrophils from bone marrow storage pools (versus 2 hours in infants with type-specific antibodies).[15] This results in decreased complement activation (and thus opsonization and phagocytosis) and inability to localize the infection, and increases the risk of a rapidly progressing overwhelming septicemia.

Because of functional and structural alterations in PMNs that decrease chemotaxis, neonates are unable to rapidly deliver adequate numbers of phagocytes to the site of initial infection. Neutropenia, rarely seen in infected adults, is a common finding in neonatal septicemia. The reasons for this neutropenia include a small marrow storage pool of neutrophils and their precursors that is rapidly depleted with sepsis, inability of the marrow to increase production of neutrophils (stem cell proliferation rate is already at maximal activity), failure of the marrow to release additional neutrophils, sequestration of neutrophils along vessel walls (margination), and the short circulating half-life (4 to 7 hours) of neutrophils in the neonate.[64]

Neonates may also be deficient in local defense mechanisms in the lungs because of decreased numbers (and possibly altered function) of lung macrophages. This deficit may predispose the infant to GBS pneumonia. Immune responses of neonates against *E. coli* are similar to those described for GBS. However, anti-K1 *E. coli* IgG antibodies are much less common in the adult population, so the mother is less likely to provide protection to her fetus against this organism. In summary, the increased susceptibility of the neonate to bacterial pathogens results primarily from lack of type-specific antibody, alterations in the functional ability of PMNs (especially decreased chemotaxis), poor bone marrow response to maintain adequate numbers of neutrophils, and decreased complement, leading to ineffective opsonic activity necessary for phagocytosis and bactericidal activity (see Table 13-1).[64]

Immune Responses to Viral Infections

Viral infections tend to be more serious and devastating disorders in neonates than in older individuals. The major defense mechanisms against viral infections are immature in neonates.[32] These limitations include immature cell-mediated immunity; reduced NK cells, IgM, IFN-γ expression, and recognition of pathogenic organisms; poorer ability of neonatal pDCs to activate CD4+ T cells; and altered ability to localize infection.[32] The decreased Th1 cytokines may also contribute to susceptibility to infection with intracellular pathogens.[173] In addition, most neonates have T lymphocytes that are not yet sensitized—that is, they are mostly still naive.

TABLE 13-3   Immune Responses to Vaccines and Infectious Pathogens in Early Life

VACCINE OR PATHOGEN	IMMUNE RESPONSES
Hepatitis B vaccine	Defective early Th1 and increased memory Th2 responses in newborns compared with naive adults; higher antibody response than adults
Oral poliomyelitis vaccine	Defective Th1 response and similar antibody response in newborns compared with immune adults
Mycobacterium bovis BCG vaccine	Adultlike Th1 response in newborns; promotes antibody, Th1, and Th2 responses to unrelated vaccines
Whole cell pertussis vaccine	Th1 response in 2-month-old infant
Measles vaccine	Lower Th1 response in 6- to 12-month-old infants compared with immune adults
Human cytomegalovirus	Mature CD8 T cell response and defective CD4 T cell response in fetuses and infants compared with adults
Human immunodeficiency virus	Defective CD4 and CD8 T cell responses in newborns and infants compared with adults
Trypanosoma cruzi	Adultlike CD8 T cell response
Herpes simplex virus	Delayed IFN-γ response in infants compared with adults
Bordetella pertussis	Th1 response in infants

BCG, Bacilli Calmette-Guerin; *IFN,* interferon; *Th,* T helper.
Modified from Marchant, A. & Goldman, M. (2005). T cell-mediated immune responses in human newborns: ready to learn? *Clin Exp Immunol, 141,* 12.

The neonate will have varied responses depending on the characteristics and robustness of specific viruses. For example, a newborn produces mature CD8+ T cell responses after fetal exposure to CMV as early as 28 weeks' gestation, which may play a role in viral persistence after birth. However, neonates have a low CD8+ response to human immunodeficiency virus (HIV). The mechanisms underlying these differences are unclear but may be related to differences in cell priming or to low CD4+ T cell responses to HIV, or HIV may inhibit responses of young T cells or prevent development of CD8+ responses.[97] Limitations in neonatal responses to selected infectious pathogens are summarized in Table 13-3.

An example of altered immune responses to viral infection is HSV infection. Neonates have impaired immune responses to both HSV1 and HSV2.[72,144] Consequently, neonatal HSV infection is often a rapidly progressing disorder that involves multiple body systems and has high morbidity and mortality rates. Severe systemic HSV infection is an age-related phenomenon, with the morbidity, mortality, and severity of illness decreasing after the first 4 weeks of life.[32] Susceptibility of neonates to severe HSV infection is related to immaturity of the immune system, alterations in neutrophil function, T cell naiveté, fewer NK cells, and less efficient cell-mediated cytolysis.[64,72,144] Alterations in the neonate's immune system that increase the risk of HSV infection include decreased NK cell cytotoxicity, reduced ability of lymphocytes and monocytes to lyse HSV, decreased antibody-dependent cell-mediated toxicity, decreased or delayed production of and response to IFN, decreased diversity of specific receptors for HSV, delayed lymphocyte proliferation in response to antigens, blunted Th1 responses, and the inability of the neonate to generate a fever (HSV is a thermolabile organism).[32,64,144]

Eradication of HSV is dependent on NK function and cell-mediated cytolysis, both of which are reduced in the newborn, probably as a result of decreased IL-12 and interferon activity.[144] Production of IFN-γ, IFN-α, and TNF-α are reduced and delayed in neonates in response to HSV infection.[32] Because IFN-γ induces NK cells and other innate mechanisms, these responses are altered in neonates.[156] The newborn develops antigen-specific T cell proliferation and responds to HSV more slowly because of altered function of T cells and DCs.[32,72] For example, it takes the neonatal CD4+ cells 3 to 6 weeks to develop the same levels of antigen-sensitive cell response as an adult develops within 2 weeks.[32] Reduced complement and immature monocyte and macrophage responses to HSV also limit the infant's ability to respond to HSV. These changes enhance dissemination of the virus in neonates.

Production of HSV IGM antibodies in the newborn is delayed, taking at least 2 to 4 weeks before these are detected.[72] Lack of maternal IgG antibodies, which are capable of neutralizing the virus and mediating antibody-dependent cell-mediated cytotoxicity, also increases the risk of neonatal HSV infection.[72] These maternal antibodies do not provide immunity to the neonate but are correlated with a lower infection rate in exposed newborns.[156] Women with primary HSV genital infection produce little IgG, and their offspring are more likely to develop severe infection. A dose-dependent relationship has been observed between the amount of maternal anti-HSV antibody and the severity of neonatal infection, in which increasing levels of maternal antibody were associated with milder neonatal infection and a decreased incidence of disseminated infection or central nervous system involvement.[156]

Diagnosis of Neonatal Infection

Although microbiologic techniques are the basic tools used in the diagnosis of infection, other parameters that reflect changes in components of the immune system can be useful. Newborns usually have low serum levels of IgM at birth. Thus elevated IgM levels (over 20 mg/dL [0.20 g/L]) in cord blood or in the first week are suggestive of an intrauterine or intrapartally acquired nonbacterial (fungal, viral, or parasitic) infection. Elevated IgM levels are not diagnostic of infection, because an infant with an intrauterine infection may have normal IgM levels and a healthy infant may have elevated levels, especially if there was maternal bleeding into the fetal circulation during labor and birth. Generally IgM levels continue to rise in infected infants but remain stable or decrease in noninfected infants. Identification of specific IgM antibodies in cord blood to CMV, rubella, or spirochetes is evidence of intrauterine infection.[15]

The total number of white blood cells (WBCs) or percentages of individual WBC types are often not useful in diagnosing neonatal sepsis, but these values may provide evidence suggestive of infection. At birth the WBC count averages 15,000/mm³ (range of 9000 to 30,000, although some healthy infants may have lower or higher values), falling to about 12,000 by the end of the first week. Total WBC counts below 4000 to 5000/mm³ or above 25,000 to 30,000/mm³ suggest infection but are not diagnostic.[14,15,64]

The neutrophil count varies significantly in normal newborns during the first few days, with lower counts seen in preterm infants. A transient neutrophilia usually occurs during this period, so neutrophil counts of 10,000 to 25,000/µL at this time are not necessarily suggestive of infection. Neutropenia can be a useful sign of sepsis in some neonates; however, a variety of clinical factors can also lead to neutropenia (Table 13-4). Mouzinho and colleagues proposed the following reference ranges for total neutrophil counts in VLBW infants less than 1500 g and 30 weeks' gestational age: 500 to 6000 at birth; 2200 to 14,000 at 18 hours; 1100 to 8800 at 60 hours; and 1100 to 5600 at 120 hours.[108]

The differential count can also be useful in the recognition of neonatal sepsis. Normally, in the first few days after birth, most WBCs are PMN neutrophils (60%), with 20% to 40% of these neutrophils being band forms. Findings associated with infection include a relative absence of PMNs, an increased shift to the left (i.e., a predominance of immature forms of PMNs [bands, metamyelocytes, occasional myelocytes] because of an outpouring of immature cells from the bone marrow), an increase in toxic granulations in the PMNs, and an increase in the absolute number of bands or metamyelocytes (even with normal total neutrophil counts). Increased numbers of total immature neutrophils can be useful but are also influenced by infant variability and clinical factors (see Table 13-4). The absolute neutrophil count (WBC count times the sum of percentages of segmented and band forms) and the ratio of immature neutrophils to total neutrophils (I:T ratio) may also be useful. Maximum normal I:T ratio levels in term infants are 0.16 at 0 to 24 hours of age and 0.12 at 60 hours of age, with a maximum of 0.2 in preterm infants younger than 31 weeks' gestational age.[15] An increased I:T ratio suggests sepsis, but increases are also seen with other clinical conditions.

In some septic infants there is evidence of a marked decrease in the bone marrow NSP, which is normally reduced in neonates. The decreased NSP probably arises from the release of stored neutrophils in response to sepsis, the increased need for phagocytes, and an inability of the bone marrow to significantly increase production of neutrophils, because production is already near maximum capacity in the neonate.

Acute phase reactions involve proteins produced by the liver in response to inflammation because of sepsis, trauma, or other cell processes.[15] Examples of these substances are C-reactive protein (CRP), erythrocyte sedimentation rate (ESR), fibronectin, and fibrinogen. Most of these substances

TABLE 13-4   Clinical Factors Affecting Neutrophil Counts

	Neonates With Abnormal Values In:[a]				
	Total Neutrophils		TOTAL IMMATURE INCREASE	INCREASED I:T RATIO[b]	APPROXIMATE DURATION (HOURS)
COMPLICATIONS	DECREASE	INCREASE			
Maternal hypertension	++++	0	+	+	72
Maternal fever, neonate healthy	0	++	+++	++++	24
≥6 hours of antepartum oxytocin	0	++	++	++++	120
Asphyxia (5-minute Apgar ≤5)	+	++	++	+++	24–60
Meconium aspiration syndrome	0	++++	+++	++	72
Pneumothorax with uncomplicated hyaline membrane disease	0	++++	++++	++++	24
Seizures: no hypoglycemia, asphyxia, or CNS hemorrhage	0	+++	+++	++++	24
Prolonged crying (≥4 minutes)	0	++++	++++	++++	1
Asymptomatic blood glucose (≤30)	0	++	+++	+++	24
Hemolytic disease	++	++	+++	++	7–28 days
Surgery	0	++++	++++	+++	24
High altitude	0	++++	++++	0	at least 6[c]

[a]+, 0% to 25% of neonates affected; ++, 25% to 50%; +++, 50% to 75%; ++++, 75% to 100%.
[b]Immature forms/total neutrophil count.
[c]Not tested after 6 hours.
CNS, Central nervous system; *I:T ratio,* immature neutrophils to total neutrophils ratio.
From Weinberg, J.A. & Powell, K.R. (2001). Laboratory aids for diagnosis of neonatal sepsis. In J.S. Remington & J.O. Klein. (Eds.). *Infectious diseases of the fetus and newborn infant* (5th ed.). Philadelphia: Saunders.

have not been useful in diagnosing neonatal infection because of low positive predictive values (positive predictive value is the number of infants with positive test results who are infected).[15] Other investigators have examined the use of laboratory panels using combinations of these substances. Use of these panels has increased the negative predictive value (negative predictive value is the number of infants with negative test results who are not infected) but has not significantly increased the positive predictive value.[15] The acute phase reactant used most often in neonates is CRP. In many infants, the CRP is normal at the onset of infection and then rises within the next day to peak at 2 to 3 days after the onset of an infection. CRP levels remain high until the infection is controlled and the inflammatory response begins to resolve, at which point the levels decline over the next 5 to 10 days.[105] A single CRP level generally has limited usefulness in initial diagnosis of infection, but serial levels may be useful in determining antibiotic effectiveness and duration of therapy.[105]

MATURATIONAL CHANGES DURING INFANCY AND CHILDHOOD

Infants and children remain at greater risk for infection because they have lower levels of immunoglobulins compared with adults. This risk is most marked during the first 6 months because of low levels of IgG associated with a physiologic hypogammaglobulinemia. Infancy is a time when sensitivity to food substances may develop because of immaturity of gut defense mechanisms. In this section, maturation of components of the host defense system is described, followed by a discussion of the physiologic

hypogammaglobulinemia of infancy, immunizations, and the development of allergies.

Maturation of Host Defense Factors

The gut microbiome continues to develop in the first year, responding to changes in the infant's diet. A typical adult microbiome is seen by 1 year with an individually distinct and more complex profile by 2 to 3 years of age.[109,140,175] Weaning from human milk is associated with marked changes in the intestinal ecosystem.[140,175]

Serum complement levels gradually increase to adult values by 12 to 18 months.[12] T cell function is relatively mature by 3 to 6 months or sooner, although T cell absolute numbers do not reach adult levels until 6 years.[144] Chemotaxis of neutrophils is underdeveloped until 2 years, and monocyte chemotaxis is similar to adults by 5 to 6 years.[15] IgG response to protein antigens is limited in infants younger than 12 months and to polysaccharide antigens until 18 to 24 months.[147] Increased secretion of antiinflammatory cytokines decreases, and production of proinflammatory cytokines (such as IL-1β and TNF-α) increase by 12 to 18 months.[12,122] The B integrin MAC1, important in PMN adhesion, reaches adult levels in early childhood.[15]

The immune responses to bacteria that have capsular polysaccharide do not reach adult capabilities until 1.5 to 2 years.[78,107] As a result, infants are more susceptible to infections from organisms such as *H. influenzae* type B, pneumococci, and meningococci. The exact age at which other components of the immune system reach maturity is unknown, although the risk of infection with many of the pathogens associated with neonatal infection decreases after 2 to 3 months of age. CD45RO[+] cells account for less than 5% of all T cells in the newborn, increasing to 35% to 45% by 16 years. Most of this increase is during the first year.[45] IFN-γ production is similar to that of adults by 2 years.[45]

Physiologic Hypogammaglobulinemia

By 1 year of life, total levels of immunoglobulins are 60% of adult values (see Figure 13-5). During the first year, the infant's B cells secrete primarily IgM. IgM reaches 50% of adult values by 6 months and 75% to 80% by 1 year in both term and preterm infants. Adult levels of IgM are attained between 1 and 2 years.[15,123] IgA levels increase after birth and reach 20% of adult levels by 1 year. Levels of sIgA reach adult values by 10 years; serum IgA levels attain adult values during adolescence.[15,123,168] Salivary and gut IgA may reach adult levels by 5 years.[95] Because IgA protects against many respiratory and GI infections, young children are more predisposed toward developing these disorders.

IgG production by the infant is minimal during the first few months but increases significantly after 6 months of age, with a gradual increase toward adult levels in childhood.[15,123] The increase in IgG and other immunoglobulins is probably stimulated by exposure to environmental antigens. IgG_1 and IgG_3 reach 50% of adult values by 1 year and 100% by 8 years; IgG_2 and IgG_4 are 50% by 2 to 3 years and 100% by 10 to 12 years.[15,64] As a result, infants and toddlers are more susceptible to infection with *H. influenzae* type B, which is dependent on IgG_2 antibodies for opsonization of its capsular coating.[64] At term, IgG is 90% to 95% of adult values, which is greater than maternal values because maternal IgG is actively transferred across the placenta. After birth, IgG levels fall gradually as maternal IgG is catabolized. Maternally derived IgG reaches a nadir at 3 to 4 months at 400 mg/dL (4.0 g/L) and has generally disappeared by 9 months of age.[78] This fall, along with minimal IgG production by the infant, results in a physiologic hypogammaglobulinemia during the first year of life. The lowest levels of IgG occur at 2 to 4 months and remain low until at least 6 months (see Figure 13-5).

The initial 6 to 12 months is therefore a period of heightened vulnerability to infection in all infants, with a higher risk in preterm infants. Preterm infants have lower IgG levels at birth, reach lowest levels of IgG sooner, and remain at low levels longer, because the ability to synthesize IgG is more closely related to postmenstrual age than to postbirth age.[63] VLBW infants may have IgG levels lower than 100 mg/dL (1.0 g/L) by 2 to 3 months of age. The lowest IgG levels during the first few months are directly proportional to gestational age and inversely proportional to postbirth age. The period of hypogammaglobulinemia is also exaggerated in SGA infants. These infants often have lower levels of maternal antibody, probably because of placental dysfunction.

Immunizations

Although immunizations have been part of well-baby care for many years, there is still controversy regarding timing, dosage, and side effects. Current recommendations for immunizations for infants and children are published each year by the Centers for Disease Control and Prevention (CDC) and the American Academy of Pediatrics and can be found on their websites. Contraindications and precautions for individual vaccinations are available on the CDC website. The American Academy of Pediatrics has recommended that immunizations be given to preterm infants at the same chronologic age as term infants.[6] However, hospitalized infants may receive blood or blood products, and vaccinations should not be given within 14 days of these treatments, because blood or blood products may contain specific antibodies against the vaccine's antigen and interfere with the development of an appropriate immune response.[166] Preterm infants tend to be underimmunized and are often not immunized on schedule.

The ability of an infant to respond to antigens with production of specific antibodies improves after vaccination and is influenced by the stage of immune system development, type of vaccine, immunogenicity of the vaccine, number of doses, interval between doses, and maternal antibody.[36,62,170] Passive immunity from maternal IgG passage provides early protection, but the duration of protection is limited to less than 6 months for many disorders.[165] Potential obstacles to effective neonatal immunization include "impaired antigen-presenting cell (APC) responses (e.g., impaired IFN-γ production) to many (but not all) stimuli, a Th2 bias to immune responses, impaired antibody (Ab) affinity maturation, and the potential inhibitory effect of maternal antibody."[127] The primary inhibitor of infant vaccination responses appears to be maternal antibody with minimal effects of T lymphocyte response.[42] In some countries oral poliovirus, hepatitis B, and bacilli Calmette-Guerin (BCG) vaccinations are given at birth with good efficacy.[36,170]

Infant responses are not dependent on either birth weight or gestational age and are influenced more by exposure to antigens than by maturation of the immune system per se.[17] Bernbaum and colleagues examined antibody responses of term and preterm infants to diphtheria-tetanus-acellular pertussis (DTaP) vaccine injections at 2, 4, and 6 months after birth.[17] Before the first immunization, 84% of preterm and 100% of term infants had adequate antibody levels to diphtheria and tetanus (but only 16% of preterm infants and 86% of term infants to pertussis) from transplacental passage of maternal IgG. Thus preterm infants would have had fewer antibodies to protect them against these pathogens if they were exposed before being vaccinated. In addition, in preterm infants antibody levels fall below protective cut-off values sooner for disorders such as measles, mumps, varicella-zoster, rubella, *H. influenzae* type B, diphtheria, pertussis, and tetanus, increasing the risk for these disorders at earlier ages.[161] Preterm infants should receive full-dose vaccines.[6,18] Fewer than half of preterm infants who received half-dose immunizations were able to mount an appropriate serologic response after three doses and required a fourth full dose to achieve this response.[18] Thus use of half-dose immunizations with preterm infants leaves about half of these infants unprotected. Preterm infants are reported to have fewer febrile or local reactions to DTaP injections, probably because of immature primary host defense mechanisms.[17,18] However, there have been several reports of transient adverse responses to immunizations in about 13% of hospitalized preterm infants with use of combination vaccinations containing either acellular or whole cell pertussis, although data are conflicting related to methodologic issues in some studies.[53]

Passively acquired maternal antibody generally does not interfere with immunizations against diphtheria, pertussis, tetanus, or polio, perhaps because maternal antibody levels to these organisms are relatively low at the time vaccination occurs. By 1 month, infants respond adequately to tetanus and diphtheria, and after 3 months, infants respond well to pertussis. This may be why several doses of pertussis are required before an adequate antibody response is observed. Adult immunization to pertussis, which is included in the adult tetanus-diphtheria booster, may change levels of passive immunization in newborns.

IgG acquired through placental transfer from the mother can interfere with live virus immunizations by neutralizing the viruses and preventing successful vaccination. The predominance of T suppressor versus T helper cells in neonates may also interfere with the ability of an infant to respond appropriately. Therefore vaccination with live viruses is usually delayed until after the first year.

Vaccination against the hepatitis B virus (HBV) is effective early in infancy because this is an inactivated protein antigen. A combination of active and passive immunization is recommended for prevention of HBV infection in neonates.[69] Thus HBV immune globulin (HBIG) and HBV vaccine are administered to infants of HBsAg-positive women. HBIG provides passive immunity by supplying antibodies to destroy HBV antigen that the infant may have acquired from the mother during the birth process. HBIG provides initial protection for the infant, although passive immunization may not completely suppress HBV infection.[69] Because infants of carrier mothers are at constant risk of reinfection, HBV vaccine is administered to provide immunization by stimulating the infant's system to produce its own antibodies against HBV.

Development of Allergic Disease

The etiology of allergic disorders is multifactorial. Hypersensitivity to cow's milk protein and foods is more common in infants than in older children. During the first year after birth, the microbiome has strong effects on the developing immune system; some of these effects may reduce or increase the risks of allergic disorders and asthma.[67] There is increasing evidence that airway, gut, and environmental microbiota play an important role in the development of allergy disorders and asthma.[52,67,131] In addition, alterations in APC function in infancy are associated with an increased risk of developing allergic disease in later life.[93,158] Exposure to potentially allergic substances in early infancy has been believed to sensitize susceptible infants to specific ingested proteins, increasing the risk of later allergic responses. Therefore food substances known to have strong antigenic potential, such as egg white and nuts, have usually not been recommended for young infants. However, data to support a relationship between early introduction of solid foods and the development of allergic disorders are limited with few controlled trials.[154] Furthermore, exposure to potential allergens in early life may also modulate immune responses, and there may be potential benefits to early rather than delayed introduction of some foods.[49] For example, a recent study reported that the "early introduction of peanuts significantly decreased the frequency of the development of peanut allergy among children at high risk for this allergy and modulated immune responses to peanuts."[41] A consensus paper of interim recommendations developed by 10 professional groups regarding early life complementary feeding practices and the risk of allergy development has been published, with specific guidelines to follow.[49] These guidelines were recently published.[157]

Breastfeeding may enhance tolerance induction of potential allergens in the infant.[155] Risk factors for the development of food allergies include "(1) genetic predisposition to atopy, (2) immature mucosal immune system, (3) inadequate normal gut flora, (4) increase in mucosal permeability, (5) IgA deficiency or other immunological defects, (6) gastrointestinal infections, (7) formula feeding, and (8) early introduction of solid foods before 4 months of age."[28, p. 397] Young infants are more at risk to develop food allergies because of immaturity of gut defense mechanisms and the ability of the immature gut to absorb intact protein macromolecules.[28] Most infants fed cow's milk early develop IgG and IgA antibodies to cow's milk antigens. These antibodies are found from 3 to 9 months and then gradually decrease, but they may return (at lower levels) with later ingestion of cow's milk. The American Academy of Pediatrics recommends delaying introduction of solids until 6 months in infants who are exclusively breastfed and 4 to 6 months in infants fed formula.[7]

SUMMARY

The immune systems of the fetus and neonate are adaptive to the intrauterine environment and transition to the extrauterine environment. However, these alterations in their host defense mechanisms increase their risk of infection. This risk is particularly evident in relation to organisms that colonize the maternal genital tract, such as GBS and sexually transmitted diseases (e.g., HSV, HBV, HIV infections). Clinical recommendations for nurses working with neonates based on changes in host defense mechanisms are summarized in Box 13-5. By understanding the limitations of the immune system in the neonate and infant, nurses can appreciate neonatal vulnerabilities to infection from specific organisms and the risk for developing sepsis, develop increased understanding of the rationales behind specific infection control policies, and provide appropriate parent teaching.

BOX 13-5 Recommendations for Clinical Practice Related to Host Defense Mechanisms in Neonates

Recognize normal parameters for immune system components and patterns of change during the neonatal period (pp. 453-461 and Table 13-1).

Obtain and evaluate a maternal history of possible exposure to infectious organisms or potential for current illness (pp. 461-463).

Recognize risk factors for development and clinical manifestations of specific infections (pp. 461-463 and Table 13-1).

Recognize the subtle signs of infection in neonates and that fever is an uncommon sign of infection (pp. 463-464).

Recognize laboratory findings associated with an increased likelihood of neonatal infection (pp. 463-464).

Monitor neonates for signs of infection, especially infants with disruption of their skin barrier; those who are preterm, ill, small for gestational age, or stressed; or those with delayed oral feedings (pp. 461-463).

Monitor for signs of group B streptococci (GBS) and *Escherichia coli* sepsis and for meningitis in infants of mothers colonized with these organisms, especially women who do not have type-specific antibody (pp. 461-463).

Teach parents regarding methods to prevent or reduce the risk of infection in their infant (pp. 461-462, 465-466).

Monitor infants of women with chronic disorders associated with transplacental passage of antibodies for antibody-related clinical problems (pp. 448-449).

Monitor Rho(D)-positive infants of Rho(D)-negative women and type A, B, or AB infants of type O mothers for jaundice and hyperbilirubinemia (pp. 449-450).

Use Standard Precautions for blood and body fluids during the perinatal period (pp. 461-463).

Know the recommended schedule of immunizations (pp. 465-466).

Monitor infants to ensure that they receive immunizations as scheduled, especially preterm infants and infants with chronic problems (pp. 465-466).

References

1. Abbas, A. K., et al. (2014). *Cellular and molecular immunology* (8th ed.). Philadelphia: Saunders.
2. Abrahams, V. M. (2011). The role of the Nod-like receptor family in trophoblast innate immune responses. *J Reprod Immunol, 88*, 112.
3. Afrazi, A., et al. (2011). New insights into the pathogenesis and treatment of necrotizing enterocolitis: Toll-like receptors and beyond. *Pediatr Res, 69*, 183.
4. Alecsandru, D., & García-Velasco, J. A. (2015). Immunology and human reproduction. *Curr Opin Obstet Gynecol, 27*, 231.
5. Aluvihare, V. R., & Kallikourdis, M. (2005). Tolerance, suppression and the fetal allograft. *J Mol Med, 83*, 88.
6. American Academy of Pediatrics, Committee on Infectious Diseases. (2015). Immunization in special circumstances. Preterm and low birth weight infants. In D. W. Kimberlin, et al. (Eds.), *Red Book: 2015 Report of the committee on infectious disease* (30th ed.). Elk Grove Village, IL: American Academy of Pediatrics.
7. American Academy of Pediatrics Committee on Nutrition. (2013). Feeding the infant. In R. E. Kleinman & F. R. Geer (Eds.), *Pediatric nutrition* (7th ed.). Elk Grove Village, IL: American Academy of Pediatrics.
8. American College of Obstetricians and Gynecologists. (2003). *Committee Opinion #282. Immunization during pregnancy*. Washington, DC: ACOG.
9. American College of Obstetricians and Gynecologists. (2013). ACOG Committee Opinion No. 566: Update on immunization and pregnancy: Tetanus, diphtheria, and pertussis vaccination. *Obstet Gynecol, 121*, 1411.
10. American College of Obstetricians and Gynecologists, Committee on Obstetric Practice. (2014). ACOG Committee Opinion No. 608: Influenza vaccination during pregnancy. *Obstet Gynecol, 124*, 1648.
11. Andreas, N. J., Kampmann, B., & Mehring Le-Doare, K. (2015). Human breast milk: a review on its composition and bioactivity. *Early Hum Dev, 91*, 629.
12. Basha, S., Surendran, N., & Pichichero, M. (2014). Immune responses in neonates. *Expert Rev Clin Immunol, 10*, 1171.
13. Battersby, A. J., & Gibbons, D. L. (2013). The gut mucosal immune system in the neonatal period. *Pediatr Allergy Immunol, 24*, 414.
14. Bellanti, J. A., Zeligs, B. J., & Pung, H. Y. (2005). Immunology of the fetus and newborn. In M. G. MacDonald, M. M. K. Seshia, & M. D. Mullett (Eds.), *Avery's Neonatology: Pathophysiology and management of the newborn* (6th ed.). Philadelphia: Lippincott Williams & Wilkins.
15. Benjamin, J. T., et al. (2015). Developmental immunology. In R. J. Martin, et al. (Eds.), *Fanaroff and Martin's Neonatal-perinatal medicine: Diseases of the fetus and infant* (10th ed.). Philadelphia: Saunders.
16. Berger, M. (2017). The complement system of the fetus and newborn. In R. A. Polin, et al. (Eds.), *Fetal and neonatal physiology* (5th ed.). Philadelphia: Saunders.
17. Bernbaum, J., et al. (1984). Development of the premature infant's host defense mechanisms and its relationship to routine immunizations. *Clin Perinatol, 11*, 73.
18. Bernbaum, J., et al. (1989). Half-dose immunization for diphtheria, tetanus, pertussis: response of preterm infants. *Pediatrics, 83*, 471.
19. Blackburn, S. (1985). Rho(D) isoimmunization: Implications for the mother, fetus, and newborn. In *NAACOG update series* (Vol. 3). Princeton, NJ: Continuing Professional Education Center.
20. Boh, E. E. (2004). Neonatal lupus erythematosus. *Clin Dermatol, 22*, 125.
21. Borzychowski, A. M., et al. (2005). Changes in systemic type 1 and type 2 immunity in normal pregnancy and pre-eclampsia may be mediated by natural killer cells. *Eur J Immunol, 35*, 3054.
22. Brinc, D., & Lazarus, A. H. (2009). Mechanisms of anti-D action in the prevention of hemolytic disease of the fetus and newborn. *Hematology Am Soc Hematol Educ Program, 2009*, 185.
23. Bromfield, J. J. (2014). Seminal fluid and reproduction: much more than previously thought. *J Assist Reprod Genet, 31*, 627.
24. Buhimschi, C. S., & Norman, J. E. (2014). Pathogenesis of spontaneous preterm labor. In R. K. Creasy, et al. (Eds.), *Creasy & Resnik's Maternal-fetal medicine: Principles and practice* (7th ed.). Philadelphia: Saunders.
25. Bulmer, J. N., & Lash, G. E. (2015). The role of uterine NK cells in normal reproduction and reproductive disorders. *Adv Exp Med Biol, 868*, 95.
26. Cappelletti, M., et al. (2016). Inflammation and preterm birth. *J Leukoc Biol, 99*, 67.
27. Centers for Disease Control and Prevention (CDC). (2012). Updated recommendations for use of tetanus toxoid, reduced diphtheria toxoid, and acellular pertussis vaccine (TDaP) in pregnant women—Advisory Committee on Immunization Practices (ACIP), 2012. *MMWR Morb Mortal Wkly Rep, 62*, 131.
28. Chahine, B. G., & Bahna, S. L. (2010). The role of the gut mucosal immunity in the development of tolerance versus development of allergy to food. *Curr Opin Allergy Clin Immunol, 10*, 394.
29. Challis, J. R., et al. (2009). Inflammation and pregnancy. *Reprod Sci, 16*, 206.
30. Chau, V., et al. (2014). Chorioamnionitis in the pathogenesis of brain injury in preterm infants. *Clin Perinatol, 41*, 83.
31. Cordeiro, C. N., Tsimis, M., & Burd, I. (2015). Infections and brain development. *Obstet Gynecol Surv, 70*, 644.
32. Crowe, J. E., Jr., et al. (2017). Host defense mechanisms against viruses. In R. A. Polin, et al. (Eds.), *Fetal and neonatal physiology* (54th ed.). Philadelphia: Saunders.
33. Cunningham F. G., et al. (2014). *Williams obstetrics* (24th ed.). New York: McGraw-Hill.

34. Curtis, B. R. (2015). Recent progress in understanding the pathogenesis of fetal and neonatal alloimmune thrombocytopenia. *Br J Haematol, 171,* 671.

35. de Man, Y. A., et al. (2008). Disease activity of rheumatoid arthritis during pregnancy: results from a nationwide prospective study. *Arthritis Rheum, 59,* 1241.

36. Demirjian, A., & Levy, O. (2009). Safety and efficacy of neonatal vaccination. *Eur J Immunol, 39,* 36.

37. DeSesso, J. M., et al. (2012). The placenta, transfer of immunoglobulins, and safety assessment of biopharmaceuticals in pregnancy. *Crit Rev Toxicol, 42,* 185.

38. Dowling, D. J., & Levy, O. (2014). Ontogeny of early life immunity. *Trends Immunol, 35,* 299.

39. Druckmann, R., & Druckmann, M. A. (2005). Progesterone and the immunology of pregnancy. *J Steroid Biochem Mol Biol, 97,* 389.

40. Duff, P. (2014). Maternal and fetal infections. In R. K. Creasy, et al. (Eds.), *Creasy & Resnik's Maternal-fetal medicine: Principles and practice* (7th ed.). Philadelphia: Saunders.

41. Du Toit, G., et al. (2015). Randomized trial of peanut consumption in infants at risk for peanut allergy. *N Engl J Med, 372,* 803.

42. Edwards, K. M. (2015). Maternal antibodies and infant immune responses to vaccines. *Vaccine, 33,* 6469.

43. Englund, J., Glezen, W. P., & Piedra, P. A. (1998). Maternal immunization against viral disease. *Vaccine, 16,* 1456.

44. Erdos, M., et al. (2017). Host defense mechanisms against fungi. In R. A. Polin, et al. (Eds.), *Fetal and neonatal physiology* (5th ed.). Philadelphia: Saunders.

45. Erdos, M., et al. (2017). T-cell development. In R. A. Polin, et al. (Eds.), *Fetal and neonatal physiology* (5th ed.). Philadelphia: Saunders.

46. Faucette, A. N., et al. (2015). Immunization of pregnant women: future of early infant protection. *Hum Vaccin Immunother, 11,* 2549.

47. Faucette, A. N., et al. (2015). Maternal vaccination: moving the science forward. *Hum Reprod Update, 21,* 119.

48. Field, C. J. (2005). The immunological components of human milk and their effect on the immune development in infants. *J Nutr, 135,* 1.

49. Fleischer, D. M., et al. (2015). Consensus communication on early peanut introduction and the prevention of peanut allergy in high-risk infants. *World Allergy Organ J, 8,* 27.

50. Forchielli, M. L., & Walker, W. A. (2005). The role of gut-associated lymphoid tissues and mucosal defense. *Br J Nutr, 3,* S41.

51. Formby, B. (1995). Immunologic response in pregnancy. Its role in endocrine disorders of pregnancy and influence on the course of maternal autoimmune diseases. *Endocrinol Metab Clin North Am, 24,* 187.

52. Fujimura, K. E., & Lynch, S. V. (2015). Microbiota in allergy and asthma and the emerging relationship with the gut microbiome. *Cell Host Microbe, 17,* 592.

53. Gagneur, A., Pinquier, D., & Quach, C. (2015). Immunization of preterm infants. *Hum Vaccin Immunother, 11,* 2556.

54. Galofre, J. C., & Davies, T. F. (2009). Autoimmune thyroid disease in pregnancy: a review. *J Womens Health, 18,* 1847.

55. Genc, M. R., & Onderdonk, A. (2011). Endogenous bacterial flora in pregnant women and the influence of maternal genetic variation. *BJOG, 118,* 154.

56. Gleeson, M., & Cripps, A. W. (2004). Development of mucosal immunity in the first year of life and relationship to sudden infant death syndrome. *FEMS Immunol Med Microbiol, 42,* 21.

57. Gomez-Gallego, C., et al. (2016). The human milk microbiome and factors influencing its composition and activity. *Semin Fetal Neonatal Med, 6,* 400.

58. Gotsch, F., et al. (2007). The fetal inflammatory response syndrome. *Clin Obstet Gynecol, 50,* 652.

59. Groer, M. W., et al. (2015). The very low birth weight infant microbiome and childhood health. *Birth Defects Res C Embryo Today, 105,* 252.

60. Harkness, U. F., & Spinnato, J. A. (2004). Prevention and management of RhD isoimmunization. *Clin Perinatol, 31,* 721.

61. Hartwell, E. A. (1998). Use of Rh immune globulin: ASCP practice parameter. *Am J Clin Pathol, 110,* 281.

62. Hodgins, D. C., & Shewen, P. E. (2012). Vaccination of neonates: problem and issues. *Vaccine, 30,* 1541.

63. Holt, P. G., & Jones, C. A. (2000). The development of the immune system during pregnancy and early life. *Allergy, 55,* 688.

64. Hong, D. K., & Lewis, D. B. (2016). Developmental immunology and role of host defenses in fetal and neonatal susceptibility to infection. In C. B. Wilson, et al. (Eds.), *Remington and Klein's infectious diseases of the fetus and newborn infant* (8th ed.). Philadelphia: Saunders.

65. Hsu, P., & Nanan, R. (2014). Foetal immune programming: hormones, cytokines, microbes and regulatory T cells. *J Reprod Immunol, 104,* 2.

66. Jabrane-Ferrat, N., & Siewiera, J. (2014). The up side of decidual natural killer cells: new developments in immunology of pregnancy. *Immunology, 141,* 490.

67. Johnson, C. C., & Ownby, D. R. (2017). The infant gut bacterial microbiota and risk of pediatric asthma and allergic diseases. *Transl Res, 179,* 60.

68. Karimi, K., & Arck, P. C. (2010). Natural killer cells: keepers of pregnancy in the turnstile of the environment. *Brain Behav Immun, 24,* 339.

69. Karnsakul, W., & Schwarz, K. (2016). Hepatitis. In C. B. Wilson, et al. (Eds.), *Remington and Klein's infectious diseases of the fetus and newborn infant* (7th ed.). Philadelphia: Saunders.

70. Kim, J. H., et al. (2016). Human milk. In C. B. Wilson, et al. (Eds.), *Remington and Klein's infectious diseases of the fetus and newborn infant* (8th ed.). Philadelphia: Saunders.

71. Kim, Y. M., et al. (2005). Toll-like receptor 4: A potential link between "danger signals," the innate immune system, and preeclampsia? *Am J Obstet Gynecol, 193,* 921.

72. Kimberlin, D. W., & Gutierrez, K. M. (2016). Herpes simplex virus infections. In C. B. Wilson, et al. (Eds.), *Remington and Klein's infectious diseases of the fetus and newborn infant* (8th ed.). Philadelphia: Saunders.

73. Kjeldsen-Kragh, J., & Skogen, B. (2013). Mechanisms and prevention of alloimmunization in pregnancy. *Obstet Gynecol Surv, 68,* 526.

74. Koenig, J. M., & Yoder, M. C. (2004). Neonatal neutrophils: the good, the bad, and the ugly. *Clin Perinatol, 31,* 39.

75. Koenig, J. M., et al. (2017). Normal and abnormal neutrophil physiology in the newborn. In R. A. Polin, et al. (Eds.), *Fetal and neonatal physiology* (5th ed.). Philadelphia: Saunders.

76. Koga, K., Aldo, P. B., & Mor, G. (2009). Toll-like receptors and pregnancy: trophoblast as modulators of the immune response. *J Obstet Gynaecol Res, 35,* 191.

77. Koga, K., et al. (2014). Toll-like receptors at the maternal-fetal interface in normal pregnancy and pregnancy complications. *Am J Reprod Immunol, 2,* 192.

78. Kollman, T. R., & Marchant, A. (2017). Host defense mechanisms against bacteria. In R. A. Polin, et al. (Eds.), *Fetal and neonatal physiology* (5th ed.). Philadelphia: Saunders.

79. Koren, O., et al. (2012). Host remodeling of the gut microbiome and metabolic changes during pregnancy. *Cell, 150,* 470.

80. Kourtis, A. P., Read, J. S., & Jamieson, D. J. (2014). Pregnancy and infection. *N Engl J Med, 370,* 2211.

81. Kumar, S. K., & Bhat, B. V. (2016). Distinct mechanisms of the newborn innate immunity. *Immunol Lett, 173,* 42.

82. Kumar, V., & Sharma, A. (2010). Mast cells: emerging sentinel innate immune cells with diverse role in immunity. *Mol Immunol, 48,* 14.

83. Landers, C. D., Chelvarajan, R. L., & Bondada, S. (2005). The role of B cells and accessory cells in the neonatal response to TI-2 antigens. *Immunol Res, 31,* 25.

84. Landor, M. (1995). Maternal-fetal transfer of immunoglobulins. *Ann Allergy Asthma Immunol, 74,* 279.

85. La Rocca, C., et al. (2014). The immunology of pregnancy: regulatory T cells control maternal immune tolerance toward the fetus. *Immunol Lett, 162,* 41.

86. Lavoie, P. M., & Levy, O. (2017). Mononuclear phagocyte system. In R. A. Polin, et al. (Eds.), *Fetal and neonatal physiology* (5th ed.). Philadelphia: Saunders.

87. Lawrence, R. A., & Lawrence, R. M. (2016). *Breastfeeding: A guide for the medical profession* (8th ed.). Philadelphia: Elsevier.

88. Lazarus, J. H. (2005). Thyroid disease in pregnancy and childhood. *Minerva Endocrinol, 30,* 71.

89. Le Bouteiller, P. (2000). HLA-G in the human placenta: expression and potential functions. *Biochem Soc Trans, 28,* 208.

90. Lee, Y. C., & Lin, S. J. (2015). Natural killer cell in the developing life. *J Perinat Med, 43,* 11.

91. Lemke, H., et al. (2009). Benefits and burden of the maternally-mediated immunological imprinting. *Autoimmun Rev, 8,* 394.

92. Li, Q., & Zhou, J. M. (2016). The microbiota-gut-brain axis and its potential therapeutic role in autism spectrum disorder. *Neuroscience, 324,* 131.

93. Lisciandro, J. G., & van den Biggelaar, A. H. (2010). Neonatal immune function and inflammatory illnesses in later life: lessons to be learnt from the developing world? *Clin Exp Allergy, 40*, 1719.

94. Lockshin, M. D., et al. (2014). Pregnancy and rheumatic diseases. In R. K. Creasy, et al. (Eds.), *Creasy & Resnik's Maternal-fetal medicine: Principles and practice* (7th ed.). Philadelphia: Saunders.

95. MacDonald, T. T., et al. (1996). The ontogeny of the mucosal immune system. In W. A. Walker, et al. (Eds.), *Pediatric gastrointestinal disease* (2nd ed.). St. Louis: Mosby.

96. Maldonado, Y. A., et al. (2016). Current concepts of infections of the fetus and newborn infant. In C. B. Wilson, et al. (Eds.), *Remington and Klein's infectious diseases of the fetus and newborn infant* (8th ed.). Philadelphia: Saunders.

97. Marchant, A., & Goldman, M. (2005). T cell-mediated immune responses in human newborns: ready to learn? *Clin Exp Immunol, 141*, 10.

98. Märker-Hermann, E., & Fischer-Betz, R. (2010). Rheumatic diseases and pregnancy. *Curr Opin Obstet Gynecol, 22*, 458.

99. McMaster, M. T., Lim, K. H., & Taylor, R. N. (1998). Immunobiology of human pregnancy. *Curr Prob Obstet Gynecol Fertil, 21*, 1.

100. Moffett, A., & Colucci, F. (2014). Uterine NK cells: active regulators at the maternal-fetal interface. *J Clin Invest, 124*, 1872.

101. Moffett, A., Hiby, S. E., & Sharkey, A. M. (2015). The role of the maternal immune system in the regulation of human birthweight. *Philos Trans R Soc Lond B Biol Sci, 370*, 20140071.

102. Moise, K. J. (2014). Hemolytic disease of the fetus and newborn. In R. K. Creasy, et al. (Eds.), *Creasy & Resnik's Maternal-fetal medicine: Principles and practice* (7th ed.). Philadelphia: Saunders.

103. Molloy, E. J. (2004). Labor promotes neonatal neutrophil survival and lipopolysaccharide responsiveness. *Pediatr Res, 56*, 99.

104. Moore, K. L., Persaud, T. V. N., & Torchia, M. G. (2015). *The developing human: Clinically oriented embryology* (10th ed.). Philadelphia: Saunders.

105. Mor, G., & Abrahams, V. M. (2014). The immunology of pregnancy. In R. K. Creasy, et al. (Eds.), *Creasy & Resnik's Maternal-fetal medicine: Principles and practice* (7th ed.). Philadelphia: Saunders.

106. Mor, G., & Kwon, J. Y. (2015). Trophoblast-microbiome interaction: a new paradigm on immune regulation. *Am J Obstet Gynecol, 213*, S131.

107. Moriyama, I., et al. (1987). Infection and the functional immaturity of the fetal immune system. In K. Maeda (Ed.), *The fetus as patient Ō¥87 (Proceedings of the Third International Symposium)*. Amsterdam: Excerpta Medica.

108. Mouzinho, A., et al. (1994). Revised reference ranges for circulating neutrophils in very-low-birth-weight neonates. *Pediatrics, 94*, 76.

109. Mueller, N. T., et al. (2015). The infant microbiome development: mom matters. *Trends Mol Med, 7*, 109.

110. Munoz-Suano, A., Hamilton, A. B., & Betz, A. G. (2011). Gimme shelter: the immune system during pregnancy. *Immunol Rev, 241*, 20.

111. Murgas Torrazza, R., & Neu, J. (2011). The developing intestinal microbiome and its relationship to health and disease in the neonate. *J Perinatol, 31*, S29.

112. Nagamatsu, T., & Schust, D. J. (2010). The immunomodulatory roles of macrophages at the maternal-fetal interface. *Reprod Sci, 17*, 209.

113. Nahmias, A. J., & Kourtis, A. P. (1997). The great balancing acts: the pregnant woman, placenta, fetus, and infectious agents. *Clin Perinatol, 24*, 497.

114. Nancy, P., & Erlebacher, A. (2014). T cell behavior at the maternal-fetal interface. *Int J Dev Biol, 58*, 189.

115. National Center for Immunization and Respiratory Diseases. (2011). General recommendations on immunization—recommendations on the Advisory Committee on Immunization Practices (ACIP). *MMWR Recomm Rep, 60*, 1.

116. Nayak, A., et al. (2010). The non-classical functions of the classical complement pathway recognition subcomponent C1q. *Immunol Lett, 131*, 139.

117. Neuman, H., & Koren, O. (2017). The pregnancy microbiome. *Nestle Nutr Inst Workshop Ser, 88*, 1.

118. Noetzel, M. J., & Burnstrom, J. E. (2001). The vulnerable oligodendrocyte, inflammatory observations on a cause of cerebral palsy. *Neurology, 66*, 1254.

119. O'Shea, T. M., & Dammann, O. (2000). Antecedents of cerebral palsy in very low-birth weight infants. *Clin Perinatol, 27*, 285.

120. Ostensen, M. (1999). Sex hormones and pregnancy in rheumatoid arthritis and systemic lupus erythematosus. *Ann N Y Acad Sci, 876*, 131.

121. Østensen, M., et al. (2015). State of the art: Reproduction and pregnancy in rheumatic diseases. *Autoimmun Rev, 14*, 376.

122. Palmeira, P., et al. (2012). IgG placental transfer in healthy and pathological pregnancies. *Clin Dev Immunol, 2012*, 985646.

123. Pappas, B. E. (1999). Primary immunodeficiency disorders in infancy. *Neonatal Netw, 18*, 13.

124. Patel, R. M., & Denning, P. W. (2015). Intestinal microbiota and its relationship with necrotizing enterocolitis. *Pediatr Res, 78*, 232.

125. Petroff, M. G., & Perchellet, A. (2010). B7 family molecules as regulators of the maternal immune system in pregnancy. *Am J Reprod Immunol, 63*, 506.

126. Petroff, M. G. (2011). Review: Fetal antigens—identity, origins, and influences on the maternal immune system. *Placenta, 32*, S176.

127. Philbin, V. J., & Levy, O. (2009). Developmental biology of the innate immune response: implications for neonatal and infant vaccine development. *Pediatr Res, 65*, 98R.

128. Piccinni, M. P. (2010). T cell tolerance towards the fetal allograft. *J Reprod Immunol, 85*, 71.

129. Polak, M., et al. (2004). Fetal and neonatal thyroid function in relation to maternal Graves disease. *Best Pract Res Clin Endocrinol Metab, 18*, 289.

130. Priddy, K. D. (1997). Immunologic adaptations during pregnancy. *J Obstet Gynecol Neonatal Nurs, 26*, 388.

131. Rachid, R., & Chatila, T. A. (2016). The role of the gut microbiota in food allergy. *Curr Opin Pediatr, 28*, 748.

132. Richani, K., et al. (2005). Normal pregnancy is characterized by systemic activation of the complement system. *J Matern Fetal Neonatal Med, 17*, 239.

133. Racicot, K., et al. (2014). Understanding the complexity of the immune system during pregnancy. *Am J Reprod Immunol, 72*, 107.

134. Riley, J. K., & Nelson, D. M. (2010). Toll-like receptors in pregnancy disorders and placental dysfunction. *Clin Rev Allergy Immunol, 39*, 185.

135. Rizzo, R., et al. (2011). The importance of HLA-G expression in embryos, trophoblast cells, and embryonic stem cells. *Cell Mol Life Sci, 68*, 341.

136. Robertson, S. A., et al. (2009). Activating T regulatory cells for tolerance in early pregnancy—the contribution of seminal fluid. *J Reprod Immunol, 83*, 109.

137. Robertson, S. A. (2010). Immune regulation of conception and embryo implantation—all about quality control? *J Reprod Immunol, 85*, 51.

138. Rodger, M., et al. (2015). Haematological problems in obstetrics. *Best Pract Res Clin Obstet Gynaecol, 29*, 671.

139. Rodríguez, J. M., et al. (2015). The composition of the gut microbiota throughout life, with an emphasis on early life. *Microb Ecol Health Dis, 26*, 1.

140. Romano-Keeler, J., & Weitkamp, J. H. (2015). Maternal influences on fetal microbial colonization and immune development. *Pediatr Res, 77*, 189.

141. Sacchi, F., et al. (1982). Differential maturation of neutrophil chemotaxis in term and preterm newborn infants. *J Pediatr, 101*, 273.

142. Saliba, E., & Henrot, A. (2001). Inflammatory mediators and neonatal brain damage. *Biol Neonate, 79*, 224.

143. Sappenfield, E., Jamieson, D. J., & Kourtis, A. P. (2013). Pregnancy and susceptibility to infectious diseases. *Infect Dis Obstet Gynecol, 2013*, 752852.

144. Schelonka, R. L., & Infante, A. J. (1998). Neonatal immunology. *Semin Perinatol, 22*, 2.

145. Schumacher, A., & Zenclussen, A. C. (2015). The paternal contribution to fetal tolerance. *Adv Exp Med Biol, 868*, 211.

146. Shynlova, O., et al. (2013). Physiologic uterine inflammation: integration of endocrine and mechanical signals. *Reprod Sci, 20*, 154.

147. Siegrist, C. A., & Aspinall, R. (2009). B-cell responses to vaccination at the extremes of age. *Nat Rev Immunol, 9*, 185.

148. Silasi, M., et al. (2015). Viral infections during pregnancy. *Am J Reprod Immunol, 3*, 199.

149. Spencer, S. J., Galic, M. A., & Pittman, Q. J. (2011). Neonatal programming of innate immune function. *Am J Physiol Endocrinol Metab, 300*, E11.

150. Srinivasan, L., et al. (2017). Cytokines and inflammatory response in the fetus and neonate. In R. A. Polin, et al. (Eds.), *Fetal and neonatal physiology* (5th ed.). Philadelphia: Saunders.

151. Stafford, I. P., & Dildy, G. A. (2005). Myasthenia gravis and pregnancy. *Clin Obstet Gynecol, 48*, 48.

152. Stagnaro-Green, A., et al. (1992). A prospective study of lymphocyte initiated immunosuppression in normal pregnancy: evidence of a T-cell etiology for postpartum thyroid dysfunction. *J Clin Endocrinol Metab, 74*, 645.

153. Svensson-Arvelund, J., et al. (2014). The placenta in toxicology. Part II: Systemic and local immune adaptations in pregnancy. *Toxicol Pathol, 42*, 327.

154. Tarini, B. A., et al. (2006). Systematic review of the relationship between early introduction of solid foods to infants and the development of allergic disease. *Arch Pediatr Adolesc Med, 160*, 502.

155. Tawia, S. (2015). Development of oral tolerance to allergens via breastmilk. *Breastfeed Rev, 23*, 35.

156. Thellin, O. (2000). Tolerance to the foetoplacental "graft": ten ways to support a child for nine months. *Curr Opin Immunol, 12*, 731.

157. Togias, A., et al. (2017). Addendum guidelines for the prevention of peanut allergy in the United States: Report of the National Institute of Allergy and Infectious Diseases-Sponsored Expert Panel. *Pediatr Dermatol, 34*, e1.

158. Upham, J. W., et al. (2009). Plasmacytoid dendritic cells during infancy are inversely associated with childhood respiratory tract infections and wheezing. *J Allergy Clin Immunol, 124*, 707.

159. Urbaniak, S. J., & Greiss, M. A. (2000). RhD haemolytic disease of the fetus and the newborn. *Blood Rev, 14*, 44.

160. Vael, C., & Desager, K. (2009). The importance of the development of the intestinal microbiota in infancy. *Curr Opin Pediatr, 21*, 794.

161. van den Berg, J. P., et al. (2011). Transplacental transport of IgG antibodies to preterm infants: a review of the literature. *Early Hum Dev, 87*, 67.

162. Verani, J. R., & Schrag, S. J. (2010). Group B streptococcal disease in infants: progress in prevention and continued challenges. *Clin Perinatol, 37*, 375.

163. Verani, J. R., et al. (2010). Prevention of perinatal group B streptococcal disease—revised guidelines from CDC, 2010. *MMWR Recomm Rep, 59*, 1.

164. Voisin, G. A. (1998). Immunology understood through pregnancy. *Am J Reprod Immunol, 40*, 124.

165. Waaijenborg, S., et al. (2013). Waning of maternal antibodies against measles, mumps, rubella, and varicella in communities with contrasting vaccination coverage. *J Infect Dis, 208*, 10.

166. Weiner, C., & Buhimschi, C. (2009). *Drugs for pregnant and lactating women* (2nd ed.). London: Churchill Livingstone.

167. Whitsett, J. A. (2010). Review: The intersection of surfactant homeostasis and innate host defense of the lung: lessons from newborn infants. *Innate Immun, 16*, 138.

168. Williams, C. B., Eisenstein, E. M., & Cole, F. S. (2012). Immunology of the fetus and newborn. In C. A. Gleason & S. Devaskar (Eds.), *Avery's Diseases of the newborn* (9th ed.). Philadelphia: Saunders.

169. Witkin, S. S., et al. (2011). Unique alterations in infection-induced immune activation during pregnancy. *BJOG, 118*, 145.

170. Wood, N., & Siegrist, C. A. (2011). Neonatal immunization: where do we stand? *Curr Opin Infect Dis, 24*, 190.

171. Wu, Y. W., & Colford, J. M. (2000). Chorioamnionitis as a risk factor for cerebral palsy. *JAMA, 284*, 1417.

172. Wynn, J., et al. (2010). The host response to sepsis and developmental impact. *Pediatrics, 125*, 1031.

173. Wynn, J. L., & Levy, O. (2010). Role of innate host defenses in susceptibility to early-onset neonatal sepsis. *Clin Perinatol, 37*, 307.

174. Yadav, A. K., Madan, T., & Bernal, A. L. (2011). Surfactant proteins A and D in pregnancy and parturition. *Front Biosci (Elite Ed), 3*, 291.

175. Yang, I., et al. (2016). The infant microbiome: implications for infant health and neurocognitive development. *Nurs Res, 65*, 76.

176. Yektaei-Karin, E., et al. (2007). The stress of birth enhances in vitro spontaneous and IL-8-induced neutrophil chemotaxis in the human newborn. *Pediatr Allergy Immunol, 18*, 643.

177. Zrour, S. H., et al. (2010). The impact of pregnancy on rheumatoid arthritis outcome: the role of maternofetal HLA class II disparity. *Joint Bone Spine, 77*, 36.

Integumentary System

The integumentary system consists of the skin and its append-ages: eccrine, apocrine, apoeccrine, and sebaceous glands; hair; and nails. Functions of the skin include protection from physical and chemical injury, infection, and ultraviolet radiation; modula-tion of transepidermal water fluxes; prevention of fluid loss and fluid and electrolyte imbalances; and thermoregulation. The skin is also important in sensation (pain, pressure, touch, and tem-perature) and tactile discrimination, contributes to maintenance of blood pressure by dilation or constriction of the peripheral capillaries, and contains precursor molecules for vitamin D.[47]

The skin and its associated structures are markedly altered during pregnancy. These changes are seen in most pregnant women, and although the changes themselves are seldom associ-ated with serious physiologic consequences, they are of concern to most women because of the subsequent cosmetic alterations, some of which may persist after delivery. In addition, there are several dermatologic disorders that are seen almost exclusively in pregnant women that can cause severe physical discomfort and may be associated with increased fetal morbidity. For the neonate, the skin is a sophisticated and critical sensory organ for obtaining and receiving information about the environment. Tactile sensation is the first sensory system to develop and ma-ture. Because the neonate is an immunologically immature host, the integrity of the skin as a barrier to that same environ-ment is essential to the survival and well-being of the infant. In addition, the skin plays a major role in the establishment of the infant microbiome at birth. Immaturity of the skin alters its permeability, immunologic capacity, bonding of the epidermis to the dermis, and role in thermoregulation and fluid balance. As a result, neonates, especially preterm and ill infants, are at risk for toxicity from topical substances, infection, skin excoriation, fluid loss, and thermal instability.

MATERNAL PHYSIOLOGIC ADAPTATIONS

Physiologic changes in the skin and its appendages during pregnancy and the postpartum period include alterations in pigmentation; connective and cutaneous tissue; integumentary vascular system; hair, nails, and secretory glands; and pruritus. Some integumentary alterations regress completely during the postpartum period; others recede but never completely disap-pear. Many of these alterations are secondary to the hormonal changes of pregnancy, although some changes are also induced by intravenous volume expansion and compression by the enlarging uterus.[96] Cells in the skin and appendages respond to these changes in various ways, depending on the tissue in-volved, including keratinocyte proliferation, angiogenesis, me-lanogenesis, collagen synthesis, and increased T helper (Th2) T lymphocytes (see Chapter 13).[96]

Antepartum Period

The basis for changes in the skin, hair, and secretory glands dur-ing pregnancy is believed to be primarily hormonal—especially the effects of estrogens and adrenocortical steroids. Similar al-terations are often seen in women using oral contraceptives. There is a familial tendency or genetic predisposition for some of the cutaneous and vascular changes.[71,110]

Alterations in Pigmentation

Alterations in pigmentation are common during pregnancy and include hyperpigmentation of specific areas of the body and melasma (chloasma). In early pregnancy, hyperpigmenta-tion is believed to result from the effects of estrogens and progesterone on β- and α-melanocyte stimulating hormone and melanocytes.[84,96,104] This finding is also consistent with reports of alterations in pigmentation associated with use of oral contraceptives.[33] Progression is also believed to be related to the effects of placental corticosteroid-releasing hormone and of proopiomelanocortin peptides such as adrenocortico-tropic hormone (ACTH), melanocyte-stimulating hormone (MSH), β-endorphin (see Chapter 19), and possibly placental lipid stimulation of tyrosinase (enzyme involved in produc-tion of melanin and thus pigmentation).[71,81,84,87,104]

Hyperpigmentation. Hyperpigmentation is the most com-mon integumentary alteration during pregnancy. Changes in pigmentation are seen in up to 91% of pregnant women, tend to be more common in women with dark hair or com-plexions, begin in the first trimester, and are progressive throughout pregnancy.[84,96] Most women experience a mild, generalized increase in pigmentation that is especially prominent in areas of the body that tend to be naturally more intensely pigmented. These areas include the areolae, genital skin, axillae, inner aspects of the thighs, and linea alba.[30,58,71,84,104]

The linea alba is a tendinous median line that extends along the anterior of the abdomen from the umbilicus to the symphysis pubis and occasionally superiorly to the xiphoid process. Hyperpigmentation during pregnancy causes the linea alba to darken and become the linea nigra. Up to one-third of women on oral contraceptives also develop a linea nigra. Pigmentary changes tend to fade during the postpartum period in fair-skinned women, but some pigmentary changes may remain in women with darker skin and hair. Hyperpigmentation may be exacerbated by sun exposure.[30,58,84,87]

Freckles, nevi, and recent scars may darken during pregnancy, perhaps because of an upregulation of receptors for estrogens and progesterone on the nevus cell surface.[96] Existing melanocytic nevi may increase in size or new nevi may develop during pregnancy, although some have reported that existing melanocytic nevi do not change significantly during pregnancy. Increased malignant degeneration of nevi is not seen during pregnancy. Prophylactic removal of nevi after pregnancy may be considered. Any nevi showing signs suggestive of malignancy should be excised immediately.[30,58,84,87]

Although rare, some women may develop pigmentary demarcation lines, which are areas of hypopigmentation that follow the distribution of peripheral cutaneous nerves and disappear after delivery. The lines are believed to be related to prolonged uterine compression of these nerves, particularly at S1-S2, leading to a sharp demarcation between pigmented and hypopigmented areas.[79,84]

Melasma. Melasma (also known as *chloasma* or the "mask of pregnancy") is a common occurrence in pregnant women (seen in 45% to 75%).[4,18,51,71,87,104] Melasma is characterized by irregular, blotchy areas of pigmentation on the face, usually bilateral and symmetric and seen most commonly on the cheeks, chin, and nose.[71,96] The areas of altered pigmentation are not elevated and can range in color from light to dark brown. Three distribution patterns have been described: centrofacial (63%), involving the cheeks, forehead, upper lip, nose, and chin; malar (21%), over the cheeks and nose; and mandibular (16%), over the ramus of the mandible.[4] Three histologic patterns have also been identified: epidermal (increased deposition of melanin in the melanocytes of the basal and suprabasal layers), which is seen in 70% of women; dermal (macrophages with large amounts of melanin can be found in both the papillary and reticular layers of the dermis), which is seen in 10% to 15%; and a mixed form, which is seen in 2%.[4,58] Although these pigmentary changes tend to fade completely within 1 year after pregnancy, they may persist (especially in dark-haired individuals).[84,87]

Melasma is associated with increased expression of α-melanocyte–stimulating hormone in the involved skin area.[84] There is a genetic predisposition toward development of melasma.[4,89] Melasma is most common in women with dark hair and complexions, is exacerbated by the sun, and tends to recur (often with increased intensity) in subsequent pregnancies or with use of oral contraceptives.[13,104] Other risk factors for development of melasma include chronic sun exposure and antidepressant or anxiolytic use.[40,96]

Avoidance of sun tanning during pregnancy, use of hats to prevent facial exposure to sun, and use of sunscreens with sun protective ratings greater than 15 may reduce the severity of melasma (Table 14-1).[96] Because melasma often fades spontaneously after pregnancy, treatment is generally limited to the less than 10% of individuals with persistent pigmentation postpartum.[71] Various depigmenting formulas have been developed to treat persistent melasma, with varying success. These formulas tend to be relatively effective on epidermal-type melasma but have little effect on the dermal type. Treatment may need to be continued for 5 to 7 weeks before satisfactory results are achieved. Topical 2% to 5% hydroquinone with or without retinoic acid and corticosteroids has also been used postpartum, again with varying success. This treatment can result in complications such as hypopigmentation, hyperpigmentation, and contact dermatitis.[4,13,84,87,110] Hydroquinone and retinoic acid have teratogenic risks and thus should be avoided during pregnancy and lactation.[96]

Changes in Connective Tissue

Striae gravidarum (also called *linear striae, striae distensae,* or *linear stretch marks*) are linear tears in dermal collagen that are commonly seen during pregnancy. These markings initially appear as irregular, pink or purple, wrinkled linear streaks that gradually become white. Striae are most prominent by 6 to 7 months and occur in 50% to 80% of pregnant women, especially those with lighter skin.[84,104] They appear initially over the abdomen oriented in opposition to skin tension lines and later on the breasts, thighs, and inguinal area. Striae are more common in younger women with greater total weight gain during pregnancy, obese women, and women with larger-birth-weight infants.[96] In addition, there appears to be a familial tendency.[4,71,84,96,110]

Striae gravidarum usually fade after pregnancy but never completely disappear, remaining as depressed, irregular white bands. Some women report striae itching, although because both pruritus and striae formation are prominent over the abdominal area during pregnancy, these two phenomena may not be related. There is no effective treatment to prevent striae formation. Topical emollients and antipruritics may be used (see Table 14-1). However, the effectiveness of topical agents such as cocoa butter, vitamin E, tretinoin, and olive oil and of massage to prevent striae formation has not been substantiated in controlled studies.[14,71,87] A meta-analysis found no evidence that any topical preparation prevented striae.[14]

Striae gravidarum are believed to arise from hormonal alterations, especially of estrogens, relaxin, and corticosteroids, along with alterations in the dermal support matrix with stretching.[96] The increased levels of estrogens, corticosteroids, and relaxin relax the adhesiveness between collagen fibers and foster formation of mucopolysaccharide ground substance, which causes separation of the fibers and striae formation. The increased glucocorticosteroids during pregnancy may decrease dermal fibroblasts and collagen synthesis. Mast cells, which contain hormonal receptors for estradiol, also increase. Mast cells release enzymes to lyse collagen.[4,58,87,110] Striae are also associated with alteration in genes that encode for elastic microfibrils.[102]

TABLE 14-1   Nursing Management and Recommendations for Common Problems During Pregnancy Related to the Integumentary System

ALTERATION	INTERVENTION
All alterations	Provide anticipatory teaching regarding the appearance of the alteration.
	Counsel regarding the basis for the alteration and course.
	Evaluate the effect on body image and relationship with partner and provide counseling.
Hyperpigmentation	Avoid sun tanning during pregnancy and use broad-spectrum (protective factor greater than 15) sunscreen.
	Use nonallergenic cover-ups.
Melasma	Avoid suntanning during pregnancy or when using oral contraceptives.
	Use broad-spectrum sunscreen (rating of 15 or greater).
	Use nonallergenic cover-ups.
	Counsel regarding the risk of similar changes with oral contraceptives.
	Counsel regarding alternative methods of birth control.
	Counsel regarding use of sunscreen and protection from sun with sunscreen use after pregnancy.
Striae gravidarum	Use topical emollients or antipruritics as required.
	Use supportive garments for the breasts and abdomen.
Spider nevi	Reassure that most fade after pregnancy.
	Use cosmetic cover-up creams.
	Suggest considering electrocauterization if of great concern to the patient.
Nonpitting edema	Elevate legs when sitting or lying down and when sleeping.
	Avoid prolonged standing or sitting.
	Rest in the left lateral decubitus position.
	Suggest water immersion (standing or with exercise).
	Exercise.
	Avoid excessive added salt.
	Avoid tight clothing and girdles.
	Try elastic stockings (although their effectiveness is controversial).
Varicosities	Elevate the legs when sitting or lying down and sleep in the Trendelenburg position.
	Avoid prolonged standing or sitting.
	Rest in the left lateral decubitus position.
	Exercise.
	Use a sitz bath for hemorrhoids.
	Avoid tight clothing.
	Wear elastic stockings or support hose.
Increased eccrine gland activity	Wear light, loose clothing.
	Increase fluid intake.
	Bathe or shower regularly.
Pruritus	Wear loose nonsynthetic clothing.
	Use cool compresses and take baths or showers.
	Use oatmeal baths.
	Use adequate skin lubrication.
	Consider topical antipruritics, emollients, and calamine lotion.

Vascular and Hematologic Changes

Vascular changes during pregnancy related to the integumentary system include development of spider angiomas, palmar erythema, nonpitting edema, cutis marmorata, purpura, hemangiomas, and varicosities. Purpura and scattered petechiae may be seen on the legs of some women and are a result of decreased capillary integrity with increased hydrostatic pressure.[4] These usually resolve postpartum. Vascular changes are a result of distention, instability, and proliferation of blood vessels mediated by changes in pituitary, adrenal, and placental hormones with increased release of angiogenic growth factors.[58,87,96] Other alterations in the hematologic and vascular systems are described in Chapters 8 and 9.

Vasomotor Instability. Vasomotor instability during pregnancy may result in facial flushing, feelings of hot or cold, pallor, and cutis marmorata.[4,43,79,96] Cutis marmorata is a transient bluish mottling of the legs that is exaggerated on exposure to cold. It arises from vasomotor instability secondary to elevated estrogens. Persistence postpartum is abnormal and may suggest underlying pathology such as collagen vascular disorders, systemic lupus erythematosus, or vasculitis. Other changes from vasomotor instability during pregnancy include pallor, facial flushing, and heat and cold sensations. Purpura secondary to increased capillary fragility and permeability occurs during the last months of pregnancy in many women.[87,110]

Spider Angioma. Spider angioma (also called *spider nevi, spider telangiectases,* or *nevus araneus*) are found in 10% to 15% of normal adults, in individuals with liver dysfunction, and in up to two-thirds of pregnant women. These lesions are more common in pregnant women of Western European descent (60% to 70% by term) than pregnant women of African descent (10% by term).[43] Spider angiomas consist of a central dilated arteriole that is flat or slightly raised with extensive radiating capillary branches. They are most prominent in areas of the skin drained by the superior vena cava (i.e., around the eyes, neck, throat, and arms). The basis for formation has been related to increased estrogen, because these structures are more common both during pregnancy and with use of oral contraceptives. However, many individuals with spider angioma associated with liver disorders do not have elevated estrogen levels.[58,110] Liver function should be evaluated in women with excessive spider angioma during pregnancy, because abnormal liver function is associated with decreased estrogen catabolism.[96]

Spider angiomas generally appear between 2 and 5 months of pregnancy and may increase in size and number as pregnancy progresses. These structures tend to regress spontaneously and fade within the first 7 weeks to 3 months after delivery, although they rarely completely disappear. They may recur or enlarge during subsequent pregnancies. Unresolved spider angiomas can be treated by pulsed-dye laser or electrodesiccation therapy.[84]

Palmar Erythema. Palmar erythema is seen with pregnancy, liver disease, hyperthyroidism, estrogen therapy, and collagen vascular diseases.[84,96] Two patterns of palmar erythema are seen during pregnancy: erythema of hypothenar and thenar eminences, palms, and fleshy portions of the fingertips and diffuse mottling of the entire palm.[96] The latter form is more common and similar to changes seen with hyperthyroidism and cirrhosis. Palmar erythema generally appears during the first two trimesters and disappears by 1 week after delivery.[96,104] This phenomenon has a familial tendency and is seen in approximately two thirds of pregnant women of Western European descent and one third of pregnant women of African descent.[104] Spider angioma and palmar erythema often occur together, suggesting a common cause, generally believed to be elevated estrogen levels with increased skin blood flow.[4,30,43,58,81,110] No treatment is needed. Palmar erythema resolves after delivery.

Nonpitting Edema. Increased vascular permeability and sodium retention because of the effects of estrogens and corticosteroids result in transient nonpitting edema of the face, hands, and feet during late pregnancy.[43,79,96] In the lower extremities, this is aggravated by pressure from the growing uterus. Nonpitting edema occurs in the face, especially the eyelids, in approximately 50% of women and in the lower extremities in 70% and is not associated with preeclampsia.[87,110] Although most pronounced in the morning, it usually improves during the day. Interventions for nonpitting edema during pregnancy are listed in Table 14-1. Vulvar edema may also be seen.

Capillary Hemangiomas. Preexisting capillary hemangiomas may increase in size during pregnancy.[4,87] In up to one-third of pregnant women, new hemangiomas appear by the end of the first trimester, with slight, slow enlargement during the remaining trimesters.[43,110] New hemangiomas usually appear on the head and neck and are unusual elsewhere.[87] Enlarged existing hemangiomas and new hemangiomas regress postpartum but may not completely disappear. Hemangioma development in pregnancy is related to elevated estrogen.[110]

Varicosities. Varicosities develop in approximately 40% of pregnant women beginning in the second month.[96] Varicosities occur most commonly in the legs but may also appear in the pelvic vessels, vulva, and anal area with hemorrhoid

formation. Varicosities arise from estrogen-induced elastic tissue fragility, vascular distension, relaxin-weakened collagen and elastin, increased venous pressure in the lower extremities and pelvis from pressure of the gravid uterus, and familial tendency for valvular incompetence.[4,58,79,87,110] Varicosities generally regress postpartum but do not completely disappear. Thrombi are rare with leg varicosities but are more common with hemorrhoids. Hemorrhoids are discussed in Chapter 12.

Alterations in Cutaneous Tissue and Mucous Membranes

The most common mucous membrane alterations are changes in the vagina and cervix, which are seen in all pregnant women, and gingivitis, which is seen in many women. A less common oral finding is a cutaneous lesion of the gums known as *angiogranuloma, epulis,* or *granuloma gravidarum.* Epulis and gingivitis are discussed in Chapter 12. Increased flow to the nasal mucosa leads to rhinitis in up to one-third of women.[59] Jacquemier-Chadwick and Goodell signs are vascular changes that are early signs of pregnancy. Jacquemier-Chadwick sign is characterized by erythema of the vestibule and vagina; Goodell sign is characterized by increased vascularity of the cervix.[58,87]

Another cutaneous change during pregnancy is the development of or increase in the number of existing skin tags called *molluscum fibrosum gravidarum* (also called *acrochordons* or, if large, *fibroepithelial polyps*).[4,71,81,87] These are soft, skin-colored or hyperpigmented skin tags, which are small (usually 1 to 5 mm), pedunculated fibromas that appear during the second half of pregnancy, primarily on the lateral aspects of the face and neck, upper axillae, groin, and between and underneath the breasts.[104] The cause of fibromata molle is unknown, but is believed to be hormonal. These skin tags are more common in the second half of pregnancy, when they may increase in size and number. These growths may regress or clear spontaneously after delivery, although many remain. Remaining skin tags can be excised.[58,71,81,84,87,110]

Alterations in Secretory Glands

Activity of the sebaceous, apocrine, and eccrine glands of the skin is altered during pregnancy. Sebaceous gland activity is generally reported to increase during pregnancy.[4,81,110] Many pregnant women report that their skin, especially on the face, feels "greasy." Some women may develop acne, often for the first time, although women with existing acne may or may not experience worsening of the acne.[4,58] These changes are related to increased ovarian and placental androgens.[58,84] Montgomery tubercles (small sebaceous glands on the areola) enlarge, beginning as early as 6 weeks' gestation.[96] Changes in Montgomery tubercles and the breasts are described in Chapter 5.

Apocrine sweat gland activity decreases during pregnancy, possibly as a result of hormonal changes.[4,96,110] Eccrine sweat gland activity increases gradually during pregnancy, possibly because of increased thyroid activity along with increased

DEVELOPMENT OF THE INTEGUMENTARY SYSTEM IN THE FETUS

Anatomic Development

The basic structure of the skin develops during the first 60 days of gestation. Around the time of transition from embryo to fetus, the skin undergoes a series of rapid morphologic changes, including keratinization of the epidermal appendages (around 15 weeks) and interfollicular epithelium (around 22 to 24 weeks).[23] By the end of the third trimester, the structure of the skin is similar to that of the adult; however, its barrier properties are still immature, especially in infants born before term.[23] Further maturation of the skin occurs within the first weeks after birth and during infancy.[11,76,97,105]

The skin consists of the epidermis and dermis with an underlying subcutaneous layer (Figure 14-1). The epidermis consists of an outer stratum corneum; the stratum granulosum; and the stratum germinativum, which consists of the stratum spinosum and stratum basale (adjacent to the epidermal-dermal junction). The basal layer contains melanocytes (pigment-producing cells) and keratinocytes. Keratinocytes, the major cell of the epidermis, develop from stem cells in the basal layer and migrate outward to cornify the outer layer.[23] The stratum corneum is the barrier layer and consists of keratinocytes linked by lipids. Underneath the epidermis lies the dermis, formed from fibrous protein, collagen, and elastin fibers woven together in a hydrated glycosaminoglycan matrix.[49] The dermis (see Figure 14-1) contains the nerves and blood vessels that nourish the skin cells and carry sensations from the skin to the brain. Mechanical properties of the dermis include tensile strength, compressibility, resilience, and elasticity.[23] The dermis and subcutaneous fat develop from the mesoderm.[49] The subcutaneous layer is composed of fatty connective tissue that provides insulation and caloric storage.[66] The epidermis and dermis, along with their vascular and neural networks, develop concurrently. Epidermal appendages such as hair follicles, sweat glands, and sebaceous glands develop from the ectoderm.[49]

Epidermis

Development of the epidermis "is characterized by coordinated establishment of increasing numbers of cell layers concomitant with expansion of skin surface area and cellular (keratinocyte) differentiation."[23] The epidermis develops from undifferentiated ectoderm at 5 to 8 weeks.[47] It initially consists of a single layer of cuboidal cells that develop from the outer germinal stratum (surface ectoderm) and can be identified during the third week of gestation (Figure 14-2, A). By 30 to 40 days, two layers are seen: the inner basal layer and the outer periderm (Figure 14-2, B).[48] The definitive epidermis develops from the basal layer.

The periderm is a transient embryonic layer that disappears in the second half of gestation.[23,48] The periderm serves as the protective barrier for the embryo and fetus until the end of the second trimester and forms part of the vernix caseosa.[47,48] Until the underlying layers develop, active transport occurs across the periderm between the amniotic fluid and the embryo; thus the periderm acts as a nutrient interface with amniotic fluid.[47,48] The outer border of the periderm rapidly proliferates between 11 and 14 weeks with formation

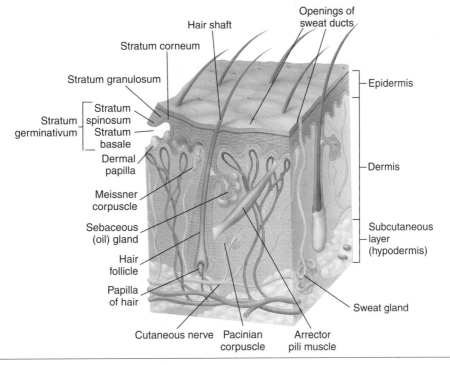

FIGURE 14-1 Structural components of the epidermis, dermis, and subcutaneous tissue. (From Thibodeau, G.A. & Patton, K.T. [2007]. *Anatomy and physiology* [6th ed.]. St. Louis: Mosby.)

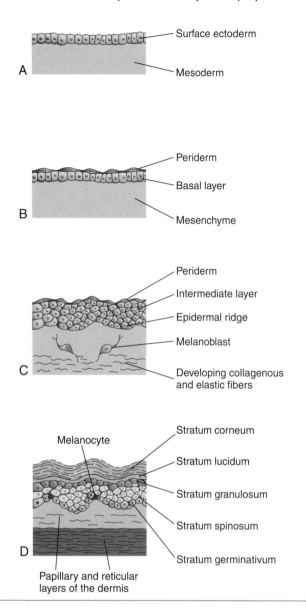

FIGURE 14-2   Successive stages of skin development. **A,** At 4 weeks. **B,** At 7 weeks. **C,** At 11 weeks. **D,** Neonate. Observe the melanocytes in the basal layer of the epidermis; their processes extend between the epidermal cells to supply them with melanin. (From Moore, K.L., Persaud, T.V.N., & Torchia, M.G. [2015]. *The developing human: Clinically oriented embryology* [10th ed.]. Philadelphia: Elsevier Saunders.)

of blebs and microvillus projections, which are coated with very fine filaments.[47] Development of the epidermis is under the influence of epidermal growth factor (EGF); matrix adhesion is believed to be mediated by actin-associated α6B4 integrin.[47,48] Cell surface receptors for EGF are found on both the basal layer and periderm.[23]

By 60 days, the epidermis has three layers (Figure 14-2, *C*): the basal layer, an intermediate layer, and the superficial periderm. The intermediate layer becomes more complex by the end of the fourth month, when the epidermis has stratified. The epidermal strata are the stratum basale; the stratum spinosum, which is made up of large polyhedral cells connected by tonofibrils; the stratum granulosum, which contains small keratohyalin granules; and the stratum corneum, which is made up of dead cells packed full of keratin.[90] Peridermal cells are replaced continuously until regression begins around 18 weeks. Shedding of peridermal cells begins in the scalp, plantar surfaces, and face, areas where keratinization first begins.[19] The periderm gradually undergoes regression and apoptosis as the stratum corneum and vernix caseosa develop. The epidermis is keratinized in skin appendages at 11 to 15 weeks and in the interfollicular area at 22 to 24 weeks.[23,29] As stem cells in the stratum germinativum proliferate, they develop down-growths (epidermal ridges) that extend into the dermis (see Figure 14-2, *D*).

Protoplasmic fibers and cellular bridges begin to form. These make up the stratum spinosum, eventually protecting the neonate from dehydration and reducing permeability to noxious substances. From 11 to 18 weeks, this layer has an abundance of glycogen to provide energy for growth.[17] Glycogen reserves decrease around 18 weeks.[47] Keratogenic structures become evident, leading to regional differences in epidermal thickness. By 24 weeks, the skin has largely concluded its period of histogenesis and moves into a period of structural and functional maturation (Figure 14-2, *D*).[23]

Ridge patterns (future fingerprints) are genetically determined, although modified by the intrauterine fluid environment, and can be seen on the surface of the hands and soles of the feet.[70] These ridges are seen between 11 and 17 weeks in the hands and between 12 and 18 weeks in the feet.[17] Because of these environmental influences, even identical twins have differences in their fingerprints. Chromosomal abnormalities such as Down syndrome modify the ridge pattern.

Keratins are produced in the stratum germinativum by 2 months and increase rapidly as the epidermis stratifies.[25] Keratinocytes are arranged in columnar fashion adjacent to the dermis.[23] Keratinocyte maturation is stimulated by several different growth factors, including EGF, transforming growth factors, insulin-like growth factors, and fibroblast growth factor.[17] The first signs of keratinization are seen by 22 to 24 weeks.[19,23]

As replacement keratinocytes mature, they rise and move through the stratum granulosum and acquire keratohyalin granules. As they continue to travel upward, the keratinocytes lose 85% of their water content and their organelles, which are replaced by keratin.[17,23,89] As the keratinocytes dehydrate and flatten, they adhere to each other to form a tough, resilient, and relatively impermeable membrane—the stratum corneum.[81] Transit time for a keratinocyte from the basal layer to the uppermost stratum takes approximately 28 days.[70] By 5 months, the periderm is completely shed, mixing with secretions from the sebaceous glands to form the vernix caseosa.[90]

The stratum corneum becomes thicker and more organized with increasing gestation, but it is not well defined until 23 to 24 weeks' gestation.[19,49] The stratum corneum is more fully developed by 34 weeks but still immature compared with older children and adults.[11,29,34,76,97,105] Formation of the scalp are in different stages of the hair cycle, depending on their location. Frontal and parietal hairs are moving to telogen; occipital hairs are in anagen and move to catagen/telogen by 8 to 12 weeks postbirth.[16] At birth the synchrony of hair growth (anagen) and hair loss (telogen) is transiently altered, so hair may become thick and coarse or be lost (temporary alopecia).[47] The postnatal hair cycle lasts 2 to 6 months; length of an individual hair is determined by the length of the anagen phase.[39] Hair on the scalp at birth reflects metabolic activity from week 28 on and therefore may be useful for assessment of prenatal exposures to drugs and other toxins.[39]

Initially the skin is covered with the yellow-white vernix caseosa that provides an insulating, protective layer. The Association of Women's Health, Obstetric and Neonatal Nurses (AWHONN) skin care guidelines recommend leaving the vernix intact after birth and allowing it to wear off with usual caregiving.[2] Removal results in exposure of the stratum corneum to the much drier postnatal environment, with desquamation of the upper layers of the stratum corneum. After the first week, visible desquamation gives way to normal proliferation and flaking, signaling adaptation. This drying out of the skin is part of the natural maturational process. Any interference in this keratinization (e.g., use of lotions or creams) only delays the development of an effective barrier and prolongs the difficulties associated with an immature cutaneous surface, such as increased water loss and thermal instability. Common neonatal skin variations are summarized in Table 14-4.

Once these initial stages are complete the skin continues to develop protective functions, providing the needed environmental barrier. This development includes the discharge of water and electrolytes, an acid mantle, resorptive capacities, generalized pigmentation, and regulation of blood circulation and nerve supply. Factors affecting infant skin condition are summarized in Figure 14-3.

TABLE 14-4   Normal Neonatal Skin Variations

CONDITION	CHARACTERISTICS
Milia	1-mm yellow-white cysts
	Appears on cheeks, forehead, nose, and nasolabial folds
	Commonly occur in clusters
	Affect 40% of all infants
Miliaria	Develops within the first 12 hours
	Caused by obstructed eccrine sweat ducts
	Appears on forehead and skin folds
	Superficial, thin-walled grouped vesicles (miliaria crystallina) or deep, grouped red papules (miliaria rubra)
Erythema toxicum	Most common transient lesion
	Irregular erythematous macules or patches with yellow or white central papule
	Can affect any area of body except palms and soles
	Appears between 24 and 72 hours after birth; may continue to appear for up to 3 weeks; lesions dissipate in a few days
	More often affects full-term infants (30%–70%)
Mongolian spots	Macular, gray-blue without sharp borders
	Most common in lumbosacral region
	Covers an area 10 cm or larger
	Caused by delayed disappearance of dermal melanocytes
	Affects up to 70%–90% of African-descent, Asian, and Native American infants and 5%–13% of white infants
	Gradually disappears over first few years of life
Harlequin color change	Transient color change usually appearing in first few days and sometimes up to 3 weeks of age, lasting a few minutes to half an hour
	Midline demarcation; dependent side red; upper side pale
	Caused by temporary autonomic imbalance of cutaneous vasculature
	Nonsignificant
	More common in preterm infants
Ecchymoses	Subcutaneous hemorrhage
	Localized
	Usually seen over presenting part
Neonatal acne (cephalic pustulosis)	Small red papules and pustules on face
	Resolves spontaneously within 2–4 weeks
	Rarely associated with comedones or cysts
Café au lait spots	Brown macules or patches
	Less than 3 cm in diameter
	Occur occasionally in newborns; more common in infants of African descent
	With six or more spots of greater than 0.5-cm diameter, the infant is at risk for underlying neurofibromatosis
Junctional (melanocytic) nevi	Flat, macular, purpura, or plaquelike pigmented lesions
	Brown to black
	Less than 1 cm
	Most develop later in childhood
	Neonatal risk minimal; with aging, risk for later melanoma, especially with large lesions

Continued

TABLE 14-4   Normal Neonatal Skin Variations—cont'd

CONDITION	CHARACTERISTICS
Hemangiomas	Relatively common Developmental vascular anomaly Capillary hemangiomas: dilated vessels Cavernous hemangiomas: large, dilated, blood-filled cavities; 65% are superficial; 15% are subcutaneous; 20% are mixed
Salmon patch hemangioma ("stork bites")	Occurs in up to 70%–75% of normal newborns Flat macular hemangioma Appears on nape of neck, eyelids, and glabellar area Indistinct borders Blanches with pressure Facial lesions disappear by 1 year of age; neck stains more permanent
Nevus flammeus	Port-wine stain hemangioma Sharply delineated Blanches only slightly Purple to red or jet black Does not involve If distributed over trigeminal territory of face, angiomatous malformation of the brain may occur (i.e., Sturge-Weber syndrome)
Strawberry hemangioma	Raised bright red capillary lesion with sharply demarcated borders Blanches with pressure Rarely seen immediately at birth; 90% manifest in neonatal period Increases in size for 4–9 months Most resolve spontaneously by early childhood Two times more common in females
Cavernous hemangioma	Deeper; less common Margins obscured by overlying epidermal tissue Reddish-blue Somewhat compressible Increases in size after birth
Cradle cap	Seborrheic eczema Reactive response to irritant Scaling lesions Greasy feeling

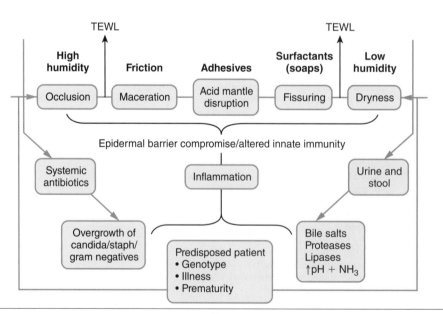

FIGURE 14-3   Factors affecting infant skin condition. The phenotype of infant skin results from the complex interplay of genotype and multiple environmental factors (humidity, friction, adhesive trauma, soap exposure). Considerations such as prematurity, illness (e.g., diarrhea), or the use of systemic antibiotics may affect regional skin health and lead to alterations in barrier function. *TEWL,* Transepidermal water loss. (From Hoath, S.B. & Narendran, V. [2011]. The skin. In R.J. Martin, A.A. Fanaroff, & M.C. Walsh. [Eds.]. *Fanaroff & Martin's neonatal-perinatal medicine: Diseases of the fetus and infant* [9th ed.]. St. Louis: Mosby, p. 1735.)

application of nonperfumed, preservative-free emollient can be used.

Umbilical Cord Care

Cord care practices are often embedded in cultural and institutional tradition. Practices range from no care to cleansing with triple dye (brilliant green, gentian violet, and proflavine hemisulfate), povidone-iodine, CHG, isopropyl alcohol, or antimicrobial ointments. There are few data on the most effective method.[52,66,94] Generally dry cord care is recommended.[91]

Aseptic cord care decreases cord bacterial colonization but not necessarily the risk of infection and delays cord separation.[3,32,52,72] The current trend in both developed and developing countries is toward dry cord care.[111] Developing countries have a high cord infection rate; however, few studies demonstrate that antiseptic cord care reduces this rate.[72] A Cochrane review by Zupan and colleagues of 21 studies (with 8959 subjects primarily from developed countries) found no difference in infection rates between dry cord care, placebo, and antiseptic use and also found that the use of antiseptics prolonged the time to cord separation.[114] Similar findings have been reported in preterm infants.[32] Aseptic care has been associated with decreased maternal concerns about the cord.[114] However, Zupan and colleagues also concluded that "there appears to be no good reason to stop use of antiseptics in situations where bacterial infection remains high."[114] A Cochrane review of studies from developing countries found use of CHG for umbilical cord care significantly reduced mortality.[95]

Use of Adhesives

Removal of adhesives can damage the skin with separation of epidermal layers or separation of the epidermis from the dermis.[68] Because the epidermis is pulled off when adhesives are removed, up to 70% to 90% of the stratum corneum can be stripped off in immature infants. In adults it takes 10 adhesive removals to disrupt the skin barrier versus only one removal of plastic tape, pectin barrier, or adhesive tape to do so in a preterm infant.[65] Silicone tapes and hydrogel-baked electrodes are gentler adhesives that may reduce skin injury.[54] Lund and colleagues compared plastic tape, pectin barrier, and hydrophilic gel use in the first week after birth in infants born at 24 to 40 weeks' gestation.[65] They found that pectin barriers and plastic tape had the highest colorimeter and vaporimeter scores, suggesting greater epidermal injury with these products than with hydrophilic gels. Skin barrier function returned to baseline by 24 hours. Although gel adhesives seemed preferable, they did not adhere as well to the skin as other products and thus required more frequent replacement.[65]

Denuded areas are a potential source of infection; they are also uncomfortable and are areas of increased fluid loss. Use of transparent semipermeable occlusive dressings, water-activated gel electrodes, and minimal tape to secure monitoring equipment and intravenous lines may reduce injury.

Transparent dressings are impermeable to water and bacteria while also providing protection to abrasions and skin irritation. These dressings can also be used to cover line insertion sites or incision sites from invasive procedures. The advantages of this type of dressing include providing an optimal moist environment for healing, allowing serous exudate to form over the wound, facilitating migration of new cells across the wound area, and preventing cellular dehydration.[45]

Skin-bonding agents such as benzoin or Mastisol should not be used to promote adhesion because of the already significant cohesion that occurs with tape.[66] These substances increase tape-epidermis adhesion and potentiate epidermal stripping upon tape removal. In addition, benzoin is absorbed through the skin, allowing acids to be released into the bloodstream. Adhesive removal products should also be avoided in immature infants because of concerns about increased skin permeability.

Protection From Infection

Protection from infection requires that the skin, as the first line of defense against infection, stay intact. Current monitoring modalities require manipulation and attachment of equipment to the infant's epidermal layer. Careful handling can reduce shear damage and epidermal sloughing. Application of noninvasive monitoring equipment needs to be done such that pressure or constriction of blood flow does not occur. Crater formation may occur in preterm infants with very thin skin. The use of heated electrodes can lead to local hyperthermia and erythema. Increasing the frequency of site changes may also reduce skin damage. Extreme care should be used when removing the adherent ring or using equipment that allows for electrode site changes without moving the ring each time.

There is a lack of clear evidence regarding the best agent for skin antisepsis with procedures in neonates, with safety and potential toxicity concerns (see Transepidermal Absorption) for all agents.[80,91] CHG or povidone-iodine with removal afterward are used, although safety issues, including skin irritation and chemical burns with CHG use, are a concern.[80] Isopropyl alcohol or alcohol-based disinfectants are not recommended for use with VLBW infants until after their stratum corneum has formed.[47]

Topical emollients have been used for preventing infection in preterm infants. However, a recent Cochrane review of 21 studies (n = 3089) from different countries did not find evidence that use of these agents prevented invasive infection or death in preterm infants in high-, middle-, or low-income settings.[24]

Transepidermal Absorption

Percutaneous absorption of substances can occur through two pathways: via the cells of the stratum corneum (the transepidermal route) and via the hair follicle–sebaceous gland complex (the transappendageal route). The major pathway is most likely the transepidermal route, with diffusion of a

---

BOX 14-3   Factors Placing Neonates at Risk for Toxic Reactions Secondary to Absorption of Topically Applied Substances

Increased permeability of the skin
Increased surface area–to–body weight ratio
Lower blood pressure
Variable skin blood flow patterns
Greater proportion of body weight being made up of brain and liver
Incomplete kidney development resulting in changes in drug excretion
Different body compartment ratios
Larger total body water content
Elevated ratio of intracellular to extracellular water
Decreased adipose tissue

From West, D., Worobec, S., & Solomon, L. (1981). Pharmacology and toxicology of infant skin. *J Invest Dermatol, 76,* 147.

---

substance through the stratum corneum and epidermis into the dermis and microcirculation. In addition, the subepidermal circulation is readily accessible, enhancing rapid absorption. Gases such as oxygen and carbon dioxide also move across the epidermal barrier, which is the basis for transcutaneous electrodes.[49]

Neonates are at increased risk for toxic reactions from absorption of topically applied substances for the reasons listed in Box 14-3. Lists of potential adverse effects of topical agents in neonates are available in the literature.[47] Along with these differences, skin metabolism is different in neonates, so drugs applied topically may result in the release of metabolites different from those that would occur if the drugs were given by other routes. This increases the risk of toxicity. Occlusion of the skin (e.g., placement against the mattress) permits more complete absorption, with longer contact enhancing absorption of the substance. In preterm infants, percutaneous absorption occurs even more rapidly and completely as a result of their increased skin permeability.

The history of neonatal practice demonstrates the problems with the use of topical agents. For example, hexachlorophene was formerly used to prevent coagulase-positive staphylococci colonization; this practice was later found to increase the risk of central nervous system damage.[56] Eventually the U.S. Food and Drug Administration modified the allowable uses of hexachlorophene. Current practices also can lead to detrimental effects if not monitored carefully. Topical application of povidone-iodine yields significantly elevated levels of iodine in blood plasma if not removed completely from the skin after completion of invasive procedures (e.g., chest tube insertion, percutaneous line insertion).[1] CHG at 0.5% has been reported to be superior to 10% povidone-iodine in decreasing colonization of peripheral catheters, possibly because of skin residues that prolong the half-life of the latter.[91]

Gentle cleansing of the skin with water removes these residues and reduces this risk. In addition to risks of epidermal stripping with use of benzoin, this substance contains many different acids, all of which can be absorbed, causing either immediate or delayed reactions.

Isopropyl alcohol is also absorbed through the skin. Alcohol use can result in dry skin, skin irritation, and skin burns. The concentration of the solution, duration of exposure, and condition of the exposed skin determine the effects of alcohol use. Tissue destruction occurs with the de-esterifying of the skin and the disruption of the cell structure. Exposure, pressure, and decreased perfusion can contribute to the development of burns from alcohol, complicating fluid management and providing portals for infection.[41]

Extremely Immature Infants

Extremely low-birth-weight (ELBW) infants have edematous, friable, gelatinous skin that is covered with abundant lanugo. These infants have decreased subcutaneous tissue and increased water content. This is compounded by a greater ratio of surface area to body weight. All of these characteristics create difficulties in fluid balance and temperature control because of the high TEWL.[88,89] Infants born at 23 weeks have little stratum corneum with TEWL of 75 $g/m^2/hour$; at 26 weeks the stratum corneum has a few cornified layers and TEWL is 45 $g/m^2/hour$, decreasing to 17 $g/m^2/hour$ by 29 weeks.[108] TEWL increases the risk of dehydration, hypothermia, and fluid and electrolyte imbalances. Double-walled incubators, plastic or thermal blankets, and polyethylene skin wraps reduce TEWL and promote thermal stability (see Chapter 20). Polyethylene wraps and bags are recommended for use with preterm infants to reduce heat loss after birth and in the early days postbirth.[8,9,10,15,85] These wraps enhance radiant heat gain and reduce evaporative losses, insensible water loss (IWL), and TEWL by creating a microenvironment under the wrap.[9] Unwrapping the infant disrupts this microenvironment, so it should be minimized.[9]

Humidity also decreases TEWL. Ambient humidity is inversely related to TEWL in VLBW infants.[49] Humidity alters breakdown of epidermal filaggrin to form NMF to hydrate the skin; NMF levels are low in preterm infants in low humidity settings.[108] Increasing the ambient humidity to 85% eliminates almost all evaporative losses; however, use of very high humidity is accompanied by concerns of infection from water-borne organisms.[49] Other products to prevent or manage barrier compromise in preterm infants include gel-filled mattresses or pads, transparent semiocclusive dressings, and hydrocolloid dressings.[45,47,49]

The preterm infant's skin is exceedingly sensitive. Skin permeability and collagen instability increase with decreasing gestational age. Cohesion at the dermoepidermal junction is also markedly reduced, which can cause stratum corneum and epidermal stripping with handling and attachment of monitoring devices. Careful handling and policies about skin adhesive practices should be used. The maintenance of skin integrity should be the goal. Denuded areas may benefit from transparent dressings, thereby reducing further damage, providing protection from microbial invasion, and reducing fluid losses.

The stratum corneum is extremely thin; therefore cutaneous permeability is greater, providing little protection against topical substances. Percutaneous absorption occurs more rapidly and completely, placing these infants at greater risk for toxic reactions.[56] The use of harsh de-esterifying substances (soaps and alcohol) should be kept to an absolute minimum. The acid mantle is easily disrupted, and cellular destruction is possible. Use of 70% isopropyl alcohol should be avoided with these infants, because alcohol is more irritating and less effective than povidone-iodine and CHG.[62] Use of any of these products should be judicious and followed by complete removal with sterile water.

Collagen instability and incomplete dermal structures result in increased cutaneous edema and decreased resiliency. This may result in skin necrosis from edema pressure within the dermis. The use of gentle handling with little compression force or friction, careful regular turning, and gentle range-of-motion exercises may help to reduce this tendency.

MATURATIONAL CHANGES DURING INFANCY AND CHILDHOOD

Although term infants' skin is functionally comparable to adult skin, loss of water content, desquamation, and drying of the stratum corneum enhance further maturation of skin function within the first few days. The stratum corneum and epidermis remain thinner than that of adults throughout infancy.[97,98] Skin barrier function development is reflected in maturation of skin water-handling (the water transport and storage properties of the stratum corneum) characteristics. For at least the first year after birth, differences between infants and adults are seen in the distribution and transport of water in superficial skin layers.[11,35,76,97,105] Stratum corneum hydration is similar to or higher than that of adults from 3 to 48 months, with higher skin surface water content for at least the first year.[34] TEWL reaches adult levels at different times depending on body part. For example, the forehead, abdomen, and legs are similar to adults after the first week, whereas the palms, soles, and forearms reach adult levels by 12 months.[12]

Collagen stability results in a decreased ability to retain fluid within the dermis. This improves with increasing gestational age and in the early postnatal period. Most of the other components of the dermis are not formed until after birth and may not be mature until 3 years of age. Skin resiliency is therefore affected and is low in term infants and even lower in preterm infants.

Melanin production and pigmentation are low during neonatal life, although high circulating maternal and placental hormones can lead to deep pigmentation of certain areas (i.e., linea alba, areolae, and scrotum). This decrease in production is even greater in preterm infants. Given that melanin protects the skin from the ultraviolet rays of the sun by absorbing their radiant energy, neonates have an increased sensitivity to sunlight.[26] Sunburn can damage the barrier effectiveness of the skin by causing dehydration and desquamation and can increase the risk of later development of skin cancer.

Although the sweat glands are functional within a short time of birth, activating influences are different in infants than in adults. For the first 2.5 years of life, the sweat glands function irregularly and the total number of glands that are active is small. Emotionally induced eccrine sweating is much less marked in the prepubertal period than in adults. The sebaceous glands are also somewhat dormant until puberty.

The sebaceous glands are large and active in utero, contributing to the lipid content of the vernix caseosa. After birth, these glands rapidly decrease in size between 2 months and 2 years and remain small and quiescent until puberty. At puberty, they once again become active structures.[23,47] The free fatty acids in the gland secretions have a fungistatic effect and provide immunity against scalp infections from these pathogens. Sebum secretion increases after birth, reaching adult values by 1 month and then decreasing after 6 months to values below those of adults until puberty.[12,34]

The vasculature also changes over the first year of life. Initially the cutaneous capillary network is underdeveloped and disorganized; a progression to an orderly mature pattern occurs during infancy.[47]

SUMMARY

The skin plays a major role in the protection of neonates from the environment into which they are born. The development of the acid mantle and microbial colonization provide protection against pathogenic organisms. The thickness of the stratum corneum determines the effectiveness of this protection and reduces permeability to the loss of fluids and absorption of topical substances.

Gestational age is the major determinant of collagen and elastin stability, the thickness of the stratum corneum barrier, and thermal regulatory abilities. Delivery results in a rapid proliferation of the stratum corneum in preterm infants as an attempt to compensate for some of the liabilities with which these infants must cope. The fragility of the premature infant's skin causes denuded areas to result from friction and shearing forces, as well as separation of the epidermis through adhesive stripping.

Understanding the normal developmental processes that the integumentary system undergoes as well as the goal of each of these processes provides the basis for nursing therapeutics. Careful assessment of skin integrity, knowledge of normal neonatal variations, and conservative therapeutics can result in appropriate and timely interventions. The care of the skin can enhance integumentary capabilities and contribute to the infant's ability to assimilate information from the environment. Clinical implications for nursing practice are summarized in Box 14-4.

BOX 14-4   Recommendations for Clinical Practice Related to the Integumentary System in Neonates

GENERAL CONSIDERATIONS FOR SKIN CARE

Know normal development and limitations of the neonatal integumentary system (pp. 484-489).

Know the normal integumentary variations encountered in the neonate (Table 14-4).

Monitor skin integrity on a routine basis (pp. 484-489).

Maintain a neutral thermal environment (pp. 488-489] and Chapter 20).

Evaluate intake, output, and hydration status (p. 488 and Chapter 11).

Avoid routine use of lubricants (pp. 485, 490-491).

Bathe only as needed using plain water (or neutral soaps if needed for highly soiled areas) (pp. 490-491).

Counsel parents to use caution in exposing the infant to direct sunlight (p. 493).

FLUID AND HEAT LOSS

Use thermal blankets or plastic wrappings to reduce losses (pp. 488, 492-493 and Chapter 20).

Monitor phototherapy equipment use and position (pp. 488, 492-493 and Chapter 18).

Monitor environmental and body temperature regularly (pp. 488, 492-493 and Chapter 20).

Avoid removing vernix (pp. 484-485).

Assess skin for stratum corneum stripping and institute measures to reduce it (pp. 489, 491-493).

Maintain appropriate humidity levels within the nursery (pp. 488, 492-493 and Chapter 20).

BARRIER MAINTENANCE

Implement minimal tape–use policies (pp. 489, 491-493).

Avoid using adhesive bandages (pp. 489, 491-493).

Remove tape carefully, using warm water to facilitate the process (pp. 489, 491-493).

Avoid benzoin preparations (pp. 491-492).

Implement plain-water bathing of preterm infants (pp. 490-491).

Ensure appropriate positioning, avoiding pressure on bony prominences and friction stress points (pp. 492-493).

Use alcohol sparingly (pp. 487, 492).

Promote careful handling of preterm infants (pp. 492-493).

Recognize activities that produce friction, shearing, or stress, and implement interventions to reduce them (pp. 488, 492-493).

PERMEABILITY

Avoid routine lubrication (pp. 490, 492-493).

Know the factors that place neonates at risk for toxic responses to topically applied substances (pp. 487, 491-492 and Box 14-3).

Practice conservative treatment of integumentary disruptions (pp. 484-485, 487, 489-493).

Counsel parents regarding the use of topical emollients and powders (pp. 490-491).

Avoid the use of benzoin (pp. 491-492).

Ensure immediate cleansing of skin prepped with antiseptic agents after invasive procedures (pp. 491-493).

Avoid alcohol, or use sparingly, on skin (pp. 487, 492).

References

1. Afsar, F. S. (2009). Skin care for preterm and term neonates. *Clin Exp Dermatol*, 34, 855.

2. Association of Women's Health, Obstetric and Neonatal Nurses. (2013). *Neonatal skin care: Evidence-based clinical practice guideline* (3rd ed.). Washington, DC: AWHONN.

3. Aygun, C., Subasi, A., & Kucukoduk, S. (2005). Timing of umbilical cord separation and neonatal intensive care unit practices. *Am J Perinatol*, 22, 249.

4. Barankin, B., Silver, S. G., & Carruthers, A. (2002). The skin in pregnancy. *J Cutan Med Surg*, 6, 236.

5. Beard, M. P., & Millington, G. W. (2012). Recent developments in the specific dermatoses of pregnancy. *Clin Exp Dermatol*, 37, 1.

6. Bechtel, M. A., & Plotner, A. (2015). Dermatoses of pregnancy. *Clin Obstet Gynecol*, 58, 104.

7. Bell, E. F., et al. (2016). Fluid and electrolyte management. In M. G. MacDonald & M. M. K. Seshia (Eds.), *Avery's Neonatology: Pathophysiology and management of the newborn* (7th ed.). Philadelphia: Wolters Kluwer.

8. Belsches, T. C., et al. (2013). Randomized trial of plastic bags to prevent term neonatal hypothermia in a resource-poor setting. *Pediatrics*, 132, e656.

9. Bissinger, R. L., & Annibale, D. J. (2010). Thermoregulation in very-low-birth-weight infants during the golden hour: results and implications. *Adv Neonatal Care, 10*, 230. Erratum in: Adv Neonatal Care (2010), 10, 351.

10. Bissinger, R. L., & Annibale, D. J. (2014). *Golden Hours: care of the very low birth weight infant*. Chicago: The National Certification Corporation.

11. Blume-Peytavi, U., et al. (2009). Bathing and cleansing in newborns from day 1 to first year of life: recommendations from a European round table meeting. *J Eur Acad Dermatol Venereol*, 23, 751.

12. Blume-Peytavi, U., et al. (2012). Skin care practices for newborns and infants: review of the clinical evidence for best practices. *Pediatr Dermatol*, 29, 1.

13. Bolanca, I., et al. (2008). Chloasma—the mask of pregnancy. *Coll Anthropol*, 32, 139.

14. Brennan, M., Young, G., & Devane, D. (2012). Topical preparations for preventing stretch marks in pregnancy. *Cochrane Database Syst Rev, 2012*(11), CD000066.

15. Butler, D. C., Heller, M. M., & Murase, J. E. (2014). Safety of dermatologic medications in pregnancy and lactation: Part II. Lactation. *Am Acad Dermatol*, 70, 417.e1–10.

16. Camacho-Martínez, F. M. (2009). Hair loss in women. *Semin Cutan Med Surg*, 28, 19.

17. Carlson, B. M. (2013). *Human embryology & developmental biology* (5th ed.). Philadelphia: Saunders.

18. Carroll, P. D., et al. (2010). Use of polyethylene bags in extremely low birth weight infant resuscitation for the prevention of hypothermia. *J Reprod Med*, 55, 9.

19. Cartlidge, P. (2000). The epidermal barrier. *Semin Neonatol*, 5, 273.

20. Ceovic, R., et al. (2013). Psoriasis: female skin changes in various hormonal stages throughout life—puberty, pregnancy, and menopause. *Biomed Res Int, 2013*, 571912. Epub 2013 Dec 28.

21. Chi, C. C., et al. (2010). Systematic review of the safety of topical corticosteroids in pregnancy. *J Am Acad Dermatol*, 62, 694.

22. Chiou, Y. B., & Blume-Peytavi, U. (2004). Stratum corneum maturation. A review of neonatal skin function. *Skin Pharmacol Physiol*, 17, 57.

23. Chu, D. H., & Loomis, C. A. (2017). Structure and development of the skin and cutaneous appendages. In R. A. Polin, et al. (Eds.), *Fetal and neonatal physiology* (5th ed.). Philadelphia: Saunders.

24. Cleminson, J., & McGuire, W. (2016). Topical emollient for preventing infection in preterm infants. *Cochrane Database Syst Rev, 2016*(1), CD001150.

25. Cohen, B. A., & Püttgen, K. B. (2012). Newborn skin: Development and basic concepts. In C. A. Gleason & S. Devaskar (Eds.), *Avery's Diseases of the newborn* (9th ed.). Philadelphia: Saunders.

26. Cypess, A. M., & Kahn, C. R. (2010). The role and importance of brown adipose tissue in energy homeostasis. *Curr Opin Pediatr*, 22, 478.

27. da Cunha, M. L., & Procianoy, R. S. (2005). Effect of bathing on skin flora of preterm newborns. *J Perinatol*, 25, 375.

28. Driscoll, M. S., & Grant-Kels, J. M. (2009). Nevi and melanoma in the pregnant woman. *Clin Dermatol, 27*, 116.

29. Dyer, J. A. (2013). Newborn skin care. *Semin Perinatol, 37*, 3.

30. Elling, S. V., & Powell, F. C. (1997). Physiological changes in the skin during pregnancy. *Clin Dermatol, 15*, 35.

31. Elser, H. E. (2013). Bathing basics: how clean should neonates be? *Adv Neonatal Care, 3*, 188.

32. Evens, K., et al. (2004). Does umbilical cord care in preterm infants influence cord bacterial colonization or detachment? *J Perinatol, 24*, 100.

33. Farage, M. A., Neill, S., & MacLean, A. B. (2009). Physiological changes associated with the menstrual cycle: a review. *Obstet Gynecol Surv, 64*, 58.

34. Fluhr, J. W., et al. (2010). Functional skin adaptation in infancy—almost complete but not fully competent. *Exp Dermatol, 19*, 483.

35. Fluhr, J. W., et al. (2012). Infant epidermal skin physiology: adaptation after birth. *Br J Dermatol, 166*, 483.

36. Fox, C. E., et al. (1998). The timing of skin acidification in very low birth weight infants. *J Perinatol, 18*, 272.

37. Furdon, S. A., & Clark, D. A. (2003). Scalp hair characteristics in the newborn infant. *Adv Neonatal Care, 3*, 286.

38. Garcia Bartels, N., et al. (2009). Influence of bathing or washing on skin barrier function in newborns during the first four weeks of life. *Skin Pharmacol Physiol, 22*, 248.

39. Gareri, J., & Koren, G. (2010). Prenatal hair development: implications for drug exposure determination. *Forensic Sci Int, 196*, 27.

40. Handel, A. C., et al. (2014). Risk factors for facial melasma in women: a case-control study. *Br J Dermatol, 171*, 588.

41. Harpin, V. A., & Rutter, N. (1982). Percutaneous alcohol absorption and skin necrosis in a premature infant. *Arch Dis Child, 57*, 477.

42. Harpin, V. A., & Rutter, N. (1982). Sweating in preterm babies. *J Pediatr, 100*, 614.

43. Henry, F., et al. (2006). Blood vessel changes during pregnancy: a review. *Am J Clin Dermatol, 7*, 65.

44. Hey, E. N., & Katz, G. (1969). Evaporative water loss in the newborn baby. *J Physiol, 200*, 605.

45. Hoath, S. B. (1997). The stickiness of newborn skin: bioadhesion and the epidermal barrier. *J Pediatr, 131*, 338.

46. Hoath, S. B., & Narendran, V. (2000). Adhesives and emollients in the preterm infant. *Semin Neonatol, 5*, 289.

47. Hoath, S. B., & Narendran, V. (2015). The skin of the neonate. In R. J. Martin, A. A. Fanaroff & M. C. Walsh (Eds.), *Fanaroff and Martin's Neonatal-perinatal medicine: Diseases of the fetus and infant* (10th ed.). Philadelphia: Saunders.

48. Hoath, S. H., & Mauro, T. (2015). Fetal skin development. In L. F. Eichenfield, et al. (Eds.), *Neonatal and infant dermatology* (3rd ed.). Philadelphia: Saunders.

49. Hoath, S. H. (2017). Physiologic development of the skin. In R. A. Polin, et al. (Eds.), *Fetal and neonatal physiology* (5th ed.). Philadelphia: Saunders.

50. Irmak, M. K., Oztas, E., & Vural, H. (2004). Dependence of fetal hairs and sebaceous glands on fetal adrenal cortex and possible control from adrenal medulla. *Med Hypotheses, 62*, 486.

51. Jadotte, Y. T., & Schwartz, R. A. (2010). Melasma: insights and perspectives. *Acta Dermatovenerol Croat, 18*, 124.

52. Janssen, P., et al. (2003). To dye or not to dye: a randomized, clinical trial of a triple dye/alcohol regime versus dry cord care. *Pediatrics, 111*, 15.

53. Jhaveri, M. B., Driscoll, M. S., & Grant-Kels, J. M. (2011). Melanoma in pregnancy. *Clin Obstet Gynecol, 54*, 537.

54. Johnson, D. E. (2016). Extremely preterm skin care: a transformation of practice aimed to prevent harm. *Adv Neonatal Care, 16*, S26.

55. Knobel, R. B., et al. (2009). Extremely low birth weight preterm infants lack vasomotor response in relationship to cold body temperatures at birth. *J Perinatol, 29*, 814.

56. Kopelman, A. E. (1973). Cutaneous absorption of hexachlorophene in low-birth-weight infants. *J Pediatr, 82*, 972.

57. Kroth, J., et al. (2008). Functional vessel density in the first month of life in preterm neonates. *Pediatr Res, 64*, 567.

58. Kroumpouzos, G., & Cohen, L. M. (2003). Specific dermatoses of pregnancy: an evidence-based systematic review. *Am J Obstet Gynecol, 188*, 1083.

59. Kumar, E., et al. (2011, Aug). Ear, nose and throat manifestations during pregnancy. *Otolaryngol Head Neck Surg, 145*(2): 188–198.

60. Lee, H. K. (2002). Effects of sponge bathing on vagal tone and behavioral responses in premature infants. *J Clin Nurs, 11*, 510.

61. Ludriksone, L., et al. (2014). Skin barrier function in infancy: a systematic review. *Arch Dermatol Res, 306*, 591.

62. Lund, C. (1999). Prevention and management of infant skin breakdown. *Nurs Clin North Am, 34*, 907.

63. Lund, C. (2016). Bathing and beyond: current bathing controversies in newborn infants. *Adv Neonatal Care, 16*, S13.

64. Lund, C., & Durant, D. J. (2016). Skin and skin care. In S. L. Gardner, et al. (Eds.), *Merenstein and Gardner's Handbook of Neonatal Intensive Care* (8th ed.). St. Louis: Elsevier.

65. Lund, C. H., et al. (1997). Disruption of barrier function in neonatal skin associated with adhesive removal. *J Pediatr, 131*, 367.

66. Maayan-Metzger, A., et al. (2004). Effect of radiant warmer on transepidermal water loss (TEWL) and skin hydration in preterm infants. *J Perinatol, 24*, 372.

67. Marschall, H. U. (2015). Management of intrahepatic cholestasis of pregnancy. *Expert Rev Gastroenterol Hepatol, 9*, 1273.

68. McNichol, L., et al. (2013). Medical adhesives and patient safety: state of the science: consensus statements for the assessment, prevention, and treatment of adhesive-related skin injuries. *J Wound Ostomy Continence Nurs, 40*, 365.

69. Meredith, F. M., & Ormerod, A. D. (2013). The management of acne vulgaris in pregnancy. *Am J Clin Dermatol, 14*, 351.

70. Moore, K. L., Persaud, T. V. N., & Torchia, M. G. (2015). *The developing human: Clinically oriented embryology* (10th ed.). Philadelphia: Saunders.

71. Muallem, M. M., & Rubeiz, N. G. (2006). Physiological and biological skin changes in pregnancy. *Clin Dermatol, 24*, 80.

72. Mullany, L. C., Darmstadt, G. L., & Tielsch, J. M. (2003). Role of antimicrobial applications to the umbilical cord in neonates to prevent bacterial colonization and infection: a review of the evidence. *Pediatr Infect Dis J, 22*, 996.

73. Murase, J. E., Heller, M. M., & Butler, D. C. (2014). Safety of dermatologic medications in pregnancy and lactation: Part I. Pregnancy. *J Am Acad Dermatol, 70*, 401. e1–14.

74. Narendran, V., et al. (2010). Biomarkers of epidermal innate immunity in premature and full-term infants. *Pediatr Res, 67*, 382.

75. Nedergaard, J., & Cannon, B. (2017). Brown adipose tissue: development and function. In R. A. Polin, et al. (Eds.), *Fetal and neonatal physiology* (54th ed.). Philadelphia: Saunders.

76. Nikolovski, J., et al. (2008). Barrier function and water-holding and transport properties of infant stratum corneum are different from adult and continue to develop through the first year of life. *J Invest Dermatol, 128*, 1728.

77. Norman, M. (2008). Low birth weight and the developing vascular tree: a systematic review. *Acta Paediatr, 97*, 1165.

78. Peters, K. L. (1998). Bathing premature infants: physiological and behavioral consequences. *Am J Crit Care, 7*, 90.

79. Ponnapula, P., & Boberg, J. S. (2010). Lower extremity changes experienced during pregnancy. *J Foot Ankle Surg, 49*, 452.

80. Ponnusamy, V., Venkatesh, V., & Clarke, P. (2014). Skin antisepsis in the neonate: what should we use? *Curr Opin Infect Dis, 27*, 244.

81. Powell, F., & Powell, B. (1987). Cutaneous changes during pregnancy. *Ir Med J, 80*, 50.

82. Quinn, D., Newton, N., & Piecuch, R. (2005). Effect of less frequent bathing on premature infant skin. *J Obstet Gynecol Neonatal Nurs, 34*, 741.

83. Ran-Ressler, R. R., et al. (2013). Branched-chain fatty acids in the neonatal gut and estimated dietary intake in infancy and adulthood. *Nestle Nutr Inst Workshop Ser, 77*, 133.

84. Rapini, R. P. (2014). The skin and pregnancy. In R. K. Creasy, et al. (Eds.), *Creasy & Resnik's Maternal-fetal medicine: Principles and practice* (7th ed.). Philadelphia: Saunders.

85. Reilly, M. C., et al. (2015). Randomized trial of occlusive wrap for heat loss prevention in preterm infants. Vermont Oxford Network Heat Loss Prevention (HeLP) Trial Study Group. *J Pediatr, 166*, 262.

86. Rissmann, R., et al. (2008). Temperature-induced changes in structural and physicochemical properties of vernix caseosa. *J Invest Dermatol, 128*, 292.

87. Rosen, C. F. (2004). The skin in pregnancy. In G. N. Burrow, T. P. Duffy, & J. A. Copel (Eds.), *Medical complications during pregnancy* (6th ed.). Philadelphia: Saunders.

88. Rutter, N., & Hull, D. (1979). Water loss from the skin of term and preterm babies. *Arch Dis Child, 54*, 858.

89. Rutter, N. (2000). Physiology of the newborn skin. In J. Harper & A. Oranje (Eds.), *Textbook of pediatric dermatology.* Oxford: Blackwell Scientific.

90. Sadler, T. W. (2015). *Langman's Medical embryology* (13th ed.). Philadelphia: Wolters Kluwer.

91. Sathiyamurthy, S., Banerjee, J., & Godambe, S. V. (2016). Antiseptic use in the neonatal intensive care unit - a dilemma in clinical practice: an evidence based review. *World J Clin Pediatr, 5*, 159.

92. Sävervall, C., Sand, F. L., & Thomsen, S. F. (2015). Dermatological diseases associated with pregnancy: pemphigoid gestationis, polymorphic eruption of pregnancy, intrahepatic cholestasis of pregnancy, and atopic eruption of pregnancy. *Dermatol Res Pract, 2015*, 979635.

93. Shwayder, T., & Akland, T. (2005). Neonatal skin barrier: structure, function, and disorders. *Dermatol Ther, 18*, 87.

94. Siegfried, E. C. (1998). Neonatal skin and skin care. *Dermatol Clin, 16*, 437.

95. Sinha, A., et al. (2015). Chlorhexidine skin or cord care for prevention of mortality and infections in neonates. *Cochrane Database Syst Rev, 2015*(3), CD007835.

96. Soutou, B., & Aractingi, S. (2015). Skin disease in pregnancy. *Best Pract Res Clin Obstet Gynaecol, 29*, 732.

97. Stamatas, G. N., et al. (2010). Infant skin microstructure assessed in vivo differs from adult skin in organization and at the cellular level. *Pediatr Dermatol, 27*, 125.

98. Stamatas, G. N., et al. (2011). Infant skin physiology and development during the first years of life: a review of recent findings based on in vivo studies. *Int J Cosmet Sci, 33*, 17.

99. Tapia-Rombo, C. A., Morales-Mora, M., & Alvarez-Vazquez, E. (2003). Variations of vital signs, skin color, behavior and oxygen saturation in premature neonates after sponge bathing. Possible complications. *Rev Invest Clin, 55*, 438.

100. Than, N. N., & Neuberger, J. (2013). Liver anomalies in pregnancy. *Best Pract Res Clin Gastroenterol, 27*, 565.

101. Tosti, A., et al. (2009). Hair loss in women. *Minerva Ginecol, 61*, 445.

102. Tung, J. Y., et al. (2013). Genome-wide association analysis implicates elastic microfibrils in the development of nonsyndromic striae distensae. *J Invest Dermatol, 133*, 2628.

103. Tyler, K. H. (2015). Dermatologic therapy in pregnancy. *Clin Obstet Gynecol, 58*, 112.

104. Tyler, K. H. (2015). Physiological skin changes during pregnancy. *Clin Obstet Gynecol, 58*, 119.

105. Visscher, M., et al. (2009). Skin care in the NICU patient: effects of wipes versus cloth and water on stratum corneum integrity. *Neonatology, 96*, 226.

106. Visscher, M. O., et al. (2005). Vernix caseosa in neonatal adaptation. *J Perinatol, 25*, 440.

107. Visscher, M. O., et al. (2011). Neonatal skin maturation-vernix caseosa and free amino acids. *Pediatr Dermatol, 28*, 122.

108. Visscher, M. O., et al. (2015). Newborn infant skin: physiology, development, and care. *Clin Dermatol, 33*, 271.

109. Walker, L., Downe, S., & Gomez, L. (2005). Skin care in the well term newborn: two systematic reviews. *Birth, 32*, 224.

110. Wong, R. C., & Ellis, C. N. (1989). Physiologic skin changes in pregnancy. *Semin Dermatol, 8*, 7.

111. World Health Organization. (1998). *Care of the umbilical cord: WHO/FHE/MSM-Cord care.* Geneva: WHO.

112. Yates, C. C., Hebda, P., & Wells, A. (2012). Skin wound healing and scarring: fetal wounds and regenerative restitution. *Birth Defects Res C Embryo Today, 96*, 325.

113. Yung-Weng, W., & Ying-Ju, C. (2004). A preliminary study of bottom care effects on premature infants' heart rate and oxygen saturation. *J Nurs Res, 12*, 161.

114. Zupan, J., Garner, P., & Omari, A. A. (2004). Topical umbilical cord care at birth. *Cochrane Database Sys Rev, 2004*(3), CD001057.

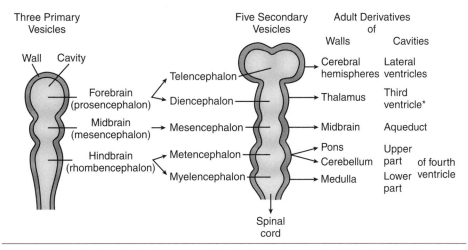

FIGURE 15-5   Embryonic development of the brain vesicles and adult derivatives. *The rostral (anterior) part of the third ventricle forms from the cavity of the telencephalon; most of the third ventricle is derived from the cavity of diencephalon. (From Moore, K.L., Persaud, T.V.N., & Torchia, M.G. [2015]. *The developing human: Clinically oriented embryology* [10th ed.]. Philadelphia: Saunders.)

are the beginning formation of the motor and sensory tracts that develop in the ventral and dorsal areas, respectively, of the cord.[169] In conjunction with formation of the spinal cord from the caudal neural tube, cells from the neural crest break into groups along the length of the cord, forming spinal and cranial ganglia and ganglia of the autonomic nervous system. Further differentiation and migration of neural crest cells and their fibers result in formation of the peripheral nerves (somatic and visceral, sensory and motor) and their connections. The primitive brain structures also go through a series of flexures or foldings and gyri formation (Figure 15-6).

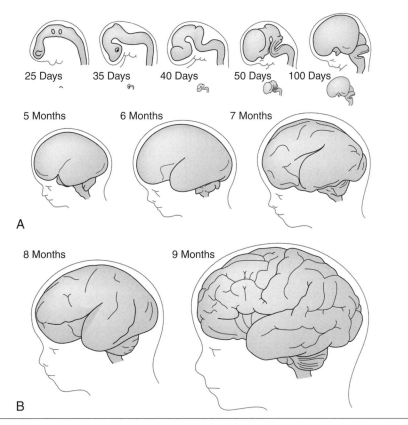

FIGURE 15-6   Folding of embryonic brain and formation of gyri. **A,** Folding during embryonic development. **B,** Development of sulci and gyri during the fetal period. (From Cowan, W.M. [1979]. The development of the brain. *Sci Am, 241,* 116.)

Anomalies Arising in the Embryonic Period

The most common CNS anomalies arise in the embryonic period during the period of primary neurulation and result from failure of neural tube closure. These anomalies include anencephaly, myelomeningocele, encephalocele, and spina bifida occulta. NTDs are usually accompanied by alterations in vertebral, meningeal, vascular, and dermal structures and arise from a complex interaction of environmental and genetic factors. NTDs have a familial pattern with an increased recurrence rate. Approximately 2% to 16% of infants with isolated NTDs have cytogenic abnormalities. NTDs also occur in infants with other congenital defects. These infants may have normal or abnormal karyotypes. A small number of NTDs occur secondary to teratogen exposure.[167]

Periconceptional folic acid supplementation significantly reduces the risk of NTDs in women with a history of a previous infant with an NTD and in the general public.[41,167] Current recommendations are that women of childbearing age consume 0.4 mg of folic acid daily, with higher recommendations (4 mg daily beginning 3 months before pregnancy and lasting through the first trimester) for women who have previously had a child with an NTD.[5] Research continues regarding folate-related and other metabolic pathways and NTDs, the role of gene polymorphisms, and the roles of other nutrients such as vitamin B_{12}.[167]

α-Fetoprotein leaks into the amniotic fluid and maternal serum in infants with open NTDs. Maternal serum screening at 16 to 18 weeks is used to identify infants at risk for NTDs, with follow-up ultrasound screening for diagnostic confirmation (see Chapter 3).

Anencephaly results from failure of the neural tube to fuse in the cranial area. Because this area forms the forebrain, anencephalic infants have minimal development of brain tissue above the midbrain. Tissue that does develop is poorly differentiated and becomes necrotic with exposure to amniotic fluid. This results in a mass of vascular tissue with neuronal and glial elements and a choroid plexus with partial absence of the skull bones.[169] Because anencephaly arises from failure of the neural tube to close cranially, the insult occurs at or before 24 days.[235] Encephaloceles also arise from failure of closure of part of the caudal portion of the neural tube and occur no later than 26 days.[235] About 70% to 80% of these defects occur in the occipital region, with the sac protruding from the back of the head or base of the neck.[57,235,245] The protruding sac varies considerably in size, but the size does not correlate with the presence of neural elements; 10% to 20% of encephaloceles contain no neural elements.[235] Hydrocephalus, present at birth or developing later, occurs in up to 50% of occipital encephaloceles because of alterations in the posterior fossa.[235]

Spina bifida is a general term used to describe defects associated with malformations of the spinal cord and vertebrae that usually arise from defects in closure of the caudal neuropore (spina bifida cystica) or with defects in secondary neurulation (spina bifida occulta). Approximately 80% of spina bifida cystica occurs in the lumbar area, which is the final area of neural tube fusion. Thus spina bifida cystica, arising from defects in primary neurulation, occurs at or before 26 days.[235] Defects range from minor malformations to disorders that result in paraplegia or quadriplegia and loss of bladder and bowel control. The degree of sensory and motor neurologic deficit depends on the level and severity of the defect. Spina bifida occulta (occult dysraphic state) is a vertebral defect at L5 or S1 that arises from failure of the vertebral arch to grow and fuse.[57,232] These are defects of secondary neurulation during formation of the caudal portion of the spinal cord. Most people with this defect have no problems, and the defect may be unrecognized. A few have underlying abnormalities of the spinal cord or nerve roots, which are manifested externally by a hemangioma, dimple, tuft of hair, or lipoma in the lower lumbar or sacral area. The cause of these findings is unclear but may be related to alterations in cell differentiation or migration with formation of hair tufts because of the absence of hair growth inhibitory factors.

Spina bifida cystica is characterized by a cystic sac, containing meninges or spinal cord elements, along with vertebral defects, covered by epithelium or a thin membrane, and usually occurring in the lumbar or lumbosacral area. Spina bifida cystica is usually caused by alterations in primary neurulation. The three main forms of spina bifida cystica are meningocele, meningomyelocele, and myeloschisis. Meningocele (5% of infants with spina bifida cystica) involves a sac containing meninges and cerebrospinal fluid (CSF) but with the spinal cord and nerve roots in their normal position. These infants usually have minimal residual neurologic deficit if the defect is covered with skin and is managed appropriately.

With a meningomyelocele, the most common (80% to 90%) form of spina bifida cystica, the sac contains spinal cord or nerve roots in addition to meninges and CSF. During development, nerve tissues become incorporated into the wall of the sac, impairing differentiation of nerve fibers.[57] These infants have a neurologic deficit below the level of the sac. Most infants have hydrocephalus and an Arnold Chiari malformation in which the medulla protrudes downward below the foramen magnum and overlaps the spinal cord.[232]

Intrauterine repair of meningomyelocele has been associated with short-term benefits including reversal of hindbrain herniation, which may enhance brain growth and reduce hydrocephalus. Some studies have found improved lower extremity function; others have not.[34] However, intrauterine repair is also associated with risks, including increased perinatal mortality, and many infants are preterm.[1,167] A large trial randomizing infants to prenatal (before 26 weeks) or postnatal repair with follow-up to 30 months found that intrauterine surgery significantly reduced the need for shunting after birth and improved outcomes at 30 months but was associated with an increased risk of preterm delivery and uterine dehiscence at delivery.[1]

Disorders of ventral induction are believed to arise no later than 5 to 6 weeks' gestation. Disorders of forebrain development often have concurrent facial anomalies and include holoprosencephaly (failure of the brain to divide into two cerebral hemispheres) and holotelencephaly (see Table 15-4).

Fetal Neurodevelopment

The earliest growth of the brain occurs in structures such as basal ganglia, thalamus, midbrain, and brainstem, whereas structures such as the cerebrum and cerebellum form somewhat later. Once the embryologic formations are established, CNS development is characterized by overlapping processes involved in formation of the neocortex and myelination. These processes include neuronal proliferation (neuronogenesis), neuronal and glial cell migration, organization, and myelination. Organization and myelination continue past birth.

Neuronal and Glial Proliferation

Neuronal proliferation (neuronogenesis) is a period of massive production of neurons and their precursors. The maximal rate of neuronal proliferation occurs between 12 and 18 weeks' gestation.[235] During proliferation the walls of the neural tube thicken, forming layers. The ependyma is the interior lining of the neural tube that later becomes the lining of the ventricles and the central spinal cord canal. In the subependymal layer, neurons and glial cells of the CNS are formed in the ventricular and subventricular zones of the germinal matrix (GM).[235] Neuronal proliferation occurs primarily from 8 to 18 weeks, followed by glial proliferation from 15 weeks on.[245] With the exception of radial glial cells, the peak in glial cell numbers occurs roughly from 5 months' gestational age through the first year of life.[235] Radial glia have two major functions. First they serve as guides during neuron migration (see next section), and second they are neuronal progenitors in the ventricular zone.[235] Thus neurons arise from both neuronal and radial glial cell progenitors. Although most of the neuronal complement is formed early in fetal life, a few areas, notably the cerebral subventricular zone and the external granular layer of the cerebellum, continue to acquire neurons during the early months after birth (see Cerebellar Development.[235,245] This pattern of neuronal formation produces a particular vulnerability in preterm infants (see Germinal Matrix and Intraventricular Hemorrhage). In late gestation the ventricular and subventricular zones disappear almost completely (a subventricular zone remnant persists to adulthood) and proliferation shifts to intermediary and subplate zones for continued production of glial cells.[235]

Alterations in neuronal proliferation can lead to increases or decreases in number and size of cells in the brain and associated structures. Micrencephaly arises from a decrease in size (microcephaly vera) or number (radial microbrain) of neuronal-glial stem cell units.[232,235] Microcephaly vera may be a result of unknown causes; have a familial basis; or be associated with teratogens such as alcohol, cocaine, radiation, and maternal phenylketonuria.[235] Excessive proliferation (macrencephaly) may also result from unknown causes, have a familial basis, or occur with growth disturbances (e.g., achondroplasia or Beckwith-Wiedemann syndrome) and chromosomal disorders (fragile X and Klinefelter syndromes). Macrencephaly is also seen with neurocutaneous syndromes (such as multiple hemangiomas and neurofibromatosis) that involve excessive proliferation of cells within the central nervous system and of mesodermal structures.[235]

Migration

Once formed, neurons travel from the germinal layer in the subependymal region below the lateral ventricles to the areas of the nervous system where they will further differentiate, forming the gray matter, and take on unique and individual functions.[235] The bulk of cerebral migration occurs from 12 to 20 weeks' gestation (usually completed by 22 weeks).[245] The two types of neuron migration are radial and tangential. Radial migration accounts for much of the cortex and involves radial glia, which appear by 10 weeks' gestation (Figure 15-7).[163,235] The nuclei of the radial glia are in the GM. The basal process of the glia is attached to the ventricle and the apical process to the pia matter. These processes guide the migrating neuron to its respective site and also act as progenitors for neuron and astrocyte generation.[235] Migration is mediated by signaling proteins, surface molecules, and receptors on both the neurons and the radial glia.[235] Radial glial–assisted migration also occurs in the cerebellum. Cortical and cerebellar neurons migrate tangentially without radial glia guidance.[163]

The neocortex develops in six zones, which are, from innermost to outermost, the ventricular zone, subventricular zone, intermediate zone, subplate, cortical plate, and marginal zone. Neurons forming in the ventricular and subventricular zones migrate through the cortical plate to form more and more superficial layers. The initial neurons migrate toward the cerebral walls to form the preplate. The next neurons migrate to areas deep within the cortex, whereas later neurons migrate further to the surface of the cortex. As a result, neurons formed early come to lie in deeper layers of cortex and subcortex; those formed later end at more superficial layers.[235] Thus neocortex formation follows an "inside-first-outside-last" pattern, except for the early neurons of the subplate.[235] The subplate and marginal zone are transient

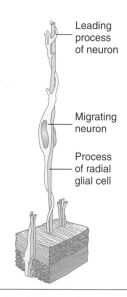

Leading process of neuron

Migrating neuron

Process of radial glial cell

FIGURE 15-7 Radial glial cells and their associations with peripherally migrating neurons during the development of the brain. (Based on Rakic, P. [1975]. Cell migration and neuronal ectopias in the brain. *Birth Defects Orig Article Series, 11,* 95.)

BOX 15-2   Major Roles of Subplate Neurons

Serve as sites of synaptic contact for "waiting" thalamic, commissural, and association (corticocortical) afferents
Establish a functional link between waiting afferents and their cortical targets
Provide axonal guidance into cerebral cortex for the ascending afferents
Facilitate cerebral cortical organization and synaptic development
Provide "pioneering" axonal guidance for efferent projections from the cortex to subcortical targets (e.g., thalamus)

From Volpe, J.J. (2009). The encephalopathy of prematurity—brain injury and impaired brain development inextricably intertwined. *Semin Pediatr Neurol, 16*, p. 172.

structures that develop in parallel with the cortical plate and then regress after the cortex is formed.[163] Most cortical neurons have reached their sites by 20 to 24 weeks' gestation.[235]

The subplate zone and subplate neurons are critical structures in neocortex development. The roles of the subplate neurons are listed in Box 15-2. The subplate is the first place where synapses form within the cortex and receive input from thalamic and other regions.[44] The subplate, located just below the developing cortex, serves as a "waiting room" or temporary site for thalamocortical and corticocortical projections and helps guide axons to cortical and subcortical targets and in establishing functional connections between brain regions.[49,52] For example, thalamic fibers enter the subplate area before their target neurons are in place and transiently form synaptic connections with subplate neurons.[235] These are held in the subplate until the cortical plate is ready and then migrate to their final location within the cortex.

Subplate formation begins at 12 weeks and reaches its maximum size at 27 to 30 weeks.[50,52,238] Thalamic afferents develop at 12 to 16 weeks and reach the subplate by 20 to 24 weeks.[114,238] Between 24 and 32 weeks axonal growth to the subplate and cortex increases and thalamocortical afferents move from the subplate to the cortex. Callosal and corticocortical axons enter the subplate from 24 to 32 weeks and enter the cortex from 32 to 36 weeks as the subplate begins to regress.[235,238] Thus the subplate is "a significant reservoir of functional connectivity in the preterm infant."[52] The subplate is vulnerable to perinatal injury in these infants.

The subplate undergoes programmed cell death after birth, although subplate neurons remain as interstitial neurons.[126,235] Interstitial neurons are embedded in superficial white matter. Alterations in interstitial neurons or in their role in cortical circuitry may play a role in some forms of schizophrenia.[126]

Disorders of migration alter gyral development and lead to hypoplasia or agenesis of the corpus callosum. Gyral development is most prominent during the last 3 months of gestation (see Figure 15-6), with the most rapid increase between 26 and 28 weeks. The increased gyri result in a change in head

shape (from oval to biparietal prominence). Gyral disorders arise secondary to inborn errors of metabolism, such as fatty acid oxidation defects, chromosomal anomalies, and exogenous insults, especially in preterm infants.[232,235]

Organization

Organization refers to the processes by which the nervous system takes on the capacity to operate as an integrated whole. This phase of neurodevelopment begins at approximately 6 months' gestation, extends many years after birth, and continues into adulthood. Neuron growth and connections lead to development of sulci and gyri (see Figure 15-6), with a brain growth spurt seen from 26 to 30 weeks. With increasing organization, fetal and infant behaviors become more complex.[4,235] Alterations in organization are seen in infants with Down, fragile X, and Angelman syndromes; periventricular leukomalacia (PVL); inflammation and infection; and hypothyroxinemia.[190,235] Injury to the cortex and subcortical area white matter can lead to disorders such as cerebral palsy. Focal lesions in the immature brain can lead to reorganization of sensory, motor, and related tracts.[44]

During the period of organization, six processes occur.[235] The first is differentiation and development of subplate neurons (see Migration). These neurons migrate to the cortex early and guide ascending and descending projections to target neurons. Subplate neurons provide a connection site for axons ascending from the thalamus and other sites, until the neurons that these axons will eventually connect with have migrated from the GM. The subplate reaches its peak from 22 to 34 weeks.[235]

The second and third processes involve arrangement of cortical neurons in layers and arborization, wherein the dendrites and axons undergo extensive branching. This latter process is sometimes referred to as the "wiring of the brain" (Figure 15-8). The increase in cellular processes and in the

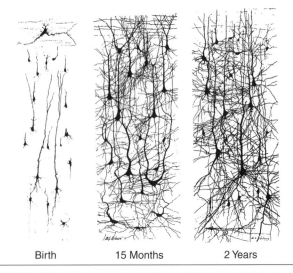

Birth   15 Months   2 Years

FIGURE 15-8   Dendritic growth. (From Dobbing, J. [1975]. Human brain development and its vulnerability. In *Biologic and clinical aspects of brain development.* [Mead Johnson Symposium on Perinatal and Developmental Medicine, no. 6.] Evansville, IN: Mead Johnson.)

size of the neuronal field is prerequisite for communication throughout the nervous system. This process is followed by the formation of connections or synapses between neurons, the fourth component of organization. The intracellular structures and enzymes that will produce neurotransmitters also develop at this time. Connections between cells are critical for integration across all areas of the nervous system. Throughout development, synapses continue to restructure; this process is believed to be the basis for memory and learning. Impulse conduction provides for functional validation of connections. Evidence suggests that use of conduction pathways may increase or alter connections.[235] Characteristics of early neuronal activity include poor spontaneous neuronal activity, slow conduction velocity, slow synaptic potentials, and synaptic transmission uncertainty. Immaturity of neurotransmitters and hypersensitivity of *N*-methyl-D-aspartate (NMDA) receptors increases the risk of receptor overstimulation with hypoxic-ischemic events (see Hypoxic-Ischemic Encephalopathy and PVL on pp. 532-534).

Synaptogenesis is mediated by excitatory neurotransmitters such as glutamate.[128] Glutamate acts on NMDA receptors to enhance neuronal proliferation, migration, and synaptic plasticity. During the brain growth spurt, NMDA receptors are hypersensitive. Blockage of these receptors in animal models by substances such as ethanol leads to apoptosis.[128,197,235] Other substances, such as erythropoietin, may also be important in enhancing brain organization and for neuroprotection.[119,159,197]

The fifth organizational process entails reduction in the number of neurons and their connections through the death of up to half of the original neurons as well as regression of many dendrites and synapses.[235] Neuronal survival has been likened to survival of the fittest, because neurons compete for resources such as nutrients, electrical impulses, and synapses. Neuronal death assists in elimination of errors within the nervous system. The appropriate number of neurons and their connections is retained, whereas neurons that are improperly located or fail to achieve adequate connections are eliminated. Numbers of neurons are maximal in the fetus, and survival is dependent on neurons or groups of neurons getting appropriate numbers of connections. From 8 months' gestation to adulthood, numbers of neurons and synapses decrease. For example, there are an estimated $620,000/m^3$ neurons in the visual cortex at 7 months' gestation versus $100,000/m^3$ at term and $40,000/m^3$ in the adult.[124]

Cell death and selective elimination of neuronal processes is important in adjusting the size of individual neurons to their anticipated need and in brain plasticity in infants. In the developing brain, neuronal processes targeted for elimination can be saved if they are needed, for example, because of damage to other processes, to preserve functional ability. Excitatory neurotransmitters, such as glutamate, mediate neural development and organization by acting on NMDA receptors.[57]

The final organizational process is differentiation of glia from the general precursor cells into specific types and glia proliferation. The increase in glia begins at approximately 30 weeks' gestation, continues into the second year, and then plateaus. There are three main types of glia: myelin-building (oligodendrocytes and Schwann cells), guiding (radial glia [for neuron migration] and Schwann cells), and "clean-up" (astroglia and microglia). The astroglia and microglia remove waste and dead tissue and occupy space left by neurons that have died, among other functions. Astrocytes also provide support for neurons. Astrocytes undergo rapid proliferation from 24 to 32 weeks (peak 26 weeks).[211,235] These glia are found primarily in deep cortical layers and white matter. They assist with axonal guidance, growth, brain structural development, and functioning of the blood-brain barrier.[211] Astrocytes can release transmitters (such as glutamate) to send signals to neighboring neurons. Each astrocyte may interact with several neurons and hundreds to thousands of synapses to integrate information.[211,235] Microglia are the brain macrophages and immune cells. They also have a role in brain development, with increased numbers seen in the third trimester. Activated microglia with white matter injury can lead to cellular injury initiated by ischemia and inflammation (mediated by reactive oxygen species, cytokines, and glutamate).[211,235] Oligodendrocytes produce myelin in the CNS. During the premyelinating period (before 32 weeks' gestation), oligodendrocytes are especially vulnerable to hypoxic-ischemic injury. Damage to these glial cells is a prominent feature in brain injury in preterm infants (see White Matter Injury).[239] Schwann cells produce myelin for the peripheral nerves. Schwann cells also act as guiding glia after peripheral nerve injury to guide regenerating axons to their targets.[235]

Myelination

Myelination refers to the laying down of myelin, the lipoprotein insulating the covering of nerve fibers. Myelination increases the speed of transmission along axons by 100-fold.[124] This process occurs in both the central and peripheral nerve systems. Glia migrate to locations along the developing nerve fibers. Myelin is formed as the glia (either Schwann cells in the peripheral nervous system or oligodendroglia in the CNS) wrap around the nerve fiber. The glia's cellular membrane, once wrapped around the fiber, fuses to become myelin.

Myelination begins during the second trimester and continues into adulthood.[235] The process of myelination occurs at differing times in areas throughout the nervous system. For example, myelination of somatosensory and auditory areas is nearly complete by term, whereas prefrontal lobe myelination is not completed until after 20 years.[124] Myelination of the forebrain is most rapid after birth. Myelination first begins in the peripheral nervous system, with motor fibers becoming myelinated before sensory fibers. In the CNS, myelination of sensory areas precedes that of motor areas, with the primary sensory areas becoming myelinated relatively early in development. Incomplete myelination does not prevent function. However, because incomplete myelination affects nerve conduction, it does alter the speed of impulse conduction. The order of myelination parallels overall nervous system functional development and generally precedes mature function.[169] Areas of the brain that support higher-level functions, such as cognition and learning, myelinate later in life.[235] Some brain areas continue to lay down myelin well into adulthood. Because myelin is a lipoprotein, dietary adequacy of fats and protein is important for normal myelination. Disorders of myelination are seen with amino and organic acidopathies, hypothyroidism, undernutrition, and perinatal insults such as PVL.[235]

Cerebellar Development

Although cerebellar development begins early in gestation, the cerebellum is one of the later brain structures to mature. The cerebellum consists of a medial section (vermis) and two lateral hemispheres. Cerebellar neuronogenesis in the cerebellar germinal matrix begins at 3 to 4 months, followed by migration of neurons to the inner granular layer from 3 to 8 months.[25] The cerebellum undergoes a rapid growth spurt from 24 to 40 weeks with a fivefold increase in volume reflecting underlying histogenic and cytogenic changes; the cerebellar cortex increases more than 30-fold during this period.[25,142] Before 20 weeks two proliferation zones are established that give rise to the major cerebellar structures. Between 20 and 40 weeks increased external surface foliation is seen with development of the external granular layer, Purkinje cell (neuron) differentiation, and migration.[142,220] The lateral hemispheres of the cerebellum are involved in cognitive and motor function; the middle layers in regulation of emotion, social behavior, and affect.[144] The cerebellum is important in cognition and acts as a node in distribution of neural networks with interconnections with the thalamus and parietal and prefrontal cortex.[179] Cerebellar damage (see Cerebellar Injury in Preterm Infants) can alter language development, behavioral function, and cognitive function; cerebellar dysfunction is also seen in autism spectrum disorders and attention deficit-hyperactivity disorder.[25,142,144,179,220,235]

Development of Specific Systems

Autonomic Nervous System. The autonomic nervous system has both central and peripheral components. Peripheral portions develop from neural crest cells. Ganglia are formed from neural crest cells that migrate beyond the neural tube. Sympathetic ganglia are derived from neural crest cells that collect along either side of the developing spinal cord at about 5 weeks' gestational age.[169] The parasympathetic ganglia and plexi also form by migration.[169] Once they reach their respective sites, neurons in the autonomic ganglia continue to differentiate. Nerve fibers, originating in the cord, grow out and make connections with the ganglia. The autonomic nervous system regulates many endocrine functions through nerve impulses. The embryonic origins of some autonomic end organs demonstrate a structural basis for these regulatory actions. The pituitary, a primary source of autonomic regulation, is derived from two forms of tissues.

The adenohypophysis is formed from ectoderm and the neurohypophysis is formed from neuroectoderm. Similarly, the adrenal gland is derived from two types of tissues. The adrenal cortex is derived from mesoderm, whereas the medulla, which secretes catecholamines, is derived from neuroectoderm (specifically neural crest cells) and is controlled by the sympathetic nervous system.

Peripheral Nervous System. The peripheral nervous system is derived from the neural crest. Through migration and specialization, cells of the neural crest develop into cranial, spinal, and visceral nerves and ganglia. Neural crest cells are precursors of the adrenal medulla chromaffin cells that secrete epinephrine.[169] Support cells of the peripheral nervous system also derive from the neural crest. Nerve fibers that eventually innervate skeletal motor fibers emerge from the spinal basal plate, combine into bundles to form the ventral root, and migrate to the developing motor fibers.[169] Sensory fibers form the dorsal root in a similar manner.

Functional Development

Studies of fetal neural activity in utero are limited to external monitoring of CNS electrical activity or noninvasive detection of fetal responses using measures of fetal movement or ultrasonography. Much of our understanding of fetal function comes from the study of preterm infants, who technically are not fetal. However, the behavior of these infants provides one means of appreciating fetal behaviors at various gestational ages. Studies of preterm infants have greatly increased information concerning operation of the fetal nervous system. The following section describes the neural function of the fetus, defined as gestational age less than 38 weeks. In many instances, information pertains to the "fetal infant" or preterm infant. Appreciation of fetal neural development provides a basis for anticipation of the many capabilities of the preterm and term infant.

Sensory Abilities

The sensory systems generally develop in the following chronologic order: tactile, proprioception, vestibular, chemoreception (smell and taste), hearing, and vision.[95,139] As noted in the section on Myelination, in the peripheral areas, motor fibers myelinate before sensory fibers, whereas in the central nervous system sensory fibers myelinate before motor fibers. Thus in terms of rate of impulse transmission, differences in myelination are one basis for limited integration of sensory and motor actions in the fetus.

The early fetus has been shown to respond to perioral touch at around 2 months of gestational age; the palmar area becomes touch sensitive by 10 to 11 weeks and most of the rest of the body as early as 15 weeks.[80,230] Somatosensory cortical pathways develop by 20 to 24 weeks.[80] Touch in utero entails contact with amniotic fluid that is approximately at body temperature and contact with body parts or the wall of the uterus. Maternal movement and buoyant amniotic fluid provide rich vestibular stimulation for the fetus in utero.

TABLE 15-5	Anatomic and Functional Development of the Different Parts of the Pain System	
PART OF THE SYSTEM	**DEVELOPMENTAL EVENT**	**TIMING (WEEKS)**
Nociceptors	Nociceptors appear (starting around the mouth and later developing over the entire body).	7–20
Peripheral afferents	Synapses appear to the spinal cord.	10–30
Spinal cord	Stimulation results in motor movements.	7.5
	Spinothalamic connections are established.	20
	Myelination of pain pathways occurs.	22
	Descending tracts develop.	Postnatally
Thalamocortical tracts	First axons appear to the cortical plate.	20–22
	Functional synapse formation of the thalamocortical tracts occurs.	26–34
Cerebral cortex	Cortical neurons migrate (cortex develops).	8–20
	First EEG burst may be detected.	20
	Symmetric and synchronic EEG activity appears.	26
	Sleep and wakefulness patterns in EEG become distinguishable.	30
	Evoked potential becomes detectable.	29

EEG, Electroencephalogram.
From Vanhatalo, S. & van Nieuwenhuizen, O. (2000). Fetal pain? *Brain Dev, 22,* 146.

Nociceptors appear at 6 to 8 weeks' gestation, initially around the mouth; by 11 weeks in the face, palms, and soles; by 15 weeks in the trunk, arms, and legs; and by 20 to 22 weeks are abundant throughout the fetus (Table 15-5).[50,114,148,163,230] The fetus can process pain at the subcortical level before cortical structures are in place.[230] Sensory fibers to dorsal interneuron areas may develop as early as 6 weeks, with development and differentiation of dorsal horn afferents beginning at 12 to 13 weeks.[148,189] Afferent synapses in the dorsal spinal cord and peripheral receptors start as early as 8 weeks' gestation.[148] Connections to the thalamus begin at 14 weeks and are complete by 20 weeks; thalamocortical connections are seen by 13 weeks and are more developed by 26 to 30 weeks.[50,148,189] These connections are myelinated by 29 weeks.[230] By at least 24 weeks noxious stimuli cause a response in the primary sensory cortex. Completion of these connections stimulates development of axons and synaptogenesis with selective elimination of excess connections and cell populations.[50]

Proprioception, which is involved with perception of joint and body movement and the position of the body, is interrelated with tactile and vestibular receptors. Vestibular sensation is a form of proprioceptive sensation involved in balance and postural control. Vestibular sensation is mediated by receptors in the ear (nonauditory labyrinth). The vestibular system connects to the cerebellum rather than the cortex and detects changes in direction and rate of head movement.[80] The vestibular system develops during the first 5 to 6 months in the fetus, initially developing concurrent with the auditory system.[177] Vestibular receptors mature by 14 to 15 weeks with structural maturation of the vestibular system by 14 to 20 weeks.[80,104,133] Myelination of the vestibular nerves begins around 20 weeks; these are the first cranial nerves to complete myelination.[177] Responses to vestibular stimulation can be observed by 25 weeks.[80] The vertex position of the fetus is thought to be induced by fetal movement in response to vestibular input.[80]

Smell is mediated by three groups of receptors that bind fragrant molecules: (1) main ciliated neuroreceptors (seen by 11 weeks), (2) trigeminal nerve endings (respond by 7 to 10 weeks), and (3) vomeronasal (appear by 5 to 6 weeks and are maximal by 20 weeks).[141,243] Olfactory marker protein is present by 28 weeks.[200] Odor molecules in amniotic fluid stimulate the fetal smell receptors by the third trimester.[243] The fetus may detect aromatic substances and flavors from the maternal diet in amniotic fluid. This stimulation may have a role in programming later dietary preferences.[16,114,129,145,162,200] Responsiveness to odors is observed in preterm infants beginning at approximately 28 weeks and is readily documented by 32 weeks' gestation in most infants.[200]

Taste occurs by activation of the taste buds and stimulation of the trigeminal nerve. Taste buds appear by 7 to 8 weeks and are morphologically mature by 13 to 15 weeks.[200] Taste receptors are present by 16 weeks, reaching adult numbers by term.[80,133] The fetus ingests amniotic fluid (see Chapter 3). Variations occur in the composition of the amniotic fluid, and flavors from the maternal diet are transferred to the fetus through amniotic fluid.[145] Injection of a sweet substance increases fetal swallowing, whereas a bitter substance decreases swallowing.[200] Preterm infants respond to sweet taste by as early as 24 weeks and consistently by 28 to 32 weeks.[80,200]

The structures of the auditory system, including the inner ear and cochlea, begin developing at 3 to 5 weeks, and all major structures are developed by 24 to 25 weeks when fetal hearing begins.[9,80,96] At this point the fluid spaces in the cochlea are still poorly developed, the basal membrane is thick, hair cell innervation and arrangement are immature, and sensitivity to sound is poor. Sound sensitivity matures rapidly from 24 to 35 weeks.[9] The tympanic membrane is similar to that in the adult by 28 weeks.[9] The cochlea matures slowly during the third trimester, undergoing "tuning" during this period. Tuning of the cochlea so that areas are frequency-specific involves mechanical maturation of the basilar membrane and outer hair cells.[9] Tuning begins in the base (high-frequency sounds) and proceeds toward the apex (low-frequency sounds). Changes in the sound environment, as occurs with preterm birth, may alter this process.

Auditory evoked potentials can be recorded as early as 25 to 26 weeks' gestation but are not reliable until after 28 weeks, when they become more complex.[9,80,92,96] In the third trimester a fetus can discriminate between maternal live voice and tape-recorded voice and familiar versus novel sounds.[86] Responses to sound are observed in preterm infants at approximately 25 to 28 weeks' gestational age.[92] Preterm infants can be observed to orient to sound, with evidence of arousal and attention. The hearing threshold decreases with gestational age. For example, in infants of 25 weeks' gestational age, the hearing threshold is approximately 65 decibels, whereas in term infants the hearing threshold is approximately 25 decibels, with the range of sensitivity increasing from 500 to 1000 Hz in the third trimester to 500 to 4000 Hz at term (versus 20,000 to 30,000 Hz in adults).[80]

Intrauterine recordings demonstrate that sounds in the external environment are audible to the fetus. High-frequency sounds are attenuated, whereas low-frequency sounds are not. External sound is reduced by about one-half its strength by the time it reaches the fetus.[129] For example, a 90-dB sound in a midrange frequency would be decreased to 45 dB by the time it reached the fetus.[86] The intrauterine auditory environment includes sounds within the mother such as breathing, movement of blood through the umbilical cord, and intestinal peristalsis, and differs significantly from the sound environment of the preterm infant.[84] Hearing in preterm infants of different gestational ages is summarized in Table 15-6.

TABLE 15-6	Development of Hearing in Preterm and Term Infants
GESTATIONAL AGE	**ANATOMIC AND FUNCTIONAL DEVELOPMENT**
Preterm infants <28 weeks	Fetal hearing begins by 24–25 weeks
	Threshold about 65 db, with a range of 500–1000 Hz
	Auditory brainstem responses by 25–26 weeks; not reliable until after 28 weeks when become more complex
Preterm infants 28–30 weeks	Rapid maturation of cochlea and auditory nerve
	Responses rapidly fatigue
	Initial auditory processing by 30 weeks
	Threshold 40 db with an increased frequency range
Preterm infants 32–34 weeks	Outer hair cells mature by 32 weeks
	Rapid maturation of cochlea and auditory nerve
Preterm infants >34 weeks	Increased speed of conduction
	Ossicles and electrophysiology complete by 36 weeks
	Hearing threshold 30 db, with increasing range
	Increasing ability to localize and discriminate
Term infants	Localize and discriminate sounds
	Hearing threshold of 25 db, with a range of 500–4000 Hz

db, Decibels; *Hz,* Hertz.
Compiled from references 24, 31, 79, 80, 95, 96, 133, and 182.

Formation of the eyes begins during embryonic development, with the optic cup present by 32 days; gross eye structures are in place by 24 weeks.[43,80] The eyelids fuse from 10 weeks until 24 to 26 weeks.[43] The fovea can be identified by 14 weeks' gestation, but maturation of the foveal region is not complete until late childhood.[82] Rod differentiation and retinal vascularization begin by 25 weeks' gestation, and myelination of the optic nerve begins at 24 weeks.[79,92] The choroid vasculature (vessels that underlie the retina and pigment epithelium) are mature by 21 weeks. Retinal vessels that supply the inner retina develop in parallel with the retina. These vessels begin to develop from the optic disk at the base of the hyaloid artery and extend peripherally to the ora serrata.[82] Growth is particularly rapid from 24 to 28 weeks and then continues at a slower pace. Zone III, the most peripheral retina, has minimal vessel development in preterm infants at 29 weeks; by 36 weeks about half of the vessels have developed, and almost all are developed by 45 to 49 weeks.[82]

The neurons forming the visual cortex are in place at 26 weeks. Between 28 and 34 weeks' gestation, visual neuronal connections and processes undergo rapid development.[92] Visual evoked potentials can be recorded between 25 and 30 weeks but have a long latency and quickly fatigue.[80,92] Visual attention begins at about 30 to 32 weeks' gestation, although it is fleeting at this age. Development of vision in preterm infants at different gestational ages is summarized in Table 15-7.

The natural sensory environment of the uterus is developmentally appropriate for the fetus. This environment provides stimuli that are rich, varied, and rhythmic. Intrauterine sensory stimulation programs have not been studied extensively and cannot be assumed to be beneficial or without risk. Because the normal uterine sensory environment is already rich, the benefits of programs to supplement intrauterine stimulation are unclear at this time.

The fetal circadian clock develops with exposure to maternal physiologic and hormonal rhythms and other signals such as melatonin, which entrain the fetal hypothalamic suprachiasmatic nucleus.[206] Fetal entrainment of 24-hour rhythms of fetal heart rate, respiratory movements, body movement, and hormones have been reported.[206]

Motor Abilities

The development of motor activity in the fetus is a function of both neural and muscular maturation. Muscle cells develop from mesoderm. Innervation during development is critical for muscle fiber development.[235] Muscle cells, as well as neurons, undergo migration and differentiation during development. Mature myocytes are present at approximately 38 weeks; muscle cells increase in size postnatally.[235]

The pattern of fetal motor development includes differences in both emergence of muscle tone and the amount of movement over time.[92] Development of muscle tone follows a caudocephalad and distal-proximal pattern; that is, lower extremities precede upper extremities and extremities precede axial or truncal muscle tone. Motor development is

effects of development on motor control mechanisms. In general, motor activities include muscle tone, motor abilities, the quality of movement, and presence and strength of reflexes. Motor control is critical to further development. Through movement and reflexes, infants are capable of expressing needs, eliciting care, taking in oral nutrients, and experiencing and manipulating their environment.

Muscle Development

The motor abilities of neonates demonstrate a characteristic pattern of development that reflects underlying changes in both nervous system control and maturation of the muscle cells themselves. Muscle is derived from mesoderm. During embryonic development, formation of muscle cells is dependent on innervation by the nervous system. The full complement of muscle cells is generally achieved at approximately 38 weeks' gestational age, with formation of few muscle cells after this time. After birth, muscle cells increase in size by increasing the diameter of the muscle fibers and also grow in length.[169] Muscle strength in particular is an outcome of muscle enlargement and growth.

Developmental changes in the innervation of muscle include myelination of afferent fibers and pathways; increasing activity in the motor cortex; and increasing coordination of system-modifying motor actions within the cerebellum, basal ganglia, and reticular activating system. Myelination improves the speed of motor nerve conduction. Maturation of the motor cortex allows conscious control of motor activities. The increasing integration of all levels of motor control results in smooth, coordinated movements; balance; and appropriate motor tone. Neonates exhibit a characteristic pattern of tone and flexion that undergoes predictable change throughout development.

Term newborns demonstrate strong muscle tone that is largely passive.[235] After birth, active motor tone, which is the tone during use of muscles, increases and passive tone decreases. Alterations in muscle tone interfere with motor activities. Hypertonicity (excessive muscle tone) and hypotonicity (inadequate muscle tone) affect the underlying muscle tension that normally supports motor function. The predominant flexed position of term newborns shows innervation of flexor muscles and reciprocal relaxation of extensor muscles. The flexed position is not only protective but also assists in conservation of energy by reducing motor movements and assists in thermoregulation by reducing the surface area for heat loss. Motor development entails inhibition of flexion and increasing extensor activity. These changes occur in part because of increasing control by the motor cortex. When cortical innervation is interrupted, as in pathologic conditions, loss of extensor innervation results in flexion. Increasing sophistication of control by the CNS improves coordination of movement, control and accuracy of movement, and synchrony and rhythmicity of movement. These capabilities support ongoing motor development, including head control, turning over, reaching, and grasping.

Neonatal Reflexes

Reflexes are automatic, built-in motor behaviors occurring at the spinal level. Reflexes therefore provide information about muscle tone and lower level motor function. Reflexes serve many neonatal needs in interacting with the extrauterine environment and provide valuable information regarding the neonate's motor and neural status. Although reflexes are automatic rather than volitional, the reflexive responses of the neonate provide evidence to parents and other caregivers of the neonate's motor capabilities, responsiveness, and individual needs. The development and strength of reflexes vary with gestational age.

Many reflexes characteristic of the neonate seemingly disappear with development. If these reflexes do not disappear at their usual time, infants should be observed for the appearance of neurologic abnormalities. Some reflexes (such as the Babinski reflex) are masked by higher-order functions but are observed in adults when pathologic conditions interfere with higher-level control. Other reflexes considered abnormal in an adult are seen in neonates. For instance, clonus of the knee and ankle is commonly observed in neonates, as is the Babinski reflex.

The Moro reflex involves abduction of the arms at the shoulder with the elbows in extension and the hands open, followed by adduction of the arms at the shoulder into an embrace position with flexion of the elbows. Portions of the Moro reflex can be observed as early as 28 weeks' gestational age, with a mature reflex seen at approximately 36 to 37 weeks.[7]

Neonates exhibit a strong palmar grasp reflex with fingers tightly flexed and curled into the palm. The palmar grasp reflex is so strong that infants can grasp, although not consciously, items placed in the hand. The palmar grasp may also be assessed in the pull-to-sit maneuver. Although the palmar grasp is first observed at approximately 28 weeks' gestational age, full strength is not achieved until approximately 32 weeks.[7]

The Babkin reflex can be elicited in term and preterm infants from birth and has been reported in infants as young as 25 weeks' gestation, although there are wide individual variations.[74] Not all neonates demonstrate this response, which is more likely to be seen in waking states and less in drowsy or sleep states. The Babkin reflex is elicited by placing the infant in a supine position and simultaneously pressing the infant's palms with the examiner's thumbs. "The predominant response in the reflex is opening of the mouth, which is often associated with flexion of the forearms and head and closing of the eyes."[74] The reflex disappears in most infants by 5 months. The area that mediates this reflex is believed to be the reticular formation of the brainstem.[74]

The tonic neck reflex (also termed the *fencing position*) is stimulated by rotation of the head to the side. The reflex movements include extension of the arm and leg on the side to which the head is turned and flexion of the arm and leg on the side opposite to which the head is turned. The movements of the extremities are similar to the crossed extensor reflex. Portions of the tonic neck reflex appear during later fetal development, but the reflex is often not well established until several weeks after birth.[235] Like the Moro reflex, the tonic neck reflex stabilizes position, preventing rolling.

Neonates demonstrate a rhythmic stepping motion of their lower extremities. When the neonate is held upright with the feet touching a solid surface, an alternating stepping motion is observed. There is some evidence that coordination exhibited in the stepping reflex may be predictive of later developmental outcomes.

The sucking and rooting reflexes are essential for oral intake of nutrients by neonates. Rooting assists the neonate in locating and latching on to the nipple and occurs at about 32 weeks' gestation. Stimulation of the perioral region results in turning of the head in the direction of the stimulus and mouthing actions in search of the nipple. The sucking reflex is present at 28 weeks' gestation but is weak and not coordinated with swallowing. Some suck-swallow synchrony is seen by 32 to 34 weeks, and synchrony is complete by 36 to 38 weeks.[7] Sucking and swallowing are discussed further on pages 413-414.

Sleep-Wake Pattern

Fetal activity records document fluctuating periods of activity and quiescence that increase in duration and regularity from midgestation to term.[181] After birth the infant exhibits alternating periods of sleep and wakefulness that initially reflect fetal activity-inactivity patterns. Sleep in neonates and infants exhibits developmental differences from that of adults. As a result, sleep is not as well defined and definitions are less precise than in adults. Consequently, neonatal and infant sleep is described in terms of state—that is, a group of physiologic and behavioral characteristics that regularly recur together.[24]

Neonates and young infants spend a large portion of the 24-hour day sleeping. Sleep therefore does not initially follow a light-dark pattern and is not diurnal, as in the adult. A major accomplishment in an infant's development is the ability to sleep through the night and adapt to the diurnal pattern of activity and sleep-wake behaviors of the family. The sleep-wake pattern is an indicator of neurologic status and the neonate's ability to organize behavior.

Definition of Infant States

A number of systems have been developed to code or score neonatal and infant sleep-wake states.[104] The major difference between conventional definitions of infant states is the number of subtypes of states and therefore the specificity and precision of the various states. Generally, the more immature the neonate is according to gestational and postmenstrual age, the grosser or less precise the definitions of state, because the quality of state and consistency among indicators improve with age. The six categories of infant state described by Wolff and Brazelton are discussed here.[31,244] Each state is complete unto itself, representing a particular form of neural control. The six sleep-wake states are as follows: quiet (deep)

sleep (QS), active (light) sleep (AS), drowsy, awake (quiet) alert, active alert, and crying. The ability to clearly differentiate these states is dependent on the infant's postmenstrual age. The proportion of time spent in each of these states also varies with postmenstrual age. Immature infants in particular have what is sometimes termed *indeterminate sleep* in which electroencephalographic (EEG), physiologic, and behavioral parameters meet neither AS nor QS criteria.[47]

QS (deep or non–rapid eye movement [NREM] sleep) is deep, restful sleep with the eyes closed; little body or facial movement, except for an occasional startle or twitch; regular respiration and heart rate; and no movement of the eyes.[180] QS is restorative and anabolic. An increase in cell mitosis and replication occurs during this state. Oxygen consumption reaches the lowest levels during QS. In addition, the release of growth hormone is associated with QS, as are high levels of serotonin and low levels of glucocorticoid.

During AS (light sleep), the eyes are closed but there are movements of the extremities and face, mouthing, grimacing, and sucking movements. Respiration and heart rate are irregular and penile erections occur. Active bouts of rapid eye movements (REM) occur in association with dreaming; the fine, rapid movement of the eyes can be observed beneath the lid. AS has been likened to "wide-awake asleep," because the level of brain activity is similar to that of the awake state. Information is processed during AS and entered into memory; thus AS has been linked to learning. Restructuring of synapses and changes in protein synthesis increase during AS.

During the drowsy state, the infant seems partially awake and partially asleep. Drowsiness usually indicates a state transition between awake and sleep states. In the quiet alert state, the infant is awake, the eyes are open, and there is little motor movement. The infant is alert and shows interest or attention by focusing on visual stimulation. The infant appears to be "drinking in" information from the surrounding environment and processing this information. This state is characterized by limited motion and activity associated with the infant attending to sensory information.

The neonate or infant's motor activity escalates in the active awake state. The eyes are less bright than in the quiet alert state. There may be spitting up or hiccoughing. Respiration often becomes increased and irregular and skin color changes may occur. The active alert state often precedes crying. In healthy infants, crying is easily recognizable. In preterm infants the motor actions associated with cry sounds are evident, but because of the infant's immaturity, the sounds may be weak or absent.

Sleep-Wake States Related to Brain Maturation

Sleep is required for brain development. "Sleep is not merely a state of rest but also is a period of intense brain activity involving higher cortical functions."[47] Sleep-wake patterns change with CNS maturation. Postnatal development of the sleep-wake state pattern reflects the underlying maturation of the reticular activating system, brainstem, and related circadian rhythms. The developmental changes in state include both alterations in temporal pattern and the integration of variables within the state. Inhibitory ability increases with CNS maturation. Increased inhibitory ability results in smoother muscle movements, reduces global responses, improves habituation and adaptation, and generally acts to improve the infant's attentional abilities as well as bring about specific changes in sleep.[104] These sleep changes include increasing duration of sleep periods, consolidation of sleep into nighttime hours, and maturation of the sleep states themselves. Within each state, synchrony among the state variables increases.

Infant development entails increasing amounts of QS as well as increasing periods of quiet alertness. Both of these states reflect sophisticated neural control. Sustaining a state consistently or making a transition from one state to another requires tremendous neural organization. Thus sleep-wake patterns are an excellent window to the infant's neurologic status. Alterations in sleep-wake patterns are observed in infants with Down syndrome, biochemical disturbances, and brain malformations and after asphyxia.[92]

Sleep is necessary for somatic and brain growth and development. As described earlier, restorative and growth processes are facilitated during QS. REM sleep is important for learning and memory. Attention behavior development parallels development of QS, indicating both inhibition and maturity.[180] The amount of quiet awake time parallels QS, and both increase with development.[92]

Development of Infant States

Before 28 to 30 weeks' gestational age, preterm infants show minimal patterns of state activity either by behavioral or EEG characteristics. Active or REM sleep appears at 28 to 30 weeks' gestation with evidence of cycling of states at 32 weeks.[60,92] Well-developed QS appears much later in development, initially becoming apparent at approximately 36 weeks' gestational age.[180] With maturation, intermediate or transitional sleep decreases, accompanied by an increase in QS; AS stays relatively stable.[166,235] General trends in sleep development include increasing QS, decreasing AS, and putting sleep cycles together consecutively, which yields longer sleep periods.[107]

The EEG of an infant is not always consistent with the behavioral expression of state. State is evidenced behaviorally before it is apparent on the EEG. Before 30 weeks' gestation, EEG activity is present but is discontinuous and of low amplitude. At 30 to 36 weeks' gestational age, AS can be determined by EEG.[235] Between 36 and 40 weeks' gestational age, both AS and QS can be determined by EEG. Maturation of EEG activity includes differentiation of discontinuous activity into mature EEG waveforms and an increase in the amplitude of EEG waves.[166] The EEG of a newborn commonly shows paroxysmal activity, asymmetry of the left and right portions of the brain, and considerable individual variation.[166]

Continued development of sleep-wake patterns after birth also involves changes in the temporal pattern of sleep and the integration of variables within states. In the first month, neonates sleep an average of 12 to 16 hours per day.[15] Periods of sleep occur around the clock. Periods of sleep are short, typically not extending beyond 3 or 4 hours. The sleep cycle is roughly 50 minutes, compared with the 90-minute adult sleep cycle. Sleep begins with active (REM) sleep versus NREM sleep in adults.[47] Initially, a sleep period may be only one to two cycles.[47] Over the first weeks, the amount of AS during the day decreases and AS increases during the nighttime hours.[181]

Circadian rhythmicity matures after birth with development of the sleep-wake rhythms and hormonal secretion prominent in the first 2 to 3 months.[193,223,224] Timing of sleep and wake is regulated by circadian clocks (entrained to light-dark cycles) and homeostatic processes (need for sleep after a certain time awake referred to as *sleep pressure*).[181] Homeostatic mechanisms are modified in early infancy; that is, infants spend relatively little time in waking before the need to sleep intervenes; thus sleep pressure accumulates more rapidly.[181] Evidence of a circadian sleep rhythm emerges at 5 to 6 weeks with progressive maturation over the next few months.[194] By 1 month, infants start to slowly shift toward more sleep at night than in the day, but they may continue daytime napping for up to 4 to 5 years.[194]

State Modulation

Some infants seem to "sleep like babies," whereas some are difficult to soothe, awaken easily, and sleep for short intervals and at unpredictable times. Other infants are overly drowsy, difficult to arouse, and sleep excessive periods of time. Differences in sleep-wake patterns reflect differences in neurologic development and the infant's ability to modulate state. *State modulation* refers to the infant's ability to make smooth transitions between states, arouse when appropriate, and sustain sleep states. By modulating or regulating state, infants can control sensory input to some extent and modulate their responses to the environment.[31] In addition, the infant can use state behaviors to guide caregiving and to modify social interactions. Problems with state modulation, therefore, entail problems regulating sensory input and responses. Infants who cannot use state changes to turn stimulation on or off may be either missing important input or become sensory overloaded. State modulation is therefore an asset in the infant's adaptation to the environment. Problems with state modulation may emanate from the infant or environment. Infant factors influencing state modulation include immaturity, pain, stress, maternal substance abuse, and illness. Environmental factors that affect state regulation and interfere with the infant's sleep-wake pattern include noise, light, temperature, and caregiver actions.

Neurobehavioral Organization

The concept of neurobehavioral organization is a means of holistically viewing the infant's response capabilities. The connectedness between elements of the nervous system is the basis for integration and organization of overall function. Neurobehavioral organization captures the essence of neonatal and infant function in the extrauterine environment and determines the infant's interaction with the surrounding physical and social environment.

Als's synactive theory of development defines five subsystems governing the infant's interaction with the environment: autonomic/physiologic, motor, state organizational, attentional/interactive, and self-regulatory capacity (synactivation is the process by which these fives subsystems interact and influence each other).[3] These subsystems are interdependent and hierarchical; that is, the order of development begins with autonomic and physiologic stability, followed in succession by motor, state, and attentional or interactive, and finally development of self-regulatory capacity. The level of organization is determined by development and is largely dependent on postmenstrual age; however, illness or injury may alter neurologic function and therefore neurobehavioral organization. In addition, organization at any level is determined by the previous levels. Thus state organization is dependent on organization and stability of the motor and autonomic-physiologic subsystems; attentional or interactive behaviors require organization of the state, motor, and autonomic-physiologic subsystems. An infant's behavioral responses or cues are indicative of the level of organization.

Autonomic organization entails regulation of cardiorespiratory activity, gastrointestinal peristalsis, and peripheral skin blood flow. Motor organization includes skeletal muscle tone, posture, and quality of movement. State organization involves orderly progression of sleep-wake states, the ability to sustain a state, and smooth state transitions. The culmination of neurobehavioral organization is in the infant's attentional or interactive and self-regulatory abilities. The attentional-interactive subsystem involves the infant's ability to orient and focus on stimuli and achieve well-defined periods of alertness. Self-regulatory capacity is the ability of the infant to maintain integrity and balance between subsystems, integrate all the subsystems, and modulate state.[3]

Neurobehavioral organization thus refers to the ability to modulate state, control internal reactions, control motor responses, self-regulate, respond to people and events in the external environment, and maintain an appropriate degree of alertness.[31] Neurobehavioral organization is critical to energy consumption, oxygen and calorie requirements, and growth, as well as the foundation for development and interactions with parents and other caregivers. Components of neurobehavioral organization include the ability to regulate sensory input, feed efficiently and effectively, coordinate sucking and swallowing, self-console, exhibit smooth coordinated movement, maintain muscle tone, and elicit caregiving through appropriate cues. Tools to assess neurobehavioral organization rely on observation of the infant in interaction with both the physical and social environments.[104]

CLINICAL IMPLICATIONS FOR NEONATAL CARE

During the neonatal period, glial proliferation, myelination, cell differentiation, dendrite expansion, and synapse formation and remodeling are occurring within the nervous system. The developing CNS is vulnerable to a number of influences, including the effects of the environment, handling, and caregiving. In addition, the immature CNS produces variations in seizure activity and influences the diagnosis and treatment of pain. These concerns are particularly important when considering infants born prematurely, because development of the nervous system is not consistent with demands posed by the extrauterine environment. A preterm infant is usually a third trimester fetus, and, with the increasing survival of extremely premature infants, viability is extending into the second trimester.

Risks Posed by the Caregiving Environment

Healthy term infants are well equipped to adapt to life outside the uterus. When neonates are compromised by illness or prematurity, adaptive abilities are challenged. The extrauterine environment is a critical factor in the development of the immature CNS and may alter developmental outcomes. The hospital care environment has been viewed as providing a deficient or inappropriate sensory environment for immature infants. Caregiving should always be individualized and based on recognition of infant cues (Box 15-3).[3,4,24] Emphasis has been placed on controlling the physical environment, including noise and light, and caregiving interactions such as pacing and individualizing caregiving to fit the infant's level of neurobehavioral maturation.[3,4,24,143,219]

Stability or engagement cues demonstrate organization and reflect the infant's readiness for interaction (see Box 15-3). Distress or disengagement cues (see Box 15-3) indicate disorganization and signal the caregiver to provide supportive measures and time for recuperation. Supportive measures include interventions such as positioning, environmental modifications, providing boundaries, swaddling, and reducing stressful stimuli.[3,24] The Neonatal Individualized Developmental Care and Assessment Program (NIDCAP) is a specialized training program for high-risk infant care providers that focuses on sensitive recognition of infant behavioral cues and individualized intervention strategies to promote and support neurobehavioral organization (http://www.nidcap.org/) in collaboration with families.[4]

Vulnerability to Brain Injury in Preterm and Term Infants

Systemic hypoxemia and decreased cerebral perfusion may lead to brain hypoxic-ischemic damage with risk of hemorrhage and edema. The usual site of injury varies with maturational changes in the vascular anatomy and metabolic activity of the brain. In term infants the site of injury usually involves the cerebral cortex with neuronal loss.[49] In older preterm and term infants, insults of this type often

BOX 15-3   Infant Neurobehavioral Cues

DISTRESS/DISENGAGEMENT CUES	STABILITY/ENGAGEMENT CUES
Bradycardia, apnea	Facial gaze
Rapid heart or respiration rate	Smiling
Grunting	Vocalization
Stooling	Feeding posture
Mottled skin	Flexion of arms and legs
Dusky color	Eyes alert
Cyanosis	Stable heart rate
Tremor	Stable respiratory rate
Finger splay	Smooth movements
Fingers interlaced	Hand to mouth
Arching	Finger folding
Hyperalert face	Smooth state transitions
Facial grimace	Sucking and mouthing
Limb extension	Consolable
Gaze aversion	"Ooh" face
Closed eyes	Alert
Slack jaw	Eye-to-eye contact
Open mouth	Grasping
Tongue thrusting	
Sighing	
Regurgitation	
Jitteriness	
Flaccidness	
Vomiting	
Hand to ear	
Worried face	
Rapid state change	
Eyes floating	
Staring	
Hyperextension	
Glassy eyed	
Tongue protrusion	
Flushed	
Hiccough	
Startle	
Yawn	
Flaccidity	
Sneezing	

Compiled from references 3, 4, 24, and 172.

result in hypoxic-ischemic encephalopathy (HIE) in the cerebral cortex and other areas.

Preterm infants are particularly vulnerable to altered brain maturation and brain injury because they are born "at a time of peak brain growth, synaptogenesis, developmental regulation of specific receptor populations, and central nervous system organization and differentiation."[218] In preterm infants, the neuropathology consists of multiple lesions including germinal matrix hemorrhage–intraventricular hemorrhage (GMH/IVH) that may include periventricular hemorrhagic infarction with posthemorrhagic hydrocephalus, and periventricular leukomalacia (PVL; *leukomalacia* refers to change in the brain's white matter reflective of softening) with accompanying neuronal and axonal abnormalities (referred to as the *encephalopathy of prematurity*).[235,238] PVL accompanied by neuronal and axonal alterations is the most common brain injury in preterm infants.[49,115,235,236,238] Preterm infants

are also at increased risk for cerebellar injury.[142,144,235,236] Reductions in both gray and white matter volume are seen in preterm infants. These reductions are seen even without documented injury (PVL or IVH) and persist into childhood.[115] In recent years severe destructive injuries have been less prevalent, with motor and cognitive disabilities more common.[12]

Because there are few specific interventions to treat these disorders, the primary emphasis of nursing care is on preventative, protective, and supportive care (see Neuroprotection Strategies and other resources).[12,21,24,25,57] Back notes "Factors such as improving nutrition, preventing infections, reducing neonatal stress, and implementing earlier behavioral interventions may all play a role in mitigating the impact of neuronal dysmaturation."[11]

Germinal Matrix and Intraventricular Hemorrhage

GMH and IVH are common forms of intracranial hemorrhage in preterm infants. The consequences of intracranial hemorrhage include direct neuronal damage from pressure and inflammation and the risk of developing posthemorrhagic hydrocephalus; severe hemorrhage may result in death.[235] Long-term outcomes are variable but include motor and sensory disabilities and cognitive delay.[14,57,241]

The occurrence of GMH/IVH is related to structural and functional differences in the immature CNS, including the nature of the GM, differences in regulation of CBF, and venous pressure. The hemorrhage usually begins as a microvascular event that spreads, presumably because of overperfusion of the area. In term infants IVH occurs predominantly in the ventricular choroid plexus and trauma is more often a precipitating factor.[235] In preterm infants, bleeding generally occurs in the subependymal GM located adjacent the lateral ventricles in the subependymal layer (GMH) in the area of the caudate nucleus and foramen of Monro, with subsequent extension of the hemorrhage into the ventricles (IVH).[235] Blood may also be found in the white matter with severe IVH because of an associated hypoxic-ischemic insult. The highest risk of GMH/IVH is during the period of GM prominence (i.e., in infants less than 34 weeks' gestation). The more immature the neonate is, the greater the risk of GMH/IVH.[235]

The GM is a highly cellular, high metabolic area characterized as gelatinous in structure with few pericytes (contractile basal membrane cells that wrap around capillaries to provide support).[14,25,235] The GM receives a rich blood supply chiefly through a large bed of irregular vessels (immature vascular rete) that are fragile because of a thin basement membrane and are prone to disruption.[14,101,241] Angiogenesis is rapid in the GM, resulting in more immature blood vessels.[14] In addition, the venous drainage in the area of the GM entails a distinctive U-shaped curve, and venous tributaries merge and flow into the vein of Galen, which is predisposed to stasis and increased venous pressure.[235] After about 35 to 36 weeks, the GM involutes and the blood vessels become true capillaries.[100,241]

The physical characteristics of the GM, along with its highly vascular nature and potential limits in venous drainage, predispose to bleeding. These characteristics interact with cerebral autoregulation and the effects of hypoxia on autoregulation. During episodes of hypoxemia, autoregulation is abolished and blood flow becomes pressure-passive. Hypercarbia and acidosis also disrupt autoregulation. Thus any condition that reduces blood oxygen levels may alter autoregulation and contribute to the development of GMH/IVH. Although cardiorespiratory problems are easily recognized as sources of hypoxia, any factor that increases oxygen demand beyond the supply capabilities (i.e., increased metabolic rate) is also suspect in producing hypoxia, altered autoregulation, and GMH/IVH.[25,241] Examples include thermoregulatory requirements, effects of handling, environmental disruptions, pain, or motor activity. During periods of pressure-passive flow, fragile capillaries of the GM may rupture if CBF or pressure increases. Once capillary disruption occurs, alterations in coagulation may perpetuate the hemorrhage.

Factors that produce fluctuating, decreased, or increased CBF also contribute to GMH/IVH.[28,235,241] If autoregulation of CBF is compromised, alterations in systemic blood pressure may also be causative factors. Examples of conditions believed to contribute to GMH/IVH include the pressure effects of ventilatory assistance, infusion of volume-expanding fluids, hypercarbia and other causes of cerebral vasodilation, increase in central venous pressure, or respiratory distress.[235] Deformation of the pliable skull of an immature infant may obstruct brain venous sinuses and increase venous pressure.[57]

Many of the health care procedures experienced by preterm infants (e.g., handling, suctioning, mechanical ventilation) alter oxygen level and blood pressure. Research on the effects of procedures has shown that blood pressure initially drops, followed by a rise; the more intensive the care is, the greater the initial drop and the greater the rebound.[28] Prevention of GMH/IVH requires sensitivity regarding the fragile nature of the capillaries within the CNS and recognition of the effects of hypoxemia on autoregulation, as well as the role of autoregulation and pressure in cerebral perfusion. Intervention bundles have been developed to prevent or minimize activities that can increase intracranial pressure or cause wide swings in arterial or venous pressure or hypoxemia, especially in the first days after birth when this disorder occurs most frequently.[21,25,57]

White Matter Injury (Periventricular Leukomalacia)

White matter hypoxic-ischemic injury (WMI) is the most common severe neurologic insult seen in preterm infants.[49,235,238,239] The primary insult is destruction of brain tissue with injury to the cerebral white matter (PVL), usually accompanied by secondary developmental disturbances (associated axonal and neuronal alterations in gray matter).[49,115,235,236,238] PVL can involve both focal necrotic lesions deep in white matter with loss of all cellular elements and diffuse injury in central cerebral

BOX 15-4	Pathogenesis of Periventricular Leukomalacia: Major Interacting Factors

CEREBRAL ISCHEMIA
- Pressure-passive cerebral circulation
- Hypocarbia

SYSTEMIC INFECTION OR INFLAMMATION
- Propensity for maternal intrauterine infection or postnatal neonatal infection
- Potentiation of cerebral ischemic injury

MATURATION-DEPENDENT INTRINSIC VULNERABILITY OF PRE-OLs
- Microglial activation
- Excitotoxicity
- Free radical (ROS/RNS) attack

Pre-OLs, Premyelinating oligodendrocytes; *ROS/RNS*, reactive oxygen species/reactive nitrogen species.
From Volpe, J.J., Kinney, H.C., Jensen, F.E., & Rosenberg, D.A. (2011). The developing oligodendrocyte: Key cellular target in brain injury in the premature infant. *Int J Dev Neurosci, 29,* 425.

white matter with damage to premyelinating oligodendrocytes (pre-OL) that may delay or alter their maturation, astrogliosis, and microglia infiltration.[25,164,239] PVL focal lesions can be either a cystic form (lesions are several millimeters or more and evolve to cysts) or a noncystic form (lesions are microscopic and evolve to glial scars).[49,115,164,235,236,238] Noncystic PVL and diffuse PVL are seen in many VLBW infants; the cystic form of PVL is seen in less than 5%.[12,239] The associated axonal and neuronal alterations in the gray matter may alter neuronal connectivity and synaptic activity and can affect multiple areas, including cerebral white matter (axons and subplate neurons), thalamus, basal ganglia, cerebral cortex, cerebellum, and brainstem.[12,238,239] Box 15-4 summarizes the mechanisms in the development of PVL and major maturation-dependent factors.

During peak vulnerability for PVL, cerebral white matter axons are undergoing rapid growth and synaptogenesis and are vulnerable to damage.[52,128] Two principal neuron types are seen in the cerebral white matter at this time: subplate neurons (in subcortical white matter) and late-migrating γ-aminobutyric acid (GABA)-ergic neurons (in central white matter).[52,236,238] Both types of neurons are critical for cerebral cortical and thalamic development.[52,238] Injury to the subplate neurons alters both afferent and efferent axons. Damage to afferent axons alters pre-OL generation and decreases cortical and thalamic development.[236] Damage to efferent axons alters cortical development.[236] Injury to the thalamus decreases axon generation and alters pre-OL development, myelination, thalamic development, and cortical development.[243] Pre-OL damage in both cystic and noncystic PVL leads to inadequate myelin-producing oligodendrocytes and cerebral hypomyelination.[49,239]

The brain is most vulnerable to WMI at 24 to 32 weeks' gestation when the white matter is immature and poorly vascularized.[49] WMI is associated with cerebral ischemia, altered cerebral autoregulation, infection and inflammation, and the vulnerability of the pre-OL in the VLBW infant (see Box 15-4).[25,236,238,239] Necrotic changes subsequent to ischemia occur in the white matter in the area of the ventricles.[235] WMI may be seen in association with GMH/IVH but often occurs in the absence of GMH/IVH.[57]

Vascular structure and factors influencing CBF place preterm infants at risk for PVL. Areas of blood flow near the lateral ventricles is impaired by hypotension.[81,235] Underperfusion of these areas leads to ischemia and necrosis. Reduction of blood oxygen decreases delivery of oxygen to these vulnerable regions, leading to hypoxic-ischemic injury. Cerebral autoregulation is immature, leading to a pressure-passive state that further alters cerebral perfusion.[238,239] Hypocarbia as a consequence of ventilator management can lead to cerebral vasoconstriction and further decreases in cerebral blood flow.[236,238,239] The pathogenesis of hypoxia-ischemia is described in Hypoxic-Ischemic Encephalopathy.

Perinatal infection and immune-mediated inflammatory response with release of proinflammatory cytokines is believed to play a prominent role in PVL pathogenesis.[49,57,191,236,238,239] Infection and inflammation may arise from intrauterine or postnatal infection. Intrauterine infection is also an important mediator of preterm labor (see Chapter 4). Infection activates the immune system, including the brain microglia with production of cytokines, free radicals, and glutamate that result in excitotoxicity and can injure the pre-OL and other brain cells (see Box 15-4).[49,239] Hypoxia and inflammation may have potentiating effects.[239] Infants with hypoxic-ischemic events, prolonged rupture of the membranes, and chorioamnionitis are at increased risk for PVL.[235]

The pre-OL are vulnerable to damage by cytokines, glutamate, adenosine, and free radicals, which can lead to alterations in cognitive, visual, and motor function.[235] Pre-OLs have low levels of antioxidant enzymes and a high oxidative metabolism, so they are vulnerable to oxidative stress with hypoxic-ischemic events.[49] Damage includes impairment of subsequent OL development and survival, altered myelination, and axonal damage and disruption.[12]

WMI and its associated neuronal and axonal alteration (referred to as the *encephalopathy of prematurity*) are the leading causes of neurologic disability in preterm infants. Sequelae may include cerebral palsy and motor, cognitive, learning, and behavioral deficits.[49,235,236] Preventative interventions being used or investigated include reducing hypoxia-ischemia, infection and inflammation, and microglia activation; increasing antioxidant defenses; and decreasing excitability.[48,191,239]

Cerebellar Injury in Preterm Infants

Preterm infants are also at risk for injury to the cerebellum. The cerebellum is one of the later brain structures to mature, is important in cognition, and acts as a node in distribution of neural networks with interconnections with the thalamus and parietal and prefrontal cortex.[73,144,179] A series of developmental events occur at the end of the second and beginning of the third trimester that are essential for the structural and functional integrity of the cerebellum.[142] The alterations seen in the cerebellum in VLBW infants may arise from direct injury (usually after cerebellar hemorrhage) leading to atrophy and growth failure; indirect injury or underdevelopment associated with cerebral injury; or underdevelopment without evidence of specific injury (e.g., because of immaturity).[25,142,144]

Cerebellar underdevelopment and hemorrhage are seen primarily in infants born at 24 to 32 weeks' gestation (and especially in those born at 24 to 28 weeks).[94,142,236,237] Infants have a bilateral, usually symmetric, decrease in cerebellar volume.[142] The exact etiology of cerebellar hemorrhage in preterm infants is unclear but includes factors similar to that of GMH/IVH.[25,73] Proposed mechanisms include immature cerebral autoregulation, increased venous pressure, fragility of the cerebellar GM blood vessels, altered GM coagulation, and vasoocclusive injury leading to bilateral infarcts of the cerebral hemispheres.[25,73,143] The cerebellar GM reaches its maximum around 25 weeks and is vulnerable to bleeding.[25] Cerebellar injury often occurs concurrently with PVL or IVH.[25,73,142,236]

Insults may lead to the altered sequences of motor development seen in some preterm infants and may contribute to alterations in language (especially expressive) and social-behavioral and cognitive function.[33,142,237] Motor disturbances include a range of findings from incoordination to cerebral palsy and deficits in motor planning and execution; cognitive deficits usually involve visual-spatial abilities, verbal fluency, reading, memory, and learning; attentional deficits involve regulation of shifts in attention; and social and affective disturbances include mood abnormalities and autistic behaviors.[33,73,142,237]

Hypoxic-Ischemic Encephalopathy

After 33 to 34 weeks' gestation, blood flow and brain metabolic activity is less prominent in the periventricular area and shifts to the cortical area. As a result, hypoxia and ischemia in older preterm and term infants are more likely to damage areas of the peripheral and dorsal cerebral cortex. The primary lesion in hypoxic injury in these infants is necrosis of neurons in the cortices of the cerebrum and cerebellum, and possibly the brainstem. The primary ischemic injury usually occurs in the posterior (boundary area) portion of the parasagittal region. This area is farthest from the original blood supply of the major cerebral vessels and with systemic hypotension or hypoperfusion receives the least blood. With asphyxia and systemic hypotension, cerebral perfusion is maintained at first by cerebral vasodilation and redistribution of blood flow to the brain from other organs. If the asphyxia continues, brain water balance and CBF are altered and ischemia and edema develop.

The primary mechanisms for cell damage with hypoxic-ischemic encephalopathy (HIE) are excitotoxicity, inflammation, and oxidative stress, which deplete energy reserves. The pathophysiology of HIE is illustrated in Figure 6-4. Damage occurs in two phases. During the first phase, damage from the initial hypoxic insult leads to cell death secondary to (1) depolarization and influx of sodium, chloride, and water leading to cell edema and lysis; (2) interference with the cell's ability to produce an action potential, leading to failure of the sodium-potassium pump and cell edema; (3) accumulation of calcium because of activation of NA/K channels and N-methyl-D-aspartate (NMDA) glutamate-mediated receptors; and (4) movement of calcium into the cell via voltage-dependent ion channels opened by the changes in the sodium-potassium pump.[57] These events may initially have a neuroprotective effect by reducing neuronal excitability and conserving oxygen. However, with reperfusion and reoxygenation, free oxygen radicals can accumulate, causing primary neuronal death. Persistence of hypoxia and ischemia activates NMDA receptors, leading to further increases in intracellular calcium via glutamate-controlled ion channels. Glutamate and nitric oxide (NO) are released and accumulate. Glutamate at high levels is neurotoxic. NO, which at normal levels promotes vasodilation and increased blood flow, at toxic levels leads to production of excess free oxygen radicals, further activation of NMDA receptors, and production of peroxynitrates, which cause further cell damage. The reperfusion phase usually begins 6 to 12 hours or more after the initial insult and is characterized by hyperexcitability; cytotoxic edema; and damage from the release of free oxygen radicals and NO, inflammatory changes, and imbalances in inhibitory and excitatory neurotransmitters. Secondary neuronal death occurs from necrosis or apoptosis.[57,235,239] Head and body cooling (therapeutic hypothermia) has become a standard of care for infants with HIE.[61,112,207] Therapeutic hypothermia is a neuroprotective strategy to reduce secondary reperfusion injuries in infants who are at risk for HIE. Studies report beneficial effects in terms of improved survival and outcome with no significant adverse effects; however, even with cooling, mortality and morbidity remain high (see Chapter 20).[61,112,205,207]

Neuroprotection Strategies

Increasing attention has been directed toward neuroprotection in recent years in efforts to prevent or ameliorate neurologic insults. Neuroprotection strategies include preventive, rescue, and reparative interventions.[143] Limperopoulos defines these as follows:

> "A *preventive therapy* is initiated before a potential insult results in injury, and requires advance knowledge of a likely or imminent insult. An example of a preventive intervention is the infant undergoing open-heart repair of complex congenital heart disease that is managed with deep hypothermia during the high-risk procedure. On a different scale is the use of individualized neonatal developmental care to optimize

brain development in premature infants by reducing the discrepancy between the premature extrauterine and fetal environments; this optimization is achieved largely through a program that reduces excessive stimulation and attempts to promote an appropriate physiological milieu for the developing brain. In a different category is neural rescue therapy, which is initiated at, or soon after, a potential brain insult occurs, but before injury becomes irreversible. An example of a rescue strategy is induced mild hypothermia in full-term infants who suffer a hypoxic-ischemic insult during perinatal asphyxia. Finally, a neural reparative strategy is one that attempts to exploit the restructuring potential of the developing brain to maximize recovery in the aftermath of irreversible brain injury."[143, p. 95]

Other examples of neuroprotection strategies include use of antenatal corticosteroids (see Chapter 10), delayed cord clamping (see Chapter 8), therapeutic hypothermia (see Hypoxic-Ischemic Encephalopathy and Chapter 20), use of antenatal magnesium sulfate (see Chapter 4) and postnatal erythropoietin (see Chapter 8), protection from infection, neutral midline head position and other positioning strategies, avoiding excessive handling in the early days after birth in VLBW infants, interventions to prevent or reduce hypoxia or asphyxia events and rapid alterations in CBF, and preventing or minimizing fluctuations in systemic blood pressure and cerebral pressure.[11,18,21,25,48,57,113,201]

Developmental care focuses on providing an environment for the infant that is individualized for that infant and supports brain development, family adaptation, and long-term developmental needs, while reducing the effects of stress in the NICU.[137,184,219] "The goal is to conserve the infant's energy for growth, facilitate physiological stability and the infant's recovery from illness and promoting neurobehavioral development and family integration."[137] Interventions include family-centered care, NIDCAP, skin-to-skin holding (kangaroo care), positioning strategies, clustering caregiving, multisensory interventions, parent collaboration in care, enhancing feeding experiences, and modifying the NICU physical and caregiving environment.[21,25,137,184,219]

Neonatal Seizures

Seizure activity is the most common sign of neurologic problems in neonates and infants.[235] Seizures result from an abnormal neuronal electrical discharge. Thus seizures are caused by a number of conditions in which the environment of neurons, which support normal electrical activity, is altered. These conditions include hypoxemia, ischemia, hypoglycemia, hypocalcemia, hyperkalemia, hypomagnesemia, hyponatremia or hypernatremia, acidosis, and meningitis.[128,235] In general, seizure activity may entail eye movements, oral movements, changes in posture, motor movements such as bicycling or rowing actions, and apnea. Types of seizures and their description are listed in Box 15-5. The timing of seizure onset and type of seizure are related to pathology and gestational age.[235]

Seizure activity is determined by brain maturation. Thus seizures are expressed differently based on gestational age

27. Bø, K., et al. (2016). Exercise and pregnancy in recreational and elite athletes: 2016 evidence summary from the IOC expert group meeting, Lausanne. Part 1-exercise in women planning pregnancy and those who are pregnant. *Br J Sports Med, 50,* 571.

28. Bonfacio, S. L., Gonzalez, F., & Ferriero, D. M. (2012). Central nervous system injury and neuroprotection. In C. A. Gleason & S. Devaskar (Eds.), *Avery's Diseases of the newborn* (9th ed.). Philadelphia: Saunders.

29. Borg-Stein, J., Dugan, S. A., & Gruber, J. (2005). Musculoskeletal aspects of pregnancy. *Am J Phys Med Rehabil, 84,* 180.

30. Bourjeily, G., Ankner, G., & Mohsenin, V. (2011). Sleep-disordered breathing in pregnancy. *Clin Chest Med, 32,* 175.

31. Brazelton, T. B., & Nugent, J. K. (2011). *Neonatal behavioral assessment scale* (4th ed.). London: MacKeith.

32. Brémond-Gignac, D., et al., European Network of Study and Research in Eye Development. (2011). Visual development in infants: physiological and pathological mechanisms. *Curr Opin Ophthalmol, 22,* S1.

33. Brossard-Racine, M., du Plessis, A. J., & Limperopoulos, C. (2015). Developmental cerebellar cognitive affective syndrome in ex-preterm survivors following cerebellar injury. *Cerebellum, 14,* 151.

34. Bruner, J. P., & Tulipan, N. (2005). Intrauterine repair of spina bifida. *Clin Obstet Gynecol, 48,* 942.

35. Buckley, S. J. (2015). Executive summary of hormonal physiology of childbearing: evidence and implications for women, babies, and maternity care. *J Perinat Educ, 24,* 145.

36. Cakmak, B., Ribeiro, A. P., & Inanir, A. (2016). Postural balance and the risk of falling during pregnancy. *J Matern Fetal Neonatal Med, 29,* 1623.

37. Camune, B. D. (2013). Challenges in the management of the pregnant woman with spinal cord injury. *J Perinat Neonatal Nurs, 27,* 225.

38. Caparroz, F. A., et al. (2016). Rhinitis and pregnancy: literature review. *Braz J Otorhinolaryngol, 82,* 105.

39. Casagrande, D., et al. (2015). Low back pain and pelvic girdle pain in pregnancy. *J Am Acad Orthop Surg, 23,* 539.

40. Chaillet, N., et al. (2014). Nonpharmacologic approaches for pain management during labor compared with usual care: a meta-analysis. *Birth, 41,* 122.

41. Chitayat, D., et al. (2015). Folic acid supplementation for pregnant women and those planning pregnancy: 2015 update. *Clin Pharmacol, 56,* 170.

42. Cipolla, M. J. (2013). The adaptation of the cerebral circulation to pregnancy: mechanisms and consequences. *J Cereb Blood Flow Metab, 33,* 465.

43. Clark-Gambelunghe, M. B., & Clark, D. A. (2015). Sensory development. *Pediatr Clin North Am, 62,* 367.

44. Clowry, G., Molnár, Z., & Rakic P. (2010). Renewed focus on the developing human neocortex. *J Anat, 217,* 276.

45. Cuero, M. R., & Varelas, P. N. (2016). Neurologic complications in pregnancy. *Crit Care Clin, 32,* 43.

46. Dabo, F., et al. (2010). Plasma levels of beta-endorphin during pregnancy and use of labor analgesia. *Reprod Sci, 17,* 742.

47. Davis, K. F., Parker, K. P., & Montgomery, G. L. (2004). Sleep in infants and young children: Part one: normal sleep. *J Pediatr Health Care, 18,* 65.

48. Davis, A. S., Berger, V. K., & Chock, V. Y. (2016). Perinatal neuroprotection for extremely preterm infants. *Am J Perinatol, 33,* 290.

49. Deng, W. (2010). Neurobiology of injury to the developing brain. *Nat Rev Neurol, 6,* 328.

50. Derbyshire, S. W. (2010). Foetal pain? *Best Pract Res Clin Obstet Gynaecol, 24,* 647.

51. de Weerd, A. W., & van den Bossche, R. A. (2003). The development of sleep during the first months of life. *Sleep Med Rev, 7,* 179.

52. Diaz, A. L., & Gleeson, J. G. (2009). The molecular and genetic mechanisms of neocortex development. *Clin Perinatol, 36,* 503.

53. Ding, X. X., et al. (2014). A systematic review and quantitative assessment of sleep-disordered breathing during pregnancy and perinatal outcomes. *Sleep Breath, 18,* 703.

54. Dinn, R. B., Harris, A., & Marcus, P. S. (2003). Ocular changes in pregnancy. *Obstet Gynecol Surv, 58,* 137.

55. DiPietro, J. A. (2000). Baby and the brain: advances in child development. *Annu Rev Public Health, 21,* 455.

56. DiPietro, J. A. (2005). Neurobehavioral assessment before birth. *Ment Retard Dev Disabil Res Rev, 11,* 4.

57. Ditzenberger, G., & Blackburn, S. T. (2014). Neurologic system. In C. Kenner & J. W. Lott (Eds.), *Comprehensive neonatal care: An interdisciplinary approach* (5th ed.). New York: Springer.

58. Doesburg, S. M., et al. (2013). Neonatal pain-related stress, functional cortical activity and visual-perceptual abilities in school-age children born at extremely low gestational age. *Pain, 154,* 1946.

59. Donaldson, J. O., & Duffy, T. P. (2004). Neurologic complications. In G. N. Burrow, T. P. Duffy, & J. A. Copel (Eds.), *Medical complications during pregnancy* (6th ed.). Philadelphia: Saunders.

60. Dreyfus-Brisac, C. (1975). Neurophysiological studies in human premature and full-term newborns. *Biol Psychol, 10,* 485.

61. Drury, P. P., Bennet, L., & Gunn, A. J. (2010). Mechanisms of hypothermic neuroprotection. *Semin Fetal Neonatal Med, 15,* 287.

62. Duley, L., Henderson-Smart, D. J., & Chou, D. (2010). Magnesium sulphate versus phenytoin for eclampsia. *Cochrane Database Syst Rev, 2010*(10), CD000128.

63. Duley, L., et al. (2010). Magnesium sulphate versus diazepam for eclampsia. *Cochrane Database Syst Rev, 2010*(12), CD000127.

64. Dzaja, A., et al. (2005). Women's sleep in health and disease. *J Psychiatr Res, 39,* 55.

65. Edward, D. P., & Kaufman, L. M. (2003). Anatomy, development, and physiology of the visual system. *Pediatr Clin North Am, 50,* 1.

66. Ek, C. J., et al. (2012). Barriers in the developing brain and neurotoxicology. *Neurotoxicology, 33,* 586.

67. Ekbom, K., & Ulfberg, J. (2009). Restless legs syndrome. *J Intern Med, 266,* 419.

68. Ellegard, E. K. (2003). The etiology and management of pregnancy rhinitis. *Am J Respir Med, 2,* 469.

69. Fitzgerald, M., & Jennings, E. (1999). The postnatal development of spinal sensory processing. *Proc Natl Acad Sci U S A, 96,* 7719.

70. Foti, T., et al. (2000). A biomechanical analysis of gait during pregnancy. *J Bone Joint Surg Am, 82,* 625.

71. Franck, L. S., et al. (2000). Pain assessment in infants and children. *Pediatr Clin North Am, 47,* 487.

72. Friend, S., et al. (2016). Evaluation of pregnancy outcomes from the Tysabri® (natalizumab) pregnancy exposure registry: a global, observational, follow-up study. *BMC Neurol, 16,* 150.

73. Fumagalli, M., et al. (2015). From germinal matrix to cerebellar haemorrhage. *J Matern Fetal Neonatal Med, 28,* 2280.

74. Futagi, Y., et al. (2013). The Babkin reflex in infants: clinical significance and neural mechanism. *Pediatr Neurol, 49,* 149.

75. Fyfe, K. L., et al. (2014). The development of cardiovascular and cerebral vascular control in preterm infants. *Sleep Med Rev, 18,* 299.

76. Giannina, G., et al. (1997). Comparison of intraocular pressure between normotensive and preeclamptic women in the peripartum period. *Am J Obstet Gynecol, 176,* 1052.

77. Gianoulakis, C., & Chretien, M. (1998). Endorphins in fetomaternal physiology. In N. Gleicher (Ed.), *Principles of medical therapy in pregnancy* (3rd ed.). Stamford, CT: Appleton & Lange.

78. Gibbs, R. S., & Karlin, B. Y. (2008). *Danforth's Obstetrics and gynecology* (10th ed.). Philadelphia: Lippincott Williams & Wilkins.

79. Glass, P. (1999). The vulnerable neonate and the neonatal intensive care environment. In G. B. Avery, M. A. Fletcher, & M. G. MacDonald (Eds.), *Neonatology: Pathophysiology and management of the newborn* (5th ed.). Philadelphia: Lippincott Williams & Wilkins.

80. Glass, P. (2016). The vulnerable neonate and the neonatal intensive care environment. In M. G. MacDonald & M. M. K. Seshia (Eds.), *Avery's Neonatology: Pathophysiology and management of the newborn* (7th ed.). Philadelphia: Wolters Kluwer.

81. Gleason, C. A., Hohimer, A. R., & Back, S. A. (2012). Developmental physiology of the central nervous system. In C. A. Gleason & S. Devaskar (Eds.), *Avery's Diseases of the newborn* (9th ed.). Philadelphia: Saunders.

82. González, E., et al. (2017). Pathophysiology of retinopathy of prematurity. In R. A. Polin, et al. (Eds.), *Fetal and neonatal physiology* (5th ed.). Philadelphia: Saunders.

83. Grant, A. D., & Chung, S. M. (2013). The eye in pregnancy: ophthalmologic and neuro-ophthalmologic changes. *Clin Obstet Gynecol, 56,* 397.

84. Graven, S. N. (2000). Sound and the developing infant in the NICU: conclusions and recommendations for care. *J Perinatol, 20,* S88.

85. Graven, S. N. (2004). Early sensory visual development of the fetus and newborn. *Clin Perinatol, 31,* 199.

86. Gray, L., & Philbin, M. K. (2004). Effects of the neonatal intensive care unit on auditory attention and distraction. *Clin Perinatol*, *31*, 243.

87. Greenough, W. T., et al. (1987). Experience and brain development. *Child Dev*, *58*, 539.

88. Greisen, G. (2005). Autoregulation of cerebral blood flow in newborn babies. *Early Hum Dev*, *81*, 423.

89. Greisen, G. (2009). To autoregulate or not to autoregulate—that is no longer the question. *Semin Pediatr Neurol*, *16*, 207.

90. Grunau, R. E. (2013). Neonatal pain in very preterm infants: long-term effects on brain, neurodevelopment and pain reactivity. *Rambam Maimonides Medical Journal*, *4*, e0025.

91. Gutke, A., et al. (2015). Treatments for pregnancy-related lumbopelvic pain: a systematic review of physiotherapy modalities. *Acta Obstet Gynecol Scand*, *94*, 1156.

92. Hack, M. (1987). The sensorimotor development of the preterm infant. In A. A. Fanaroff & R. J. Martin (Eds.), *Behrman's neonatal-perinatal medicine* (4th ed.). St. Louis: Mosby.

93. Haider, B., & von Oertzen, J. (2013). Neurological disorders. *Best Pract Res Clin Obstet Gynaecol*, *27*, 867.

94. Haines, K. M., Wang, W., & Pierson, C. R. (2013). Cerebellar hemorrhagic injury in premature infants occurs during a vulnerable developmental period and is associated with wider neuropathology. *Acta Neuropathol Commun*, *1*, 69.

95. Haith, M. M. (1986). Sensory and perceptual processes in early infancy. *J Pediatr*, *109*, 158.

96. Hall, J. W. (2000). Development of the ear and hearing. *J Perinatol*, *20*, S12.

97. Hamdan, A. L., et al. (2009). Effect of pregnancy on the speaking voice. *J Voice*, *23*, 490.

98. Han, I. H. (2010). Pregnancy and spinal problems. *Curr Opin Obstet Gynecol*, *22*, 477.

99. Harden, C. L., et al. (2009). Practice parameter update: Management issues for women with epilepsy—focus on pregnancy (an evidence-based review): obstetrical complications and change in seizure frequency: Report of the Quality Standards Subcommittee and Therapeutics and Technology Assessment Subcommittee of the American Academy of Neurology and American Epilepsy Society. *Neurology*, *73*, 126.

100. Harden, C. L., et al. (2009). Practice parameter update: management issues for women with epilepsy—focus on pregnancy (an evidence-based review): teratogenesis and perinatal outcomes: Report of the Quality Standards Subcommittee and Therapeutics and Technology Assessment Subcommittee of the American Academy of Neurology and American Epilepsy Society. *Neurology*, *73*, 133.

101. Hardy, P., et al. (1997). Control of cerebral and ocular blood flow autoregulation in neonates. *Pediatr Clin North Am*, *44*, 137.

102. Harvey, V. L., & Dickenson, A. H. (2008). Mechanisms of pain in nonmalignant disease. *Curr Opin Support Palliat Care*, *2*, 133.

103. Hensley, J. G. (2009). Leg cramps and restless legs syndrome during pregnancy. *J Midwifery Womens Health*, *54*, 211.

104. Holditch-Davis, D., & Blackburn, S. T. (2013). Neurobehavioral development. In C. Kenner & J. W. Lott (Eds.), *Comprehensive neonatal nursing* (5th ed.). New York: Springer.

105. Holmes, G. L. (2009). The long-term effects of neonatal seizures. *Clin Perinatol*, *36*, 901.

106. Holmes, G. L., & Ben-Ari, Y. (2001). The neurobiology and consequences of epilepsy in the developing brain. *Pediatr Res*, *49*, 320.

107. Hoppenbrouwers, T., et al. (1988). Sleep and waking states in infancy: normative studies. *Sleep*, *11*, 387.

108. Hunter, L. P., Rychnovsky, J. D., & Yount, S. M. (2009). A selective review of maternal sleep characteristics in the postpartum period. *J Obstet Gynecol Neonatal Nurs*, *38*, 60.

109. Hutchison, B. L., et al. (2012). A postal survey of maternal sleep in late pregnancy. *BMC Pregnancy Childbirth*, *12*, 144.

110. Ireland, M. L., & Ott, S. M. (2000). The effects of pregnancy on the musculoskeletal system. *Clin Orthop*, *372*, 169.

111. Ito, M. (2004). "Nurturing the brain" as an emerging research field involving child neurology. *Brain Dev*, *26*, 429.

112. Jacobs, S. E., et al. (2013). Cooling for newborns with hypoxic ischaemic encephalopathy. *Cochrane Database Syst Rev*, *2013*(1), CD003311.

113. Jelin, A. C., et al. (2016). Perinatal neuroprotection update. *F1000Res*, *5*, F1000.

114. Jensen, F. E. (2009). Neonatal seizures: an update on mechanisms and management. *Clin Perinatol*, *36*, 881.

115. Jobe, A. H. (2010). "Miracle" extremely low birth weight neonates: examples of developmental plasticity. *Obstet Gynecol*, *116*, 1184.

116. Johnson, A. C., & Cipolla, M. J. (2015). The cerebral circulation during pregnancy: adapting to preserve normalcy. *Physiology (Bethesda)*, *30*, 139.

117. Johnston, C. C., Fernandes, A. M., & Campbell-Yeo, M. (2011). Pain in neonates is different. *Pain*, *152*, S65.

118. Jones, L., et al. (2012). Pain management for women in labour: an overview of systematic reviews. *Cochrane Database Syst Rev*, *2012*(3), CD009234.

119. Juul, S. E., & Pet, G. C. (2015). Erythropoietin and neonatal neuroprotection. *Clin Perinatol*, *42*, 469.

120. Karacan, I., et al. (1968). Characteristics of sleep patterns during late pregnancy and the postpartum periods. *Am J Obstet Gynecol*, *10*, 579.

121. Khazaie, H., et al. (2013). Insomnia treatment in the third trimester of pregnancy reduces postpartum depression symptoms: a randomized clinical trial. *Psychiatry Res*, *210*, 901.

122. Kirby, M. A., Groves, M. M., & Yellon, S. M. (2010). Retrograde tracing of spinal cord connections to the cervix with pregnancy. *Reproduction*, *139*, 645.

123. Klein, A. M., & Loder, E. (2010). Postpartum headache. *Int J Obstet Anesth*, *19*, 422.

124. Koizumi, H. (2004). The concept of developing the brain: a new natural science for learning and education. *Brain dev*, *26*, 434.

125. Kojić, Z., et al. (2007). Labor pain—physiological basis and regulatory mechanisms (Abstract). *Srp Arh Celok Lek*, *135*, 235.

126. Kostović, I., Judaš, M., & Sedmak, G. (2011). Developmental history of the subplate zone, subplate neurons and interstitial white matter neurons: relevance for schizophrenia. *Int J Dev Neurosci*, *29*, 193.

127. Kumar, R., Hayhurst, K. L., & Robson, A. K. (2011). Ear, nose, and throat manifestations during pregnancy. *Otolaryngol Head Neck Surg*, *145*, 188.

128. Lagercrantz, H., & Changeux, J. P. (2009). The emergence of human consciousness: from fetal to neonatal life. *Pediatr Res*, *65*, 255.

129. Lagercrantz, H., & Changeux, J. P. (2010). Basic consciousness of the newborn. *Semin Perinatol*, *34*, 201.

130. Lam, J., & Koren, G. (2014). P-glycoprotein in the developing human brain: a review of the effects of ontogeny on the safety of opioids in neonates. *Ther Drug Monit*, *36*, 699.

131. Lawrence, R. A., & Lawrence, R. M. (2016). *Breastfeeding: a guide for the medical profession* (8th ed.). Philadelphia: Elsevier.

132. Lawson, W., Reino, A. J., & Biller, H. F. (2000). Ear, nose & throat disorders in pregnancy. In W. R. Cohen, S. H. Cherry, & I. R. Merkatz (Eds.), *Cherry and Merkatz's Complications of pregnancy* (5th ed.). Philadelphia: Lippincott Williams & Wilkins.

133. Lecanuet, J. P., & Schaal, B. (1996). Fetal sensory competencies. *Eur J Obstet Gynecol*, *68*, 1.

134. Lee, K. A., et al. (2000). Parity and sleep patterns during and after pregnancy. *Obstet Gynecol*, *95*, 14.

135. Lee, K. A., et al. (2008). The influence of reproductive status and age on women's sleep. *J Womens Health (Larchmt)*, *17*, 1209.

136. Lentz, M. J., & Killien, M. G. (1991). Are you sleeping? Sleep patterns during postpartum hospitalization. *J Perinatal Neonatal Nurs*, *4*, 30.

137. Lester, B. M., et al. (2011). Infant neurobehavioral development. *Semin Perinatol*, *35*, 8.

138. Lickliter, R. (2000). The role of sensory stimulation in perinatal development: insights from comparative research for care of the high-risk infant. *J Behavioral Dev Pediatr*, *21*, 437.

139. Lickliter, R. (2011). The integrated development of sensory organization. *Clin Perinatol*, *38*, 591.

140. Liddle, S. D., & Pennick, V. (2015). Interventions for preventing and treating low-back and pelvic pain during pregnancy. *Cochrane Database Syst Rev*, *2015*(9), CD001139.

141. Liem, K. D., & Greisen, G. (2010). Monitoring of cerebral haemodynamics in newborn infants. *Early Hum Dev*, *86*, 155.

142. Limperopoulos, C., et al. (2007). Does cerebellar injury in premature infants contribute to the high prevalence of long-term cognitive, learning, and behavioral disability in survivors? *Pediatrics, 120,* 584.

143. Limperopoulos, C. (2010). Advanced neuroimaging techniques: their role in development of future fetal and neonatal neuroprotection. *Semin Perinatol, 34,* 93.

144. Limperopoulos, C. (2010). Extreme prematurity, cerebellar injury, and autism. *Semin Pediatr Neurol, 17,* 25.

145. Lipchock, S. V., Reed, D. R., & Mennella, J. A. (2011). The gustatory and olfactory systems during infancy: implications for development of feeding behaviors in the high-risk infant. *Clin Perinatol, 38,* 627.

146. Liporace, J., & D'Abreu, A. (2003). Epilepsy and women's health: family planning, bone health, menopause, and menstrual-related seizures. *Mayo Clin Proc, 78,* 497.

147. Lowe, N. K. (1996). The pain and discomfort of labor and birth. *J Obstet Gynecol Neonatal Nurs, 25,* 82.

148. Lowery, C. L., et al. (2007). Neurodevelopmental changes of fetal pain. *Semin Perinatol, 31,* 275.

149. Mabie, W. C. (2005). Peripheral neuropathies during pregnancy. *Clin Obstet Gynecol, 48,* 57.

150. Macgregor, E. A. (2014). Headache in pregnancy. *Continuum (Minneap Minn), 20,* 128.

151. Mackensen, F., et al. (2014). Ocular changes during pregnancy. *Dtsch Arztebl Int, 111,* 567.

152. Maloni, J. A. (2010). Antepartum bed rest for pregnancy complications: efficacy and safety for preventing preterm birth. *Biol Res Nurs, 12,* 106.

153. Marchenko, A., et al. (2015). Pregnancy outcome following prenatal exposure to triptan medications: a meta-analysis. *Headache, 55,* 490.

154. Martin, S. R., & Foley, M. R. (2005). Approach to the pregnant patient with headache. *Clin Obstet Gynecol, 48,* 2.

155. McCool, W. F., Smith, T., & Aberg, C. (2004). Pain in women's health: a multifaceted approach toward understanding. *J Midwifery Womens Health, 49,* 473.

156. McCrory, J. L., et al. (2010). Dynamic postural stability during advancing pregnancy. *J Biomech, 43,* 2434.

157. McCrory, J. L., et al. (2010). Dynamic postural stability in pregnant fallers and non-fallers. *BJOG, 117,* 954.

158. McMahon, E., Wintermark, P., & Lahav, A. (2012). Auditory brain development in premature infants: the importance of early experience. *Annals of the New York Academy of Science, 1252,* 17.

159. McPherson, R. J., & Juul, S. E. (2010). Erythropoietin for infants with hypoxic-ischemic encephalopathy. *Curr Opin Pediatr, 22,* 139.

160. Melzack, R., & Wall, P. D. (1983). *The challenge of pain.* New York: Basic Books.

161. Melzack, R. (2005). Evolution of the neuromatrix theory of pain. The Prithvi Raj Lecture: Presented at the Third World Congress of World Institute of Pain, Barcelona 2004. *Pain Pract, 5,* 85.

162. Mennella, J. A., et al. (2011). The timing and duration of a sensitive period in human flavor learning: a randomized trial. *Am J Clin Nutr, 93,* 1019.

163. Meyer, G. (2001). Human neocortical development: the importance of embryonic and early fetal events. *Neuroscientist, 7,* 303.

164. Miller, S. P., & Back, S. A. (2017). Pathophysiology of neonatal white matter injury. In R. A. Polin, et al. (Eds.), *Fetal and neonatal physiology* (5th ed.). Philadelphia: Saunders.

165. Mindell, J. A., Cook, R. A., & Nikolovski, J. (2015). Sleep patterns and sleep disturbances across pregnancy. *Sleep Med, 16,* 483.

166. Mirmiran, M., Maas, Y. G., & Ariagno, R. L. (2003). Development of fetal and neonatal sleep and circadian rhythms. *Sleep Med Rev, 7,* 321.

167. Mitchell, L. E. (2005). Epidemiology of neural tube defects. *Am J Med Genet C Semin Med Genet, 135,* 88.

168. Montirosso, R., & Provenzi, L. (2015). Implications of epigenetics and stress regulation on research and developmental care of preterm infants. *J Obstet Gynecol Neonatal Nurs, 44,* 174.

169. Moore, K. L., Persaud, T. V. N., & Torchia, M. G. (2015). *The developing human: clinically oriented embryology* (10th ed.). Philadelphia: Saunders.

170. Nagandla, K., & De, S. (2013). Restless legs syndrome: pathophysiology and modern management. *Postgrad Med J, 89,* 402.

171. Nappi, R. E., et al. (2011). Headaches during pregnancy. *Curr Pain Headache Rep, 15,* 289.

172. *NCAST learning resource manual.* (1987). Seattle: NCAST, University of Washington.

173. Nishihara, K., et al. (2000). Mothers' wakefulness at night in the post-partum period is related to their infants' circadian sleep-wake rhythm. *Psychiatry Clin Neurosci, 54,* 305.

174. Ohel, I., et al. (2007). A rise in pain threshold during labor: a prospective clinical trial. *Pain, 132,* S104.

175. Okun, M. L. (2015). Sleep and postpartum depression. *Curr Opin Psychiatry, 28,* 490.

176. Omoti, A. E., Waziri-Erameh, J. M., & Okeigbemen, V. W. (2008). A review of the changes in the ophthalmic and visual system in pregnancy. *Afr J Reprod Health, 12,* 185.

177. O'Reilly, R., et al. (2011). Development of the vestibular system and balance function in the pediatric population. *Otolaryngol Clin North Am, 44,* 251.

178. Oyiengo, D., et al. (2014). Sleep disorders in pregnancy. *Clin Chest Med, 35,* 571.

179. Parker, J., et al. (2008). Cerebellar growth and behavioral & neuropsychological outcome in preterm adolescents. *Brain, 131,* 344.

180. Parmelee, A. H., & Stern, E. (1972). Development of states in infants. In C. D. Clemente, D. P. Purpura, & F. E. Mayer (Eds.), *Sleep and the maturing nervous system.* New York: Academic Press.

181. Peirano, P., Algarin, C., & Uauy, R. (2003). Sleep-wake states and their regulatory mechanisms throughout early human development. *J Pediatr, 143,* S70.

182. Philbin, M. K., & Klaas, P. (2000). Hearing and behavioral responses to sound in full-term newborns. *J Perinatol, 20,* S68.

183. Picchietti, D. L., et al. (2015). Consensus clinical practice guidelines for the diagnosis and treatment of restless legs syndrome/Willis-Ekbom disease during pregnancy and lactation. *Sleep Med Rev, 22,* 64.

184. Pickler, R. H., et al. (2010). A model of neurodevelopmental risk and protection for preterm infants. *J Perinat Neonatal Nurs, 24,* 356.

185. Pihko, E., & Lauronen, L. (2004). Somatosensory processing in healthy newborns. *Exp Neurol, 190,* S2.

186. Pillai Riddell, R. R., et al. (2015). Nonpharmacological management of infant and young child procedural pain. *Cochrane Database Syst Rev, 2015(12),* CD006275.

187. Pleasure, J. R., et al. (2017). Trophic factor and nutritional and hormonal regulation of brain development. In R. A. Polin, et al. (Eds.), *Fetal and neonatal physiology* (5th ed.). Philadelphia: Saunders.

188. Qureshi, I. A., et al. (2000). The ocular hypotensive effect of late pregnancy is higher in multigravidae than in primigravidae. *Graefes Arch Clin Exp Ophthalmol, 238,* 64.

189. Ranger, M., et al. (2017). Developmental aspects of pain. In R. A. Polin, et al. (Eds.), *Fetal and neonatal physiology* (5th ed.). Philadelphia: Saunders.

190. Rees, S., & Inder, T. (2005). Fetal and neonatal origins of altered brain development. *Early Hum Dev, 81,* 753.

191. Rees, S., Harding, R., & Walker, D. (2011). The biological basis of injury and neuroprotection in the fetal and neonatal brain. *Int J Dev Neurosci, 29,* 551.

192. Ritchie, J. R. (2003). Orthopedic considerations during pregnancy. *Clin Obstet Gynecol, 46,* 456.

193. Rivkees, S. A., & Hao, H. (2000). Developing circadian rhythmicity. *Semin Perinatol, 24,* 232.

194. Rivkees, S. A. (2003). Developing circadian rhythmicity in infants. *Pediatrics, 112,* 373.

195. Rowlands, S., & Permezel, M. (1998). Physiology of pain in labour. *Baillieres Clin Obstet Gynaecol, 12,* 347.

196. Sahota, P. K., Jain, S. S., & Dhand, R. (2003). Sleep disorders in pregnancy. *Curr Opin Pulm Med, 9,* 477.

197. Sanchez, R. M., & Jensen, F. E. (2001). Maturational aspects of epilepsy mechanisms and consequences for the immature brain. *Epilepsia, 42,* 577.

198. Santiago, J. R., et al. (2001). Sleep and sleep disorders in pregnancy. *Ann Intern Med, 134,* 396.

199. Sarberg, M., et al. (2014). Snoring during pregnancy and its relation to sleepiness and pregnancy outcome—a prospective study. *BMC Pregnancy Childbirth, 14,* 15.

200. Sarnat, H. B. (2017). Development of olfaction and taste in the human fetus and neonate. In R. A. Polin, et al. (Eds.), *Fetal and neonatal physiology* (5th ed.). Philadelphia: Saunders.

201. Saugstad, O. D. (2001). Resuscitation of the asphyxic newborn infant: new insight leads to new therapeutic possibilities. *Biol Neonate, 79,* 258.

202. Saxby, A. J., et al. (2013). The rhinological manifestations of women's health. *Otolaryngol Head Neck Surg, 148,* 717.

203. Schmidt, P. M., et al. (2010). Hearing and vestibular complaints during pregnancy. *Braz J Otorhinolaryngol, 76,* 29.

204. Schultz, K. L., Birnbaum, A. D., & Goldstein, D. A. (2005). Ocular disease in pregnancy. *Curr Opin Ophthalmol, 16,* 308.

205. Selway, L. D. (2010). State of the science: Hypoxic ischemic encephalopathy and hypothermic intervention for neonates. *Adv Neonatal Care, 10,* 60.

206. Serón-Ferré, M., et al. (2012). Circadian rhythms in the fetus. *Mol Cell Endocrinol, 349,* 68.

207. Shankaran, S. (2015). Therapeutic hypothermia for neonatal encephalopathy. *Curr Opin Pediatr, 27,* 152.

208. Sharif, K. (1997). Regression of myopia induced by pregnancy after photorefractive keratectomy. *J Refract Surg, 13,* S445.

209. Sheth, B. P., & Mieler, W. F. (2001). Ocular complications of pregnancy. *Curr Opin Ophthalmol, 12,* 455.

210. Shnol, H., Paul, N., & Belfer, I. (2014). Labor pain mechanisms. *Int Anesthesiol Clin, 52,* 1.

211. Sizun, J., & Browne, J. V. (2006). *Research on early developmental care in preterm neonates.* New Barnet, UK: John Libbey Publishing.

212. Smith, C. A., et al. (2006). Complementary and alternative therapies for pain management in labour. *Cochrane Database Syst Rev, 2006*(4), CD003521.

213. Smith, M. W., Marcus, P. S., & Wurtz, L. D. (2008). Orthopedic issues in pregnancy. *Obstet Gynecol Surv, 63,* 103.

214. Smith, R. P., et al. (2000). Pain and stress in the human fetus. *Eur J Obstet Gynecol Reprod Biol, 92,* 161.

215. Stafford, I. P., & Dildy, G. A. (2005). Myasthenia gravis and pregnancy. *Clin Obstet Gynecol, 48,* 48.

216. Sterman, M. B. (1972). The basic rest-activity cycle and sleep: developmental considerations in man and cats. In C. D. Clemente, D. P. Purpura, & F. E. Mayer (Eds.), *Sleep and the maturing nervous system.* New York: Academic Press.

217. Stevens, B., et al. (2016). Sucrose for analgesia in newborn infants undergoing painful procedures. *Cochrane Database Syst Rev, 2016*(7), CD001069.

218. Symes, A. (2016). Developmental disabilities. In M. G. MacDonald & M. M. Seshia (Eds.), *Avery's Neonatology: Pathophysiology & Management of the Newborn* (7th ed.). Philadelphia: Wolters Kluwar.

219. Symington, A., Pinelli, J. (2006). Developmental care for promoting and preventing morbidity in preterm infants. *Cochrane Database Syst Rev, 2006*(2), CD001814.

220. Tam, E. W. Y., et al. (2017). Cerebellar development – the impact of preterm birth and co-morbidities. In R. A. Polin, et al. (Eds.), *Fetal and neonatal physiology* (5th ed.). Philadelphia: Saunders.

221. Teich, S. A. (1998). Common disturbances of vision and ocular movement and surgery of the eye. In N. Gleicher (Ed.), *Principles of medical therapy in pregnancy* (3rd ed.). Stamford, CT: Appleton & Lange.

222. Thabah, M., & Ravindran, V. (2015). Musculoskeletal problems in pregnancy. *Rheumatol Int, 35,* 581.

223. Thomas, K. A., et al. (2014). Mother–infant circadian rhythm: development of individual patterns and dyadic synchrony. *Early Human Development, 90,* 885.

224. Thomas, K. A., Burr, R. L., & Spieker, S. (2015). Maternal and infant activity: analytic approaches for the study of circadian rhythm. *Infant Behav Dev, 41,* 80.

225. Tingåker, B. K., & Irestedt, L. (2010). Changes in uterine innervation in pregnancy and during labour. *Curr Opin Anaesthesiol, 23,* 300.

226. Tomson, T., & Battino, D. (2012). Teratogenic effects of antiepileptic drugs. *Lancet Neurol, 11,* 803.

227. Torelli, P., Allais, G., & Manzoni, G. C. (2010). Clinical review of headache in pregnancy. *Neurol Sci, 31,* S55.

228. Torsiglieri, A. J., et al. (1990). Otolaryngologic manifestations of pregnancy. *Otolaryngol Head Neck Surg, 102,* 293.

229. Trout, K. K. (2004). The neuromatrix theory of pain: implications for selected nonpharmacologic methods of pain relief for labor. *J Nurs Midwifery, 49,* 482.

230. Vanhatalo, S., & van Nieuwenhuizen, O. (2000). Fetal pain? *Brain Dev, 22,* 145.

231. van Pampus, M. G., & Aarnoudse, J. G. (2005). Long-term outcomes after pre-eclampsia. *Clin Obstet Gynecol, 48,* 489.

232. Verity, C., Firth, H., & French-Constant, C. (2003). Congenital abnormalities of the central nervous system. *J Neurol Neurosurg Psychiatry, 74,* i3.

233. Vermani, E., Mittal, R., & Weeks, A. (2010). Pelvic girdle pain and low back pain in pregnancy: a review. *Pain Pract, 10,* 60.

234. Visser, G. H. A., et al. (1987). Fetal behavior at 30 to 32 weeks' gestation. *Pediatr Res, 22,* 655.

235. Volpe, J. J. (2008). *Neurology of the newborn* (5th ed.). Philadelphia: W.B. Saunders.

236. Volpe, J. J. (2009). Brain injury in premature infants: a complex amalgam of destructive and developmental disturbances. *Lancet Neurol, 8,* 110.

237. Volpe, J. J. (2009). Cerebellum of the premature infant: rapidly developing, vulnerable, clinically important. *J Child Neurol, 24,* 1085.

238. Volpe, J. J. (2009). The encephalopathy of prematurity—brain injury and impaired brain development inextricably intertwined. *Semin Pediatr Neurol, 16,* 167.

239. Volpe, J. J., et al. (2011). The developing oligodendrocyte: key cellular target in brain injury in the premature infant. *Int J Dev Neurosci, 29,* 423.

240. Walker, S. M. (2013). Biological and neurodevelopmental implications of neonatal pain. *Clin Perinatol, 40,* 471.

241. Walsh, B. W., et al. (2017). Intraventricular hemorrhage in the neonate. In R. A. Polin, et al. (Eds.), *Fetal and neonatal physiology* (5th ed.). Philadelphia: Saunders.

242. Wang, S. M. (2004). Low back pain during pregnancy: prevalence, risk factors, and outcomes. *Obstet Gynecol, 104,* 65.

243. Winberg, J., et al. (1998). Olfaction and human neonatal behaviour: clinical implications. *Acta Paediatr, 87,* 6.

244. Wolff, P. H. (1966). The causes, controls, and organization of behavior in the neonate. *Psychol Issues, 5,* 1.

245. Yuskaitis, C. J., & Pomeroy, S. L. (2017). Development of the nervous system. In R. A. Polin, et al. (Eds.), *Fetal and neonatal physiology* (5th ed.). Philadelphia: Saunders.

246. Zafarghandi, N., et al. (2012). The effects of sleep quality and duration in late pregnancy on labor and fetal outcome. *Med, 25,* 535.

247. Zanardo, V., et al. (2001). Labor pain effects on colostral milk beta-endorphin concentrations of lactating mothers. *Biol Neonate, 79,* 87.

248. Zupanc, M. L. (2004). Neonatal seizures. *Clin Perinatol, 51,* 961.

Carbohydrate, Fat, and Protein Metabolism

Georgia R. Ditzenberger

Metabolic processes in the pregnant woman, fetus, and neonate are closely linked with and mediated by the function of various endocrine glands. Major alterations in metabolic processes arise during pregnancy. These changes are essential for the mother to provide adequate nutrients to support fetal growth and development. Maternal metabolic changes also alter the course of pregnancy in women with chronic disorders such as diabetes mellitus. After birth, major changes occur in both the sources of nutrients and the use of substrates by the infant. Limitations in metabolic processes and related endocrine function during this period can compromise neonatal extrauterine adaptation and health, and increase the risk of adult-onset disorders. This chapter examines alterations in carbohydrate, fat, and protein metabolism and related endocrinology during pregnancy and in the fetus and neonate.

MATERNAL PHYSIOLOGIC ADAPTATIONS

Metabolic adaptations during pregnancy are directed toward (1) ensuring satisfactory growth and development of the fetus; (2) providing the fetus with adequate stores of energy and substrates needed for transition to extrauterine life; (3) meeting maternal needs to cope with the increased physiologic demands of pregnancy; and (4) providing energy and substrate stores for the demands of pregnancy, labor, and lactation.[8] The first two demands compete with the third and fourth demands. As a result, alterations in maternal metabolic processes can significantly affect maternal and fetal health status.

Pregnancy involves a "coordinated series of physiologic adjustments which act in concert to preserve maternal homeostasis while at the same time providing for fetal growth and development."[66] Pregnancy is primarily an anabolic state in which food intake and appetite are increased, activity is decreased, approximately 3.5 kg of fat is deposited, energy reserves of approximately 30,000 kcal (125,550 J) are established, and 900 g of new protein is synthesized by the mother, fetus, and placenta. The overall energy cost of reproduction is estimated at 75,000 to 85,000 kcal (313,875 to 355,725 J).[8,27,99,128,154] Anabolic aspects are most prominent during the first two trimesters when, because of enhanced lipogenesis, accumulation of maternal fat and increased blood volume lead to maternal weight gain (Figure 16-1).[29,97,128,154] Protein and glycogen synthesis increase in muscle with increased glycogenolysis (breakdown of glycogen to form glucose) and decreased glycolysis in the liver. Insulin increases in response to glucose with a normal or slight increase in peripheral insulin sensitivity and serum glucose levels. This results in uptake of nutrients and maternal fat accumulation. During the third trimester, the woman's metabolic status becomes more catabolic as stored fat is used (see Figure 16-1). Gluconeogenesis (formation of glucose from amino acids and glycerol) in the liver decreases and intestinal dietary fat absorption increases.[44,97,128,154] Lipolytic activity within adipose tissue is enhanced with increases in plasma free fatty acids and glycerol. Maternal ketone production is increased. Counterinsulin hormones increase, leading to insulin resistance. During this phase, maternal weight gain is primarily due to the growing fetus and placenta; the fetus gains 90% of its growth in the last half of pregnancy.[18,29,99,105,128,140,154]

Antepartum Period

Pregnancy is associated with major changes in metabolic processes and endocrine function. Pregnancy has been characterized as a metabolic "tug of war" between the competing needs of the mother and the fetus.[66] The fetus and placenta influence maternal metabolic alterations in that these tissues become an additional site for metabolism of maternal hormones as well as new sites for hormonal biosynthesis. Many of the metabolic changes during pregnancy are aimed at providing substances (especially glucose, lipids, and amino acids) for the growth and development of the fetus. As the fetus and placenta grow, maternal fuel economy is altered to support this growth.[131,140]

Human chorionic somatomammotropin (hCS), also called human placental lactogen (hPL), estrogen, progesterone, and possibly leptin influence metabolic processes during pregnancy, primarily by altering glucose utilization and insulin action. These changes contribute to the diabetogenic effects of pregnancy, stimulate alterations in lipid and protein metabolism, and increase the availability of glucose and amino acids for transfer to the fetus, while at the same time providing an alternative energy substrate (free fatty acids) to meet maternal needs and maintain homeostasis. The changes in

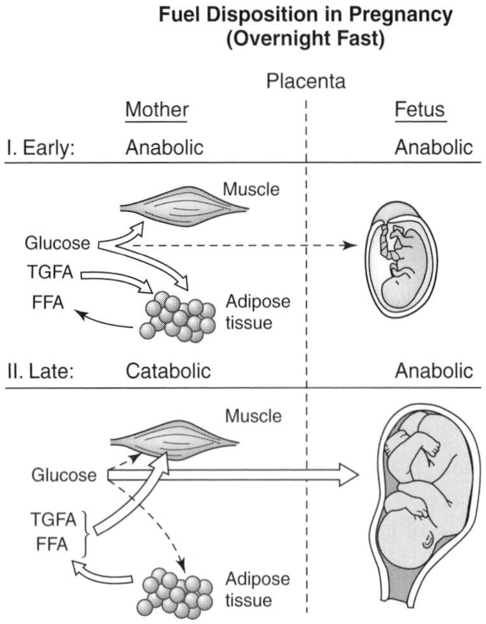

Fuel Disposition in Pregnancy
(Overnight Fast)

FIGURE 16-1 Fuel disposition in pregnancy during early (I) and late (II) gestation. *FFA,* Free fatty acids; *TGFA,* tryglyceride fatty acids. (From Knopp, R.H., Childs, M.T., & Warth, M.R. [1979]. Dietary management of the pregnant diabetic. In M. Winick. [Ed.]. *Nutritional management of genetic disorders.* New York: Wiley-Interscience.)

carbohydrate and lipid metabolism parallel the energy needs of the mother and fetus, whereas the changes in maternal nitrogen and protein metabolism occur early in pregnancy, before fetal demand.

Basal Metabolic Rate

The basal metabolic rate (BMR) increases during pregnancy (see Figure 12-1). The rate of change varies with maternal prepregnant nutritional status and fetal growth. Significant variations are seen among individual women, with up to an eightfold increase reported. Similar variations are reported for fat accretion.[27,37,54,98,110] If a woman has low energy reserves at conception, there is less of an increase in the BMR and energy is conserved.

The total energy required for pregnancy can be divided into three parts: (1) obligatory energy needed for the fetus, placenta, uterus, and breasts (which is the smallest part); (2) energy for maternal fat storage; and (3) energy maintenance of these new tissues.[27,54,98] If a woman has lower energy stores, less of the maternal energy intake is needed to maintain new tissues and energy is conserved for maternal basic needs and the fetal-placental unit.[98,99,129,131,135] For example, in undernourished women, fetal weight accounts for 60% of the pregnancy weight gain, versus 25% in a well-nourished woman.[54,131,135] This energy-sparing response may allow the woman to sustain the pregnancy but is often at the expense of fetal growth, with decreased birth weight and risk of fetal growth restriction.[131] Prentice and Goldberg suggest that leptin might monitor a woman's prepregnancy energy stores and adjust or coordinate maternal metabolic resources.[131]

Women with large-for-gestational-age (LGA) infants tend to have increased BMR with less maternal energy storage.[98,133]

The pregnant woman meets the energy demands of pregnancy by increasing her intake, decreasing her activity, or limiting fat storage.[99,128,129,135] King and colleagues propose three examples of how women in different situations might alter their energy to sustain pregnancy.[98] First, an underweight impoverished woman with limited food, poor fat stores, and need for physical work cannot increase food intake or limit physical activity during pregnancy. Her body responds by decreasing basal energy expenditures so that pregnant energy needs are similar to prepregnant needs. Second, a normal-weight woman in a resource-rich country with fat stores before pregnancy and adequate nutrition during pregnancy increases fat stores in pregnancy and increases her BMR slightly. Finally, an overweight woman in a resource-rich country increases her BMR by 20% or more, perhaps to reduce additional fat deposition.[98]

Carbohydrate Metabolism

Basal endogenous hepatic glucose production remains sensitive to insulin and increases up to 30% by the third trimester to meet fetal and placental needs.[18,54,117,128] Endogenous glucose production increases with gestational age, paralleling fetal and maternal needs. Maternal glucose levels are generally 10% to 20% lower than in nonpregnant women. In addition, during the overnight fasting period, maternal plasma glucose values fall to levels 15 to 20 mg/dL (0.8 to 1.1 mmol/L) lower than in nonpregnant women.[10,13] This decrease in glucose leads to lower insulin levels during the postabsorptive state (between meals and overnight) and a tendency toward hypoglycemia and ketosis. The decreased glucose level in the postabsorptive state is caused by increased plasma volume in early pregnancy and later to placental transport of glucose to the fetus, which increases during gestation as fetal glucose needs increase.[117,128]

During the first two trimesters, the pregnant woman is in an anabolic state. Insulin secretion increases with increased peripheral glucose use without increases in insulin resistance.[42,66,128] As pregnancy progresses, peripheral glucose use by the mother decreases because of increasing insulin resistance. This reduces maternal glucose utilization and makes glucose more readily available to the fetus. The mother compensates by using fat stores to meet her energy needs with breakdown of glycerol to glucose.[105] Insulin resistance in the latter part of pregnancy is believed to be a result of a decrease in sensitivity of cell receptors that results from the insulin antagonism effects of hCS, progesterone, and cortisol.[66,86] The insulin antagonism is partially modulated by pancreatic β-cell hyperplasia and hypertrophy with increased insulin availability after a meal. Pregnancy is also characterized by greater oscillations in insulin and glucagon levels.[42,66,86] A reduction in the extraction of insulin by the liver may contribute to the peripheral hyperinsulinemia. Variations in hepatic insulin binding may lead to alterations in the ratio of insulin to glucagon.[8,42]

Progesterone augments insulin secretion, decreases peripheral insulin effectiveness, and increases insulin levels after a meal. Estrogen increases the level of plasma cortisol (an insulin antagonist), stimulates β-cell hyperplasia (and thus insulin production), and enhances peripheral glucose utilization. Increased levels of both bound and free cortisol decrease hepatic glycogen stores and increase hepatic glucose production. These changes further increase glucose availability for the fetus.[10,13,42,117]

hCS levels correlate with fetal and placental weight and are higher in multiple pregnancies.[121] hCS increases synthesis and availability of lipids. Lipids can be used by the mother as an alternative fuel, enhancing availability and transfer of glucose and amino acids to the fetus. A mild form of the metabolic changes seen during pregnancy can be induced by giving hCS to nonpregnant women.

Protein Metabolism

Decreased serum amino acid and serum protein levels are found in pregnancy.[8,21,62] This decrease is related to increased placental uptake, increased insulin levels, hepatic diversion of amino acids for gluconeogenesis, and transfer of amino acids to the fetus.[8,21,62] The fetus uses some of these amino acids for glucose formation. Maternal plasma levels of glucogenic amino acids (e.g., those that can be converted into glucose), such as alanine, threonine, glutamate, and serine, are reduced because of placental transfer of these amino acids.[47,92] Maternal plasma alanine levels, in particular, are lower because alanine is a key precursor for glucose formation (via gluconeogenesis) by the fetal liver.[92]

Alterations in protein metabolism during pregnancy have a biphasic pattern.[92] During the first half of gestation, maternal protein storage increases, with a net retention of 1.3 g/day of nitrogen.[99] Most of this is transported to the fetus, but some is retained in maternal tissues. During the second half, maternal protein use is more economic, with decreased urinary nitrogen excretion, thus conserving protein.[104] These changes may be mediated by decreased activity of hepatic enzymes involved in amino acid deamination and urea synthesis.

Lipid Metabolism

Pregnancy results in significant alterations in lipid metabolism with a markedly different lipoprotein profile, with marked increases in triglycerides, as well as increases in phospholipids and cholesterol. Basal oxidation of fatty acids increases 70% during pregnancy, leading to a relative hyperlipidemia.[38] Synthesis of very-low-density lipoprotein (VLDL), low-density lipoprotein (LDL), and high-density lipoprotein (HDL), which are contained in triglycerides, and LDL and HDL, which are found in cholesterol, also increase.[77]

Lipid metabolism in pregnancy is characterized by two phases and is analogous to the patterns of change in carbohydrate and protein metabolism.[29,105] During the first two trimesters, triglyceride synthesis and fat storage increase. VLDL increases threefold in the second and third trimesters. LDL decreases slightly initially, followed by a progressive rise. HDL increases progressively to 24 weeks, then decreases to 32 weeks and stabilizes for the remainder of pregnancy.[120] Triglycerides increase 40% by 18 weeks and 250% by term.[106] Phospholipids and cholesterol levels also increase; the triglyceride-to-cholesterol level remains stable because cholesterol also increases.[76,77] By late pregnancy, cholesterol levels are 50% higher than before pregnancy, regardless of maternal dietary intake.[62] These changes enhance the availability of substrates for the fetus.[105]

Maternal fat storage is most prominent from 10 to 30 weeks, before the peak of fetal energy demands.[98] Promotion of lipogenesis and suppression of lipolysis during this phase are mediated by progressive increases in insulin responsiveness and enhanced by progesterone, cortisol, leptin, and prolactin.[8,43,62,77] Estrogens decrease lipoprotein lipase activity.[28] During this period the pregnant woman experiences a physiologic ketosis with a twofold to threefold increase in baseline ketone body production, with an acute increase after fasting, suggesting enhanced fat utilization.[51,142]

Lipid metabolism in late pregnancy is illustrated in Figure 16-2. The third trimester is characterized by both lipogenesis and lipolysis, with increased breakdown of fat deposits.[29,48,76,105] These changes are mediated by increased adipose tissue lipolytic activity and decreased lipoprotein lipase (LPL) activity (because of estrogens).[29,76] LPL, which is present in the capillary endothelium of extrahepatic tissues, hydrolyzes circulating triglycerides, including VLDL, producing free fatty acids and glycerol.[76] Adipose tissue is broken down into free fatty acids and glycerol, which circulate to the liver and are converted to active forms (acyl-CoA and glycerol-3-phosphate) and reesterified into triglycerides (circulated as VLDL).[29,76] Glycerol can also be used for glucose synthesis (gluconeogenesis). The increased lipolysis is related to the rise of hCS levels with its antiinsulinogenic and lipolytic effects, as well as the effects of cortisol, glucagon, and prolactin, resulting in increased lipolytic activity in adipose tissue.[29,76,97,105] Enhanced ketogenesis in the liver is a consequence of increased oxidation of free fatty acids for energy and release of ketone bodies.[76] The fat mobilization is associated with increased glucose and amino acid uptake by the fetus. Thus fats are used by the mother as an alternative energy substrate, allowing the mother to conserve glucose for the fetus and her central nervous system (CNS) during the second half of gestation.[8,76,77] Fetal glucose and ketone uptake increases. Ketones are used by the fetus for oxidative metabolism, lipogenesis, triglyceride production, and as substrate for brain lipid synthesis.[51,76,97,142]

The changes in lipid metabolism during pregnancy are reflected in changes in maternal serum free fatty acid concentrations as well as plasma triglyceride, cholesterol, and phospholipid levels. These changes may be exaggerated in obese women.[38] The minimal change in free fatty acids during early pregnancy is probably related to increased fat storage and augmented fat utilization. As maternal fat stores are mobilized, serum levels of triglycerides, free fatty acids, glycerol, and triglyceride-rich lipoproteins (VLDL) increase to peak near term.[29,76,77] Because elevations in free fatty acids are a result of catabolism of stored triglycerides (into free fatty acid and glycerol), changes in free fatty acids are mirrored by changes in glycerol.[8] Hypertriglyceridemia during the third

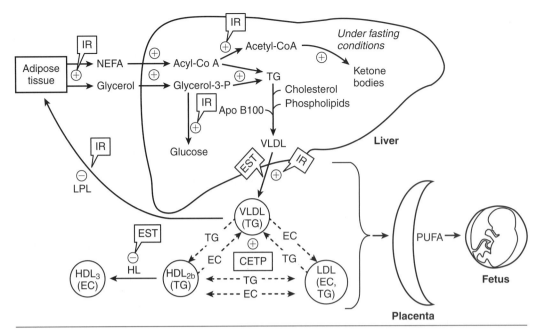

FIGURE 16-2   Major lipid metabolism interactions during late pregnancy, with indications of control roles of insulin resistance *(IR)* and enhanced estrogen *(EST)*. +, Activated steps; −, inhibited steps; *CETP*, cholesteryl ester transfer protein; *EC*, esterified cholesterol; *HDL*, high density lipoprotein; *HL*, hepatic lipase; *LDL*, low density lipoprotein; *LPL*, lipoprotein lipase; *NEFA*, nonesterified fatty acids; *PUFA*, polyunsaturated fatty acids; *TG*, triglyceride; *VLDL*, very low density lipoprotein. (From Herrera, E. & Ortega-Senovilla, H. [2010]. Disturbances in lipid metabolism in diabetic pregnancy—Are these the cause of the problem? *Best Pract Res Clin Endocrinol Metab, 24,* 517.)

trimester is primarily caused by increases in VLDLs and decreased peripheral clearance.[29,76,77] The increase is related to reduced VLDL clearance secondary to decreased activity of LPL in the liver and adipose tissue, enhanced activity of cholesterol ester transferase, increased gastrointestinal absorption of lipids, and increased hepatic triglyceride production.[48,76,77] The decrease in lipoprotein lipase is a result of increases in estrogens in late pregnancy and the increasing insulin resistance.[76,97] Near term, lipoprotein lipase activity increases in the mammary glands. This enhances availability of triglycerides for milk production.[105]

Changes in lipid metabolism are accompanied by functional and morphologic changes in the adipocytes. Hypertrophy of these cells accommodates the increased fat storage during the first two-thirds of pregnancy. In the last trimester, maximal glucose transport, glucose oxidation, and lipogenesis within the adipocytes decrease.[62] The number of insulin receptors on the adipocytes increases in the first part of pregnancy and returns to prepregnant levels by term.[8,62] Because responsiveness of adipose tissue to insulin is not diminished as much as that of other tissues, these changes in the adipocytes facilitate fat storage.[62] After a meal, maternal fat stores are replenished by increased glucose uptake, incorporation of glucose into glycerol, and esterification of fatty acids by adipocytes.[8]

Insulin

Insulin levels and responsiveness of tissues to insulin change dramatically during pregnancy, leading to peripheral insulin resistance. Peripheral insulin resistance is "the decreased ability of insulin to affect glucose uptake, primarily in skeletal muscle and to a lesser degree in adipose tissue."[117] Actions of insulin are summarized in Table 16-1.[60] Insulin production and sensitivity during pregnancy differ in early compared with later pregnancy. During early pregnancy (up to 12 to 14 weeks), insulin responses are enhanced, sending glucose to the embryo and young fetus. The pregnant woman has a normal glucose tolerance, basal glucose production, and peripheral muscle sensitivity to insulin.[42,86,132] Adipose tissue is more sensitive to insulin during this period, resulting in lipogenesis and fat storage.[42,132]

In later pregnancy (from 20 weeks to term), insulin sensitivity decreases and insulin secretion and resistance increase with decreased glucose uptake by muscle and adipose tissue.[42,86,118,155] Maternal insulin levels increase 2.5- to 3-fold by the third trimester.[66,97,117,118] These changes are accompanied by maternal pancreatic hypertrophy and hyperplasia.[122,132] Increased insulin secretion ensures adequate maternal protein synthesis in the face of increasing resistance of peripheral tissues to the effects of insulin. With increasing gestation, mean insulin sensitivity decreases up to 50% to 70%.[97,118,122] Tissue resistance is most prominent in liver, adipose, and muscle cells and is further altered in women with preeclampsia.[113,144] The increasing insulin resistance promotes nutrient flux from the mother to the fetus and promotion of adipose tissue accumulation.[97,118] Insulin resistance is often exaggerated in overweight and obese women.[23,38,122]

TABLE 16-1	Metabolic Effects of Insulin and Glucagon

HORMONE	METABOLIC ACTIONS

Insulin	Acts in the liver to:
	  Increase glycogen synthesis from carbohydrate (glycogenesis) or fat and protein (glyconeogenesis)
	  Decrease formation of glucose from fats and protein (gluconeogenesis)
	  Increase protein synthesis
	Acts in muscle to:
	  Increase glucose uptake
	  Increase glycogen and protein synthesis
	  Retard proteolysis
	Acts in adipose cells to:
	  Increase glucose uptake
	  Increase conversion of carbohydrate to fat
	  Decrease lipolysis
	  Increase uptake of free fatty acids

Glucagon	Acts in the liver to:
	  Decrease glycogen synthesis and increase conversion of glycogen to glucose (glycogenolysis)
	  Increase uptake of amino acids
	  Increase conversion of alanine to glucose
	  Increase ketogenesis
	Acts in adipose tissue to:
	  Increase lipolysis

Compiled from Guyton, A.C. & Hall, J.E. (2010). *Textbook of medical physiology* (12th ed.). Philadelphia: Saunders Elsevier; and Widmaier, E., Raff, H., & Strang, K.T. (2005). *Vander's human physiology: The mechanism of body function* (10th ed.). New York: McGraw-Hill.

Insulin receptor binding does not change significantly during pregnancy; however, the postreceptor insulin signaling cascade, and thus handling of glucose by cells, is altered in skeletal muscle and adipose tissue.[122,132] During pregnancy insulin receptor substrate 1 (IRS-1) is downregulated, affecting insulin uptake and use by cells.[113,117,122] The postreceptor handling of glucose during pregnancy is altered by decreased IRS-1 expression (especially in skeletal muscle), altered expression of tyrosine kinase activity, and decreased expression of GLUT-4 glucose transporter protein in adipose tissue, which normally promotes glucose uptake.[117,132]

Insulin resistance is mediated by the increasing levels of placental hormones, especially estrogens, progesterone, and hCS, as well as prolactin and cortisol, and is minimally affected by changes in blood glucose levels.[113,117,122] Other factors that play an important role in the insulin resistance of pregnancy are tumor necrosis factor-α and other cytokines, circulating free fatty acids, leptin, and placental growth hormone, which stimulates insulin-like growth factor 1 (IGF-1).[22,97,149] In late pregnancy, although basal insulin levels are elevated, maternal blood glucose values are similar to prepregnant levels.[8,36,113,140,154] Increased insulin secretion after a meal (in response to the higher blood glucose) offsets the contrainsulin effects of the placental hormones and facilitates movement of nutrients to the fetus. The insulin resistance of late pregnancy enhances maternal fat breakdown and increased gluconeogenesis and ketogenesis in the postabsorptive

state, the state in which changes in insulin response are most apparent.[36,66,76,140,154] If the pregnant woman is not able to elevate her insulin secretion to overcome the increasing pregnancy-induced insulin resistance, maternal and fetal hyperglycemia will result and metabolic abnormalities such as gestational diabetes may develop or existing metabolic problems such as diabetes will be aggravated.

Alterations in insulin production and responsiveness are critical in integrating changes in carbohydrate and fat metabolism throughout the course of pregnancy. Baird summarizes these interactions as follows: During early pregnancy, increased insulin in response to glucose, minimal changes in insulin sensitivity, and increased number of insulin receptors on the adipocytes result in normal or slightly enhanced carbohydrate tolerance. The increased hepatic synthesis and secretion of triglycerides during this period, along with a normal or slightly elevated removal of triglycerides from the circulation, lead to a net storage of fat. During late pregnancy, the elevated plasma insulin, decrease in numbers of adipocyte insulin receptors to prepregnant levels, and increasing insulin resistance result in reduced assimilation of glucose and triglycerides by maternal tissues, greater transfer of these substances to the fetus, and increased lipolysis. The net result is a decrease in maternal blood glucose, increased glucose turnover, and greater maternal reliance on lipid catabolism for energy.[8] Changes in lipid, carbohydrate, and protein metabolism are summarized in Table 16-2.

TABLE 16-2	Maternal Metabolic Processes During Pregnancy: Relationship Between Hormonal and Metabolic Changes

HORMONAL CHANGE	EFFECT	METABOLIC CHANGE
Increased hCS	Diabetogenic Decreased glucose tolerance	Facilitated anabolism during feeding Accelerated starvation during fasting
Increased prolactin	Insulin resistance	Facilitated anabolism during feeding Accelerated starvation during fasting
Increased bound and free cortisol	Decreased hepatic glycogen stores Increased hepatic glucose production	Ensures glucose and amino acids to fetus
Increased estrogen, progesterone, and insulin during early pregnancy	Increased fat synthesis Fat cell hypertrophy Inhibition of lipolysis	Anabolic fat storage during early pregnancy
Increased hCS in late pregnancy	Lipolysis	Catabolic fat mobilization in late pregnancy

hCS, Human chorionic somatomammotropin (also known as human placental lactogen).
Adapted from Moore, T.R. (2004). Diabetes and pregnancy. In R.K. Creasy, R. Resnik, & J.D. Iams. (Eds.). *Maternal-fetal medicine: Principles and practice* (5th ed.). Philadelphia: Saunders.

Absorptive Versus Postabsorptive States

In addition to phasic changes in metabolic processes in early versus late pregnancy, metabolism of amino acids, carbohydrates, and fats also varies on a daily basis depending on whether the mother is in the absorptive (fed) or postabsorptive (fasting) state (Figures 16-3 and 16-4). As a result of these changes, pregnancy has been characterized as a time of both "accelerated starvation" and "facilitated anabolism."[115]

Absorptive State. During the absorptive (fed) state, ingested nutrients (amino acid, glucose, triglyceride) are entering the blood from the gastrointestinal tract (see Chapter 12) and must be oxidized for energy, used for protein synthesis, or stored. The average meal takes 4 to 6 hours for complete absorption. In this state anabolism exceeds catabolism and glucose is the major energy source. Small amounts of amino acid and fat are converted into energy or used to resynthesize body proteins or for structural fat. Most of the amino acids and fat and any extra carbohydrates are transformed into adipose tissue; carbohydrates are also stored as glycogen.

Insulin has an anabolic and anticatabolic role during this state.[97] Insulin secretion increases and plasma insulin levels rise. Insulin promotes glucose uptake by the hepatocytes and peripheral tissues, inhibits glycogen breakdown, and inhibits lipolysis in adipose tissue. Glucose is converted to glycogen for storage in the liver, cardiac muscle, and skeletal muscle. Muscle amino acid uptake is enhanced and proteolysis inhibited.[97]

After a meal the pregnant woman has higher glucose, insulin, and triglyceride levels and suppression of glycogen compared with nonpregnant women. Thus the absorptive state during pregnancy (see Figure 16-3, *A*) is characterized by relative hyperinsulinemia (related to decreased insulin sensitivity), hyperglycemia (because of failure of liver glucose uptake), insulin resistance (especially in skeletal muscle), hypertriglyceridemia, and lipogenesis (more glucose is converted to triglyceride for storage).[8,97,144,153] As mentioned previously, pregnancy has been called a state of facilitated anabolism to describe these metabolic alterations that conserve energy, especially during early pregnancy.[114] These changes increase glucose availability for transport to the fetus; increase availability of an alternate energy source (triglycerides) for maternal needs; and provide fewer stimuli for maternal gluconeogenesis, glycogenolysis, and ketogenesis.[62,66]

Maternal blood glucose levels may rise transiently to 130 to 140 mg/dL (7.2 to 7.8 mmol/L) (see Figure 16-4). Gluconeogenesis and circulating free fatty acids are decreased. Under the influence of placental hormones, resistance of the liver and peripheral tissues to insulin is increased by as much as 60% to 70%.[36,128,144,153,154] The hyperinsulinemic response is most marked during the third trimester because of hypertrophy and hyperplasia of pancreatic islet β cells. These cells become more responsive to alterations in blood glucose and amino acid levels. The increased insulin levels after eating overcome the insulin resistance to allow glucose uptake by muscles for storage as glycogen.[113,122,144] Even with increased production of insulin, however, overall glucose levels are maintained, although at a relatively lower level than in nonpregnant women because of the counterbalancing effects of estrogen, progesterone, and hCS.

Postabsorptive and Fasting State. In the postabsorptive state (i.e., when nutrients are not entering the blood from the intestines, beginning 4 to 6 hours after a meal) and fasting state (12 or more hours after the last meal), energy must be supplied by body stores (see Figure 16-3, *B*). Insulin levels are low. Fat and protein synthesis are decreased and catabolism exceeds anabolism. Gluconeogenesis (production of new glucose from lactate, amino acids [especially alanine], and

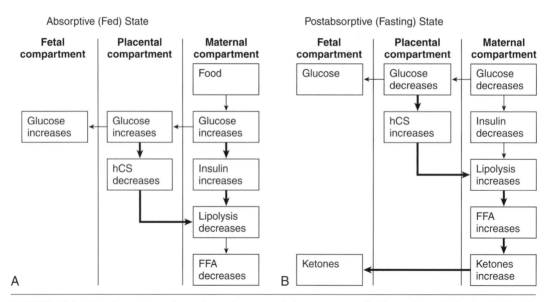

FIGURE 16-3   The absorptive and postabsorptive states during pregnancy. **A,** Absorptive or fed state. **B,** Postabsorptive or fasting state. *FFA,* Free fatty acid; *hCS,* human chorionic somatomammotropin. (From Speroff, L., Glass, R.H., & Kase, N.G. [1999]. *Clinical gynecologic endocrinology and fertility* [6th ed.]. Baltimore: Williams & Wilkins.)

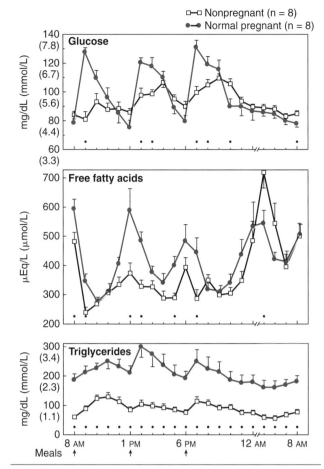

FIGURE 16-4 Glucose and insulin response to 24 hours of feeding and fasting in the third trimester of pregnancy *(closed circles)* and the nonpregnant state *(open squares)*. In the fed state, pregnancy is associated with elevated levels of both circulating glucose and insulin. In the fasting state, pregnancy is associated with decreases in glucose below those seen in the nonpregnant state. (From Phelps, R.L., Metzger, B.E., & Freinkel, N. [1981]. Carbohydrate metabolism in pregnancy. *Am J Obstet Gynecol, 140*, 730.)

glycerol) and catabolism of fat are the main sources of energy.[36,97,128,135,140] Plasma glucose levels are maintained during the postabsorptive state by use of these alternate sources of glucose and glucose-sparing or fat-utilization reactions.[36,62,135,140] The CNS continues to use glucose, while other organs and tissues become glucose sparing, depending on fat as the primary energy source.

During the fasting state (e.g., overnight between the evening meal and breakfast), plasma glucose levels decline (see Figure 16-4). The magnitude of the decline is greater in pregnant women than in nonpregnant women, because of the continuous transfer of glucose to the fetus, and is associated with a more rapid conversion to fat metabolism. Fatty acids are liberated by breakdown of triglycerides. Lipolysis yields glycerol (converted to glucose by the liver) and free fatty acids, which are catabolized to ketone bodies (oxidized for energy). Under homeostatic conditions ketones do not accumulate in the body to produce ketoacidosis, because excess

ketones not needed for energy are rapidly cleared by the kidneys.[57,97,105]

This response is an exaggeration of the changes normally seen during the overnight fast in nonpregnant women. These changes would normally raise blood glucose levels, but in pregnant women the fasting glucose level tends to be lower because of the limited availability of substrate for gluconeogenesis. For example, as early as 15 weeks' gestation, maternal glucose levels after a 12- to 14-hour overnight fast are 15 to 20 mg (0.8 to 1.1 mmol/L) lower than levels in nonpregnant women. The decrease in glucose during the overnight fasting period is especially prominent during the second and third trimesters.[8,57,97,105]

The exaggerated maternal responses during the fasting state are influenced by (1) continuous placental uptake of glucose and amino acids from the maternal circulation; (2) decreased peripheral utilization of glucose as plasma concentrations of ketones and free fatty acids increase; (3) decreased renal absorption of glucose; and (4) decreased hepatic glucose production. This response, seen primarily in late pregnancy, is characterized by lower fasting glucose and amino acid levels; increased blood glucose levels after eating; and increased plasma free fatty acids, triglycerides, ketones, and insulin secretion in response to glucose.[18,62,97] Thus the postabsorptive fasting state in pregnancy is characterized by a relative hypoglycemia (because of the fetal siphon, increased renal losses, and decreased liver production), hyperketonuria (ketones used as an alternative energy source), hypoamino-acidemia (because of placental transfer for use in fetal glucose production), and hypoinsulinemia (see Figures 16-3, *B*, and 16-4).[18,92,97,105,117] Hypoalaninemia also develops because maternal protein stores can provide only limited substrate, which is insufficient to meet both maternal and fetal amino acid needs.[66] Increased insulin during the postabsorptive state enhances uptake of glucose into the maternal skeletal muscle and adipose tissue. In lean women, this leads to suppression of hepatic glucose production in late pregnancy. Less suppression is seen in obese women; therefore the alteration in insulin sensitivity is greater in obese than nonobese women.[23,117,122]

Levels of lipoprotein lipase are increased, enhancing triglyceride breakdown with release of free fatty acids and glycerol (which is broken down into glucose) and production of ketone bodies to provide energy when plasma glucose supply is low.[57,105] Glycerol is a source for hepatic gluconeogenesis. The elevated free fatty acids prevent glucose uptake and oxidation by maternal cells, thus preserving glucose for the maternal CNS and the fetus.[18] In nonpregnant women this switch to fat oxidation occurs after 14 to 18 hours of fasting; during pregnancy the switch occurs after 2 to 3 hours and has been termed *accelerated starvation*.[18,29,62,115]

Metabolic changes characteristic of this state are primarily related to hCS, which promotes lipolysis to increase free fatty acid levels and opposes insulin action, thus increasing glucose availability to the fetus. Other factors influencing this response include increased glucose utilization by the fetus (the fetal siphon) and mother, along with an increase in the volume of distribution for glucose (i.e., hemodilution due to increased plasma volume). During the second half of pregnancy, effectiveness of insulin in translocating glucose into cells is reduced.[97] Because insulin is the ultimate arbitrator of both the absorptive and postabsorptive states, alterations in insulin secretion alter substrate availability to the mother and fetus.[66] The insulin antagonism in pregnancy is progressive, paralleling the growth of the fetoplacental unit, and disappears immediately after delivery. Placental hormones and other substances are major factors in producing this insulin antagonism.

Drainage of glucose and amino acids by the fetus may lead to increased maternal appetite and a feeling of faintness sometimes experienced in pregnancy. Pregnant women may experience more rapid development of ketosis and fasting hypoglycemia after food deprivation. With greater maternal reliance on fat utilization during pregnancy, production of ketone bodies and risks of abnormalities such as acidosis are increased. Dieting and caloric restriction to lose weight during pregnancy should be considered potentially dangerous to both the mother and fetus.[26,58]

Effects of Placental Hormones and Other Substances

The phasic changes in carbohydrate, lipid, and protein metabolism during pregnancy are due to the interplay of placental hormones, especially estrogen, progesterone, hCS, and leptin.[95,105,113,117] During the first half of pregnancy, metabolism is affected primarily by estrogens and progesterone. In late pregnancy the influences of increasing concentrations of hCS and leptin become more prominent. Maternal metabolic changes are also influenced by prolactin and cortisol.[18,113,140]

Estrogen stimulates pancreatic β-cell hyperplasia and insulin secretion, enhances glucose utilization in peripheral tissues, and increases plasma cortisol, an insulin antagonist. As a result, particularly in the first half of gestation, estrogen decreases fasting glucose levels, improves glucose tolerance, and increases glycogen storage.[97,113,122,140] Progesterone augments insulin secretion, increases fasting plasma insulin concentrations, and diminishes peripheral insulin effectiveness. Cortisol mediates these changes by inhibiting glucose uptake and oxidation, increasing liver glucose production, and possibly augmenting glucagon secretion.[18,122,140] Cortisol increases to 2.5 times normal levels by late pregnancy.[18,122,140,154,155] Prolactin increases 5-fold to 10-fold and stimulates insulin production and, in animal models, increases the number of β-cell receptors.[155]

hCS is a polypeptide hormone produced by the syncytiotrophoblast (see Chapter 3). hCS is the most potent insulin antagonist of the placental hormones. This hormone is secreted primarily into the maternal circulation, although some is also secreted into fetal circulation after around 6 weeks. Levels of hCS increase markedly after 20 weeks. Because the effects of hCS are similar to those of growth hormone, it has been called the "growth hormone" of the second half of pregnancy.[18] hCS action increases availability of maternal glucose

and amino acids to the fetus. Other effects of hCS include diminished tissue response to insulin; increased β-cell mass; lipolysis, which increases plasma free fatty acids; enhanced nitrogen retention; decreased urinary potassium excretion; and increased calcium excretion. The major effect is sparing of maternal carbohydrates (glucose) by providing alternative energy sources such as free fatty acids for the mother.[57,105]

Several adipokines, including leptin, adiponectin, and retinal binding protein 4 (RBP4), are also important for ensuring adequate substrate for fetal growth.[76] Leptin, a protein product of the obese (ob) gene, is produced and secreted by adipose tissue and other tissues, including the placenta during pregnancy. Leptin is involved in regulating appetite and food intake, modulating metabolism, and enhancing energy expenditure and may also be important in signaling readiness for sexual maturation at puberty.[23,45,74,151] Leptin receptors are found in the hypothalamus, placenta, muscle, liver, lymphoid tissue, uterus, chorion, amnion, pancreas, ovary, and adipose tissue.[23,97,149] Placental leptin is secreted into both maternal and fetal circulations.[23,104]

Leptin plays a role in maturation and regulation of reproduction and may serve as a detector of long-term metabolic fuel availability, signaling the presence of significant maternal fat stores to initiate reproduction.[23,74] Leptin modulates glucose metabolism, insulin sensitivity, and adipose tissue lipolysis during pregnancy, enhancing breakdown of maternal fat stores in the second half of pregnancy and availability of glucose and lipids for the fetus.[23,46,74,76] Other roles of leptin in pregnancy may be to mediate changes in appetite, thermogenesis, and lipid metabolism.[23,45,46,74] Leptin may also modulate fetal growth. Concentrations of leptin increase from 6 to 8 weeks' gestation, rising further in the second and (especially) third trimesters.[23,46] The increase is probably primarily related to increased placental leptin production. Levels in early pregnancy correlate with maternal weight and body mass index; this correlation is not found in later pregnancy and may reflect a form of leptin resistance (similar to that seen with obesity).[23,45,46,74]

Adiponectin is a protein, secreted by adipose tissue, that is involved in modulating glucose and lipid metabolism and enhancing insulin sensitivity.[76] Changes in leptin and adiponectin have been reported in complicated pregnancies.[9,102,104] A significant increase in placental leptin production is associated with placental insufficiency, suggesting that leptin may be a bio-marker for fetal stress and placental dysfunction.[46] Serum leptin levels increase with worsening preeclampsia.[9,46,102,104] Adiponectin is decreased in women with gestational diabetes mellitus, whereas tumor necrosis factor-α (an inflammatory marker) and cord blood leptin are increased.[45,74,76,109,134] Low levels of adiponectin in women with gestational diabetes may play a role in the increased insulin resistance seen in these women.[45,76] Low leptin levels are associated with spontaneous abortion.[55,101] RBP4 may also have a role in glucose metabolism and insulin sensitivity. RBP4 increases with increasing gestational age (probably because of placental production) and is increased in pregnancies complicated by gestational diabetes.[23,76]

Intrapartum Period

The processes of parturition are dependent on an available supply of glucose and triglycerides as energy sources. In addition, essential fatty acids are important as precursors of prostaglandins (arachidonic acid, from which prostaglandins are derived, is a derivative of essential fatty acid), which are critical to the onset of labor. These relationships are described in Chapter 4.

During labor and delivery, maternal glucose consumption increases markedly to produce the energy required by the uterus and skeletal muscles. As a result, maternal insulin requirements fall. Oxytocin may augment or supplant insulin during this period. In animals, oxytocin has been demonstrated to act similarly to insulin; that is, oxytocin stimulates glucose oxidation, lipogenesis, glycogen synthesis, and protein formation.[42,54,66,128,140]

Postpartum Period

With removal of the placenta, concentrations of placental hormones such as hCS, estrogens, and progesterone fall rapidly within hours after delivery (see Chapter 5). The postpartum woman is in a state of relative hypopituitarism with blunted production of gonadotropins and growth hormone. This hypopituitarism may result from the feedback effects of elevated hCS and prolactin levels during pregnancy on the pituitary gland. hCS is similar to growth hormone, and its disappearance with removal of the placenta leaves the woman without its contrainsulin effects during a period of relative deficiency of growth hormone.[66,121] Plasma leptin levels decrease by 24 hours after delivery.[101]

Fasting plasma glucose levels fall within a few days, then increase, reaching late pregnancy fasting levels by 5 days.[62] It is unclear when these levels return to prepregnant values.[13,62,135] The insulin resistance of late pregnancy is reversed soon after delivery.[42,117,135]

Plasma free fatty acids fall to prepregnant levels by 3 days; triglycerides by 2 weeks.[28,57,62,105] During the first week the decrease in triglycerides coincides with the fall in hCS. This fall is more rapid in women who are breastfeeding.[28,76] In these women, free fatty acids rise to late pregnancy levels by 6 weeks, followed by a decrease to prepregnant levels by 3 to 6 months.[8] The increasing levels of fatty acids from 1 to 6 weeks postpartum may reflect maternal use of other nutrients for milk production.[8,57,105] Cholesterol levels slowly decrease to prepregnant levels over the first few weeks postpartum.[62,113,135] Maternal plasma amino acid levels return to prepregnant values of approximately 4.3 mg/dL (0.043 g/L) (versus pregnant values of 3.5 mg/dL [0.35 g/L]) by several days after birth.[1,21,52]

CLINICAL IMPLICATIONS FOR THE PREGNANT WOMAN AND HER FETUS

The metabolic adaptations of pregnancy safeguard against variations in maternal caloric intake, changes in activity, increased metabolic efficiency, and changes in the metabolism of carbohydrates, fats, and proteins.[8,42,105,128] These metabolic changes occur in a phasic pattern—probably programmed by placental hormones—that spreads the energy costs and protein requirements of pregnancy over the entire 9 months of gestation. In early pregnancy, energy is conserved (facilitated anabolism), followed by later redirection of energy (glucose) to the fetus (accelerated starvation), whereas throughout pregnancy the mother uses protein more economically to provide adequate amino acids for development of the fetal brain and other organs.[8,21,66,128] Pregnancy has also been characterized as a diabetogenic state. This state is reflected in the elevated blood glucose levels in association with increasing insulin resistance. This state is described in this section along with the basis for alterations in the glucose tolerance test (GTT) and the effects of the normal metabolic changes of pregnancy on the diabetic woman and her fetus.

The diabetogenic effects of pregnancy are reflected by alterations in the GTT, with higher glucose values after a meal reflecting an acquired resistance to insulin. The alterations in carbohydrate metabolism are most evident during late pregnancy in the absorptive state (see Figure 16-3, A). When the woman is in this state and glucose is being added to the plasma from the gut, her blood glucose levels do not drop as rapidly as usual, even in the face of higher circulating insulin levels. This response results from decreased maternal sensitivity to insulin because of the action of hormones such as hCS, progesterone, and cortisol. Secretion of these hormones increases during the second half of pregnancy; therefore diabetogenic effects are most prominent during this period. Insulin resistance is somewhat compensated for by increased plasma insulin concentrations.[13,86,98]

The changes in insulin sensitivity tend to protect the fetus if the mother is fasting by keeping glucose in the blood and thus available for placental transfer. hCS decreases insulin effectiveness (and thus movement of glucose out of the blood into maternal cells) by decreasing tissue sensitivity and mobilizes free fatty acids and amino acids. The result is an increase in available glucose and amino acids for transfer to the fetus and increased free fatty acids for maternal energy.

Effects of Metabolic Changes on Glucose Tolerance Tests

The alterations in carbohydrate metabolism in the absorptive state during pregnancy result in an elevated blood glucose response to a carbohydrate load. The progressive decrease in glucose tolerance is reflected in the criteria for an abnormal GTT in pregnancy. These changes are most marked in the third trimester.

Two methods commonly used to evaluate glucose tolerance in pregnancy are (1) a one-step 75-g, 2-hour test (recommended by the World Health Organization); and (2) a two-step test with a 1-hour 50-g glucose challenge (screening test) followed by a 100-g, 3-hour oral glucose tolerance test (OGTT) if challenge levels are either 135 mg/dL (7.5 mmol/L) or greater (more women meet criteria for the 3-hour test, but a greater proportion of women with gestational diabetes mellitus [GDM] are identified) or 140 mg/dL (7.8 mmol/L).[97,117,148,152] The Fifth International Workshop Conference on Gestational Diabetes

Mellitus recommended the two-step test.[13,116,148] The two-step test has been used most commonly in the United States, whereas the one-step test is used most commonly in other countries.[13,116,117,148,152]

During pregnancy, the initial fasting blood glucose value is lower than in nonpregnant individuals, because of decreased glucose utilization and increased fat utilization by the mother (making increased glucose available to the fetus) and the subsequent effects of the fetal siphon. Blood glucose levels tend to remain high after ingestion of carbohydrates for a longer period of time secondary to insulin antagonism and decreased insulin sensitivity. Normally the magnitude of the increase in blood glucose after a carbohydrate feeding is a reflection of failure in glucose uptake by the liver. During pregnancy the increased glucose response in the face of increased endogenous insulin confirms the relative insensitivity and resistance of the liver (as well as peripheral tissues such as muscle and adipose tissue) to insulin.[97,117]

Maternal-Fetal Relationships

Growth and development of the fetus is dependent on the availability of a constant supply of glucose, amino acids, and lipids from the mother for energy, protein synthesis, and production of new tissues. The fetus must also develop adequate stores of these substances to meet the demands of the intrapartum period and transition to extrauterine life. Placental transfer of selected nutrients and hormones is summarized in Figure 16-5. Fetal requirements for substrates involved in carbohydrate, fat, and protein metabolism are discussed in the next section.

Alterations in maternal metabolic processes or in placental transfer of essential nutrients that increase the availability of specific substrates are usually an advantage to the fetus but can be a disadvantage in altered maternal metabolic states. For example, because fetal energy requirements are met almost exclusively by glucose, the metabolic changes in pregnancy increase availability of glucose in maternal plasma for placental transfer by reducing the efficiency of maternal glucose storage. If the usual metabolic changes of pregnancy or placental function are altered, however, variations in fetal growth—such as occur in the infant of a mother with diabetes or in an infant with fetal growth restriction—may develop.[139,147] Maternal glucose infusions during the intrapartum period can lead to a fetal hyperglycemia that stimulates insulin and inhibits glucagon secretion. This may delay gluconeogenesis after birth and increase the risk of neonatal hypoglycemia.

The placenta is a highly metabolic organ with its own substrate needs. Placental metabolic activities include glycolysis, gluconeogenesis, glycogenesis, oxidation, protein synthesis, amino acid interconversion, triglyceride synthesis, and alterations in the length of fatty acid chains (see Chapter 3). The placenta can modify nutrient uptake to meet fetal growth demands.[21,42,105,121,141] The degree of glucose uptake by the placenta is similar to that of the brain. Cholesterol from the mother is essential for placental synthesis of estrogens and progesterone. Fatty acids are needed by the placenta for oxidation and membrane formation.[57,105] Leptin may have a role in coordinating placental metabolism.[23,45,74]

Glucose is the nutrient that crosses the placenta in highest concentrations. The increased maternal reliance on fats as an alternative energy source, especially during the maternal postabsorptive fasting state, conserves maternal glucose for transfer to the fetus. The fetal-placental unit uses approximately 50% of the total maternal glucose needed for pregnancy.[23,45,105,113] Glucose crosses via facilitated transport by insulin-dependent glucose transporters. Amino acids are transferred via active transport because levels are higher in the fetus than in the mother. Amino acids are removed from maternal circulation and concentrated in the placental intercellular matrix. As fetal amino acid levels fall, these placental stores are transferred to the fetus. Mechanisms for amino acid transfer include direct transfer from mother to fetus without modification in the placenta, metabolism of maternally derived amino acids by the placenta to produce other amino acids (which are then transferred to the fetus), and production of new amino acids by the placenta for fetal transfer.[82,105,113] Maternal lipoproteins do not cross the placenta directly, but are taken up by the placenta where placental lipoprotein lipase along with other lipases, enzymes, receptors, and fatty acid binding proteins facilitate transfer of fatty acids to the fetus.[76,77,97,105] Essential fatty acids and long-chain polyunsaturated fatty acids needed for fetal growth and development cross the placenta.[77,105] Free fatty acids are

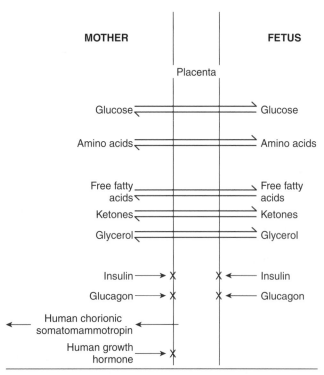

FIGURE 16-5   Maternal-fetal substrate, hormone relationships. (From Devaskar, S.L. & Garg, M. [2015]. Disorders of carbohydrate metabolism in the neonate. In R.J. Martin, A.A. Fanaroff, & M.C. Walsh. [Eds.]. *Fanaroff and Martin's neonatal-perinatal medicine: Diseases of the fetus and infant* [10th ed.]. Philadelphia: Saunders.)

transferred to the fetus according to maternal-fetal concentration gradients mediated by specific fatty acid carriers. The pattern of essential and other fatty acids in the fetus reflect maternal concentrations.[57,82,105] Ketones, especially acetoacetate and β-hydroxybutyrate, diffuse readily across the placenta; concentrations are similar in the mother and fetus.[97] Inadequate maternal dietary fatty acids such as docosahexaenoic acid (DHA) increase the risk of altered neurologic and vision development in offspring.[28,63]

The Pregnant Diabetic Woman

The classification system for diabetes proposed by the National Diabetes Data Group and adopted by the American Diabetes Association includes (1) type 1 diabetes ("β-cell destruction, usually leading to absolute insulin deficiency"), (2) type 2 diabetes ("ranging from predominantly insulin resistance with relative insulin deficiency to predominantly an insulin secretory defect with insulin resistance"), (3) other specific types of diabetes (including genetic defects; pancreas alterations; or endocrine, drug-induced, or infectious etiologies), and (4) gestational diabetes mellitus.[5] Individuals with impaired fasting glucose and/or impaired glucose tolerance are referred to as having "prediabetes."[5]

The metabolic changes during pregnancy contribute to alterations in insulin requirements in insulin-dependent pregnant diabetic women. Because the metabolic changes in pregnancy normally lead to increased insulin availability by the end of pregnancy, it is not surprising that pregnant diabetic women experience an increase in insulin requirements by this time.[66,97,117]

Management of a pregnant diabetic woman or a woman who develops gestational diabetes is complex. There are many controversies regarding screening, diagnosis, treatment, and outcomes of women with gestational diabetes.[65,91,97,106] Leary et al summarized guidelines for screening and diagnosis of gestational diabetes from various groups around the world.[106] Some of the current controversies relate to the findings and subsequent recommendations from the Hyperglycemia and Adverse Pregnancy Outcomes (HAPO) study.[61,64,65,106] The HAPO study was a prospective, randomized, controlled, multinational study of 25,000 pregnant women in 10 countries who did not have a diagnosis of diabetes on study entry.[64,65] This study examined the relationship between maternal glucose concentrations lower than those diagnostic of diabetes and adverse perinatal outcomes.[64,103] Findings demonstrated a linear association between findings on the 75-g OGTT and the following fetal and maternal outcomes: birth weight greater than 90th percentile; increased cord blood C-peptide level; and risks of neonatal hypoglycemia, fetal shoulder dystocia, neonatal hyperbilirubinemia, and maternal preeclampsia.[64,65] In the HAPO study, both fasting and post 75-g OGTT levels were correlated to maternal and neonatal outcomes.[35,61,64,103] In response to the HAPO study, an International Association of Diabetes and Pregnancy Study Groups (IADPSG) consensus panel published guidelines on screening and diagnosis of GDM at the first prenatal visit for all or high-risk women and screening all women at 24 to 28 weeks. With the IADPSG recommendations women would be diagnosed with GDM earlier on the basis of an initial fasting glucose of 92 to 126 mg/dL (5.1 to 7.0 mmol/L) or an abnormal fasting (92 mg/dL or 5.1 mmol/L), 1-hour (180 mg/dL or 10.0 mmol/L), or 2-hour (153 mg/dL or 8.5 mmol/L) 75-g OGTT, with a single abnormal glucose considered adequate for the diagnosis.[85] These recommendations are controversial, and their effect on current practice and policies is unclear.[61,106,156] Wendland et al compared the diagnostic criteria recommended by WHO with those suggested by IADPSG and showed that both criteria diagnosed women at risk for gestational diabetes.[152] However, the IADPSG diagnostic criteria was more inconsistent in diagnostic determination and further studies were suggested.

GDM is defined as "carbohydrate intolerance of various degrees of severity with onset or first recognition during pregnancy."[117] GDM occurs in 3% to 9% of pregnancies in the United States.[117] Women with GDM have a pronounced peripheral insulin resistance, decreased numbers of insulin receptors, and decreased binding of insulin to target cells, which results in a progressive alteration in glucose tolerance. Fasting, postprandial, and 24-hour glucose and lipid and amino acid concentrations are altered. Possible causes include an autoimmune defect in the β cells, impaired β-cell function, increased insulin degradation, and decreased tissue sensitivity to insulin, either because of impaired insulin-receptor binding or intracellular insulin signaling.[13,113,118,122,132] Between 2% and 13% of women with GDM have specific antibodies against β-cell antigens. Most women with GDM have impaired β-cell function and adaptation during pregnancy with chronic insulin resistance, which has an additive effect in pregnancy. It is unclear whether insulin resistance occurs before alterations in β-cell function or if these events occur together. A decrease in IRS-1 concentration and decreased ability of insulin receptor-B (found inside skeletal muscle cells) to be phosphorylated by tyrosine have been reported. These changes further alter insulin signaling and reduce glucose transport activity. In late pregnancy, the pregnant woman normally increases insulin secretion, but women with GDM, because of underlying chronic insulin resistance, have even greater insulin resistance, producing less insulin compared with the amount of resistance.[13,113,117,118,122]

During the postpartum period, women with GDM continue to show defects in insulin action and sensitivity, even after glucose tolerance tests have normalized.[3] Women with GDM have an increased risk for later development of diabetes, primarily type 2. Approximately 10% develop diabetes in the first months postpartum, 50% by 5 years postpartum, and 70% by 10 years postpartum.[3,13,27,79,152] The risk is greater with weight gain after pregnancy or GDM in a subsequent pregnancy.[3,13,79] Several studies suggest that infant outcomes, including macrosomia and shoulder dystocia, could be reduced by treating women with mild hyperglycemia who did not reach diagnostic criteria for GDM.[35,103]

Pregnant women with type 1 diabetes may experience no change or decreased insulin requirements during the first trimester because of increased glucose siphoning by the fetus, which decreases maternal blood glucose levels. Maternal food intake may also decrease during this period because of the nausea and vomiting of pregnancy. Because circulating glucose levels are reduced, maternal insulin requirements are often lowered. As pregnancy progresses, the diabetogenic actions of increasing amounts of placental hormones and the increasing insulin insensitivity outweigh the effects of the fetal siphon. Women with type 1 diabetes appear to have similar alterations in insulin sensitivity during pregnancy to woman with normal glucose tolerance.[117] Thus maternal insulin requirements usually increase during the second half of gestation to levels two to three times higher than prepregnancy values.[66,97,117]

Women with diabetes may have altered insulin requirements during labor, probably because of an increase in energy needs (and thus glucose utilization) and the presence of oxytocin, with its insulin-like effects. After delivery and removal of the placenta, levels of estrogens, progesterone, and hCS fall rapidly. This quickly reverses the insulin insensitivity of pregnancy. Maternal insulin requirements usually fall rapidly to prepregnancy levels or even below (because of a rebound phenomenon). Oxytocin may also contribute to these changes. As a result, an insulin-dependent diabetic woman may need little or no exogenous insulin the first few days after delivery. Insulin requirements generally return to prepregnancy levels by 4 to 6 weeks postpartum.[58]

Levels of glycosylated hemoglobin and other glycosylated proteins are useful in monitoring glucose concentrations over time and in genetic counseling and have been used to evaluate fetal and maternal risks for complications in a pregnancy complicated by maternal diabetes. Glycosylated hemoglobin is formed slowly over the lifespan of the red blood cell and represents an overall measure of glycemia. The parameters used most are hemoglobin A1c (HbA1c; the most abundant component of hemoglobin A) and total amounts of hemoglobin A. Levels of glycosylated hemoglobin A reflect ambient glucose concentrations over the previous 4 to 6 weeks and have been used to monitor maternal glycemic control on a monthly basis. HbA1c testing is widely used for screening, diagnosing, and monitoring prediabetes states and diabetes mellitus in the general population.[25,80] HbA1c is higher in pregnant diabetic women than in other pregnant women but lower than in nonpregnant diabetic women. Maternal levels of HbA1c correlate with the development of fetal anomalies, with the lowest levels having the least risk.[117,133] However, HbA1c may not be as useful as an independent measure of glycemic control in pregnancy, because these levels may not be a good predictor of capillary blood glucose levels in the woman. Studies regarding the efficacy of using HbA1c testing during pregnancy to diagnose or monitor gestational diabetes have been equivocal thus far.[25,80]

Fetus of a Diabetic Mother

Maternal metabolic abnormalities, particularly hyperglycemia during the period of embryonic organogenesis (up to 8 weeks' gestation), have been associated with an increased risk of congenital anomalies.[1,74,97,117] The most common anomalies involve the cardiovascular system (especially atrial septal defects, ventricular septal defects, and transposition of the great vessels) and central nervous system (neural tube defects), with urinary tract malformations, anal-rectal atresias, and caudal regression syndrome also seen with increased frequency.[97] The risk is increased four- to eight-fold in women with overt diabetes before conception, with no increase in women who develop GDM after the first trimester or in offspring of diabetic fathers.[117] Rigid glycemic control before conception and during early pregnancy has been associated with a reduction in the frequency of congenital anomalies, but the risk is still higher than in nondiabetic women.[83,117] Preconception counseling and glycemic control are critical for improving pregnancy outcome in a woman with diabetes. Using data from a meta-analysis, Ray and colleagues reported that mean fasting capillary glucose levels of 70 to 130 mg/dL (3.9 to 7.2 mmol/L) and a glycosylated hemoglobin level less than 4 standard deviations above normal during the periconceptional period minimized the risk of glycemia-related anomalies.[133] The basis for the increase in anomalies is not completely understood. Possible etiologies include excessive formation of free oxygen radicals in the mitochondria; inhibition of prostacyclin formation resulting in an excess of thromboxane A2, compared with prostacyclin (thromboxane A2 is a potent vasoconstrictor that alters vascularization of tissues); altered levels of arachidonic acid and myoinositol; lipid peroxidation; increased somatomedin inhibitors; accumulation of sorbitol and trace metals; and hyperglycemia-induced apoptosis with exaggerated programmed cell death (glucose alters the expression of regulating genes).[97,117,125]

Macrosomia is seen in up to 20% of infants of women with GDM and 35% of women with other forms of diabetes.[142] This phenomenon is generally believed to arise from increased fetal production of insulin and other growth factors, especially IGF-1 and leptin, in response to fetal hyperglycemia.[87,117,119,126] This leads to excessive transfer of nutrients across the placenta. Because maternal insulin does not cross the placenta (see Figure 16-5), fetal hyperinsulinemia arises as a response to increased placental transfer of substrates, particularly glucose. Maternal hyperglycemia increases fetal insulin, IGFs, and leptin, which upregulates glucose transporters (GLUT) that move glucose across the placenta and into fetal cells.[61,76,83,124] Upregulation of these glucose transporters in women with type 1 diabetes may lead to excessive transfer of glucose to the fetus even with good maternal glucose control.[48,88] Hyperglycemia in pregnant women with diabetes results in fetal hyperglycemia and subsequent hyperplasia of the fetal pancreatic islet cells, with increased production of insulin, enhanced glycogen synthesis, lipogenesis, and increased protein synthesis.[117,153]

Increased levels of other substances ("mixed nutrients"), particularly amino acids and fatty acids, are also believed to be important in the development of fetal macrosomia, because fetal overgrowth remains a problem even with strict glycemic control.[21,57,76,105] Maternal diabetes alters lipid metabolism and increases transfer of fatty acids to the fetus and the amount of triglyceride stored in the placenta.[10,76] These changes are secondary to alterations in several factors that influence fatty acid transfer, including maternal and fetal blood flow and concentrations of serum proteins and placental fatty acid–binding protein. Elevated levels of triglycerides in pregnant women with diabetes also enhance lipid availability to the fetus.[10,76] Maternal triglycerides and nonesterified fatty acid levels in women with well-controlled GDM correlate with fat mass and weight in the newborn.[143] Increased intrauterine fat deposition may also be related to altered fat metabolism in the fetus of women with GDM.[10,124]

Levels of endogenous insulin and IGF-1 in the fetus are correlated with the development of macrosomia.[42,105,113,119] Insulin and IGF-1 are major mediators of fetal growth; therefore fetal hyperinsulinemia leads to increased body fat and organ size. The major organs affected are the heart, lungs, liver, spleen, thymus, and adrenal gland. The brain and kidney are not significantly affected. The organomegaly probably arises from increased protein synthesis. Even short-term fetal hyperinsulinemia promotes storage of excess nutrients. Stringent maternal glucose control, especially during the third trimester, when fetal growth peaks, reduces the risk of macrosomia, primarily by reducing fetal adipose tissue mass.[26,126] However, the accelerated growth velocity seen in these infants may continue into childhood and adulthood.

The placenta is also affected, especially in women whose diabetes is poorly controlled, with increased peripheral and capillary surface area and intervillous space volume. These changes may result from the increased glucose load and abnormal metabolic environment with fetal hyperinsulinemia or as a compensatory mechanism to increase oxygen delivery. The fetus of a mother with diabetes shows increases in metabolic rate and oxygen consumption related to metabolism of excessive glucose and other substrates.[8,108] The risk of later development of type 1 diabetes in an infant whose mother has type 1 diabetes is 1.3%. The risk of later development of type 2 diabetes is 15% if one parent (up to 60% if both parents) has type 2 diabetes.[73,97,108] Additional morbidities in infants of women with diabetes are discussed on pages 565-566.

SUMMARY

Maternal adaptations during pregnancy alter the woman's metabolic processes. These changes are critical for protection of the mother and promote her ability to adapt to pregnancy. Maternal adaptations are essential to ensure that the fetus obtains an adequate supply of nutrients to support growth and development. Alterations in metabolic processes in the mother also interact with the course of disorders such as diabetes mellitus. An understanding of the normal metabolic

---

BOX 16-1   Recommendations for Clinical Practice Related to Changes in Carbohydrate, Fat, and Protein Metabolism in Pregnant Women

Recognize the usual changes in carbohydrate, fat, and protein metabolism during pregnancy (pp. 543-547 and Table 16-2).

Assess and monitor maternal nutrition in terms of carbohydrate, fat, and protein intake (pp. 544-547 and Chapter 12).

Counsel women regarding nutrient and energy requirements to meet maternal and fetal needs during pregnancy (pp. 544-547, 552-553).

Monitor maternal glucose and ketone status (pp. 548, 552-553).

Monitor fetal growth (pp. 552-554).

Understand the implications of changes in the absorptive and postabsorptive states for the pregnant woman and her fetus (pp. 548-550 and Figures 16-3 and 16-4).

Monitor maternal energy status during the intrapartum period (p. 551).

Counsel women regarding changes in appetite and weight during pregnancy (p. 543 and Chapter 12).

Know how glucose tolerance test parameters are altered during pregnancy (pp. 551-552).

Recognize the effects of metabolic changes on insulin requirements of women with diabetes during the prenatal, intrapartum, and postpartum periods (pp. 553-554).

Evaluate and monitor metabolic and insulin status in the pregnant woman with diabetes (pp. 553-554).

Counsel women with diabetes regarding the effects of diabetes on pregnancy and the fetus and of pregnancy on diabetes (pp. 553-555 and Figure 16-11).

Counsel women with diabetes regarding strategies before pregnancy to optimize maternal and fetal outcomes (pp. 553-555).

Recognize the potential effects of diabetes on the fetus and newborn (pp. 554-555, 565-566 and Figure 16-11).

---

changes during pregnancy increases understanding of the alterations seen in the pregnant diabetic woman, the fetus, and the newborn. Implications for clinical practice are summarized in Box 16-1.

DEVELOPMENT OF CARBOHYDRATE, FAT, AND PROTEIN METABOLISM IN THE FETUS

The placenta and fetal liver function as a "coordinated multiorgan system for the exchange of nutrients and for ensuring the production of nutrients sufficient to meet fetal requirements."[12] Fetal metabolic processes are dominated by anabolism and governed primarily by glucose with little oxidation of fat. The fetus must produce energy and maintain oxidative phosphorylation in the face of a low-oxygen environment. Although energy is produced in the fetus under aerobic conditions, the fetus has a greater capacity for anaerobic metabolism and is efficient in using lactate. Oxygen consumption in a fetus is 8 mL/kg/minute. Glucose contributes more than half of the substrate for oxygen consumption.[12,130]

The fetal caloric requirement has been estimated to average 90 to 100 kcal/kg/day. Almost all of the fetal fuel requirements are met by metabolism of glucose; lactate; and amino acids such as alanine, glutamate, and serine.[12,70] The fetus also uses these substrates as major precursors for storage of fuels (e.g., fatty acids, glycogen). The stored fuels are critical energy sources during the intrapartum period and transition to extrauterine life. By term, the fetus has increased its weight 175-fold, protein content 400-fold, and fat content 5000-fold. Fetal nutrient uptake and growth is influenced by maternal nutrition and health; uterine blood flow; placental nutrient uptake, metabolism, and transfer; umbilical blood flow; and the fetal endocrine system.[113,140]

Substances are transported across the placental syncytiotrophoblast (see Chapter 3) from maternal to fetal circulations. The syncytiotrophoblast is "the transporting epithelium of the human placenta,"[48] consisting of two polarized plasma membranes. The microvillous membrane (MVM) faces maternal blood in the intervillous space; the basal membrane (BM) faces the fetal capillary epithelium.[48]

Insulin-like growth factors (IGF-1 and IGF-2) are the dominant endocrine regulators of fetal growth; cord blood levels are correlated with birth weight.[2,20,30,119] IGF-1 and IGF-2 levels increase longitudinally to about 33 weeks, then increase twofold to threefold more to term. IGF-1 is believed to be the primary controller of fetal size in the second half of pregnancy. IGF-1 (but not IGF-2) is significantly lower in infants with fetal growth restriction.[2,30,108] Cord blood IGF-1 levels are lower in women who smoke.[30]

Fetal leptin, adiponectin, and other adipokines (resistin, visfatin, and apelin) are involved in controlling fetal growth.[22,113,128,154] Leptin may act by modulating growth hormone secretion and may have a role in hematopoiesis and angiogenesis. Leptin has been found in immature subcutaneous fat cells by 6 to 10 weeks' gestation.[6,23,36,140] Circulating levels of leptin, an adipostatic hormone (see p. 550), increase after 32 to 34 weeks' gestation, around the time of increasing body fat mass.[123,126] Levels of leptin decrease rapidly after birth and may help limit energy expenditure and conserve the infant's nutrient reserves for later growth and development.[23,74] Leptin levels at birth have been reported to correlate with intrauterine growth and be a predictor of neonatal bone mass.[30,90] Concentrations of leptin are higher in large-for-gestational-age (LGA) infants than in infants of appropriate size for gestational age; concentrations are also higher in LGA infants than in small-for-gestational-age (SGA) infants.

The nutritional, metabolic, and hormonal status during fetal and early postbirth life can alter organ development, including the hypothalamus and other endocrine structures (see Chapter 19).[28] The mechanisms by which the fetal environment influences later status are believed to be related to placental adaptive responses to the intrauterine environment. After birth these adaptations may no longer be appropriate for the extrauterine environment and lead to altered glucose-insulin metabolism, lipid metabolism, and endocrine programming. Alterations in fetal and early neonatal nutrition "result in neuroendocrine, pancreatic, skeletal muscle, and

adipose tissue dysfunction, and increased food intake and decreased energy expenditure. This leads to increased adiposity and adult disease."[28] These adult-onset disorders include insulin resistance and type 2 diabetes, obesity, hypertensive disorders, coronary artery disease, and osteoporosis.[28,39,49,53,59,73]

Carbohydrate Metabolism

The fetus has been described as a "glucose-dependent parasite" and uses glucose from the mother as the major substrate for energy production.[100] Eighty percent of fetal energy comes from carbohydrate (glucose) oxidation.[40,137] Fetal glucose utilization rates (averaging 5 mg/kg/min) are higher than in adults (2 to 3 mg/kg/min).[40,70] Even with fetal growth restriction, maternal glucose is the major energy substrate for the fetus, although the placenta can produce alternate substrates such as lactate and ketone bodies for use as energy and for glycogen synthesis.[40]

Glucose is transported across the placenta via sodium-independent carrier-mediated facilitated diffusion.[89,142] The placenta has a high facility for glucose uptake and transport via a family of membrane transport proteins (GLUTs, which is the gene symbol for facilitated glucose transporter) on the microvillous membrane facing maternal blood and fetal-facing basal membrane of the placenta.[83,89,130] Various GLUT isoforms are expressed in the syncytiotrophoblast, including GLUT-1, -3, -4, and -12. GLUT-4 and -12 are sensitive to insulin.[89] GLUT-1 and GLUT-2 are expressed early in development and are found on both the trophoblast and blastocyst.[125] GLUT-1 is the major fetal glucose transporter; fetal GLUT-2 levels remain low.[68] GLUT-1 is expressed on almost all fetal tissues, enhancing cellular glucose uptake.[146] In animal models maternal hyperglycemia during early gestation downregulates these receptors, increasing the risk of apoptosis and neural tube and limb defects. There is a fivefold greater increase in GLUT-1 on the microvillous membrane facing maternal blood than on the fetal-facing basal membrane during the first trimester.[83,89,130] This increases the movement of maternal glucose into the placenta, where approximately 30% to 40% is used by the placenta for oxidation or converted to glycogen and lactate to meet its energy needs.[89]

Basal membrane glucose transport is the rate-limiting step in fetal glucose transfer.[11,89] In the second half of pregnancy, basal membrane GLUT-1 receptors increase at least twofold, and their activity increases 50% to meet increasing demands with fetal growth in late pregnancy.[83,130] If the uteroplacental nutrient supply is diminished, the fetus consumes nutrients and oxidizes them at the usual rate, but the placenta reduces consumption of both nutrients and oxygen. Increased placental GLUT-1 receptors with increased glucose transport to the fetus have been found in women with diabetes who are hyperglycemic.[145] Placental glucose transport, and alterations with maternal obesity and diabetes mellitus, is summarized in Figure 16-6.

During the first few days after fertilization, the zygote has a limited ability to metabolize glucose. After the embryonic genome is activated, glucose metabolism increases.[41] Both

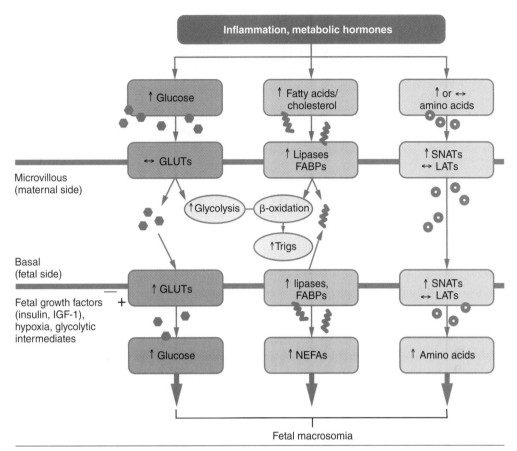

FIGURE 16-6 Placental transfer and metabolism of energy substrates in maternal overweight, obesity, and/or diabetes mellitus. Usual placental transfer mechanisms for glucose, lipids, and amino acids are illustrated (in the box in the middle of the figure) along with changes that occur when maternal circulating levels of glucose, fatty acids/cholesterol, and amino acids may be altered. Glucose: The expression of GLUTs remains unaffected in the microvillous membrane but is upregulated in the basal membrane, facilitating enhanced glucose transport across the placental-fetal side. Placental metabolism of glucose (glycolysis) is also enhanced. Fatty acids/cholesterol: The expression of some lipases and FABPs are increased, allowing for enhanced maternal-fetal transfer of NEFAs and/or cholesterol across microvillous and basal membranes. Byproducts of glycolysis are thought to inhibit fatty acid oxidation (β-oxidation), shifting placental fatty acid metabolism to NEFA esterification and triglyceride accumulation. Amino acids: Maternal amino acid levels are increased in type 1 diabetes and transport via SNAT is increased. In obesity and GDM, amino acid levels are not altered but SNAT expression and activity are higher. Collectively, these modifications to substrate transport and metabolism across the placenta contribute to adverse fetal outcomes, the most common being macrosomia (weighting of block arrows signifies the magnitude of contribution). *FABPs*, Fatty acid binding proteins; *GLUTs*, facilitated glucose transporters; *IGF-1*, insulin-like growth factor-1; *LATs*, system L amino acid transporters; *NEFA*, non-esterified fatty acids; *SNATs*, system A amino acid transporters; *trigs*, triglycerides. (From Gallo, L.A., Barrett H.L., & Dekker Nitert M. [2017]. Review: Placental transport and metabolism of energy substrates in maternal obesity and diabetes, *Placenta, 54,* 59.

glucose and pyruvate uptake increase initially; glucose uptake remains high throughout pregnancy, whereas pyruvate uptake falls.

The major regulators of fetal growth are IGF-1 and IGF-2, which stimulate cell proliferation, differentiation, and metabolism.[2,119,140] IGFs act via cell membrane receptors and are modulated by a group of binding proteins. The liver is the main source of IGFs, which have autocrine, paracrine, and endocrine functions. IGF-1 can be detected in fetal tissue by 9 weeks' gestation and in fetal circulation by 15 weeks' gestation.[2,50,119,140] Both IGF-1 and IGF-2 increase with gestational age. In early gestation, IGF-2 activity, which is not significantly affected by nutritional factors, is predominant. In late pregnancy, IGF-1, which is regulated by nutrient availability, is predominant. Fetal growth in later gestation is regulated by the interaction of glucose, insulin, and IGF-1.[36,44,140] Glucose transfer across the placenta stimulates fetal insulin release. Insulin in turn stimulates lipogenesis and IGF, which increases fetal anabolism and placental uptake of glucose and other nutrients for fetal (versus placental) use.

Lower levels of IGF-1 are seen in preterm and growth-restricted infants.[2,107,119] Levels are also reduced in infants of mothers who smoke.[136,139] Even though glucose and insulin concentrations are lower with fetal growth restriction, the fetus maintains glucose uptake and utilization because of increased insulin sensitivity, enhancing movement of glucose into cells. This is mediated by increased expression of GLUT and insulin-responsive glucose transporters.[69,142] With chronic substrate deprivation, a growth-restricted fetus will develop systems for glucose production, initially by glycogenolysis (breakdown of glycogen to glucose) and later by gluconeogenesis (production of new glucose from lactate, amino acids [especially alanine], and glycerol) along with the reduction in fetal growth.[142] Poor fetal nutrition may alter the ability to produce and respond to insulin in adulthood, increasing the risk of type 2 diabetes, or may alter fetal low-density lipoprotein metabolism, increasing the risk of later coronary artery disease.[28,53,94,107,108,155]

Under basal, nonstressed conditions, the fetal glucose pool is in equilibrium with the maternal pool.[156] Enzymes for fetal gluconeogenesis are present by 3 months' gestation, but fetal glucose production is minimal and maternal glucose remains the source of fetal glucose.[40,71,142] Ambient fetal glucose levels are generally 20 to 40 mg/dL (1.1 to 2.2 mmol/L) less than maternal levels (or 70% to 80% of maternal values) and increase slightly toward the end of gestation.[40,97] This gradient is regulated by the placenta and favors transfer of glucose across the placenta from the mother through carrier-mediated facilitated diffusion (GLUTs) (see Figure 16-6).

The usual lower limit for fetal glucose is 54 mg/dL (3 mmol/L), especially after 30 weeks.[69,70] If fetal glucose supply decreases, then placental glucose uptake increases, and vice versa, as seen with the infants of mothers with diabetes.[40,89] Extra glucose is stored by the fetus as glycogen and triglycerides.[93] The levels at which glucose carriers become saturated are significantly higher than the usual maternal blood glucose level, which promotes a constant supply of glucose to the fetus. There is no net transfer of insulin or glucagon to the fetus (see Figure 16-5). With adequate maternal nutrition, gluconeogenesis and ketogenesis are not seen in the fetus.[112,142] If the placental supply of glucose is inadequate, the fetus can use ketone bodies and other substrates as alternative energy sources.[142] As noted previously, with prolonged glucose deprivation, the fetus can produce some glucose initially by glycogenolysis and later by gluconeogenesis, probably mediated by cortisol.[70,142]

Fetal glucose utilization is independent of maternal glucose availability. The linear relationship between maternal and fetal glucose levels is maintained during maternal euglycemia, hypoglycemia, and hyperglycemia.[93] The mother meets this demand by an increasing reliance on fat metabolism for her own fuel needs. If the maternal system is not able to meet the fetal demand for gluconeogenic precursors, hypoglycemia can result. Because fetal blood glucose levels are 70% to 80% of maternal values, maternal hypoglycemia leads to even lower fetal blood glucose levels.[97] Placental glucose transfer increases with increasing gestational age not only by increases in GLUT, but also by increases in insulin receptors on fetal tissues, particularly adipose tissue and skeletal muscle. Glucose is also needed by the fetus for protein synthesis, as a

precursor for fat synthesis, for conversion to glycogen for storage, and as the primary substrate for oxidative metabolism. Most of the transferred glucose is oxidized to carbon dioxide and water with release of energy by the tricarboxylic acid cycle and oxidative phosphorylation.

The fetus has an active capacity for anaerobic metabolism, which has a greater role in fetal metabolic processes than it does in adults. The fetus has increased amounts of glycolytic isoenzymes such as hexokinase, glucose-6-phosphate dehydrogenase (G6PD), and pyruvate dehydrogenase, which favor anaerobic glycolysis.[93] Fetal and especially placental tissues actively metabolize glucose to lactate. The lactate generated by the placenta serves as an important fuel for the fetus.[70] Lactate is a major precursor of fetal hepatic glycogen and fatty acid synthesis.[93] Under aerobic conditions the fetus is a net consumer of lactate. The placenta produces large amounts of lactate and ammonia, which may help in regulating metabolic activities in the fetal hepatocytes.[70] The fetus can also use ketone bodies produced from β-oxidation of fatty acids as another alternative fuel source.[142]

The fetal liver contains enzymes needed to both synthesize and catabolize glycogen to store and release glucose. The fetus can also synthesize glycogen from pyruvate, acetate, and alanine.[93] Glycogen synthesis is greater than glycogenolysis in the fetus. Glycogen synthetase and other gluconeogenic enzymes can be found in the liver from the eighth week and increase to term, with a rapid increase seen after 36 weeks' gestation.[93,112] Deposition of hepatic glycogen during the perinatal period is regulated by glucocorticoids and insulin. Glucocorticoids may induce glycogen synthetase, which is then activated by insulin. Fetal cells have increased insulin receptors, greater receptor affinity for glucose, and delayed maturation of hepatic glucagon receptors. These changes promote storage of glucose as glycogen and fat. Glycogen can be synthesized from lactate, pyruvate, alanine, and glycerol as well as glucose.[130]

Glycogen is stored in fetal tissues from 9 weeks' gestation on and increases slowly from 15 to 20 weeks, then more rapidly during the third trimester.[40] Until 20 to 24 weeks, the fetal liver is the main glycogen storehouse; after that time, glycogen is also stored in cardiac and skeletal muscle, and to a lesser extent in the kidneys, intestines, and brain (primarily in the astrocytes).[129,130] Liver and skeletal muscle glycogen concentrations peak at term.[130] Compared with adults, the term fetus has significantly more liver, skeletal muscle, and cardiac muscle glycogen stores. Liver glycogen synthesis is regulated by fetal insulin, the hypothalamic-pituitary axis, and thyroid hormones.[130]

Immunoreactive insulin is present in fetal plasma and islet tissue as early as 8 weeks' gestation.[40,145] Insulin levels are dependent on fetal glucose levels.[70] Insulin production is stimulated by increasing glucose and amino acid concentrations, especially after 20 weeks.[40] Fetal glucose metabolism is relatively independent of the insulin-glucagon regulatory mechanisms seen after birth, however. Acute changes in glucose concentrations leading to hypoglycemia or hyperglycemia do not significantly alter fetal insulin or glucagon secretion.[68] Secretion of these hormones is markedly altered by chronic changes such as long-term hyperglycemia in a woman with diabetes, which augments insulin secretion by β-cell hyperplasia and suppresses glucagon, or by chronic maternal malnutrition, which depresses insulin and stimulates release of fetal glucagon.[40,156] Because insulin is a fetal growth hormone, fetal hyperinsulinemic states are associated with fetal and neonatal macrosomia.[40,105]

Glucagon is found in fetal plasma by 15 weeks' gestation and reaches peak concentrations at 24 to 26 weeks. Compared with adults, the number of fetal hepatic glucagon receptors is decreased and insulin receptors are increased. Fetal liver cells, erythrocytes, monocytes, and lung cells have an increased affinity for insulin. These attributes promote insulin-mediated anabolic processes such as glycogen formation and decrease glucagon-mediated catabolism.[156]

The fetal liver receives the highest net flux of maternal glucose because it is the first organ system encountered by blood returning from the placenta (see Chapter 9). Fetal hepatic enzymes for glycogenesis (carbohydrate to glycogen) are increased, whereas enzymes for glycolysis (carbohydrate to pyruvate and lactate) and gluconeogenesis (fat and protein to glucose) are present but decreased. For example, glucose-6-phosphatase, an enzyme involved in gluconeogenesis and inhibited by glucose and amino acids, is at 20% to 50% of adult levels at midgestation. These relationships are maintained until birth, when decreased glucose availability and onset of feedings with higher fat content stimulate decreases in glycogenolytic enzymes.

Lipid Metabolism

Lipids are a critical component of brain development, of retinal development, and for structural and functional integrity of neuronal and glial membranes, and are the main component of the myelin sheath.[48,76,84,150] Fetal fat content increases during gestation from 0.5% of body weight in early gestation to approximately 3.5% by 28 weeks and 16% by term or by approximately 3.4 g/kg/day in the third trimester.[150] This increase is due to transfer of fatty acids from the mother and active lipogenesis in the fetal liver and other tissues. Lipogenesis is primarily through the fatty acid synthetase pathway, which is highly active in the fetus. The placenta modulates the fatty acid supply for its use and for fetal use.[29] Placental leptin stimulates lipolysis and is excreted to both maternal and fetal circulations. As a result the placenta may have a role in modulating fatty acid supply based on fetal demands.[63]

Long-chain polyunsaturated fatty acids in the mother are primarily found in the form of esterified fatty acids such as triglycerides, phospholipids, and esterified cholesterol. Maternal lipoproteins do not cross the placenta but are taken up by the placenta, where they are broken down and their products used for energy or steroid hormone production or released to the fetus.[77] The placenta contains various tissue receptors, enzymes, and fatty acid binding proteins to upload these lipoproteins and to transport polyunsaturated fatty acids and nonesterified fatty acids to the fetus.[48,89] Free fatty acids cross by diffusion in limited amounts, with a net flux of unesterified fatty acids to the fetus.[76,77] These fatty acids are derived primarily from maternal circulating free fatty acids or cleavage of maternal triglycerides by lipoprotein lipase.[75] The maternal diet is reflected in the fatty acid content of fetal tissues. Ketone bodies and glycerol also cross the placenta.[77] Placental lipid transport and alterations with maternal obesity and diabetes mellitus is illustrated in Figure 16-6. Because transport of fatty acids is partly controlled by maternal concentrations, increased maternal levels are associated with increased transfer and fetal storage.[29,78,83] Other factors influencing free fatty acid transfer include serum albumin level, fatty acid chain length, lipid solubility, uteroplacental and umbilical blood flow, α-fetoprotein, placental proteins that bind fatty acids, and binding affinity.[40,76]

Essential fatty acids (EFA), such as linoleic and α-linolenic acids, cannot be synthesized by the fetus and must be transported across the placenta.[48,76,77,89] These substances can then be desaturated by the fetus to form other fatty acids.[76] Transfer of EFA increases in late pregnancy, when demand for brown and white adipose tissue development and for vascular and neural growth increases; however, some early transfer is needed for uteroplacental vascular development. Long-chain polyunsaturated fatty acids (LCPUFA) from the mother are critical for development of the brain and retinal and brain growth. The fetus has limited capacity to synthesize LCPUFA because of low levels of desaturating enzymes.[57,63,76,105] In the third trimester when fetal neuronal and vascular growth is high, selective transport of LCPUFA derivatives such as arachidonic acid and docosahexaenoic acid (DHA) increases.[76,77] Preterm infants thus need a diet that includes these critical substances.[63] Linoleic acid is converted to arachidonic acid, the main precursor for prostaglandins, thromboxanes, and leukotrienes; α-linolenic acid is converted to DHA (needed for fetal growth and development) and eicosapentaenoic acid (precursor of prostaglandins that inhibit platelet aggregation).[29]

Increased fat deposition during the third trimester is associated with increasing fetal weight and decreased serum triglycerides because these are used in fat deposition.[33] Most (80%) of the fetal fat accretion during this period is a result of de novo synthesis from acetyl coenzyme A (CoA) with formation of palmitic acid, especially in the brain and liver.[17,57,75]

Fetal lipid metabolism is characterized by early development of mechanisms for cholesterol metabolism and lipogenesis with decreased lipolytic activity throughout gestation, except in the liver.[77] Fetal fatty acid synthesis occurs through lipogenesis and desaturation of essential fatty acids. Lipogenesis is dependent on substrate availability. Lipogenic precursors include glucose, lactate, and ketone bodies; the latter two are the most important.[75,131]

The rate of synthesis is primarily controlled by the ratio of plasma insulin-to-glucagon levels. Insulin stimulates and glucagon inhibits fatty acid synthesis (see Table 16-1). The action of glucagon is mediated by cyclic adenosine monophosphate (cAMP), which inhibits acetyl-CoA enzymes.[75] The high insulin-to-glucagon ratio in the fetus promotes fatty acid synthesis. Lipogenesis is increased by glucose, fatty acids, and T4 (see Chapter 19) and reduced by catecholamines. The fetal liver and brain contain enzymes for ketone oxidation as an alternative energy substrate; the fetal brain can use ketones for energy by 10 to 12 weeks' gestation.[17,77,130] Lipolytic activity becomes active after delivery, when the infant can no longer rely on a constant glucose supply from the mother and must cope with a much higher fat intake.

By 15 weeks the fetus has developed enzymes to convert acetate or citrate to fatty acid and thus the potential to use fat as an alternative source of energy. Blood lipid and free fatty acid levels are relatively stable after about 26 weeks but remain low until after delivery. The free fatty acids that cross the placenta are used by the fetus in organ development; synthesis of pulmonary surfactant, other phospholipids, bile, and serum lipoprotein; formation of cell membranes; precursors for prostaglandins; and as second messenger precursors. Fatty acids needed by developing neuronal and glial cells and in formation of the myelin sheath are synthesized within the brain.[75]

The fetus needs cholesterol for cell membranes, bile acid synthesis, embryogenesis (cell proliferation and differentiation), synaptogenesis, production of steroid hormones, and cell-cycle regulation.[76] The fetus obtains cholesterol from endogenous biosynthesis and placental transport.[77] Fetal cholesterol levels are high in early pregnancy, decrease, then rise, peaking in the third trimester.[77] Fetal and maternal cholesterol levels are not correlated.[77] Activity of the pentose phosphate intermediary metabolic pathway is also high in the fetus. Activity of this pathway is associated with cell proliferation and an increased requirement for ribose phosphate precursors of nucleic acids and provision of nicotinamide-adenine dinucleotide (NADH) for synthesis of long-chain fatty acids.

Protein Metabolism

At least 10 amino acids are essential for the fetus, including those essential for adults plus cysteine and histidine, with a dependency on arginine and tyrosine. Arginine and leucine are insulin secretogogues; arginine may also enhance vascular development. Taurine helps regulate metabolism and is needed in the development of the heart, eye, and brain. Because of the relative inactivity of hepatic enzymes such as cystathionase and phenylalanine hydroxylase, the fetus cannot synthesize tyrosine and cysteine from phenylalanine and methionine. The fetus uses amino acids for protein synthesis or oxidation because organ development involves continuous remodeling (breakdown and resynthesis) of tissue. The availability of glucose and other substances influences fetal amino acid catabolism and protein accretion.[24]

There is a net flux of most amino acids from the mother to the fetus.[21] Because concentrations of most amino acids are higher in fetal than maternal blood, amino acids are actively transported from maternal blood across the placental microvillous membrane. Amino acid levels in the syncytiotrophoblast are higher than in either maternal or fetal circulations. Facilitated diffusion moves substances across the syncytiotrophoblast basal membrane to fetal blood. There are at least 15 different amino acid transporters, each mediating uptake of several different amino acids, and each amino acid may use multiple transport systems.[21,89,118]

Placental amino acid transport and alterations with maternal obesity and diabetes mellitus is illustrated in Figure 16-6. Fetal-to-maternal amino acid nitrogen ratios average 1.03 to 3.0, with a net active transfer of nitrogen to the fetus of 54 nmol/day and a total accumulation of about 400 g of protein by term.[8,24] Amino acid transport is not significantly affected by fluctuations in uterine or placental blood flow.[24] Transport may be downregulated in a growth-restricted fetus.[89]

Amino acids are supplied to the fetus in greater amounts than are needed for nitrogen accretion. The fetus uses the carbon from excess amino acids for oxidation and to make nonessential amino acids.[24] Some critical amino acids are not transferred across the placenta directly but are, instead, produced in the placenta. For example, glutamate, which is needed for neurotransmitters and brain development, is not transferred from mother to fetus. Instead glutamine is transferred from the mother to the placenta, where it is used to produce glutamate. Similarly, asparagine is used by the placenta to produce aspartate, another neurotransmitter. Both glutamate and aspartate are toxic, so by transferring precursors, the placenta can produce only the amounts that are needed by the fetus. The placenta also produces ammonia, which is used by the fetal liver for additional protein synthesis.

NEONATAL PHYSIOLOGY

Neonates must develop a homeostatic balance between energy requirements and the supply of substrates as they move from the constant glucose supply of fetal life to the normal intermittent variations in the availability of glucose and other fuels that characterize the absorptive and postabsorptive states. The development of this homeostasis is dependent on substrate availability and maturation of hormonal, neuronal, and enzymatic systems and is influenced by gestational age, health status, and intake.

Transitional Events

Metabolic transition is characterized by a shift from the anabolic-dominant fetal state to the catabolic state of the neonate. This transition is influenced by genetic, environmental, and endocrine factors as well as by major alterations in energy metabolism within the mitochondria. Changes in metabolism with birth are regulated by the expression of specific genes and gene products that alter the activity of various enzymes.[33] Shortly before term birth, induction of hepatic glucose production begins; it is enhanced postbirth by increased glucocorticoids and glucagon.[142] The ability of the fetus to use glucose anaerobically and to readily metabolize lactate may be important in maintaining homeostasis during the stresses of labor and delivery. The fetus prepares for this transition during the last weeks of gestation by increasing fuel storage in the form of glycogen and lipids. Glycogen is critical to maintain glucose homeostasis immediately after birth, whereas the fat stores, through lipolysis of fatty acids and ketone bodies, serve as an alternate energy source. Postnatal changes in metabolism involve the transition from the almost exclusive reliance on glucose for energy production in the fetus to markedly increased use of fatty acid oxidation and ketone body use for energy production in the neonate. An increase in epinephrine, norepinephrine, and glucagon and a decrease in insulin at birth promote mobilization of fatty acids and glycogen metabolism.[93]

Carbohydrate Metabolism

Birth results in the loss of the maternal glucose source. As a result, neonatal blood glucose normally falls after birth, reaching a nadir at 30 to 90 (generally around 60) minutes after birth (Figure 16-7).[40] This fall in glucose is believed to be necessary for activating postnatal glucose production processes.[142] Glucose values then rise and stabilize by 2 to 3 hours after birth.[40,71] The glucose nadir and timing of the nadir are influenced by maternal glucose infusion during the intrapartum period.[40] Steady-state hepatic release of glucose at 4 to 6 mg/kg/minute is seen by 2 to 3 hours in term infants.[60,129] Mean glucose levels in term healthy infants in

TABLE 16-3	Basis for Changes in Blood Glucose Levels Immediately After Birth
CHARACTERISTIC	**BASIS**
Immature liver enzyme systems	Promotes glucose storage rather than release
Larger brain in proportion to body size	Obligatory glucose user
Increased red blood cell volume	Obligatory glucose user
Decreased liver response to glucagons	Limits release of glucose from glycogen stores
Increased energy needs	Increased metabolic and motor activity with birth

the first week average 80 mg/dL.[40] The basis for the fall in blood glucose is summarized in Table 16-3.

Newborns respond to the decrease in blood glucose in several ways. The rapid glycogenolysis (liberation of glucose from glycogen) after birth is stimulated by a fall in the insulin-to-glucagon ratio and sluggish insulin secretion (because of the decreased blood glucose with removal of the placenta), increased serum glucagon, stimulation of the sympathetic nervous system with catecholamine release, increased thyroid stimulating hormone, and increases in hepatic cAMP.[33,68,129] Because insulin promotes transfer of glucose out of the blood into cells, the lowered levels decrease transfer and elevate blood glucose levels. Glucagon stimulates conversion of glycogen into glucose, also raising blood glucose levels.

Hepatic glycogen stores decrease markedly during this period. In term infants, glycogen stores only last an estimated 10 hours after birth before glucose must be produced by gluconeogenesis (production of new glucose from lactate, amino acids [especially alanine], and glycerol).[60] As glycogen falls, the newborn responds by mobilizing fat stores with release of free fatty acids. This response is stimulated by the catecholamine release associated with cooling at birth (see Chapter 20), which rapidly increases free fatty acids.[146] Increased secretion of catecholamines at birth increases glucagon secretion (together these activate hepatic glycogen phosphorylase and glycogenolysis), suppresses insulin, reverses the fetal insulin-to-glucagon ratio, increases lipolysis to provide an alternate energy source, activates enzymes needed for gluconeogenesis, and augments growth hormone secretion.[142,146,156] Healthy infants are able to readily mobilize free fatty acids and oxidize ketones to maintain their blood glucose levels.

Breastfed infants have lower blood glucose levels and higher ketone bodies than bottle-fed infants.[71,142] The elevated ketone bodies may provide an alternate fuel during the period of lower nutrient intake as breastfeeding is being established. This may be especially important for the brain, which can readily use ketones as an alternate energy source.[33,71,142,146] Production of glucose from amino acids, especially alanine, increases and accounts for 4% to 10% of the glucose used for energy in term infants.

Gluconeogenesis also contributes to systemic glucose production after birth. Substrates metabolized by the liver to

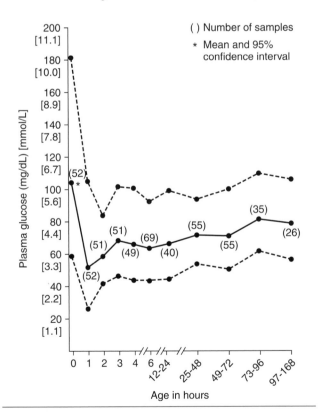

FIGURE 16-7   Plasma glucose levels in healthy term neonates delivered vaginally with birth weights between 2.5 and 4 kg. (From Srinivasan, G., Pildes, R.S., Cattamanchi, G., Voora, S., & Lilien, L.D. [1986]. Plasma glucose values in normal neonates: A new look. *J Pediatr, 109,* 114.)

produce glucose include glycerol, lactate, alanine, and pyruvate.[40,60,93,146] Lactate may account for up to 30% of hepatic glucose production, with 5% to 10% from alanine and glycerol via gluconeogenesis.[114] Gluconeogenic enzyme activity increases after birth. Both glycogenolysis and gluconeogenesis pathways are dependent on the hepatic microsomal glucose-6-phosphatase (G6PD) enzyme system, which has only about 10% of adult activity at birth.[81] The cortisol surge with birth stimulates G6PD activity in the liver and hepatic glucose release.[142] Adult values are reached by about 3 days in term infants but take longer in preterm infants.[81] By 12 to 24 hours after birth, both gluconeogenesis and ketogenesis are active.[112,146] From late fetal life to 3 days after birth, blood glucose regulation is glucose dominant. As a result, gluconeogenesis is diminished during this period. After this period, blood glucose regulation becomes insulin dominant (the adult pattern). The increased gluconeogenesis after birth is regulated by changes in the serum insulin-to-glucagon ratio, catecholamine secretion, fatty acid oxidation, and activation of hepatic enzyme systems.[146] Very-low-birth-weight (VLBW) infants are able to produce glucose to meet basal metabolic needs with appropriate responses to exogenous glucose and amino acid infusions, although hepatic glucose production may be sluggish or incomplete. In the first day after birth in term infants, about 50% of glucose is produced via glucogenolysis and 30% to 40% by gluconeogenesis (primarily from glycerol, but also from alanine and lactate).[71]

After birth, GLUT-1 glucose transporters decrease, whereas GLUT-2 (involved in uptake of glucose by the liver, pancreatic β cells, and intestinal and renal epithelium) and GLUT-3 (involved in uptake by neurons, especially in the cerebellum, skeletal muscle, and other tissues) increase rapidly.[52,69,71,145,147] Activity of GLUT-4 (involved in uptake by muscle and adipose tissue) and other GLUTs increases more slowly.[145,147] GLUT-1, although lower in neonates than in fetuses, remains active and needed for transfer of glucose into red blood cells and across the blood-brain barrier. Both GLUT-1 and GLUT-3 are important in regulating brain glucose supply and are prominent in the blood-brain barrier epithelial cells, astrocytes, oligodendrocytes, choroid plexus, and cerebral cortex.[69,71] Major alternative fuels for the brain are pyruvate, lactate, and ketones. These are transported across the blood-brain barrier by monocarboxylate transporters.[71]

Increased glucagon concentrations and norepinephrine are important in subsequent activation of the hepatic gluconeogenic enzymes.[40,93,147] The predominant enzymes activated during this period are hepatic glycogen phosphorylase, glucose-6-phosphate dehydrogenase (G6PD), and phosphoenolpyruvate carboxykinase (PEP-CK). Hepatic glycogen phosphorylase is activated by norepinephrine and glucagon and stimulates glycogenolysis.[60,142] G6PD activity increases markedly after birth, increasing hepatic release of glucose.[142] This is probably related to surges of glucagon and cAMP, which help shift the activity of the liver from glycogen storage to glucose production. PEP-CK, which is inhibited by insulin, is the rate-limiting enzyme for gluconeogenesis.[60,142] With changes in the insulin-to-glucagon ratio after birth, this enzyme increases about 20-fold, reaching adult levels by 24 hours after birth and thus increasing gluconeogenesis.[60,146]

The resumption of a carbohydrate source (i.e., feeding) generally stabilizes the infant's glucose concentration, and most neonates achieve a steady state in their glucose concentrations by about 5 days. The first enteral feeding immediately increases blood glucose levels. This increase is accompanied by an increase in plasma insulin levels in term infants and development of cyclic changes in insulin and blood glucose levels. In preterm infants the initial feeding is not accompanied by similar hormonal changes, and the cyclic responses in insulin and blood glucose take 2 to 3 days to develop (and longer in VLBW infants or infants who are not fed). Enteral feeding also stimulates production of digestive hormones and secretion of peptides critical for induction of gastrointestinal tract maturation and development of the enteroinsular axis (see Chapter 12). These changes lead to additional modifications of hepatic metabolism.

Basal glucose production in newborns is 4 to 6 mg/kg/minute, versus 2 to 3 mg/kg/minute in adults and approximately 6 to 8 mg/kg/minute in preterm infants and infants with symmetric growth restriction.[60,70,71,142] The high glucose needs in neonates reflect the increased brain mass-to-body weight ratio, in that the brain has a high obligatory glucose use.[83,93] For infants who weigh less than 1000 g, glucose is the major energy source for most of the neonatal period.[52] Newborns are able to use ketone bodies and lactate for brain energy metabolism if inadequate glucose is available, although excess levels can be damaging. This mechanism is present in term, large preterm, and term SGA infants but is absent in VLBW infants and other intrauterine growth–restricted infants who are at risk for hypoglycemia. Glycogen stores in astrocytes may provide another alternative source of glucose for the neurons during periods of low glucose.[4,56]

Lipid Metabolism

The inability of the fetus to readily oxidize fatty acids is rapidly reversed at birth because of changes in the functional ability of enzymes such as carnitine palmitoyltransferase. During this period the levels of glucose and free fatty acids are mirror images of each other. Lipolysis, with enhanced oxidation of free fatty acids and ketogenesis, increases quickly after birth, reaching a maximum within a few hours.[53,75,78,129] This increase is reflected in changes in plasma free fatty acid levels, which rise rapidly beginning 4 to 6 hours after birth and reach adult levels by 24 hours. By this time, 60% to 70% of the infant's energy is produced from oxidation of fat.[137]

Fat is the major form of stored calories in newborns and the preferred energy source for tissues such as the heart and adrenal cortex, which have high energy demands. Fat stores are significantly reduced in low-birth-weight infants. After birth, mobilization of fatty acids from these stores is reflected in the rise in serum levels over the first few hours. This process is initiated by the increase in catecholamines and glucagon, resulting in increased cAMP followed by an increase in protein kinases, phosphorylation, and activation of adipose tissue lipase with release of fatty acids.[53,75]

The transition from glucose to fatty acid oxidation after birth is reflected in the fall of the respiratory quotient from 0.9 to less than 0.8 by 2 hours.[78,137] This indicates that the infant has moved from obtaining nearly two-thirds of its energy from oxidation of glycogen immediately after birth to deriving most of its energy from fat metabolism, conserving glucose to ensure an adequate glucose supply for the central nervous system.[40,60,129] This transition reflects increasing dependence on oxidative metabolism and is associated with an increase in the number of mitochondria and enzymes of the Krebs cycle and changes in serum free fatty acid levels. The shift to fat metabolism is delayed in infants of diabetic mothers with hyperinsulinemia.[40,93] The neonate's brain may use free fatty acids, along with branched-chain amino acids and ketones, as additional energy sources.[60]

The increase in fatty acid oxidation and ketogenesis after birth, stimulated by the thyroid-stimulating hormone surge and increased thyroid hormones with birth, is related to increased enzyme activity, especially of carnitine palmitoyltransferase. Carnitine activity enhances fatty acid oxidation. Concentrations of carnitine are high in human milk for 2 to 3 days after delivery. Another factor influencing this change is alteration in the insulin-to-glucagon ratio, with increased glucagon. This increases the availability of substrates such as acetyl-CoA and carnitine for fatty acid oxidation in the mitochondria.

Serum cholesterol levels in cord blood are about one-half adult values, and serum triglycerides average 30 to 50 mg/dL (0.3 to 0.6 mmol/L). Cholesterol in preterm infants may be high if they are born during the time of the normal fetal cholesterol peak in the third trimester. Low-density lipoprotein cholesterol concentrations decrease with increasing gestational age and are about one-fifth adult values at term; high-density lipoprotein cholesterol values are about one-half adult values at term. Very-low-density lipoprotein (VLDL) transports less than one-third of the total serum triglycerides in the term infant versus that in the adult, in whom VLDL is the major transporter of triglycerides. Serum cholesterol and lipoprotein increase rapidly after birth, especially in breastfed infants.[77]

Protein Metabolism

Serum amino acid levels are higher during the first few weeks of life.[111] Urinary amino acids are elevated immediately after birth, with excretion of 8.8 mg/day in preterm and 7.6 mg/day in term infants versus 2.5 mg/day in older children. The average body nitrogen content at birth is 2%.[111]

Newborns have a limited capacity to synthesize protein, primarily because of the relative inactivity of several hepatic enzymes. This limitation is especially marked in preterm infants, whose capacity to use excess amino acid is reduced. Preterm infants who receive excess protein or an unbalanced amino acid intake are at risk for hyperammonemia, azotemia, metabolic acidosis, and altered plasma amino acid profiles. The latter changes are associated with altered protein synthesis, growth, central nervous system (CNS) function, and bile

acid uptake. The ability to metabolize excess amino acids may also be altered in newborns depending on the maturity of enzyme systems in the liver and skeletal muscle and activity of the urea cycle to eliminate nitrogen.

CLINICAL IMPLICATIONS FOR NEONATAL CARE

The newborn's transitional state in relation to glucose homeostasis can result in problems even for healthy newborns as they attempt to provide adequate energy for maintenance and growth. Alterations in metabolic processes in newborns can result in clinical problems, most notably hypoglycemia. The status of metabolic function in newborns also influences nutritional needs (see Chapter 12).

Neonatal Hypoglycemia

Neonates may develop hypoglycemia if glycogen stores are insufficient to provide fuel during transition until production of energy by fat oxidation is adequate, or if the infant fails to adequately mobilize available glycogen stores. The physiologically optimal range for plasma glucose is given as 70 to 100 mg/dL (3.9 to 5.6 mmol/L).[96,147] Plasma glucose levels (whole blood glucose levels are 10% to 15% lower than plasma levels) below 40 mg/dL (2.2 mmol/L) are uncommon in the first few hours after birth in healthy infants with early feeding, and the lowest optimal level of glucose is most likely around 60 mg/dL (3.3 mmol/L).[14,40,147] Arterial samples are slightly higher than venous samples (by 10% to 15%), with capillary samples intermediate.[14] Elevated hematocrits can lead to lower glucose levels because of the high glucose utilization by the red blood cells. Newer technologies for continuous interstitial glucose monitoring, currently being investigated for use in neonates, have identified more episodes of intermittent blood glucose levels than previously recognized; however, the physiologic significance and long-term significance of these episodes are unknown.[67,72]

Four approaches have been used to define hypoglycemia.[33,34] These include approaches based on appearance of clinical manifestations, measured glucose value ranges, acute metabolic changes and endocrine responses, and long-term neurologic outcomes.[33] None have been satisfactory. Aynsley-Green and Hawdon note that "hypoglycemia is a continuum, no single blood glucose concentration reflecting functional changes in every infant at that level."[7] Similarly, an expert panel concluded that the "rational definition of hypoglycemia is clearly not a specific value but a continuum of falling blood glucose values, creating thresholds for neurologic dysfunction, which may vary from one cause of hypoglycemia or clinical circumstance to another."[32]

Focus should be on promoting normoglycemia with prompt intervention for less optimal values.[32,125] The optimal glucose value and risk for neurologic sequelae probably varies from infant to infant depending on their brain maturity, glycogen stores, presence of hypoxia or ischemia, activity of gluconeogenic pathways, glucose transport status, and brain glucose demand.[4,56] Most sources cite levels below 40 to

45 mg/dL (2.2 to 2.5 mmol/L) as cutoff values for neonatal hypoglycemia.[14,40,67,71,142] There is no evidence that preterm infants are able to tolerate low glucose better than term infants.[7,147] Infants who are very immature or ill (hypoxia, ischemia, sepsis) may have greater glucose needs and be more vulnerable to the effects of hypoglycemia. The American Academy of Pediatrics Committee on Fetus and Newborn has published a practice guideline and algorithm for the screening and management of hypoglycemia in late preterm and term newborns.[31] This guideline suggests that for these infants, a "reasonable (although arbitrary) cutoff for treating symptomatic infants is 40 mg/dL. This value is higher than the physiologic nadir and higher than concentrations usually associated with clinical signs."[31] The guidelines conclude that "a reasonable goal is to maintain plasma glucose concentrations in symptomatic infants between 40 and 50 mg/dL."[31]

Clinical signs of hypoglycemia include tremors, jitteriness, irregular respiration, hypotonia, apnea, cyanosis, poor feeding, high-pitched cry, lethargy, irritability, hypothermia, and seizures. Because hypoglycemic infants may be symptomatic or asymptomatic and signs of hypoglycemia are often nonspecific, careful monitoring of infants at risk for development of hypoglycemia is critical. Multiple factors influence the outcome of infants with hypoglycemia, including severity and duration of the episode, cerebral blood flow and central nervous system (CNS) glucose levels, rates of glucose uptake, maturity, availability of alternative substrates, response to intervention, and type of clinical manifestation.[32,112,138,142]

Glucose is critical for the brain, and hypoglycemia increases the risk of brain injury. Decreased glucose availability increases release of glutamate, free radicals, and other toxic metabolites that can lead to mitochondrial damage, altered adenosine triphosphate (ATP)-dependent ion transport across neuronal membranes, changes in cell membranes, cellular edema, and neuronal necrosis (see Chapter 15). Unfortunately many studies on the outcome of infants with hypoglycemia have significant methodological limitations, and there have been no controlled prospective studies.[4,19,56,129,142] Infants with persistent and recurrent hypoglycemia have the poorest neurologic outcomes.[4,56,142] Hypoglycemia and hypoxic ischemic events may have an additive effect on neuronal injury.[16,142] Brain neuroprotective responses to hypoglycemia include increased epinephrine, increased cerebral blood flow, use of alternative fuels such as ketone bodies and lactate, and degradation of glycogen stored in astrocytes.[16,129,141] This may contribute to the lack of clinical signs even with low blood glucose levels.[16,60] Devaskar and Garg concluded that "transient asymptomatic hypoglycemia in an otherwise healthy neonate has been associated with a good prognosis. Several studies of small groups of subjects have suggested that symptomatic hypoglycemia in the infant results in long-term neurologic damage. However, these data should be interpreted with caution because of a number of confounding variables."[40]

Neonatal hypoglycemia can arise from an inadequate supply of glucose, alterations in endocrine regulation, or increased glucose regulation.[34,40,138] Preterm and SGA infants tend to develop hypoglycemia because of insufficient glycogen and fat stores and a decreased rate of gluconeogenesis. Normally with hypoglycemia, brain glucose utilization decreases by up to 50%, with increased reliance on ketones and lactate for energy. Preterm infants may be limited in their ability to mobilize these responses and thus more vulnerable to the effects of hypoglycemia.[52] Infants of diabetic mothers usually have sufficient stores; however, glycogenolysis is prevented by their high insulin levels and inability to secrete glucagon despite falling blood glucose levels. Infants at risk for neonatal hypoglycemia and associated mechanisms are summarized in Table 16-4.

TABLE 16-4   Causes and Time Course of Neonatal Hypoglycemia

MECHANISM	CLINICAL SETTING	EXPECTED DURATION
Decreased substrate availability	Fetal growth restriction	Transient
	Prematurity	Transient
	Reduced glycogen storage	Transient
	Reduced fat stores	Transient
	Reduced ketogenesis	Transient
	Glycogen storage disease	Prolonged
	Inborn errors of metabolism (e.g., fructose intolerance)	Prolonged
Endocrine disturbances: hyperinsulinemia	Infant of a diabetic mother	Transient
	Persistent hyperinsulinism of infancy	Transient
		Prolonged
	Congenital hyperinsulinism	Prolonged
	Beckwith-Wiedemann syndrome	Transient
	Erythroblastosis fetalis	Transient
	Exchange transfusion	Prolonged
	Islet cell dysplasia	Transient
	Maternal β-agonist tocolytics	Transient
	Improperly placed umbilical artery catheter	Transient
	Inadvertent insulin administration	
Other endocrine disorders	Immaturity of hepatic enzymes necessary for glucose production	Transient
		Prolonged
		Prolonged
	Reduced or failed counterregulation	Prolonged
		Prolonged
	Hypopituitarism	
	Hypothyroidism	
	Adrenal insufficiency	
Increased utilization	Increased brain weight to body weight and liver weight ratio with increased brain consumption of glucose	Prolonged
		Transient
		Transient
	Perinatal asphyxia	
	Hypothermia	
Miscellaneous or multiple mechanisms	Sepsis	Transient
	Congenital heart disease	Transient
	Central nervous system abnormalities	Prolonged

Adapted from Rozance, P.J., McGowan, J.E., Price-Douglas, W., & Hay, W.W., Jr.. (2016). Glucose homeostasis. In S.L. Gardner, B.S. Carter, M.E. Hines, & J.A. Hernandez. (Eds.). *Merenstein & Gardner's handbook of neonatal intensive care* (8th ed.). St. Louis: Mosby.

The Preterm Infant

Hypoglycemia is a common problem of preterm infants. Preterm infants usually develop hypoglycemia secondary to inadequate intake or decreased hepatic glucose production. These infants have decreased glycogen and fat reserves (accumulation of these stores occurs during the third trimester) and immature hepatic function, with low levels of gluconeogenic and glycogenolytic enzymes, especially glucose-6-phosphatase, which is important in glycogenolysis and gluconeogenesis.[40,81] Their initial hormonal response to low glucose levels may be limited.[81] Preterm infants are less able to produce alternate substrates such as ketone bodies. These infants may also have altered metabolic demands from tachypnea, respiratory distress syndrome, hypoxia, hypothermia, or other events that increase glucose use. Infants of mothers treated long term with β-adrenergic agonists for preterm labor (these agents are currently used less commonly) may develop hypoglycemia secondary to hyperinsulinemia.[125] These agents rapidly cross the placenta and stimulate β-cell receptors on the fetal pancreas, with subsequent insulin release and altered glucose homeostasis in the fetus and newborn. Maternal treatment with benzothiazide diuretics can also stimulate fetal β-cell receptors and increase maternal and thus fetal glucose levels. Maternal propranolol, which can interfere with the catecholamine surge at birth, may also increase the risk of hypoglycemia.[40]

The Growth-Restricted Infant

Growth-restricted infants are at risk for hypoglycemia primarily because of alterations in hepatic glucose production and increased glucose utilization.[40,96] These infants may have reduced glycogen stores because of altered placental transport of substrates during fetal life, delayed maturation of gluconeogenesis, and a tendency toward hyperinsulinemia.[112] Insulin sensitivity is decreased in the liver and increased in the peripheral cells. Growth restricted infants have increased energy demands because of their greater brain mass–to-body weight ratio, increased metabolic rate, and tendency toward polycythemia, but have smaller energy stores. Because the brain and red blood cells are obligatory glucose users, these factors can markedly increase glucose needs even in nonstressed infants. Glucose utilization may be further increased by chronic or acute perinatal hypoxia. Secretion of hepatic gluconeogenic enzymes (especially PEP-CK) is impaired in these infants, further limiting their ability to increase glucose production to meet metabolic demands.[142] Growth-restricted infants are at risk for later obesity and other long-term health risks (see Chapter 12).[15,94,155]

The Infant of a Diabetic Mother

Although improved preconceptional care and careful metabolic control of pregnant women with diabetes have reduced the incidence of significant macrosomia and improved perinatal mortality, infants of diabetic mothers (IDMs) continue to be at risk for these as well as other health problems.[51] The cause of these problems relates to fetal and neonatal responses to maternal metabolic alterations and consequences to the neonate of cessation of placental transfer of substrates after birth. Many IDMs are large for gestational age (LGA), lethargic, poor feeders, and at risk for the problems summarized in Figure 16-8 (see also pp. 554-555 for a discussion of the

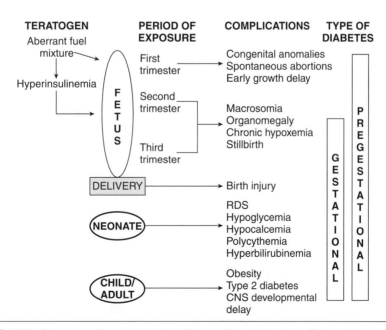

FIGURE 16-8 Diagrammatic representation of the multiple deleterious effects of the pregnancy of a diabetic patient on the offspring during the various periods of fetal and postnatal life. *CNS,* Central nervous system; *RDS,* respiratory distress syndrome. (Adapted from Hod, M., Rabinerson, D., & Peled, Y. [1995]. Gestational diabetes mellitus: Is it a clinical entity? *Diabetes Rev, 3,* 605.)

proposed basis for macrosomia and risk of congenital anomalies in IDMs). Infants born to diabetic mothers with significant vascular involvement are often SGA, but with more mature liver enzyme systems and lungs because of the effects of intrauterine stress. This group of infants is at particular risk for problems associated with chronic hypoxia such as asphyxia and polycythemia.

A prominent problem seen in IDMs is hypoglycemia. Hyperinsulinemia and a blunted glucagon response, aggravated by decreased hepatic responsiveness to glucose, are responsible for the hypoglycemia.[68] Levels of epinephrine and norepinephrine are also elevated, suggesting that hypoglycemia in these infants also may be related to adrenal medullary exhaustion.[34] In addition, exposure in utero to marked increases in glucose (because of higher maternal glucose levels) upregulates insulin secretion and alters glucose disposal. This leads to rapid insulin secretion and rebound hypoglycemia after an intravenous glucose bolus in the newborn.[142]

Large-for-Gestational-Age Infants. LGA infants (weight greater than the 90th percentile or greater than 2 standard deviations for their gestational age) who are not offspring of women with diabetes are also at higher risk for developing hypoglycemia and hyperinsulinemia.[129,142] The exact mechanism is unclear but may be related to increased insulin sensitivity or to borderline maternal glucose tolerance.[40,129,142]

The Infant With Asphyxia

After intrauterine stress, levels of insulin-like growth factor-2 (IGF-2) are low, with increased insulin-like growth factor binding protein 1 and interleukin 6. This leads to decreases in peripheral glucose consumption, conserving glucose for the CNS.[60] Hypoxia and asphyxia alter glucose production and utilization with an increase in glycogenolysis to meet the increased metabolic and energy demands. Because oxygen availability is compromised, the infant switches from aerobic to anaerobic glycolysis. Anaerobic metabolism is less efficient than aerobic metabolism, producing a net increase of only two molecules of ATP per molecule of glucose oxidized (versus 36 molecules of ATP per glucose molecule under aerobic conditions). These changes rapidly deplete glucose (glycogen) reserves, with decreased energy production that may be inadequate to maintain normal cell biologic processes and lead to accumulation of lactic acid.[34] Hypoxic-ischemic damage to the liver may further impair glucose production and delay the postnatal increase in gluconeogenesis. These infants may also develop a transient hyperinsulinemia.[16,34,112]

Because a fetus normally produces large amounts of lactate, intermediary pathways to metabolize lactate are relatively mature and efficient in fetuses and newborns. As a result, metabolic acidosis with birth and asphyxia—if it is not severe enough to overwhelm these pathways or associated with postnatal alterations in oxygenation—is often reversed without administration of sodium bicarbonate.

The ability of the infant to mobilize fat stores may be impaired in hypoxia. During hypoxia, release of catecholamines and fatty acids is impaired and oxidation of fats is inhibited. These changes impair the ability of the infant to generate the energy necessary for normal cell functions and to meet the increased demands of the hypoxic state. IDMs may be further compromised, because although this infant has adequate (or excessive) fat stores, the concomitant hyperinsulinemia and reduced glucagon secretion result in inadequate lipolysis.

Neonatal Hyperglycemia

Neonatal hyperglycemia is a plasma glucose level greater than 180 mg/dL.[40] Hyperglycemia is less common than hypoglycemia but has the potential for significant alterations in neurodevelopmental outcome.[32,40,52,96] Hyperglycemia is seen predominantly in preterm infants, especially those weighing less than 1000 g and receiving parenteral glucose infusions.[34,52] Hyperglycemia is negatively correlated with birth weight and positively correlated with the rate of glucose infusion. Markedly increased blood glucose levels can lead to osmotic changes and fluid shifts within the CNS (with a risk of intraventricular hemorrhage) and to glycosuria (with increased fluid and electrolyte losses and subsequent dehydration).

Hyperglycemia in low-birth-weight infants "is most likely related to the secretion of glucose counter regulatory hormones as a result of stress, or to the release of cytokines in infected infants."[40] Other mechanisms that have been suggested for neonatal hyperglycemia include an inability of the immature infant to suppress endogenous glucose production while receiving a glucose infusion.[34,52] This inability may be related to a decrease in expression of GLUT-2 on hepatocytes, an increased ratio of GLUT-1/GLUT-2 transporters, decreased sensitivity and response to glucose and insulin with hyperglycemia, and decreased ability of the pancreatic β cells to adequately increase insulin in response to increased glucose.[35,52,98,117] Stressed infants seem to be at particular risk for hyperglycemia because of the simultaneous increase in catecholamine release (as a stress response), which further increases glucose levels by inhibiting insulin release and glucose utilization. Other infants at risk for hyperglycemia include infants treated with methylxanthines for apnea or with lipid infusions given at rates greater than 0.25 g/kg/hour, infants with sepsis or after surgery, and term newborns with severe growth restriction who develop transient neonatal diabetes. Chronic glucose deficiency in a growth-restricted fetus leads to fewer pancreatic β cells with a decreased ability to secrete insulin. As a result, these infants may develop hepatic insulin resistance with increased PEP-CK and an increased hepatic glucose production rate, which can lead to a persistent hyperglycemia.[142] Hyperglycemia can also occur, rarely, in infants with very-early-onset diabetes mellitus.[132]

MATURATIONAL CHANGES DURING INFANCY AND CHILDHOOD

Energy and calorie requirements per unit of body weight remain higher in children than in adults because of their higher metabolic rate and growth needs. The relative requirement for carbohydrates is similar for children and adults. For infants, generally not more than 40% of the total calories should be carbohydrates; for children and adults, this value is 40% to 60%.[111] Cerebral glucose utilization is increased until childhood.

The fasting response pattern is similar in infants and children as in adults; however, it proceeds more rapidly because of the greater brain mass–to–body weight ratio and increased glucose utilization rates. Therefore infants and young children develop fasting hyperketonemia more rapidly (within 24 hours) than do adults (36 to 48 hours).[147]

IGF-1 levels along with insulin continue as important growth regulators during infancy and have an inverse relationship with body weight. Catch-up growth is associated with IGF-1 elevations during early childhood. Growth hormone receptors increase in the first 2 years with a gradual transition to growth hormone regulation of growth.[127]

Serum amino acid levels decrease and urinary excretion increases until early childhood. Total body protein increases and reaches adult proportions (3%) by 4 years. Retention of nitrogen decreases during this time to adult values (11 mg/kg/day).[111] Diet alters the fatty acid composition of adipose tissue and possibly the composition of structural lipids during periods of rapid weight gain in the first year of life. This may affect the functional ability of tissues and structures.

SUMMARY

Growth "is an accretion of materials brought together in a synergism involving anabolism and catabolism."[100] Growth

---

> **BOX 16-2**   Recommendations for Clinical Practice Related to Changes in Carbohydrate, Fat, and Protein Metabolism in Neonates
>
> Know the usual changes in carbohydrate, fat, and protein metabolism during the fetal and neonatal periods (pp. 555-563).
> Monitor neonates for alterations in metabolic processes (pp. 560-566).
> Monitor newborn glucose status during transition and in the early neonatal period (pp. 560-562 and Table 16-3).
> Initiate early enteral feeding as appropriate (pp. 560-563 and Table 16-3).
> Monitor neonates for signs of excessive and inadequate intake of carbohydrates, fat, and protein (pp. 560-564).
> Recognize infants at risk for hypoglycemia (pp. 563-566 and Table 16-4).
> Know the clinical signs of hypoglycemia (p. 564).
> Assess and monitor infants at risk for neonatal hypoglycemia (pp. 563-566 and Table 16-4).
> Recognize infants at risk for hyperglycemia (p. 566).
> Assess and monitor infants at risk for hyperglycemia (p. 566).
> Monitor infants at risk for hyperglycemia for alterations in fluid and electrolyte balance (p. 566).
> Recognize and monitor for problems for which the infant of a diabetic mother is at increased risk (pp. 554-555, 565-566 and Figure 16-11).

involves increases in cell size and in the complexity of cells, tissues, and organs. Alterations in growth during the perinatal period arise from maternal, fetal, or placental factors that alter the availability, accretion, or use of substrates or nutrients. These events are influenced by metabolic processes involved in carbohydrate, protein, and lipid metabolism. When this occurs the fetus or neonate may be unable to adapt to environmental stress and is at increased risk for morbidity and mortality. Implications for clinical practice are summarized in Box 16-2.

References

1. Aberg, A., et al. (2001). Congenital malformations among infants whose mothers had gestational or preexisting diabetes. *Early Hum Dev, 61*, 85.
2. Agrogiannis, G. D., et al. (2014). Insulin-like growth factors in embryonic and fetal growth and skeletal development. *Mol Med Rep, 10*, 579.
3. Albareda, M., et al. (2005). Metabolic syndrome at follow-up in women with and without gestational diabetes mellitus in index pregnancy. *Metabolism, 54*, 1115.
4. Alkalay, A. L., et al. (2005). Neurologic aspects of neonatal hypoglycemia. *IMAJ, 7*, 188.
5. American Diabetes Association. (2010). Diagnosis and classification of diabetes mellitus. *Diabetes Care, 33*(Suppl. 1), S62.
6. Atanassova, P., & Popova, L. (2000). Leptin expression during the differentiation of subcutaneous adipose cells of human embryos in situ. *Cells Tissues Organs, 166*, 15.
7. Aynsley-Green, A., & Hawdon, J. M. (1997). Hypoglycemia in the neonate: current controversies. *Acta Paediatr Jpn, 39*, S12.
8. Baird, J. D. (1986). Some aspects of the metabolic and hormonal adaptation to pregnancy. *Acta Endocrinol, 112*, 11.
9. Baksu, A., et al. (2005). Serum leptin levels in preeclamptic pregnant women: relationship to thyroid-stimulating hormone, body mass index, and proteinuria. *Am J Perinatol, 22*, 161.
10. Barrett, H. L., et al. (2014). Normalizing metabolism in diabetic pregnancy: is it time to target lipids? *Diabetes Care, 37*, 1484.
11. Barta, E., & Drugan, A. (2010). Glucose transport from mother to fetus—a theoretical study. *J Theor Biol, 263*, 295.
12. Battaglia, F. C., & Thureen, P. J. (1997). Nutrition of the fetus and premature infant. *Nutrition, 13*, 903.
13. Baz, B., Riveline, J., & Gautier, J. (2016). Gestational diabetes mellitus: definition, aetiological and clinical aspects. *Euro J Endocrinol, 174*, R43.
14. Beardsall, K. (2010). Measurement of glucose levels in the newborn. *Early Human Dev, 86*, 263.
15. Beltrand, J., Meas, T., & Levy-Marchal, C. (2010). Pathophysiology of insulin resistance in small for gestational age subjects: a role for adipose tissue? *Endocr Dev, 19*, 73.
16. Boardman, J. P., & Hawdon, J. M. (2015). Hypoglycaemia and hypoxic-ischaemic encephalopathy. *Dev Med Child Neurol, 57*, 29.
17. Bobinski, R., & Mikulska, M. (2015). The ins and outs of maternal-fetal fatty acid metabolism. *ACTA ABP, 62*, 499.
18. Boden, G. (1996). Fuel metabolism in pregnancy and in gestational diabetes mellitus. *Obstet Gynecol Clin North Am, 23*, 1.

19. Boluyt, N., van Kempen, A., & Offringa, M. (2006). Neurodevelopment after neonatal hypoglycemia: a systematic review and design of an optimal future study. *Pediatrics, 117*, 2231.

20. Boyne, M. S., et al. (2003). The relationship among circulating insulin-like growth factor (IGF)-I, IGF-binding proteins-1 and -2, and birth anthropometry: a prospective study. *J Clin Endocrinol Metab, 88*, 1687.

21. Brett, K. E., et al. (2014). Maternal-fetal nutrient transport in pregnancy pathologies: the role of the placenta. *Int J Mo Sci, 15*, 16153.

22. Briana, D. D., & Malamitsi-Puchner, A. (2010). The role of adipocytokines in fetal growth. *Ann N Y Acad Sci, 1205*, 82.

23. Briffa, J. F., et al. (2015). Leptin in pregnancy and development: a contributor to adulthood disease? *Am J Physiol Endocrinol Metab, 308*, E335.

24. Brown, L. D., et al. (2017). Fetal requirements and placental transfer of nitrogenous compounds. In R. A. Polin, et al. (Eds.), *Fetal and neonatal physiology* (5th ed.). Philadelphia: Saunders.

25. Burlingame, J. M., et al. (2015). Can we really diagnose diabetes during pregnancy? *J Perinat Med, 43*, 277.

26. Buschur, E., & Kim, C. (2012). Guidelines and interventions for obesity during pregnancy. *Int J Gynaecol Obstet, 119*, 6.

27. Butte, N. F., et al. (2004). Energy requirements during pregnancy based on total energy expenditure and energy deposition. *Am J Clin Nutr, 79*, 1078.

28. Calkins, K., & Devaskar, S. U. (2011). Fetal origins of adult disease. *Curr Probl Pediatr Adolesc Health Care, 41*, 158.

29. Cetin, I., Berti, C., & Calabrese, S. (2010). Role of micronutrients in the periconceptional period. *Hum Reprod Update, 16*, 80.

30. Christou, H., et al. (2001). Cord blood leptin and insulin-like growth factor levels are independent predictors of fetal growth. *J Clin Endocrinol Metab, 86*, 935.

31. Committee on Fetus and Newborn & Adamkin, D. H. (2011). Postnatal glucose homeostasis in late-preterm and term infants. *Pediatrics, 127*, 575.

32. Cornblath, M., & Ichord, R. (2000). Hypoglycemia in the neonate. *Semin Perinatol, 24*, 136.

33. Cornblath, M., et al. (1990). Hypoglycemia in infancy: the need for a rational definition. *Pediatrics, 85*, 834.

34. Cowett, R. M., & Farrag, H. M. (2004). Selected principles of perinatal-neonatal glucose metabolism. *Semin Neonatol, 9*, 37.

35. Crowther, C. A., et al. (2005). Australian Carbohydrate Intolerance Study in Pregnant Women (ACHOIS) Trial Group. Effect of treatment of gestational diabetes mellitus on pregnancy outcomes. *N Engl J Med, 352*, 2477.

36. Crume, T. L., et al. (2015). Maternal fuels and metabolic measures during pregnancy and neonatal body composition: the healthy start study. *J Clin Endocrinol Metab, 100*, 1673.

37. Damjanovic, S. S., et al. (2009). Relationship between basal metabolic rate and cortisol secretion throughout pregnancy. *Endocrine, 35*, 262.

38. Dennedy, M. C., & Dunne, F. (2010). The maternal and fetal impacts of obesity and gestational diabetes on pregnancy outcome. *Best Pract Res Clin Endocrinol Metab, 24*, 573.

39. Desai, M., & Ross, M. G. (2011). Fetal programming of adipose tissue: Effects of intrauterine growth restriction and maternal obesity/high-fat diet. *Semin Reprod Med, 29*, 237.

40. Devaskar, S. U., & Garg M. (2015). Disorders of carbohydrate metabolism. In R. J. Martin, A. A. Fanaroff, & M. C. Walsh (Eds.), *Fanaroff & Martin's Neonatal-perinatal medicine: Diseases of the fetus and infant* (10th ed.). Philadelphia: Saunders.

41. Devreker, F., & Englert, Y. (2000). In vitro development and metabolism in the human embryo up to the blastocyst stage. *Eur J Obstet Gynecol Reprod Biol, 92*, 51.

42. Diaz, P., Powell, T. L., & Jansson, T. (2014). The role of placental nutrient sensing in maternal-fetal resource allocation. *Biol of Repro, 91*, 82.

43. Di Simone, N., et al. (2009). Resistin modulates glucose uptake and glucose transporter-1 (GLUT-1) expression in trophoblast cells. *J Cell Mol Med, 13*, 388.

44. Donnelly, J. M., et al. (2015). Fetal metabolic influences on neonatal anthropometry and adiposity. *BMC Ped, 15*, 175183.

45. Dos Santo, E., et al. (2015). The roles of leptin and adiponectin at the fetal-maternal interface in humans. *Horm Mol Biol Clini Investig, 24*, 47.

46. Doster, Y., et al. (2016). The possible role of serum leptin in preeclampsia. *Clin Exp Obstet Gynecol, 43*, 98.

47. Duggleby, S. L., & Jackson, A. A. (2002). Protein, amino acid and nitrogen metabolism during pregnancy: how might the mother meet the needs of her fetus? *Curr Opin Clin Nutr Metab Care, 5*, 503.

48. Duttaroy, A. K. (2009). Transport of fatty acids across the human placenta: a review. *Prog Lipid Res, 48*, 52.

49. Dyer, J. S., & Rosenfeld, C. R. (2011). Metabolic imprinting by prenatal, perinatal and postnatal overnutrition: a review. *Semin Reprod Med, 29*, 266.

50. Engstrom, E., et al. (2005). The role of maternal factors, postnatal nutrition, weight gain, and gender in regulation of serum IGF-I among preterm infants. *Pediatr Res, 57*, 605.

51. Ercal, B., & Crawford, P. A. (2017). Ketone body metabolism in the neonate. In R. A. Polin, et al. (Eds.), *Fetal and neonatal physiology* (5th ed.). Philadelphia: Saunders.

52. Farrag, H. M., & Cowett, R. M. (2000). Glucose homeostasis in the micropremie. *Clin Perinatol, 27*, 1.

53. Fernandez-Twinn, D. S., & Ozanne, S. E. (2010). Early life nutrition and metabolic programming. *Ann N Y Acad Sci, 1212*, 78.

54. Forsum, E., & Lof, M. (2007). Energy metabolism during human pregnancy. *Annu Rev Nutr, 27*, 277.

55. Garrido-Gimenez, C., & Alijotas-Reig, J. (2015). Recurrent miscarriage: causes, evaluation and management. *Postgrad Med J, 91*(1073), 151.

56. Georgieff, M. K., Brunette, K. E., & Tran, P. V. (2015). Early life nutrition and neural plasticity. *Dev Psychopathol, 27*, 411.

57. Gil-Sanchez, A., Kolezko, B., & Larque, E. (2012). Current understanding of placental fatty acid transport. *Curr Opin Clin Nutr Metab Care, 15*, 272.

58. Gleicher, N., et al. (1998). *Principles and practice of medical therapy in pregnancy* (3rd ed.). New York: McGraw-Hill.

59. Godfrey, K. M., Inskip, H. M., & Hanson, M. A. (2011). The long term effects of prenatal development on growth and metabolism. *Semin Reprod Med, 29*, 257.

60. Gustafsson, J. (2009). Neonatal energy substrate production. *Indian J Med Res, 130*, 618.

61. Hadar, E., & Hod, M. (2010). Establishing consensus criteria for the diagnosis of diabetes in pregnancy following the HAPO study. *Ann N Y Acad Sci, 1205*, 88.

62. Hadden, D. R., & McLaughlin, C. (2009). Normal and abnormal maternal metabolism during pregnancy. *Semin Fetal Neonatal Med, 14*, 66.

63. Hanebutt, F. L., et al. (2008). Long-chain polyunsaturated fatty acid (LC-PUFA) transfer across the placenta. *Clin Nutr, 27*, 685.

64. HAPO Study Cooperative Research Group. (2008). Hyperglycemia and adverse pregnancy outcomes. *N Engl J Med, 358*, 1991.

65. HAPO Study Cooperative Research Group. (2009). Hyperglycemia and Adverse Pregnancy Outcome (HAPO) Study: Associations with neonatal anthropometrics. *Diabetes, 58*, 453.

66. Hare, J. W. (1989). *Diabetes complicating pregnancy: The Joslin Clinic method.* New York: Alan R. Liss.

67. Harris, D. L., et al. (2010). Continuous glucose monitoring of newborn babies at risk of hypoglycemia. *J Pediatric, 157*, 198.

68. Hawkes, C. P., & Stanley, C. A. (2017). Pathophysiology of hypoglycemia. In R. A. Polin, et al. (Eds.), *Fetal and neonatal physiology* (5th ed.). Philadelphia: Saunders.

69. Hay, W. W. (2006). Placental-fetal glucose exchange and fetal glucose metabolism. *Trans Am Clin Climatol Assoc, 117*, 321 (discussion 339).

70. Hay, W. W., Jr. (2006). Recent observations on the regulation of fetal metabolism by glucose. *J Physiol, 572*, 17.

71. Hay, W. W., Jr., et al. (2009). Knowledge gaps and research needs for understanding and treating neonatal hypoglycemia: workshop report from Eunice Kennedy Shriver National Institute of Child Health and Human Development. *J Pediatr, 155*, 612.

72. Hay, W. W., Jr., & Rozance, P. J. (2010). Continuous glucose monitoring for diagnosis and treatment of neonatal hypoglycemia. *J Pediatr, 157*, 180.

73. Heerwagen, M. J., et al. (2010). Maternal obesity and fetal metabolic programming: a fertile epigenetic soil. *Am J Physiol Regul Integr Comp Physiol, 299*, R711.

74. Henson, M. C., & Castracane, V. D. (2006). Leptin in pregnancy: an update. *Biol Reprod, 74*, 218.

75. Herrera, E. (2000). Lipid metabolism in the fetus and the newborn. *Diabetes Metab Res Rev, 16*, 202.

76. Herrera, E., & Ortega-Senovilla, H. (2010). Disturbances in lipid metabolism in diabetic pregnancy—are these the cause of the problem? *Best Pract Res Clin Endocrinol Metab*, *24*, 515.

77. Herrera, E., & Lasuncion, M. A. (2017). Maternal-fetal transfer of lipid metabolites. In R. A. Polin, et al. (Eds.), *Fetal and neonatal physiology* (5th ed.). Philadelphia: Saunders.

78. Herrera, E., & Ortega-Senovilla, H. (2017). Lipids as an energy source for the premature and term neonate. In R. A. Polin, et al. (Eds.), *Fetal and neonatal physiology* (5th ed.). Philadelphia: Saunders.

79. Hod, M., Hadar, E., & Cabero-Roura, L. (2015). Prevention of type 2 diabetes among women with prior gestational diabetes mellitus. *Inter J Gynecol Obstet*, *131*, 516.

80. Hughes, R. C., Rowan, J., & Florkowski, C. M. (2016). Is there a role for HbA1c in pregnancy? *Curr Diab Rep*, *16*, 5.

81. Hume, R., et al. (2005). Glucose homeostasis in the newborn. *Early Hum Dev*, *81*, 95.

82. Illsley, N. P. (2000). Glucose transporters in the human placenta. *Placenta*, *21*, 14.

83. Illsley, N. P. (2000). Placental glucose transport in diabetic pregnancy. *Clin Obstet Gynecol*, *43*, 116.

84. Innis, S. M. (2005). Essential fatty acid transfer and fetal development. *Placenta*, *26*, S70.

85. International Association of Diabetes and Pregnancy Study Groups. (2010). International Association of Diabetes and Pregnancy Study Groups recommendations on the diagnosis and classification of hyperglycemia in pregnancy. *Diabetes Care*, *33*, 676.

86. Jahromi, A. S., et al. (2016). Association of tumor growth factor-β and interferon-γ serum levels with insulin resistance in normal pregnancy. *Global J Health Science*, *8*, 25.

87. Jaksic, J., et al. (2001). Effect of insulin and insulin-like growth factor I on fetal macrosomia in healthy women. *Coll Antropol*, *25*, 535.

88. Jansson, T., & Powell, T. L. (2000). Placental nutrient transfer and fetal growth. *Nutrition*, *16*, 500.

89. Jansson, T., Myatt, L., & Powell, T. L. (2009). The role of trophoblast nutrient and ion transporters in the development of pregnancy complications and adult disease. *Curr Vasc Pharmacol*, *7*, 521.

90. Javaid, M. K., et al. (2005). Umbilical cord leptin predicts neonatal bone mass. *Calcif Tissue Int*, *76*, 341.

91. Jovanovic, L., & Nakai, Y. (2006). Successful pregnancy in women with type 1 diabetes: from preconception through postpartum care. *Endocrinol Metab Clin North Am*, *35*, 79.

92. Kalhan, S. C. (2000). Protein metabolism in pregnancy. *Am J Clin Nutr*, *71*, 1249S.

93. Kalhan, S. C. (2017). Metabolism of glucose and methods of investigation in the fetus and newborn. In R. A. Polin, et al. (Eds.), *Fetal and neonatal physiology* (5th ed.). Philadelphia: Saunders.

94. Kanaka-Gantenbein, C. (2010). Fetal origins of adult diabetes. *Ann N Y Acad Sci*, *1205*, 99.

95. Kapoor, N. (2007). Diabetes in pregnancy: a review of current evidence. *Curr Opin Obstet Gynecol*, *19*, 586.

96. Katz, L. L., & Stanley, C. A. (2005). Disorders of glucose and other sugars. In A. R. Spitzer (Ed.), *Intensive care of the fetus and neonate* (2nd ed.). St. Louis: Mosby.

97. Kenshole, A. B. (2004). Diabetes and pregnancy. In G. N. Burrow, T. P. Duffy, & J. A. Copel (Eds.), *Medical complications during pregnancy* (6th ed.). Philadelphia: Saunders.

98. King, J. C., et al. (1994). Energy metabolism during pregnancy: influence of maternal energy status. *Am J Clin Nutr*, *59*, 439S.

99. King, J. C. (2000). Physiology of pregnancy and nutrient metabolism. *Am J Clin Nutr*, *71*, 1218S.

100. Kretchmer, N., Schumacher, L. B., & Silliman, K. (1989). Biological factors affecting intrauterine growth. *Semin Perinatol*, *13*, 169.

101. Lage, M., et al. (1999). Serum leptin levels in women throughout pregnancy and the postpartum period and in women suffering spontaneous abortion. *Clin Endocrinol*, *50*, 211.

102. Laivuori, H., et al. (2000). Leptin during and after pre-eclamptic or normal pregnancy: its relation to serum insulin and insulin sensitivity. *Metabolism*, *49*, 259.

103. Landon, M. B., et al. (2009). A multicenter, randomized trial of treatment for mild gestational diabetes. *N Engl J Med*, *361*, 1339.

104. Lappas, M., et al. (2005). Release and regulation of leptin, resistin and adiponectin from human placenta, fetal membranes, and maternal adipose tissue and skeletal muscle from normal and gestational diabetes mellitus-complicated pregnancies. *J Endocrinol*, *186*, 457.

105. Larque, E., Ruiz-Palacios, M., & Koletzko, B. (2013). Placental regulation of fetal nutrient supply. *Curr Opin Clin Nutr Metab Care*, *16*, 292.

106. Leary, J., Pettitt, D. J., & Jovanovic, L. (2010). Gestational diabetes guidelines in a HAPO world. *Best Pract Res Clin Endocrinol Metab*, *24*, 673.

107. Levy-Marchal, C., Jaquet, D., & Czernichow, P. (2004). Long-term metabolic consequences of being born small for gestational age. *Semin Neonatol*, *9*, 67.

108. Lewis, R. M., et al. (2013). The placental exposome: placental determinants of fetal adiposity and postnatal body composition. *Ann Nutr Metab*, *63*, 208.

109. Lindsay, R. S., et al. (2004). The relation of insulin, leptin and IGF-1 to birthweight in offspring of women with type 1 diabetes. *Clin Endocrinol (Oxf)*, *61*, 353.

110. Lof, M., et al. (2005). Changes in basal metabolic rate during pregnancy in relation to changes in body weight and composition, cardiac output, insulin-like growth factor I, and thyroid hormones and in relation to fetal growth. *Am J Clin Nutr*, *81*, 678.

111. Lowrey, G. (1986). *Growth and development of children*. Chicago: Year Book.

112. Lteif, A. N., & Schwenk, W. F. (1999). Hypoglycemia in infants and children. *Endocrinol Metab Clin North Am*, *28*, 619.

113. Meo, S. A., & Hassain, A. (2016). Metabolic physiology in pregnancy. *J Pak Med Assoc*, *66*, S8.

114. Mericq, V. (2006). Prematurity and insulin sensitivity. *Horm Res*, *65*, 131.

115. Metzger, B. E. (2003). The Freinkel legacy. In M. Hod, et al. (Eds.), *Textbook of diabetes and pregnancy*. London: Martin Dunitz.

116. Metzger, B. E., et al. (2007). Summary and recommendations of the fifth international workshop-conference on gestational diabetes mellitus. *Diabetes Care*, *30*, S251.

117. Moore, T. R., Hauguel-De Mouzon, S., & Catalano, P. (2014). Diabetes and pregnancy. In R. K. Creasy, et al. (Eds.), *Creasy & Resnik's Maternal-fetal medicine: Principles and practice* (7th ed.). Philadelphia: Saunders.

118. Mouzon, S. H., & Lassance, L. (2015). Endocrine and metabolic adaptations to pregnancy; impact of obesity. *Horm Mol Biol Clin Invest*, *24*, 65.

119. Nawathe, A. R., et al. (2016). Insulin-like growth factor axis in pregnancies affected by fetal growth disorders. *Clinical Epigenetics*, *8*, 11.

120. Nelson, S. M., Matthews, P., & Poston, L. (2009). Maternal metabolism and obesity: modifiable determinants of pregnancy outcome. *Hum Repro Update*, *16*, 1.

121. Newbern, D., & Freemark, M. (2011). Placental hormones and the control of maternal metabolism and fetal growth. *Curr Opin Endocrinol Diabetes Obes*, *18*, 409.

122. Nielsen, J. H., et al. (2014). Impact of fetal and neonatal environment on beta cell function and development of diabetes. *ACTA Obs Gyn Scand*, *93*, 1109.

123. Ong, K., et al. (2002). Circulating IGF-I levels in childhood are related to both current body composition and early postnatal growth rate. *J Clin Endocrinol Metab*, *87*, 1041.

124. Ortega-Senovilla, H., et al. (2009). Gestational diabetes mellitus upsets the proportion of fatty acids in umbilical arterial but not venous plasma. *Diabet Care*, *32*, 120.

125. Pampfer, S. (2000). Peri-implantation embryopathy induced by maternal diabetes. *J Reprod Fertil Suppl*, *55*, 129.

126. Persson, B. (2009). Neonatal glucose metabolism in offspring of mothers with varying degrees of hyperglycemia during pregnancy. *Semin Fetal Neonatal Med*, *14*, 106.

127. Phillips, A. F. (2017). Oxygen consumption and general carbohydrate metabolism of the fetus. In R. A. Polin, et al. (Eds.), *Fetal and neonatal physiology* (5th ed.). Philadelphia: Saunders.

128. Plecas, D., Plesinac, S., & Vucinic, O. K. (2014). Nutrition in pregnancy: basic principles and recommendations. *Srp Arh Celok Lek*, *142*, 125.

129. Poppitt, S. D., et al. (1993). Evidence of energy-sparing in Gambian women during pregnancy: a longitudinal study using whole-body calorimetry. *Am J Clin Nutr*, *57*, 353.

130. Poston, L. (2010). Developmental programming and diabetes—the human experience and insight from animal models. *Best Pract Res Clin Endocrinol Metab*, *24*, 541.

131. Prentice, A. M., & Goldberg, G. R. (2000). Energy adaptations in human pregnancy: limits and long-term consequences, *J Clin Nutr, 71*, 1226S.

132. Pridjian, G., & Benjamin, T. D. (2010). Update on gestational diabetes. *Obstet Gynecol Clin North Am, 37*, 255.

133. Ray, J. G., O'Brien, T. E., & Chan, W. S. (2001). Preconception care and the risk of congenital anomalies in the offspring of women with diabetes mellitus: a meta-analysis. *QJM, 94*, 435.

134. Retnakaran, R., et al. (2004). Reduced adiponectin concentration in women with gestational diabetes: a potential factor in progression to type 2 diabetes. *Diabetes Care, 27*, 799.

135. Reynolds, C. M., et al. (2015). Early life nutrition and energy balance disorders in offspring in later life. *Nutrients, 7*, 8090.

136. Rozance, P. J., & Hay, W. W., Jr. (2006). Hypoglycemia in newborn infants: features associated with adverse outcomes. *Biol Neonate, 90*, 74.

137. Rozance, P. J., & Hay, W. W., Jr. (2010). Describing hypoglycemia—definition or operational threshold? *Early Hum Dev, 86*, 275.

138. Rozance, P. J. (2014). Update on neonatal hypoglycemia. *Curr Opin Endocrinol Diabetes Obes, 21*, 45.

139. Sehested, L. T., & Pedersen, P. (2014). Prognosis and risk factors for intrauterine growth retardation. *Dan Med J, 61*, A4826.

140. Sferruzzi-Perri, A., et al. (2013). Hormonal and nutritional drivers of intrauterine growth. *Curr Opin Clin Nutr Metab Care, 16*, 298.

141. Sibley, C. P., et al. (2010). Review: Adaptation in placental nutrient supply to meet fetal growth demand: implications for programming. *Placenta, 31*, S70.

142. Siddiqui, F., & James, D. (2003). Fetal monitoring in type 1 diabetic pregnancies. *Review. Early Hum Dev, 72*, 1.

143. Simmons, R. A. (2017). Cell glucose transport and glucose handling during fetal and neonatal development. In R. A. Polin, et al. (Eds.), *Fetal and neonatal physiology* (5th ed.). Philadelphia: Saunders.

144. Sugden, M. C., & Holness, M. J. (1998). Fuel selection: the maternal adaptation to fetal nutrient demand. *Biochem Soc Trans, 26*, 79.

145. Tieu, J., et al. (2010). Oral anti-diabetic agents for women with pre-existing diabetes mellitus/impaired glucose tolerance or previous gestational diabetes mellitus. *Cochrane Database Syst Rev, 2010*(10), CD007724.

146. Tieu, J., et al. (2014). Screening and subsequent management for gestational diabetes for improving maternal and infant health. *Cochrane Database Syst Rev, 2014*(2), CD007222.

147. Touger, L., et al. (2005). Early growth in offspring of diabetic mothers. *Diabetes Care, 28*, 585.

148. van Leeuwen, M., et al. (2012). Glucose challenge test for detecting gestational diabetes mellitus: a systematic review. *BJOG, 119*, 393.

149. Vitoratos, N., et al. (2001). Maternal plasma leptin levels and their relationship to insulin and glucose in gestational-onset diabetes. *Gynecol Obstet Invest, 51*, 17.

150. Weindling, M. A. (2009). Offspring of diabetic pregnancy: short-term outcomes. *Semin Fetal Neonatal Med, 14*, 111.

151. Wells, J. C. (2011). The thrifty phenotype: an adaptation in growth or metabolism? *Am J Hum Biol, 23*, 65.

152. Wendland, E. M., et al. (2012). Gestational diabetes and pregnancy outcomes – a systematic review of the world health organization (WHO) and the international association of diabetes in pregnancy study groups (IADPSG) diagnostic criteria. *BMC Pregnancy and Childbirth, 12*, 23.

153. Widmaier, E., Raff, H., & Strang, K. T. (2005). *Vander's Human physiology: The mechanism of body function* (10th ed.). New York: McGraw-Hill.

154. Wu, G., Imhoff-Kunsch, B., & Girard, A. W. (2012). Biological mechanisms for nutritional regulation of maternal health and fetal development. *Paediatr Perinat Epidemiol, 26*(Suppl. 1), 4.

155. Yamashita, H., Shao, J., & Friedman, J. E. (2000). Physiologic and molecular alteration in carbohydrate metabolism during pregnancy and gestational diabetes mellitus. *Clin Obstet Gynecol, 43*, 87.

156. Yogev, Y., Metzger, B. E., & Hod, M. (2009). Establishing diagnosis of gestational diabetes mellitus: impact of the hyperglycemia and adverse pregnancy outcome study. *Semin Fetal Neonatal Med, 14*, 94.

Calcium and Phosphorus Metabolism

Georgia R. Ditzenberger

Calcium and phosphorus are critical in cardiovascular, nervous, homeostatic, and muscular processes and in the function of many hormones and enzyme systems. Maternal calcium metabolism during pregnancy and lactation undergoes a series of hormone-mediated adjustments to enhance transport of this mineral to the infant without long-term alterations in the maternal skeleton.[87,100] Calcium serves as a second messenger; this calcium signaling is important in many reproductive processes, including fertilization, implantation, placental development and function, and labor.[8]

Calcium, phosphorus, and other minerals are transported across the placenta for fetal bone mineralization and skeletal growth. After birth the newborn loses the placental supply of calcium and must quickly establish homeostasis of this system to prevent metabolic derangements. This chapter discusses alterations in these substances and related hormones during pregnancy and the neonatal period. Calcium and phosphorus homeostasis in nonpregnant individuals is summarized in Box 17-1 and in Figure 17-1. The roles of the major calciotropic hormones (parathyroid hormone, calcitonin, and vitamin D) are summarized in Table 17-1.

MATERNAL PHYSIOLOGIC ADAPTATIONS

Calcium and phosphorus metabolism is altered during pregnancy, with an increase in the amount and efficiency of intestinal calcium absorption. During pregnancy, absorption increases to 50%, versus 20% to 25% in nonpregnant individuals.[70,78] The increased absorption is mediated primarily by increased 1,25-dihydroxyvitamin D (1,25-[OH]$_2$D).[75] Calcium accumulation in the fetus by term is approximately 30 g.[50,65,100] At least 80% of calcium accretion occurs in the third trimester and is used for fetal bone formation and mineralization.[50,100] Maternal calcium metabolism undergoes further changes during lactation to meet the calcium needs of the growing infant. Understanding of changes in maternal calcium metabolism in pregnancy and lactation has grown in recent years with improved assay techniques and recognition of the roles of parathyroid hormone–related peptide (PTHrP) (Box 17-2).[21] PTHrP increases in the first trimester and is critical for placental calcium transport and believed to help protect the maternal skeleton from excess bone loss.[21,61]

PTHrP may also help mediate changes in vitamin D and parathyroid hormone (PTH).[90]

Antepartum Period

Calcium homeostasis during pregnancy is interrelated with changes in extracellular fluid volume, renal function, and fetal needs. The mother meets the fetal requirement for calcium primarily by increasing intestinal calcium absorption. These changes are mediated by increased production of 1,25-(OH)$_2$D and PTHrP and under the influence of hormones and growth factors such as estrogens, prolactin (PRL), human chorionic somatomammotropin (hCS), also called human placental lactogen (hPL), placental growth factor, and insulin-like growth factor 1.[65,70] These substances increase intestinal absorption of calcium in pregnancy, decrease urinary excretion, alter maternal bone calcium turnover, and stimulate synthesis of both PTHrP and 1,25-(OH)$_2$D.[56,70,78] Changes in calcium and phosphorus homeostasis during pregnancy are summarized in Table 17-2 and Figure 17-2.

Calcium

Maternal total serum calcium levels fall progressively beginning soon after fertilization and decrease by an average of 1 to 1.5 mg/dL (0.25 to 0.38 mmol/L). Calcium reaches its lowest levels at 28 to 32 weeks, followed by a plateau or slight rise to term.[75,105] Serum calcium levels during pregnancy average 9 to 10 mg/dL (2.3 to 2.5 mmol/L)—a decrease of 5% to 6%.[75] The decrease in serum calcium is a relative decrease, in that it is primarily related to and parallels the fall in serum proteins, especially albumin, with a decrease in both total and bound calcium.[21,65,70] Other factors that contribute to alterations in serum calcium include increased plasma volume and hemodilution, increased urinary calcium excretion, and fetal transfer (primarily in the third trimester).[58,75] Ionized calcium (physiologically active form) does not change significantly and is stable or in the low normal range.[58,65,87]

Calcium absorption occurs by active transport in the duodenum and proximal jejunum and by passive mechanisms in the distal jejunum and ileum. Intestinal absorption of calcium doubles during pregnancy, with a positive calcium balance noted by as early as 12 weeks' gestation that continues to the third trimester.[23,65,69] The early increase allows the

BOX 17-1   Calcium and Phosphorus Homeostasis

Serum calcium is present in three forms: (1) bound to albumin and globulins (40%), (2) complexed to bicarbonate and other buffers (up to 10%), and (3) physiologically active ionized calcium (50%). Calcium is also found in extracellular fluid (ECF) and cytoplasm. Calcium is needed for muscle contraction, neurotransmitter secretion, and hormonal secretion.[60] Parathyroid hormone (PTH), vitamin D, and calcitonin are the major hormones involved in calcium homeostasis. Actions of PTH and intestinal absorption of vitamin D are enhanced by magnesium. Hormonal regulation of calcium metabolism is summarized in Figure 17-1.

Calcium and phosphorus are absorbed in the small intestine under the influence of 1,25-dihydroxyvitamin D (1,25-[OH]$_2$D), which stimulates calcium-binding protein carriers. PTH mobilizes calcium and phosphorus in bone by stimulating osteolysis. Active transport of calcium across intestinal cells is vitamin D–dependent and releases calcium and phosphorus into the ECF. In the kidneys, 98% of the filtered calcium is reabsorbed, 70% in the proximal tubule, 20% in the distal tubule, and 10% in the ascending loop of Henle. Reabsorption is regulated by PTH and 1,25-(OH)$_2$D.

PTH inhibits proximal tubular reabsorption of phosphate, leading to increased urinary loss and decreased ECF levels. PTH increases distal tubular reabsorption of Ca^{2+} to conserve calcium by decreasing renal excretion. Thus PTH increases the release of both calcium and phosphorus from the bones, increasing ECF levels. PTH alters both osteoblast and osteoclast activity in the bone.[9] Because concentrations of Ca^{2+} and PO_4 in ECF are closely tied to each other, if ECF PO_4 levels increase, further release of calcium from the bones would normally be decreased to keep the total concentration of calcium and phosphorus constant. If the kidneys increase PO_4 excretion, however, extracellular phosphorus

decreases and more calcium is released from bone. The net result is increased serum and ECF calcium and decreased phosphorus. Decreased serum PO_4 occurs because the phosphaturic actions of PTH exceed serum phosphate–elevating activities. Release of PTH is regulated by concentrations of serum calcium. Even small changes in serum ionized calcium stimulate PTH release. Calcium reabsorption is also influenced by ionized calcium levels, acid-base balance, and phosphate concentrations.[4] Phosphorus excretion is regulated primarily by PTH, which inhibits renal phosphorus reabsorption. Decreased plasma phosphorus levels stimulate increased 1,25-(OH)$_2$D, which increases plasma calcium and suppresses PTH.[4] Phosphorus is also regulated by phosphatonin peptides such as FGF23, which acts on the bone and kidney.[79]

Vitamin D enhances PTH action to increase calcium release from bone and tubular reabsorption of these minerals (see Figure 17-1). Vitamin D can be produced endogenously in the epidermal layer of skin by ultraviolet light irradiation of 7-dehydrocholesterol to D_3 (cholecalciferol) or ingested as D_2 (ergocalciferol) or D_3. Ingested vitamin D requires bile salts for intestinal absorption and is converted in the liver to serum 25-hydroxyvitamin D (25-[OH]D) (major circulating metabolite). This metabolite is usually transported in the blood bound to vitamin-D binding protein. In the kidneys, 25-(OH)D is hydroxylated to 1,25-(OH)$_2$D$_3$ by 1α-hydroxylase (CYP27B1). This enzyme is found in the proximal tubule and is upregulated by PTH and downregulated by fibroblast growth factor.[54] Regulation of vitamin D also occurs through negative feedback from 25-(OH)D levels. 1,25-(OH)$_2$D is also produced in other tissues, including possibly the decidua and placenta during pregnancy, and may play a role in glucose metabolism, skeletal muscle, skin, and cardiovascular and immune system function.[9,54]

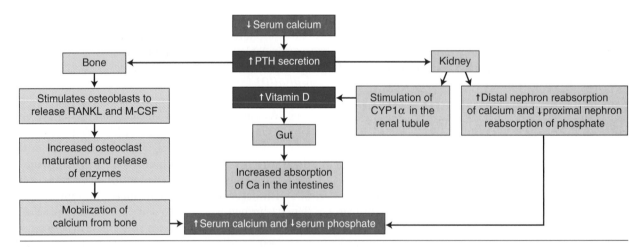

FIGURE 17-1   Normal calcium metabolism regulated by parathyroid hormone *(PTH)* and vitamin D. *CYP1α,* Cytochrome P4501α-hydrolase; *M-CSF,* macrophage colony-stimulating factor; *RANKL,* receptor activator of nuclear factor-κ-B (NF-κB) ligand. (From McCance, K.L. & Huether, S. [2010]. *Pathophysiology: The biological basis for disease in adults & children* [6th ed.]. St. Louis: Mosby, p. 712.)

mother to store calcium throughout pregnancy to meet the high fetal demands in the latter part of the third trimester.[26,58,69] The rise in calcium absorption parallels the rise in 1,25-(OH)$_2$D, which is the primary mediator of this change. However, because the increased intestinal absorption begins before the increase in 1,21,25-(OH)$_2$D, there are likely other

undetermined mechanisms.[54] Estrogens and other hormones may upregulate intestinal calcium transporter genes independent of the influence of vitamin D.[98] PRL has a calciotropic role during pregnancy as well as during lactation.[20]

Urinary calcium excretion parallels the rise in intestinal calcium absorption.[21,50] Urinary excretion increases by 12 weeks,

TABLE 17-1 Hormonal Actions Controlling Calcium and Phosphorus Levels

HORMONE	BONE	INTESTINE	KIDNEY
Parathyroid hormone	Increased calcium release Increased phosphorus release		Increased calcium reabsorption Decreased phosphorus reabsorption
Calcitonin	Decreased calcium release	May inhibit calcium and phosphorus reabsorption	Increased calcium excretion
	Decreased phosphorus release		Increased phosphorus excretion
Vitamin D	Increased calcium release	Increased calcium absorption Increased phosphorus absorption	Increased calcium reabsorption Increased phosphorus reabsorption

---

BOX 17-2   Roles of Parathyroid Hormone–Related Peptide (or Protein)

Parathyroid hormone–related peptide or protein (PTHrP), first isolated in 1987, is produced from a single gene similar in origin and sequencing to the parathyroid hormone (PTH) gene.[57,99,107] The gene is processed into different circulating fragments or iso-forms, each with a different function.[37,99] PTHrP is produced in most tissues of the body and has a broad range of functions. Because few of these functions directly relate to calcium, the name is somewhat of a misnomer. Sources of PTHrP during pregnancy include the breasts, decidua, placenta, fetal membranes, parathyroid gland, and umbilical cord.[58,99]

PTHrP is divided into three peptides that can each produce other peptides, each with differing functions.[58,99,107] The major functions of PTHrP are as follows: (1) stimulation of transepithelial calcium transport, especially in the kidneys, placenta, and breast; (2) smooth muscle (uterus, bladder, stomach, intestines, arterial wall) relaxation; and (3) regulation of cellular proliferation, differentiation, and apoptosis (see Chapter 3).[57,58,99,107] Critical perinatal functions of PTHrP include roles in milk production, labor onset (see Chapter 4), fetal-maternal calcium gradient, and placental calcium transport. Disruption of the PTHrP gene in a fetus or neonate is lethal.

TABLE 17-2   Minerals and Hormones Involved in Calcium Homeostasis

MINERAL/ HORMONES	MOTHER	FETUS	NEWBORN
Total calcium*	Low	High	Decreases‡
Ionized calcium*	Low-normal	High	Decreases
Magnesium*	Low-normal	High-normal	Decreases
Phosphorus*	Low	High	Increases‡
Parathyroid hormone	Low	Low	Increases
Calcitonin	Normal or high	High	Decreases
25(OH)D*	Variable	Variable	Variable
1,25(OH)₂D	High	Low	Increases
Parathyroid hormone– related peptide	High†	High	Decreases

*Placental transfer.
†Of fetal origin.
‡Toward nonpregnant adult values.
Adapted from Nader, S. (2014). Other endocrine disorders of pregnancy. In R.K. Creasy, R. Resnik, & J.D. Iams. (Eds.). *Maternal-fetal medicine: Principles and practice* (7th ed.). Philadelphia: Saunders.

with an average increase from the nonpregnant value of 160 to 240 mg/dL (40 to 60 mmol/L) in the third trimester.[70,75] This change is related to upregulation of 1α-hydroxylase (the enzyme involved in 1,25-[OH]₂D synthesis) activity by PTHrP, estrogens, prolactin, and hCS as well as the increased glomerular filtration rate and occurs even when the maternal diet is calcium deficient.[23,78] After 36 weeks, urinary calcium excretion decreases by about 35%, increasing calcium availability by

approximately 50 mg/day. Because fetal needs at this point are approximately 350 mg/day, however, other maternal calcium sources (i.e., dietary sources or the maternal skeleton) are essential.[75]

Phosphorus and Magnesium

Serum inorganic phosphate levels are generally stable during pregnancy, as is renal tubular reabsorption of this mineral.[56,58] Magnesium is at or below the lower reference range limit. These changes are related to hemodilution and decreased serum albumin.

Parathyroid Hormone

PTH levels fall to low-normal in the first trimester and may become undetectable in women with adequate calcium and vitamin D intake and increase to midnormal ranges by term in these women.[23,58,100] Newer assays suggest PTH levels decrease to 10% to 30% of prepregnant values before increasing to term.[65] The initial decrease is related to the increased 1,25-(OH)₂D in response to increased PTHrP, which may contribute to changes in parathyroid function during pregnancy.[9,36,65,107]

Vitamin D

Both free and bound levels of 1,25-(OH)₂D rise early in pregnancy, double by 10 to 12 weeks' gestation, and remain high to term.[9,58,65,78] Maternal serum levels of 1,25-(OH)₂D are 50% to 100% higher by the second trimester and up to 100% higher in the third trimester.[54] Vitamin D–binding protein also increases, possibly because of the increased estrogen.[9,74]

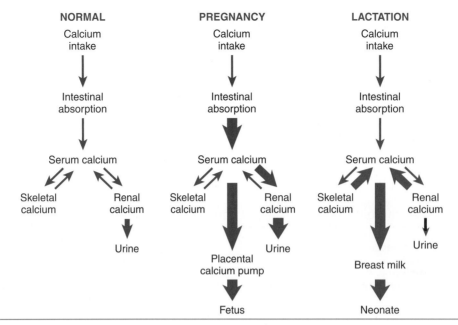

FIGURE 17-2   Adaptive processes of calcium homeostasis in human pregnancy and lactation compared with the normal nonpregnant state. The thickness of the arrows indicates the relative increase or decrease with respect to the normal, nonpregnancy state. (From Kovacs, C.S. & Kronberg, H.M. [1997]. Maternal-fetal calcium and bone metabolism during pregnancy, puerperium and lactation. *Endocrin Rev, 18,* 859.)

Changes in 1,25-(OH)$_2$D are not mediated by PTH, because levels of this hormone are low-normal during the first trimester but are under the influence of estrogens, PRL, hCS, and especially PTHrP, which increases levels of the enzyme 1α-hydroxylase needed for production of 1,25-(OH)$_2$D and suppresses maternal PTH.[9,23,54,65] The increased 1,25-(OH)$_2$D comes primarily from increased production by the maternal kidney, with some from the decidua and fetoplacental unit.[9,48,54,58,78,107] 1,25-(OH)$_2$D opens voltage-dependent calcium channels in intestinal cells to increase calcium absorption.[65] Thus the doubling of 1,25-(OH)$_2$D is paralleled by a twofold increase in intestinal calcium absorption. Serum 25-hydroxyvitamin D (25-[OH]D) levels (stored form) do not change significantly during pregnancy. The increase in 1,25-(OH)$_2$D after 34 to 36 weeks has been associated with an increase in a vitamin D–binding protein and bound vitamin D. Thus intestinal absorption of vitamin D is enhanced throughout gestation. Renal clearance of 1,25-(OH)$_2$D does not change during pregnancy.[9,48]

Calcitonin

Calcitonin levels are generally reported to be normal to high during pregnancy, particularly in the latter half, with about 20% of women having values outside the normal range.[21,56,65] During pregnancy calcitonin is synthesized by the breasts and placenta in addition to the usual synthesis by the C cells of the thyroid gland. The increase in calcitonin with advancing pregnancy may stimulate the proximal renal tubule to increase 1,25-(OH)$_2$D production.[36,48] Increased calcitonin inhibits calcium and phosphorus release from the bones,

counteracting the action of PTH (see Table 17-1). This may help prevent excessive reabsorption of bone calcium and conserve the maternal skeleton while simultaneously permitting the intestinal and renal actions of PTH and 1,25-(OH)$_2$D to provide the additional calcium needed by the fetus.

Changes in Bone Formation and Density

Uncoupling of bone reabsorption and formation is seen during pregnancy, with increased reabsorption during the first two trimesters and increased formation in the third trimester.[65] Markers of bone reabsorption are reported to increase through 28 weeks' gestation, whereas bone formation markers remain stable to 28 weeks and then increase to term.[23,65] Maternal bone formation increases early in pregnancy with increased storage of calcium in maternal bones. Maternal bone growth is associated with increases in bone formation and reabsorption markers such as bone alkaline phosphatase and procollagen peptides in the blood.[48,70,78] Osteocalcin, which normally increases with bone formation, is lower in pregnancy, although some increase is noted in late pregnancy. This may be related to increased placental calcium uptake.[58,107] Bone turnover increases in the third trimester at the time of peak calcium transfer to the fetus. During this time, maternal bone stores are mobilized to meet fetal demands.[48,75] However, the fetal calcium accumulation of 28 to 30 g represents only a small proportion of maternal skeletal stores. The changes in maternal bone are transient.[42,48,70]

Studies of bone mineral density during pregnancy have been inconsistent, with small sample sizes and other methodologic problems, including time of follow-up and other confounding factors.[23,28,41,42,48,63] However, most indicate that bone mineral density decreases by 2% to 5% during pregnancy and lactation, especially in the trabecular bone sites (lumbar spine and hips).[13,23,48,54,68] This is balanced by increases in the periosteal and endosteal surfaces of cortical bones (arms, legs).[70,78,106] Individual variations are seen, with an increased risk of bone density loss associated with frequent pregnancies, short time between pregnancies, adolescent women, lower calcium intake during pregnancy, multiple gestation, and heparin use.[26,78] There do not appear to be any long-term effects of maternal skeletal mass or bone density changes during pregnancy, and bone mineral density has been found to be similar in postmenopausal women whether they have or have not been pregnant.[42,70] A decrease in hip fractures has been reported in several studies in women who have had children, perhaps because pregnancy-associated changes in calcium and phosphorus metabolism may improve mechanical resistance of the upper femur.[70,71,74]

Intrapartum Period

Calcium is essential for the activation of myosin light chain kinase in smooth muscle and thus myometrial contraction. Without calcium, much of which comes from extracellular sources, myometrial contraction does not occur. PTHrP levels in the myometrium and amnion decrease at the onset of labor. The role of calcium in uterine contractions is discussed in Chapter 4.

Postpartum Period

Serum calcium, PTH, and calcitonin gradually return to prepregnant values by 6 weeks postpartum in nonlactating women.[75,100] Resumption of menses is associated with increases in calcium absorption, PTH, and, in most studies, 1,25-$(OH)_2$D. In lactating women, changes in calcium metabolism continue so the mother can provide adequate calcium for infant growth and development.[78] Lactation is a greater challenge to calcium homeostasis than pregnancy. During lactation the woman must provide 280 to 400 mg/day of calcium.[58,70] Exclusive breastfeeding for 6 months leads to four times the calcium loss than what occurs in pregnancy. In lactating women, serum calcium levels are slightly decreased, with a slight increase in ionized calcium (although still within normal limits), whereas phosphorus, PTH, PTHrP, and 1,25-$(OH)_2$D levels are all increased. PTH levels are low-normal or slightly lower if the woman has adequate calcium and vitamin D intake.[21,39,56]

PTHrP, primarily from mammary tissue, increases and plays an important role in controlling breast calcium content.[9,43,58,65,70] PTHrP is important in regulating movement of calcium and phosphorus from maternal bone to breast milk, renal tubular calcium reabsorption, and suppressing PTH.[65] Suckling and prolactin increase PTHrP, which in conjunction with low estradiol levels upregulates bone reabsorption of calcium. PTHrP levels may show a pulsate pattern in response to suckling. Intestinal calcium absorption is not

increased in lactation as it is during pregnancy. However, renal calcium excretion is reduced, conserving calcium for milk production.[22,58,65] Thus the calcium demands of lactation are met primarily through reabsorption of maternal skeletal calcium, probably mediated primarily by PTHrP, and reduction in renal excretion of calcium.[39,100] Changes in calcium metabolism during lactation are summarized in Figure 17-2.

Markers of bone turnover are increased in early lactation but decrease after 6 to 12 months, even with continuation of lactation.[78] Maternal bone density decreases during lactation, with up to 7% of the maternal bone mass lost by 9 months' lactation.[22,53] These changes are most prominent in the trabecular bones of the axial skeleton and hip (e.g., pregnancy and lactation are associated with a 2% to 10% loss of bone mass in the spine and hip) in the first 6 months of lactation, with wide individual variation.[6,23,65,70,78,85] Calcium losses do not continue beyond 6 months even with continued lactation.[65] Calcium supplementation during lactation does not prevent these losses.[23,85] These are reversible changes with no long-term adverse effects in most women, because the maternal skeleton recovers the calcium within 3 to 6 months of weaning (with a regain of bone mineral density of 0.5% to 2% per month).[23,39,70,78,85] Very rarely bone reabsorption may be excessive, with fractures and a clinical diagnosis of osteoporosis.[58,78]

As noted above, changes in the maternal skeleton are reversed in the later stages of lactation and with weaning. Markers of bone reabsorption increase in the first 5 to 12 months of lactation and then decrease.[78,85] During weaning, there is decreased suckling and milk volume and increase in estradiol levels. PTHrP levels decrease.[70] After weaning, PTHrP and PTH levels are elevated, intestinal absorption increases, and urinary calcium losses decrease.[58,78] These changes may help the woman regain her stores. By 3 to 5 months after lactation, bone mineral status is similar or higher in lactating women compared with nonlactating women, regardless of the length of lactation.[78] Increases in PTH and 1,25-$(OH)_2$D after weaning help restore the maternal skeleton.[78] Lactation physiology is discussed further in Chapter 5.

CLINICAL IMPLICATIONS FOR THE PREGNANT WOMAN AND HER FETUS

Changes in calcium and phosphorus metabolism are essential to provide adequate substrate for fetal growth and development and to simultaneously ensure maternal homeostasis. To support these changes, maternal calcium and phosphorus intake must increase during pregnancy and lactation. This section considers these needs as well as implications of alterations in calcium, phosphorus, and magnesium in relation to leg cramps and selected disorders complicating pregnancy.

Maternal Nutritional Needs

During pregnancy an additional 400 mg/day of both calcium and phosphorus is recommended, especially during the second and third trimesters. This results in a recommended total calcium intake of 1200 mg/day in a pregnant woman (or 1600 mg/day in a pregnant adolescent).[58] The effect of supplemental calcium intake on bone density during pregnancy is unclear, because changes in bone metabolism occur even with increased calcium intakes.[18,22,78] There is no consistent correlation between dietary calcium intake or 1,25-$(OH)_2$D bioavailability and intestinal calcium absorption. Hoskings notes that because the fetal skeleton contains only 28 to 30 g of calcium (far less than the average 1000 g of calcium in the adult skeleton), it is unlikely that fetal calcium needs cause clinical bone disease in the mother, but these needs may exacerbate the effects of existing low peak bone mass.[36]

Most studies have not shown a significant increase in maternal bone mineral density with the use of calcium supplements, although neonatal bone mineral density may be improved.[18,22,65,93,95] However, women with low calcium intakes (less than 600 mg/day), adolescents, or women with a multiple pregnancy may benefit from increased calcium intake or supplementation during pregnancy.[1,22,51,70,78] Calcium supplementation during pregnancy has been associated with a reduced risk of preeclampsia (see Maternal Calcium Metabolism and Pregnancy Complications), increased birth weight, decreased risk of preterm delivery, decreased fetal lead exposure (calcium decreases circulating lead in the mother), and lower infant blood pressures.[9,34,35,95,97,101] Calcium and phosphorus needs during lactation are discussed further in Chapter 5.

Vitamin D intake is critical in maintaining calcium homeostasis. Vitamin D intakes of 400 international units (10 μg) per day are recommended in pregnancy, although some question whether these values are too low.[9,88,104] Vitamin D helps ameliorate fluctuations in the calcium-to-phosphorus ratio and enhances calcium absorption. Between 5% and 29% of pregnant women in the United States may have an inadequate vitamin D status.[17,103,104] Alterations in calcium and bone metabolism, including increased risk of maternal osteomalacia and neonatal hypocalcemia, tend to occur primarily in women who have diets that are low in both calcium and vitamin D.[58] Supplementation is recommended for women with low levels before pregnancy, low dietary intakes, and minimal sunlight exposure, although studies of the efficacy of supplementation are limited.[54,64,72,100,103] Low intake of vitamin D during pregnancy has been associated with preeclampsia, gestational diabetes, increased cesarean section, bacterial vaginosis, preterm delivery, and lower weight gain and altered fetal mineral accretion, although some data for these effects are contradictory.[5,9,14,17,52,54,101]

Milk is an excellent source of calcium, vitamin D, and phosphorus. Alternatives for women who are lactose intolerant include cheese, yogurt, lactose-free milks, sardines, whole or enriched grains, and green leafy vegetables. Some substances alter calcium absorption. For example, lactose increases calcium absorption, possibly by decreasing luminal pH or through chelate formation. Excessive fats, phosphate, phytates (found in many vegetables), or oxalates interfere with calcium absorption by forming insoluble calcium salts within the intestinal lumen. High sodium concentrations may also decrease calcium absorption by interfering with active transport mechanisms.

Adequate intake of phosphorus is as important as that of calcium, because these two minerals exist in a constant of solubility in the blood (see Box 17-1 on p. 572). Excess dietary phosphorus binds calcium in the intestine, limiting absorption; excess blood phosphorus leads to increased urinary excretion of calcium. Therefore it is essential for the diet of pregnant and lactating women to be balanced in regard to these substances. Foods such as processed meats, snack foods, and cola drinks have high phosphorus but low calcium levels.

Leg Cramps

Sudden tonic or clonic contraction of the gastrocnemius muscles and occasionally the thigh and gluteal muscles is experienced by 25% to 50% of all pregnant women.[32,76,110] These cramps are most common at night or on awakening and predominantly after 24 weeks' gestation.[110] Leg cramps are also more common in sedentary versus active pregnant women.

Cramps may be associated with a lower threshold for increased neuromuscular irritability because of decreased serum ionized calcium levels combined with increased serum inorganic phosphate levels, along with the hormonal and biochemical alterations of pregnancy.[75,76] Systemic relaxin may decrease calcium movement into muscle, increasing the risk of leg cramps. The incidence of leg cramps is not correlated with ionized calcium levels. Muscular irritability in pregnancy also arises from the lowered calcium levels and mild alkalosis caused by changes in the respiratory system (see Chapter 10).[76] Interventions have included reducing milk intake (although milk is rich in calcium, it also contains large amounts of phosphate); supplementation with magnesium lactate or citrate; or use of aluminum hydroxide antacids to promote formation of insoluble aluminum phosphate salts in the gut, thus reducing absorption of phosphorus.[75] Young and Jewell found the best evidence for treatment with magnesium lactate or citrate.[110] Other oral supplements have often been used, although data to support the efficacy of oral calcium, magnesium, vitamin B or vitamin C supplements are weak.[32,110,111] Thus the specific basis for leg cramps in pregnant women and the most effective interventions remain unclear.

Maternal Calcium Metabolism and Pregnancy Complications

Women with acute and chronic hypertension during pregnancy tend to have lower serum calcium and higher magnesium levels.[34,65] Decreased calcium increases vascular resistance.[34,77] The incidence of preeclampsia has been reported to vary inversely with calcium intake, primarily in women at high risk for low calcium intake.[34,35,97] The risk for preeclampsia was decreased by 50% (range 31% to 67% reduction) with the use of calcium supplementation, particularly for those with low dietary intake.[34,35] Calcium supplementation during pregnancy was also found to reduce the risk of preterm birth in some but not all studies.[18,35]

Women undergoing long-term heparin therapy for thromboembolism during pregnancy may occasionally develop heparin-induced osteopenia. Heparin inhibits 1α-hydroxylation of 25-(OH)D, decreasing levels of 1,25-(OH)$_2$D; altering calcium homeostasis; and increasing bone calcium absorption.[58,65] Calcium status should be monitored carefully in women receiving this therapy.

Disorders of the parathyroid glands are rare. The diagnosis of primary hyperparathyroidism may be obscured by pregnancy changes in calcium metabolism. Pregnancy may provide some protection to women with this disorder, with 39% to 80% becoming asymptomatic during pregnancy. This is often followed by an acute exacerbation postpartum. Moderate to severe forms of this disorder may lead to maternal hypercalcemia with fetal parathyroid suppression and hypocalcemia and risk for neonatal tetany. In women with hypoparathyroidism the normal replacement dose of vitamin D may need to be increased because of the increased vitamin D–binding hormone in pregnancy.[58,65,77]

Osteoporosis is a rare complication of pregnancy and seems to be associated with various factors—such as chronic heparin, anticonvulsant, or steroid use; low bone mineral density prepregnancy; skeletal abnormalities; or excessive reabsorption secondary to chronic inadequate calcium intake, low 1,25-(OH)$_2$D stores, or excessive parathyroid hormone–related peptide (PTHrP)—rather than pregnancy-induced alteration in calcium metabolism.[23,33,58,85] Similarly, pregnancy-associated osteoporosis of the hip, which is also rare, is believed to be unrelated to alterations in mineral balance in pregnancy.[16,85] This condition, seen primarily in primigravida lactating women with small body builds, is self-limiting and usually resolves by 6 to 12 months postpartum.[42,85]

Maternal-Fetal Interactions

Maternal-placental-fetal calcium metabolism is interrelated. As noted earlier, fetal calcium accumulation is mediated by increased maternal absorption of calcium. Calcium is actively transported across the placenta, mediated primarily by PTHrP to maintain a 1:1.4 maternal-to-fetal calcium gradient.[4,37,75,107] Calcium transport increases from 50 mg/day (20 weeks) to greater than 150 mg/day (mean 200 to 300 mg/day) at term.[8,20,42,60] About 80% of fetal mineral accretion occurs after 25 weeks, with peak accretion occurring from 34 to 38 weeks' gestation coinciding with bone development.[23,44,45] Total fetal calcium accretion increases during pregnancy from 100 mg (4 months) and averages 25 to 30 g (generally 28 to 30) at term.[4,48,65,77] Fetal serum calcium (10 to 11 mg/dL

[2.5 to 2.8 mmol/L]) is about 1 mg/dL (0.25 mmol/L) above maternal values.[58] The higher fetal values are primarily related to increased ionized calcium.

Fetal calcium accretion and active transport across the placenta are independent of maternal calcium levels and stores. Calcium movement across the placenta involves three phases: (1) passive bidirectional movement across the maternal-facing microvillous trophoblast membrane into the syncytiotrophoblast cytosol; (2) binding of calcium to calcium-binding proteins such as calmodulin for transport through the syncytiotrophoblast cytosol (binding buffers the calcium so that it does not disrupt cellular processes in the trophoblast); and (3) active transport across the fetal-facing basolateral trophoblast membrane into fetal circulation via several calcium channels and transporters.[8,10,36] Placental transport of both calcium and phosphorus also involves insulin–like growth factor, which also stimulates 1,25-(OH)$_2$D synthesis.[4]

PTHrP (see Box 17-2 on p. 573) regulates control of calcium transport across the placenta.[33,37,47] PTHrP is the major factor in maintaining the fetal calcium level higher than maternal levels. PTHrP is also important for bone development.[21,33,47,50] PTHrP is produced by the fetal parathyroid glands, skeletal growth plate, umbilical cord, amnion, chorion, and placenta.[36,47,107] PTHrP levels are higher in fetuses than in adults.[47,107] Fetal calcium levels are set at a specific level and appear to be maintained at that level regardless of maternal calcium level, even with maternal hypocalcemia. Although fetal calcium levels are maintained primarily by PTHrP-mediated placental calcium transport, movement of calcium in and out of fetal bone, fetal renal tubular reabsorption and excretion of calcium, and swallowing of amniotic fluid also have a role in maintaining fetal homeostasis. Lack of adequate PTHrP and parathyroid hormone (PTH) can lead to fetal growth restriction, because both substances are critical for skeletal mineral accretion.[4,21,33,47,50]

A fetus accumulates 16 g of phosphorus, primarily in the third trimester, and 0.75 g of magnesium (with a peak of 60 to 75 mg/kg/day in the third trimester).[4,60,83] Most of the fetal phosphorus is used for bone mineralization.[4] Fetal phosphorus and magnesium levels are higher than maternal levels; these minerals are actively transported across the placenta.[4,53,75,89] Magnesium is transported to the fetus in increasing amounts after the fifth month.[25] Fetal magnesium levels depend on adequate placental function and maternal stores. Placental insufficiency and inadequate nutritional intake increase the risk of neonatal hypomagnesemia. Transplacental passage of magnesium is influenced by maternal level; for example, administration of large amounts of magnesium sulfate to the mother leads to elevated magnesium in both the mother and fetus.[29]

Fetal mineral homeostasis is not heavily dependent on vitamin D.[60] Placental transport of 1,25-(OH)$_2$D is low, and the fetus is a main source of this substance.[7,54,75,93] The placenta also synthesizes 1,25-(OH)$_2$D and contains 1,25-(OH)$_2$D receptors and key enzymes such as 1-hydroxylase needed for vitamin D metabolism.[7] The fetus is dependent on maternal 25-(OH)D, which is readily transported across the placenta, because fetal hepatic enzyme processes are limited. The 25-(OH)D is 1α-hydroxylated to 1,25-(OH)$_2$D in the fetal kidneys.[4,58,66] Maternal vitamin D deficiency is associated with an increased incidence and severity of neonatal hypocalcemia. PTH and calcitonin do not appear to cross the placenta.[58,75,93] Vitamin D is an important factor in the regulation of cellular differentiation and apoptosis. Insufficient vitamin D during gestation can affect development of the fetal skeleton, immune system, and brain and may alter fetal programming, increasing the risk of adult-onset disorders.[55] Maternal vitamin D deficiency during pregnancy has been associated with neonatal hypocalcemia, impaired growth, and later problems in offspring, including skeletal problems, type 1 diabetes, altered immunotolerance, risk of autoimmune disease, food allergies, and altered programming of long bone development.[4,9,15,54,55,66,86,101]

SUMMARY

Calcium and phosphorus are essential minerals for many body processes and growth. Alterations in metabolic processes related to these elements during pregnancy can alter maternal, fetal, and infant health status. Health can be promoted by careful assessment and monitoring of maternal and fetal status and initiation of appropriate interventions. Recommendations for clinical practice related to calcium and phosphorus metabolism during pregnancy are summarized in Box 17-3.

BOX 17-3 Recommendations for Clinical Practice Related to Changes in Calcium and Phosphorus Metabolism in Pregnant Women

Recognize the usual changes in calcium and phosphorus metabolism during pregnancy (pp. 571-573, Figure 17-2, and Table 17-2).

Assess and monitor maternal nutrition in terms of calcium, phosphorus, and vitamin D intake (pp. 575-576).

Counsel women regarding calcium, phosphorus, and vitamin D requirements to meet maternal and fetal needs during pregnancy (pp. 575-576).

Monitor fetal growth (pp. 577-578, 579).

Know the usual parameters for serum calcium during pregnancy (p. 572).

Evaluate the diet of women complaining of leg cramps (p. 576).

Counsel women regarding leg cramps and appropriate interventions (p. 576).

Recognize usual changes in calcium and phosphorus metabolism during lactation (p. 575, Figure 17-2).

Assess and monitor nutrition during lactation in terms of calcium, phosphorus, and vitamin D intake (p. 575).

Counsel women regarding calcium, phosphorus, and vitamin D requirements to meet maternal needs during lactation (p. 575 and Chapter 5).

Counsel women with pregnancy complications regarding calcium intake during pregnancy (pp. 576-577).

DEVELOPMENT OF CALCIUM AND PHOSPHORUS METABOLISM IN THE FETUS
Anatomic Development

Calcium and phosphorus metabolism is regulated by a variety of hormones, including parathyroid hormone (PTH), vitamin D, and calcitonin. This section reviews development of the parathyroid glands; development of the thyroid glands (site of calcitonin synthesis) is discussed in Chapter 19. Because calcium and phosphorus are critical for bone mineralization processes, skeletal growth is also considered.

Parathyroid Glands

Many structures of the head and neck—the maxillary process, mandibular arch, several muscles of the jaw, hyoid and ear bones, thyroid, and cricoid cartilage—develop from the branchial or pharyngeal arches. These are bars of mesenchymal tissue separated by pharyngeal clefts. The pharyngeal pouches are outpouchings along the lateral walls of the pharyngeal gut. Structures that develop from these pouches include the palatine tonsils, thymus, primitive tympanic cavity, and (from the third and fourth pouches) the parathyroid glands (Figure 17-3).[62]

The third and fourth pharyngeal pouches develop bulbar and ventral portions. The inferior parathyroid glands differentiate from the dorsal bulbar portion of the third pharyngeal pouch during the sixth week. The ventral portion of this pouch forms the thymus. The parathyroid glands initially migrate caudally and medially with the thymus, later separating and attaching to the inferior portion of the dorsal surface of the descending thyroid gland (see Chapter 19).

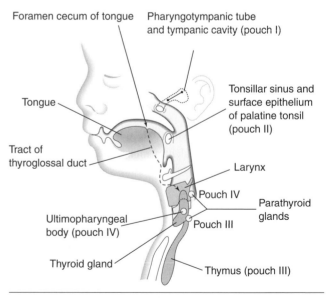

FIGURE 17-3 Schematic sagittal section of the head and neck of a 20-week fetus showing the adult derivatives of the pharyngeal pouches and descent of the thyroid gland. (From Moore, K. [1998]. *The developing human* [6th ed.]. Philadelphia: Saunders.)

The superior parathyroid glands develop from the dorsal bulbar portion of the fourth pharyngeal pouch by the sixth week and attach to the superior portion of the dorsal side of the caudally migrating thyroid gland (see Figure 17-3).[62] Parathyroid glands are active by 12 weeks, but function is suppressed by the high serum calcium concentrations in the fetus.[4,29,65]

Skeletal Development and Growth

Skeletal growth occurs in two phases. During fetal life a cartilage anlage (primordium) is formed that is later replaced by bone. Bone formation also occurs by differentiation of mesenchyme directly into bone cells. Later linear growth depends on cartilaginous growth in the endochondral ossification centers at the epiphyses; appositional growth of the skeleton depends on the laying down of new bone by bone-forming cells with subsequent remodeling (reabsorption of existing bone followed by formation of new bone). Bone formation and remodeling are a cyclic process that occurs continuously throughout life. During growth, bone formation is greater than remodeling. Once maximal growth is achieved, the skeletal mass is stable for 10 to 15 years, and remodeling and bone formation occur at the same rate. With aging, remodeling is greater than bone formation, with a gradual loss of bone mass. Excessive differences between bone formation and remodeling can lead to osteoporosis and compromised skeletal integrity. Stress, such as subjecting bone to heavy loads, or stress that occurs with strenuous exercise, stimulates osteoblastic deposition of new bone, leading to thickening of bones.[30,80,88]

Skeletal development begins in early embryonic life (apparent by the eighth week) and continues well into postnatal life.[65] Bone consists primarily of organic matrix and bone salts. Compact bone is 30% organic matrix and 70% bone salts; newer bone has a more organic matrix. The organic matrix is composed primarily of collagen fibers that give the bone its tensile strength. The rest of the matrix is ground substance, consisting of extracellular fluid and proteoglycans, which may assist in controlling deposition of calcium salts. Crystalline bone salts (hydroxyapatites) give bone compressional strength and consist primarily of calcium and phosphorus with small deposits of sodium, potassium, magnesium, and carbonate salts.[30,80,88]

Bone is formed by either intramembranous or endochondral ossification. Intramembranous ossification is the process involved in formation of bones such as the skull, mandible, and maxilla.[4,80] With intramembranous ossification, the fibrous mesenchyme condenses to form a collagenous membrane in which some cells differentiate into osteoblasts. Osteoblasts produce a collagenous material and ground substance to fill the extracellular spaces. The collagen polymerizes to form collagen fibers and the tissue becomes osteoid and similar to cartilage.[4,62,80] Osteoblasts later secrete alkaline phosphatase, which leads to deposition of calcium salts in the form of calcium hydroxyapatite crystals, with gradual conversion of the osteoid to bone. Some osteoblasts are trapped within lacunae in the bone matrix and develop into osteocytes. The bone matrix grows in all directions as spicules, and ossification centers are established.

The osteoblasts deposit spongy bone first, followed by plates of compact bone (periosteal ossification). Spongy bones are filled with fibrous and cellular mesenchymal derivatives that later differentiate into elements characteristic of red bone marrow (reticular tissue, fat cells, sinusoids, and developing blood cells). Bone growth is accompanied by remodeling, in which much of the original matrix is reabsorbed by osteoclasts simultaneously with formation of new bone by osteoblasts. During this process the osteoclasts project villi that secrete proteolytic enzymes to dissolve the organic matrix and citric, lactic, and other acids that cause solution of bone salts.[30]

The long bones of the appendicular and axial skeleton form by endochondral ossification in which the condensed mesenchymal cells give rise to hyaline cartilage models that are shaped like the eventual bone. This cartilage is eroded locally and destroyed as bone is formed. Endochondral ossification involves the progressive destruction of cartilage, deposition of calcium salts, and formation of a central area of spongy bone (that will later develop a red marrow matrix) surrounded by compact bone. This process begins in the middle of the bone shaft and progresses toward the epiphysis. At birth the long bones consist of central ossification centers and bony shafts with cartilaginous ends. Secondary areas of ossification later appear in the epiphyses.[62,80]

Bone growth and mineralization are mediated by a variety of regulating hormones and growth factors, including calciotropic hormones (e.g., PTH, vitamin D, calcitonin); parathyroid hormone–related peptide (PTHrP); systemic growth-regulating hormones (e.g., growth hormone, insulin, glucocorticoids, thyroid hormones, sex steroids); circulating growth factors (e.g., somatomedin, insulin-like growth factor, epidermal growth factor, platelet-derived growth factor, fibroblast growth factor); and local factors (e.g., osteoclast activity factor, cartilage-derived growth factor).[4,48,49,80,89] In addition, maternal diet (especially vitamin D), physical activity, and smoking during pregnancy may also influence fetal bone mineral acquisition.[24,40,49]

Functional Development

Fetal mineral requirements are met by transport of calcium, phosphorus, magnesium, and other minerals across the placenta (see Maternal-Fetal Interactions). Eighty percent of calcium and phosphorus accretion occurs in the third trimester.[89] From 25 weeks' gestation to term, bone mineralization increases fourfold and fetal calcium acquisition ranges from 92 to 119 mg/kg/day or higher (up to 350 mg/day or a mean of 200 mg/day at term) and phosphorous from 2.51 to 3.44 mg/kg/day (Figure 17-4).[4,44,48,49,66] In contrast, calcium accretion immediately after birth increases from 15 mg/kg on day 1 to 45 mg/kg on day 3.[4,25,48,49,50,66] Phosphate levels peak at midgestation (15 mg/dL [4.8 mmol/L]) and then decrease to 5.5 to 7 mg/dL (1.8 to 2.3 mmol/L) by term.[4,66]

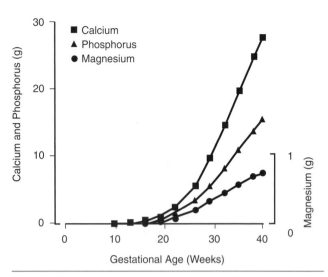

FIGURE 17-4   Calcium, phosphorus, and magnesium accretion in the human fetus from 16 to 40 weeks' gestation. (From Greer, F.R. [2005]. Disorders of calcium homeostasis. In A.R. Spitzer. [Ed.]. *Intensive care of the fetus and neonate* [2nd ed.]. St. Louis: Mosby.)

1,25-(OH)$_2$D and PTH levels are low in the fetus and probably have a limited role in fetal calcium physiology.[33,48,60,88] The parathyroid gland contains PTH by 10 to 12 weeks and actively secretes PTH by 25 to 26 weeks in response to decreased extracellular fluid calcium.[9,62] The fetal parathyroid is less responsive to decreased serum calcium, perhaps because of suppression of the parathyroid by the relative fetal hypercalcemia or placental PTH production.[9,33,37,47,75] The predominant hormone regulating fetal calcium homeostasis is PTHrP (see Box 17-2 on p. 573) rather than PTH (as occurs after birth and in adults), although PTHrP and PTH act synergystically.[4,33,36,46]

Cord concentrations of vitamin D metabolites are only about 20% of maternal levels.[9,46,104,108] 25-(OH)D is transferred from the mother, because fetal liver processes for vitamin D metabolism are limited.[46,100] Renal 1α-hydroxylation to form 1,25-(OH)$_2$D occurs in the fetal kidneys, placenta, and decidua.[46,60,104] The fetus needs to store vitamin D to cope with the relatively high calcium requirements of the early postbirth period. Vitamin D deficiency during fetal development can alter bone growth and development and other areas of development in the infant and child and has implications for the development of other disorders.[1,60,100] These implications and fetal vitamin D synthesis are described further in Maternal-Fetal Interactions on pages 577-578.

Calcitonin-containing cells appear in the thyroid at about 14 weeks' gestation and secrete immunoreactive calcitonin from 28 weeks.[48,60,104] Calcitonin levels are high in the fetus, with increasing concentrations during the third trimester. The role of calcitonin in the fetus is unclear; however, animal evidence suggests that calcitonin does not have a major role in fetal bone metabolism.[46,47,60,104]

NEONATAL PHYSIOLOGY

Newborns are relatively hypercalcemic and hyperphosphatemic compared with maternal levels. The infant must quickly move from the intrauterine dependence on maternal calcium sources and placental hormones to independent extrauterine control of calcium and phosphorus metabolism and homeostasis with reliance on oral intake and bone stores. Failure to do so may lead to hypocalcemia or other metabolic abnormalities. Calcium and phosphorus homeostasis is summarized in Box 17-1 on page 572 and in Figure 17-1. The roles of the major calciotropic hormones (parathyroid hormone, calcitonin, and vitamin D) are summarized in Table 17-1.

Transitional Events

At birth, maternal supplies of calcium and other minerals are no longer available to the infant. Within 24 to 48 hours of birth, the infant moves from the hypercalcemic, peptide PTHrP-dominated calcium metabolism to a parathyroid hormone (PTH) and 1,25-(OH)$_2$D environment. In this environment, the infant must mobilize bone calcium and increase intestinal absorption to maintain serum calcium levels.[4,66] Total and ionized calcium levels are higher in cord blood than in maternal serum; PTH is decreased, but PTHrP is increased.[27,33,47,48,49,75,83] Cord blood magnesium levels are slightly increased and related to maternal levels, whereas phosphorus levels are low.[4,27] Cord blood levels of calcitonin are reported to be 68% to 108% of maternal levels and correlate with maternal levels.[29,85]

Maternal serum 25-(OH)D levels at term correlate with cord blood levels, although cord blood values are about 20% lower; 1,25-(OH)$_2$D levels are about half maternal values.[9,60] At birth serum osteocalcin levels are two to three times higher than in adults. This reflects the rapid rate of fetal bone formation in the last weeks of pregnancy. Osteocalcin is a noncollagenous bone-specific protein that is released into the blood in proportion to the amount of bone formation. Levels increase from birth to 1 to 5 days and then decrease. Markers of bone formation decrease and markers of bone reabsorption increase for a few days after birth due to the transition to dependence on intestinal mineral absorption and the relatively low intake immediately after birth. After that time, both types of markers increase over the next few weeks.[23]

Calcium

The relative hypercalcemia at birth is followed by a physiologic hypocalcemia as both total and ionized calcium fall to levels lower than those found in older infants and about 1 mg/dL (0.25 mmol/L) lower than birth values.[29,60,75] There is a rapid decrease in ionized calcium, especially in the first 4 to 6 hours after birth, reaching a nadir of 4.4 to 5.4 mg/dL (1.1 to 1.4 mmol/L) by 16 to 24 hours.[51,60,66,67,88] Calcium levels generally stabilize in the next 24 to 48 hours and then increase along with increases in PTH and 1,25-(OH)$_2$D.[4,66] The fall in calcium is believed to result from parathyroid suppression in late gestation (from elevated fetal calcium levels), loss of placental transport of calcium, and an increased PTH response.[47,48,49,60,66] This nadir is more pronounced in infants who are preterm or born to mothers with diabetes or vitamin D deficiency.[3,6,40,48,49,108] In term infants, total calcium values average 8 to 9 mg/dL (2 to 2.2 mmol/L), with a range of 8 to 11 mg/dL (2 to 2.8 mmol/L), and are slightly lower in preterm infants. Ionized calcium levels are 4 to 4.6 mg/dL (1 to 1.5 mmol/L).[3,4,37] Calcium levels at birth correlate inversely with gestational age.[4,44,75] The length and degree of the postbirth physiologic hypocalcemia are also correlated inversely with gestational age.[3,4,29] In very-low-birth-weight (VLBW) infants this hypocalcemia may persist despite increasing levels of PTH and 1,25-$(OH)_2$D.[47,49,66,82]

Intestinal absorption of calcium is correlated with both gestational and postbirth age, but the major factor in determining absorption is postnatal age.[4,29,66] Immature intestinal function and decreased intake may limit calcium absorption. Much of the intestinal transport is primarily passive (via paracellular transport) in preterm infants, because transcellular active transport, which is vitamin D–dependent, is not yet mature.[4] Renal calcium excretion is relatively efficient in both term and preterm infants, although increased renal sodium losses in VLBW infants may also increase calcium loss (see Chapter 11).[4,29] Renal calcium excretion increases with gestational and postbirth age, ranging from 60 to 88 mg/day during the first 2 weeks to 180 mg/day by 3 to 12 weeks in term infants and from less than 8 to 80 mg/day to 120 mg/day by 2 weeks of age in preterm infants.[25]

Phosphorus

Phosphorus levels may decrease slightly during the first 1 to 2 days after birth but remain higher than those of adults.[4,66,75] Renal excretion of phosphorus is delayed because of a decreased glomerular filtration rate and increased tubular reabsorption of phosphorus. Increased energy demands during birth with conversion of adenosine triphosphate (ATP) to adenosine diphosphate (ADP) lead to additional phosphorus release. Delayed feeding further elevates phosphorus levels because of tissue catabolism. Phosphorus levels are lower in small-for-gestational-age (SGA) infants and correlate with the degree of growth restriction. Levels are higher in formula-fed than breastfed infants and inversely related to serum calcium concentrations. The fractional excretion of phosphorus is increased in preterm infants, increasing the risk of phosphate deficiency.[4]

Parathyroid Hormone

As serum calcium levels decrease over the first few days after birth, PTH levels gradually increase by about 24 to 48 hours.[51,66] Levels are higher in hypocalcemic preterm infants. Preterm infants may have a transient pseudohypoparathyroidism for the first 72 hours secondary to immature bone and renal responses to PTH.[29,66] By 3 to 4 days of age, the preterm infant's parathyroid gland generally responds effectively to calcium. The infant of a diabetic mother may also have impaired PTH production initially; after a perinatal hypoxic ischemic event, an infant may have a decreased PTH response to low calcium.[4] PTH levels do not appear to change with oral administration of calcium supplements, but intravenous bolus administration of calcium can suppress parathyroid function.[29,66] PTHrP decreases rapidly after birth to the low levels normally seen in adults. Its role in neonatal calcium homeostasis is unclear, but PTH is the major calciotropic hormone by 48 hours of age.[33,47] The response of the neonatal kidneys to PTH is not well understood, although both term and preterm infants do respond to exogenous PTH.[66] The amount of calcium excreted by the kidneys increases over the first 2 weeks after birth, perhaps mediated by the increasing glomerular filtration rate (see Chapter 11).[66]

Vitamin D

Plasma concentrations of 25-(OH)D are lower than and correlate with maternal serum values and remain stable in both term and preterm infants in the first week.[29,66] Term infants are able to effectively metabolize vitamin D in the liver and kidneys. The kidneys can convert 25-(OH)D to 1,25-$(OH)_2$D by 28 to 32 weeks' gestational age. However, vitamin D metabolism remains limited in preterm infants because 25-hydroxylation by the liver does not occur at significant rates until 36 to 38 weeks' gestation.[66,93] In VLBW infants born before 28 weeks' gestation, the vitamin D activation pathway may remain immature.[4] Absorption of exogenous vitamin D may also be limited because of immature fat absorption. Serum 1,25-$(OH)_2$D levels increase during the first 48 hours, probably because of decreased serum calcium or increased PTH, and elevated levels persist for the first week.[66,70] The increase parallels the decrease in serum calcium and increase in PTH in both term and preterm infants. This helps maintain calcium levels within physiologic limits by stimulating bone and intestinal reabsorption. In preterm infants, levels may remain higher for up to 7 to 9 weeks, reflecting rapid prenatal growth.[3,4,29,66,82]

Calcitonin

Calcitonin levels may be normal or slightly elevated at birth, followed by a surge that is reported to peak anywhere from 2- to 10-fold over cord blood levels by 24 to 48 hours of age.[4] Levels then plateau and decrease to childhood levels by 1 month.[4,29,66] Calcitonin levels are inversely correlated with gestational age.[66] Increased calcitonin may protect the infant from excessive bone reabsorption and promote mineralization during a period of active bone growth in the face of increased PTH and 1,25-$(OH)_2$D. High calcitonin levels may contribute to the lower serum calcium levels and increased risk of hypocalcemia seen in preterm infants. Calcitonin levels remain high in preterm infants for a longer period, slowly decreasing over the first 2 to 3 months to reach normal levels by about 40 weeks' postmenstrual age.[66]

Magnesium

Serum magnesium levels increase initially after birth and then fall to levels similar to those in adults (range, 1.5 to 2.8 mg/dL [0.6 to 1.2 mmol/L]) by 2 weeks. Urinary excretion of magnesium may be low for the first few days after birth.

CLINICAL IMPLICATIONS FOR NEONATAL CARE

Bone mineralization and synthesis of new tissues continue after birth and are dependent on adequate substrate. Alterations in calcium and phosphorus metabolism in the neonatal period have implications for nutritional needs of term and preterm infants and are critical in ensuring adequate postnatal growth and development. In addition, these alterations may increase the risk for disorders such as hypocalcemia. This section examines postnatal nutritional needs related to calcium and phosphorus metabolism and the demands of bone mineralization and the basis for common disorders.

A calcium-to-phosphorus ratio of 1.7:1 to 2.0:1 is considered ideal for human infants.[3,4,25] The ratio of calcium to phosphorus can have a significant effect on mineral homeostasis. Hyperphosphatemia may lead to hypocalcemia by blunting the responsiveness of the bone to parathyroid hormone (PTH) and vitamin D. Conversely, low serum phosphorus levels can lead to reduction of calcium entry into bone, bone demineralization, and hypercalcemia.[2,3,25] Infant formulas have higher phosphorus and lower ionized calcium concentrations than human milk. However, currently most commercial formulas have ratios that more closely approximate those of human milk.[2,3,4,82,93] Although levels of calcium are lower in human milk than in cow's milk formulas, the ratio of calcium to phosphorus in human milk promotes calcium-phosphorus homeostasis. The efficiency of intestinal calcium absorption increases up to twofold with human milk feedings. The American Academy of Pediatrics recommends that exclusively breastfed infants receive 400 international units of vitamin D daily (10 μg/day) beginning soon after birth, although compliance with this recommendation is low.[2,73,102] Calcium and phosphorus levels of human milk are not adequate initially for VLBW infants, and supplementation is recommended (see Chapter 12).[2,3,82,96]

Calcium Intake in Preterm Infants

Preterm infants may have difficulty maintaining an adequate calcium intake because of increased growth needs and a low intake. Calcium needs are increased in preterm VLBW infants because they have missed the third trimester when much of the fetal calcium accretion occurs.[2,3,89] In addition medications such as phenytoin, phenobarbital, and glucocorticoids can decrease intestinal calcium absorption.[4] Calcium levels in mature breast milk and standard formulas are significantly below daily intrauterine calcium accretion rates in the third trimester.[89] As a result, bone mineralization is reduced in infants fed these. Preterm infants fed breast milk do have increased calcium absorption (60% to 70% versus 35% to 60% with formulas).[2,3,29,80] Initially, extremely low-birth-weight (ELBW) infants will need parenteral nutrition to supply calcium and phosphorus, although this often does not match intrauterine accretion rates.[3,29,80] Increased levels of calcium and phosphorus can be delivered with formulations containing calcium glycerophosphate and monobasic phosphate (up to 86 mg/dL [21.5 mmol/L] of calcium and 46 mg/dL

[14.9 mmol/L] of phosphorus). Fortification of human milk can increase calcium retention up to 60 mg/kg/day; if the fortifier contains calcium glycerophosphate, this increases to up to 90 mg/kg/day.[80] If supplementation is used for preterm infants fed human milk, calcium-to-phosphorus ratios of 1.7:1 are recommended to maximize intake and retention.[4,80] Ratios should not be greater than 2:1 to prevent hyperphosphatemia. Preterm formulas come closer to duplicating intrauterine calcium accretion rates during the last weeks of the third trimester (120 to 150 mg/kg/day) but have a lower bioavailability of calcium than human milk.[2,4,29,44,81] Vitamin D levels are increased in these formulas to enhance intestinal calcium absorption. Medium-chain triglycerides (MCTs) are also added to increase fat absorption and thus absorption of vitamin D and calcium.

Bone Mineralization

After birth the neonatal skeleton continues to accrete calcium at a rate of approximately 150 mg/kg/day.[4,51,66] To accomplish this, the infant must have adequate vitamin D and intestinal absorption of calcium. This may be difficult to achieve in VLBW and ELBW infants. Rigo and colleagues note that the goal for VLBW infants is postnatal growth similar to the intrauterine rate, with a slightly higher rate in ELBW infants.[80] To reach this goal, these infants need not only adequate supplies of calcium, phosphorus, and other minerals, but also protein and energy for formation of the collagen matrix.[4,80] VLBW infants have decreased postnatal bone mineralization and a significant delay in completing bone development compared with intrauterine rates.[12] Prolonged (longer than 5 days) maternal magnesium sulfate administration has been reported to alter neonatal bone mineralization.[109]

Preterm infants are at risk for both rickets and osteopenia (reduction of bone mass with demineralization of the bone with or without signs of rickets). By term-corrected age, VLBW infants are still of lower weight and length than term infants, with linear growth restriction and lower bone mineral mass and density seen in up to 22% of appropriate for gestational age (AGA) preterm infants.[11,51] Land and Schoenau suggest that one reason for this difference is that the fetus in utero experiences higher mechanical resistance to extremity movement than occurs after birth.[51] Thus the preterm infant's movements occur against lower resistance, which provides less stimulation for development.[51,88] Significant bone mineralization problems, ranging from osteopenia to rickets (see p. 595), are seen in more than 30% of ELBW infants.[2,44,80] Mineralization may also be delayed in SGA infants. Longitudinal follow-up is important after discharge to promote catch-up growth and optimal bone mineralization.[80] Factors leading to inadequate bone mineralization are illustrated in Figure 17-5.

Alterations in Neonatal Calcium Homeostasis
Neonatal Hypocalcemia

The serum calcium level below which an infant is considered to be hypocalcemic varies in the literature from 7 to 8 mg/dL (1.75 to 2 mmol/L).[4,44,75,83] Most sources use a lower limit of 7 mg/dL (1.75 mmol/L) in preterm and 7.8 to 8 mg/dL (1.95

Bilirubin Metabolism

Physiologic jaundice is a common problem in term and preterm infants during the first week after birth. For most of these infants, this phenomenon is mild and resolves without treatment. A small group of infants develop neonatal hyperbilirubinemia, which may be an exaggeration of normal physiologic processes or may herald underlying disorders such as hemolytic disease of the newborn or sepsis. When any infant develops significant hyperbilirubinemia, concerns arise about possible sequelae in the form of bilirubin encephalopathy. This chapter focuses on bilirubin metabolism in fetuses and neonates along with issues related to neonatal hyperbilirubinemia and its management. Maternal adaptations are discussed only briefly, because bilirubin metabolism is not normally significantly altered in pregnancy. Bilirubin synthesis, transport, and metabolism are summarized in Figure 18-1 and Box 18-1.

MATERNAL PHYSIOLOGIC ADAPTATIONS

Alterations in liver and hepatic function during pregnancy are described in Chapter 12. Bilirubin metabolism is not significantly altered in the pregnant woman, with bilirubin levels generally reported to be similar or slightly lower than those in nonpregnant women.[22,105,114,120] Values of 0.3 to 1 mg/dL (5.3 to 17.1 μmol/L) for total bilirubin and an upper limit of 0.2 mg/dL (3.4 μmol/L) for direct bilirubin have been reported.[103] Both total and free bilirubin levels, although still within the normal nonpregnant range, have been reported to be slightly lower than nonpregnant values, with a decreased range in all three trimesters and reduction in the upper limit toward the end of pregnancy; the direct bilirubin was lower in the second and third trimesters.[7,49,136] These changes are believed to be related to hemodilution and decreased albumin.[7,49] Reference ranges for liver function tests during pregnancy have been proposed, with the upper limit of normal values lower than previous values for both pregnant and nonpregnant women of childbearing age.[7,35,49] Activity of phase II enzymes involved in bilirubin metabolism is increased in pregnant women.[82] Elevated serum bilirubin levels in pregnancy warrant further evaluation for liver or hematologic dysfunction.[73,103,136]

CLINICAL IMPLICATIONS FOR THE PREGNANT WOMAN AND HER FETUS

A major difference between fetal and adult handling of bilirubin is that a fetus uses the placenta rather than its own intestines as the major elimination pathway. Most of the bilirubin produced by the fetus remains in the indirect state, a form that can be readily cleared by the placenta. The indirect fetal bilirubin eliminated across the placenta is conjugated and excreted by the maternal liver. Even with severe hemolysis, infants are rarely born jaundiced, because the placenta efficiently clears excess fetal indirect bilirubin.[56] However, these infants may have an accumulation of direct bilirubin and are often severely anemic because of the ongoing hemolysis. The maternal system efficiently handles the fetal bilirubin load and has sufficient reserve, so maternal hyperbilirubinemia secondary to fetal hemolysis is rare.[103] Immunologic aspects of hemolytic disorders secondary to blood group incompatibility are discussed on pages 449-451.

Maternal Hyperbilirubinemia

Elevated total and direct serum bilirubin levels during pregnancy may occur with viral hepatitis, hyperemesis gravidarum (usually less than 5 mg/dL [85.5 μmol/L]; jaundice is uncommon in this disorder), intrahepatic cholestasis of pregnancy (usually less than 4 to 5 mg/dL [68.4 to 85.8 μmol/L]), preeclampsia/eclampsia (often normal but if increased levels are generally less than 5 mg/dL [85.5 μmol/L]), acute fatty liver of pregnancy (usually less than 10 mg/dL [171 μmol/L]), cholelithiasis, and hepatic rupture.[49,85,103,114,120] Jaundice occurs in approximately 10% of women with intrahepatic cholestasis of pregnancy and usually begins 2 to 4 weeks after the onset of pruritus.[114,120] Low maternal bilirubin levels in women with preeclampsia have been associated with poorer maternal and fetal outcomes, possibly because of a reduction in the usual antioxidant protection from bilirubin.[15] The most common cause of jaundice in the first two trimesters of pregnancy is viral hepatitis.[103] Other causes of jaundice in early pregnancy include drug-induced hepatotoxicity, septicemia, or

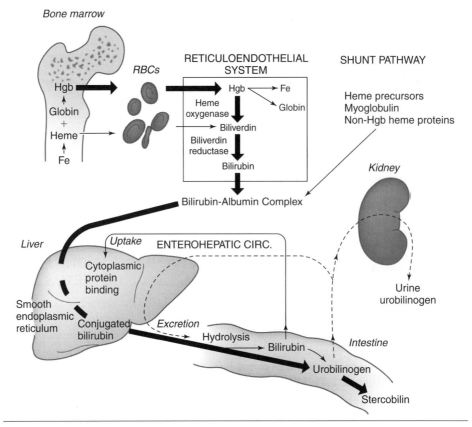

FIGURE 18-1   Bilirubin synthesis, transport, and metabolism. *Hgb,* Hemoglobin; *RBCs,* red blood cells. (From Gartner, L.M. & Hollander, M. [1972]. Disorders of bilirubin metabolism. In N.S. Assali. [Ed.]. *Pathophysiology of gestation* [Vol. 2]. New York: Academic Press.)

BOX 18-1   Bilirubin Synthesis, Transport, Metabolism, and Excretion

Bilirubin is a chain of four pyrrole rings with carbon bridges that is an end-product of hemoglobin catabolism. Hemoglobin is broken down into a heme iron–porphyrin complex and globin in the reticuloendothelial system (see Figure 18-1). Heme is degraded by a series of oxidation-reduction reactions releasing ferrous iron (Fe++) and carbon monoxide (CO) to form biliverdin under the influence of heme oxygenase (HO). HO is a membrane-bound isoenzyme with several forms and is found primarily in the spleen, liver, and bone marrow, although it is also found in the lungs, vascular endothelium, and nervous system.[18,118] HO is the rate-limiting step in bilirubin production.[20,118] The iron is stored and reused. The CO is excreted via the lungs. Bilirubin, iron, and CO are formed in equimolar proportions, so CO production can be used as an index of bilirubin production.[20,118] About 80% of the CO produced by the newborn comes from bilirubin.[20,118] Biliverdin is a water-soluble, nontoxic, blue-green pigment that is catabolized to indirect (unconjugated) bilirubin (4Z-15Z-bilirubin-IXa) by action of nicotinamide adenine dinucleotide phosphate (NADPH)–dependent biliverdin reductase.[118] Most of the heme comes from catabolism of senescent red blood cells (RBCs) and ineffective erythropoiesis (each gram of catabolized hemoglobin produces 34 mg of unconjugated bilirubin).[67] Bilirubin also comes from catabolism of nonhemoglobin heme proteins and free heme in the liver.

Indirect bilirubin is orange-yellow, fat-soluble, and not readily excreted in bile or urine. Indirect bilirubin is transported in plasma, bound to albumin (1 g albumin binds 7–8 mg of unconjugated bilirubin) with a small amount of free bilirubin, to the liver for metabolism and excretion.[56] Direct (conjugated) bilirubin is a water-soluble complex that has been metabolized by the liver to form bilirubin monoglucuronides or diglucuronides (see Figure 18-1).

Bilirubin is dissociated from albumin and transported into the hepatocyte mediated by four transport proteins.[41] These intracellular carrier proteins move bilirubin from the hepatocyte plasma membrane to the liver's smooth endoplasmic reticulum. A cytosolic form of glutathione S-transferase, ligandin, is the major intracellular carrier protein for bilirubin.[18,56,81] Indirect bilirubin is conjugated in the smooth endoplasmic reticulum of the liver to form polar (water soluble) bilirubin monoglucuronide or diglucuronide. The major conjugation pathway involves action of the microsomal enzyme uridine diphosphate-glucuronosyltransferase (UGT). There are multiple isoforms of this liver enzyme, including a bilirubin-specific isoform (UGT1A1) coded by genes on chromosome 2q37.[81] Mutations in this gene lead to diseases such as Gilbert syndrome and Crigler-Najjar syndrome, which are characterized by an indirect hyperbilirubinemia. Other isoforms are involved in conjugation of various drugs, bile acids, and hormones. Polymorphisms in this gene can increase the risk of hyperbilirubinemia in newborns by altering enzyme activity and decreasing production of conjugated bilirubin production or delaying bilirubin clearance.[56,81,130]

Conjugation of each bilirubin molecule involves an enzymatic combination with sugars and glucuronic acid to produce bilirubin

BOX 18-1   Bilirubin Synthesis, Transport, Metabolism, and Excretion—cont'd

monoglycerides and diglycerides.[81] In children and adults, about two thirds of the monoglucuronides are conjugated to form diglucuronides. In neonates, most of the conjugated bilirubin is monoglucuronide. The glucuronyl-conjugating system is dependent on adequate supplies of glucose and oxygen for proper functioning. Most conjugated bilirubin is transported into the intestines in bile and is excreted in feces. A small amount is reabsorbed in the colon and subsequently excreted in urine (increases with elevated serum direct bilirubin levels).[13,39,56] The excretion of bilirubin into the biliary tree is by carrier-mediated active transport. These carriers may become saturated at high bilirubin levels.[24,165] This is a rate-limiting step in clearance of bilirubin from the blood. If these carriers become saturated (as occurs with hepatocellular disorders such as hepatitis), direct hyperbilirubinemia develops.[14,56,81] Some direct bilirubin is also found in circulation bound to albumin to form δ-bilirubin. δ-bilirubin is not seen in the first 2 weeks.[56] Direct or conjugated bilirubin is relatively unstable in the circulation, so the monoglucuronide and

diglucuronide isomers that make up its structure can be rearranged to form other isomers, reducing the accuracy of direct bilirubin measurements.[87]

In the intestines, conjugated bilirubin is further catabolized by intestinal bacteria into tetrapyrroles known as *urobilinogen*.[41] Urobilinogen is oxidized by intestinal bacteria to stercobilin, which is excreted in stool. Direct bilirubin is unstable and can be hydrolyzed by the relatively alkaline environment of the duodenum and jejunum, intestinal brush border enzymes such as β-glucuronidase, and intestinal bacteria back into glucuronic acid and unconjugated (indirect) bilirubin. β-glucuronidase is found in high concentrations in both term and preterm newborns.[56] Some urobilinogen is also deconjugated in the small intestine by β-glucuronidase, absorbed across the intestinal mucosa, and returned to the circulation and portal venous system through enterohepatic circulation (see Figure 18-1) and is a significant contributor to physiologic jaundice.[56,41] Recirculated bilirubin eventually is reconjugated by the liver.

---

cholelithiasis, with biliary tract disease becoming more prominent in the second trimester.[100] Causes of jaundice in the third trimester include intrahepatic cholestasis of pregnancy (see Table 14-2), viral hepatitis, gallstone disease, HELLP syndrome (characterized by hemolysis [H], elevated liver enzymes [EL], and a low platelet [LP] count), acute fatty liver of pregnancy (jaundice is progressive), and disseminated herpes. Postpartum jaundice is most often a result of septicemia, drug use, viral hepatitis, or cholelithiasis.[49,73] Liver function and hepatic disorders during pregnancy are discussed further in Chapter 12.

The effects of excessive maternal bilirubin production on the fetus depend on whether the woman has direct or indirect hyperbilirubinemia. Direct (conjugated) bilirubin is not transferred across the placenta in either direction.[72,103] Therefore the fetus of a woman with direct hyperbilirubinemia and jaundice secondary to hepatitis or other functional liver disorders does not have an elevated direct bilirubin level. Indirect (unconjugated) bilirubin has been reported to be transferred across the placenta from mother to fetus (as well as the usual transfer from fetus to mother), and prolonged exposure to elevated levels may increase the risk of neurologic complications in the infant.[81,103] HELLP syndrome is associated with an increase in indirect bilirubin, although levels in the mother are typically less than 5 mg/dL (85.5 μmol/L) and the mother usually does not appear jaundiced.[103] Neonatal hyperbilirubinemia is seen in about half of the infants in pregnancies complicated by this syndrome. Isolated indirect hyperbilirubinemia is rare in adults; however, several cases of elevated indirect bilirubin levels in cord blood have been reported in infants of women with end-stage cirrhosis.[103] It is unclear whether this increase results from maternal-to-fetal transfer or whether the elevated maternal bilirubin levels prevented the normal fetal-to-maternal transfer of indirect bilirubin. Intrahepatic cholestasis of pregnancy (See Table 14-2) can

alter the removal of bile acids and bilirubin from the fetus across the placenta. If this occurs, these substances may accumulate in the maternal liver and eventually in the placenta and fetal liver.[72,82]

DEVELOPMENT OF BILIRUBIN METABOLISM IN THE FETUS

In early pregnancy, the fetus begins producing bile acids and bile pigments (the most prominent being biliverdin and bilirubin). Elimination of these cholephilic organic anions requires a complex interplay of the mother, placenta, and fetus.[72,82] The placenta contains detoxifying enzymes (expression and activity of phase II enzymes are increased in the placenta) and organic anion carrier transport systems, which facilitate this removal and prevent fetal accumulation of these potentially harmful substances.[72,82] As a result, bile acids and bilirubin levels remain low in the fetus.[72] Biliverdin crosses the placenta poorly; thus conversion to bilirubin facilitates carrier-mediated transport across the placenta.[72] Most fetal bilirubin remains in an unconjugated state.[18,72] This is facilitated by immaturity of the liver and intestine, decreased hepatic blood flow as a result of shunting of some placental blood away from the fetal liver by the ductus venosus, and increased recirculation of bilirubin by the enterohepatic shunt (see Figure 18-1 and Box 18-1). Bilirubin production from biliverdin before liver maturation may play a role in protecting the fetus from oxidative stress and in inducing expression of antioxidant systems.[72,110]

Hepatic uptake is reduced by very low levels of the intracellular carrier protein ligandin.[81] Conjugation of indirect bilirubin by the fetal liver is reduced because of immaturity of a hepatic microsomal enzyme 1A1 isoform of uridine diphosphate-glucuronosyltransferase (UGT) and other liver enzyme systems and decreased hepatocyte uptake and excretion of bilirubin. UGT1A1 can be detected by 16 weeks' gestation.[58] Activity of this enzyme remains low in the fetus and is 0.1% of adult activity at 17 to 30 weeks, increasing to 1% by 30 to 40 weeks.[41,58,81,130]

Elevated concentrations of β-glucuronidase in the fetal small intestine lead to increased deconjugation of direct bilirubin with recirculation to the blood (enterohepatic shunting) for removal by the placenta. Limited intestinal motility also promotes intestinal reabsorption of bilirubin by lengthening the time available for β-glucuronidase to act. Fetal total bilirubin levels are slightly higher than maternal values (averaging 1.5 ± 0.3 mg/L [25.6 ± 5.1 μmol/L]), which may facilitate diffusion across the placenta.[102] The fetus demonstrates little hepatobiliary elimination of bilirubin. Unconjugated bilirubin levels are also greater in the fetus than the mother.[72] Bilirubin and its conjugates can be detected in fetal bile by 22 to 24 weeks' gestation.[36] Fetal total and direct bilirubin increases with increasing gestational age, probably because of increasing numbers of red blood cells (RBCs) that eventually undergo physiologic hemolysis. Bilirubin production increases about 150% per unit of body weight in late gestation as RBCs formed earlier in gestation undergo normal degradation.

Indirect bilirubin can be found in the amniotic fluid beginning at about 12 weeks' gestation.[56,81] Amniotic fluid bilirubin levels initially rise, plateau between 16 and 25 weeks, and then decrease, essentially disappearing by about 36 weeks.[56,81,102] This pattern has been plotted on graphs used to monitor and manage the fetus in pregnancies complicated by Rh sensitization and other blood group incompatibilities. The increased bilirubin reflects increased RBC destruction by maternal antibodies (see pp. 449-451).

The mechanisms by which bilirubin reaches amniotic fluid are uncertain.[56] The fetal kidney excretes small amounts of organic anions into amniotic fluid.[18] Bilirubin may be transferred directly across placental tissue from the mother or across the amnion or umbilical cord from fetal blood vessels.[56,58] The lipid-soluble indirect bilirubin may enter the amniotic fluid dissolved in phospholipids from tracheobronchial secretions.[56] Failure of amniotic fluid bilirubin levels to decrease during gestation is associated with hemolytic disease (see Chapter 13) or disorders that interfere with the normal production and turnover of amniotic fluid (see Chapter 3), such as high intestinal obstruction or anencephaly with decreased fetal swallowing.

Heme oxygenase, an enzyme involved in bilirubin production, is found in the placenta. Heme oxygenase catabolizes heme into carbon monoxide and biliverdin, which is subsequently catabolized to bilirubin (see Figure 18-1 and Box 18-1). Carbon monoxide is a potent vasodilator and bilirubin a potent antioxidant (see Benefits of Bilirubin). Thus these substances may have a local role in control of placental vascular tone and protection of fetal-placental endothelium and syncytiotrophoblast from oxidative injury.[20,117,118]

NEONATAL PHYSIOLOGY

Before birth, bilirubin clearance is handled efficiently by the placenta and mother. After birth, the liver of the newborn must assume full responsibility for bilirubin metabolism. Immaturity of liver and intestinal processes for metabolism, conjugation, and excretion can result in physiologic jaundice and interact with other factors to increase the risk of neonatal hyperbilirubinemia.

Transitional Events

Cord blood bilirubin levels are normally less than 2 mg/dL (34.2 μmol/L) and range from 1.4 to 1.9 mg/dL (23.9 to 32.5 μmol/L).[81] With clamping of the umbilical cord, blood flow and pressure in the venous circulation decrease, the ductus venosus constricts, and flow of relatively desaturated blood to the liver increases. Persistent or fluctuating patency of the ductus venosus, which occurs in some immature or ill infants, results in shunting of portal blood past the liver sinusoidal circulation (reducing the amount of blood perfusing the liver) and may interfere with normal clearance of bilirubin from the plasma.[86]

At birth the meconium in the intestines may contain 100 to 200 mg of bilirubin.[36] About half of this is deconjugated bilirubin and equals 5 to 10 times the daily bilirubin production rate from heme catabolism in a term neonate. Meconium passage usually occurs within 6 to 12 hours (69% of infants) and occurs in 94% of term infants by 24 hours of age (see Chapter 12). Any delay in passage of meconium through the intestinal tract increases the likelihood that conjugated bilirubin will be deconjugated (see Box 18-1 on pp. 590-591) and returned to the circulation.

Benefits of Bilirubin

The byproducts of heme degradation (CO, iron, and bilirubin) have both toxic and beneficial effects.[20,118] Unconjugated bilirubin can diffuse into any cell. Although high levels of bilirubin are toxic, at low levels bilirubin acts as a potent intracellular antioxidant by binding to membranes to prevent their peroxidation and scavenging reactive oxygen species.[20,56,72,81,87,110,111] Levels of bilirubin correlate with total blood oxidative capacity in newborns.[110] Highly reactive metabolites of oxygen (free radicals) are a byproduct of oxidative phosphorylation. Cellular enzymes normally scavenge for and destroy these radicals before they can interfere with cell metabolic functions and destroy cell lipid membranes. Bilirubin accumulation after birth may augment other antioxidant systems and help protect the fetus in moving from the lower oxygenation of the intrauterine environment to the oxygen-rich extrauterine environment.[18,72,81,110] Infants with neonatal disorders associated with free radical production (e.g., respiratory distress syndrome, intraventricular hemorrhage, necrotizing enterocolitis, and retinopathy of prematurity) have been found to have lower serum bilirubin levels than those of similar gestational ages with nonoxidative disorders, which is suggestive that bilirubin is being used to cope with oxidative stress.[110] Bilirubin may also have a protective role against cardiovascular disease in adults.[72] Low bilirubin levels are associated with worse outcomes in adults with coronary artery disease and other vascular respiratory disorders.[15,107]

Bilirubin Production in the Neonate

The usual destruction of circulating red blood cells (RBCs) accounts for about 75% of the bilirubin produced in a healthy term newborn.[41] Catabolism of nonhemoglobin heme, ineffective erythropoiesis, and enterohepatic recirculation (enterohepatic shunt) account for approximately 25% of the bilirubin produced in the neonate.[81] In newborns the amount of nonhemoglobin heme is increased by heme from the large pool of hematopoietic tissue, primarily in the liver, that ceases to function after birth.[41,56] Bilirubin produced by catabolism of nonhemoglobin heme and immature RBCs is sometimes referred to as early bilirubin.

The newborn produces up to 8 to 10 mg/kg/day of bilirubin (more than twice as much as adults).[81] Bilirubin production is inversely correlated with gestational age and remains higher (per kilogram) for 3 to 6 weeks.[56] Increased bilirubin production in the newborn is related to a greater circulating RBC volume per kilogram (and subsequent breakdown of senescent cells), decreased RBC life span (80 to 100 days in term, 60 to 80 days in preterm, and 35 to 50 days in extremely low-birth-weight [ELBW] infants, versus 120 days in adults), increased numbers of immature or fragile cells, and an increase in early bilirubin.[48,81]

Levels of unbound bilirubin may also be higher in newborns, especially preterm infants, because of lower albumin concentrations, decreased albumin-binding capacity, and decreased affinity of albumin for bilirubin.[3,18,41,56] This may be related to a maturational defect in albumin structure, or endogenous metabolic products produced during periods of stress or abnormal metabolism may block or interfere with albumin-binding sites.[18] Bilirubin processing (conjugation) by the liver and excretion are also altered in newborns (see Causes of Physiologic Jaundice).

Physiologic Jaundice

Physiologic jaundice is seen in up to 85% of newborns during the first days after birth.[81,132] Visible jaundice in neonates usually appears as the bilirubin levels reach 5 to 6 mg/dL (85.5 to 103 μmol/L).[56] Almost all term infants develop bilirubin levels over 2 mg/dL (34.2 μmol/L) in the first week, and most will develop clinical jaundice.[81]

Patterns of Physiologic Jaundice

The usual pattern of bilirubin change is a two-phase process.[34,56] These general phases are seen in term and preterm infants and in breastfed and formula-fed infants, although characteristics of the phases vary depending on gestation,

ethnicity, and method of feeding. Phase I is primarily related to reduced hepatic UGT1A1 activity and phase II to low levels of ligandin binding.[48] Both phases are influenced by increased enterohepatic shunting. During phase I in term infants of Western European or African descent, total bilirubin levels peak at 48 to 120 hours (most infants peak at 72 to 96 hours) at 5 to 6 mg/dL (86 to 103 μmol/L) and then decrease to less than 3 mg/dL (51 μmol/L) by day 5.[56] Infants of African descent tend to have slightly lower bilirubin levels than those of Western European descent.[81] Infants of East Asian ethnicity usually peak slightly later (72 to 120 hours) at 10 to 14 mg/dL (171 to 239 μmol/L) and fall to less than 3 mg/dL (51 μmol/L) by 7 to 10 days.[56] Levels also tend to be higher in Hispanic (primarily Mexican) and Native American infants.[81] All groups gradually fall to adult values of less than 2 mg/dL (34 μmol/L) over the first 1 to 2 weeks (phase II).

The rate of bilirubin synthesis may be slightly elevated in infants of East Asian ethnicity.[56] These infants are also more likely to have glucose-6-phosphate dehydrogenase (G6PD) deficiency. In addition, genomic polymorphisms (variations in gene sequencing) in the genes involved in bilirubin production and conjugation are seen with greater frequency.[56,130] Polymorphisms in these genes increase the risk of hyperbilirubinemia and are seen in other infants as well. For example, alterations in UGT1A1, which is involved in bilirubin conjugation, and soluble carrier organic anion transporter polypeptide (SLCO1B1), which is involved in uptake of unconjugated bilirubin by the hepatocyte, alone or in conjunction with environmental influences, can alter bilirubin clearance and increase the risk of hyperbilirubinemia.[130]

Patterns of physiologic jaundice in term breastfed infants are similar to phases in term formula-fed infants, except that the peak is higher (may be up to 7 to 14 mg/dL [119.7 to 239.4 μmol/L]) and later and phases I and II are longer (see Breastfeeding and Neonatal Jaundice). The usual mean peak levels of total serum bilirubin in breastfed infants has been reported as 8 to 9 mg/dL (137 to 16 μmol/L).[81] In breastfed infants, bilirubin levels generally decrease over 2 to 4 weeks, although it may take up to 6 weeks.[48,56,81] Maisels et al. found that 20% to 30% of breastfed newborn born at 35 or greater weeks were still jaundiced at 3 to 4 weeks of age, and of these infants, 30% to 40% had bilirubin levels of 5 mg/dL (85.5 μmol/L) or greater.[80]

Preterm infants also have two phases with a higher peak and longer phase I and II. The mean peak total bilirubin is 10 to 12 mg/dL (171 to 205 μmol/L) by day 5.[56] These patterns are only seen if early prophylactic phototherapy is not used. The greater the immaturity of the infant, the greater the alterations in phases and the greater the risk of hyperbilirubinemia. The term *physiologic jaundice* has little usefulness with preterm and especially very-low-birth-weight (VLBW) infants, because these infants are treated with phototherapy even at physiologic levels.[81]

TABLE 18-1   Factors Associated With the Development of Physiologic Jaundice

BASIS	CAUSES
INCREASED BILIRUBIN AVAILABILITY	
Increased bilirubin production	Increased red blood cells (RBCs) Decreased RBC lifespan Increased early bilirubin
Increased recirculation via enterohepatic shunting	Increased β-glucuronidase activity Reduced bacterial flora Delayed passage of meconium
DECREASED CLEARANCE OF BILIRUBIN	
Decreased clearance from plasma	Deficiency of carrier proteins
Decreased hepatic metabolism	Decreased uridine diphosphate-glucurosyltransferase (UDPGT1A1) activity

Causes of Physiologic Jaundice

Physiologic jaundice is not caused by a single factor, but rather reflects a combination of factors related to the newborn's physiologic maturity (Table 18-1 and Figure 18-2). The increased levels of circulating indirect bilirubin in newborns are related to the combination of increased bilirubin availability and decreased clearance. Phase I bilirubin elevations are primarily a result of a sixfold increase in bilirubin load, decreased bilirubin-specific hepatic UGT1A1 activity, and increased enterohepatic shunting.[56] Phase II elevations are primarily related to the continuing high bilirubin load from increased reabsorption of bilirubin by the enterohepatic shunt (see Figure 18-1), increased bilirubin production, and decreased hepatic uptake of bilirubin.[34] Table 18-2 and Figure 18-2 summarize other factors associated with the development of increased bilirubin levels in newborns.

Increased bilirubin availability results from greater bilirubin production (with more RBCs per kilogram), decreased RBC life span, and greater early bilirubin. Active recirculation of bilirubin by the enterohepatic shunt also raises serum indirect bilirubin levels (see Figure 18-1 and Box 18-1). Increased recirculation of bilirubin is promoted by reduced bacterial flora (which normally further metabolizes direct bilirubin for excretion in feces), high levels of β-glucuronidase activity (which deconjugates direct bilirubin back into indirect bilirubin), and decreased intestinal motility.[41] Concentrations of β-glucuronidase, an intestinal brush border enzyme, are 10 times higher in newborns than in adults, in whom little bilirubin is normally reabsorbed from the small intestine.[48]

The longer direct bilirubin remains in the small intestine, the greater the likelihood it will be deconjugated. Thus infants who are fed earlier (before 4 hours of age versus after 24 hours) or fed more frequently and infants with meconium staining or early passage of meconium may have a lower incidence of physiologic jaundice, although the effects of early meconium passage are probably not significant.[81] Infants with delayed passage of meconium, meconium ileus, or intestinal obstructions are more likely to develop physiologic jaundice. Recirculated bilirubin puts an additional load on an already stressed and functionally immature liver.

Clearance of bilirubin from the plasma and metabolism by the liver are impaired in newborns because of deficient ligandin (the main hepatocyte intracellular bilirubin-binding protein), reduced UGT1A1 activity, and diminished excretion by a liver overloaded with bilirubin. Levels of ligandin reach adult values by 5 days of age.[48,81]

UGT1A1 activity is 0.1% at 17 to 30 weeks' gestation and remains minimal (less than 1% of adult activity) from 30 to 40 weeks and during the first 24 hours after birth.[41,81,130] Activity of this enzyme increases rapidly after the first 24 hours because of a gradual upregulation of UGT1A1 activity. This upregulation is seen across all gestational ages.[130] Activity is lower initially in preterm than term infants; however, increases in activity after birth are related more to postbirth age than to gestational age. The increase in bilirubin levels in newborns helps induce UGT1A1 activity and bilirubin conjugation in the liver after birth.[18] UGT1A1 activity does not reach adult levels for 6 to 14 weeks.[41,56,58,130] The major bilirubin conjugate formed in newborns is monoglucuronide rather than diglucuronide, as in older individuals (see Box 18-1 on pp. 590-591). Monoglucuronide is more easily hydrolyzed to indirect bilirubin than diglucuronide, and only indirect bilirubin is reabsorbed across the intestinal mucosa via enterohepatic shunting.[34]

Hypoglycemia or hypoxemia may interfere with bilirubin conjugation. Decreased liver perfusion may impede clearance of bilirubin from plasma. Hypoxemia further reduces blood flow to the liver and alters hepatocyte function. The ability of the newborn's liver to excrete conjugated bilirubin may also be decreased. This may be critical in disorders with large bilirubin loads (e.g., severe erythroblastosis fetalis) and leads to the direct hyperbilirubinemia seen in these infants.[56,81]

Preterm infants are more likely to develop physiologic jaundice and hyperbilirubinemia than term infants. All of the factors previously described that contribute to physiologic jaundice in term infants are more prominent in preterm infants and are magnified with decreasing gestational age. For example, RBC life span is related to gestational age and may be only 35 to 50 days in an ELBW infant. The lower serum albumin levels in ELBW infants may limit extracellular binding and transport of bilirubin when concentrations are high.[18] These infants often have delayed feeding, with a low caloric intake initially and slower intestinal transit time. Feeding provides a substrate for intestinal flow and bacterial colonization. A major factor contributing to the increased risk in preterm infants is decreased UGT1A1 activity. Postnatal maturation of UGT1A1 and ligandin and canalicular transportation pathways for bile may be slower in ELBW infants.[18]

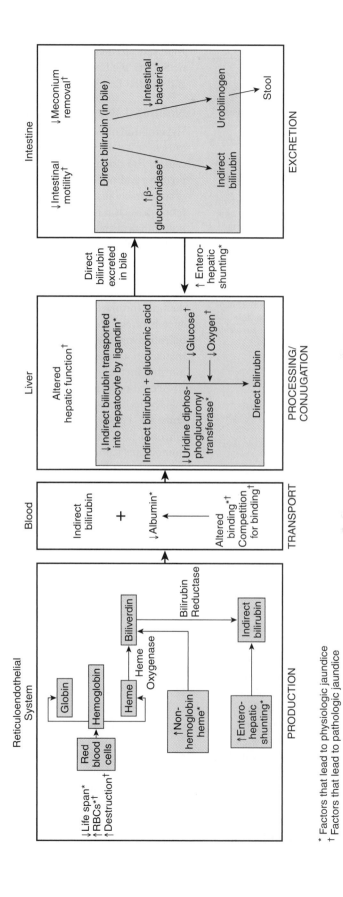

FIGURE 18-2   Basis for increased bilirubin levels in the newborn. *RBCs,* Red blood cells.

TABLE 18-2   Factors Associated With Neonatal Indirect Hyperbilirubinemia

BASIS	CAUSES
INCREASED PRODUCTION OF BILIRUBIN	
Increased hemoglobin destruction	Fetomaternal blood group incompatibility (Rh, ABO)
	Congenital red blood cell abnormalities
	Congenital enzyme deficiencies (glucose-6-phosphate dehydrogenase deficiency, galactosemia)
	Enclosed hemorrhage (e.g., cephalohematoma, bruising, intracranial bleeding)
	Sepsis
Increased amount of hemoglobin	Polycythemia (maternal-fetal or twin-twin transfusion, small for gestational age)
Increased enterohepatic circulation	Fasting or delayed initiation of feeding
	Intestinal ileus, stenosis or atresia
ALTERED CLEARANCE OF BILIRUBIN	
Alteration in UDT1A1 production or activity	Immaturity
	Metabolic/endocrine disorders (e.g., Crigler-Najjar syndromes, Gilbert syndrome, hypothyroidism, disorders of amino acid metabolism, galactosemia)
Alteration in hepatic function and perfusion (and thus conjugating ability)	Asphyxia, hypoxia, hypothermia, hypoglycemia
	Sepsis (also causes inflammation)
	Drugs and hormones (e.g., novobiocin, pregnanediol)
Hepatic obstruction (associated with direct hyperbilirubinemia)	Congenital anomalies (biliary atresia, cystic fibrosis)
	Biliary stasis (hepatitis, sepsis)
	Excessive bilirubin load (often seen with severe hemolysis)

CLINICAL IMPLICATIONS FOR NEONATAL CARE

Alteration in bilirubin metabolism is a relatively common event during the first week after birth. Neonatal jaundice accounts for the majority of hospital readmissions in the first week after birth. Neonatal jaundice results from either physiologic or pathologic causes (see Figure 18-2). Physiologic jaundice is a normal process in the first days after birth and is related to normal physiologic adaptations. Physiologic jaundice is seen up 85% of all infants.[81,132] Pathologic jaundice results from pathologic factors, such as Rh or ABO incompatibility (see Chapter 13 pp. 449-451), polycythemia, glucose-6-phosphate dehydrogenase (G6PD) deficiency, intestinal obstruction, sepsis, and other factors that alter normal bilirubin metabolism. Neonatal jaundice reflects an increase in bilirubin. At times these increases may reach levels that characterize hyperbilirubinemia. Readmission rates for treatment of jaundice have increased twofold to threefold in recent years, especially in late preterm infants born between 35 and 36⁶/₇ weeks' gestation.[10,18,81] In addition, although still rare, bilirubin encephalopathy and kernicterus continues to occur with breastfed and late preterm infants at higher risk.[18,36,50] This section addresses these issues and discusses the basis for phototherapy and other methods of managing hyperbilirubinemia. Guidelines for the management of neonatal hyperbilirubinemia are available from professional groups in several countries, including the American Academy of Pediatrics (AAP), the Canadian Pediatric Society, the United Kingdom's National Institute for Health and Clinical Excellence, and others.[5,16,26,41]

Neonatal Hyperbilirubinemia

Hyperbilirubinemia can be related to physiologic or pathologic causes or to a combination of physiologic and pathologic causes. The risk of this disorder is increased in breastfed, late preterm, and preterm infants. Neonatal hyperbilirubinemia is of concern because it may be a sign of an underlying pathologic problem, such as hemolysis or sepsis, and because of its association with acute bilirubin encephalopathy and kernicterus.

Neonatal hyperbilirubinemia is caused by increased production or decreased clearance of bilirubin (see Table 18-2 and Figure 18-2). Significant hyperbilirubinemia within the first 36 hours after birth is usually a result of increased production (primarily from hemolysis), because hepatic clearance is rarely altered enough during this period to produce bilirubin values greater than 10 mg/dL (171 μmol/L).[56,81] An increase in the hemoglobin destruction rate by 1% leads to a fourfold increase in the bilirubin production rate.[41]

According to the AAP, the major risk factors for developing severe hyperbilirubinemia in late preterm and term infants are a total serum bilirubin (TSB) or transcutaneous bilirubin (TcB) level in the high-risk zone on the bilirubin nomogram; jaundice in the first 24 hours after birth; blood group incompatibility with a positive direct Coombs test; other known hemolytic disease (e.g., G6PD deficiency); gestational age of 35 to 36 weeks; previous sibling who received phototherapy; cephalohematoma or significant bruising; East Asian ethnicity; and exclusive breastfeeding, particularly in infants with difficulties with nursing and excessive infant weight loss.[5] Any infant born prematurely is also at greater risk for hyperbilirubinemia, with the risk increasing with decreasing gestational age and the factors listed previously.

There is no consistent definition for neonatal hyperbilirubinemia; the diagnostic range varies with population characteristics and postbirth age. Maisels and Watchko defined *hyperbilirubinemia* as "TSB [total serum bilirubin] exceeds the 95th percentile for that infant's age in that population. After 96 hours, a TSB >20 mg/dL (342 μmol/L) is 'severe hyperbilirubinemia' and levels >30 mg/dL (513 μmol/L) are considered 'extreme hyperbilirubinemia.'"[81] A TSB of 8 to 10 mg/dL (136 to 171 μmol/L) in the first 24 hours is above the 95th percentile.[81] Kaplan et al. define *unconjugated (indirect) hyperbilirubinemia* in the newborn as bilirubin levels greater than 20 mg/dL (342 μmol/L) and *conjugated (direct) hyperbilirubinemia* as bilirubin levels greater than 1.5 mg/dL (26 μmol/L).[56] Bhutani et al. calculated that about 1 in 10 infants will have TSB levels equal to or greater than 17 mg/dL (290.7 μmol/L); 1 in 70 will have levels equal to or greater than 20 mg/dL (342 μmol/L); 1 in 700 will have levels equal to or greater than 25 mg/dL (425 μmol/L); and 1 in 10,000 will have levels equal to or greater than 30 mg/dL (513 μmol/L).[10] Jaundice within the first 24 hours after birth; increases of more than 0.25 mg/dL/hour (4.3 μmol/L/hour), which is equivalent to greater than 6 mg/dL/day; and jaundice associated with other abnormal findings such as feeding problems, G6PD deficiency, irritability, hepatosplenomegaly, acidosis, or metabolic abnormalities are also of concern.[5,52,56] Infants with G6PD deficiency are at high risk for both hyperbilirubinemia and kernicterus. G6PD deficiency is an inherited X-linked metabolic disorder that is one of the most common genetic diseases in the world. G6PD is an enzyme that normally protects the red blood cells (RBCs) and other cells from oxidative injury and hemolysis.[56] G6PD deficiency leads to increased heme turnover, possibly in association with UGT1A1 gene polymorphisms.[81]

Investigators have attempted to predict the risk of later significant hyperbilirubinemia in healthy term infants before early hospital discharge.[5,9,41,125] As a result hour-specific nomograms are available for determining normal and at-risk bilirubin levels (using either TSB or TcB) in infants 35 weeks' gestation or older.[5,9,27,41] For example, Bhutani and colleagues developed an hour-specific nomogram by plotting total serum bilirubin levels with age in hours to identify infants at high, intermediate, and low risk of later requiring phototherapy.[9] They reported that no infant who fell into the low-risk area of the graph later required phototherapy. This nomogram has been incorporated into the revised AAP guidelines for management of hyperbilirubinemia in newborns of 35 weeks' gestational age and older.[5] In a comparison of the predictive value of predischarge bilirubin measurement with this nomogram and clinical risk factor assessment, Keren and colleagues reported that the predischarge bilirubin measurement was more accurate in identifying infants at risk for severe hyperbilirubinemia (TSB greater than 95th percentile) and generated a wider risk stratification.[59] Several investigators have noted that the factors most predictive of readmission for phototherapy are infants with a peak TcB greater than the 75th percentile (or high-intermediate to high zone) on the nomogram, exclusive breastfeeding, and birth at less than 38 weeks' gestation.[60,77] Concerns have been raised about methodologic flaws in the development of the nomogram and the risks of false positives and, particularly, false negatives.[30] These nomograms were not developed for infants born at less than 35 weeks' gestation and are not useful in this group, because prophylactic phototherapy is often begun for VLBW and ELBW infants while bilirubin levels are in physiologic ranges. Recommendations are available for the management of bilirubin in these infants.[56,79,81]

Direct Hyperbilirubinemia

Direct or conjugated hyperbilirubinemia (obstructive jaundice), which is common in adults with jaundice, is rare in neonates. A direct bilirubin greater than 1 mg/dL (17.1 μmol/L) with TSB levels of 5 mg/dL (85.5 μmol/L) or less, or TSB levels greater than 5 mg/dL (85.5 μmol/L) with the direct bilirubin equal to 20% of the TSB, are abnormal.[5] Elevations of direct bilirubin involve cholestasis and are associated with alterations in hepatic function and interference with excretion of bilirubin into bile or obstruction of bile flow in the biliary tree. In neonates this can occur with hepatitis, severe erythroblastosis, sepsis, biliary atresia, inborn errors of metabolism (including galactosemia, α1-antitrypsin deficiency, tyrosinemia, and cystic fibrosis), or prolonged parenteral alimentation.

Breastfeeding and Neonatal Jaundice

The increased incidence of hyperbilirubinemia in the United States in recent years has been attributed primarily to the increase in breastfeeding. Most infants with hyperbilirubinemia for which no specific cause can be found are breastfed.[81] Bilirubin levels are higher in breastfed than formula-fed infants for at least the first 3 to 4 weeks.[81] Two forms or phases of neonatal jaundice are described in breastfed infants: the more common early (breastfeeding-associated) jaundice, and late (breast milk) jaundice. However, these forms overlap and may not be readily distinguishable from each other.[35,36,48,56,81]

The early-onset form, often referred to as *breastfeeding-associated jaundice,* is believed to be related primarily to the process of feeding.[34,36] A major factor leading to breastfeeding-associated jaundice is increased enterohepatic shunting caused by lower fluid and caloric intake, less frequent feedings, stooling patterns, increased β-glucuronidase activity, and decreased formation of urobilins.[36,41,78,81] Decreased caloric intake results in increased fat breakdown for energy and fatty acid production that increases intestinal fat absorption and may indirectly interfere with UGT1A1 and ligandin.[81] When fatty acids reach the liver, they may inhibit UGT1A1 activity or saturate the hepatic protein carrier system.[24] The increased absorption of fat from breast milk may also increase intestinal bilirubin absorption. Breastfed infants produce lower-weight individual stools, have a lower initial stool output, and have stools that contain less bilirubin than formula-fed infants.[41] Greater weight loss after birth and less stooling are associated with higher bilirubin production. These infants also have slower urobilinogen formation, possibly related to different intestinal colonization patterns after birth (see Chapter 13). Breastfed infants excrete less bilirubin in stools than formula-fed infants because more conjugated direct bilirubin is changed back to indirect bilirubin by β-glucuronidase, which has greater activity in breastfed infants.[36,37,41] Breastfeeding-associated jaundice is not associated with increased new bilirubin production or abnormal hepatic uptake or conjugation of bilirubin, suggesting that the most likely mechanism is increased enterohepatic shunting.[34]

Breastfed infants may also develop a later onset, prolonged hyperbilirubinemia. The late-onset form is less common (occurs in less than 1 in 200 births) and is believed to be related primarily to attributes of breast milk that interfere with normal conjugation and excretion.[34,56,67] Many of these infants also have a history of the early-onset form of jaundice. Late-onset jaundice is characterized by increasing bilirubin levels after 3 to 5 days, peaking at 5 to 10 mg/dL (86 to 171 μmol/L) by 2 weeks, followed by a slow decrease in bilirubin values to normal limits over the next 3 to 12 weeks.[56,67] These infants do not have any signs of hemolysis or abnormal liver function, and the jaundice has not been correlated with changes in weight or stool patterns.[67]

The cause of late-onset jaundice in breastfed infants is unknown but has been attributed to the presence of specific factors in breast milk that appear to be minimal or absent in colostrum but appear in transitional and mature milk, and it tends to recur with subsequent pregnancies.[34,67] Although the specific factor or factors have not been identified, these may include the following: the progesterone metabolite pregnane-$3\alpha,20\beta$-diol (which may interfere with UGT1A1 activity or release of conjugated bilirubin from the hepatocyte); increased lipoprotein lipase (bile salt-stimulated lipase) activity with subsequent release of free fatty acids in the intestines; UGT1A1 gene polymorphisms, inhibition of conjugation by the increased amounts of unsaturated fatty acids found in breast milk; and other factors in breast milk that may increase enterohepatic shunting.[34,36,56,67,81,83] No correlation was reported between bilirubin and β-glucuronidase at 3 to 6 days postpartum.[67]

Prevention of Hyperbilirubinemia in Breastfed Infants

Hyperbilirubinemia in breastfed infants may be reduced by preventive interventions. Encouraging feeding soon after delivery will increase intestinal activity and establishment of gut flora. Frequent feeding stimulates intestinal activity and meconium removal (less bilirubin for enzymes to convert back to the indirect form), reduces enterohepatic shunting, and stimulates maternal milk production.[5,56] Feeding stimulates the gastrocolonic reflex, increases intestinal motility, and stimulates meconium passage (colostrum acts as a laxative). This removes conjugated bilirubin from the small intestine, thus reducing the likelihood that this bilirubin will be deconjugated and recirculated by the enterohepatic shunt.

A critical factor in reducing the risk of jaundice in breastfed infants is enhancing breast milk intake.[5,56] Bilirubin levels in these infants tend to correlate negatively with breast milk intake; that is, as intake decreases, bilirubin levels tend to rise. Supplements should be avoided, because they can interfere with the establishment of breastfeeding.[5] If supplementation is required for medical reasons, supplementation with formula provides more calories. Supplementation of breastfeeding with water or dextrose water does not lower bilirubin levels in healthy breastfeeding infants. Supplemental feedings with dextrose water have been found to decrease breast milk intake, increase bilirubin levels, and possibly increase the risk of hyponatremia.[23,67] Dextrose water supplementation may satiate the infant but lead to inadequate caloric intake; caloric deprivation increases bilirubin levels. Use of any form of supplementation can alter intake of breast milk and establishment of the mother's milk supply (see Chapter 5) and lead to early discontinuance of breastfeeding.

An inverse relationship between the number of feedings per day and bilirubin levels has been reported.[24] Bilirubin levels were lowest in infants who were breastfed more than eight or nine times in 24 hours during the first 3 days after birth.[137] Increasing the frequency of feedings may stimulate gut motility and decrease intestinal absorption of bilirubin.[24] Current AAP recommendations are to breastfeed at least 8 to 10 times per 24 hours initially to ensure adequate milk intake.[5] Signs of inadequate milk intake include delayed meconium passage, fewer bowel movements (less than three to four stools per day by day 4), decreased urine output (less than four to six thoroughly wet diapers in 24 hours), and weight loss greater than 7%.[5,34,67]

Initial and continuing support of the mother and other family members is essential to enhance breastfeeding success.[31,67] The AAP guidelines recommend that all newborns be seen by 72 hours if discharged before 24 hours of age, at 96 hours if discharged at 24 to 47.9 hours of age, and at 120 hours if discharged at 48 to 72 hours of age, with earlier and more frequent follow-up for infants at risk for hyperbilirubinemia.[5] Some infants discharged before 48 hours may need multiple follow-up visits at 24 to 72 hours depending on their clinical status.[5]

Management of Hyperbilirubinemia in Breastfed Infants

Management of hyperbilirubinemia in breastfed infants is often challenging. Multiple issues and concerns, including maternal desire to breastfeed, advantages of breastfeeding to both mother and infant, effects on maternal-infant interaction, parental stress with the potential for bilirubin toxicity, and legal implications related to "safe" bilirubin values must be balanced.[34,51,56] This has been further complicated by the continuing reports of kernicterus (although still rare) in breastfed term and late preterm infants.[41,50,52,60,68] In the early 1990s, less aggressive treatment of hyperbilirubinemia in term infants was advocated and reflected in guidelines released by the AAP in 1994. One of the bases for these guidelines was the estimate that the risk of kernicterus in well term infants with bilirubin levels of 20 to 25 mg/dL (342 to 428 μmol/L) was lower than the risks associated with exchange transfusion.[95]

The AAP guidelines recommend that breastfeeding be continued whenever possible, but that supplementation with expressed breast milk or formula be considered if "the infant's intake is inadequate, weight loss is excessive, or the infant seems dehydrated."[5] Interruption of breastfeeding should be avoided, unless the infant develops bilirubin levels above 25 mg/dL (428 μmol/L); rather the infant should continue frequent breastfeeding (every 2 to 3 hours) while using intensive phototherapy, unless the infant's weight loss from birth is greater than 12% or there is clinical evidence of dehydration.[5,81] Amato and colleagues report no difference in the time needed to reduce bilirubin levels with jaundice managed by discontinuing breastfeeding versus the use of phototherapy and continued breastfeeding.[4] Martinez and associates compared four interventions (continue breastfeeding and observe; discontinue breastfeeding and begin formula feeding; discontinue breastfeeding, begin formula feeding, and start phototherapy; and continue breastfeeding and start phototherapy) once bilirubin levels reached 17 mg/dL (291 μmol/L).[84] They found that if an adequate dosage of phototherapy was provided, there was no significant advantage to stopping breastfeeding.[84] Lawrence and Lawrence emphasize an approach focusing on prevention and modifying factors (particularly inadequate frequency of feeding) that are associated with early-onset jaundice in breastfed infants (Box 18-2).[67] Any interruption of breastfeeding must be accompanied by parental emotional support and facilitation of breast pumping or manual expression of milk.

Measurement of Serum Bilirubin

Serum bilirubin levels are measured by laboratory and transcutaneous methods. Clinical estimations of serum bilirubin levels by the cephalopedal progression of jaundice are correlated with serum bilirubin concentrations in most but not all studies.[62,63,90] Cephalopedal progression is most useful at low bilirubin levels and is less reliable at levels greater than 12 mg/dL (205 μmol/L).[81] Knudsen suggests that the basis for this progression may be conformational changes in the bilirubin-albumin complex and in the binding affinity of bilirubin for albumin.[62,63] Indirect bilirubin leaving the reticuloendothelial system, where it is produced, binds to albumin. Initially binding affinity is lower, with less-effective binding, so bilirubin is more likely to be deposited in this area (i.e., in more proximal tissues). By the time bilirubin reaches more distal areas, it is more tightly bound and less likely to be deposited in the peripheral tissues unless bilirubin levels are high (overwhelming the available albumin-binding capacity).[62,63] This progression may also be related to decreased capillary blood flow in distal areas.[81] Several studies suggest that visual assessment may be useful for determining which infants need a transcutaneous bilirubin assessment.[17,53,61,74,104] These assessments are not predictive of who will develop severe hyperbilirubinemia; thus laboratory assessments are also necessary.[52,60]

Laboratory methods involve measurement of total and direct bilirubin and calculation of indirect values. TSB is the gold standard for assessment of neonatal jaundice.[68] Peak total bilirubin concentrations are poorly associated with development of bilirubin toxicity.[2] Plasma unbound bilirubin is a better predictor of abnormal outcomes but more difficult to measure.[2,135]

Transcutaneous bilirubinometry is an alternative method that is most appropriate for screening and monitoring healthy term infants with physiologic jaundice because it prevents repeated heel sticks. These devices work by either calculating changes in light optical density between reflected light sources or measuring the amount of light reflected from light transmitted into the skin.[27,33,68] TcB is linearly related to laboratory measurements of TSB, and levels have been reported to also correlate with TSB, including in preterm and late preterm infants.[27,29,32,41,92,121] Current TcB instruments have a correlation that is within 2 to 3 mg/dL (34.2 to 51.3 μmol/L) of TSB if the TSB is less than 15 mg/dL (356.5 μmol/L) in term and late preterm infants.[52,56] This correlation is poorer once infants are under phototherapy.[27,38,81] Some TcB units tend to overestimate bilirubin levels in infants with darker skin pigment and underestimate in infants with lighter skin pigment.[27,41,57] TcB instruments also tend to underestimate TSB at high TSB levels.[41] Across four TcB nomograms, mean TcB values at 73 to 96 hours of age were 8.6 ± 3.3 mg/dL (147.1 ± 56.4 μmol/L) with a range of 6.9 to 10.4 mg/dL (118 to 177.8 μmol/L).[25] Measurement of TcB at the sternum or intrascapular area has been reported to more closely approximate TSB than forehead measurements.[27,96] If therapy is being considered, a TSB should be obtained.[75] Universal bilirubin screening has been recommended by some, whereas others have noted the lack of evidence that this will prevent acute bilirubin encephalopathy and concerns about excessive use of phototherapy.[66,75,93,97,122,124] Implementation of universal screening has been associated with a lower incidence of hyperbilirubinemia but increased phototherapy use.[46,122,124]

Serum albumin levels and bilirubin/albumin ratios may also be measured in addition to the TSB and may be useful as additional data in those infants at risk for an exchange transfusion.[5] Lower albumin levels or low albumin binding of bilirubin suggests that these infants may be at increased risk for deposition of bilirubin in the brain. However, the bilirubin/albumin ratio does not correlate well with unbound bilirubin, and significant differences can occur among newborns.[5] Recent studies did not find that use of bilirubin/albumin ratios in preterm infants improved neurodevelopmental outcomes.[46]

Management of Neonatal Hyperbilirubinemia

Various techniques have been used to manage neonates with indirect hyperbilirubinemia. Strategies have included prevention, use of pharmacologic agents, exchange transfusion, and phototherapy. Prevention has focused on early initiation of feedings and frequent breastfeeding to decrease enterohepatic shunting, promote establishment of normal bacterial flora, and stimulate intestinal activity. Specific pharmacologic agents have been used to prevent hyperbilirubinemia or reduce bilirubin levels.

Pharmacologic Agents

Pharmacologic agents have been used in the management of hyperbilirubinemia to stimulate the induction of hepatic enzymes and carrier proteins, to interfere with heme degradation, or to bind bilirubin in the intestines to decrease enterohepatic reabsorption. Inert nonabsorbable substances such as charcoal and agar have been tried for the latter purpose with equivocal results and are not recommended.[81] Intravenous immunoglobulin has been used with infants with severe Rh and ABO incompatibility to suppress isoimmune hemolysis and decrease the number of exchange transfusions; however, a recent systematic review found an unclear benefit.[5,48,69] Phenobarbital has also been used, although generally only with some rare forms of congenital hyperbilirubinemia.[56] Phenobarbital stimulates activity and concentrations of UGT1A1 and ligandin and may increase the number of bilirubin-binding sites.[81] β-glucuronidase inhibitors, such as L-aspartic acid and enzymatically hydrolyzed casein, and other nonabsorbable substances that bind bilirubin in the intestines (and thus possibly reduce enterohepatic shunting) have also been examined, but further investigation is needed.[37,56] Kaplan suggests that frequent breastfeeding may be as effective as these interventions.[56]

Prevention of hyperbilirubinemia with the use of synthetic metalloprotoporphyrins has also been investigated.[48,118,119] These substances are synthetic heme analogs. Protoporphyrin has been shown to be an effective competitive inhibitor of heme oxygenase, the enzyme necessary for catabolism of heme to biliverdin (see Figure 18-1), and the rate-limiting step in the formation of bilirubin. With use of these substances, the heme that is prevented from being catabolized does not accumulate but is excreted intact in bile.[48] In studies with both term and preterm infants, and in infants with and without hemolytic diseases, tin-protoporphyrin (Sn-PP) and tin-mesoporphyrin (Sn-MP) have decreased serum bilirubin levels and the need for phototherapy.[12,20,48,118,119] Use of phototherapy after the administration of Sn-PP has been associated with phototoxic erythema. Sn-MP is a less toxic variant, especially when used in conjunction with phototherapy. Studies continue with use of Sn-MP and other metalloprotoporphyrins such as chromium mesoporphyrin and zinc deuteropophyrin.[12,20,56] Long-term outcomes have not been established.

Exchange Transfusion

Exchange transfusions are used in the management of indirect hyperbilirubinemia and hemolytic disease of the newborn. An exchange transfusion removes antibody-coated blood cells and bilirubin and helps to correct the anemia associated with hemolytic disease. A double volume exchange replaces 85% of the circulating RBC volume and reduces the bilirubin by approximately 45% to 60%.[81] After the exchange, bilirubin rebounds by up to 60% to 80% of preexchange values as bilirubin diffuses into the vascular space from extravascular tissues.[81] The frequency of exchange transfusions has been significantly reduced with the availability of Rho(D) immune globulin (see pp. 449-450) and phototherapy.

Phototherapy

Phototherapy was first introduced in 1958 and has been used extensively and effectively in treating neonatal indirect hyperbilirubinemia since the late 1960s.[21] Multiple studies have documented the effectiveness of phototherapy in preventing and treating neonatal hyperbilirubinemia.[11,81,93] Prophylactic phototherapy in preterm infants lowers bilirubin concentrations and may reduce the risk of exchange transfusion and later hearing loss, motor dysfunction, and neurodevelopmental impairment.[52,88] Consensus-based and other protocols are available to guide the initiation of phototherapy in healthy term and late preterm infants (greater than or equal to 35 weeks' gestational age) and in preterm infants.[5,16,26,56,79,81,98]

Physics of Phototherapy. Absorbance of light by unconjugated bilirubin is strongest in the blue light spectrum at about 460-nm wavelength.[106] Absorption of a photon of light excites the bilirubin molecule with the accumulation of excess energy. To lose this excess energy, the bilirubin molecule can reemit the light photon (rare), it can use the excess energy to produce heat (accounts for about 80% of the excess energy), or the energy can alter the bilirubin molecule (about 20% of the excess energy) by photochemical reactions.[18] These photochemical reactions are photoisomerization and photooxidization. Indirect bilirubin is composed of four pyrrole rings. Photoisomerization involves conversion of poorly soluble indirect bilirubin into water-soluble reversible configurational (rearrangement of chemical groups in the molecule by temporarily disrupting the chemical bonds between carbon atoms in the molecule, resulting in a 180-degree rotation of the pyrrole rings) or irreversible structural (rearrangement of the atoms) photoisomers (i.e., photobilirubin, lumirubin).[11,48,56,106,126] The photoisomers can be excreted into bile without conjugation. Because these photoisomers are polar and need transporters to reach neurons, they may be less likely to cross the blood-brain barrier than unconjugated bilirubin.[106] Decomposition of bilirubin under phototherapy occurs primarily in the superficial capillaries and in interstitial spaces. Formation of configurational isomers is rapid, but these isomers are excreted slowly in bile, with a serum half-life of 12 to 21 hours.[13,48,87,91] By 6 to 12 hours after conventional phototherapy has been initiated, 20% of TSB has been converted to configurational isomers.[13] These isomers are unstable and may be changed back into unconjugated bilirubin in the intestines and recirculated via enterohepatic shunting.

Lumirubin, a structural nonreversible isomer, is formed at a slower rate but is excreted in bile more rapidly, with a serum half-life of 2 hours. Lumirubin is the major pathway through which bilirubin is eliminated during phototherapy. Lumirubin accounts for 2% to 6% of the TSB under steady-state conditions during phototherapy.[11,13,48,106,126] There is a dose-response relationship between lumirubin formation and phototherapy irradiance.[48] Formation of lumirubin is irreversible; it is excreted in bile or, to a lesser extent, in urine. Excretion of these isomers increases bile flow, which may stimulate intestinal activity and more rapid removal of bilirubin. As a result, phototherapy is often more effective in infants being fed and less effective in infants who are not being fed or infants with bowel obstruction.

Photooxidization has a minor role in elimination of bilirubin with phototherapy.[13,56] In this process the bilirubin molecule absorbs light energy from the phototherapy lights. Some of this energy is transferred to oxygen, leading to the formation of a highly reactive oxygen molecule (singlet oxygen). This molecule aids in oxidation and breakdown of bilirubin into water-soluble breakdown products (e.g., mono-pyrroles, dipyrroles) that are excreted primarily in urine.

Side Effects of Phototherapy. Concerns have been raised about the safety of phototherapy and possible short-term and long-term effects. These concerns focus on complications of photoisomerization and photooxidization; long-term concerns focus on irradiation damage, retinal damage (eye protection is always needed), and neurodevelopmental issues.[5,56] However, investigations have generally failed to demonstrate any significant long-term problems with phototherapy usage in human infants, and side effects are usually transient.[5,47,56] Transient effects include thermal and metabolic changes, hemodynamic changes, increased insensible water loss (IWL) and stool water loss, altered physiologic function and weight gain, skin and ocular effects, behavioral alterations, and hormonal changes (Table 18-3).[1,37,47,81] IWL may increase up to

TABLE 18-3   Side Effects of Phototherapy

SIDE EFFECT	SPECIFIC CHANGES	IMPLICATIONS
Thermal and other metabolic changes	Increased environmental and body temperature Increased oxygen consumption Increased respiratory rate Increased skin blood flow	Influenced by maturity, caloric intake (energy to respond to thermal changes), adequacy of heat dissipation from phototherapy unit, distance of unit from infant and incubator hood (related to space for air flow and radiant heat loss), use of servocontrol
Cardiovascular changes	Transient changes in cardiac output and decrease in left ventricular output	Reopening of ductus arteriosus, possibly related to photorelaxation; usually not hemodynamically significant Hemodynamic changes seen primarily in the first 12 hours of phototherapy use; after that, return to previous levels or higher
Fluid status	Increased peripheral blood flow Increased insensible water loss	Increases fluid loss May alter uptake of intramuscular medications Related to increases in evaporative water loss, metabolic rate, and possibly respiratory rate Influenced by environment (e.g., air flow, humidity, temperature); characteristics of phototherapy unit (e.g., heat dissipation, distance from infant); ambient temperature alteration; infant alterations in skin and core temperature, heart rate, respiratory rate, metabolic rate, caloric intake; type of bed (increased with radiant warmer and incubator)
Gastrointestinal function	Increased number, frequency of stools Watery, greenish brown stools Decreased time for intestinal transit Decreased absorption; retention of nitrogen, water, electrolytes Altered lactose activity, riboflavin	May be related to increased bile flow, which stimulates gastrointestinal activity Increases stool water loss Increases stool water loss and risk of dehydration Transient alterations in fluids and electrolytes Temporary lactose intolerance with decreased lactase at epithelial brush border and increased frequency and water content of stools
Altered activity	Lethargy or irritability Decreased eagerness to feed	May affect parent-infant interaction May alter fluid and caloric intake
Altered weight gain	Decreased initially but generally catches up in 2–4 weeks	Resulting from poor feeding and increased gastrointestinal losses
Ocular effects	Not documented in humans, but continued concerns about effects of light versus effect of eye patches	Lack of appropriate sensory input and stimulation Increased risk of infection, corneal abrasion, and increased intracranial pressure (if too tight) from eye patches
Skin changes	Tanning Rashes Burns Bronze baby syndrome	Related to induction of melanin synthesis or dispersion by ultraviolet light Resulting from injury to skin mast cells with release of histamine; erythema from ultraviolet light From excessive exposure to short-wave emissions from fluorescent light Result of interaction of phototherapy and cholestasis jaundice, producing a brown pigment (bilifuscin) that stains the skin; reversible change that may take months to resolve
Endocrine changes	Alterations in serum gonadotropins (increased luteinizing hormone and follicle-stimulating hormone)	Significance unclear
Hematologic changes	Increased rate of platelet turnover Injury to circulating red blood cells with decreased potassium and increased adenosine triphosphate activity	May be a problem in infants with low platelets and sepsis May lead to hemolysis, increased energy needs
Psychobehavioral concerns	Isolation or lack of usual sensory experiences, including visual deprivation Alteration in state organization and neurobehavioral organization	Effects can be mediated by provision of appropriate nursing care May interfere with parent-infant interaction and increase parental stress May also affect circadian rhythms (unclear)

25%, increasing the needs for fluids and monitoring. Compared to other methods, IWL is decreased with light-emitting diode (LED) units.[56] Some infants with an elevated direct bilirubin and cholestasis develop bronze baby syndrome, which is characterized by a dark gray-brown discoloration of the skin, serum, and urine. This syndrome may be related to retention of bile pigments with accumulation of porphyrins and other metabolites secondary to impaired bile excretion resulting from cholestasis.[5,56]

Some studies have reported evidence of deoxyribonucleic acid (DNA) damage, changes in cytokine levels, and oxidative stress with the use of phototherapy.[41] No increased risk of later neurodevelopmental problems is linked to phototherapy use, and improved outcomes have been reported in preterm infants.[6,45,123] However, a small increase in mortality has been reported in ELBW infants treated with aggressive phototherapy (possibly because of deeper light penetration through the thin skin of these infants, causing cell membrane oxidative injury).[6,45,88,123]

Psychobehavioral concerns associated with the use of phototherapy include the potential effect of isolation and the lack of usual sensory experiences, behavioral and activity changes (including lethargy, irritability, and altered feeding behavior), and alterations in state organization and biologic rhythms as well as effects of parental stress (see Table 18-3). These concerns may influence parental perceptions of their infant and early parent-infant interactions.

Methods of Providing Phototherapy. Phototherapy can be provided using a bank of fluorescent lights, tungsten-halogen or quartz halide spotlights, high-intensity blue gallium nitride LEDs, bilirubin blankets, or a bassinet system that provides simultaneous phototherapy above and below the infant.[56,81,125] A disadvantage of bilirubin blankets is lower spectral power because of the small surface area, making them less useful in treating infants with severe hyperbilirubinemia, unless used in conjunction with overhead bililights to provide intensive phototherapy. Filtered sunlight (not recommended by AAP), being careful to avoid sunburn, has been used effectively to provide phototherapy in resource-limited countries.[65,115,116]

Plexiglas covering lights and in an incubator hood protects against ultraviolet irradiation.[56] Tungsten-halogen spotlights cover a smaller infant surface area; therefore they also provide less spectral power than fluorescent bank lights.[81] High-intensity blue gallium nitride LEDs produce less ultraviolet light, infrared radiation, and heat, and the amount of blue-green light can be customized.[11,56,64,127] Because these units generate little heat, the unit can be placed a shorter distance from the infant to deliver high irradiances, enhancing lumirubin formation.[56,127] Use of broad-spectrum LED phototherapy in term and late preterm infants with nonhemolytic hyperbilirubinemia reduced duration of phototherapy, possibly because of the different peak light emissions.[101] An examination of different phototherapy devices with ELBW infants found that LED lights achieved the highest initial reduction in TSB and were similar to spotlights on other measures.[89]

An issue in caring for infants under phototherapy is whether to turn off the "lights" or remove the infant from under them during feeding and other caregiving. The benefits to both the infant and the parents of removing the eye shields and holding the infant during feeding seem to outweigh concerns regarding the effectiveness of bilirubin reduction in most situations.[5] The most rapid catabolism of bilirubin appears to take place within the first few hours after the start of each phototherapy period. It takes bilirubin about 3 hours to return to the skin after removal of photoisomers.[48] Thus for infants with mild to moderate hyperbilirubinemia, the irradiance, area of skin exposed, and initial effects of phototherapy on bilirubin in the skin seem to have more influence than whether the infant is removed for short periods of feeding or holding.[18,81] A recent study found that in term and late preterm infants with nonhemolytic anemia, intermittent phototherapy was as effective as continuous exposure.[108] Intensive phototherapy should be used continuously until TSB levels decrease.[81] A postphototherapy bilirubin rebound has been reported, particularly in infants who are preterm, have a positive direct Coombs test, have phototherapy initiated in the first few days after birth, or are under phototherapy for less than 72 hours.[56] Alternating positions from supine to prone while under phototherapy has not been reported to affect the pattern of decreased TSB.[28]

Effective phototherapy requires sufficient illumination over an adequate area of exposed skin at a sufficiently short distance to produce the desired effect of light on bilirubin molecules.[5,56] Therefore the effectiveness of phototherapy is influenced by the spectrum of light delivered by the phototherapy unit, intensity of the energy output (power output) or irradiance, peak wavelength of the light delivered, the surface area of the infant exposed to the light, and the transmission of the light through the infant's skin.[6,11,41,81,106] The surface area of exposure can be increased with the use of intensive phototherapy.

Irradiance is the radiant power of light on a surface per unit of surface area ($\mu W/cm^2/nm$). Irradiance is directly related to the distance of the light source from the infant.[81] Spectral irradiance—the irradiance of the light source (radiant power per unit area) within the therapeutic wavelength of maximum light absorbance by the bilirubin molecule (425 to 550 nm)—not the intensity (i.e., illumination or brightness)—determines effectiveness.[81] Maximal absorbance of albumin-bound bilirubin is about 460-nm wavelength; for unbound bilirubin it is 440-nm wavelength.[56] The intensity of the light is inversely related to the distance between the light source and the skin surface.[5] There is a significant linear relationship between the spectral irradiance received by the infant and the decrease in serum bilirubin levels over a 24-hour period.[5,43,81]

Phototherapy units vary in effectiveness, and light emission may decrease over time. Irradiance levels can be monitored with a radiometer using the instructions in equipment manuals or unit protocol. The radiometer has a wide bandwidth so the effective irradiance of the phototherapy unit (as amount of blue light) can be measured. Measurement is in $\mu W/cm^2/nm$ and evaluates the spectral irradiance. A spectral irradiance of 6 $\mu W/cm^2/nm$ in the 425- to 475-nm waveband is sufficient for production of configurational isomers; however, for production of the structural isomer lumirubin, a higher spectral irradiance of 8 to 10 $\mu W/cm^2/nm$ is required.[5,18] A spectral radiance of 10 $\mu W/cm^2/nm$ should reduce the TSB 20% to 50% during the first 24 hours of therapy.[106] Intensive phototherapy requires a greater spectral irradiance.[5,11,56] When comparing different devices, spectral power may be a more useful measure, because it measures the average spectral irradiance across the skin surface area of the infant.[81]

For phototherapy to be effective, light photons must penetrate the skin and be absorbed by bilirubin molecules. Only certain wavelengths are absorbed by bilirubin; longer waves penetrate deeper into the skin. Light wavelengths in the blue-green spectrum (425 to 550 nm) are most effective in reducing bilirubin levels. Daylight white, blue, green, and special blue (super blue) fluorescent bulbs have been used in conventional phototherapy devices. Special blue (narrow spectrum) bulbs are the most effective because they provide more irradiance at 450 nm (maximal blue wavelength absorbance).[81] Green light favors formation of lumirubin, and its longer waves penetrate farther into the skin.[48]

Intensive phototherapy is used for infants with severe hyperbilirubinemia to produce irradiance in the 430- to 490-nm wavelength with an irradiance of 30 $\mu W/cm^2/nm$ or more.[5,11,41] Rapid formation of bilirubin photoisomeres has been reported beginning early in the use of intensive phototherapy.[40] By using multiple (fluorescent or halogen) phototherapy units or combining overhead phototherapy with bilirubin LED blankets or using special blue lights on an uninterrupted schedule, over as much of the infant's body as possible, the intensity and thus effectiveness of phototherapy can be increased.[56,81] Simultaneous use of overhead phototherapy and bilirubin blankets increases the surface area exposed to light and spectral irradiance, which can also increase effectiveness. Compared with single phototherapy, double phototherapy has been reported to be twice as effective in preterm infants and 50% more effective in term infants.[109] Exposure can be increased by using a reflective surface (such as a white sheet) around the incubator or bassinet or two to three LED blankets to cover more surface area.[56,81] The spectral irradiance can also be increased by placing the lights at the minimum safe distance from the infant's surface.[56] Care must be taken to keep all phototherapy lights, halogen lights in particular, at the manufacturer's recommended distance from the infant's skin, because these lights can cause burns if positioned too close.[48,81]

Competition for Albumin Binding

Most indirect bilirubin is transported in plasma bound to albumin. Two terms used to describe albumin binding are *capacity* and *affinity*. Each molecule of albumin has a certain number of binding sites available (the binding capacity). The tightness by which bilirubin is bound to sites available for binding is the affinity. Avidity increases with increasing plasma albumin concentration as well as the ability of the albumin to bind bilirubin.[2]

Each molecule of albumin can bind at least two molecules of bilirubin, with the first molecule bound more tightly.[56] Binding sites may be primary (tight or high affinity) or secondary (weak affinity). Each albumin molecule has one primary binding site and one or more secondary sites. If the primary site is saturated, there is a rapid increase in loosely bound or free bilirubin.[81] Albumin-binding capacity is lower in neonates because of lower albumin levels and decreased albumin-binding capacities.[3,56] Albumin-binding capacity increases with both gestational and postnatal age and is impaired in sick infants.[8,131] Unbound bilirubin can leave the vascular system and enter the skin, brain, and other organs. Albumin-bound bilirubin generally does not enter the brain if the blood-brain barrier is intact.[106] The unbound fragment of bilirubin is believed to be more closely associated with bilirubin levels in the central nervous system and risk of bilirubin encephalopathy than TSB.[56,134] An infant with a greater binding capacity may have a greater TSB but lower risk of toxicity, because more of the bilirubin is bound to albumin.[2] Various techniques have been developed to measure albumin binding of bilirubin, but to date none are currently used for widespread clinical management because of issues with either application or interpretation.[18,56,81,87]

Many substances can influence bilirubin binding to albumin.[8] Competing substances easily displace bilirubin bound to secondary sites. Drugs such as sulfisoxazole and other sulfonamides, salicylate, chlorothiazide, ceftriaxone, cefmetazole, ibuprofen, certain x-ray contrast substances, and benzyl alcohol and its derivatives (a preservative that has been used in some multiple-injection vials) may displace bilirubin.[18,48,56] Combinations of drugs may exacerbate these effects. Other drugs may alter brain-bilirubin uptake but not affect albumin-bilirubin binding.[81] Bilirubin also displaces some drugs (including ampicillin, phenobarbital, and phenytoin) from albumin (see Chapter 7).

Albumin binding of bilirubin can be altered by pathologic events. Plasma free fatty acids compete with bilirubin for albumin-binding sites.[48] Hypothermia increases metabolism and catabolism of fatty acids, which may displace bilirubin from albumin. However, the risk is minimal if molar concentrations of free fatty acids to albumin are less than 4:1.[48] Fatty acids are also elevated with sepsis and hypoxemia.[56,131] Although concerns have been raised about risks with the use of emulsified lipid solutions (e.g., Intralipid) in neonates, dosages of 2 to 3 g/kg every 15 hours produce fatty acid to albumin ratios of only 0.1 to 1.8.[81] ELBW infants with lipid infusions of 3 g/kg/day may have elevated unbound free fatty acid levels.[44] The amount of unbound indirect bilirubin may also be increased if there is more bilirubin than available albumin because of excess production of bilirubin or decreased albumin (e.g., with malnourishment). Serum pH per se may not alter binding but may influence deposition of unbound bilirubin in the central nervous system.[81,106] Thus there may be an advantage to monitoring bilirubin/albumin ratios as well as TSB levels in determining the need for exchange transfusions.[5]

Acute Bilirubin Encephalopathy and Kernicterus

Development of acute bilirubin encephalopathy and kernicterus is a concern for any infant with elevated bilirubin levels. These complications, although rare, still occur.[2,54,76,78] Early discharge, breastfeeding, and lack of adequate early follow-up may increase the risk.[2,19,76,78] Other infants at higher risk are late preterm infants, other preterm infants, male infants, and infants with low albumin levels and other factors that alter the blood-brain barrier, such as asphyxia, hypoxia, infection, drugs, and hypothermia.[5,18,75,76,126] An incidence of 0.4 to 2.7 cases per 100,00 live births has been reported in North American and Europe, with a higher incidence in some other countries.[132]

Acute bilirubin encephalopathy refers to early, acute clinical central nervous system symptoms of bilirubin toxicity, whereas kernicterus (or chronic bilirubin encephalopathy) refers to the chronic, permanent changes to the brain secondary to deposition of bilirubin in brain cells, with yellow staining and neuronal necrosis.[48,50,52,76,113] Another term used is *bilirubin-induced neurologic dysfunction (BIND)*, characterized by disturbances in sensorimotor integration and processing, coordination, and muscle tone.[41,71,112,113] The effects of bilirubin on the brain are influenced by the characteristics of the developing brain in interaction with the duration and level of brain exposure to unbound bilirubin.[132] The risk of neurotoxicity is also related to blood pH, albumin-binding capacity, and blood-brain barrier permeability; comorbidities such as infection, hemolysis, and hypoxic-ischemic injury may increase the risk.[5,41,47,75,112,132]

Early signs of acute bilirubin encephalopathy, which is reversible in early stages, include progressive lethargy, poor feeding, vomiting, temperature instability, hypotonia, alternating hypotonia and hypertonia of the extensor muscles, and a high-pitched cry.[87,113] Many infants, especially VLBW infants, are asymptomatic or have subtle manifestations in the neonatal period.[113,128] Signs of kernicterus include ataxia, choreoathetosis, opisthotonos, extrapyramidal disturbances, auditory abnormalities with hearing loss, oculomotor paresis, dental enamel hypoplasia of the primary teeth, seizures, and developmental and motor abnormalities. The neurotoxic effects of bilirubin are exacerbated by other pathologic conditions such as hypoxia, asphyxia, and hypercapnia.[41,48,81,113,132]

Bilirubin has a high affinity for phospholipids in cell membranes.[18] Although the specific effects of bilirubin on the brain are still unclear, unbound bilirubin uncouples oxidative phosphorylation in the mitochondria, interfering with cellular respiration; blocking adenosine triphosphate (ATP) production; inhibiting cellular enzymes; altering cerebral glucose metabolism, water and electrolyte transport, and protein synthesis; and damaging or interfering with DNA.[18,48,56,81,106,113,132] Damage from the resulting increased neural excitotoxicity, oxidative stress, lipid peroxidation, mitochondrial energy failure, and increased intracellular calcium leads to activation of proteolytic enzymes, microglia and astrocytes, neural inflammation, and apoptosis.[41,81,132] Areas of the brain most often affected include the basal ganglia, brainstem auditory pathways, and oculomotor nuclei. The reason for the increased risk in these area may be related to increased blood flow and metabolic activity in these areas.[48] Bilirubin toxicity may be prevented in individual cells by specific transporter proteins (such as p-glycoprotein) that maintain intracellular bilirubin levels at nontoxic levels and the presence of bilirubin metabolizing enzymes.[94,132] Genetic differences in the expression and function of these proteins might lead to differences in susceptibility to the effects of unbound bilirubin and risk of kernicterus.[129,130,132]

For bilirubin to pass into neural tissue, it must cross the blood-brain barrier.[14] The blood-brain barrier has tight junctions between endothelial cells of the cerebral blood vessels. These junctions are permeable to lipid-soluble substances but usually are impermeable to water-soluble substances, proteins, and other large molecules (see Chapter 15).[48] Unbound (free) indirect bilirubin crosses the blood-brain barrier in both directions, although its passage is slowed by this barrier. Factors that influence the passage of bilirubin include the amount of free bilirubin, blood flow, the bilirubin-albumin dissociation rate, transit time in the capillary bed, permeability and surface area of the capillary epithelium, and perhaps energy-dependent and multidrug-resistant transporters such as P-glycoprotein.[14] Because indirect bilirubin is fat soluble, at high levels it accumulates in the brain, especially in the basal ganglia and in other areas with a high lipid content. The intact blood-brain barrier is normally impermeable to albumin-bound bilirubin.[14,52] However, if the blood-brain barrier is damaged, reversible alterations ("openings") in the blood-brain barrier (caused by infection, dehydration, hyperosmolality, severe respiratory acidosis, hypoxemia, or other injury) allow entry of albumin-bound bilirubin as well as increased movement of unbound bilirubin.[14,18,52,81,134]

The critical level of bilirubin beyond which brain damage occurs is not certain.[56] Most healthy term and late preterm infants with kernicterus in the recent resurgence have had bilirubin levels greater than 30 mg/dL (513 μmol/L).[81] Most infants with kernicterus are term or late preterm infants. Kernicterus is rarer in preterm infants, possibly related to early prophylactic treatment, but the risk is increased by comorbidities such as hypoalbuminemia, infection, inflammation, and central nervous system insults.[55,133] Ip and colleagues examined reports of outcomes of infants with kernicterus over 30 years and concluded that "kernicterus, although infrequent, has at least 10% mortality and at least 70% long-term morbidity. It is evident that the preponderance of cases of kernicterus occurred in infants with bilirubin levels higher than 20 mg/dL (342 μmol/L)."[47]

Reanalysis of data from the Collaborative Perinatal Project as well as follow-up studies of bilirubin in healthy term infants shows no consistent association between bilirubin levels, hearing loss, and neurologic abnormalities.[41,47,81,99] Low bilirubin values are not safe for all infants, because pathologic changes associated with bilirubin encephalopathy have been clearly demonstrated on autopsy at much lower values.[41,81,131] Factors associated with greater risk for developing kernicterus at lower bilirubin levels are prematurity, respiratory distress syndrome, G6PD deficiency, hypoxia, and acidosis.[5,18,75] However, there has not been a consistent pattern of hazardous bilirubin levels related to birth weight or gestational age with low-bilirubin-level kernicterus, nor have serum bilirubin concentrations or treatment been significant independent variables affecting long-term neurodevelopmental outcome.[18,41,70,88,131] As a group, peak bilirubin levels in VLBW infants are associated with an increased risk of hearing loss, altered psychomotor development, and possibly neurodevelopmental problems, although these findings are confounded by many comorbidities in this group of infants.[41,70,81,88,131]

MATURATIONAL CHANGES DURING INFANCY AND CHILDHOOD

The bilirubin load tends to remain higher in infants for 3 to 6 weeks after birth. In older children and adults, visible jaundice may be noticed at bilirubin levels as low as 2 mg/dL (34.2 μmol/L). Bilirubin-specific UGT1A1 activity increases to adult values by 3 months of age.[56] Plasma levels of indirect bilirubin reach adult values by 2 to 4 weeks after birth in most healthy infants.[18] δ-bilirubin, absent in the first 2 weeks, is seen in older neonates and children and is increased in children with congenital hyperbilirubinemia associated with liver problems.[56]

SUMMARY

Alterations in bilirubin metabolism that occur with birth result in one of the more common problems seen in the neonate: physiologic jaundice. These changes also interact with pathologic factors in the development of hyperbilirubinemia. Hyperbilirubinemia is of concern because it may be a sign of underlying pathologic processes, such as hemolysis or sepsis, and may lead to adverse consequences—namely, kernicterus. Therefore it is essential for caregivers to appreciate the processes involved in bilirubin metabolism and its maturation, to understand the basis for physiologic jaundice and hyperbilirubinemia, and to recognize infants at risk for these disorders. Clinical recommendations are summarized in Box 18-3.

BOX 18-3   Recommendations for Clinical Practice Related to Bilirubin Metabolism in Neonates

Know the usual cord blood values for serum bilirubin (p. 592).

Know the usual patterns for serum bilirubin in term and preterm neonates and for breastfed infants (p. 593).

Recognize infants at risk for physiologic jaundice (pp. 593-595, Figure 18-2, and Table 18-1).

Monitor fluid intake and stooling patterns (pp. 594, 598).

Assess and monitor infants at risk for physiologic jaundice (pp. 593-596).

Recognize infants at risk for hyperbilirubinemia (pp. 596-597 and Table 18-2).

Know the substances and pathophysiologic events that may compete with bilirubin for albumin-binding sites and monitor the status of exposed infants (pp. 603-604).

Counsel and support the family of a jaundiced infant (p. 602 and Table 18-3).

Monitor breastfed infants for early and late hyperbilirubinemia (pp. 597-599).

Institute interventions to prevent early-onset jaundice in breastfed infants (pp. 598-599 and Box 18-2).

Counsel and support parents of a jaundiced breastfed infant (pp. 598-599).

Teach parents to monitor for hyperbilirubinemia and the importance of health care after early hospital discharge (pp. 598-599).

Plan with parents of term newborns for follow-up care with the primary care provider after discharge (pp. 596-598).

Assess and monitor infants at risk for hyperbilirubinemia (pp. 596-597 and Table 18-2).

Know the methods of monitoring serum bilirubin levels and factors that can alter the accuracy of measurement (p. 599).

Monitor infants during and after exchange transfusion for alterations in fluid, electrolyte, and acid-base status (p. 600).

Recognize and monitor for physiologic and psychobehavioral side effects associated with phototherapy (pp. 601-602 and Table 18-3).

Provide a safe environment for an infant under phototherapy (pp. 600-603 and Table 18-3).

Recognize infants at risk for bilirubin encephalopathy and kernicterus (pp. 604-605).

Monitor for signs of bilirubin encephalopathy and kernicterus (pp. 604-605).

References

1. Abrol, P., & Sankarasubramanian, R. (1998). Effect of phototherapy on behavior of jaundiced neonates. *Indian J Pediatr, 65,* 603.

2. Ahlfors, C. E., (2010). Predicting bilirubin neurotoxicity in jaundiced newborns. *Curr Opin Pediatr, 22,* 129.

3. Ahlfors, C. E., & Parker, A. E. (2010). Bilirubin binding contributes to the increase in total bilirubin concentration in newborns with jaundice. *Pediatrics, 126,* e639.

4. Amato, M., Howald, H., & van Murah, G. (1985). Interruption of breastfeeding versus phototherapy as treatment of hyperbilirubinemia in full term infants. *Helv Paediatr Acta, 40,* 127.

5. American Academy of Pediatrics, Subcommittee on Hyperbilirubinemia. (2004). Management of hyperbilirubinemia in the newborn infant 35 or more weeks of gestation. *Pediatrics, 114,* 297.

6. Arnold C., Pedroza C., & Tyson J. E. (2014). Phototherapy in ELBW newborns: does it work? Is it safe? The evidence from randomized clinical trials. *Semin Perinatol, 38,* 452.

7. Bacq, Y., et al. (1996). Liver function tests in normal pregnancy: a prospective study of 103 pregnant women and 103 matched controls. *Hepatology, 23,* 1030.

8. Bender, G. J., Cashore, W. J., & Oh, W. (2007). Ontogeny of bilirubin-binding capacity and the effect of clinical status in premature infants born at less than 1300 grams. *Pediatrics, 120,* 1067.

9. Bhutani, V. K., Johnson, L., & Silveri, E. M. (1999). Predictive ability of a predischarge hour-specific serum bilirubin for subsequent significant hyperbilirubinemia in healthy term and near-term newborns. *Pediatrics, 103,* 6.

10. Bhutani, V. K., et al. (2004). Kernicterus: epidemiological strategies for its prevention through systems-based approaches. *J Perinatol, 24,* 650.

11. Bhutani, V. K., Committee on Fetus and Newborn & American Academy of Pediatrics. (2011). Phototherapy to prevent severe neonatal hyperbilirubinemia in the newborn infant 35 or more weeks of gestation. *Pediatrics, 128,* 1046.

12. Bhutani, V. K., et al. (2016). Clinical trial of tin mesoporphyrin to prevent neonatal hyperbilirubinemia. *J Perinatol. 36,* 533.

13. Bhutani V. K., & Lamola, A. A. (2017). Mechanistic actions of phototherapy for neonatal hyperbilirubinemia. In R. A. Polin, et al. (Eds.), *Fetal and neonatal physiology* (5th ed.). Philadelphia: Saunders.

14. Bratlid, D. (1990). How bilirubin gets into the brain. *Clin Perinatol, 17,* 449.

15. Breslin, E., Kaufmann, A., & Quenby, S. (2013). Bilirubin influences the clinical presentation of pre-eclampsia. *Eur J Obstet Gynecol Reprod Biol, 170,* 111.

16. Canadian Paediatric Society, Fetus and Newborn Committee. (2007). Guidelines for detection, management and prevention of hyperbilirubinemia in term and late preterm newborn infants (35 or more weeks' gestation). *Paediatr Child Health, 12,* 1B (guidelines reaffirmed 2/2016).

17. Carceller-Blanchard, A., Cousineau, J., & Delvin, E. E. (2009). Point of care testing: transcutaneous bilirubinometry in neonates. *Clin Biochem, 42,* 143.

18. Cashore, W. J. (2017). Neonatal bilirubin metabolism. In R. A. Polin, et al. (Eds.), *Fetal and neonatal physiology* (5th ed.). Philadelphia: Saunders.

19. Centers for Disease Control and Prevention. (2001). Kernicterus in full-term infants—United States, 1994-1998. *JAMA, 18,* 299.

20. Cohen, R. S., Wong, R. J., & Stevenson, D. K. (2010). Understanding neonatal jaundice: a perspective on causation. *Pediatr Neonatol, 51,* 143.

21. Cremer, R. J., Perryman, P. W., & Richards, D. H. (1958). Influence of light on the hyperbilirubinemia of infants. *Lancet, 1,* 1094.

22. Cunningham F. G., et al. (2014). *Williams obstetrics* (24th ed.). New York: McGraw-Hill.

23. De Carvalho, M., Holl, M., & Harvey, D. (1981). Effects of water supplementation on physiological jaundice in breastfed babies. *Am J Dis Child, 56,* 568.

24. De Carvalho, M., Klaus, M., & Merkatz, R. B. (1982). Frequency of breast-feeding and serum bilirubin concentration. *Am J Dis Child, 136,* 737.

25. De Luca, D., et al. (2009). Transcutaneous bilirubin nomograms: a systematic review of population differences and analysis of bilirubin kinetics. *Arch Pediatr Adolesc Med, 163,* 1054.

26. De Luca, D. (2010). NICE guidelines on neonatal jaundice: at risk of being too nice. *Lancet, 376,* 771.

27. De Luca, D., Jackson, G. L., & Engle, W. D. (2013). *Transcutaneous bilirubinometry.* New York: Nova Biomedical.

28. Donneborg, M. L., Knudsen, K. B., & Ebbesen, F. (2010). Effect of infants' position on serum bilirubin level during conventional phototherapy. *Acta Paediatr, 99,* 1131.

29. Engle, W. D., Jackson, G. L., & Engle, N. G. (2014). Transcutaneous bilirubinometry. *Semin Perinatol, 38,* 438.

30. Fay, D. L., Schellhase, K. G., & Suresh, G. K. (2009). Bilirubin screening for normal newborns: a critique of the hour-specific bilirubin nomogram. *Pediatrics, 124,* 1203.

31. Feldman-Winter, L. (2013). Evidence based interventions to support breastfeeding. *Pediatr Clin North Am. 60,* 169.

32. Fouzas, S., et al. (2010). Transcutaneous bilirubin levels in late preterm neonates. *Pediatrics, 157,* 762.

33. Fouzas, S., et al. (2010). Transcutaneous bilirubin levels for the first 120 postnatal hours in healthy neonates. *Pediatrics, 125,* e52.

34. Gartner, L. M., & Lee, K. S. (1999). Jaundice in the breastfed infant. *Clin Perinatol, 26,* 431.

35. Girling, J. C., Dow, E., & Smith, J. H. (1997). Liver function tests in pre-eclampsia: importance of comparison with a reference range derived from normal pregnancy. *Br J Obstet Gynaecol, 104,* 246.

36. Gourley, G. R. (1998). Pathophysiology of breast-milk jaundice. In R. A. Polin & W. W. Fox (Eds.), *Fetal and neonatal physiology* (2nd ed.). Philadelphia: Saunders.

37. Gourley, G. R., et al. (2005). A controlled, randomized, double-blind trial of prophylaxis against jaundice among breastfed newborns. *Pediatrics, 116,* 385.

38. Grabenhenrich, J., et al. (2014). Transcutaneous bilirubin after phototherapy in term and preterm infants. *Pediatrics, 134,* 1324.

39. Guyton, A. C., & Hall, J. E. (2015). *Textbook of medical physiology* (13th ed.). Philadelphia: Saunders.

40. Hansen T. W. R. (2010). Phototherapy for neonatal jaundice—therapeutic effects on more than one level? *Semin Perinatol, 34,* 231.

41. Hansen, T. W. R., & Bratlid, D. (2012). Physiology of neonatal unconjugated hyperbilirubinemia. In: D. K. Stevenson, M. J. Maisels, & J. F. Watchko. (Eds.), *Care of the jaundiced neonate.* New York: McGraw Hill.

42. Hansen T. W. R. (2017). Pathophysiology of kernicterus. In R. A. Polin, et al. (Eds.), *Fetal and neonatal physiology* (5th ed.). Philadelphia: Saunders.

43. Hart, G., & Cameron, R. (2005). The importance of irradiance and area in neonatal phototherapy, *Arch Dis Child Fetal Neonatal Ed, 90,* F437.

44. Hegyi, T., et al. (2013). Unbound free fatty acids from preterm infants treated with intralipid decouples unbound from total bilirubin potentially making phototherapy ineffective. *Neonatology, 104,* 184.

45. Hintz, S. R., et al. (2011). Is phototherapy exposure associated with better or worse outcomes in 501- to 1000-g-birth-weight infants? *Acta Paediatr, 100,* 960.

46. Hulzebos, C. V., & Dijk, P. H. (2014). Bilirubin–albumin binding, bilirubin/albumin ratios, and free bilirubin levels: where do we stand? *Seminars in Perinatology, 38,* 412.

47. Ip, S., et al. (2004). An evidence-based review of important issues concerning neonatal hyperbilirubinemia, *Pediatrics, 114,* 130.

48. Ives, N. K. (2012). Neonatal jaundice. In J. M. Rennie (Ed.), *Textbook of neonatology* (4th ed.). Edinburgh: Churchill Livingstone. In J. M. Rennie (Ed.), *Rennie & Roberton's textbook of neonatology* (5th ed.). London: Churchill Livingstone.

49. Jamjute, P., et al. (2009). Liver function test and pregnancy. *J Matern Fetal Neonatal Med, 22,* 274.

50. Joint Commission on Accreditation of Healthcare Organizations (JCAHO). (2001). Kernicterus threatens healthy newborns. *Sentinel Event Alert, 18,* 1.

51. Kamath-Rayne, B. D., et.al. (2015). Neonatal Hyperbilirubinemia. In S. L. Gardner, et al. (Eds.), *Merenstein & Gardner's Handbook of neonatal intensive care* (8th ed.). St. Louis: Elsevier.

52. Kaplan, M., & Hammerman, C. (2005). Understanding severe hyperbilirubinemia and preventing kernicterus: adjuncts in the interpretation of neonatal serum bilirubin. *Clin Chim Acta, 356,* 9.

53. Kaplan, M., et al. (2008). Visual screening versus transcutaneous bilirubinometry for predischarge jaundice assessment. *Acta Paediatr, 97,* 759.

54. Kaplan, M., Bromiker, R., & Hammerman, C. (2011). Severe neonatal hyperbilirubinemia and kernicterus: Are these still problems in the Third Millennium? *Neonatology, 100,* 354.

55. Kaplan, M., Bromiker, R., & Hammerman, C. (2014). Hyperbilirubinemia, hemolysis,

and increased bilirubin neurotoxicity. *Semin Perinatol*, 38, 429.

56. Kaplan, M., et al. (2015). Neonatal jaundice and liver disease. In R. J. Martin, A. A. Fanaroff, & M. C. Walsh (Eds.), *Neonatal-perinatal medicine: Diseases of the fetus and infant* (10th ed.). Philadelphia: Saunders.

57. Karon, B. S., et al. (2010). BiliChek transcutaneous bilirubin meter overestimates serum bilirubin as measured by the Doumas reference method. *Clin Biochem*, 43, 1009.

58. Kawade, N., & Onishi, S. (1981). The prenatal and postnatal development of UGT-glucuronyl transferase activity towards bilirubin and the effect of premature birth on this activity in the human liver. *Biochem J*, 196, 257.

59. Keren, R., et al. (2005). Identifying newborns at risk of significant hyperbilirubinaemia: a comparison of two recommended approaches. *Arch Dis Child*, 90, 415.

60. Keren, R., et al. (2008). A comparison of alternative risk-assessment strategies for predicting significant neonatal hyperbilirubinemia in term and near-term infants. *Pediatrics*, 121, e170.

61. Keren, R., et al. (2009). Visual assessment of jaundice in term and late preterm infants. *Arch Dis Child Fetal Neonatal Ed*, 94, F317.

62. Knudsen, A. (1990). The cephalocaudal progression of jaundice in newborns in relation of transfer of bilirubin from plasma to skin. *Early Hum Dev*, 22, 23.

63. Knudsen, A. (1991). The influence of the reserve albumin concentration and pH on the cephalocaudal progression of jaundice in newborns. *Early Hum Dev*, 25, 37.

64. Kumar, P., Chawla, D., & Deorari, A. (2011). Light-emitting diode phototherapy for unconjugated hyperbilirubinaemia in neonates. *Cochrane Database Syst Rev*, 2011(12), CD007969.

65. Kumar, P. (2016) Filtered sunlight reduces serum bilirubin levels as effectively as conventional phototherapy in late preterm and term neonates with mild jaundice. *Evid Based Med. 21*, 87.

66. Kuzniewicz, M. W., et al. (2009). Impact of universal bilirubin screening on severe hyperbilirubinemia and phototherapy use. *Pediatrics*, 124, 1031.

67. Lawrence, R. A., & Lawrence R. M. (2016). *Breastfeeding: A guide for the medical profession* (8th ed.). Philadelphia: Elsevier.

68. Lease, M., & Whalen, B. (2010). Assessing jaundice in infants of 35-week gestation and greater. *Curr Opin Pediatr*, 22, 352.

69. Louis, D., et al. (2014). Intravenous immunoglobulin in isoimmune haemolytic disease of newborn: an updated systematic review and meta-analysis. *Arch Dis Child Fetal Neonatal Ed*, 99, 325.

70. Lunsing, R. J., Pardoen, W. F. H., & Hadders-Algra, M. (2013). Neurodevelopment after moderate hyperbilirubinemia at term. *Pediatr Res*, 73, 655.

71. Lunsing, R. J. (2014). Subtle bilirubin-induced neurodevelopmental dysfunction (BIND) in the term and late preterm infant: does it exist? *Semin Perinatol*, 38, 465.

72. Macias, R. I., Marin, J. J., & Serrano, M. A. (2009). Excretion of biliary compounds during intrauterine life. *World J Gastroenterol*, 15, 817.

73. Mackillop, L., & Williamson, C. (2010). Liver disease in pregnancy. *Postgrad Med J*, 86, 160.

74. Maisels, M. J., & Kring, E. (2006). Transcutaneous bilirubin levels in the first 96 hours in a normal newborn population of ≥ 35 weeks' gestation. *Pediatrics*, 117, 1169.

75. Maisels, M. J., et al. (2009). Hyperbilirubinemia in the newborn infant ≥35 weeks' gestation: An update with clarifications. *Pediatrics*, 124, 1193.

76. Maisels, M. J. (2009). Neonatal hyperbilirubinemia and kernicterus—not gone but sometimes forgotten. *Early Hum Dev*, 85, 727.

77. Maisels, M. J., et al. (2009). Routine transcutaneous bilirubin measurements combined with clinical risk factors improve the prediction of subsequent hyperbilirubinemia. *J Perinatol*, 29, 612.

78. Maisels, M. J. (2010). Screening and early postnatal management strategies to prevent hazardous hyperbilirubinemia in newborns of 35 or more weeks of gestation. *Semin Fetal Neonatal Med*, 15, 129.

79. Maisels, M. J., et al. (2012). An approach to the management of hyperbilirubinemia in the preterm infant less than 35 weeks of gestation. *J Perinatol*, 32, 660.

80. Maisels, M. J., et al. (2014). The natural history of jaundice in predominantly breast-fed infants. *Pediatrics*, 134, 340.

81. Maisels, M. J., & Watchko, J. F. (2016). Jaundice. In M. G. MacDonald & M. M. K. Seshia, (Eds.), *Avery's Neonatology: Pathophysiology and management of the newborn* (7th ed.). Philadelphia: Wolters Kluwer.

82. Marin, J. J., et al. (2008). Molecular bases of the fetal liver-placenta-maternal liver excretory pathway for cholephilic compounds. *Liver Int*, 28, 435.

83. Maruo, Y., et al. (2014). Bilirubin uridine diphosphate-glucuronosyltransferase variation is a genetic basis of breast milk jaundice. *J Pediatr*, 165, 36.

84. Martinez, J. C., et al. (1993). Hyperbilirubinemia in the breast-fed newborn: a controlled trial of four interventions. *Pediatrics*, 91, 470.

85. Matsubara, S., et al. (2012). Connection between hyperemesis gravidarum, jaundice or liver dysfunction, and biliary sludge. *Obstet Gynaecol Res*, 38, 446.

86. McDonagh, A. F. (1990). Is bilirubin good for you? *Clin Perinatol*, 17, 359.

87. McDonagh, A. F. (2010). Controversies in bilirubin biochemistry and their clinical relevance. *Semin Fetal Neonatal Med*, 15, 141.

88. Morris, B. H., et al. (2008). Aggressive vs. conservative phototherapy for infants with extremely low birth weight. *N Engl J Med*, 359, 1885.

89. Morris, B. H., et al. (2013). Efficacy of phototherapy devices and outcomes among extremely low birth weight infants: multicenter observational study. *J Perinatol*, 33, 126.

90. Moyer, V. A., Ahn, C., & Sneed, S. (2000). Accuracy of clinical judgment in neonatal jaundice. *Arch Pediatr Adolesc Med, 154,* 301.

91. Mreihil, K., et al. (2010). Early isomerization of bilirubin in phototherapy of neonatal jaundice. *Pediatr Res, 67,* 656.

92. Nagar, G., et al. (2013). Reliability of transcutaneous bilirubin devices in preterm infants: a systematic review. *Pediatrics. 132,* 871.

93. National Institute of Child Health and Human Development. (1985). Randomized controlled trial of phototherapy for neonatal hyperbilirubinemia. *Pediatrics*, 75, 365.

94. Newman, T. B., & Klebanoff, M. A. (1993). Neonatal hyperbilirubinemia and longterm outcome: another look at the Collaborative Perinatal Project. *Pediatrics*, 92, 651.

95. Newman, T. B., & Maisels, M. J. (2000). Less aggressive treatment of neonatal jaundice and reports of kernicterus: lessons about practice guidelines. *Pediatrics*, 105, 242.

96. Newman, T. B. (2009). Data suggest visual assessment of jaundice in newborns is helpful. *J Pediatr*, 154, 466.

97. Newman, T. B. (2009). Universal bilirubin screening, guidelines, and evidence. *Pediatrics*, 124, 1199.

98. Okwundu C. I., Okoromah C. A., & Shah, P. S. (2012). Prophylactic phototherapy for preventing jaundice in preterm or low birth weight infants. *Cochrane Database Syst Rev*, 2012(1), CD007966.

99. Palmer, R. H., et al. (2004). National Institute of Child Health and Human Development NICHD) conference on kernicterus: a population perspective on prevention of kernicterus. *J Perinatol*, 24, 723.

100. Pathak, B., Sheibani, L., & Lee, R. H. (2010). Cholestasis of pregnancy. *Obstet Gynecol Clin North Am*, 37, 269.

101. Pratesi S., et al. (2015). Broad-spectrum light versus blue light for phototherapy in neonatal hyperbilirubinemia: a randomized controlled trial. *Am J Perinatol*, 32, 779.

102. Ramsay, M. M., et al. (2000). *Normal values in pregnancy* (2nd ed.). Philadelphia: Saunders.

103. Riely, C. A., & Fallon, H. J. (2004). Liver diseases. In G. N. Burrow, T. P. Duffy, & J. A. Copel (Eds.), *Medical complications during pregnancy* (5th ed.). Philadelphia: Saunders.

104. Riskin, A., et al. (2008). Is visual assessment of jaundice reliable as a screening tool to detect significant neonatal hyperbilirubinemia? *J Pediatr*, 152, 782.

105. Ruiz-Extremera, A., et al (2005). Activity of hepatic enzymes from week sixteen of pregnancy. *Am J Obstet Gynecol*, 193, 2010.

106. Ruud Hansen, T. W. (2010). Phototherapy for neonatal jaundice—therapeutic effects on more than one level? *Semin Perinatol*, 34, 231.

107. Ryter, S. W. (2012). Bile pigments in pulmonary and vascular disease. *Front Pharmacol*, 3, 39.

108. Sachdeva M., et al. (2015). Intermittent versus continuous phototherapy for the treatment of neonatal non-hemolytic moderate hyperbilirubinemia in infants more than 34 weeks of gestational age: a randomized controlled trial. *Eur J Pediatr*, 174, 177.

109. Sarici S., et al. (2000). Double versus single phototherapy in term newborns with significant hyperbilirubinemia. *J Trop Pediatr*, 46, 36.

110. Sedlak, T. W., & Snyder, S. H. (2004). Bilirubin benefits: cellular protection by a biliverdin reductase antioxidant cycle. *Pediatrics, 113*, 1776.

111. Sedlak, T. W., et al. (2009). Bilirubin and glutathione have complementary antioxidant and cytoprotective roles. *Proc Natl Acad Sci U S A, 106*, 5171.

112. Shapiro, S. M. (2005). Definition of the clinical spectrum of kernicterus and bilirubin-induced neurologic dysfunction (BIND). *J Perinatol, 25*, 54.

113. Shapiro, S. M. (2010). Chronic bilirubin encephalopathy: diagnosis and outcome. *Semin Fetal Neonatal Med, 15*, 157.

114. Shekhar, S., Diddi, G., & Taiwan, J. (2015). Liver disease in pregnancy. *Obstet Gynecol, 5*, 475.

115. Slusher, T. M., et al. (2014). Safety and efficacy of filtered sunlight in treatment of jaundice in African neonates. *Pediatrics, 133*, 1568.

116. Slusher, T. M., et al. (2015). A randomized trial of phototherapy with filtered sunlight in African neonates. *N Engl J Med, 373*, 1115.

117. Soares, M., & Bach, F. (2009). Heme oxygenase-1: from biology to therapeutic potential. *Trends Mol Med, 15*, 50.

118. Stevenson, D. K., & Wong, R. J. (2010). Metalloporphyrins in the management of neonatal hyperbilirubinemia. *Semin Fetal Neonatal Med, 15*, 164.

119. Suresh, G. K., Martin, C. L., & Soll, R. F. (2003). Metalloporphyrins for treatment of unconjugated hyperbilirubinemia in neonates. *Cochrane Database Syst Rev, 2*, CD004207.

120. Than, N. N., & Neuberger, J. (2013). Liver anomalies in pregnancy. *Best Pract Res Clin Gastroenterol, 27*, 565.

121. Thayyil, S., & Marriott, L. (2005). Can transcutaneous bilirubinometry reduce the need for serum bilirubin estimations in term and near term infants? *Arch Dis Child, 90*, 1311.

122. Trikalinos, T., et al. (2009). Systematic review of screening for bilirubin encephalopathy in neonates. *Pediatrics, 124*, 1162.

123. Tyson, E., et al. (2012). Does aggressive phototherapy increase mortality while decreasing profound impairment among the smallest and sickest newborns? *J Perinatol, 32*, 677.

124. U.S. Preventive Services Task Force. (2010). Screening of infants for hyperbilirubinemia to prevent chronic bilirubin encephalopathy: recommendation statement. *Am Fam Physician, 82*, 408.

125. Varvarigou, A., et al. (2009). Transcutaneous bilirubin nomogram for prediction of significant neonatal hyperbilirubinemia. *Pediatrics, 124*, 1052.

126. Vitek, L., & Ostrow, J. D. (2009). Bilirubin chemistry and metabolism: harmful and protective aspects. *Curr Pharm Des, 15*, 2869.

127. Vreman, H. J., et al. (2008). Standardized bench method for evaluating the efficacy of phototherapy devices. *Acta Paediatr, 97*, 308.

128. Wallenstein, M. B., & Bhutani, V. K. (2013). Jaundice and kernicterus in the moderately preterm infant. *Clin Perinatol, 4*, 679.

129. Watchko, J. F., Daod, M. J., & Biniwale, M. (2002). Understanding neonatal hyperbilirubinaemia in the era of genomics. *Semin Neonatol, 7*, 143.

130. Watchko, J. F., & Lin, Z. (2010). Exploring the genetic architecture of neonatal hyperbilirubinemia. *Semin Fetal Neonatal Med, 15*, 169.

131. Watchko, J. F., & Maisels, M. J. (2010). Enduring controversies in the management of hyperbilirubinemia in preterm neonates. *Semin Fetal Neonatal Med, 15*, 136.

132. Watchko, J. F., & Tiribelli, C. (2013). Bilirubin-induced neurologic damage—mechanisms and management approaches. *N Engl J Med, 369*, 2021.

133. Watchko, J. F., & Maisels, M. J. (2014). the enigma of low bilirubin kernicterus in premature infants: Why does it still occur, and is it preventable? *Semin Perinatol, 38*, 397.

134. Wennberg, R. P., et al. (2006). Toward understanding kernicterus: a challenge to improve the management of jaundiced newborns. *Pediatrics, 117*, 474.

135. Wennberg, R. P., Ahlfors, C. E., & Aravkin, A. Y. (2009). Intervention guidelines for neonatal hyperbilirubinemia: an evidence based quagmire. *Curr Pharm Des, 15*, 2939.

136. Williamson, C., et al. (2014). Diseases of the liver, biliary system, and pancreas. In R. K. Creasy, et al. (Eds.), *Creasy and Resnik's Maternal-fetal medicine: Principles and practice* (7th ed.). Philadelphia: Saunders.

137. Yamauchi, Y., & Yamanouchi, H. (1990). Breast-feeding frequency during the first 24 hours after birth in full-term neonates. *Pediatrics, 86*, 171.

Pituitary, Adrenal, and Thyroid Function

Pituitary, adrenal, and thyroid function; the hypothalamic-pituitary-adrenal (HPA) axis; and the hypothalamic-pituitary-thyroid (HPT) axis are critical for normal function and adaptation during pregnancy, growth, and development of the fetus and adaptation of the newborn to the extrauterine environment. HPA axis function in the mother and fetus are closely interrelated with placental function. The hormones of the HPA and HPT axes (see Figure 2-7) are necessary for many body functions, for development of the central nervous system (CNS) and other growth processes, and for reproductive function. Disorders of these systems are associated with infertility, alterations in normal changes at puberty, and complications of pregnancy. Concentrations of HPA and HPT axis hormones are altered in pregnant women and neonates. Marked changes in adrenal and thyroid function occur in neonates with birth. This chapter examines changes in the glands and hormones of the HPA and HPT axes during pregnancy; development of neuroendocrine function in fetuses and neonates; and implications for mothers, fetuses, and neonates.

MATERNAL PHYSIOLOGIC ADAPTATIONS

Pregnancy is associated with significant alterations in the morphology of the pituitary, adrenal, and thyroid glands. Concentrations of adrenocorticotropin (ACTH), corticotropin-releasing hormone (CRH), growth hormone (GH), cortisol, thyroid hormones (thyroxine [T_4] and triiodothyronine [T_3]), and thyroxine-binding globulin (TBG) are altered during pregnancy. Placental hormones, particularly estrogen, human chorionic gonadotropin (hCG), placental growth hormone, and placental CRH, and alterations in liver and kidney function influence these changes.

Antepartum Period
Hypothalamic-Pituitary-Adrenal Axis

Marked changes occur in the hypothalamic-pituitary-adrenal (HPA) axis during pregnancy, resulting in a state of increased HPA function.[24,76,112] (See Figure 2-7 for an illustration of the HPA axis.) These changes are mediated primarily by placental hormones, including placental ACTH, GH, and CRH. Maternal hypothalamic-pituitary function is discussed further in Chapter 2 in conjunction with the hypothalamic-pituitary-ovarian axis.

Changes in the hypothalamus and pituitary during pregnancy are summarized in Box 19-1.

Anterior Pituitary Function. The anterior pituitary is composed of six cell types, each of which produces different hormones. These types of cells and their major hormones include lactotroph (prolactin), corticotroph (proopiomelanocortin [POMC] and its derivatives, including ACTH, β-endorphin, and β-lipotropin), somatotroph (GH), gonadotroph (follicle-stimulating hormone [FSH] and luteinizing hormone [LH]), and cells producing thyroid-stimulating hormone (TSH) (thyrotropin). The anterior pituitary gland increases in size and weight, from an average of 660 mg in the nonpregnant woman to 760 mg or greater (up to 136%) during pregnancy, as a result of an estrogen-induced hyperplasia of lactotroph cells.[25,37,82,91,95] These changes are evident by 1 month and continue to term.[97] The anterior pituitary also develops a more convex, dome-shaped surface, which may cause it to bulge upward in some women, compressing the optic chiasma.[37] For these women, this can result in a transient hemianopia. Changes in pituitary function during pregnancy are summarized in Box 19-1.

In a nonpregnant woman, the prolactin-producing lactotroph cells make up approximately 20% of the anterior pituitary; this increases to around 60% during pregnancy.[25] Prolactin isoforms increase during pregnancy, with the nonglycosylated forms exceeding the N-linked glycosylated form that is most common in nonpregnant women.[25,37] The nonglycosylated form may be more bioactive and functions to prepare the breast for lactation (see Chapter 5). Prolactin increases 10-fold during pregnancy to peak at delivery at 140 ng/mL (6068 pmol/L).[29,37,95] Most of the increase in maternal prolactin is from the maternal anterior pituitary, although prolactin is also produced by the maternal decidua. Decidual prolactin is found primarily in amniotic fluid; little enters the maternal circulation. Prolactin levels in the amniotic fluid peak in the second trimester at 6000 ng/mL (260,886 pmol/L).[25,37]

Corticotroph cells do not change in size during pregnancy.[25] However, ACTH secretion and plasma ACTH levels increase progressively from approximately 10 pg/mL (2.2 pmol/L) in nonpregnant women to 50 pg/mL (11 pmol/L) at term, peaking during the intrapartum period (Figure 19-1).[25,37,95] ACTH secretion is stimulated by CRH and, in turn, stimulates release of cortisol by the adrenal gland. Changes in ACTH parallel the

BOX 19-1 Physiologic Changes in the Hypothalamic-Pituitary Axis During Pregnancy

Lactotroph hypertrophy and hyperplasia
Progressive increase in serum prolactin
Doubling or more of anterior pituitary volume
Decline in gonadotropins, luteinizing hormone, and follicle-stimulating hormone
Decline in pituitary growth hormones
Production of a placental variant of growth hormone
Increase in corticotropin-releasing hormone (CRH), mainly of placental origin
Activation of maternal and fetal pituitary gland by placental corticotropin-stimulating hormone
Increased adrenocorticotropic hormone and cortisol
Increase in cortisol stimulating placental CRH and leading to hypercortisolism
Decline in thyroid-stimulating hormone in first trimester because of the thyrotropic effect of human chorionic gonadotropin
Decline in plasma osmolality by 5–10 mOsm/kg as a result of resetting of osmoreceptors for vasopressin release
Decline in osmotic threshold for thirst
Increase in metabolic clearance of vasopressin as a result of a placental vasopressinase

From Nader, S. (2004). Thyroid disease and other endocrine disorders in pregnancy. *Obstet Gynecol Clin North Am, 31*, 258.

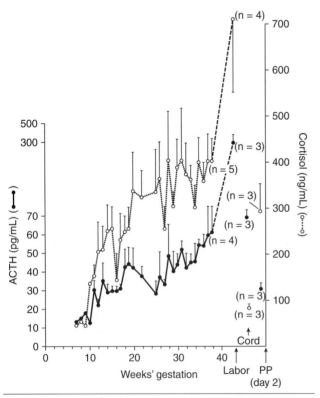

FIGURE 19-1 Adrenocorticotropic hormone *(ACTH)* and cortisol concentration in maternal circulation throughout gestation. *PP*, postpartum. (From Carr, B.R., Parker, C.R., Jr., Madden, J.D., MacDonald, P.C., & Porter, J.C. [1981]. Maternal plasma adrenocorticotropin [ACTH] and cortisol relationships throughout human pregnancy. *Am J Obstet Gynecol, 139*, 416.)

increase in free and total cortisol (see Figure 19-1).[82] During pregnancy, the adrenal gland is more responsive to ACTH, with a blunted HPA axis response to exogenous glucocorticoids.[76] There is a twofold to fourfold increase in ACTH from the first to third trimesters, despite the increased bound and free plasma cortisol.[95] The increase in ACTH in the face of increased cortisol suggests a change in the set point for cortisol release that alters the ACTH-cortisol feedback loop.[95] ACTH maintains its diurnal variation during pregnancy, although this cycling may be blunted.[76,82,95] Placental ACTH increases in the second and third trimesters. It is unclear how much of the increased maternal serum ACTH comes from the maternal anterior pituitary versus the placenta.[91] The effects of ACTH on the adrenal gland and changes in cortisol during pregnancy are described further under Adrenal Function.

The increased ACTH secretion during pregnancy is believed to be primarily because of increased placental (and some decidua and fetal membrane) CRH, rather than maternal hypothalamic CRH (Figure 19-2).[25,37,76,82,154] Other factors that may contribute to this increase are the decreased pituitary gland sensitivity to cortisol feedback, enhanced pituitary responsiveness to corticotropin-releasing factors such as vasopressin, and CRH.[76,154] Maternal serum CRH increases beginning by 8 to 10 weeks and rises from prepregnant values of 10 to 100 pg/mL (47.6 to 476 pmol/L) to 300 to 1000 pg/mL (1429 to 4762 pmol/L) by the third trimester (peaking at delivery), with most of the increase related to increased placental CRH.[25,82,154] CRH-binding protein (CRH-BP) decreases the bioactivity of CRH throughout most of gestation. CRH-BP levels are similar to nonpregnant levels until the third trimester and then fall by two-thirds during the last 6 weeks in preparation for birth. CRH increases markedly near term because of the decrease in CRH-BP as well as increased CRH secretion by the placenta, decidua, fetal membranes, and fetus.[132]

CRH has multiple roles in establishing and maintaining pregnancy and is produced by placental and uterine tissues in addition to the hypothalamus.[154] CRH plays a critical role in the onset of parturition (see Chapter 4). With maturation of the fetal HPA system in late gestation, fetal and placental CRH are increased, altering myometrial responsiveness and the local (uterine) hormonal milieu. These changes increase myometrial excitability, activity, and responsiveness to prostaglandins and oxytocin. Early elevations of CRH have been associated with an increased risk of spontaneous preterm delivery. Maternal or fetal stress may activate labor via increases in CRH and cortisol leading to increased estriol production and an increase in prostaglandins and other substances associated with labor onset (see Figure 4-7).[154]

Somatotroph and gonadotroph cells of the anterior pituitary decrease during pregnancy.[3] Hypothalamic gonadotropin-releasing hormone (GnRH) is suppressed in pregnancy by the elevated CRH, β-endorphins, and cortisol, with a blunted response of the pituitary to GnRH and low LH and FSH levels by 6 to 7 weeks.[154] By midpregnancy, LH and FSH levels are undetectable.[25,37,95] Gonadotropin function is described in Chapter 2. β-endorphins during pregnancy and the intrapartum period are described in Chapter 15.

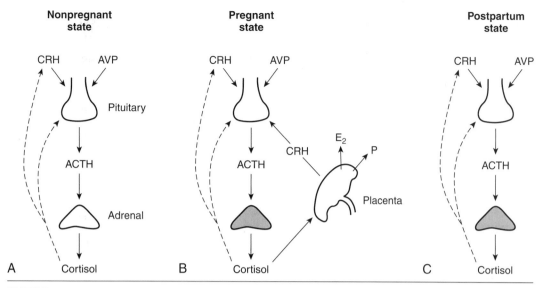

FIGURE 19-2   The hypothalamic-pituitary-adrenal (HPA) axis in nonpregnant, pregnant, and postpartum women. *ACTH,* Adrenocorticotropin; *AVP,* arginine vasopressin; *CRH,* corticotropin-releasing hormone; *E₂,* estradiol; *P,* progesterone. Shaded areas represent relative hypertrophy of the adrenals. (From Mastorakos, G. & Ilias, I. [2000]. Maternal hypothalamic-adrenal axis in pregnancy and the postpartum period: Postpartum-related disorders. *Ann N Y Acad Sci, 900,* 100.)

Pituitary GH (GH-N) decreases after the first trimester as placental GH (GH-V) increases.[91,95] GH-V is a GH variant that stimulates bone growth and regulates maternal insulin-like growth factor 1 (IGF-1; also called *somatomedin C*), which in turn alters maternal metabolism, stimulating gluconeogenesis and lipolysis.[91] GH-V is secreted continuously, as opposed to the pulsatile secretion characteristic of GH-N. GH-N is the main maternal GH until 15 to 20 weeks; then it decreases and becomes undetectable by term. GH-V increases progressively from 15 to 20 weeks until term.[95] GH-V stimulates IGF-1, with negative feedback suppression of maternal GH-N.[37]

Posterior Pituitary Function. The major posterior pituitary hormones are arginine vasopressin (AVP, also called antidiuretic hormone) and oxytocin. Posterior pituitary function changes are associated with osmoregulatory changes and parturition. AVP levels are within normal ranges during pregnancy; however, the threshold at which AVP is secreted is reset so that AVP is secreted at a lower plasma osmolality during pregnancy, with a decline in plasma osmolality by 5 to 10 mOsm/kg less than the nonpregnant mean of 285 mOsm/kg (see Chapter 11).[95,96] AVP also modulates ACTH release.[47] Oxytocin levels progressively increase during pregnancy, with further increase at term (see Chapter 4) and with lactation (see Chapter 5).[95]

Adrenal Function. Pregnancy is characterized by a transient hypercortisolism that begins by at least 12 weeks (see Figure 19-1).[82] Both total serum cortisol (the primary glucocorticoid) and free cortisol increase, with total cortisol peaking at levels threefold to eightfold times higher by term.[95,122] Salivary cortisol increases twofold by 25 weeks and then plateaus to term.[21] The pregnant woman does not demonstrate signs of hypercortisolism because the free cortisol fraction is still within normal range.[21] Urinary cortisol increases at least 180% by term.[95] The diurnal secretion of cortisol—with higher levels in the morning versus evening—is blunted but maintained.[24,76,82,95] Physiologic responses to

stress are maintained during pregnancy but appear to be blunted.[21,154] This blunted response may help protect the fetus from adverse effects of stress, because maternal stress and the intrauterine environment can influence fetal HPA programming (see Maternal Stress Responses and Fetal Endocrine Programming).

The increase in plasma cortisol parallels the increase in ACTH (see Figure 19-1). The increase in total cortisol is primarily a result of an estrogen-stimulated increase in cortisol-binding globulin (CBG) that increases twofold to threefold during pregnancy.[95] Increased CBG reduces liver catabolism and clearance of cortisol, yielding a twofold increase in cortisol half-life.[82,95] The increase in free cortisol is also partially related to displacement of cortisol from CBG by progesterone and increased placental secretion of CGH, which stimulates the maternal pituitary gland to increase ACTH and thus cortisol.[24] Maternal cortisol stimulates synthesis of placental CRH, further increasing maternal cortisol (see Figure 19-2).[24]

The adrenal gland becomes hypertrophic as the zona fasciculata (site of glucocorticoid production) widens, with no changes in the size of the zona glomerulosa or reticularis (Box 19-2). Levels of aldosterone (the primary mineralocorticoid) are markedly increased in pregnancy (see Chapter 11). Synthesis of androgens also increases, especially during the second half of pregnancy.[95] An increase in sex hormone–binding globulin during pregnancy increases total and protein-bound testosterone levels. Levels of free testosterone are low to normal to 28 weeks and then increase along with levels of androstenedione.[95] Maternal serum dehydroepiandrosterone (DHEA-S) levels remain low because of placental uptake and metabolic clearance.[95]

In summary, major changes in HPA function during pregnancy include the following:

1. Plasma levels of CRH increase, peaking at term—the primary source is believed to be placental CRH.

BOX 19-2 Adrenal Hormones

The adrenal gland is composed of the outer adrenal cortex and the inner adrenal medulla. The mature adrenal cortex is divided into three zones: zona fasciculata, zona glomerulosa, and zona reticularis. Although the adrenal cortex produces more than 50 steroid hormones, the major hormones are cortisol and aldosterone. The zona fasciculata is the site of glucocorticoid and cortisol production, which is regulated by corticotropin-releasing hormone (CRH) from the hypothalamus and adrenocorticotropic hormone (ACTH) from the pituitary gland (see Figure 19-2, A). ACTH is derived from proopiomelanocortin (POMC) precursors. Placental cortisol inhibits ACTH release and POMC synthesis. ACTH binds to membrane receptors on cells of the adrenal gland, activating adenylate cyclase. This increases movement of cholesterol, a precursor for pregnenolone, into the cells. Pregnenolone is metabolized in the smooth endoplasmic reticulum

to cortisol, the main glucocorticoid. Glucocorticoids, primarily cortisol, are involved in the regulation of fluid and electrolyte balance, metabolism, vascular permeability, endothelial integrity, and blood glucose; maintain hemodynamic stability; increase with stress; and suppress immune functions.[30] The zona glomerulosa produces mineralocorticoids, the major one being aldosterone. Mineralocorticoids regulate fluid and electrolyte balance (see Chapter 11). The zona reticularis produces androgens that are important for sexual differentiation (see Chapter 1), although the major source of androgens is the gonads (see Chapter 2). A major androgen is androstenedione, which is converted to testosterone, estrone, and estriol in peripheral tissues.[95] The adrenal medulla is the source of epinephrine and norepinephrine, which are also involved in stress responses and cardiovascular function.

---

2. Total serum cortisol increases, peaking threefold to eightfold higher by term because of increased CBG.
3. Elevated CRH stimulates the maternal pituitary gland to increase ACTH and thus cortisol (which stimulates further placental CRH secretion).
4. Physiologic responses to stress are maintained during pregnancy but appear to be blunted, perhaps to protect the fetus and fetal HPA programming.
5. Areas of the adrenal gland involved in glucocorticoid production hypertrophy.
6. Aldosterone levels markedly increase (see Chapter 11).[24,76,82,95]

Hypothalamic-Pituitary-Thyroid Axis

Marked changes are also seen in the hypothalamic-pituitary-thyroid (HPT) axis during pregnancy. These changes occur primarily in the first half of gestation so that the woman achieves a new steady state in HPT function by midgestation that is maintained until delivery.[61,69] The net result of changes in thyroid function during pregnancy is to significantly increase the availability of thyroid hormones. Morreale de Escobar et al. summarized the major changes in thyroid function during pregnancy: (1) Increased estrogen leads to a twofold to threefold increase in thyroid-binding globulin production by the liver. This decreases

levels of free thyroid hormone and stimulates the HPT axis. (2) Increased hCG, which has a structure similar to TSH, stimulates increased T_3 and T_4. This leads to negative feedback to the pituitary gland and a decrease in TSH (especially during weeks 8 to 14 when hCG is peaking). (3) Peripheral metabolism of thyroid hormones increases in the second and third trimesters because of increased production of type II and III monodeiodinases (Box 19-3) by the placenta.[94]

Adaptations during pregnancy related to thyroid physiology mimic hyperthyroidism. A pregnant woman can be described as being in a state of euthyroid hyperthyroxinemia, however, because thyroid function per se does not change during pregnancy.[94] Thyroid hormone changes are important in supporting the altered carbohydrate, protein, and lipid metabolism of pregnancy and changes in basal metabolic rate (see Chapter 16).[77] The factors primarily responsible for changes in HPT axis function during pregnancy are the elevated hCG and thyroid-binding globulin (TBG) levels and the increased urinary iodide excretion that lowers maternal plasma iodine.[43,47,113] Box 19-3, Box 19-4, and Figure 19-3 review thyroid hormone production and regulation. Figure 19-4 illustrates regulation of maternal thyroid hormone function during pregnancy.

BOX 19-3 Thyroid Function

The thyroid gland consists of multiple colloid-filled follicles that serve as a storage site for thyroid hormone (see Figure 19-3). The major component of the colloid is thyroglobulin. Thyroid cellular functions include iodine transport and thyroxine (T_4) and triiodothyronine (T_3) formation and release into the blood. T_4 acts as a prohormone for T_3 and by itself has little intrinsic metabolic activity.[15] Iodide is actively transported into the thyroid cell, where it is stored and oxidized. Oxidized iodide is bound to tyrosine to form monoiodotyrosines (MIT) and diiodotyrosines (DIT). T_3 is composed of 1 MIT and 1 DIT; T_4 is formed from 2 DIT. These substances are held within the thyroglobulin and used to form T_4 and T_3. T_4 and T_3 are stored in

the thyroid, bound to thyroglobulin. Under the influence of thyroid-stimulating hormone (TSH), T_4 and a small amount of T_3 are cleaved from thyroglobulin and secreted. In peripheral tissue, T_4 is deiodinated to T_3 (80% of T_3 in tissues is derived from this process).[15] The iodine released by this process is reconcentrated by the thyroid or excreted by the kidneys. T_4 can also be metabolized to reverse T_3 (rT_3), which is an inactive compound. T_3 and rT_3 are in a reciprocal relationship. Nearly all of the thyroid hormones circulate in plasma bound to proteins, including thyroxine-binding globulin (TBG) (the major carrier), transthyretin (TTR), or albumin. Changing levels of TBG, such as occurs during pregnancy, alter serum thyroxine levels

---

BOX 19-3 Thyroid Function—cont'd

without changing thyroid status. The small amount of free T_3 in the blood forms the most physiologically active fraction.

Three types of the iodothyronine monodeiodinase (MDI) enzymes catabolize thyroid hormones: D1 (found in the liver, kidney, thyroid, and pituitary); D2 (found in the brain, pituitary, brown adipose tissue, keratinocytes, and placenta); and D3 (found in the brain, liver, epidermis, placenta, uterus, and amnion). D1 and D2 act on the outer ring of the iodothyronine molecule; D3 acts primarily on the inner ring to catabolize T_4 to the inactive rT_4 or T_3 to the inactive T_2. D1 acts on the outer ring converting T_4 to T_3. D1 is the major enzyme for producing circulating T_3; D2 generates localized T_3 in the pituitary, brown adipose tissue, keratinocytes, and placenta.[36] During pregnancy, D3

helps regulate placental function and transfer of maternal thyroid hormones to the fetus.[36]

Thyroid hormones bind to nuclear thyroid hormone protein receptors in cells, which have a 10-fold greater affinity for T_3 than for T_4, that regulate gene transcription, resulting in the production of proteins that affect a variety of metabolic and other processes.[15,32,97] Thyroid hormones are involved in the regulation of protein and lipid metabolism, glucose absorption and utilization, increasing the rate of cellular oxidation, heat production, fluid balance, calcium and vitamin D homeostasis, and liver functions.[15] Thyroid hormones are also critical for maturation of the retina, cochlea, and brain, including neural differentiation and migration (see Chapter 15).[15]

From references 15, 32, 36, 52, and 97.

BOX 19-4 Regulation of Thyroid Hormone Secretion

Thyroid-stimulating hormone (TSH) acts through receptors on the thyroid cell membrane to activate adenyl cyclase. This stimulates formation of cyclic adenosine monophosphate (cAMP), which activates cellular systems to increase iodide uptake and thyroid hormone production and synthesis. TSH secretion is stimulated by thyrotropin-releasing hormone (TRH). TRH is secreted primarily by paraventricular nuclei of the hypothalamus and is released into the hypothalamic-pituitary portal system. TRH binds to receptors on the plasma membrane of thyrotropic cells within the anterior pituitary to activate synthesis and secretion

of TSH. Secretion of thyroid hormones decreases the responsiveness of the pituitary to TRH. Secretion of TSH is also influenced by circulating levels of free thyroid hormone and intrapituitary triiodothyronine (T_3) levels via negative feedback to the pituitary gland; that is, increased free thyroid hormone levels decrease secretion of TSH by the pituitary and vice versa. Circulating thyroxine (T_4) regulates TSH primarily through intrapituitary deiodination of T_4 to T_3. The pituitary-thyroid axis is controlled in turn by the hypothalamus and TRH. TSH is inhibited by excess circulating thyroid hormone.

From references 15, 32, 52, and 97.

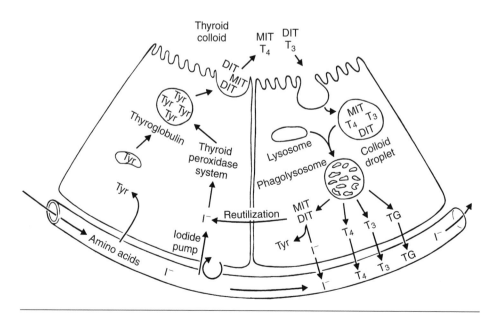

FIGURE 19-3 Thyroid hormone synthesis. *DIT,* Diiodotyrosine; *MIT,* monoiodotyrosine; TG, thyroglobulin; *Tyr,* tyrosine. (From Lane, A.H. & Wilson, T.A. [2005]. Neonatal thyroid disorders. In A.R. Spitzer. [Ed.]. *Intensive care of the fetus & neonate* [2nd ed.]. St. Louis: Mosby, p. 1141.)

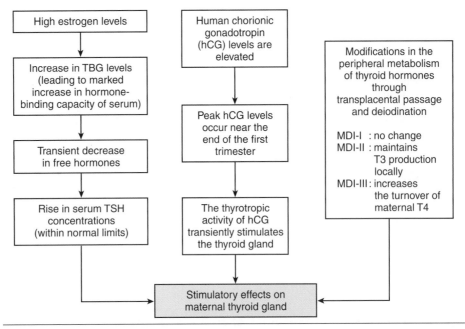

FIGURE 19-4   Regulation of maternal thyroid function in normal pregnancy. Three series of separate events exert stimulatory effects on maternal thyroid function. The first event is linked to the progressive rise in thyroid binding *(TBG)* levels during the first trimester; the second event takes place transiently near the end of the first trimester and is related to the thyrotropic action of peak human chorionic gonadotropin *(hCG)* concentrations; the third event takes place mainly during the second half of gestation and is related to modifications in peripheral metabolism of maternal thyroid hormones, mainly at the placental level. *MDI,* Monodeiodinase; *TSH,* thyroid-stimulating hormone. (From Glinoer, D. [1999]. Thyroid regulation and disease in pregnancy. In M.I. Surks. [Ed.]. *Atlas of clinical endocrinology-thyroid disease* [Vol. 1]. Philadelphia: Blackwell Science, p. 161.)

Thyroid hormones are transported in the blood bound to binding proteins, such as TBG, albumin, and transthyretin (TTR; formerly called *thyroxine-binding prealbumin*). In a nonpregnant individual, about two-thirds of the T_4 is bound to TBG, increasing to 75% or greater during pregnancy.[39,47,113] Under the influence of estrogen, hepatic synthesis and sialylation of TBG increase twofold to threefold beginning within a few weeks after fertilization and plateau from midgestation to delivery.[39,69,97,99,113,138] Increased sialylation increases the half-life of TBG. The ability of TBG to bind thyroxine doubles during this period; TTR, also influenced by estrogen, decreases.[47] These changes increase serum TBG levels, decrease the percentage of T_4 bound to TTR, and increase total T_4 and T_3.[99] The increased TBG is accompanied by a 10% to 15% decrease in free T_4 and free T_3 if iodine is sufficient; if iodine is inadequate, T_4 levels increase.[97]

A transient increase in free T_4 is reported in the first trimester, related to the increase in hCG, with a 10% to 15% decrease in the second and third trimesters.[65,69,70,90,113] Variations in findings are most often related to differences in the iodine status of the populations studied and measurement techniques.[73] Free T_3 changes parallel those of free T_4.[72] Concentrations of free T_3 and free T_4, although low, remain within normal physiologic limits.[70,97] The basis for these changes is believed to be primarily related to the interaction of estrogen, TSH, and thyroid-binding proteins.[70]

Resin T_3 uptake (RT$_3$U) decreases during pregnancy. RT$_3$U measures TBG-binding capacity by quantifying the number of unbound sites and approximates the amount of free T_4. Although T_4-binding sites and binding capacity increase in pregnancy, the number of binding sites exceeds the available T_4. The increased number of unbound sites is reflected by decreased RT$_3$U.

In contrast to changes in free T_3 and free T_4, total T_3 and T_4 increase, peaking at 10 to 15 weeks' gestation and then plateauing at levels higher than nonpregnant values.[113,138] This increase is primarily related to increases in TBG and hCG and the production of iodothyronine monodeiodinase (MDI)-III (see Box 19-3 on p. 613) enzymes (also called *D3*) by the placenta.[69,97] This enzyme converts T_4 to reverse T_3 (rT_3), an inactive compound, and T_3 to T_2, another inactive compound.[96,97] Levels of T_3 are elevated because of the increased availability of T_4 for deiodination to T_3 in peripheral tissue rather than because of increased T_3 production per se.

The increased T_3 and T_4 are also related to increased TSH bioactivity stimulated by hCG, which peaks at about the same time.[59] hCG has a mild TSH-like activity that increases secretion of T_4.[39,99] hCG is a partial inhibitor of the pituitary gland and has β subunits similar to TSH (as well as luteinizing and follicle-stimulating hormone).[113] Thus hCG has thyrotropic activity and can activate TSH receptors.[39,99] Serum hCG is positively correlated with free T_4 and inversely correlated with TSH levels in early pregnancy.[43,73] Elevated T_3 and T_4 suppress endogenous TSH secretion by the anterior pituitary.[96] TSH decreases transiently from 8 to 14 weeks' gestation at the time of the hCG peak, progressively returning to prepregnancy levels by term.[25,39,97,99] Approximately 10% to 20% of otherwise healthy pregnant women will experience a transient hyperthyroxinemia (generally without clinical signs) associated with higher-than-usual hCG levels in the first trimester and a greater fall in TSH.[47,70,97] The increase in total T_3 and T_4 is less than the increase in TBG, resulting in a decreased T_4/TBG ratio, leading to a state of relative hypothyroxinemia during pregnancy.

Pregnancy is characterized by significant changes in iodide metabolism with increased renal iodide clearance and increased iodine needed to make thyroid hormones.[42,69] The increased total T_4 and T_3 stimulate increased serum protein-bound iodine (PBI).[42] Because circulating levels of free thyroid hormone are not significantly altered, increased PBI does not reflect maternal hyperthyroidism. Thyroid iodine uptake increases because of a decrease in the total body iodine pool. This pool is altered because of increased renal iodide loss secondary to the increased renal blood flow and glomerular filtration rate (see Chapter 11) and placental transfer of iodine to the fetus.[47,69,97,138]

The thyroid compensates for the increased loss of iodine by hyperplasia and increased plasma iodine clearance, reducing plasma iodine levels.[84,97] Iodine is stored in the colloid of the thyroid gland follicles (see Figure 19-3). With TSH stimulation, thyroglobulin is catabolized to form T_4 and T_3.[97] Serum thyroglobulin increases in the first trimester but is most marked in later pregnancy. This increase is associated with an increase in thyroid volume, especially in areas of low iodine intake.[47,70,97] The degree of hyperplasia is related to the degree of imbalance between iodine needs versus iodine intake and stores (see Iodine Needs During Pregnancy).[70] Mild thyroid hyperplasia (10% to 15% increase), caused primarily by increased vascularity, is seen in areas such as North America, where diets are generally believed to be iodine sufficient.[42,97,99] Moderate to marked thyroid enlargement in these women cannot be considered normal and requires further evaluation. Women who live in iodine-poor areas have an increase in thyroid volume of 15% to 30% during pregnancy.[41,97] Goiter is generally not a risk if iodine levels are greater than 0.08 μg/dL (0.006 μmol/L); in North America, levels average 0.3 μg/dL (0.023 μmol/L). Goiter is a significant risk in areas with low iodine intake.

Intrapartum Period

The HPA and HPT axes undergo further alterations during the intrapartum period. CRH appears to be a trigger in the initiation of labor, and activation of the HPA axis may serve as a "biologic clock" timing the length of gestation.[97] Maternal plasma CRH, ACTH, β-endorphin, and cortisol levels increase up to sevenfold with labor onset and during labor (see Chapter 4).[17,76,82,91,166] ACTH reaches its highest level, increasing from 50 pg/mL (11 pmol/L) at term to 300 pg/mL (66 pmol/L) during labor (see Figure 19-1).[25,37,76] Further increases in ACTH and cortisol are seen in women with poor progress in labor.[34] Low β-endorphin levels at term have been associated with an increased need for pain medication during labor, although a causal relationship is unclear.[17]

Levels of total and free T_3 increase during labor. This change probably reflects the energy demands of labor on the maternal system. T_3 and T_4 have similar functions, but T_3 is three to five times more active. T_3 and T_4 increase intracellular enzymes (increased cellular metabolism), the number and activity of mitochondria (to provide energy for cellular enzyme systems), and Na-K adenosine triphosphatase (ATPase) (because of the increased energy use during myometrial contractions).[52]

Postpartum Period

The alterations in the HPA (see Figure 19-2, *C*) and HPT axes during pregnancy are reversed during the postpartum period. CRH levels drop rapidly with removal of the placenta and placental CRH.[24,25] Maternal ACTH and cortisol levels decrease rapidly in the immediate postpartum period and reach nonpregnant values by 1 to 4 days postpartum.[76,82] The HPA axis is depressed with a reduction in hypothalamic CRH for 3 to 6 weeks, returning to normal levels by 12 weeks (longer in lactating women).[24,82,97] This depression of the HPA axis may play a role in postpartum "blues" and depression or in exacerbation of autoimmune disorders in the postpartum period.[18,24,46,61,109] Although ACTH secretion may be suppressed, total serum cortisol is within normal limits, probably secondary to a mild hypertrophy of the adrenal cortex.[82] Hyperplasia of the lactotrophs of the anterior pituitary gland peaks in the first 3 days postpartum. This tissue decreases in size by 1 month in nonlactating and more slowly in lactating women but never returns to nulliparous size.[37,91,95] Prolactin falls at delivery and returns to nonpregnant values by 3 months; in breastfeeding women, prolactin increases after delivery.[25,37] β-endorphins decrease by 24 hours after birth and are higher in colostrum than in maternal plasma.[167] Serum growth hormone levels may remain elevated for several months.[37] Postpartum changes in prolactin, FSH, and LH are described in Chapter 5.

After delivery with removal of the placenta and reduction in estrogen, hepatic synthesis of TBG decreases, and renal excretion of iodine returns to prepregnancy levels. As a result, the metabolic alterations in thyroid processes gradually reverse over 4 to 6 weeks, although they may persist for up to 6 to 12 weeks.[47,138] Thyroid-releasing hormone (TRH) is a (minor) stimulus of prolactin release and has been used to induce relactation.[68] Free T_4 may be low and TSH elevated in the first 3 to 4 days, which may confound assessment of thyroid function.[63] Transient disorders in thyroid function are seen in some postpartum women (see Postpartum Thyroid Disorders).

Thyroid hormones are secreted in breast milk. Levels are low initially and then rise. Breast milk T_4 and T_3 have been reported to delay the development of hypothyroidism in some infants with this disorder.[15]

CLINICAL IMPLICATIONS FOR THE PREGNANT WOMAN AND HER FETUS

Changes in the hypothalamic-pituitary-adrenal (HPA) and hypothalamic-pituitary-thyroid (HPT) axes are critical for maintenance of pregnancy. In addition, the maternal and fetal HPA axes and the interrelationship between maternal and fetal-placental function are essential for initiation of labor (see Chapter 4 and Figure 4-4). Alterations in the HPA axis from inflammation or infection or because of stress may lead to preterm labor. These risks are discussed further in Chapter 4. Thyroid disorders are more common in women and are not uncommon in pregnant women; they are the second most common endocrine disorder (after diabetes mellitus) found in pregnant women. Disorders of the adrenal and pituitary gland, such as prolactinomas, which may increase in size during pregnancy because of the stimulating effects of elevated prolactin levels, and Cushing disease are uncommon.[91,95,96] Cushing disease tends to be exacerbated during pregnancy with remission postpartum and is more often related to adrenal lesions than excess adrenocorticotropin (ACTH).[95] Diagnosis of thyroid dysfunction during pregnancy may be more difficult, because symptoms of thyroid disorders often mimic some of the usual physiologic changes of pregnancy, and radioactive iodine tests cannot be used because of fetal risks. Implications of alterations in thyroid function and changes in laboratory tests during pregnancy are discussed in this section, along with disorders of thyroid function unique to the postpartum period.

Iodine Needs During Pregnancy

Adequate iodine stores and nutrition are essential for normal function of the maternal and fetal thyroid.[20,41] Iodine needs increase during pregnancy because of increased renal loss and increased placental—and thus fetal—uptake, particularly during the second half of pregnancy when fetal thyroid hormone production increases.[15,33,41,97] Dietary iodine is converted to iodide; 20% of this is absorbed by the thyroid gland, the rest is cleared by the kidney. During pregnancy renal iodide clearance doubles because of the increased renal blood flow and glomerular filtration rate (see Chapter 11).[97] The World Health Organization and Endocrine Society recommend an iodine intake of 250 µg/day during pregnancy and lactation; others recommend 200 or up to 300 µg/day.[4,15,18,33,75,84,95,168] Iodine needs can be met by iodine in prenatal vitamins and use of iodinated salt.[47] Mean urinary iodine excretion, used to assess iodine deficiency, is insufficient if less than 150 µg/L during pregnancy or less than 100 µg/L during lactation.[33]

Iodine deficiency is lowest in North America and higher in Europe, with Southeast Asia accounting for nearly one-fourth of the worldwide population with insufficient iodine uptake.[84] Iodine stores are low in iodine-deficient areas and have been falling in many iodine-sufficient areas. 50% to 65% of women in western and central Europe were found to be iodine deficient (versus 11% of women in the United States).[41,168] Recent reports suggest a decline in iodine sufficiency in childbearing women in the United States, with moderate iodine deficiency reported in 15% of women of childbearing age and 7% of pregnant women.[97,116] Women who enter pregnancy in an iodine-deficient state fall even further behind, so iodine deficiency in the first trimester tends to become more severe in later pregnancy.[69,73] Iodine deficiency is the most common cause of preventable mental retardation worldwide, and often the damage is done by the time of birth.[84,168] Significant iodine deficiency is also associated with an increased risk of spontaneous abortion, perinatal mortality, and congenital anomalies.[4,84,168] Even in iodine-sufficient areas, there has been increasing concern that iodine deficiency may increase the risk of later neurodevelopmental impairment of offspring in women with marked subclinical thyroid dysfunction.[70] Various professional groups have differing recommendations regarding whether all pregnant women should be routinely screened to identify subclinical hypothyroidism.[2,10,18,33,61,162]

Thyroid Function Tests During Pregnancy

Because changes in thyroxine-binding globulin (TBG) and thyroid hormones during pregnancy alter the parameters for many tests used to assess thyroid status, nonpregnant thyroid reference ranges do not apply during pregnancy.[115] Pregnancy alterations in thyroid function, which vary with trimester, must be considered when evaluating thyroid function in pregnant and postpartum women. If nonpregnant reference ranges are used, a hypothyroid pregnant woman may be classified as euthyroid and a euthyroid woman classified as hyperthyroid.[113] Reference ranges for thyroid function tests during pregnancy have been described, with variations by trimester of testing, number of fetuses, and testing method.[1,33,113] Ranges for each trimester are also available at http://perinatology.com/Reference/Reference%20Ranges/Reference%20for%20Serum.htm. Use of trimester-specific ranges has been recommended by many groups.[18,40,113,115,145]

Free T_3 and T_4 assays, rather than total values, are generally preferred because of the increased TBG.[33] Free T_4 immunoassays tend to be unreliable during pregnancy, with an increased risk of both false positives and false negatives reported, because of interference from the high serum TBG levels.[97,115] Total T_4 and T_3 levels are elevated (because of increased TBG and reduced clearance), RT_3U is lower (because of increased binding of T_3 by TBG resulting in a reduction in the amount of T_3 available to bind to the resin), and the free thyroxine index ($T_4 + RT_3U$) falls to within normal limits during pregnancy.[97] Glinoer and Spencer indicate that serum TSH assay "is the most sensitive index to reliably detect thyroid

TABLE 19-1 Thyroid Function Changes During Pregnancy

PHYSIOLOGIC CHANGES	RESULTING CHANGE IN THYROID ACTIVITY
↑ Serum estrogens	↑ Serum TBG
↑ Serum TBG	↑ Demand for T_4 and T_3
	↑ Total T_4 and T_3
↑ hCG	↓ TSH in first trimester (in reference range unless hCG is >50,000 IU/L)
	↑ Free T_4 in first trimester (still within normal reference range unless hCG is >50,000 IU/L)
↑ Iodine (I) clearance	↑ Dietary requirement for iodine
	↓ Thyroid hormone production in iodine-deficient areas
	↑ Goiter in iodine-deficient areas
↑ Type III deiodinase	↑ T_4 and T_3 degradation
	↑ Demand for T_4 and T_3
↑ Demand for T_4 and T_3	↑ Serum thyroglobulin
	↑ Thyroid volume
	↑ Goiter in iodine-deficient areas

hCG, Human chorionic gonadotropin; *T3*, triiodothyronine; *T4*, thyroxine; *TBG*, thyroxine-binding globulin; *TSH*, thyroid-stimulating hormone.
Modified from Brent, G.A. (1997). Maternal thyroid function: Interpretation of thyroid function test in pregnancy. *Clin Obstet Gynecol, 40*, 3, by Fantz, C.R., Dagogo-Jack, S., Ladenson, J.H., & Gronowski, A.M. (1999). Thyroid function during pregnancy. *Clin Chem, 45*, 2250.

function abnormalities" during pregnancy.[43] Table 19-1 summarizes the changes in thyroid function during pregnancy that lead to alterations in these tests. As noted in the previous section, recommendations for routine thyroid screening during pregnancy vary among different professional groups worldwide.[2,10,18,33,61,71,113,153,162]

Antithyroid peroxidase enzymes have been reported in 10% to 14% of women at 14 weeks' gestation and may increase the risk of gestational thyroid dysfunction and postpartum thyroiditis.[70] Most women are euthyroid, but some have increased thyroid-stimulating hormone (TSH), decreased free T_4, or both.[70]

Thyroid Function and Nausea and Vomiting in Pregnancy

Nausea and vomiting in pregnancy (NVP) has been linked to alterations in T_4, TSH, and human chorionic gonadotropin (hCG) (which has TSH-like activity). hCG stimulates receptors for both TSH (increases T_4) and hCG (increases estriol and possibly NVP). NVP severity has been correlated with increased free T_4 and decreased TSH, with values returning to normal pregnant ranges as the nausea and vomiting resolve.[69] These findings may lead to or be a consequence of emesis during early pregnancy. NVP is discussed further in Chapter 12.

Hyperemesis gravidarum in women without any history or evidence of thyroid dysfunction has also been associated with increased free T_4 and decreased TSH. These findings, seen in about 60% of women with hyperemesis, are similar to those of the euthyroid sick syndrome seen with severe illness.[73] T_4 levels in women with hyperemesis return to usual values in 1 to 4 weeks after resolution with or without treatment with antithyroid drugs.[18,47,70,96]

The Pregnant Woman With Hyperthyroidism

A transient hyperthyroidism is seen in 10% to 20% of otherwise healthy pregnant women during the first trimester and may be associated with increased hCG levels, multiple gestation, or NVP.[39,41] This transient form of subclinical hyperthyroidism is characterized by normal free T_4 and decreased TSH.

Another form of transient clinical hyperthyroidism, characterized by increased free T_4 and decreased TSH, is less common and may be associated with multiple gestation, hyperemesis gravidarum, and gestational trophoblast disorders with markedly increased hCG production.[39,61,70] Trophoblast disorders such as a molar pregnancy occasionally cause biochemical and, in some women (5% to 64%), clinical findings of hyperthyroidism because of the high levels of hCG secreted by the trophoblastic mass.[99]

Chronic hyperthyroidism occurs in 0.05% to 0.2% of pregnant women.[97] Hyperthyroidism during pregnancy is defined as "serum TSH level below the trimester-specific reference range with elevated levels of T_3 and or free T_4."[115] The diagnosis of hyperthyroidism during pregnancy may be difficult, because the signs and symptoms associated with this disorder are often seen normally during pregnancy. Findings common to hyperthyroidism and certain stages of pregnancy include fatigue, heat intolerance, warm skin, emotional lability, insomnia, increased appetite, sweating, breathlessness, ankle edema, palpitations, and increased pulse pressure.[33,39,47,70,97,99] Failure to gain weight with a good appetite and persistent tachycardia (greater than 100 beats/min) are most suggestive of hyperthyroidism in pregnancy.[47] Increased free T_3 and total T_4 (greater than 15 μg/dL [193 nmol/L]) and increased or high-normal RT_3U are seen with hyperthyroidism. Alterations in thyroid function (see Table 19-1) and thus thyroid function tests during pregnancy must be considered when interpreting test results. For example, because RT_3U is decreased in pregnancy, values in the nonpregnant range suggest hyperthyroidism. TSH levels less than 0.05 μU/L (mIU/mL) and increased free T_4 levels greater than 11.6 μg/dL (149 pmol/L) are diagnostic.[97]

Hyperthyroidism in pregnant women in North America is usually related to either an autoimmune disorder or an unknown cause; it is rarely related to goiter. The risk of goiter during pregnancy is attributed to increased avidity of the thyroid for iodine in response to increased renal loss and placental transport. In most women these losses are compensated for by a higher dietary iodine intake.

Hyperthyroidism in pregnant women is almost always (90% to 95%) a result of Graves' disease.[97] Graves' disease is an autoimmune disorder in which thyroid-stimulating immunoglobulins (TSIs), such as TSH receptor antibody (TRAb), attach to and activate TSH receptors on the thyroid follicular cells. This leads to increased production of thyroid hormones and the clinical finding of hyperthyroidism.

Women with mild hyperthyroidism generally do well during pregnancy because increased serum TBG offsets the increased secretion of thyroid hormones. In women with Graves' disease, their disorder may be aggravated in the first trimester (because of the increased hCG) and then improve during the third trimester, with remission and occasionally complete resolution.[33,160] This improvement is related to suppression of maternal immune system responses by fetal cytokines with lower TSI levels and decreased thyroid hormone production. Relapse or exacerbation generally occurs postpartum, usually within several weeks of delivery, as immune system alterations and production of TBG return to prepregnancy levels.[99,160]

Pregnant women with hyperthyroidism usually require a caloric intake that is higher than that generally recommended during pregnancy to compensate for their increased metabolic rate. These women are also at risk for fluid loss and dehydration as a result of the diarrhea and tachycardia that often accompany hyperthyroidism.[97] Women with hyperthyroidism, particularly if it is poorly controlled, are at increased risk for placental abruption, miscarriage, preterm labor, fetal growth restriction, congestive heart failure, and thyroid storm.[33,39,41,70,97] Their infants can develop transient hyperthyroidism from transplacental passage of TSIs (see Chapter 13) or hypothyroidism secondary to the effects of maternal antithyroid drugs.[41] Hyperthyroidism also alters sex steroid metabolism, sperm motility, and fertility.[15]

Transplacental passage of TSIs, especially TRAb, leads to a transient neonatal hyperthyroidism in about 1% to 5% of infants of mothers with Graves' disease (see p. 448).[4,18,33] The risk is present even if the woman is euthyroid in pregnancy or has had thyroid ablation via surgery or radiation before pregnancy because TSIs are still present.[99] The fetal risk increases after 20 weeks when fetal TSH receptors become responsive to TSH.[78] TSH-binding inhibitory immunoglobulins may also cross the placenta, causing a transient neonatal hypothyroidism.[15]

Hyperthyroidism is treated with antithyroid drugs (thioamides), surgical removal, or thyroid ablation with radioactive iodine-131 (I-131 or ^{131}I). The most common thioamides are propylthiouracil (PTU) and methimazole (MMI) (Tapazole or Carbimazole, which is metabolized to MMI). All of these agents cross the placenta and have potential risks for the fetus and neonate from lowered thyroid hormone levels.[97] The lower hormone levels stimulate increased TSH production, which can lead to fetal goiter and tracheal obstruction. Infants of mothers treated with thioamides may have decreased T_4 and increased TSH levels after birth. These values are generally within normal neonatal limits by 4 to 5 days of age. PTU is recommended as the first-line drug during pregnancy.[18,39,41] Although MMI has the advantage of less frequent dosing and fewer tablets per dose, MMI is associated with a risk of fetal scalp defects (cutis aplasia) and possibly esophageal and choanal atresia.[33,41,73,99] PTU is of concern primarily because of the

risk of hepatotoxicity.[97] Some guidelines recommend using PTU during the first trimester and MMI in the second and third trimesters, although this approach has not been well studied.[18,97,145] Pharmacologic effects must be monitored carefully in women with Graves' disease, particularly during the third trimester, when remission can lead to decreased thyroid hormone production and a transient decrease in required drug dosage by 32 to 36 weeks.[97] In some women, the drug can be transiently discontinued in late pregnancy.[160]

Pregnant women may also develop a transient subacute thyroiditis that often occurs in association with viral infections. The inflammation and destruction of thyroid tissue lead to release of stored thyroid hormone into serum and a transient hyperthyroxinemia. As the disorder resolves, the woman may develop hypothyroidism because the released thyroid hormones are used up before the thyroid gland can produce an adequate new supply. If treatment is initiated, β-blockers such as short term propranolol therapy are used rather than antithyroid drugs that block thyroid hormone production, because with subacute thyroiditis the thyroid is not making hormones.[47,70] Propranolol is generally not indicated for long-term treatment of pregnant women with hyperthyroidism. This drug crosses the placenta and has been associated with fetal growth restriction and impaired responses to anoxia and neonatal hypoglycemia and bradycardia.

The Pregnant Woman With Hypothyroidism

Hypothyroidism in iodine-sufficient pregnant women is usually secondary to autoimmune disorders (after surgical removal or ablation of the thyroid with radioactive iodine for Graves' disease and idiopathic myxedema) or Hashimoto thyroiditis.[4,33,61] Worldwide, iodine deficiency is the most common cause of hypothyroidism and can lead to mental retardation, deafness, and other neurologic symptoms in the infant.[41,53,61,97,99] Iodine deficiency leads to hypothyroxinemia, thyroid stimulation from thyroid-releasing hormone (TRH) and TSH feedback loops, and development of goiter.[69] Women with untreated hypothyroidism have a high incidence of infertility and spontaneous abortion.[33,39,47,73]

The worldwide incidence of hypothyroidism during pregnancy is 0.4% to 11%, with a mean of 2.5%; approximately two-thirds are subclinical hypothyroidism.[113] The diagnosis of hypothyroidism during pregnancy may be missed because some of the signs and symptoms associated with this disorder—fatigue, weight gain, muscle cramps, constipation, and amenorrhea—are also seen normally during pregnancy.[33,47,97] The increase in TBG in pregnancy may mask the decrease in thyroid hormones; however, levels are usually still low for pregnant norms. In addition, free T_4 is low and TSH is elevated.[70]

Pregnancy in women with primary hypothyroidism or autoimmune thyroiditis may be complicated by an increased risk of fetal loss or prolonged pregnancy, possibly because of compromised placental blood flow or the inability of the thyroid gland to meet the metabolic demands of pregnancy. These women are also at greater risk for preterm delivery, low birth weight, preeclampsia, and cesarean section.[4,33,39,41,61,107,113] Weight gain patterns must be carefully monitored in women with hypothyroidism. These women may also have difficulty with fatigue and constipation during pregnancy.

Thyroid hormone replacement doses usually need to be increased as a result of the increased TBG and T_4 demand.[70,99,139] For example, levothyroxine may need to be increased 25% to 40% to maintain normal serum TSH levels.[39,73,113,145] Increased requirements may occur as early as the fifth week of gestation and are influenced by maternal estrogen levels, pregestational TSH levels, maternal volume of distribution, parity, and etiology of the hypothyroidism.[39] Postpartum levothyroxine levels usually decrease to prepregnancy levels, but some women continue to have a greater requirement.[33,39]

The rationale for treatment of subclinical hypothyroidism is the fetal dependence on maternal thyroid hormone, especially early in gestation, and concerns about the risk of fetal neurocognitive impairment from inadequate thyroid hormone.[113] Multiple, and sometimes conflicting, guidelines are available.[2,18,40,140,145] Although overt hypothyroidism is associated with neurodevelopmental problems in offspring, the role of subclinical hypothyroidism is less clear.[18,53,84,100] Subclinical hypothyroidism (elevated TSH but normal free T_4) occurs in 2% to 5% of pregnancies and has been reported to increase the risk of prematurity, abruption, and impaired neurologic outcome in infants.[18,33,53,70,84,101] However, the role of subclinical hypothyroidism in infants' later development is still an area of debate because of inadequate data on the causal relationship between subclinical hypothyroidism and lower IQ levels.[33,53,72,114,140,145] Routine screening for thyroid disorders is also controversial and has been recommended for either all pregnant women or for all who are high risk for this disorder by some, but not all, professional organizations.[2,10,13,18,61,97,162] Universal screening for thyroid dysfunction in pregnancy increased the numbers of women diagnosed and treated for hypothyroidism but was not found to have a clear effect on either maternal or fetal outcomes.[144]

Postpartum Thyroid Disorders

The postpartum period is associated with transient thyroid disorders. Physiologic alterations and experiences of pregnancy can mask clinical findings of hypothyroidism or hyperthyroidism. As a result, these disorders may first become apparent in the postpartum period. Although less common than these transient disorders, postpartum women are also at increased risk of developing Graves' disease, especially women older than 35 years.[6]

Postpartum thyroiditis (PPT) is a transient disorder seen in 4% to 9% of postpartum women.[4,97] The incidence of PPT is 33% to 50% in women with thyroid peroxidase antibodies in early pregnancy (versus 0.5% in those without these antibodies).[61,70] PPT is more prevalent in women with type 1 diabetes.[61] Classic PPT accounts for about 28% of these cases

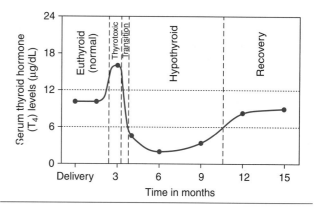

FIGURE 19-5 Thyroid function during postpartum thyroiditis. T_4, Thyroxine. (From Smallridge, R.C., et al. [1988]. Postpartum thyroiditis. *The Bridge, 3,* 3. Newsletter of the Thyroid Foundation of America, Inc.)

and generally appears in the first 6 months (usually by 6 to 8 weeks after delivery). PPT (Figure 19-5) is generally characterized by weeks or months (average, 2 to 4 months, median 13 weeks, but can be up to 6 months) of mild hyperthyroidism, followed by weeks or months (up to a year) of hypothyroidism, and finally a return to normal thyroid function in most women—usually by 12 months postpartum.[18,47,61,70,97,99] Many women present with only hypothyroidism or hyperthyroidism.[97] A 69% recurrence rate has been reported in subsequent pregnancies.[4,97]

The exact cause of PPT is unclear, but it appears to be an autoimmune disorder with increased susceptibility in postpartum women as the immune system rapidly changes from Th2 to Th1 T-lymphocyte dominance (see Chapter 13).[18,70] The initial hyperthyroid phase is characterized by thyroid cell destruction with excessive release of thyroid hormone. PPT may reflect postpartum exacerbation of a subclinical autoimmune disorder that, with release of pregnancy-induced immunosuppression, leads to rebound of immune components with excessive production of thyroid autoantibodies.[47,61] The subsequent hypothyroid phase is related to decreased thyroid hormones from excessive loss of thyroid cells during the first phase. As the thyroid cells regrow, normal function returns.

Up to 30% to 50% of women with PPT remain hypothyroid or develop permanent hypothyroidism within 5 to 15 years.[18,61] Biochemical abnormalities include elevated free T_4, suppression of TSH, presence of microsomal antibodies, and a low I-131 uptake.[70] PPT may be misdiagnosed as postpartum depression and often recurs with subsequent deliveries.[33,70] Transient hypothyroidism is also seen occasionally during the postpartum period. Findings include fatigue, weight gain, low free T_4 and elevated TSH levels, and elevated antimicrosomal and antithyroglobulin antibody titers.

Breastfeeding in Women With Thyroid Disorders

Breastfeeding is not contraindicated in women with hypothyroidism, because thyroid hormones cross in only small amounts and the infant should receive a dose no higher than that from a euthyroid woman.[59,68] Breastfeeding in women with hyperthyroidism may be a concern because of the passage of antithyroid medications and their metabolites in breast milk.[86,143] However, PTU is excreted in breast milk in relatively small amounts (0.025% to 0.077% of the maternal dose).[68] Generally breastfeeding is not routinely contraindicated in women taking PTU who are carefully monitored, but each woman needs to weigh the risks and benefits and infants must be carefully monitored.[68,143,145] The American Thyroid Association recommends that breastfeeding women on antithyroid drugs take the drug in divided doses immediately after breastfeeding to avoid exposure of the infant to peak doses (peak plasma levels are about 1 hour after dosing for MMI and 1 to 1.5 hours for PTU) and that infants have TSH levels monitored.[143,145] Thiouracil is actively transported into breastmilk and in significant amounts and is thus contraindicated in breastfeeding women.[68]

The mammary glands actively take up, concentrate, and secrete iodine in breast milk. Thus breastfeeding is interrupted if the woman requires thyroid uptake studies or scans involving use of radioactive iodine-123 (I-123 or ^{123}I) or I-131. If radioactive iodine is needed, I-123 is preferred over I-131, because breastfeeding generally needs to be stopped for only about 48 hours with I-123 versus the prolonged period needed with I-131.[47]

Use of Radioiodine and Iodides

Iodine is actively transported across the placenta and taken up by the fetal thyroid (Figure 19-6). Avidity of the fetal thyroid for iodine is 20 to 50 times greater than that of the mother.[47] Administration of any form of iodine to pregnant women results in significantly higher concentrations per weight in fetal tissues and can lead to development of a goiter, especially after 10 to 12 weeks' gestation, when the fetal thyroid begins to concentrate iodine.[97] Fetal risks of radioactive substances include thyroid damage, microcephaly, growth restriction, mental retardation, later malignancy, and death. As a result, radioiodine is contraindicated during pregnancy. Radioiodine also alters spermatogenesis, so a waiting period is recommended for in men between therapy and fertilization.

All women should have a pregnancy test before radioactive iodine studies. If these studies are performed with I-123 in a woman who is later found to be pregnant, however, the risks are minimal, because the dose of I-123 used is generally low. The use of I-131 for definitive diagnosis and therapy of Graves' disease is associated with increased pregnancy loss and potential damage to the fetal thyroid; thus this agent is avoided during pregnancy.[39]

The use of nonradioactive iodides has also been reported to increase the risk of fetal goiter, tracheal obstruction, and hypothyroidism. Iodides are found in Betadine-containing vaginal suppositories and douches, saturated solution of potassium iodide (SSKI), iodinated medications for asthmatics, and some contrast materials.[15,47] The incidence of drug-induced

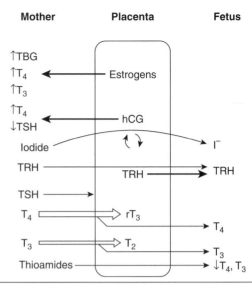

FIGURE 19-6　Placental role in maternal and fetal thyroid function. Heavy arrows indicate placental production of estrogens and human chorionic gonadotropin *(hCG)*, which predominantly moves into maternal blood, and of thyroid-releasing hormone *(TRH)*, which moves primarily into fetal blood. Iodide is actively transported from mother to fetus. The placenta is impermeable to thyroid-stimulating hormone *(TSH)* in either direction. Transfer of thyroxine *(T4)* and triiodothyronine *(T3)* is controlled by placental type III iodothyronine deiodinase, which convert T_4 to rT_3 and T_3 to T_2 (rT_3 and T_2 are inactive compounds). Thyroid hormones from the mother cross the placenta throughout gestation and are critical for fetal development. The relatively free transport of antithyroid drugs (thioamides, such as propylthiouracil *[PTU]* and methimazole) can inhibit fetal thyroid hormone production. *TBG,* Thyroxine-binding globulin. (From Fisher, D.A. & Polk, D.H. [1994]. The ontogenesis of thyroid function and actions. In D. Tulchinsky & A.B. Little. [Eds.]. *Maternal-fetal endocrinology* [2nd ed.]. Philadelphia: Saunders.)

fetal goiter is 1 in 10,000 and is seen primarily with daily iodide doses over 12 μg.

Maternal-Fetal Endocrine Relationships

Maternal, fetal, and placental HPA functions are closely interrelated. The placenta produces significant amounts of some hypothalamic and pituitary hormones such as corticotropin-releasing hormone (CRH) and growth hormone (GH). The fetus and placenta, via CRH production, influence the timing of parturition (see Chapter 4). Large quantities of steroids are produced by interaction of the mother, placenta, and fetus. Some of these substances are dependent on the viability and well-being of the fetus and placenta, whereas others, such as progesterone, do not require the fetus to be viable for production to continue. Steroid-producing cells appear early in placental development. They can be seen first in the trophoblast tissue of the placenta; however, the syncytiotrophoblast lacks several of the key enzymes necessary for steroid metabolism. Therefore the placenta is an incomplete steroidogenic tissue and must receive precursors from the fetus or maternal system (see Chapter 3 and Figure 3-12).

During early gestation, maternal cortisol crossing the placenta provides negative feedback to the fetal HPA axis. This suppresses fetal cortisol production. Later in pregnancy, as placental metabolic activity matures, less maternal cortisol reaches the fetus as much of this cortisol is converted to inactive cortisone in the placenta. In late pregnancy, there is less negative feedback to the fetal HPA axis and increased fetal cortisol production. Placental CRH, which increases during gestation, has a stimulatory effect on the fetal HPA axis and is stimulated by cortisol.[157]

The fetal HPT axis develops relatively independently of maternal influences.[31] Maternal TRH does cross the placenta but does not seem to have a major influence on fetal pituitary or thyroid function, probably because maternal TRH levels are low and much of the maternal TRH is degraded in the placenta.[32,99] Maternal TSH does not cross the placenta.[15,97] Administration of thyroid hormone to the mother does not significantly increase fetal hormone levels.[31]

Maternal T_4 crosses the placenta to the fetus and is critical for normal development of the central nervous system (CNS) and other organ systems, especially in the first trimester before the fetal thyroid is functional and the mother is the only source of T_4 (see Role of Maternal Thyroid Hormones on p. 627).[32,47,69,94,97,138] Transfer continues throughout pregnancy but is decreased in later pregnancy because of increased placental deiodination of T_4 (to inactive rT_3) and T_3 (to T_2) by D3.[15,32] MDI-I (D1) and MDI-II (D2) are expressed by the placenta to produce T_3 locally, especially if maternal T_4 levels are low.[97] Inadequate maternal iodine may decrease transfer of maternal T_4 to the fetus.[75,80,84,168] Increased T_4 transfer has been reported in late gestation with fetuses with severe congenital hypothyroidism.[31] Athyroid fetuses have T_4 levels that are 25% to 50% of normal.[15] The fetus is also dependent on the mother for iodides—either via direct transfer or breakdown of maternal T_4 by the placenta (see Figure 19-6).[31] The placenta is permeable to commonly used antithyroid drugs (PTU and methimazole), β-blockers (propranolol), and iodine.[15] Placental permeability to TSIs can lead to development of transient neonatal hyperthyroidism in infants of women with Graves' disease (see The Pregnant Woman With Hyperthyroidism and p. 448).

Maternal Stress Responses and Fetal Endocrine Programming

Even though both ACTH and cortisol are elevated during pregnancy, physiologic responses (e.g., blood pressure, heart rate, and cortisol reactivity) to stress, although maintained, appear to be blunted in pregnant women, particularly in later pregnancy, as increasing serum cortisol downregulates hypothalamic CRH production.[9,21,23,24] However, data are limited, and wide individual differences have been reported. This blunting may be related to glucocorticoid negative feedback, possibly nitric oxide, urocortins, β-endorphins, and other endogenous opioids.[9] Maternal stress and the intrauterine environment can influence fetal programming.

Fetal programming is "the process whereby early adaptation to adverse environment results in permanent physiologic changes that may be beneficial during fetal life but are less advantageous postnatally."[132] These changes can influence susceptibility to later disorders either via gene-environment interactions producing persistent epigenetic changes or by altering normal development of an organ system.[24,38,67] For example, the nutritional and hormonal status during fetal and early postbirth life can alter organ development, including the hypothalamus and other endocrine structures. Increases in cortisol with maternal stress can lead to increases in fetal cortisol. This is important because before birth, fetal systems such as the fetal HPA axis are programmed for postnatal function, with adverse consequences for later function if programming is altered.[9,154] Normally most of the cortisol reaching the placenta is broken down into inert metabolites by placental enzymes, such as 11-β-hydroxysteroid dehydrogenase, in the syncytiotrophoblast. These enzymes convert active glucocorticoids, such as cortisol and corticosterone, to inactive metabolites.[24,27,76] As a result, fetal circulating cortisol levels are normally maintained lower than maternal levels; however, with adverse events such as maternal physiologic or psychological stress, fetal stress, excessive anxiety or depression, infection, or inflammation, fetal cortisol levels may become elevated.[24,27,132]

Wide individual differences have been reported in both maternal stress reactivity and in the activity and sensitivity of these placental enzymes.[21,23] Human and animal studies demonstrate the effects of prenatal stress on offspring, including prematurity, low birth weight, delivery complications, and impaired prenatal and postnatal growth and development.[14,21,24,27,44,108,154,161] For example, the risk of early pregnancy loss with maternal stress may be mediated by alterations in glucocorticoids, progesterone and prolactin, and the immune system, leading to alterations in the early pregnancy cytokine environmental balance (see Chapter 13) needed for implantation and early pregnancy maintenance.[9] Early stress may also induce epigenetic changes in gene expression that increase the risk of later metabolic, vascular, and neurodevelopmental disorders in offspring.[14,27,38,85,154] Prolonged exposure to maternal stress mediators may permanently reset the HPA axis and increase the risk of adult-onset disorders such as type 2 diabetes, hypertension, obesity, coronary artery disease, end-stage renal disease, and depression.[9,24,27,38,147,154,157]

The specific mechanisms by which maternal stress affects the fetus are unclear but probably involve changes in the fetal HPA axis from maternal increases in sympathetic nervous system and HPA activity, and perhaps changes in the limbic system, with stress.[22] Glucocorticoids are believed to have a major role in fetal tissue programming, because excess levels can inhibit growth; alter expression of receptors, enzymes, ion channels, and transporters; and alter growth factors, structural proteins, binding proteins, and signaling pathways.[112,132] Several possible mechanisms have been proposed:[21,112,154,161]

1. A stress-induced increase in maternal cortisol results in increased fetal cortisol and changes in the feedback regulation of the fetal HPA axis.
2. Hormones from the maternal HPA axis stimulate the placenta to increase CRH, which alters brain glucocorticoid receptor development and function in the fetus.
3. Increased cortisol and catecholamines seen with stress may alter uteroplacental blood flow, leading to poorer fetal growth, prematurity, and other complications.

Figure 19-7 illustrates a proposed model of factors contributing to indirect and direct effects of stress on the fetus. Fetal programming is discussed further in Chapters 11, 12, and 16.

SUMMARY

Changes in the HPA axis during pregnancy enhance maternal adaptations and availability of nutrients to the fetus. Maternal HPA function is interrelated with placental function, because the placenta produces hypothalamic and pituitary hormones such as CRH and GH. Placental CRH plays a major role in initiation of parturition (see Chapter 4). Changes in HPA and HPT function can alter reproductive processes. A pregnant woman is in a state of euthyroid hyperthyroxinemia and transient hypercortisolism, although control set points are reset so the woman responds to stress in a manner that is similar to that of nonpregnant individuals. As a result, values for some endocrine function tests are altered. These changes must be considered when evaluating neuroendocrine function during pregnancy. Thyroid disorders are not uncommon in pregnant women. Knowledge of the effects of these disorders and their treatment is important to optimize fetal and neonatal outcome. Clinical recommendations related to changes in pituitary, adrenal and thyroid function in pregnant women are summarized in Box 19-5.

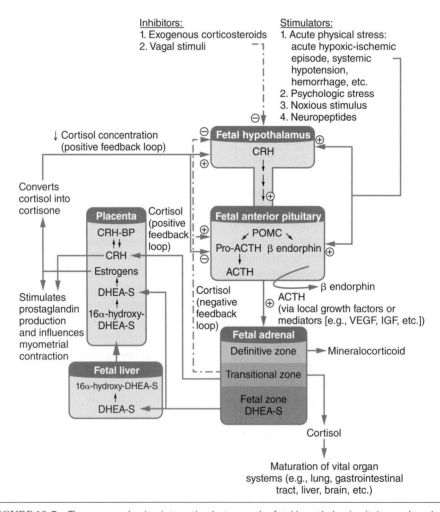

FIGURE 19-7 The neuroendocrine interaction between the fetal hypothalamic-pituitary-adrenal axis and the placenta. The *solid arrows* represent positive stimulatory pathways, including effects of stressors, and the *broken arrows* represent negative inhibitory pathways. *ACTH,* Adrenocorticotropin; *CRH,* corticotropin-releasing hormone; *CRH-BP,* corticotropin-releasing hormone binding protein; *DHEA-S,* dehydroepiandrosterone sulfate; *IGF,* insulin-like growth factor; *POMC,* proopiomelanocortin; *pro-ACTH,* proadrenocorticotropin; *VEGF,* vascular endothelial growth factor. (From Ng, P.C. [2000]. The fetal and neonatal hypothalamic-pituitary-adrenal axis. *Arch Dis Child Fetal Neonatal Ed, 82,* F250.)

DEVELOPMENT OF HYPOTHALAMIC, PITUITARY, ADRENAL, AND THYROID FUNCTION IN THE FETUS

Maturation of thyroid and adrenal function is interrelated with that of the hypothalamic and pituitary glands and the hypothalamic-pituitary-adrenal (HPA) and hypothalamic-pituitary-thyroid (HPT) axes. This process can be divided into three overlapping phases: embryogenesis (phase I), hypothalamic maturation (phase II), and maturation of thyroid and adrenal system function (phase III).[32] During the first phase (10 to 12 weeks), the adrenal and thyroid glands develop morphologically. Hypothalamic function matures during phase II (from 4 to 5 until 35 to 40 weeks). Thyroid-releasing hormone (TRH), gonadotropin-releasing hormone (GnRH), and growth hormone (GH) are detected in the hypothalamus by 10 to 12 weeks (by radioimmunoassay) and in fetal blood in the third trimester.[45] Phase III lasts from midgestation until term or 1 month after birth if transitional changes are considered. This stage involves increasing maturation and integration of endocrine system function.

Hypothalamus and Pituitary Gland
Anatomic Development

The hypothalamus and anterior pituitary glands develop simultaneously but independently of each other. As a result, growth of the various cell types within the anterior pituitary is not dependent on the presence of the hypothalamus. For example, anencephalic infants do not have a hypothalamus but have thyroid-stimulating hormone (TSH) cells within their rudimentary anterior pituitary gland.

The hypothalamus develops from 6 to 12 weeks from the ventral portion of the diencephalon. Hypothalamic nuclei and supraoptic track fibers develop by 12 to 14 weeks, with maturation of the hypothalamic neurons by 30 to 35 weeks.[31,98] The anterior pituitary arises from the anterior wall of the Rathke pouch, an upward offshoot of the primitive oral cavity.[129] The posterior pituitary and stalk develop from the infundibulum, a thickening on the floor of the diencephalon.[129] The anterior pituitary can be seen by 4 weeks and is independent of the oral cavity by 12 weeks. During the fifth week, the primitive anterior pituitary becomes connected with the infundibulum.

Cell types within the anterior pituitary develop in a specific order controlled by coordinated expression and upregulation and downregulation of various transcription factors.[98] Cellular differentiation within the anterior pituitary gland begins at 7 to 8 weeks, under the influence of Pit-1 (a transcription regulator) that activates expression of genes encoding GH and prolactin and differentiation of the different anterior pituitary cell types.[129] Thyrotropic cells appear at 12 to 13 weeks. An increase in TSH-secreting cell volume occurs by 23 weeks. Corticotroph cells can be identified by 6 weeks and express adrenocorticotropic hormone (ACTH) by 7 weeks; somatotroph can be seen by 8 weeks. TSH and gonadotropin β subunits are seen by 12 weeks. Lactotroph cells do not produce prolactin until after 24 weeks.[37]

Hypothalamic and Pituitary Function

The HPA axis is essential for regulating intrauterine homeostasis and maturation of the lungs, liver, and central nervous system (CNS); in conjunction with the placenta, this axis essential in the timing of parturition (see Chapter 4).[103] The hypothalamus and pituitary gland also play major roles in regulating the principal fetal steroid-secreting glands (adrenal glands and gonads) via a negative feedback mechanism. Figure 19-7 summarizes the HPA axis in the fetus and its interaction with placental function.

The fetal hypothalamus is visible by 7 weeks' gestation.[120] The hypothalamus-pituitary axis is generally complete by 12 to 18 weeks' gestation.[120] The HPA axis is established by 20 weeks and matures throughout the remainder of gestation; integrated HPA function matures postnatally.[32] The hypothalamic-pituitary portal system is functional by 10 to

12 weeks, and most of the hormones of the HPA axis are present by 10 to 16 weeks' gestation.[32,86,96] For example, ACTH is seen in pituitary cells by 5 to 8 weeks and is measurable in fetal plasma by 16 weeks.[120] Plasma concentrations of these hormones rise for the first half of gestation. At this time the negative feedback loop comes into operation, and production and release of pituitary hormones become more finely regulated, and fetal plasma ACTH levels are similar to or greater than maternal levels.[132] Corticotropin-releasing hormone (CRH) from the fetus and placenta stimulates ACTH, which controls growth, differentiation, and function of the adrenal cortex in conjunction with growth factors (GFs) and other mediators.[103]

Fetal GH and prolactin appear early in gestation. Prolactin may be involved in regulation of amniotic fluid osmolality and lung metabolism.[51] GH does not have a major role in fetal growth but acts primarily on metabolic functions and protection from hypoglycemia (see Chapter 16).[51] GH levels are higher in the fetus than after birth because of immature inhibitory control and lack of GH receptors on fetal tissues.[45] Increases in cortisol before delivery are believed to induce GH receptors and changes in insulin-like growth factor 1 (IGF-1).

Hypothalamic-Pituitary-Gonadal Axis. GnRH has been identified as early as 4 to 5 weeks, is found in the hypothalamus by 8 to 13 weeks, and increases to 30 weeks.[86,98] The fetal pituitary releases gonadotropins in response to GnRH by the second trimester.[98] Luteinizing hormone (LH) and follicle-stimulating hormone (FSH) appear in the fetal pituitary gland by 9.5 to 11 weeks and reach their peaks at about 25 to 29 weeks' gestation in girls and 35 to 40 weeks in boys.[98] These differences in female versus male fetuses may be related to inhibition of pituitary gonadotropin production by testosterone production in boys.[98] After peaking, LH and FSH decrease to low levels (similar to prepuberty levels) by term.[98] The concentration of LH is higher than that of FSH, and girls have higher levels than boys.[86] FSH promotes development of follicles in girls.[98] In boys FSH stimulates growth of seminiferous tubules and initiates spermatogenesis and phallic growth in late gestation.[98] LH increases the synthesis and secretion of testosterone in the male embryo and stimulates steroid synthesis in ovarian cells. Development of the hypothalamic-pituitary-gonadal axis is discussed further in Chapter 2 and summarized in Box 2-3 on page 40.

Adrenal Glands
Anatomic Development

The adrenal cortex arises in the fourth to fifth week from the intermediate mesoderm in the notch between the primitive urogenital ridge and the dorsal mesentery.[16,126] These cells proliferate and form cords migrating medially and laterally to the cranial end of the mesonephros (primitive transitional renal structures).[86] Neural crest cells form a medial mass on the primitive cortex. These cells are surrounded by the cortex cells and differentiate into the adrenal medulla. Later, another wave of cells surrounds the initial cortical cells to form the

definitive cortex.[16,129,165] By 8 weeks, the cortex is organized into the fetal zone, with the definitive zone appearing a week later.[16,86,165] The fetal zone increases in size from 10 to 15 weeks and dominates from 16 to 20 weeks, being similar in size to the fetal kidneys.[16,126,159] At 22 to 24 weeks, a transitional zone that is initially similar to the fetal zone appears between the fetal and definitive zones. During the second and third trimesters, the adrenal glands continue to enlarge, with hypertrophy of the fetal zone and hyperplasia of the definitive zone.[16,86]

By midgestation, the fetal zone occupies 85% of the adrenal volume and is highly vascularized.[122,123] The adrenals double in size between 20 and 30 weeks and double again between 30 and 40 weeks as steroidogenic activity increases.[16,159] At term, the adrenal glands each weigh 3 to 4 g and, relative to adult proportions, are 20 to 30 times larger.[16,86,122] After birth, the adrenal undergoes extensive remodeling, with a decrease in size and disappearance of the fetal zone.

Adrenal Function

The fetal adrenal gland in conjunction with the placenta is responsible for maintaining pregnancy, initiating parturition (see Chapter 4), promoting maturation of the lungs, and kidneys; liver accumulation of glycogen; gluconeogenesis; and, via cortisol, enhancing production of thyroid hormones and catecholamines.[159] As noted previously, the fetal adrenal gland initially consists of two zones: the fetal zone (analogous to the adult zona reticularis) and the definitive zone (which becomes the postnatal adrenal neocortex, or zona glomerulosa, producing aldosterone. During the third trimester, the transitional zone, which gives rise to the glucocorticoid-producing zona fasciculata, develops between the fetal and definitive zones. The fetal zone contains large lipid-containing steroidogenic cells, which are the major source of dehydroepiandrosterone (DHEA) and its sulfate (DHEA-S), which are precursors for production of estrone and estradiol-17β in the placenta. DHEA-S is also the precursor for 16-hydroxydehydroepiandrosterone, which is needed for estriol production by the placenta (see Chapter 3). Cholesterol is the precursor for these steroid hormones, and the fetus uses both endogenous cholesterol synthesized from low-density lipoproteins and cholesterol transferred across the placenta.[122]

The placenta does not produce these precursors and thus is dependent on the fetal adrenal (primary source) or mother. In fetuses with decreased adrenal function, such as anencephalic fetuses, estriol production by the placenta remains low. Enzymes to synthesize DHEA-S are present by 6 to 8 weeks.[86,120] High levels of 17α-hydroxylase (17-OH or CYP17) and probably 21-hydroxylase (21-OH or CYP21) are seen early in gestation (Figure 19-8). 17-OH and 21-OH are cytochrome P-450 enzymes not expressed by the placenta.[159] Deficiency of 21-OH is the most common cause of congenital adrenal hyperplasia (see p. 633); a lack of 21-OH can result in virilization of the female external genitalia. Because the

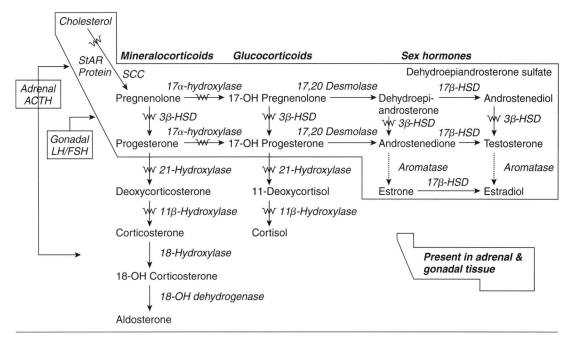

FIGURE 19-8 Adrenal and gonadal steroidogenesis. The *solid line* represents a major pathway; the *dotted line* represents a major pathway in the ovaries and minor pathway in the adrenals; w represents one of the potential areas of deficient enzymatic activity causing congenital adrenal hyperplasia. 3β-HSD, 3β-hydroxysteroid dehydrogenase; 17β-HSD, 17β-hydroxysteroid dehydrogenase; *SCC*, cholesterol side-chain cleavage enzyme; *StAR*, steroidogenic autoregulatory protein. (From Pang, S. [1997]. Congenital adrenal hyperplasia. *Endocrinol Metab Clin North Am, 26*, 854.)

genital tract differentiates at 7 to 10 weeks (see Chapter 1), this enzyme must be present early in gestation.[16] Levels of 3β-hydroxysteroid dehydrogenase (involved in cortisol production) are low in fetuses.[16] The large size of the adrenal glands allows the fetus to secrete larger amounts of adrenal androgens daily, predominantly DHEA-S, than do adults. The fetus supplies 90% of the DHEA-S to the placenta after 16-hydroxylation by the fetal liver (see Figure 19-7).[122,123]

Cortisol is produced as early as 8 to 12 weeks, but in small amounts and primarily from progesterone.[16,86,120,159] Production of cortisol from cholesterol, the usual precursor in later life, requires 3β hydroxysteroid dehydrogenase (3β-HSD).[157] 3β-HSD is not consistently expressed before 22 to 24 weeks' gestation, with limited adrenal capacity for synthesis until after 30 weeks.[95,120] Cortisol secretion is present by 20 to 24 weeks' gestation.[32] Fetal cortisol levels gradually increase from 5 to 10 μg/mL at 30 weeks to 20 μg/mL after 36 weeks and 45 μg/mL before term labor onset.[57] Cortisol is essential for fetal maturation of the lungs, gut, liver, and CNS.[103] Cortisol is also found in amniotic fluid. During labor, fetal cortisol levels double.[57,159] Most fetal tissues and especially the placenta contain enzymes such as 11β hydroxysteroid dehydrogenase type 2 (11β-HSD2) that convert cortisol to inactive cortisone. This serves as a protective mechanism against elevated cortisol in the fetus.

Maternal cortisol enters the placenta. However, because about 85% is deactivated by 11β-HSD2, little reaches the fetus.[157] Maternal cortisol that does reach the fetus has a negative feedback effect on the fetal HPA axis, suppressing fetal cortisol production. Placental CRH stimulates pituitary

ACTH production that in turn stimulates the fetal adrenal to produce cortisol, DHEA, and DHEA-S.[157] In the third trimester, placental 11β-HSD2 activity increases with increased conversion of both fetal and maternal cortisol to cortisone. This reduction in active cortisol reaching the fetal hypothalamus and pituitary further reduces negative feedback to the HPA axis that would normally reduce CRH, ACTH, and cortisol levels. This increases adrenal DHEA-S synthesis. DHEA-S production increases estrogen production, which in turn stimulates increased 11β-HSD2.[32,103,122,157]

CRH plays a major role in regulating fetal adrenal steroidogenesis in late gestation and in labor onset (see Chapter 4).[122,159] Placental CRH stimulates the fetal HPA axis and is itself stimulated by fetal cortisol (whereas hypothalamic CRH is inhibited by high cortisol levels). Seven to ten weeks before birth fetal adrenal cortisol production increases with a decrease in the conversion of cortisol to inactive cortisone, mediated by an increase in 11β-HSD activity (stimulated by estrogens) (see Figure 19-7).[32,159] Factors influencing fetal adrenal function are summarized in Table 19-2 and Figure 19-7.

Growth of the adrenal glands is probably not dependent on ACTH, because an anencephalic fetus with low ACTH levels develops adrenal glands, but ACTH is required for adrenal function.[16,123] ACTH may exert its effect via local GFs and other mediators such as fibroblast GF, epidermal GF, transforming growth factor-α (TGF-α), IGF-1, IGF-2, transforming growth factor-β (TGF-β), activin, and inhibin.[16,86,126,155,159,165] ACTH, estrogens, and IGF-2 stimulate growth of the definitive zone and activation of 3β-HSD and

TABLE 19-2 Factors Affecting Fetal Adrenal Function

FACTOR	EFFECT
Maternal cortisol passively transferred to the fetus, suppressing the fetal HPA axis	Increased production during maternal stress
	Increased transfer during early gestation
	Increased transfer in the presence of decreased placental 11β-HSD2 activity
Placental 11β-HSD2	Converts maternal cortisol to cortisone
	Modulates exposure of fetus to maternal cortisol
Placental CRH	Stimulates fetal HPA axis
	Is in turn stimulated by increased fetal cortisol
	Increases exponentially before delivery
Chorioamnionitis	Proinflammatory cytokines stimulate fetal HPA axis
Fetal responses to maternal and placental signaling during development	HPA axis suppressed by maternal cortisol
	HPA axis stimulated by placental CRH or chorioamnionitis

11β-HSD2, 11β hydroxy-steroid dehydrogenase type 2; *CRH,* corticotropin-releasing hormone; *HPA axis,* hypothalamus-pituitary-adrenal axis.
From Watterberg, K.L. (2004). Adrenocortical function and dysfunction in the fetus and neonate. *Semin Neonatol, 9,* 14.

P450 17α-hydroxylase, which mediate the increase in fetal cortisol production in late gestation.[32,159]

Fisher summarizes the significance of this increase in fetal cortisol in late gestation in anticipation of transition to extrauterine life: "The increase in fetal circulating cortisol concentration during the final weeks of gestation is associated with a variety of physiologic responses. These include (a) increased conversion of T_4 to T_3 by stimulation of hepatic iodothyronine monodeiodinase (MDI-I; also called D1) and inhibition of MDI-III (also called D3) leading to an increase in circulating T_3 and decrease in rT_3 levels; (b) increased epinephrine secretion by sympathetic chromaffin tissue (including adrenal medulla) because of augmented phenylethanolamine transferase activity (which converts norepinephrine to epinephrine); (c) augmented synthesis and secretion of surfactant and maturation of surfactant composition; (d) stimulation of maturation of hepatic gluconeogenic enzyme activities; (e) increased β-adrenergic receptor density in a variety of tissues, including lung, heart, and brown adipose tissue; and (f) induction and maturation of a variety of gut enzymes for nutrient absorption and maturation of gut transport processes, motility, and structure."[32, p. 390]

Intrauterine stress may activate adrenal cortisol secretion (see Maternal Stress Responses and Fetal Endocrine Programming on p. 621). This often occurs at the cost of decreased DHEA-S production and thus lowered estriol production. The fetus may be exposed to elevated cortisol passively (because of increased maternal cortisol secondary to maternal stress or lowered placental 11β-HSD2 activity) or actively secondary to proinflammatory cytokine secretion.[157] Passive exposure tends to suppress the fetal HPA axis and may increase the risk of low birth weight, prematurity, and other complications as well as alter growth and development and increase the risk of adult-onset disorders; active exposure tends to enhance cortisol production after birth.[21,157,161] The fetus also responds to stress after 18 to 19 weeks by increasing β-endorphin (BE) levels.[121,137]

Thyroid Gland
Anatomic Development

The thyroid gland develops during the first 12 weeks of gestation in three stages: precolloid (7 to 13 weeks), colloid (13 to 14 weeks), and follicular (after 14 weeks), the stage in which thyroid hormone secretion begins.[36] The thyroid begins as an epithelial thickening at the base of the tongue around 20 to 22 days.[15] As the primordial gland migrates downward, it becomes bilobular with a small median isthmus and begins to form follicles.[62] The thyroid initially descends in front of the pharyngeal gut. Later the thyroid descends in front of the hyoid bone and larynx to reach its final position in front of the trachea by 45 to 50 days of gestation.[15] Thyroid gland volume further increases 8- to 10-fold between 30 and 42 weeks' gestation with increasing iodine, thyroglobulin, iodothyronine, and thyroid hormone reserves.[32]

Thyroid Function

The bioavailability of TSH, T_4, and T_3 is determined by (1) activity of the HPT axis, (2) T_4 and T_3 production, (3) peripheral conversion of T_4 to more biologically active T_3 or to inactive metabolites, (4) binding of T_4 and T_3 to thyroid hormone receptors on various target tissues, and (5) T_4 and T_3 uptake and subsequent activation of cellular processes.[36] TRH synthesis begins in the hypothalamus by 6 to 8 weeks and is found in fetal serum by 8 to 9 weeks.[86,99,124] TRH is also synthesized by the placenta, fetal pancreas, and gut. Fetal serum TRH levels are high during the first and second trimesters because of these extrahypothalamic sources; hypothalamic TRH production matures by 35 to 40 weeks along with maturation of the hypothalamic-pituitary portal system.[32,103] TSH can be detected in fetal serum by 10 to 12 weeks.[15,36] Levels are low until 18 weeks, then increase to 28 weeks, and then plateau and decrease to term.[15,47,86]

By 10 to 12 weeks, the thyroid gland begins to accumulate and concentrate iodine and has begun to synthesize and secrete iodothyronines.[36] T_4 can be detected in fetal serum by 12 to 14 weeks, increasing to 2 μg/dL by 20 weeks and 10 μg/dL by term.[15,33,62,86,97,99,124,149] Fetal thyroid function remains at basal levels until midgestation, even though the capacity to secrete these hormones as well as TSH and TRH develops earlier.[31,47,86] As a result, significant amounts of fetal thyroid hormone are not produced before 18 to 20 weeks' gestation, when fetal iodide uptake and serum T_4

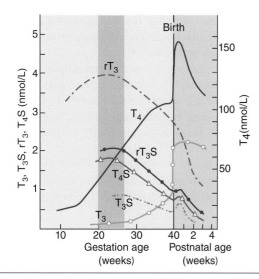

FIGURE 19-9   Maturation of serum iodothyronine concentrations in the human fetus and newborn. T_3, Triiodothyronine; T_4, thyroxine; rT_3, reverse T_3. T_4S, T_3S, and rT_3S are sulfated analogs. The neonatal TSH surge peaks at 60 to 70 mU/L. The shaded area highlights levels in extremely low-birth-weight fetuses. (From Fisher, D.A. [2008]. Thyroid system immaturities in very low–birth weight premature infants. *Semin Perinatol, 32*, 389.)

increase.[94,97] TSH, T_4, and free T_4 increase from 15 to 42 weeks.[163] At term, T_4 levels in cord blood are 10% to 20% lower than maternal values; most fetal T_4 is bound to TTR and albumin.[15] Free T_4 concentrations in fetal fluids reflect the interaction between T_4-binding proteins and maternal T_4, which maintains sufficient free T_4 for fetal needs but prevents toxic levels.[94] Thyroxine-binding globulin (TBG) can be detected by 10 to 12 weeks and reaches term values by midgestation.[15,36] Concentrations of iodine increase after 13 to 15 weeks, with peak concentrations at 20 to 24 weeks.[70] Changes in fetal thyroid hormones are summarized in Figure 19-9.

Serum T_3 levels remain low until 30 weeks and then increase slightly, but they never approach maternal values.[31,36,99,149] At term, fetal T_3 and free T_3 levels are 30% to 50% of maternal values.[15] T_3 levels remain low, because the fetus is unable to convert T_4 to T_3 peripherally as a result of the incomplete enzyme systems. The increase in T_3 after 30 weeks is associated with maturation of these enzymes.[31] Type II (D2) and type III (D3) monodeiodinases (see Box 19-3 on pp. 612-613) are present by midgestation; D1 (which converts T_4 to the highly active T_3) matures later, and levels are low during gestation.[32,149] As a result, a greater proportion of T_4 is converted to the inactive rT_3 in fetuses than in adults.[31,36,96] Iodothyronines are inactivated by sulfation as well, which also helps to regulate the amount of active thyroid hormone; these analogs are also metabolized to the inactive rT_3S.[36,163] Increased production of sulfated analogs of thyroid hormones are seen in fetuses.[32] In a hypothyroid fetus, D3 increases and D1 is suppressed, so T_4 is shunted to the CNS, where it is converted to T_3 by D2.[32] The control by these monodeiodinases of the levels of active thyroid hormones at different stages of development is an important protective mechanism, because too much T_3 could damage cells. Organs such as the brain, which are dependent on T_3 for normal development, have higher levels of enzymes such as D2 and D3 needed to convert T_4 to T_3.[21,84,96,97]

Serum rT_3 levels rise early in the third trimester and then progressively decrease to term as monodeiodinase activity increases.[15,86,149] As noted earlier, the elevated serum rT_3 levels in the fetus are a result of increased D3 activity (see also Box 19-3 on pp. 612-613).[31] D3 is the predominant monodeiodinase in the fetus and placenta, with levels 10 to 15 times greater than in adults.[31,32] This increases conversion of T_4 to the biologically inactive rT_3 (rather than to biologically active T_3) and T_3 to the inactive T_2; this may be a way the fetus counteracts high T_4 levels and maintains metabolic homeostasis.[31,32,58] Thyroid maturation in the late fetal and early neonatal period is related to progressive increases in hypothalamic TRH secretion, TRH responsiveness by the pituitary (by 26 to 28 weeks, the fetus responds to TRH in a manner similar to that of adults), sensitivity of the thyroid to TSH, and maturation of feedback mechanisms.[31,32]

Role of Maternal Thyroid Hormones

Thyroid hormones are critical for brain development, neuronogenesis, neuron migration, axon and dendrite formation, and organization. Thyroid hormone receptors develop early in the fetal brain, appearing by at least 9 weeks' postmenstrual age and increasing 10-fold by 18 weeks; 25% to 30% of the receptors are occupied by T_3 during this time.[94] Thyroid hormones are much higher in the brain than fetal serum at each stage of development because of activity of D2 and brain D3.[94]

Maternal thyroid hormones are transferred via specific transporter proteins to the fetus in the first trimester, beginning soon after conception, and increase rapidly over the next weeks to biologically relevant values that correlate with maternal values.[58,84,93,94,99] During the second and third trimesters when the fetal thyroid is producing hormone, additional T_4 needed for development and neuroprotection is of maternal origin.[36,58] This has implications for infants born prematurely, especially very-low-birth-weight (VLBW) infants, who lose this protection by their early birth.[94] Maternal hypothyroidism is particularly damaging to the fetal brain in the first half of pregnancy when fetal T_4 production is low.[93,124] T_3 generation from T_4 by D2 increases in the cerebral cortex until midgestation, reaching values similar to those in the adult brain. Cerebral T_3 levels are dependent on local production in the brain, via D2 that converts T_4 to T_3, and are thus not affected by circulating T_3 levels, but by circulating T_4.[36] Therefore if the mother has low T_4 levels, the fetal brain may have a deficiency of T_3 for normal development, even if circulating T_3 is normal or increased.[93] Maternal iodine deficiency results in altered thyroid function and inadequate thyroid hormone for development; maternal iodine excess can also block thyroid hormone synthesis and secretion.[119,124]

NEONATAL PHYSIOLOGY
Transitional Events

Catecholamines and cortisol surge at birth. Catecholamines, including epinephrine, norepinephrine, and dopamine, increase to levels 20 times greater than those of adults.[32] This increase is greater with vaginal birth than with cesarean birth and greater in preterm than term infants, although the response is slower in preterm infants.[57] The catecholamine response is lower in preterm infants receiving antenatal corticosteroid therapy to induce lung maturation.[57] Levels decrease after the first few hours. The increase in catecholamines with labor and delivery promotes extrauterine cardiorespiratory transition and adaptation (see Chapters 9 and 10) and adaptation of energy metabolism (see Chapter 16) and fluid homeostasis (see Chapter 11); initiates brown adipose tissue thermogenesis (see Chapter 20); and is accompanied by a surge in other hormones, including renin, angiotensin II, arginine vasopressin (AVP; see Chapter 11), adrenocorticotropic hormone (ACTH), β-endorphins (BEs), and cortisol.[57,28] Cortisol helps regulate the responses of the newborn to the catecholamine surge and, along with thyroid hormones, helps activate the sodium pump to clear lung fluid after birth (see Chapter 10).[57] Cord blood AVP is higher in infants delivered vaginally versus cesarean birth, decreasing rapidly after birth in both groups, and is correlated with evidence of fetal distress.[28] Thyroid hormones are involved in the regulation of thermogenesis, cardiac contractility, and metabolic function during transition to extrauterine life.[7]

Hypothalamic-Pituitary-Adrenal Axis

Remodeling of the adrenal glands after birth occurs via apoptosis of the fetal zone, remodeling of the fetal zone cells, and development of the other zones.[16,86,159] Apoptosis of the fetal zone is mediated by activin and transforming growth factor-β (TGF-β). The size of the adrenals decreases 25% in the first 4 days after birth.[159] Adequate pituitary function is seen in both term and preterm infants.[82]

The cortisol surge that began in late gestation increases during labor and transition to extrauterine life.[32] This surge is blunted in VLBW infants.[32,57] Cortisol levels, which doubled during labor, increase further in the first 1 to 2 hours after birth, and then gradually fall during the first week.[57,159] There is an inverse relationship between cortisol levels and gestational age. ACTH and cortisol levels are higher in infants delivered vaginally than in those delivered by cesarean.[87] ACTH and BE levels are elevated in cord blood and decrease significantly by 24 hours and reach adult levels by 4 to 5 days in healthy infants.[74,79,121] After birth the high placental corticotropin-releasing hormone (CRH) levels fall. This may lead to a refractory period over the first few days during which newborn CRH production by the hypothalamus is transiently suppressed, accompanied by a refractory pituitary gland response.[159] These changes result in a decreased ability to increase ACTH to stimulate the adrenal gland. This transition is tolerated well in healthy infants but in immature or ill infants may lead to a relative adrenal insufficiency and cardiovascular compromise (see Adrenal Cortex Insufficiency).[30,105,120,159] Pituitary and steroidal hormone reference ranges for preterm infants have been published.[48,49]

BEs are endogenous opioid-like substances that are derived, along with ACTH and other substances, from a large precursor molecule (proopiomelanocortin). BEs increase markedly with birth in both term and preterm infants. The BE increase at birth is greater with perinatal hypoxic-ischemic events or other stress such as forceps delivery and is reported to be inversely related to PO_2.[121,146] Other endogenous opioids, such as the enkephalins, are also increased at birth and further increased with hypoxia, acidosis, and ischemia.

Both term and preterm infants in the neonatal intensive care unit (NICU) have higher BE levels than healthy term infants. Preterm infants (especially preterm males) have higher BE levels than both healthy term and ill term infants.[74] Elevated BE levels are seen in stressed preterm infants with apnea, but not in nonstressed infants.[79] Release of BE is a component of neonatal respiratory control and is triggered by hypoxia.[79] BE levels are also higher in infants with respiratory distress.[74]

The administration of antenatal corticosteroids (see Chapter 10) leads to a transient suppression of the pituitary and adrenal glands. Long-term effects on hypothalamic-pituitary-adrenal (HPA) function have not been well studied.[83] Even with this suppression, healthy, preterm infants respond to stress with increased cortisol.[103] An ill infant, however, is less able to respond to stress and is more vulnerable to stress-related morbidity (see Neonatal Stress and Adrenal Cortex Insufficiency).

Growth hormone (GH) decreases after birth as free fatty acids, which block GH release, increase with nonshivering thermogenesis.[45,51] GH levels are higher in preterm infants than in term infants.[51] Prolactin increases in the late fetal and early neonatal periods. Levels are higher in preterm infants than in term infants because of increased sensitivity to thyroid-stimulating hormone (TSH) and estrogens, pituitary insensitivity to dopaminergic inhibition, and reduced renal excretion by the immature kidney (with its lower glomerular filtration rate).[51,146] Prolactin may have a role in lung maturation and fluid homeostasis with transition.[51] Dopamine levels are twice those of adults and function as a prolactin release–inhibiting factor.[86] Luteinizing hormone (LH) and follicle-stimulating hormone (FSH) increase with birth, then decrease over the months to prepuberty levels. Patterns are different for female and male infants (see Maturational Changes During Infancy and Childhood).[98]

Hypothalamic-Pituitary-Thyroid Axis

A newborn is in a state of physiologic hyperthyroidism because of marked changes in thyroid function at birth.[15,58] These changes are summarized in Figure 19-9. Thyroid-releasing hormone (TRH) and TSH levels increase rapidly after birth, followed by increases in T_4, free T_4, T_3, and free T_3.[149] Exposure of the newborn to the cooler extrauterine environment increases TSH and iodothyronine monodeiodinase (MDI)-II (also called D2) expression in brown adipose tissue. MDI-III (also called D3) production is suppressed by the rising PO_2 levels.[58] These changes, along with stimulation of skin thermal receptors, lead to TRH release by the hypothalamus and TSH release by the pituitary gland.[32] The TSH surge is also stimulated by the cutting of the umbilical cord and the catecholamine surge at birth.[32,58] The increase in TSH (and T_4) with cord cutting is limited in extremely low-birth-weight (ELBW) infants.[32] TSH increases from 9 to 10 μU/mL (IU/L) at birth to peak at 60 to 70 mU/L within the first hour after birth.[32] TSH rapidly decreases to 50% of peak values by 2 hours and to 20% by 24 hours, followed by a progressive decrease over the next 2 to 3 days to levels similar to or lower than cord blood values (see Figure 19-9).[29,31,32,86] During the first week, periodic oscillations in serum TSH have been reported, possibly reflecting an establishment of a new equilibrium in the negative feedback exerted by the thyroid hormone on the anterior pituitary.[129] Although TSH generally falls to adult ranges within 3 to 10 days, TSH may remain somewhat elevated for several months.[15,124]

The TSH surge leads to a rapid threefold to sixfold increase in T_4.[32,163] T_3 and twofold increase in free T_4.[32,163] T_3 and rT_3 levels are correlated with gestational age and birth weight.[124] T_4 levels peak at 24 to 48 hours after birth (see Figure 19-9), then slowly decrease over the next few weeks.[15,32,99,124,149] Free T_4 reaches adult values by 4 to 6 weeks.[15]

Cord blood T_3 values average 45 to 50 ng/dL (0.69 to 0.77 pmol/L) (30% to 50% of maternal values). The newborn quickly changes from a state of T_3 deficiency to T_3 excess. T_3 levels increase rapidly with birth, with a sixfold increase in T_3 secretion and eightfold increase in free T_3.[149] T_3 peaks at 24 to 48 hours at 260 to 300 ng/mL (4 to 4.62 pmol/L) (values exceeding those in adults) in most infants and then gradually fall.[15,31,32,124] The increase in T_3 is related to the TSH surge and increased MDI-I (also called D1) activity (see Box 19-3 on pp. 612-613), with increased conversion of T_4 to T_3 and removal of the placenta (with its high levels of D3) that convert T_3 to inactive forms.[32,149] The increase in T_3 is also related to cutting the umbilical cord, which increases liver blood flow and conversion of T_3 to T_4.[32] Serum T_3 and T_4 levels gradually fall to values seen in infancy within the first few weeks after birth.[124]

Levels of rT_3 remain high for 3 to 5 days and then gradually decrease to adult values by 1 to 2 months.[15] Thyroxine-binding globulin (TBG) tends to be high because of placental passage of estrogens that stimulate its production. TBG-binding capacity in the infant is higher than in the pregnant woman and about 1.5 times that of the adult.[15] Radioactive iodine uptake by the thyroid is higher in the newborn because of increased avidity of the neonatal thyroid for iodine. Iodine concentrations in the thyroid gland at birth are correlated with gestational age, with increased 24-hour radioactive iodine 123 (I-123 or ^{123}I) uptake for the

first month and a greater concentration of I-123 in infants than adults.[15]

The TSH surge is also seen in preterm and small-for-gestational-age infants, although it may be blunted, especially in VLBW infants less than 28 weeks' gestation.[32,58,163] Thyroid hormones in preterm infants follow patterns similar to those in term infants but may take longer to reach stable values.[15,47,124,168] Thyroid hormone levels are inversely related to gestational age.[32,97,124] Free T_4 and T_3 levels are lower and rT_3 levels higher in preterm infants than in term infants for the first weeks because of persistence of fetal levels of MDI enzymes (see p. 627) and higher sulfated iodothyronine analogs.[32,99,149,163] TSH levels and response are generally similar to those in term infants, but TSH may be in the normal adult range.[99] In ELBW infants, TSH response to low T_4 levels is limited.[32] Serum T_4 and T_3 levels may decrease to below birth levels in VLBW preterm infants during the first week to levels two to three times lower than in term infants.[124,149] In addition, some ill and VLBW preterm infants develop a characteristic syndrome of transient hyperthyroxinemia with normal or low TSH and low free T_4 levels without other evidence of hypothyroidism (see Transient Alterations in Thyroid Function in Preterm Infants).[32,97,124,149,163] T_4 levels are higher in infants of mothers who received a course of antenatal glucosteroids.[81] A preterm infant may take 3 to 8 weeks to reach term levels of thyroid hormones.[149]

CLINICAL IMPLICATIONS FOR NEONATAL CARE

Endocrine adaptation at birth is influenced by gestational age, stresses of delivery, postnatal disease states, and hypoxic-ischemic events.[146] Normal endocrine function is critical for normal growth and development both before and after birth. For example, biochemical maturation of the lungs and surfactant production (see Chapter 10) are dependent on the hypothalamic-pituitary-adrenal (HPA) axis and its hormones, including corticotropin-releasing hormone (CRH) and cortisol, as well as thyroid hormones. Thyroid hormones are important in cell metabolism, proliferation, and differentiation and are needed for lung development and surfactant production, growth, bone growth (including calcium and vitamin D homeostasis), thermogenesis, and central nervous system (CNS) maturation.[7,12,36,58,128] Within the CNS, these hormones are critical for differentiation of neural stem cells, cerebral neuronogenesis, gliogenesis, myelination, synaptogenesis, neuronal migration, axon development, and growth (see Chapter 15).[7,12,36,52,58,69,128,138] Effects on bone growth and CNS development continue into early childhood. An intact HPA axis is necessary for the infant to respond appropriately to stress and to prevent maladaptation.

Alterations in HPA and hypothalamic-pituitary-thyroid (HPT) function influence the transition to extrauterine life. For example, thyroid function is closely linked to thermoregulation and production of heat from brown adipose tissue. Alterations in health status from immaturity or acute illness can result in transient adrenal or thyroid dysfunction. Screening for hypothyroidism and congenital adrenal hyperplasia and recognition of hyperthyroidism and hypothyroidism has important ramifications for the infant's future growth and development. This section examines the implications of these events.

Neonatal Stress

Although definitions and depictions of the stress response may vary, all or most propose an integrated biologic response pattern during or after stressor exposure. Activation of endocrine and neurotransmitter systems represents the major mechanisms upon which other aspects of this response are built. Responses to stressors are normally of short duration (acute stress) and are aimed at survival followed by a return to a state of dynamic homeostasis.[118] Stress responses that go on for extended periods (chronic stress) can produce long-term changes in stress response systems, leading to decreases in adaptive capacity and increased susceptibility to disease. Susceptibility to disease is influenced by both genetic and environmental factors, especially during the intrauterine (see Maternal Stress Response and Fetal Endocrine Programming on pp. 621-622) and early postbirth periods. Adverse stress exposures "may determine propensity for diseases in later life (by shaping phenotypic responsivity to endogenous and exogenous disease-related conditions [such as stress or altered nutrition]."[27] These adult-onset disorders include hypertension and other cardiovascular disorders, renal disease (see Chapter 11), obesity (see Chapter 12), respiratory disorders (Chapter 10), and metabolic disorders (see Chapter 16).[38,67,125,135]

The NICU has the potential for significant stress during a period of critical brain development. There are many sources of stress in the NICU from both internal (e.g., pain, distress, pathologic processes) and external (e.g., physical environment, caregiver interventions, medical or surgical procedures, multiple simultaneous modes of stimulation) demands. Stress and pain (see Chapter 15) interact. Preterm infants may be simultaneously exposed to pain stimuli and other potentially noxious sensations (e.g., handling, light, sound, and temperature changes) that cause further activity in nociceptive pathways and systemic stress responses. An infant's stress tolerance may be reached or exceeded repeatedly, contributing to short- and long-term morbidity. Infants in the NICU experience both acute and chronic stress. Many handling procedures for small and sick infants lead to stress, which, if not controlled, may cause cumulative harm.[3]

Baseline responses to stress are set early in life and can influence later responses and adaptation.[9,44,108,154] Stress activates the HPA axis with release of catecholamines, CRH, adrenocorticotropin (ACTH), β-endorphins (BEs), and cortisol. Stress responses affect many systems: cardiovascular (increased blood pressure and heart rate), gastrointestinal (increased gut motility and splanchnic vasoconstriction), renal (sodium and water retention), and respiratory (increased

oxygen consumption, decreased tidal volume, and functional residual capacity or ventilation-perfusion mismatch). Stress can alter coagulation, immune function, and cytokine production. Stress has profound short and long term metabolic consequences; metabolic stability may be more difficult to maintain in stressed neonates, especially in immature infants.[3] Stress can lead to hyperglycemia or hypoglycemia. Stress increases counterregulatory hormones (e.g., glucagon, ACTH, catecholamines, cortisol) that decrease insulin secretion. Glucagon, fat, and protein are converted to glucose, which—in the face of insulin resistance from the counterregulatory hormones—results in hyperglycemia. In immature infants, this response and the infant's nutrient stores may become exhausted, so over time the infant becomes hypoglycemic.[3]

Term infants, whether healthy or ill, have an HPA axis that identifies and responds to stress.[117] Healthy preterm infants older than 28 weeks' gestational age respond to stress with increased cortisol secretion, although at lower levels than in term infants.[117] Healthy term infants have relatively low basal cortisol levels that rapidly increase with stress.[54] Salivary cortisol has been used to examine responses of both term and preterm infants to stressful or soothing events.[50,87,92,111,131,141,142]

However, in preterm infants who are ill or younger than 28 weeks' gestational age, the HPA is suppressed during the first few weeks after birth. These VLBW infants seem unable to "recognize" stress and to respond by increasing cortisol secretion.[54] Preterm infants—especially those who are ill or weigh less than 1000 g—have lower basal cortisol levels and are less able to increase cortisol production with stress. In these infants there is an increase in precursors but not in cortisol, suggesting immature activity of enzymes to convert these precursors to cortisol. In very immature infants, this may reflect the persistence of fetal protective responses against higher maternal cortisol levels.[56]

Exposure of VLBW infants to significant early pain and stress has been reported to alter later cortisol response patterns, with a "resetting" of the basal arousal system postulated.[50] Early stress in the fetus and neonate may produce permanent changes in neural pathways, increasing the risk of later disorders such as adult psychopathology, hypertension, and cardiovascular disease (see Maternal Stress Responses and Fetal Endocrine Programming on p. 612).[3,9,27,44,130,154] Maternal stress in the third trimester is associated with increased ACTH and cortisol and increased placental CRH. Because CRH is a primary factor in labor onset, this may lead to preterm labor (see Chapter 4) and decrease the sensitivity of the fetal-neonatal anterior pituitary to CRH, with permanent elevations in cortisol and BEs.[130]

Adrenal Cortex Insufficiency

A transient adrenal cortex insufficiency is seen in some ELBW infants. These infants have poor or limited ability to respond to shock and develop hypotension unresponsive to fluid and pressor management.[26,104,157] In these infants the adrenal cortex may be unable to produce enough cortisol to

---

BOX 19-7 Recommendations for Clinical Practice Related to Pituitary, Adrenal, and Thyroid Function in Neonates

---

Know the usual changes in pituitary and adrenal function in the fetus and during the neonatal period (pp. 623-626, 628, Table 19-2, and Figure 19-7).

Know the usual changes in thyroid function during the neonatal period in term infants (pp. 628-629, Figure 19-9, Box 19-7).

Know the usual changes in thyroid function during the neonatal period in preterm infants (pp. 628-629, 631-632 and Box 19-8).

Recognize the normal parameters related to thyroid function in term and preterm neonates (pp. 628-629).

Recognize and monitor for transient alterations in thyroid function in a preterm infant (pp. 631-632).

Recognize the signs of and monitor for transient hyperthyroidism in infants of mothers with Graves' disease (pp. 632-633).

Recognize the clinical signs of hypothyroidism in infants (p. 633).

Screen newborns for congenital hypothyroidism and congenital adrenal hyperplasia per state newborn screening protocol (pp. 633-634).

Monitor growth and neurologic status in infants with congenital hypothyroidism (p. 633).

Monitor for signs of stress and pain in neonates (p. 630 and Chapter 15).

---

at birth. Newborns normally have a relative hyperthyroidism, but immaturity or illness can lead to transient hypothyroidism. Screening for congenital hypothyroidism and congenital adrenal hyperplasia is a part of newborn metabolic screening. Use of this screening is essential for early identification and reduction of mortality and morbidity in these infants. All neonates should be monitored for stress, and protective interventions should be initiated. Preterm infants, especially those who are ill or younger than 28 weeks' gestational age, are particularly vulnerable to the adverse consequences of stress. Box 19-7 summarizes clinical recommendations related to neonatal pituitary, adrenal, and thyroid function.

References

1. Abbassi-Ghanavati, M., Greer, L. G., & Cunningham, F. G. (2009). Pregnancy and laboratory studies: a reference table for clinicians. *Obstet Gynecol, 114*, 1326.
2. ACOG Committee Opinion. (2007). Subclinical hypothyroidism in pregnancy. *Obstetrics & Gynecology, 110*, 959.
3. Anand, K. J., & Scalzo, F. M. (2000). Can adverse neonatal experiences alter brain development and subsequent behavior? *Biol Neonate, 77*, 69.
4. Andersen, S. L., et al. (2013). Birth defects after early pregnancy use of antithyroid drugs: a Danish nationwide study. *J Clin Endocrinol Metab, 98*, 4373.
5. Baud, O., et al. (2016). Effect of early low-dose hydrocortisone on survival without bronchopulmonary dysplasia in extremely preterm infants (PREMILOC): a double-blind, placebo-controlled, multicentre, randomised trial. *Lancet, 387*, 1827.
6. Benhaim, R. D., & Davies, T. F. (2005). Increased risk of Graves disease after pregnancy. *Thyroid, 15*, 1287.
7. Blackburn, S. (2009). Maternal-fetal thyroid interactions. *J Perinat Neonatal Nurs, 23*, 312.
8. Bongers-Schokking, J. J., et al. (2013). Cognitive development in congenital hypothyroidism: is overtreatment a greater threat than undertreatment? *J Clin Endocrinol Metab, 98*, 4499.
9. Brunton, P. J. (2010). Resetting the dynamic range of hypothalamic-pituitary-adrenal axis stress responses through pregnancy. *J Neuroendocrinol, 22*, 1198.
10. Burman, K. D. (2009). Controversies surrounding pregnancy, maternal thyroid status, and fetal outcome. *Thyroid, 19*, 323.
11. Carrascosa, A., et al. (2004). Thyroid function in seventy-five healthy preterm infants thirty to thirty-five weeks of gestational age: a prospective and longitudinal study during the first year of life. *Thyroid, 14*, 435.
12. Carreón-Rodríguez, A., & Pérez-Martínez, L. (2012). Clinical implications of thyroid hormones effects on nervous system development. *Pediatr Endocrinol Rev, 9*, 644.
13. Casey, B., & de Veciana, M. (2014). Thyroid screening in pregnancy. *Am J Obstet Gynecol, 211*, 351.
14. Charil, A., et al. (2010). Prenatal stress and brain development. *Brain Res Rev, 65*, 56.
15. Chuang, J. (2015). Thyroid disorders in the neonate. In A. A. Fanaroff & R. J. Martin (Eds.), *Neonatal-perinatal medicine: Diseases of the fetus and infant* (8th ed.). Philadelphia: Saunders.
16. Coulter, C. L. (2004). Functional biology of the primate fetal adrenal gland: advances in technology provide new insight. *Clin Exp Pharmacol Physiol, 31*, 475.
17. Dabo, F., et al. (2010). Plasma levels of beta-endorphin during pregnancy and use of labor analgesia. *Reprod Sci, 17*, 742.
18. De Groot, L., et al. (2012). Management of thyroid dysfunction during pregnancy and postpartum: an Endocrine Society Clinical Practice Guideline. *J Clin Endocrinol Metab, 97*, 2543.
19. Delahunty, C., et al. (2010). Levels of neonatal thyroid hormone in preterm infants and neurodevelopmental outcome at 5½ years: millennium cohort study. *J Clin Endocrinol Metab, 95*, 4898.
20. Delange, F. (2007). Iodine requirements during pregnancy, lactation and the neonatal period and indicators of optimal iodine nutrition. *Public Health Nutr, 10*, 1571.
21. de Weerth, C., & Buitelaar, J. K. (2005). Physiological stress reactivity in human pregnancy—a review. *Neurosci Biobehav Rev, 29*, 295.
22. DiPietro, J. A., Costigan, K. A., & Gurewitsch, E. D. (2003). Fetal response to induced maternal stress. *Early Hum Dev, 74*, 125.
23. Douglas, A. J. (2005). Central noradrenergic mechanisms underlying acute stress responses of the hypothalamic-pituitary-adrenal axis: adaptations through pregnancy and lactation. *Stress, 8*, 5.
24. Duthie, L., & Reynolds, R. M. (2013). Changes in the maternal hypothalamic-pituitary-adrenal axis in pregnancy and postpartum: influences on maternal and fetal outcomes. *Neuroendocrinology, 98*, 106.
25. Edlow, A. G., & Norwtiz, E. R. (2014). Endocrine diseases of pregnancy. In J. F. Strauss & R. Barbieri (Eds.), *Yen and Jaffe's Reproductive endocrinology: Physiology, pathophysiology, and clinical management* (7th ed.). Philadelphia: Saunders.
26. Efird, M. M., et al. (2005). A randomized-controlled trial of prophylactic hydrocortisone supplementation for the prevention of hypotension in extremely low birth weight infants. *J Perinatol, 25*, 119.
27. Entringer, S., Buss, C., & Wadhwa, P. D. (2015). Prenatal stress, development, health and disease risk: a psychobiological perspective-2015 Curt Richter Award Paper. *Psychoneuroendocrinology, 62*, 366.
28. Evers, K. S., & Wellmann, S. (2016). Arginine vasopressin and copeptin in perinatology. *Front Pediatr, 4*, 75.
29. Feldman P. M., & Lee, M. M. T. (2016). Endocrine disorders of the newborn. In M. G. Macdonald & M. M. K. Sheshia (Eds.), *Neonatology: Pathophysiology and management of the newborn* (7th ed.). Philadelphia: Wolters Kluwer.
30. Fernandez, E. F., & Watterberg, K. L. (2009). Relative adrenal insufficiency in the preterm and term infant. *J Perinatol, 29*, S44.

31. Fisher, D. A. (1997). Fetal thyroid function: diagnosis and management of fetal thyroid disorders. *Clin Obstet Gynecol, 40*, 16.

32. Fisher, D. A. (2008). Thyroid system immaturities in very low birth weight premature infants. *Semin Perinatol, 32*, 387.

33. Fitzpatrick, D. L., & Russell, M. A. (2010). Diagnosis and management of thyroid disease in pregnancy. *Obstet Gynecol Clin North Am, 37*, 173.

34. Florido, J., et al. (1997). Plasma concentrations of β-endorphin and adrenocorticotropic hormone in women with and without childbirth preparation. *Eur J Obstet Gynecol Reprod Biol, 73*, 121.

35. Ford, G., LaFranchi, S. H. (2014). Screening for congenital hypothyroidism: a worldwide view of strategies. *Best Pract Res Clin Endocrinol Metab, 28*, 175.

36. Forhead, A. J., & Fowden, A. L. (2014). Thyroid hormones in fetal growth and prepartum maturation. *J Endocrinol, 221*, R87.

37. Foyouzi, N., Frisbaek, Y., & Norwitz, E. R. (2004). Pituitary gland and pregnancy. *Obstet Gynecol Clin North Am, 31*, 873.

38. Friedman, J., & Baker, P. R. (2017). Fetal origins of adult disease: a classic hypothesis with new relevance. In R. A. Polin, et al. (Eds.), *Fetal and neonatal physiology* (5th ed.). Philadelphia: Saunders.

39. Galofre, J. C., & Davies, T. F. (2009). Autoimmune thyroid disease in pregnancy: a review. *J Womens Health (Larchmt), 18*, 1847.

40. Garber, J. R., et al. (2012). Clinical practice guidelines for hypothyroidism in adults: cosponsored by the American Association of Clinical Endocrinologists and the American Thyroid Association. *Endocr Pract, 18*, 988.

41. Gartner, R. (2009). Thyroid diseases in pregnancy. *Curr Opin Obstet Gynecol, 21*, 501.

42. Glinoer, D. (2004). The regulation of thyroid function during normal pregnancy: importance of the iodine nutrition status. *Best Pract Res Clin Endocrinol Metab, 18*, 133.

43. Glinoer, D., & Spencer, C. A. (2010). Serum TSH determinations in pregnancy: how, when and why? *Nat Rev Endocrinol, 6*, 526.

44. Glover, V., O'Connor, T. G., & O'Donnell, K. (2010). Prenatal stress and the programming of the HPA axis. *Neurosci Biobehav Rev, 35*, 17.

45. Gluckman, P. D., et al. (1999). The transition from fetus to neonate—an endocrine perspective. *Acta Paediatr Suppl, 88*, 7.

46. Glynn, L. M., Davis, E. P., & Sandman, C. A. (2013). New insights into the role of perinatal HPA-axis dysregulation in postpartum depression. *Neuropeptides, 47*, 363.

47. Golden, L. H., & Burrow, G. N. (2004). Thyroid diseases. In G. N. Burrow, T. P. Duffy, & J. A. Copel (Eds.), *Medical complications during pregnancy* (6th ed.). Philadelphia: Saunders.

48. Greaves, R. F., et al. (2014). Establishment of hormone reference intervals for infants born < 30 weeks' gestation. *Clin Biochem, 47*, 101.

49. Greaves, R. F., et al. (2015). Hormone modeling in preterm neonates: establishment of pituitary and steroid hormone reference intervals. *J Clin Endocrinol Metab, 100*, 1097.

50. Grunau, R. E., Weinberg, J., & Whitfield, M. F. (2004). Neonatal procedural pain and preterm infant cortisol responses to novelty at 8 months. *Pediatrics, 114*, e77.

51. Gurtunca, N., & Sperling, M. A. (2017). Growth hormone, prolactin, and placental lactogen in the fetus and newborn. In R. A. Polin, et al. (Eds.), *Fetal and neonatal physiology* (5th ed.). Philadelphia: Saunders.

52. Guyton, A. C., & Hall, J. E. (2015). *Textbook of medical physiology* (13th ed.). Philadelphia: Saunders Elsevier.

53. Gyamfi, C., Wapner, R. J., & D'Alton, M. E. (2009). Thyroid dysfunction in pregnancy: the basic science and clinical evidence surrounding the controversy in management. *Obstet Gynecol, 113*, 702.

54. Hanna, C. E., et al. (1993). Hypothalamic-pituitary adrenal function in the extremely low birth weight infant. *J Clin Endocrinol Metab, 76*, 384.

55. Havelock, J. C., Auchus, R. J., & Rainey, W. E. (2004). The rise in adrenal androgen biosynthesis: adrenarche. *Semin Reprod Med, 22*, 337.

56. Heckmann, M., et al. (2005). Cortisol production rates in preterm infants in relation to growth and illness: a noninvasive prospective study using gas chromatography-mass spectrometry. *J Clin Endocrinol Metab, 90*, 5737.

57. Hillman, N. H., Kallapur, S. G., & Jobe, A. H. (2012). Physiology of transition from intrauterine to extrauterine life. *Clin Perinatol, 39*, 769.

58. Huang, S. A. (2017). Fetal and neonatal thyroid physiology. In R. A. Polin, et al. (Eds.), *Fetal and neonatal physiology* (5th ed.). Philadelphia: Saunders.

59. Karras, S., et al. (2010). Pharmacological treatment of hyperthyroidism during lactation: review of the literature and novel data. *Pediatr Endocrinol Rev, 8*, 25.

60. Kidd, S., et al. (2005). Lack of adult-type salivary cortisol circadian rhythm in hospitalized preterm infants. *Horm Res, 64*, 20.

61. Krassas, G. E., Poppe, K., & Glinoer, D. (2010). Thyroid function and human reproductive health. *Endocr Rev, 31*, 702.

62. Kratzsch, J., & Pulzer, F. (2008). Thyroid gland development and defects. *Best Pract Res Clin Endocrinol Metab, 22*, 57.

63. Kurioka, H., Takahashi, K., & Miyazaki, K. (2005). Maternal thyroid function during pregnancy and puerperal period. *Endocr J, 52*, 587.

64. LaFranchi, S. H. (2014). Screening preterm infants for congenital hypothyroidism: better the second time around. *J Pediatr, 164*, 1259.

65. La Gamma, E. F., & Paneth, N. (2012). Clinical importance of hypothyroxinemia in the preterm infant and a discussion of treatment concerns. *Curr Opin Pediatr, 24*, 172.

66. Lajic, S., Nordenström, A., & Hirvikoski, T. (2008). Long-term outcome of prenatal treatment of congenital adrenal hyperplasia. *Endocr Dev, 13*, 82.

67. Lane, R. H. (2014). Fetal programming, epigenetics, and adult onset disease. *Clin Perinatol, 41*, 815.

68. Lawrence, R. A., & Lawrence R. M. (2016). *Breastfeeding: A guide for the medical profession* (8th ed.). Philadelphia: Saunders.

69. Lazarus, J. H. (2005). Thyroid disease in pregnancy and childhood. *Minerva Endocrinol, 30*, 71.

70. Lazarus, J. H. (2005). Thyroid disorders associated with pregnancy: etiology, diagnosis, and management. *Treat Endocrinol, 4*, 31.

71. Lazarus, J. H. (2011). Screening for thyroid dysfunction in pregnancy: is it worthwhile? *J Thyroid Res, 2011*, 397012.

72. Lazarus, J. H., et al. (2012). Antenatal thyroid screening and childhood cognitive function. *N Engl J Med, 366*, 493.

73. LeBeau, S. O., & Mandel, S. J. (2006). Thyroid disorders during pregnancy. *Endocrinol Metab Clin North Am, 35*, 117.

74. Leuschen, M. P., et al. (1991). Plasma beta-endorphin in neonates: effect of prematurity, gender, and respiratory status. *J Clin Endocrinol Metab, 73*, 1062.

75. Li, M., & Eastman, C. J. (2010). Neonatal TSH screening: is it a sensitive and reliable tool for monitoring iodine status in populations? *Best Pract Res Clin Endocrinol Metab, 24*, 63.

76. Lindsay, J. R., & Nieman, L. K. (2005). The hypothalamic-pituitary-adrenal axis in pregnancy: challenges in disease detection and treatment. *Endocr Rev, 26*, 775.

77. Lof, M., et al. (2005). Changes in basal metabolic rate during pregnancy in relation to changes in body weight and composition, cardiac output, insulin-like growth factor I, and thyroid hormones and in relation to fetal growth. *Am J Clin Nutr, 81*, 678.

78. Luton, D., et al. (2005). Management of Graves disease during pregnancy: the key role of fetal thyroid gland monitoring. *J Clin Endocrinol Metab, 90*, 6093.

79. MacDonald, M. G., et al. (1990). Cerebrospinal fluid and plasma beta-endorphin-like immunoreactivity in full-term neonates and in preterm neonates with and without apnea of prematurity. *Dev Pharmacol Ther, 15*, 8.

80. Marco, A., et al. (2010). Patterns of iodine intake and urinary iodine concentrations during pregnancy and blood thyroid-stimulating hormone concentrations in the newborn progeny. *Thyroid, 20*, 1295.

81. Martin, C. R., Van Marter, L. J., & Allred, E. N. (2005). Antenatal glucocorticoids increase early total thyroxine levels in premature infants. *Biol Neonate, 87*, 273.

82. Mastorakos, G., & Ilias, I. (2003). Maternal and fetal hypothalamic-pituitary-adrenal axes during pregnancy and postpartum. *Ann N Y Acad Sci, 997*, 136.

83. Matthews, S. G., et al. (2004). Fetal glucocorticoid exposure and hypothalamo-pituitary-adrenal (HPA) function after birth. *Endocr Res, 30*, 827.

84. Melse-Boonstra, A., & Jaiswal, N. (2010). Iodine deficiency in pregnancy, infancy and childhood and its consequences for brain development. *Best Pract Res Clin Endocrinol Metab, 24*, 29.

85. Merlot, E., Couret, D., & Otten, W. (2008). Prenatal stress, fetal imprinting and immunity. *Brain Behav Immunol, 22*, 42.

86. Mesiano, S. (2014). The endocrinology of human pregnancy and fetoplacental neuroendocrine development. In J. F. Strauss & R. Barbieri (Eds.), *Yen and Jaffe's Reproductive endocrinology: Physiology, pathophysiology, and clinical management* (7th ed.). Philadelphia: Saunders.

87. Miller, N. M., et al. (2005). Stress responses at birth: determinants of cord arterial cortisol and links with cortisol response in infancy. *BJOG, 112,* 921.

88. Miller, W. L. (2015). Fetal endocrine therapy for congenital adrenal hyperplasia should not be done. *Best Pract Res Clin Endocrinol Metab, 29,* 469.

89. Mitchell, M. L., Hsu, H. W., & Sahai, I. (2014). Changing perspectives in screening for congenital hypothyroidism and congenital adrenal hyperplasia. *Curr Opin Endocrinol Diabetes Obes, 21,* 39.

90. Moleti, M., Trimarchi, F., & Vermiglio, F. (2014). Thyroid physiology in pregnancy. *Endocr Pract, 21,* 1.

91. Molitch, M. E. (2006). Pituitary disorders during pregnancy. *Endocrinol Metab Clin North Am, 35,* 99.

92. Mörelius, E., et al. (2015). A randomized trial of continuous skin-to-skin contact after preterm birth and the effects on salivary cortisol, parental stress, depression, and breastfeeding. *Early Hum Dev, 91,* 63.

93. Morreale de Escobar, G., Obregon, M. J., & Escobar del Rey, F. (2004). Maternal thyroid hormones early in pregnancy and fetal brain development. *Best Pract Res Clin Endocrinol Metab, 18,* 225.

94. Morreale de Escobar, G., et al. (2008). The changing role of maternal thyroid hormone in fetal brain development. *Semin Perinatol, 32,* 380.

95. Nader, S. (2014). Other endocrine disorders of pregnancy. In R. K. Creasy, et al. (Eds.), *Maternal-fetal medicine: Principles and practice* (6th ed.). Philadelphia: Saunders.

96. Nader, S. (2004). Thyroid disease and other endocrine disorders in pregnancy. *Obstet Gynecol Clin North Am, 31,* 257.

97. Nader, S. (2014). Thyroid disease and pregnancy. In R. K. Creasy, et al. (Eds.), *Maternal-fetal medicine: Principles and practice* (6th ed.). Philadelphia: Saunders.

98. Narasimhan, S., Clemente, E. G., & Vyas, N. V. (2017). Luteinizing hormone and follicle-stimulating hormone secretion in the fetus and newborn. In R. A. Polin, et al. (Eds.). *Fetal and neonatal physiology* (5th ed.). Philadelphia: Saunders.

99. Neale, D., & Burrow, G. (2004). Thyroid disease in pregnancy. *Obstet Gynecol Clin North Am, 31,* 893.

100. Negro, R., et al. (2010). Universal screening versus case finding for detection and treatment of thyroid hormonal dysfunction during pregnancy. *J Clin Endocrinol Metab, 95,* 1699.

101. Nelson, D. B., et al. (2014). Subsequent pregnancy outcomes in women previously diagnosed with subclinical hypothyroidism. *Am J Perinatol, 31,* 77.

102. New, M. I. (2004). An update of congenital adrenal hyperplasia. *Ann N Y Acad Sci, 1038,* 14.

103. Ng, P. C. (2000). The fetal and neonatal hypothalamic-pituitary-adrenal axis. *Arch Dis Child Fetal Neonatal Ed, 82,* F250.

104. Ng, P. C., et al. (2004). Transient adrenocortical insufficiency of prematurity and systemic hypotension in very low birthweight infants. *Arch Dis Child Fetal Neonatal Ed, 89,* F119.

105. Ng, P. C. (2011). Effect of stress on the hypothalamic-pituitary-adrenal axis in the fetus and newborn. *J Pediatr, 158,* e41.

106. Nimkarn, S., & New, M. I. (2010). Congenital adrenal hyperplasia due to 21-hydroxylase deficiency: a paradigm for prenatal diagnosis and treatment. *Ann N Y Acad Sci, 1192,* 5.

107. Nor Azlin, M. I., et al. (2010). Thyroid autoantibodies and associated complications during pregnancy. *J Obstet Gynaecol, 30,* 675.

108. O'Donnell, K., O'Connor, T. G., & Glover, V. (2009). Prenatal stress and neurodevelopment of the child: focus on the HPA axis and role of the placenta. *Dev Neurosci, 31,* 285.

109. O'Keane, V., et al. (2011). Changes in the maternal hypothalamic-pituitary-adrenal axis during the early puerperium may be related to the postpartum 'blues'. *J Neuroendocrinol, 23,* 1149.

110. Osborn, D. A., & Hunt, R. W. (2007). Prophylactic postnatal thyroid hormones for prevention of morbidity and mortality in preterm infants. *Cochrane Database Syst Rev, 1,* CD005948.

111. Osman, M., Elsharkawy, A., & Abdel-Hady, H. (2015). Assessment of pain during application of nasal-continuous positive airway pressure and heated, humidified high-flow nasal cannulae in preterm infants. *J Perinatol, 35,* 263.

112. Parker, V. J., & Douglas, A. J. (2010). Stress in early pregnancy: maternal neuroendocrine-immune responses and effects. *J Reprod Immunol, 85,* 86.

113. Patton, P. E., et al. (2014). Controversies in the management of hypothyroidism during pregnancy. *Obstet Gynecol Surv, 69,* 346.

114. Pearce, E. N., & Stagnaro-Green, A. (2010). hypothyroidism in pregnancy: Do guidelines alter practice? *Thyroid, 20,* 241.

115. Pearce, E. N. (2015). Thyroid disorders during pregnancy and postpartum. *Best Pract Res Clin Obstet Gynaecol, 29,* 700.

116. Perrine, C. G., et al. (2010). Some subgroups of reproductive age women in the United States may be at risk for iodine deficiency. *J Nutr, 140,* 1489.

117. Peters, K. L. (1998). Neonatal stress reactivity and cortisol. *J Perinat Neonat Nurs, 11,* 45.

118. Pierro, A. (1999). Metabolic response to neonatal surgery. *Curr Opin Pediatr, 11,* 230.

119. Puig-Domingo, M., & Vila, L. (2013). The implications of iodine and its supplementation during pregnancy in fetal brain development. *Current Clinical Pharmacology, 8,* 97.

120. Quintos, J. B., & Boney, C. M. (2010). Transient adrenal insufficiency in the premature newborn. *Curr Opin Endocrinol Diabetes Obes, 17,* 8.

121. Radunovic, N., et al. (1992). Beta-endorphin concentrations in fetal blood during the second half of pregnancy. *Am J Obstet Gynecol, 167,* 740.

122. Rainey, W. E., Rehman, K. S., & Carr, B. R. (2004). Fetal and maternal adrenals in human pregnancy. *Obstet Gynecol Clin North Am, 31,* 817.

123. Rainey, W. E., Rehman, K. S., & Carr, B. R. (2004). The human fetal adrenal: making adrenal androgens for placental estrogens. *Semin Reprod Med, 22,* 327.

124. Raymond, J., & LaFranchi, S. H. (2010). Fetal and neonatal thyroid function: review and summary of significant new findings. *Curr Opin Endocrinol Diabetes Obes, 17,* 1.

125. Roggero, P., et al. (2013). Consequences of prematurity on adult morbidities. *Eur J Intern Med, 24,* 624.

126. Ross, I. L., & Louw, G. J. (2015). Embryological and molecular development of the adrenal glands. *Clin Anat, 28,* 235.

127. Rouet, J. F. (2002). Congenital hypothyroidism: an analysis of persisting defects and associated factors. *Child Neuropsychol, 8,* 150.

128. Rovet, J. F. (2014). The role of thyroid hormones for brain development and cognitive function. *Endocr Dev, 26,* 26.

129. Sadler, T. W. (2015). *Langman's Medical embryology* (13th ed.). Philadelphia: Wolters Kluwar.

130. Sandman, C. A., et al. (1997). Maternal stress, HPA activity, and fetal/infant outcome. *Ann N Y Acad Sci, 24,* 266.

131. Santiago, L. B., et al. (1996). Longitudinal analysis of the development of salivary cortisol rhythm in infancy. *Clin Endocrinol (Oxf), 44,* 157.

132. Schwartz, J., & Rose, J. C. (2017). Development of the corticotropin-releasing hormone–corticotropin system in the mammalian fetus. In R. A. Polin, et al. (Eds.). *Fetal and neonatal physiology* (5th ed.). Philadelphia: Saunders.

133. Scratch, S. E., et al. (2014). Free thyroxine levels after very preterm birth and neurodevelopmental outcomes at age 7 years. *Pediatrics, 133,* e955.

134. Shih, J. L., & Agus, M. S. (2009). Thyroid function in the critically ill newborn and child. *Curr Opin Pediatr, 21,* 536.

135. Simeoni, U., et al. (2014). Epigenetics and neonatal nutrition. *Early Hum Dev, 90,* S23.

136. Slaughter, J. L., et al. (2010). The effects of gestational age and birth weight on false-positive newborn-screening rates. *Pediatrics, 126,* 910.

137. Smith, R. P., et al. (2000). Pain and stress in the human fetus. *Eur J Obstet Gynecol Reproduct Biol, 92,* 161.

138. Soldin, O. P., et al. (2004). Trimester-specific changes in maternal thyroid hormone, thyrotropin, and thyroglobulin concentrations during gestation: trends and associations across trimesters in iodine sufficiency. *Thyroid, 14,* 1084.

139. Soldin, O. P., et al. (2010). Longitudinal comparison of thyroxine pharmacokinetics between pregnant and nonpregnant women: a stable isotope study. *Ther Drug Monit, 32,* 767.

140. Soldin, O. P. (2012). When thyroidologists agree to disagree: comments on the 2012 Endocrine Society pregnancy and thyroid disease clinical practice guideline. *J Clin Endocrinol Metab, 97,* 2632.

141. Sonir, R. R., et al. (2000). The emergence of salivary cortisol circadian rhythm and its relationship to sleep activity in preterm infants. *Clin Endocrinol, 52,* 423.

142. South, M. M., et al. (2005). The use of non-nutritive sucking to decrease the physiologic pain response during neonatal circumcision: a randomized controlled trial. *Am J Obstet Gynecol, 193,* 537.

143. Speller, E., & Brodribb, W. (2012). Breast-feeding and thyroid disease: a literature review. *Breastfeed Rev, 20,* 41.

144. Spencer, L., et al. (2015). Screening and subsequent management for thyroid dysfunction pre-pregnancy and during pregnancy for improving maternal and infant health. *Cochrane Database Syst Rev, 2015*(9), CD011263.

145. Stagnaro-Green, A., et al. (2011). Guidelines of the American Thyroid Association for the diagnosis and management of thyroid disease during pregnancy and postpartum. *Thyroid, 21,* 1081.

146. Sulyok, E. (1989). Endocrine factors in the neonatal adaptation. *Acta Physiol Hung, 74,* 329.

147. Swamy, G. K., Ostbye, T., & Skjaerven, R. (2008). Association of preterm birth with long-term survival, reproduction, and next-generation preterm birth. *JAMA, 299,* 1429.

148. Van Vliet, G., Polak, M., & Ritzén, E. M. (2008). Treating fetal thyroid and adrenal disorders through the mother. *Nat Clin Pract Endocrinol Metab, 4,* 675. Erratum in: *Nat Clin Pract Endocrinol Metab* (2009). *5,* 122.

149. van Wassenaer, A. G., & Kok, J. H. (2004). Hypothyroxinaemia and thyroid function after preterm birth. *Semin Neonatol, 9,* 3.

150. van Wassenaer, A. G., & Kok, J. H. (2008). Trials with thyroid hormone in preterm infants: clinical and neurodevelopmental effects. Semin Perinatol, *32,* 423.

151. van Wassenaer-Leemhuis, A., et al. (2014). Thyroid hormone supplementation in preterm infants born before 28 weeks gestational age and neurodevelopmental outcome at age 36 months. *Thyroid, 24,* 1162.

152. Vigone, M. C., et al. (2014). Evolution of thyroid function in preterm infants detected by screening for congenital hypothyroidism. *J Pediatr, 164,* 1296.

153. Vila, L., et al. (2014). On the need for universal thyroid screening in pregnant women. *Eur J Endocrinol, 170,* R17.

154. Vrekoussis, T., et al. (2010). The role of stress in female reproduction and pregnancy: an update. *Ann N Y Acad Sci, 1205,* 69.

155. Wassner, A. J., & Modi, B. P. (2013). Endocrine physiology in the newborn. *Semin Pediatr Surg, 22,* 205.

156. Wassner, A. J., & Brown, R. S. (2015). Congenital hypothyroidism: recent advances. *Curr Opin Endocrinol Diabetes Obes, 22,* 407.

157. Watterberg, K. L. (2004). Adrenocortical function and dysfunction in the fetus and neonate. *Semin Neonatol, 9,* 13.

158. Watterberg, K. L., et al. (2004). Prophylaxis of early adrenal insufficiency to prevent bronchopulmonary dysplasia: a multicenter trial. *Pediatrics, 114,* 1649.

159. Watterberg, K. L., & Muglia, L. J. (2017). Fetal and neonatal adrenocortical physiology. In R. A. Polin, et al. (Eds.), *Fetal and neonatal physiology* (5th ed.). Philadelphia: Saunders.

160. Weetman, A. P. (2010). Immunity, thyroid function and pregnancy: molecular mechanisms. *Nat Rev Endocrinol, 6,* 311.

161. Weinstock, M. (2005). The potential influence of maternal stress hormones on development and mental health of the offspring. *Brain Behav Immun, 19,* 296.

162. Wier, F. A., & Farley, C. L. (2006). Clinical controversies in screening women for thyroid disorders during pregnancy. *J Midwifery Womens Health, 51,* 152.

163. Williams, F., & Hume, R. (2011). The measurement, definition, aetiology and clinical consequences of neonatal transient hypothyroxinaemia. *Ann Clin Biochem, 48,* 7.

164. Williams, F. L., & Hume, R. (2008). Perinatal factors affecting thyroid hormone status in extreme preterm infants. *Semin Perinatol, 32,* 398.

165. Xing, Y., et al. (2015). Development of adrenal cortex zonation. *Endocrinol Metab Clin North Am, 44,* 243.

166. Yildirim, M., Oktem, M., & Yilmaz, A. O. (2004). Fetal and maternal adrenal steroid levels and labor. *Int J Gynaecol Obstet, 85,* 274.

167. Zanardo, V., et al. (2001). Labor pain effects on colostral milk beta-endorphin concentrations of lactating mothers. *Biol Neonate, 79,* 87.

168. Zimmermann, M. B. (2009). Iodine deficiency in pregnancy and the effects of maternal iodine supplementation on the offspring: a review. *Am J Clin Nutr, 89,* 668S.

Thermoregulation

Thermoregulation is the balance between heat production and heat loss involved in maintaining thermal equilibrium. Heat is produced by the body as a byproduct of metabolic processes and muscular activity; thus a major function of the thermoregulatory system is dissipation of this heat.[18] The thermoregulatory system must also respond appropriately to alterations in environmental temperature to preserve thermal equilibrium. Maintenance of thermal stability is particularly critical for newborns, because exposure to cold environments and lowered body temperatures are closely correlated with survival, especially in very-low-birth-weight (VLBW) infants. Maternal temperature changes are also important in relation to fetal well-being and the potential adverse consequences of maternal hyperthermia. Regulation of body temperature is summarized in Figure 20-1 and Box 20-1.

MATERNAL PHYSIOLOGIC ADAPTATIONS

Hormonal and metabolic alterations during pregnancy result in changes in maternal temperature. These changes are transient and may cause discomfort but are generally not associated with significant physiologic alterations.

Antepartum Period

The amount of heat generated increases 30% to 35% during pregnancy because of the thermogenic effects of progesterone, alterations in maternal metabolism and basal metabolic rate (see Chapter 16), and maternal dissipation of heat generated by the fetus.[33,114] As a result, many pregnant women develop an increased tolerance for cooler weather and decreased tolerance for heat. The additional heat is dissipated by peripheral vasodilation, with a fourfold to sevenfold increase in cutaneous blood flow and increased activity of the sweat glands (see Chapter 14). Cutaneous vasodilation leads to skin warmth.

The maternal temperature usually increases by 0.5° C (0.3° F). Both core and skin temperature increase during pregnancy, with a slight decrease reported in late pregnancy. The core temperature peaks by midpregnancy.[106] The decrease in core temperature in late pregnancy may be related to decreases in progesterone and physical activity (which generates heat) during this time. The rise in skin temperature is particularly evident in the hands and feet, probably because of

arteriovenous shunting in these areas.[157] In general, heat accumulation may be slower and heat dissipation faster in later pregnancy than before pregnancy or in early pregnancy. The increased plasma volume during pregnancy provides a greater area for heat storage and may enhance heat transfer from the fetus to the mother.[106] A pregnant woman has decreased vasoconstriction in response to cold during pregnancy, which may alter her ability to conserve heat during cold stress.[106] Body temperature may increase with exercise because of heat generated by increased metabolic energy production. Some of this heat is dissipated by increased skin blood flow; the remainder is stored transiently, increasing the core temperature (see Maternal Exercise and Temperature Elevations on pp. 641-642).

Intrapartum Period

An increase in body temperature, averaging 1° C (1.7° F), may occur during labor as a result of physical activity with uterine contractions, release of substances from the fetal-placental unit that may stimulate the maternal hypothalamic thermoregulatory center, or delivery room temperatures.[60,108,114,128] Panzer and colleagues reported that women during labor do not show the same relationship between temperature, sweating, and shivering as nonpregnant individuals.[114] In the parturient, shivering was not necessarily triggered by decreased temperature, nor was sweating necessarily triggered by increased temperature; the woman might shiver and sweat simultaneously. Temperature increases can lead to an increased maternal heart rate, cardiac output, oxygen consumption, and catecholamine production.[128] Bartholomew and colleagues reported that 95% of 147 women had temperatures between 36.2° C and 37.8° C (97.2° F and 100.0° F) during labor.[11] Diurnal variations were noted with a nadir at midday and peak in the evening.[11]

In some women the increase in temperature during labor is high enough to generate concern that the mother is infected. Although this can be the case, maternal temperature alterations during labor in the absence of infection are usually attributed to epidural anesthesia.[3,11,60,66,121,128] Histologic chorioamnionitis and use of epidural anesthesia were reported to be independently associated with a risk of intrapartum fever.[34] Temperature elevations are reported in approximately 20% of laboring women with epidurals and are most common in

Control signals

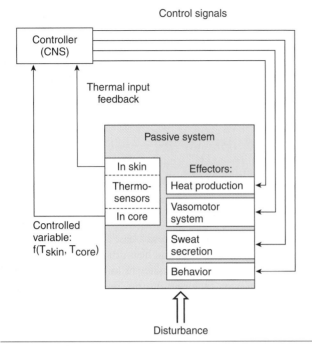

FIGURE 20-1 Regulation of body temperature. The diagram represents the biocybernetic concept of temperature regulation in humans. Temperature is sensed at various sites of the body, and the temperature signals are fed into the central controller *(multiple input system)*. *CNS*, Central nervous system; *f(T_skin, T_core)*, skin temperature and core temperature gradient. (From Sahni, R. & Schulze, K. [2012]. Temperature control in newborn infants. In R.A. Polin, W.W. Fox, & S.H. Abman. [Eds.]. *Fetal and neonatal physiology* [4th ed.]. Philadelphia: Saunders.)

BOX 20-1 **Body Temperature Regulation**

Regulation of temperature depends on the ability to (1) sense temperature changes in the external environment by skin receptors; (2) regulate heat production by increasing or decreasing metabolic rate; (3) conserve or dissipate heat (by sweating or altering skin blood flow); and (4) coordinate sensory input about environmental changes with appropriate body-temperature-regulating responses.[87] Thermoregulation involves a "multiple-input system" controlled by the anterior and posterior portions of the hypothalamus. The anterior hypothalamus is temperature-sensitive and controls heat loss mechanisms. The preoptic and anterior nuclei of the anterior hypothalamus are the sites of the set point or threshold temperature. The set point is a mechanism through which heat production and loss are regulated to maintain the core temperature within a narrow range. The posterior hypothalamus, which is the central controller of responses (heat production or dissipation) to cold or heat stimuli, receives input from central receptors (in deep body structures such as the hypothalamus, abdominal organs, and spinal cord) and peripheral receptors (skin, abdomen, spinal cord, hypothalamic preoptic nuclei, and internal organs). The peripheral receptors are free nerve endings in the skin that send impulses to the hypothalamus via afferent nerve fibers as well as to the thalamus and cerebral cortex, when there is conscious perception of temperature changes.[83] With cold stress, the thermoregulatory center acts to conserve heat (through cutaneous vasoconstriction and abolition of sweating) or increase heat production (through voluntary skeletal muscle activity, shivering, or nonshivering thermogenesis). This center dissipates heat by activation of sweat glands to increase evaporative loss, peripheral vasodilation, and respiration. Thermal regulation is also influenced by thyroid hormones and the sympathetic nervous system.[70]

---

nulliparous women with prolonged labor.[5,61] The fever seen with epidurals has been characterized by a slow increase in temperature of approximately 0.07° C/hour, although the temperature may rise to greater than 37.5° C (99.5° F) or 38° C (100.4° F) in some women.[66,128] The basis for the increased risk of fever may be decreased heat dissipation (because of a decreased sweating threshold, alterations in ventilation, and altered hypothalamic responses) and an increase in heat production, possibly related to increased shivering.[3,34,128] The autonomic block with epidural analgesia inhibits peripheral vasoconstriction and sweating in the lower body. This impairment of sweating and behavioral responses may decrease heat loss.[11,23,114] Maternal fever with epidural anesthesia is associated with a noninfectious inflammatory state with increased proinflammatory cytokines, but the exact pathophysiology is not well understood.[3,5,121,128] Maternal fever during labor can have both maternal and neonatal consequences, including an increased risk of sepsis workup and antibiotic use.[5]

Laboring women are also at risk for hypothermia during the intrapartum period because of vasodilation (limiting usual vasoconstrictive responses to cold); administration of anesthetics, narcotics, and other pharmacologic agents; blood loss; rapid fluid replacement, especially if cool fluids are used; or other events that increase maternal heat loss (e.g., cold drafts, wet drapes or towels). Fluid and air warming with cesarean birth have been found effective in reducing the incidence of

hypothermia and shivering.[115,144] Prolonged exposure to a cool environment can aggravate heat loss. Hypothermia can result in shivering, hypotension, and hemodynamic and cardiorespiratory instability.[114]

Postpartum Period

Maternal temperature is monitored closely during the postpartum period, because elevations may indicate infection or dehydration. A transient postpartum chill or shivering is often experienced about 15 minutes after birth of the infant or delivery of the placenta. The cause of this chill is unknown, and various causes have been proposed. This phenomenon may represent muscular exhaustion or result from disequilibrium between the internal and external thermal gradients secondary to muscular exertion during labor and delivery, sudden changes in intraabdominal pressure with emptying of the uterus, or small amniotic fluid emboli. Most women who experience early postpartum shivering are normothermic, suggesting that this phenomenon is nonthermoregulatory in origin.[114] Shivering is seen in about 20% of women who did not receive neuraxial analgesia and is more common in women who have received epidural analgesia.[114]

Transient maternal temperature elevations up to 38° C (100.4° F) occur in up to 6.5% of vaginally delivering women during the first 24 hours after delivery. In most women this resolves spontaneously and is secondary to noninfectious causes such as dehydration or to a transient bacterial endometritis.[55] Maternal fever in the postpartum period may be a sign of puerperal infection, mastitis, endometritis, or urinary tract infection, although these infections are usually the cause of fever after 24 hours. Any temperature elevation merits close monitoring, especially with increasingly early discharge.[1,33]

CLINICAL IMPLICATIONS FOR THE PREGNANT WOMAN AND HER FETUS

The fetal ambient environmental temperature is the maternal temperature. Fetal temperature is linked to maternal temperature and the maternal-fetal thermal gradient (see Development of Thermoregulation in the Fetus), so if maternal temperature rises, so will the fetal temperature. Maternal oral temperature has been reported to correlate with intrauterine temperature, with maternal oral temperature lower than intrauterine temperature by 0.8° C (1.3° F).[10] In this study a maternal "oral temperature greater than 37.2° C (99.0° F) detected an intrauterine temperature greater than 38° C (100.4° F) with a sensitivity of 81% and a specificity of 96%."[10]

The increase in maternal temperature during pregnancy may cause transient discomfort and alter the woman's heat tolerance. The major concerns related to thermoregulation during pregnancy are the effects of maternal hyperthermia and fever on the fetus.

Maternal Hyperthermia and Fever

Maternal fever has three potential detrimental effects on the fetus: (1) hypoxia secondary to maternal and fetal tachycardia and altered hemodynamics; (2) teratogenesis; and (3) preterm labor (see Chapter 4) from the fever per se, underlying infection, or associated hemodynamic alterations.[33] Maternal intrapartum fever related to infection also has been linked to a risk of cerebral palsy, cognitive defects, and neonatal seizures and encephalopathy, as well as later disorders such as schizophrenia and autism.[5,101,128] Maternal hyperthermia increases maternal oxygen consumption and shifts the oxygen-hemoglobin dissociation curve to the right. Although this latter change increases the oxygen supply to the placenta, fetal oxygen uptake becomes more difficult because of the altered thermal gradient. Proposed mechanisms for alterations in fetal development with exposure to maternal fever suggest that pyrogenic cytokines alter protein synthesis and energy production, leading to changes in cell proliferation, migration, differentiation, and apoptosis.[41,118] Fever may also induce production of heat shock proteins that also alter protein synthesis and cell proliferation.[41] Alterations in these cellular processes can lead to alterations in embryologic development, particularly in the first trimester, when cell differentiation is most prominent.[118]

Research regarding adverse fetal effects has focused primarily on maternal temperature elevations from fever secondary to illness, exercise, and the use of saunas or hot tubs. Animal studies show specific effects of maternal hyperthermia, especially when the maternal core temperature increases to 2° C or more above baseline; the longer the temperature elevation is maintained or the higher the temperature, the greater the risk to the fetus.[24] Some human studies have been retrospective and suggestive but inconclusive, whereas others have demonstrated a clear association.[6,21,24,41,49,106,111] A metaanalysis of studies, including both retrospective case-controlled and prospective cohort studies, reported an overall odds ratio of neural tube defects (NTDs) when associated with maternal hyperthermia of 1.92 (95% confidence interval = 1.16 to 2.29).[111] Definitions of hyperthermia in the various studies ranged from temperature above 37.8° C (100.4° F) to temperature above 38.9° C (102.0° F). Most of the hyperthermia was a result of maternal influenza or other febrile illness. A more recent metaanalysis of studies since 1990 reported adverse outcomes in infants with maternal fever during the first trimester, with the most consistent significant associations being a 1.5- to almost 3-fold increased risk of NTD, congenital heart defects, and oral clefs.[41] A dose-response relationship between fever and duration and between maternal fever and the risk of stillbirth or preterm delivery was not found in this analysis.[41]

Maternal febrile illness is believed to pose the greatest hyperthermia risk; however, susceptibility may be modified by genotype.[41] Elevated maternal temperature secondary to illness-induced fever during early pregnancy has been associated with increased risk of anencephaly and spina bifida, especially around the time of neural tube closure (22 to 28 days), microcephaly, and other central nervous system disorders; alterations in growth; cleft lip; and facial dysmorphogenesis in humans.[10,24] In a prospective study, Chambers and colleagues reported a 10-fold increase in NTDs in women who had a temperature of 38.9° C (102° F) or greater lasting for more than 24 hours in the first month of pregnancy.[24] Whether these disorders are primarily related to the elevated temperature, the underlying infection, its treatment, or a combination of these events is unclear.[41] Reductions in risk have also been reported with folic acid supplementation.[49] Antifever medications and folic acid may reduce the risk of vascular disruption and apoptosis leading to congenital anomalies.[49]

Several studies have reported an increase in neural tube defects and oral clefts in infants born to women with an extended heat exposure secondary to sauna or hot tub use in the first trimester, suggesting that an elevated temperature may be the critical factor.[24,45] Milunsky and colleagues found that the hot tub exposure, especially in the first 2 months of pregnancy (and the risk increased with number of exposures during this time), posed a greater risk than sauna use, with no risk from electric blanket use.[109] Duong et al reported that there may be an increased risk of anencephaly and gastroschisis with repeated use of hot tubs and for long periods in early pregnancy.[45] Prospective studies from Finland of sauna use in pregnancy have not shown an increased risk. However, in these studies, maximal temperature was 38.1° C (100.6° F), below the value of 38.9° C (102° F) considered to be critical.[106]

Maternal Exercise and Temperature Elevations

Maternal exercise is associated with increased heat production and body temperature increases that may alter the maternal-fetal thermal gradient and fetal heat dissipation. Uterine blood flow decreases during exercise, further altering the ability of the mother to dissipate fetal heat.[143] However, most women seem to be able to tolerate moderate intensity exercise without significant changes in core temperature.[143] With strenuous exercise or exercise in high ambient temperatures, maternal temperature and thus fetal temperature may increase, but fetal changes lag behind maternal changes.[118]

Changes in temperature with exercise are smaller during pregnancy than in nonpregnant women, with some investigators reporting a slight decrease or no change.[54,98] The enhanced thermoregulatory capacity of pregnant women may help protect them against hyperthermia.[106] The increased plasma volume in pregnancy may assist in maintaining uterine and placental blood flow during exercise and in maximizing heat transfer from the fetus and heat dissipation in the mother.

The ability of the mother to dissipate the heat generated by exercise may improve as pregnancy progresses.[106,143] The risks from temperature changes during exercise in late pregnancy are related to decreases in uterine blood flow, which can be potentiated by dehydration. Prolonged exercise or exercise in heat (increased ambient heat reduces the thermal gradient between the skin and environment) or high humidity (decreases evaporative heat loss) may result in a higher maternal temperature than exercise in a cool, dry environment or water environment (e.g., aerobic exercise in water).[106,117,157]

Low-impact aerobic exercise (to 70% of maximal heart rate) has not been associated with hyperthermia.[91,99] Aerobic exercise in water is associated with minimal changes in either core or skin temperature.[106,157] Physical conditioning before pregnancy can improve thermoregulatory capacity and may decrease the effect of heat stress.[106,117] Exercise-related hyperthermia has not been associated with teratogenic effects.[54] Exercise during pregnancy is discussed further in Chapters 9 and 10.

SUMMARY

Alterations in thermal status during pregnancy increase the risk of alterations in fetal health and development. Ongoing assessment and monitoring of thermal status in the pregnant woman and neonate and initiation of appropriate interventions to maintain thermal stability can prevent or minimize these risks. Clinical recommendations related to maternal thermoregulation are summarized in Box 20-2.

DEVELOPMENT OF THERMOREGULATION IN THE FETUS

Because fetal temperature is linked to maternal temperature and the maternal-fetal thermal gradient, a fetus cannot control its temperature independently. Under normal resting conditions, the temperature of the fetus is approximately 0.5° C (0.9° F) higher (range, 0.3° C to 1° C [0.5° F to 1.7° F]) than that of the mother, or about 37.6° C to 37.8° C (99.7° F to 100.0° F).[12,14,53,73,76,108,118] About half of this difference is a result of placental and uterine heat production.[118] In animal studies,

---

BOX 20-2 Recommendations for Clinical Practice Related to Changes in Thermoregulation in Pregnant Women

Counsel pregnant women regarding the basis for heat intolerance during pregnancy and intervention strategies (pp. 639-640).

Counsel pregnant women to avoid activities that may lead to hyperthermia (pp. 641-642).

Encourage adequate fluid intake before and during exercise (pp. 641-642).

Discourage prolonged exercise, especially in a hot, humid environment (pp. 641-642).

Maintain adequate ambient temperature in the delivery area (pp. 639-640).

Protect from cold drafts during delivery (p. 640).

Avoid infusing cold solutions (p. 640).

Avoid contact of maternal skin with wet drapes and towels (p. 640).

Monitor maternal temperature and assess thermoregulatory status during the intrapartum and postpartum periods (pp. 639-641).

Evaluate women with elevated temperatures for signs of infection (pp. 639-641).

---

this difference between maternal and fetal temperatures is seen by the time the fetus achieves one-third of its body weight, which would be around the beginning of the third trimester in a human fetus.[108] The fetus produces about 5 calories (20.9 J) of heat per milliliter of oxygen used.[118] Fetal metabolic rate varies to match oxygen availability (adaptive hypometabolism), so if PO_2 decreases, fetal oxygen consumption also decreases, and if fetal PO_2 increases, so does fetal oxygen consumption.[118] Any increase in fetal oxygen consumption increases heat production.[143]

Fetal core and skin temperature and the temperature of amniotic fluid are all similar. The fetal temperature must be higher than the maternal temperature to maintain a gradient to offload heat from the fetus to the mother. Fetal heat dissipation is influenced by fetal and placental metabolic activity; thermal diffusion capacity of heat exchange sites within the placenta; and rates of blood flow in the umbilical cord, placenta, and intervillous spaces.[106]

Heat generated by fetal metabolism is dissipated by the amniotic fluid to the uterine wall (conductive pathway) or via the umbilical cord and placenta to maternal blood in the intervillous spaces (convective pathway). Most heat (approximately 85%) is transferred via the convective pathway through the placenta via the umbilical circulation, with only 10% to 20% dissipated via amniotic fluid.[53,118] The large placental surface area, thin membrane barrier, and high blood flow rate enhance thermal exchange. Transfer of heat is facilitated by the maternal-fetal temperature gradient. Therefore if the mother has an elevated temperature (from exercise, illness, or exposure to environments such as a hot tub or sauna), this gradient may be reduced or reversed, leading to an increase in the fetal temperature (see Maternal Hyperthermia and Fever).[26] Changes in fetal temperature lag behind maternal changes, because amniotic fluid provides some insulation.[118]

Fetal heat production and loss mechanisms are suppressed in utero. Fetal temperature is "heat-clamped" to the maternal system, preventing the fetus from independent thermoregulation before birth.[118] Fetal responses to cooling are minimal and primarily involve shivering-like skeletal muscle contractions and endocrine response. Cooling of the fetus does not activate nonshivering thermogenesis (NST). The inability to initiate NST is believed to be linked to placental inhibitors of an uncoupling protein essential for brown adipose tissue (BAT) metabolism that are present in fetal blood. Both BAT and the uncoupling protein (UCP-1) that regulates its metabolism increase from 25 to 26 weeks' gestation to term (see Brown Adipose Tissue Metabolism).[36] The placental inhibitors, primarily prostaglandin E_2 and adenosine, are an advantage to the fetus in promoting accumulation of BAT. The rapid decrease in these inhibitors with clamping of the umbilical cord at birth promotes BAT metabolism in the newborn to maintain thermal stability with transition to extrauterine life.[118] Fetal cord occlusion thus leads to an increase in body temperature, although brain temperature tends to remain constant.[36,118]

The fetal-maternal temperature gradient is sustained during labor, although it may widen with prolonged labor, during the latent phase, or with infection or prolonged rupture of the membranes, or it may decrease with compression of the umbilical cord (decreasing blood flow from the fetus and thus the ability of the fetus to dissipate heat).[76,118] If the maternal temperature rises in labor, as often occurs with epidural analgesia (see Intrapartum Period), the fetal temperature will also increase.[76,128] In the second and third trimesters, increased fetal temperature leads to increased fetal heart rate but not to other thermoregulatory responses. Maternal fever in labor, especially temperature greater than 38° C (100.4° F), in noninfected women has been associated with lower Apgar scores, hypotonia, hypoxia, and an increased need for resuscitation and oxygen at birth.[5,10]

NEONATAL PHYSIOLOGY

Thermoregulation is a critical physiologic function in neonates that is closely linked to infant survival and health status.[51] An understanding of transitional events and neonatal physiologic adaptations is essential for provision of an appropriate environment to maintain thermal stability. Heat losses are greater and more rapid and can easily exceed heat production in both term and preterm neonates if infants are left unclothed in an environment comfortable for an adult. This is because of the infant's larger surface area–to–body mass ratio, decreased insulating subcutaneous fat, increased skin permeability to water, and small radius of curvature of exchange surfaces.[37] Newborns (even most preterm infants) have a relatively well-developed thermoregulatory capacity. Their major thermoregulatory limitation is a narrow control range that makes them more vulnerable to alterations in the thermal environment.[51]

Transitional Events

With birth the fetus moves from the warm, moist intrauterine environment to the colder, drier extrauterine environment.

The infant's temperature falls after birth, triggering cold-induced metabolic responses and heat production.[14,18,127] As noted previously, because fetal thermoregulation is linked to the mother, thermoregulatory processes are suppressed in the fetus. These processes, especially initiation of nonshivering thermogenesis (NST), must be activated rapidly after birth for the infant to survive the transition to extrauterine life. Stimulation of cutaneous cold receptors and spinal cord and hypothalamic thermal receptors at birth activates the sympathetic nervous system. This leads to the release of norepinephrine and a twofold to threefold increase in metabolic rate, oxygen consumption, and heat production.[53,118] Occlusion of the umbilical cord, which removes placental factors that suppress NST, increases a brown adipose tissue (BAT)–specific uncoupling protein (UCP-1) with a rapid increase in BAT metabolism (see Brown Adipose Tissue Metabolism) and heat production.[118,123] Thermal transition at birth and BAT metabolism are interrelated with changes in thyroid function (see Chapter 19). In very-low-birth-weight (VLBW) infants, the immature thermoregulatory system limits the adaptive responses of their hypothalamus thermoreceptors to the release of thyroxine and norepinephrine with birth.[32,127]

Newborns lose heat rapidly after birth, especially through evaporative losses (0.58 kcal/mL [2.4 J/mL] of water loss) from their moist body surface, as well as via convection to cooler room air and radiation to cooler room walls. A newborn's temperature may fall 0.2° C to 1° C/minute (0.5° F to 1.7° F/minute) if thermal interventions are not initiated.[26,51,53] Rutter estimated that in a cool room, the body temperature of a 1000 g preterm infant falls 1° C (1.7° F) every 5 minutes.[76] Initial temperatures of infants born by cesarean birth are on average 0.3° C (0.5° F) lower than infants born vaginally, perhaps because of slightly lower levels of sympathetic activity, catecholamines, and thyroid activity with a transient depression of BAT activation and UCP-1 levels.[118]

Admission temperature is a predictor of mortality and morbidity across all gestational ages.[116] Every 1° C below 36° C on admission temperature increases mortality by 28%.[88,161] Interventions in the delivery room to reduce evaporative and other losses support transition, reduce cold stress, and have been associated with a higher PO_2 at 1 hour of age, lower mortality, and decreased morbidity.[51] Because much of the heat loss that occurs immediately after birth results from evaporative losses, infants should be quickly dried and wrapped in a warm, dry towel or blanket and either given to the mother for skin-to-skin contact or placed under a radiant warmer or in a prewarmed incubator.[53,62] A polyethylene bag or wrap and thermal mattresses can be used with VLBW infants to reduce heat loss after birth (see Methods of Promoting Thermal Stability).[14,31,83,116] Heat loss in VLBW infants immediately after birth can also be reduced by maintaining adequate ambient temperatures and humidity in the delivery and stabilization room.[148] Bissinger and Annibale recommend 50% humidity and room temperatures of 25.5° C to 26.6° C (78° F to 80° F) for infants 28 weeks' gestation or earlier (less than or equal to 1000 g) and with a temperature of 22.2° C (72° F) or higher, with a goal of 23.8° C (75° F) for infants 29 to 32 weeks' gestation (1001-1500 g).[14] Golden hour strategies have been developed to improve delivery and transitional management of extremely-low-birth-weight (ELBW) infants.[15,23,161] Thermal management is a critical component of golden hour management and includes increased delivery room ambient temperature, placement of the infant in a polyethylene wrap or bag (which is kept in place during resuscitation and stabilization), covering the infant's head using a polyethylene or woolen hat, and careful thermal monitoring to prevent both hypothermia and hyperthermia.[15,23,52,77,161] Other interventions to reduce evaporative, radiant, conductive, and convective losses are listed in Table 20-1.

Term newborns can increase their metabolic rate by up to 200% to 300% in response to cold stress.[18,53] This response is delayed in larger preterm infants, who do not approximate term values until 2 to 3 weeks of age; further delay is seen in VLBW infants.[18,40] VLBW infants may only have a maximal increase in metabolic activity of 25% with cold stress.[26] In ELBW infants, an increase in thermal maturational skills has been reported at 28 weeks' postmenstrual age, possibly related to decreased evaporative losses as the skin matures.[40]

Most healthy infants increase their temperatures by 2 to 3 hours after birth. Thermal stabilization may be affected by timing of the first bath, thermal status at time of bathing, and method of bathing.[107] VLBW infants are more likely than

TABLE 20-1   Prevention of Heat Loss and Overheating in the Neonate

MECHANISM	SOURCES OF HEAT LOSS OR OVERHEATING	INTERVENTIONS
Conduction	Cool mattress, blanket, scale, table, x-ray plate, or clothing	Place warm blankets on scales, x-ray plates, and other surfaces in contact with the infant. Warm blankets and clothing before use. Use skin-to-skin care. Preheat incubators, radiant warmers, and heat shields.
	Heating pads, hot water bottles, chemical bags	Avoid placing the infant on any surface or object that is warmer than the infant.
Convection	Cool room, corridors, or outside air	Maintain the room temperature at levels adequate to provide a safe thermal environment for infants according to their gestational ages. Transport the infant in an enclosed, warmed incubator through internal hallways and between external environments (e.g., ambulance to nursery). Open incubator portholes only when necessary and for brief periods. Swaddle with warm blankets (unless under radiant warmer). Use polyethylene bags or wraps with VLBW infants from birth; use transparent plastic across the infant between the radiant warmer side guards; use caps with adequate insulation quality or hooded blankets.
	Convective air flow incubator	Monitor the incubator temperature to avoid temperatures warmer than the infant's body temperature.
	Drafts from air vents, windows, doors, heaters, fans, and air conditioners	Place infants away from air vents, drafts, and other sources of moving air particles. Use side guards on radiant warmers to decrease cross-current air flow across the infant; stretch transparent plastic across the infant between the radiant warmer and side guards.
	Cold oxygen flow (especially near facial thermal receptors)	Warm oxygen and monitor the temperature inside the oxygen hood.
Evaporation	Wet body surface and hair in the delivery room or from bathing	Dry the infant, especially the head, immediately after birth with a warm blanket or towel. Use caps with adequate insulation quality or hooded blankets. Use polyethylene bags or wraps with VLBW infants from birth. Replace wet blankets with dry, warm ones and place in a warm environment. Delay the initial bath until the infant's temperature has stabilized; then give a sponge bath. Bathe the infant in a warm, draft-free environment, place on warmed towels, and dry immediately; bathe under a radiant warmer.
	Application of lotions, solutions, wet packs, or soaks to the infant	Prewarm solutions and soaks; maintain warmth during use. Avoid overheating solutions and soaks.
	Water loss from lungs	Warm and humidify oxygen.
	Increased insensible water loss in VLBW or ill infants	Increase incubator humidity levels as needed for VLBW infants.
Radiation	Placement near cold or hot external windows or walls; placement in direct sunlight	Place incubators, cribs, and radiant warmers away from external walls and windows and direct sunlight. Use thermal shades on external windows.
	Cold incubator walls	Use double-walled incubators or heat shields, or cover with plastic film. Prewarm incubators, radiant warmers, and heat shields.
	Heat lamps	Avoid use whenever possible; if used, do not place close to infant skin and monitor temperature every 10–15 minutes to avoid burns.

VLBW, Very-low-birth-weight.

the humidity, so infants in environments with greater humidity will lose less water and fewer calories. For example, TEWL at 85% to 95% humidity is approximately 10% that at 50% humidity.[102,127] Evaporative insensible water loss (IWL) increases with activity and tachypnea, under radiant warmers, or with phototherapy (see Chapter 18).[74] Rapid maturation of the skin occurs in the first few weeks after birth in infants of all gestational ages, reducing the degree of TEWL (see Chapter 14). Even at 4 weeks of age, TEWL is still twice as high in preterm versus term infants.[124] Term and older preterm infants can increase evaporative losses via the skin by sweating in response to a warm environment.[76]

In term and preterm infants, the evaporative heat loss is inversely proportional to the partial pressure of water vapor.[82,93] The neutral thermal environment temperature has been calculated to be reduced approximately 0.5° C (0.8° F) for each 1 mm of increase in water vapor pressure.[139] Increasing relative humidity reduces evaporative losses; at a relative humidity of 100%, evaporative loss is nonexistent.[146] Incubator humidity levels may need to be increased to reduce evaporative losses in VLBW infants. These infants may have subnormal temperatures despite incubator temperatures above their body temperatures. The elevated air temperature reduces convective and radiant losses but does little to reduce the extremely high transepidermal evaporative loss in these infants. Vapor pressure increases with higher temperatures, so as long as the infant's skin is warmer than the environment, evaporative losses can occur even with 100% humidity.[127]

Evaporative losses may be minimized by drying infants immediately after delivery or bathing, swaddling them in warm blankets, warming soaks and solutions, and warming and humidifying oxygen (see Table 20-1). Use of occlusive wraps (polyethylene wrappings or bags) with preterm infants in the delivery room and intensive care nursery can also reduce evaporative losses (see Methods of Promoting Thermal Stability) while allowing radiant heating.[13,15,22,92,104,116,127,154] Evaporative water losses in infants under radiant warmers can also be reduced by stretching a layer of plastic wrap or bubble wrap across the infant between the side guards of the radiant warmer, which is especially useful during procedures when the occlusive wrap around the infant must be removed.[15]

Radiation

A major form of heat loss in infants in incubators is radiation. Radiation involves the transfer of radiant energy from the body surface (through absorbance and emission of infrared rays) to surrounding cooler or warmer surfaces (walls, windows, heat lamps, lightbulbs) not in contact with the infant. The rate of transfer depends on the temperature gradient, surface absorption, and geometry (the amount and angle of the infant's surface area facing the object).[53,93,127] Radiant heat losses are independent of ambient temperature, air speed, and other heat loss mechanisms.[118] The infant can also gain heat by radiation, which is the principle of radiant warmers in which the (cooler) infant is placed under the warm radiant heat source.

Regulating incubator temperature alone does not prevent heat loss by radiation. Thus infants can get cold in a room containing air warmer than the infant if the walls and windows are cold. Infants in warm incubators can be cold stressed if they radiate body heat to cooler incubator walls or cooler windows and walls or to the cool outside air during transport. The amount of radiant loss is related to the temperatures of the window and walls rather than the temperature of the air in the incubator. Conversely, a baby in a cool incubator can get overheated if the incubator walls or room windows or walls are too hot.[51,53,127] Heat loss by radiation is reduced in double-walled versus single-walled incubators. Loss of heat by radiation is also influenced by the infant's position and amount of exposed radiating surface area.[26]

Incubators tend to act as greenhouses by trapping heat. The acrylic walls of the incubator are opaque to infrared rays. The walls allow short light waves to enter the incubator and subsequently the infant's body. The infant converts the short waves to heat and reemits them as longer infrared rays. Because these rays cannot escape from the incubator, they heat the incubator and then the infant ("greenhouse effect"). Radiant heat losses can be reduced by placing vulnerable infants away from the cooler exterior walls and windows, use of thermal shades, and use of double-walled incubators. Overheating of infants by radiation can be prevented by placing infants away from windows and walls that are warmer than the infant.[51,53,127]

Monitoring Temperature

Neonatal temperature is usually monitored by skin or axillary measurements and by manual or servocontrol methods. Although rectal temperature provides an approximation of core temperature, it is not used because of the risks associated with taking rectal temperatures, including trauma, perforation, and cross-contamination with repeated insertions. Axillary temperatures are noninvasive and approximate core temperature.[141] The optimal length of time to obtain an accurate assessment of temperature with axillary measurement using a mercury glass thermometer carefully placed in the axilla is 3 to 5 minutes in most studies.[96,135] Correlations have been reported between rectal and tympanic temperatures (with lower sensitivity of the tympanic measurements) in term infants, and between temporal artery and axillary temperatures, although some studies have shown poorer correlations between temporal and rectal temperatures.[27,46,47,59,71,94,125,156]

In a cold environment, core temperature may not indicate thermal stability. In a cold-stressed infant, the core temperature may be within normal limits because the infant has successfully compensated by increasing nonshivering thermogenesis. By the time the core temperature falls, the infant may be significantly compromised and difficult to rewarm.[127] Skin temperature measurement is used with preterm and other neonates at risk for thermoregulatory problems. Skin temperature changes provide an early indication of cold or heat stress, because an early mechanism to preserve body heat is peripheral vasoconstriction, which is detected by measuring skin temperature.[51]

Thermocouples or thermistors must be carefully placed, because skin temperature can vary widely. The best area for skin temperature probe placement is not known, although sites usually recommended in textbooks are the skin surface over the liver, between the umbilicus and pubis, or the back in a prone infant. Commonly suggested sites to avoid are over areas of BAT, poorly vasoreactive areas, and excoriated or bruised areas or near transcutaneous gas–monitoring transducers.[16] A recent study of a small sample of hemodynamically stable preterm infants in supine position reported no differences between skin sensor temperatures from the abdomen, flank, or axilla or between skin sensor temperatures and axillary temperatures.[125] However, there have been few probe placement site studies to determine either the best areas or which areas to avoid. Differences have been reported between various sites used for probe placement, with lower temperatures found in sites not exposed to radiant heat.[16,96] Lying on the probe may raise temperature by increasing skin insulation and lead to variable skin temperatures with repositioning.[16]

Disadvantages of skin temperature monitoring include accidental displacement of the probe, risk of skin irritation, misleading values with rapid temperature changes, and artifacts altering accuracy of measurement.[1,16,53] Artifacts that can alter readings include inadvertent insulation of the probe and the underlying skin; partial loss of skin contact with the probe; radiant or convective heating or cooling of the probe; increased probe temperature if covered with clothing or blankets or if the infant is lying on the probe (producing falsely high readings); and alteration in evaporative loss in skin covered with probes. This may occur with the use of probe covers; the temperature of the skin under the probe may be different from the skin temperature at other sites.[1,76,126,127,149] Insulated probes provide different information than exposed probes.[127,149] Insulated probes may result in probe temperatures greater than skin temperatures in either a radiant warmer or incubator and have been reported to alter incubator servocontrol with lower incubator temperatures and a higher skin-to-environment temperature gradient.[76,127,149] Therefore it is important to follow the manufacturer's directions regarding the types of probes and probe covers used.

Servocontrol

Servocontrol methods are used to maintain an infant's temperature within specified ranges. Servocontrol systems regulate both skin and air temperatures. A change in air temperature results in a change in the wall temperature and in heat exchange via convection and radiation.[127] Infant skin servocontrol using proportional control units is standard in modern convective incubators.[53] Air and skin servocontrol produce different thermal environments (Figure 20-6).[4,126,149,150] Air servocontrol tends to provide a more stable thermal environment with greater infant temperature variability, whereas skin servocontrol leads to greater variability in air temperature but is more effective in maintaining an NTE.[4,140,149,150] With infant skin servocontrol, the temperature from a skin probe is electronically monitored and used to control heater

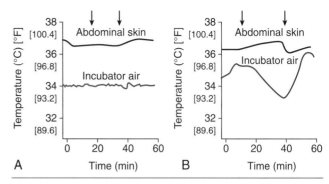

FIGURE 20-6 Fluctuations in incubator and air temperature when used in **(A)** air mode and **(B)** servo mode. In air mode, the set temperature (air) is 34° C (93.2° F), and in the servo mode, the set temperature (skin) is 36.3° C (97.3° F). Handling for brief spells of routine nursing care is indicated by the arrows. (From Rutter, N. [2005]. Temperature control and its disorders. In J.M. Rennie. [Ed.]. *Roberton's textbook of neonatology* [4th ed.]. London: Churchill Livingstone.)

output decisions in either a convectively heated incubator or radiant warmer. Considerations related to use of skin probes and probe artifacts are discussed in the preceding section. Risks of servocontrol include hyperthermia, if the probe becomes detached or is left in the manual mode, and failure to detect early signs of sepsis, because alterations in body temperature are masked.

Servocontrol may be affected by high evaporative water losses. The servocontrol system is based on the assumption that the temperature of the skin under the probe represents that of the surrounding skin; however, attaching the probe to the skin reduces evaporative losses at the site where temperature is being monitored. Thus the servocontrol system may record skin temperatures that are higher than those of the rest of the infant's body and fail to keep the infant warm.[4,53,127] Increasing humidity may reduce these differences. Opening of the portholes may lead to overdamping of the servocontrol system, with undershooting or overshooting of the air temperature for up to 1 hour later.[53] This problem has been reduced with the newer combination convection incubator–radiant warmer devices.

Methods of Promoting Thermal Stability

A major consideration in monitoring thermal status and promoting thermal stability in neonates involves issues related to the various types of equipment that are currently available. Other methods of supporting thermoregulation are summarized in Table 20-1.

High-risk neonates are generally cared for in convectively heated incubators; open, radiantly heated beds; or hybrid devices. The hybrid devices combine these two methods with an incubator mode in which plastic walls enclose the infants and a radiant warmer mode in which the radiant warmer is turned on and the plastic walls retract. Each of these pieces of equipment and methods has inherent advantages and disadvantages, as do adjuncts to these beds such as humidity and heat shields, thermal blankets, occlusive or polyethylene skin wraps, and warmed mattresses.[14,15,31,81,89,104,142]

Convective Incubators

Convective incubators operate by circulation of warmed air. Air entering the incubator is filtered, providing a barrier against airborne pathogenic organisms from the environment. Air leaving the incubator is not filtered, so nearby personnel or infants in open warmers and cribs are not protected from airborne organisms in the incubator air. In double-walled incubators, walls are warmed by a layer of warm water or by computer-controlled, electrically conductive plastic panels, thus decreasing heat loss and reducing radiant losses and oxygen consumption.[51,90]

Up to 60% to 70% of total heat loss in infants cared for in convectively heated incubators is by radiation.[26,146] Because Plexiglas is relatively opaque to radiant waves, infants radiate their body heat primarily to the inner side of the incubator wall. Radiant losses are reduced with double-walled incubators, which place a second layer of Plexiglas between the infant and the outer incubator wall. The infant radiates heat to the inner wall, which is surrounded on both sides by warmed incubator air. Increasing the ambient temperature of the room and placing the infant away from windows or exterior walls can also reduce radiant losses in infants in incubators. Further alterations in radiant losses occur when infants are clothed or incubators are covered with blankets or quilts to reduce light and noise levels. As a result of extremely high transepidermal evaporative losses, VLBW infants may have subnormal temperatures even though incubator temperatures are above their body temperatures and double-walled incubators are used.

Temperature fluctuations may occur with opening and closing of the portholes or hood, because the temperature of the air in the incubator falls rapidly and recovers slowly.[160] Laminar flow and double-walled incubators minimize temperature fluctuations with the opening of portholes, providing a more stable thermal environment during caregiving. The inner wall in a double-walled incubator acts as a heat reservoir; in some models warm air is redirected across the front of the incubator when it is opened.[126] The air thermometer or thermistor in an incubator should be near the infant's body and protected from being covered with bedding, clothing, or cool air flow from a resuscitation bag left in the incubator.[26]

Convective losses can also occur in incubators because of either natural convection or forced air convection. Natural convection is the thermal gradient between the skin surface and the surrounding air. Warm air rises from the infant's skin, carrying heat and moisture. This air then cools and falls back to the infant's skin surface, especially over the curvature of the body. Infants positioned in flexion have less exposed surface area and less heat loss than infants in an extended posture.[26,53] Forced convection usually occurs at air velocities equal to or greater than 0.2 m/sec.[127] Lower air velocities (especially less than 0.1 m/sec) minimize these losses, as can swaddling or clothing and humidity. In most incubators, the primary route of convective loss is through natural convection, because the air velocities near the infant's body are minimal.[53,126]

Air in the incubator is usually humidified by active methods. Active methods use a modular integral or external humidifier, so water vapor is continuously added to the circulating air via vaporization. This method generally uses servocontrol, and the amount of humidity can be individualized. Advantages of active humidification include reduction in infection risk, easier cleaning, and reduced recovery time after incubator doors are opened.[102]

Radiant Warmers

Radiant warmers maintain the infant's temperature using a proportional servocontrol system that maintains skin temperature at a constant level. The optimal skin temperature is not known and may vary from infant to infant.[126] Radiant heat is produced in the infrared spectrum and penetrates below the skin surface, where epidermal cells with a high water content absorb the radiant energy and convert it to heat. This heat is transferred to deeper tissues by conduction and circulating blood. The heat source is usually about 80 to 90 cm from the infant's surface.[53,76]

Radiant warmers are convenient to use, allow direct access to the infant, decrease radiant losses, and eliminate temperature fluctuations with opening of the portholes. Evaporative and convective—and possibly radiant—losses may increase, however, with a risk of dehydration.[12,56,127] Evaporative losses are primarily increased because of the lower humidity and can be reduced by the use of plastic wrap or blankets. IWL in infants in radiant warmers is increased 50% to 200%.[70] These losses may counteract the reduction in radiant losses in VLBW infants. Further IWL occurs if infants are simultaneously being treated with phototherapy (see Chapter 18). Although it may be possible to compensate for variations in evaporative and convective heat losses, the increased evaporative water losses are more difficult to manage.[53] Radiant warmers have been associated with an increase in oxygen consumption and metabolic rate, although the increase has not been statistically significant in most trials.[76,139] As mentioned, manufacturer's directions regarding temperature probes and probe covers should be followed, because insulated probes may result in probe temperatures greater than skin temperatures.[76,127,149] Use of servocontrol is discussed on page 652.

Convective losses can be reduced by using the sides on the warming bed or by stretching a layer of plastic wrap across the infant between the radiant warmer's side guards or use of occlusive wrappings. Plastic wrap does not block radiant heat waves as does Plexiglas; thus heat shields made from this material are not recommended for use with radiant warmers.[53,139] Plastic wrap also reduces IWL; plastic shields do not have a similar effect.[53]

Skin-to-Skin Care

At birth, term infants who are dried and covered with a warm blanket and placed skin to skin against their mother or who experience skin-to-skin contact later maintain their temperature as well as infants cared for in standard heating units.[12,62,110,113,145] Studies of skin-to-skin (kangaroo) care across all gestational ages demonstrate that infants maintain adequate thermal control during this type of holding, especially if the infant is wearing a hat and is covered with a blanket.[17,25,29] In some infants, skin temperature transiently increases during kangaroo care.[17,25,29,95,126] Somewhat less thermal stability has been reported in some infants less than 26 weeks' gestation, with a decrease in axillary temperature after transfer.[20,79] Others have found no significant differences in skin temperature before, during, and after skin-to-skin care in clinically stable ELBW infants if transfer techniques were standardized to prevent heat loss.[100,158] During kangaroo care, the parent's clothing around the sides and back of the infant forms a "pouch" that provides insulation and allows conduction of heat from parent to infant.[20,79,139] ELBW infants require careful temperature monitoring during kangaroo care to avoid both heat stress and cooling.

Use of Head Coverings, Clothing, Blankets, and Polyethylene Wraps

Clothing and head coverings can provide thermal insulation, reducing radiant and convective losses, and can, depending on the fabric, also reduce evaporative loss.[89,126,138] A neonate's head accounts for one-fifth of the total body surface area. Brain heat production is estimated to account for 55% of total metabolic heat production in newborns. Thus a neonate's head is poorly insulated and accounts for a significant proportion of total heat loss. Head coverings are often used to reduce heat loss from this area and may be especially useful immediately after birth and after a bath when the infant's hair is wet.[127] Head coverings or caps made of stockinette, which is a poor insulator, are relatively ineffective in reducing heat loss.[104] More effective materials include caps made of insulated fabrics, wool, or polyolefin; lined with Gamgee; or insulated with a liner.[104] Head coverings have been found to decrease heat loss after delivery and in neonates cared for in cribs and incubators.[107,126] These coverings are most effective in a cool environment and are less effective in a thermoneutral environment or with use of infant servocontrol.[126] Head coverings and clothing can interfere with radiant heat loss and gain and are not appropriate for infants under radiant warmers. There has been little research on the use of hats with VLBW infants.

Clothing and blankets alter the thermal environment by both widening and lowering the neutral thermal range.[76] Insulation from swaddling with blankets decreases evaporative loss by reducing the amount of exposed surface area and by changing airflow patterns and skin emissivity. In addition, swaddling and nesting maintain flexion, which reduces exposed surface area and thus convective and radiant losses.[53] Swaddled infants in servocontrolled double-walled incubators have been reported to have higher abdominal skin temperatures and require lower incubator temperatures.[136] Swaddling appears to have a greater effect on skin than core temperature. Others have found that nested infants have closer approximation of skin and rectal temperatures.[96]

Occlusive polyethylene wraps and bags are recommended for use with preterm infants to reduce heat loss after birth.[22,31,104,116,127,154] These wraps enhance radiant heat gain and reduce evaporative losses, IWL, and TEWL by creating a microenvironment under the wrap.[14,15,31] Reilly and associates found that use of occlusive wraps with preterm infants younger than 27 weeks' gestation increased mean body temperature but did not alter mortality.[120] Unwrapping the infant disrupts this microenvironment, so it should be minimized.[14] Occlusive wraps, skin-to-skin care, plastic bags (reported to be especially useful in resource-poor settings), and warming mattresses have all been effective in maintaining temperature in preterm infants.[13,92,104,120]

Neonatal Hypothermia and Cold Stress

Alterations in health status or maturity can compromise the ability of the newborn to efficiently and effectively regulate heat production and respond to cold stress. Infants at risk and the basis for this risk are summarized in Table 20-3.

Signs of hypothermia are often absent or nonspecific in neonates. Clinical findings may include lethargy, restlessness, pallor, cool skin, tachypnea, grunting, poor feeding, or decreased weight gain.[127] Hypothermia may be a sign of neonatal sepsis, because newborns have an altered response to pyrogens and as a result may not increase their temperature and run a fever with infection.[12,127] The neonatal response to pyrogens is not well understood.[12] Hypothermia in ELBW infants has been associated with abnormal heart rates (either less than the 25th percentile or greater than the 75th percentile of the individual infant's baseline heart rate), with a correlation between heart rate and abdominal temperature reported.[85]

"Cold stress occurs when an exposed infant loses more heat than he or she produces."[83] Cold stress can interfere with interpretation of pH, because pH is temperature-dependent.[76] Cold stress may delay transition from fetal to neonatal circulation.[14,83] With severe cold stress the infant may develop peripheral edema and sclerema. The initial temperature decrease is peripheral with stimulation of cutaneous receptors and initiation of NST. If the heat generated by this method is insufficient, the core temperature will drop. ELBW infants are at increased risk of cold stress because of poor vasomotor control with decreased peripheral vasoconstrictive responses, lack of both white and brown adipose tissue, thin skin, increased surface area and weight, and inefficient BAT metabolism related to decreased BAT, UCP-1, and thyroid hormones.[83]

A hypothermic or cold-stressed neonate tries to compensate by conserving heat and increasing heat production. These compensatory mechanisms can lead to physiologic alterations that may set off a series of adverse metabolic events (Figure 20-7). If uninterrupted, this chain of events can result in hypoxemia, metabolic acidosis, glycogen depletion, hypoglycemia, and altered surfactant production.[69] Physiologic effects of hypothermia and their consequences are summarized in Table 20-4.

Prevention of hypothermia and cold stress is a major component of neonatal health care. Strategies include careful monitoring of all infants, especially those at increased risk for hypothermia; decreasing heat losses by preventing evaporative, convective, conductive, and radiant losses; reducing the frequency and duration of cold exposure; and monitoring both infant and environmental temperatures.

Use of Hypothermia for Neuroprotection

Mild induced hypothermia is used as a neuroprotective strategy to reduce secondary reperfusion injuries in infants who

TABLE 20-3   Infants at Risk for Problems in Thermoregulation

INFANT CATEGORY	BASIS FOR RISK
Preterm infants	Decreased subcutaneous fat for insulation
	Decreased BAT and ability to mobilize norepinephrine and fat
	Large surface area–to–weight ratio
	Inadequate caloric intake
	Inability to effectively increase oxygen consumption
	Increased open resting posture with less flexion
	Immature thermal regulatory mechanisms
	Increased evaporative water losses and higher body water content
Infants with neurologic problems	Alterations in hypothalamic control of body temperature
Infants with endocrine problems	Impairment of BAT metabolism because of inadequate catecholamines, thyroxine, or other hormones
Hypoglycemic infants	Decreased substrate for energy and ATP production in BAT
	Decreased metabolic response to cold stress
Infants with cardiorespiratory problems	Inability to increase oxygen consumption or minute ventilation further
	Inability to increase metabolic rate and reduce metabolic response to cold
	Impairment of BAT metabolism by hypoxia (impaired with PO_2 of 45–55 torr; essentially ceases at values below 30 torr)
	Inadequate caloric intake to meet metabolic demands
	Increased risk of metabolic acidosis
	Increased temperature losses through evaporation of water from lungs
Infants with nutritional problems	Inadequate caloric intake to meet increased metabolic demands
Infants with electrolyte imbalances	Alterations in sodium and potassium possibly leading to sodium pump failure interfering with BAT metabolism
Infants with congenital anomalies (e.g., meningomyelocele, omphalocele, gastroschisis)	Increased surface area for heat loss
	Increased evaporative losses
Small-for-gestational-age infants	Decreased subcutaneous fat for insulation
	Increased surface area for weight
	Higher basal metabolic rate and energy demands
Sedated infants or maternal intrapartal analgesia	Limited physical activity to generate heat
	Possible transient alteration of thermal stability

ATP, Adenosine triphosphate; *BAT,* brown adipose tissue.
Compiled from references 18, 51, 53, 62, 114, and 127.

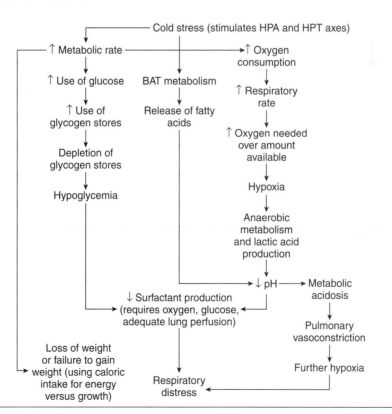

FIGURE 20-7   Physiologic consequences of cold stress. *BAT,* Brown adipose tissue; *HPA,* hypothalamic-pituitary-adrenal; *HPT,* hypothalamic-pituitary-thyroid.

TABLE 20-4   Consequences of Neonatal Hypothermia

PHYSIOLOGIC EFFECT	PHYSIOLOGIC CONSEQUENCE
Peripheral vasoconstriction	Increased internal (core to skin) gradient and tissue insulation
	Can lead to reduced tissue perfusion and metabolism with accumulation of ketone bodies and development of metabolic acidosis if persistent
Increased metabolic rate	Increased oxygen consumption by increasing minute ventilation and respiratory rate
	Risk of hypoxia and respiratory failure in infants unable to increase oxygen intake (e.g., infant with respiratory distress syndrome or other respiratory problems, VLBW)
Increased requirements for oxygen, glucose, and calories	Exhaustion of supplies with subsequent development of hypoglycemia, hypoxia, aggravation of respiratory distress syndrome, or weight loss
Increased production of ketone bodies and accumulation of lactic acid from anaerobic metabolism	Metabolic acidosis with subsequent pulmonary vasoconstriction with further reduction in pulmonary perfusion
	Risk of hypoxia and altered surfactant synthesis
Norepinephrine release	Increased pulmonary vascular resistance with altered ventilation-perfusion relationships and increased right-to-left shunting through the patent ductus arteriosus
	Risk of hypoxia and altered surfactant synthesis
Elevation in plasma nonesterified fatty acids	Alteration in glucose–fatty acid relationship with fall in blood glucose
	Risk of hypoglycemia and altered surfactant synthesis
	Competition with bilirubin for albumin-binding sites with risk of bilirubin encephalopathy
Dissociation of albumin and bilirubin because of acidosis	Increased indirect (unbound) bilirubin
	Risk of bilirubin encephalopathy

VLBW, Very-low-birth-weight.
Compiled from references 18, 38, 51, 53, 62, and 127.

are at risk for postasphyxia hypoxic-ischemic encephalopathy (HIE).[7,8,43,44,72,75,129,130,131,132,152] Damage from HIE occurs in two phases: an initial phase and a secondary reperfusion phase. The phases of cerebral injury are described in Chapters 6 and 15 and Figure 6-4. Hypothermia is initiated during the latent stage to prevent or reduce the secondary phase changes associated with secondary mitochondrial failure.[44] Mild hypothermia during the latent phase of cerebral injury reduces anoxic depolarization, excitotoxicity, production of free radicals, and dysfunction of the blood-brain barrier and may suppress apoptosis and microglia activation (which along with production of inflammatory cytokines and neurotoxins can result in secondary inflammation and consequent neural damage).[44] Hypothermia reduces brain metabolism (approximately 5% for every degree of temperature reduction), thus delaying anoxic cell depolarization.[44]

Both selective cooling of the head with mild systemic hypothermia (34° C to 35° C [93.2° F to 95° F]) and whole-body cooling have been studied in multiple multinational trials.[7,65,72,75,122,130,131,134] The cooling generally begins within 6 hours after birth and continues for 48 to 72 hours. Metaanalyses have confirmed decreased mortality without increased disability, with reductions in the combined outcomes of mortality and neurodevelopmental disability and with neurodevelopmental disability in both systemic hypothermia and selective head cooling.[48,63,68,75,130,133,134] Decreases in cognitive delay, psychomotor delay, and cerebral palsy were also reported in infants with systemic hypothermia.[130] Long-term safety and efficacy are still being evaluated, as are the ideal cooling temperatures, method of cooling, and duration of cooling.[129]

Hyperthermia and Fever in the Neonate

Although discussions regarding alterations in neonatal thermoregulation often focus primarily on hypothermia, neonates are also at risk for hyperthermia (heat stress). Hyperthermia increases metabolic demands, so even a slight increase in temperature can result in a significant increase in oxygen consumption, especially in preterm infants. Other consequences of hyperthermia include increased heart, respiratory, and metabolic rates; increased IWL; dehydration; peripheral vasodilation with a risk of decreased blood pressure; alteration in weight gain; and the risk of hypoxia and metabolic acidosis.[26,51,127] Neonatal hyperthermia (i.e., temperature above 37.5° C to 37.8° C [99.5° F to 100.0° F]) is primarily related to overheating and less often to hypermetabolism. Hyperthermia also results from dehydration, drugs, or alterations in hypothalamic control mechanisms secondary to birth trauma. Maternal and neonatal fever is also associated with maternal epidural anesthesia (see pp. 639-640).[5,60,67]

Overheating because of increased environmental temperatures or radiant gains from exposure to sunlight or heat lamps is associated with peripheral vasodilation, a "flushed" appearance especially prominent in extremities, warm extremities, increased activity, irritability, increased IWL, extended posture, and sweating (in older preterm or term infants). Skin temperatures are higher than core temperatures. Infants, particularly VLBW infants, are at risk for thermal injury from environmental sources (see Table 20-3).

Neonates are more vulnerable to overheating than are older individuals, because they have a lower capacity for normothermic heat storage, a larger surface-to-volume ratio, and a narrower control range than an adult does.[51] At environmental temperatures above the neutral thermal zone, thermal equilibrium is reestablished by increasing evaporative losses.[18] Adults respond by increasing skin water losses and sweating. A neonate's initial response is to increase respiratory water loss (via tachypnea). Infants more than 30 weeks' gestation can sweat if the environmental temperature exceeds their threshold.[58]

Hyperthermia secondary to hypermetabolism can result from sepsis, cardiac problems, drug withdrawal, or other metabolic alterations. Clinical signs include peripheral vasoconstriction; pale, cool extremities; and a core body temperature that is higher than skin temperature.[12,127] Foot temperature is more than 3° C (5° F) cooler than abdominal skin temperature.[76,127] Fever is less commonly seen with infections in neonates because of an immature, weak, or absent response to fever-producing substances such as bacterial endotoxins.[12] Regardless of the cause, hyperthermia, especially if prolonged, increases the risk of heat stroke, dehydration, and brain damage in neonates.

MATURATIONAL CHANGES DURING INFANCY AND CHILDHOOD

Nonshivering thermogenesis (NST) is believed to be the major mechanism for thermoregulation in infancy, especially during the first 3 to 6 months.[18,36,97] With increasing age, NST becomes less prominent, and the infant begins to rely more on physical methods of heat generation, such as activity and shivering.[18]

Brown adipose tissue (BAT) is found in the thorax and abdomen of children and adolescents and is inversely correlated with body mass, with BAT activity peaking prepuberty.[39,42,63] BAT is higher in adolescent males and correlated with muscle volume, so testosterone and growth hormone and insulin-like growth factor may play a role.[63,64] Activation of BAT in children and adolescents is associated with changes in weight and adiposity (increased weight and subcutaneous and visceral fat is greater in children without BAT activation).[64] BAT in children and adults continues to play a role in energy balance and is believed to have a role in weight control and prevention of obesity.[36,39,97] BAT cells can be induced within white adipose tissue (inducible brown fat or beige fat). This type of fat is associated with higher bone mineral density and is being investigated as a treatment for obesity, because BAT tends to burn energy rather than storing it as fat.[39,153]

Much of the BAT is gradually replaced by white adipose tissue. This change is correlated with the switch in the major thermoregulatory mechanism from NST to shivering.[64] Sweating becomes more efficient as a method of heat dissipation. The threshold body temperature for sweating decreases and maximal sweat production increases.[146] Infants continue to have a decreased hypothalamic response to pyrogens for the first 2 to 3 months.[105]

Differences in thermoregulation may persist in preterm infants after discharge, with smaller preterm infants more likely to be underheated at home.[151] Infants increase their temperature more easily with heat exposure and are less able to lose the heat via sweating.[155] By 3 months of age the thermal balance has shifted to favor heat conservation. Mass-to-surface differences and metabolic rate, however, continue to increase, so net heat loss per unit of surface area in a 3-month-old is 50% higher than at birth.[80] Children have a greater surface area–to–body mass ratio than adults. "In a warm environment this allows them to rely more on dry heat loss and less on evaporative cooling. However, in extreme conditions, hot or cold, the greater surface area–to–body mass ratio results in a higher rate of heat absorption or heat loss, respectively."[50]

Higher mean temperatures predominate in infants. Average temperatures at 18 months of age are 37.7° C (99.8° F), with marked daily variations seen in some children. Body temperatures gradually decrease from 2 years to puberty, stabilizing at 13 to 14 years of age in girls and 16 to 17 years in boys.[86]

SUMMARY

Thermal stability is one of the most critical processes during the transition to extrauterine life. Thermoregulation is essential for survival and has priority over most other metabolic demands. An infant who does not achieve thermal stability after birth or who is cold stressed in the neonatal period is more likely to experience health problems, poor growth, and increased morbidity and mortality. Ongoing assessment and monitoring of thermal status in the neonate and initiation of appropriate interventions to maintain thermal stability can prevent or minimize these risks. Clinical recommendations related to neonatal thermoregulation are summarized in Box 20-3.

BOX 20-3   Recommendations for Clinical Practice Related to Thermoregulation in Neonates

Know the mechanisms of heat production and dissipation in neonates (pp. 645-648).

Initiate interventions to conserve body heat and reduce neonatal heat loss during transition (pp. 643-645 and Table 20-1).

Implement golden hour interventions in extremely preterm infants (p. 644 and Table 20-1).

Recognize usual values for neonatal temperature (pp. 643-645).

Avoid overheating or cooling the trigeminal area of the neonate's face (pp. 646, 650).

Recognize and monitor for events that increase heat loss by conduction, convection, evaporation, and radiation (pp. 649-651 and Table 20-1).

Institute interventions to reduce heat loss in term and preterm infants by conduction, convection, evaporation, and radiation (pp. 649-651 and Table 20-1).

Provide term and preterm neonates with an appropriate thermal environment (pp. 648-652).

Know the methods for monitoring thermal status and their advantages and limitations (pp. 651-652).

Understand the differences between and implications of core versus skin temperature (pp. 651-652).

Know the advantages and limitations of infant incubators and radiant warmers (pp. 652-653).

Use infant incubators and radiant warmers appropriately to maintain neonatal thermal status and reduce heat loss (pp. 652-653).

Monitor insensible water loss in infants (pp. 650-651).

Provide opportunities for skin-to-skin care (pp. 643, 649, 653-654).

Use head coverings made of appropriate materials to reduce heat loss in infants in incubators and cribs (p. 654).

Continued

BOX 20-3   Recommendations for Clinical Practice Related to Thermoregulation in Neonates—cont'd

Recognize and monitor infants at risk for hypothermia and cold stress (p. 654 and Table 20-3).

Provide neuroprotective interventions as ordered to reduce injury in infants at risk for postasphyxia hypoxic-ischemic encephalopathy (pp. 654, 656).

Monitor hypothermic or cold-stressed infants for adverse physiologic effects (pp. 654-655, Figure 20-7, and Table 20-4).

Recognize infants at risk for and signs of hyperthermia and thermal injury (pp. 656-657).

Monitor hyperthermic infants for adverse physiologic effects (pp. 656-657).

Use occlusive polyethylene wraps or bags with very-low-birth-weight infants (pp. 643, 644, 651, and 654).

References

1. American Academy of Pediatrics and American College of Obstetricians and Gynecologists. (2012). *Guidelines for perinatal care* (7th ed.). Elk Grove Village, IL: American Academy of Pediatrics; and Washington, D.C.: American College of Obstetricians and Gynecologists.
2. Ammari, A., et al. (2009). Effects of body position on thermal, cardiorespiratory and metabolic activity in low birth weight infants. *Early Hum Dev, 85*, 497.
3. Anim-Somuah, M., et al. (2011). Epidural versus non-epidural or no analgesia in labour. *Cochrane Database Syst Rev, 2011*(4), CD000331.
4. Antonucci, R., Porcella, A., & Fanos, V. (2009). The infant incubator in the neonatal intensive care unit: unresolved issues and future developments. *J Perinat Med, 37*, 587.
5. Arendt, K. W., & Segal, B. S. (2013). The association between epidural labor analgesia and maternal fever. *Clin Perinatol, 40*, 385.
6. Au, K. S., Ashley-Koch, A., & Northrup, H. (2010). Epidemiologic and genetic aspects of spina bifida and other neural tube defects. *Dev Disabil Res Rev, 16*, 6.
7. Azzopardi, D., et al. (2008). The TOBY Study: whole body hypothermia for the treatment of perinatal asphyxia encephalopathy: A randomized controlled trial. *BMC Pediatr, 8*, 17.
8. Azzopardi, D. V., et al. (2009). Moderate hypothermia to treat perinatal asphyxial encephalopathy. *N Engl J Med, 361*, 1349.
9. Baka, S., et al. (2015). Cord blood irisin at the extremes of fetal growth. *Metabolism, 64*, 1515.
10. Banerjee, S., et al. (2004). Maternal temperature monitoring during labor: concordance and variability among monitoring sites. *Obstet Gynecol, 103*, 287.
11. Bartholomew, M. L., et al. (2002). Maternal temperature variation during parturition. *Obstet Gynecol, 100*, 642.
12. Baumgart, S. (2008). Iatrogenic hyperthermia and hypothermia in the neonate. *Clin Perinatol, 35*, 183.
13. Belsches, T. C., et al. (2013). Randomized trial of plastic bags to prevent term neonatal hypothermia in a resource-poor setting. *Pediatrics, 132*, e656.
14. Bissinger, R. L., & Annibale, D. J. (2010). Thermoregulation in very-low-birth-weight infants during the golden hour: results and implications. *Adv Neonatal Care, 10*, 230. Erratum in: *Adv Neonatal Care, 10*, 351.
15. Bissinger, R. L., & Annibale, D. J. (2014). *Golden hours: care of the very low birth weight infant*. Chicago: National Certification Company.
16. Blackburn, S., et al. (2001). Neonatal nursing thermal care: the effect of position and temperature probe placement. *Neonatal Netw, 20*, 19.
17. Boundy, E. O., et al. (2016). Kangaroo mother care and neonatal outcomes: a meta-analysis. *Pediatrics, 137*, 1.
18. Bruck, K. (1978). Heat production and temperature regulation. In U. Stave (Ed.), *Perinatal physiology*. New York: Plenum.
19. Cannon, B., & Nedergaard, J. (2004). Brown adipose tissue: function and physiological significance. *Physiol Rev, 84*, 277.
20. Carbasse, A., et al. (2013). Safety and effectiveness of skin-to-skin contact in the NICU to support neurodevelopment in vulnerable preterm infants. *J Perinat Neonatal Nurs, 27*, 255.
21. Carolan-Olah, M., & Frankowska, D. (2014). High environmental temperature and preterm birth: a review of the evidence. *Midwifery, 30*, 50.
22. Carroll, P. D., et al. (2010). Use of polyethylene bags in extremely low birth weight infant resuscitation for the prevention of hypothermia. *J Reprod Med, 55*, 9.
23. Castrodale, V., & Rinehart, S. (2014). The golden hour: improving the stabilization of the very low birth-weight infant. *Adv Neonatal Care, 14*, 9.
24. Chambers, C. D. (2006). Risks of hyperthermia associated with hot tub or spa use by pregnant women. *Birth Defects Res A Clin Mol Teratol, 76*, 569.
25. Chan, G. J., et al. (2016). Kangaroo mother care: a systematic review of barriers and enablers. *Bull World Health Organ, 94*, 130J.
26. Chandra, S., & Baumgart, S. (2005). Fetal and neonatal thermal regulation. In A. R. Spitzer (Ed.), *Intensive care of the fetus & neonate* (2nd ed.). St. Louis: Mosby.
27. Charafeddine, L., et al. (2014). Axillary and rectal thermometry in the newborn: do they agree? *BMC Res Notes, 31*, 584.
28. Cioffi, F., et al. (2009). Uncoupling proteins: a complex journey to function discovery. *Biofactors, 35*, 417.
29. Conde-Agudelo, A., & Díaz-Rossello, J. L. (2014). Kangaroo mother care to reduce morbidity and mortality in low birthweight infants. *Cochrane Database Syst Rev, 2014*(4), CD002771.
30. Contreras, C., et al. (2015). The brain and brown fat. *Ann Med, 47*, 150.
31. Cramer, K., et al. (2005). Heat loss prevention: a systematic review of occlusive skin wrap for premature neonates. *J Perinatol, 25*, 763.
32. Cummings, K. J., Li, A., & Nattie, E. E. (2011). Brainstem serotonin deficiency in the neonatal period: autonomic dysregulation during mild cold stress. *J Physiol, 589*, 2055.
33. Cunningham, F. G., et al. (2014). *Williams obstetrics* (24th ed.). New York: McGraw-Hill.
34. Curtin, W. M., et al. (2015). Intrapartum fever, epidural analgesia and histologic chorioamnionitis. *J Perinatol, 35*, 396.
35. Cypess, A. M., et al. (2009). Identification and importance of brown adipose tissue in adult humans. *N Engl J Med, 360*, 1509.
36. Cypess, A. M., & Kahn, C. R. (2010). The role and importance of brown adipose tissue in energy homeostasis. *Curr Opin Pediatr, 22*, 478.
37. Darnell, R. A. (1987). The thermophysiology of the newborn infant. *Med Instrum, 21*, 16.
38. Davis, V. (1980). The structure and function of brown adipose tissue in the neonate. *J Obstet Gynecol Neonatal Nurs, 9*, 368.
39. Devlin, M. J. (2015). The "Skinny" on brown fat, obesity, and bone. *Am J Phys Anthropol, 156*, 98.
40. Dollberg, S., Mimouni, F. B., & Weitraub, V. (2004). Energy expenditure in infants weaned from a convective incubator. *Am J Perinatol, 21*, 253.
41. Dreier, J. W., Andersen, A. M., & Berg-Beckhoff, G. (2014). Systematic review and meta-analyses: fever in pregnancy and health impacts in the offspring. *Pediatrics, 133*, e674.
42. Drubach, L. A., et al. (2011). Pediatric brown adipose tissue: detection, epidemiology, and differences from adults. *J Pediatr, 159*, 939.
43. Drury, P. P., Bennet, L., & Gunn, A. J. (2010). Mechanisms of hypothermic neuroprotection. *Semin Fetal Neonatal Med, 15*, 287.
44. Drury, P. P., et al. (2014). Mechanisms of Hypothermic neuroprotection. *Clin Perinatol, 41*, 161.
45. Duong, H. T., et al. (2011). Maternal use of hot tub and major structural birth defects. *Birth Defects Res A Clin Mol Teratol, 91*, 836.
46. Duran, R., et al. (2009). Comparison of temporal artery: mid-forehead and axillary temperature recordings in preterm infants, 1500g of birthweight. *J Paediatr Child Health, 45*, 444.
47. Duru, C. O., Akinbami, F. O., & Orimadegun, A. E. (2012). A comparison of tympanic and rectal temperatures in term Nigerian neonates. *BMC Pediatr, 12*, 86.

48. Edwards, A. D., et al. (2010). Neurological outcomes at 18 months of age after moderate hypothermia for perinatal hypoxic ischaemic encephalopathy: synthesis and meta-analysis of trial data. *BMJ, 340*, 363.

49. Edwards, M. J. (2006). Review: Hyperthermia and fever during pregnancy. *Birth Defects Res A Clin Mol Teratol, 76*, 507.

50. Falk, B. (1998). Effects of thermal stress during rest and exercise in the paediatric population. *Sports Med, 25*, 221.

51. Fanaroff, A. A., & Fanaroff, J. M. (2013). *Care of the high risk infant* (6th ed.). Philadelphia: Elsevier Saunders.

52. Fawcett, K. (2014). Preventing admission hypothermia in very low birth weight neonates. *Neonatal Netw, 33*, 143.

53. Feiedman M., & Baumgardt, S. (2005). Thermal regulation. In M. G. Macdonald, M. M. K. Sheshia, & M. D. Mullett (Eds.), *Avery's Neonatology: Pathophysiology and management of the newborn* (6th ed.). Philadelphia: Lippincott, Williams & Wilkins.

54. Fieril, K., Glantz, A., & Fagevik Olsen, M. (2016). Hemodynamic responses to single sessions of aerobic exercise and resistance exercise in pregnancy. *Acta Obstet Gynecol Scand, 95*, 1042.

55. Filker, R., & Monif, G. R. G. (1979). The significance of temperature during the first 24 hours postpartum. *Obstet Gynecol, 53*, 358.

56. Flenady, V. J., & Woodgate, P. G. (2003). Radiant warmers versus incubators for regulating body temperature in newborn infants. *Cochrane Database Syst Rev, 2003*(2), CD000435.

57. Fluhr, J. W., et al. (2010). Functional skin adaptation in infancy—almost complete but not fully competent. *Exp Dermatol, 19*, 483.

58. Foster, K. G., Hey, E. N., & Katz, G. (1969). The response of the sweat glands of the newborn baby to thermal stimuli and to intradermal acetylcholine. *J Physiol, 203*, 13.

59. Friedrichs, J., et al. (2013). Axillary temperatures in full-term newborn infants: using evidence to guide safe and effective practice. *Adv Neonatal Care, 13*, 361.

60. Frölich, M. A., et al. (2012). What factors affect intrapartum maternal temperature? A prospective cohort study: maternal intrapartum temperature. *Anesthesiology, 117*, 302.

61. Frölich, M. A. (2014). Labor epidural fever and chorioamnionitis. *Int Anesthesiol Clin, 52*, 101.

62. Gardner, S. L., & Hernandez, J. A. (2015). Heat balance. In S. L. Gardner, et al. (Eds.), *Merenstein & Gardner's Handbook of Neonatal Intensive Care* (8th ed.). St. Louis: Elsevier Mosby.

63. Gilsanz, V., et al. (2012). Changes in brown adipose tissue in boys and girls during childhood and puberty. *J Pediatrics, 160*, 604.

64. Gilsanz, V., Hu, H. H., & Kajimura, S. (2013). Relevance of brown adipose tissue in infancy and adolescence. *Pediatr Res, 73*, 3.

65. Gluckman, P. D., et al. (2005). Selective head cooling with mild systemic hypothermia after neonatal encephalopathy: multicentre randomized trial. *Lancet, 365*, 663.

66. Goetzl, L., et al. (2007). Intrapartum epidural analgesia and maternal temperature regulation. *Obstet Gynecol, 109*, 687.

67. Goetzl, L. (2014). Epidural fever in obstetric patients: it's a hot topic. *Anesth Analg, 118*, 494.

68. Guillet, R., et al. (2012). Seven- to eight-year follow-up of the CoolCap trial of head cooling for neonatal encephalopathy. *Pediatr Res, 71*, 205.

69. Gunn, A. J., & Bennet, L. (2017). Responses of the fetus and neonate to hypothermia. In R. A. Polin, et al. (Eds.), *Fetal and neonatal physiology* (5th ed.). Philadelphia: Elsevier Saunders.

70. Guyton, A. C., & Hall, J. E. (2015). *Textbook of medical physiology* (13th ed.). Philadelphia: Elsevier Saunders.

71. Haddad, L., et al. (2012). Comparison of temporal artery and axillary temperatures in healthy newborns. *J Obstet Gynecol Neonatal Nurs, 41*, 383.

72. Higgins, R. D., et al. (2006). Hypothermia and perinatal asphyxia: executive summary of the National Institute of Child Health and Human Development Workshop. *J Pediatr, 148*, 170.

73. Hillman, N. H., Kallapur, S. G., & Jobe, A. H. (2012). Physiology of transition from intrauterine to extrauterine life. *Clin Perinatol, 39*, 769.

74. Horns, K. (1994). Physiological and methodological issues: neonatal insensible water loss. *Neonatal Netw, 13*, 83.

75. Jacobs, S. E., et al. (2013). Cooling for newborns with hypoxic ischaemic encephalopathy. *Cochrane Database Syst Rev, 2013*(4), CD003311.

76. Jain A. (2012). Temperature control and disorders. In J. M. Rennie (Ed.), *Rennie & Roberton's textbook of neonatology* (5th ed.). London: Churchill Livingstone.

77. Jia, Y. S., et al. (2013). Effect of delivery room temperature on the admission temperature of premature infants: a randomized controlled trial. *J Perinatol, 33*, 264.

78. Joung, K. E., et al. (2015). Cord blood irisin levels are positively correlated with birth weight in newborn infants. *Metabolism, 64*, 1507.

79. Karlsson, V., et al. (2012). Early skin-to-skin care in extremely preterm infants: thermal balance and care environment. *J Pediatr, 161*, 422.

80. Khorshid, L., et al. (2005). Comparing mercury-in-glass, tympanic and disposable thermometers in measuring body temperature in healthy young people. *J Clin Nurs, 14*, 496.

81. Kim, S. M., et al. (2010). Improved care and growth outcomes by using hybrid humidified incubators in very preterm infants. *Pediatrics, 125*, e137.

82. Knobel, R., & Holditch-Davis, D. (2007). Thermoregulation and heat loss prevention after birth and during neonatal intensive-care unit stabilization of extremely low-birth weight infants. *J Obstet Gynecol Neonatal Nurs, 36*, 280.

83. Knobel, R., & Holditch-Davis, D. (2010). Thermoregulation and heat loss prevention after birth and during neonatal intensive-care unit stabilization of extremely low-birthweight infants. *Adv Neonatal Care, 10*, S7.

84. Knobel, R. B., et al. (2009). Extremely low birth weight preterm infants lack vasomotor response in relationship to cold body temperatures at birth. *J Perinatol, 29*, 814.

85. Knobel, R. B., Holditch-Davis, D., & Schwartz, T. A. (2010). Optimal body temperature in transitional extremely low birth weight infants using heart rate and temperature as indicators. *J Obstet Gynecol Neonatal Nurs, 39*, 3.

86. Kornienko, I. A., & Gokhblit, I. I. (1980). Age differences of temperature regulation in children age 5-12 years. *Human Physiol, 6*, 443.

87. Kruse, J. (1988). Fever in children. *Am Fam Physician, 37*, 127.

88. Laptook, A. R., Salhab, W., & Bhaskar, B. (2007). Admission temperature of low birth weight infants: predictors and associated morbidities. *Pediatrics, 119*, e643.

89. Laptook, A. R., & Watkinson, M. (2008). Temperature management in the delivery room. *Semin Fetal Neonatal Med, 13*, 383.

90. Laroia, N., Phelps, D. L., & Roy, J. (2007). Double wall versus single wall incubator for reducing heat loss in very low birth weight infants in incubator. *Cochrane Database Syst Rev, 2007*(2), CD004215.

91. Larsson, L., & Lindqvist, P. G. (2005). Low-impact exercise during pregnancy—a study of safety. *Acta Obstet Gynecol Scand, 84*, 34.

92. Leadford, A. E., et al. (2013). Plastic bags for prevention of hypothermia in preterm and low birth weight infants. *Pediatrics, 132*, e128.

93. LeBlanc, M. H. (1987). The physics of thermal exchange between infants and their environment. *Med Instrum, 21*, 11.

94. Lee, G., et al. (2011). Accuracy of temporal artery thermometry in neonatal intensive care infants. *Adv Neonatal Care, 11*, 62.

95. Legault, M., & Goulet, C. (1995). Comparison of kangaroo and traditional methods of removing preterm infants from incubators. *J Obstet Gynecol Neonatal Nurs, 24*, 501.

96. Leick-Rude, M. K., & Bloom, L. F. (1998). A comparison of temperature taking methods in neonates. *Neonatal Netw, 17*, 21.

97. Lidell, M. E., & Enerbäck, S. (2010). Brown adipose tissue—a new role in humans? *Nat Rev Endocrinol, 6*, 319.

98. Lotgering, F. K. (2014). 30(+) years of exercise in pregnancy. *Adv Exp Med Biol, 814*, 109.

99. Lynch, A. M., et al. (2007). Maternal physiological responses to swimming training during the second trimester of pregnancy. *Res Sports Med, 15*, 33.

100. Maastrup, R., & Greisen, G. (2010). Extremely preterm infants tolerate skin-to-skin contact during the first weeks of life. *Acta Paediatr, 99*, 1145.

101. Malaeb, S., & Dammann, O. (2009). Fetal inflammatory response and brain injury in the preterm newborn. *J Child Neurol, 24*, 1119.

102. Marshall, A. (1997). Humidifying the environment for the premature neonate: maintenance of a thermoneutral environment. *J Neonatal Nurs, 3*, 32.

103. Mattson, M. P. (2010). Perspective: Does brown fat protect against diseases of aging? *Ageing Res Rev, 9*, 69.

104. McCall, E. M., et al. (2010). Interventions to prevent hypothermia at birth in preterm and/or low birthweight infants. *Cochrane Database Syst Rev, 2010*(3), CD004210.

105. McCarthy, P. L. (1998). Fever. *Pediatr Rev, 19*, 401.

106. McMurray, R. G., et al. (1993). Thermoregulation of pregnant women during aerobic

exercise on land and in the water. *Am J Perinatol, 10*, 178.

107. Medves, J. M., & O'Brien, B. (2004). The effect of bather and location of first bath on maintaining thermal stability in newborns. *J Obstet Gynecol Neonatal Nurs, 33*, 175.

108. Miller, M. W., et al. (2007). Fetal thermal dose considerations during the obstetrician's watch: implications for the pediatrician's observations. *Birth Defects Res C Embryo Today, 81*, 135.

109. Milunsky, A., et al. (1992). Maternal heat exposure and neural tube defects. *JAMA, 268*, 882.

110. Moore, E. R., et al. (2012). Early skin-to-skin contact for mothers and their healthy newborn infants. *Cochrane Database Syst Rev, 2012*(5), CD003519.

111. Moretti, M. E., et al. (2005). Maternal hyperthermia and the risk for neural tube defects in offspring: systematic review and meta-analysis. *Epidemiology, 16*, 216.

112. Nedergaard, J., & Cannon, B. (2017). Brown adipose tissue: development and function. In R. A. Polin, et al. (Eds.), *Fetal and neonatal physiology* (5th ed.). Philadelphia: Elsevier Saunders.

113. Nimbalkar, S. M., et al. (2014). Effect of early skin-to-skin contact following normal delivery on incidence of hypothermia in neonates more than 1800 g: randomized control trial. *J Perinatol, 34*, 364.

114. Panzer, O., et al. (1999). Shivering and shivering-like tremor during labor with and without epidural analgesia. *Anesthesiology, 90*, 1609.

115. Paris, L. G., et al. (2014). A randomized controlled trial to improve outcomes utilizing various warming techniques during cesarean birth. *J Obstet Gynecol Neonatal Nurs, 43*, 719.

116. Perlman, J. M., et al. (2015). Part 7: Neonatal Resuscitation: 2015 International Consensus on Cardiopulmonary Resuscitation and Emergency Cardiovascular Care Science With Treatment Recommendations. *Circulation, 132*, S204.

117. Pivarnik, J. M., Perkins, C. D., & Moyerbrailean, T. (2003). Athletics and pregnancy. *Clin Obstet Gynecol, 46*, 403.

118. Power, G. G., & Blood, A. B. (2012). Perinatal thermal physiology. In R. A. Polin, W. W. Fox, & S. H. Abman (Eds.), *Fetal and neonatal physiology* (4th ed.). Philadelphia: Saunders.

119. Ravussin, E., & Galgani, J. E. (2011). The implications of brown adipose tissue for humans. *Annu Rev Nutr, 21*, 33.

120. Reilly, M. C., et al., & Vermont Oxford Network Heat Loss Prevention (HeLP) Trial Study Group. (2015). Randomized trial of occlusive wrap for heat loss prevention in preterm infants. *J Pediatr, 166*, 262.

121. Riley, L. E., et al. (2011). Association of epidural-related fever and noninfectious inflammation in term labor. *Obstet Gynecol, 117*, 588.

122. Rutherford, M., et al. (2010). Assessment of brain tissue injury after moderate hypothermia in neonates with hypoxic-ischaemic encephalopathy: a nested substudy of a randomised controlled trial. *Lancet Neurol, 9*, 39.

123. Rutter, N. (1999). Thermal adaptation to extrauterine life. In C. H. Rodeck & M. J.

Whittle (Eds.), *Fetal medicine: Basic science and clinical practice*. London: Churchill Livingstone.

124. Sahni, R. (2017). Temperature control in newborn infants. In R. A. Polin, et al. (Eds.), *Fetal and neonatal physiology* (5th ed.). Philadelphia: Elsevier Saunders.

125. Schafer, D., et al. (2014). Comparison of neonatal skin sensor temperatures with axillary temperature: does skin sensor placement really matter? *Adv Neonatal Care, 14*, 52.

126. Sedin, G. (2012). Physics and physiology of human neonatal incubation. In R. A. Polin, W. W. Fox, & S. H. Abman (Eds.), *Fetal and neonatal physiology* (4th ed.). Philadelphia: Saunders.

127. Sedin, G. (2015). The thermal environment of the intensive care nursery. In R. J. Martin, A. A. Fanaroff, & M. C. Walsh (Eds.), *Fanaroff & Martin's Neonatal-perinatal medicine: Diseases of the fetus and infant* (10th ed.). St. Louis: Elsevier Saunders.

128. Segal, S. (2010). Labor epidural analgesia and maternal fever. *Anesth Analg, 111*, 1467.

129. Selway, L. D. (2010). State of the science: Hypoxic ischemic encephalopathy and hypothermic intervention for neonates. *Adv Neonatal Care, 10*, 60.

130. Shah, P. S. (2010). Hypothermia: a systematic review and meta-analysis of clinical trials. *Semin Fetal Neonatal Med, 15*, 238.

131. Shankaran, S., et al. (2008). Outcomes of safety and effectiveness in a multicenter randomized controlled trial of whole-body hypothermia for neonatal hypoxic-ischemic encephalopathy. *Pediatrics, 122*, e791.

132. Shankaran, S. (2009). Neonatal encephalopathy: treatment with hypothermia. *J Neurotrauma, 26*, 437.

133. Shankaran, S., et al. (2012). Brain injury following trial of hypothermia for neonatal hypoxic-ischaemic encephalopathy. *Arch Dis Child Fetal Neonatal Ed, 97*, F398.

134. Shankaran, S., et al. (2012). Childhood outcomes after hypothermia for neonatal encephalopathy. *N Engl J Med, 366*, 2085.

135. Sheenan, M. S. (1996). Obtaining an accurate axillary temperature measurement. *J Neonatal Nurs, 2*, 6.

136. Short, M. (1998). A comparison of temperature in VLBW infants swaddled versus unswaddled in a double-walled incubator in skin control mode. *Neonatal Netw, 17*, 25.

137. Silva, J. E. (2011). Physiological importance and control of non-shivering facultative thermogenesis. *Front Biosci (Schol Ed), 3*, 352.

138. Simbruner, G., et al. (2005). Premature infants are less capable of maintaining thermal balance of head and body with increases of thermal environment than with decreases. *Am J Perinatol, 22*, 25.

139. Sinclair, J. (1992). Management of the thermal environment. In J. C. Sinclair & M. B. Brocker (Eds.), *Effective care of the newborn infant*. Oxford: Oxford University Press.

140. Sinclair, J. (2002). Servo-control for maintaining abdominal skin temperature at 36° C in low birth weight infants. *Cochrane Database Sys Rev, 2002*(1), CD001074.

141. Smith, J., Alcock, G., & Usher, K. (2013). Temperature measurement in the preterm and term neonate: a review of the literature. *Neonatal Netw, 32*, 16.

142. Soll, R. (2008). Heat loss prevention in neonates. *J Perinatol, 28*, S57.

143. Soultanakis-Aligianni, H. N. (2003). Thermoregulation during exercise in pregnancy. *Clin Obstet Gynecol, 46*, 442.

144. Sultan, P., et al. (2015). The effect of patient warming during Caesarean delivery on maternal and neonatal outcomes: a meta-analysis. *Br J Anaesth, 115*, 500.

145. Sundin, C. S., & Mazac, L. B. (2015). Implementing skin-to-skin care in the operating room after Cesarean birth. *MCN Am J Matern Child Nurs, 40*, 249.

146. Swyer, P. R. (1987). Thermoregulation in the newborn. In L. Stern & P. Vert (Eds.), *Neonatal medicine*. New York: Masson.

147. Symonds, M. E., Pope, M., & Budge, H. (2012). Adipose tissue development during early life: novel insights into energy balance from small and large mammals. *Proc Nutr Soc, 71*, 363.

148. te Pas, A. B., et al. (2010). Humidified and heated air during stabilization at birth improves temperature in preterm infants. *Pediatrics, 125*, e1427.

149. Thomas, K. A., & Burr, R. (1999). Preterm infant thermal care: differing thermal environments produced by air versus skin servo-control incubators. *J Perinatol, 19*, 264.

150. Thomas, K. A. (2003). Preterm infant thermal responses to caregiving differ by incubator control mode. *J Perinatol, 23*, 640.

151. Thomas, K. A. (2003). Infant weight and gestational age effects on thermoneutrality in the home environment. *J Obstet Gynecol Neonatal Nurs, 32*, 745.

152. Thoresen, M., et al. (2013). Time is brain: starting therapeutic hypothermia within three hours after birth improves motor outcome in asphyxiated newborns. *Neonatology, 104*, 228.

153. Townsend, K. L., & Tseng, Y. H. (2014). Brown fat fuel utilization and thermogenesis. *Trends Endocrinol Metab TEM, 25*, 168.

154. Trevisanuto, D., et al. (2010). Heat loss prevention in very preterm infants in delivery rooms: a prospective, randomized, controlled trial of polyethylene caps. *J Pediatr, 156*, 914.

155. Tsuzuki-Hayakawa, K., Tochihara, Y., & Ohnaka, T. (1995). Thermoregulation during heat exposure of young children compared to their mothers. *Eur J Appl Physiol Occup Physiol, 72*, 12.

156. Uslu, S., et al. (2011). A comparison of different methods of temperature measurements in sick newborns. *J Trop Pediatr, 57*, 418.

157. Vaha-Eskeli, K., Erkkola, R., & Seppanen, A. (1991). Is the heat dissipating ability enhanced during pregnancy? *Eur J Obstet Gynecol Reprod Biol, 39*, 169.

158. Van Zanten, H. A., et al. (2007). The kangaroo method is safe for premature infants under 30 weeks of gestation during ventilator support. *J Neonatal Nurs, 12*, 186.

159. Virtanen, K. A., et al. (2009). Functional brown adipose tissue in healthy adults. *N Engl J Med, 360*, 1518.

160. Wrobel, L. C., et al. (2010). An overview of recent applications of computational modeling in neonatology. *Philos Transact A Math Phys Eng Sci, 368*, 2817.

161. Wyckoff, M. H. (2014). Initial resuscitation and stabilization of the periviable neonate: the Golden-Hour approach. *Semin Perinatol, 38*, 12.

List of Abbreviations

1,25-[OH]2D	1,25-dihydroxyvitamin D
2,3-DPG	2,3-diphosphoglycerate
3β-HSD	3β hydroxysteroid dehydrogenase
11β-HSD	11-β-hydroxysteroid dehydrogenase
17-OH	17α-hydroxylase
17-OHPC	17-α-hydroxyprogesterone caproate
21-OH	21-hydroxylase
AaDO$_2$	alveolar-arterial PO$_2$ gradient
AAP	American Academy of Pediatrics
Ab	antibody
ABC	APT-binding cassette
AC	adenyl cyclase
ACE	angiotensin-converting enzyme
aCGH	array comparative genome hybridization
ACIP	Advisory Committee on Immunization Practices
ACOG	American College of Obstetricians and Gynecologists
ACS	antenatal corticosteroids
ACTH	adrenocorticotropic hormone
ADP	adenosine diphosphate
AED	antiepileptic drug
AEP	atopic eruptions of pregnancy
AFI	amniotic fluid index
AFP	α-fetoprotein
AGA	appropriate for gestational age
AIT	alloimmune thrombocytopenia
ALT	alanine aminotransferase
ANF	atrial natriuretic factor
ANP	atrial natriuretic peptide
AOS	antioxidant system
APC	antigen presenting cells
aPC	activated protein C
aPTT	activated partial thromboplastin time
AQP	aquaporin
ARDS	adult respiratory distress syndrome
ART	assisted reproductive technologies
AS	active (light) sleep
ASB	asymptomatic bacteriuria
ASD	atrial septal defect
AST	aspartate aminotransferase
AT	antithrombin
ATP/ATPase	adenosine triphosphate/-ase
AT$_1$R	angiotensin 1 receptor
AV	atrioventricular
AVP	arginine vasopressin
AWHONN	Association of Women's Health, Obstetric and Neonatal Nurses
BAT	brown adipose tissue
BBB	blood brain barrier
BCG	bacilli Calmette-Guerin
BCRP	breast cancer resistance protein
BE	β-endorphin
BFU	burst forming unit
BH4	tetrahydrobiopterin
BIND	bilirubin-induced neurologic dysfunction
BM	basal membrane
BMI	body mass index
BMP	bone morphogenetic protein
BMR	basal metabolic rate
BNP	B-type natriuretic peptide
BPD	bronchopulmonary dysplasia
BPP	biophysical profile
BUN	blood urea nitrogen
BV	bacterial vaginosis
CaD	caldesmon
CAH	congenital adrenal hyperplasia
cAMP	cyclic adenosine monophosphate
CAP	contraction-associated protein
CBF	cerebral blood flow
CBG	cortisol-binding globulin
CC	closing capacity
CCHD	critical congenital heart defects
CCO	combined cardiac output
C$_{cr}$	creatinine clearance
CDC	Centers for Disease Control and Prevention
CDH	congenital diaphragmatic hernia
CDKS	cyclin-dependent kinases
CDP-choline	cytidine diphosphate choline
CF	cystic fibrosis
cfDNA	cell-free DNA
CFTR	CF transmembrane conductance regulator
CFU	colony-forming unit
CFU-GM	colony-forming unit–granulocyte macrophage
cGMP	cyclic guanosine monophosphate
CGRP	calcitonin gene-related protein
CHD	congenital heart defects
CHG	chlorhexidine gluconate
CHF	congestive heart failure
C$_3$H$_6$O$_3$	lactic acid

CLD	chronic lung disease		FDA	Food and Drug Administration
CM	calmodulin		FDP	fibrin-fibrinogen degradation products
CMV	cytomegalovirus		Fe	iron
CNS	central nervous system		FE_{Na}	fractional sodium excretion
CO	cardiac output		FET	frozen embryo transfer
CO_2	carbon dioxide		FEV_1	forced expiratory volume in 1 second
CoA	coenzyme A		FGF	fibroblast growth factor
COX-2	cyclooxygenase-2		FHR	fetal heart rate
CPAP	continuous positive airway pressure		FIL	feedback inhibitor of lactation
CRF/H	corticotropin-releasing factor/hormone		FIO_2	fractional inspired oxygen
CRH-BP	CRH-binding protein		FIRS	fetal inflammatory response syndrome
CRP	C-reactive protein		FISH	fluorescent in situ hybridization
CST	contraction stress test		FMP	final menstrual period
CV	closing volume		FNAIT	fetal and neonatal alloimmune
CVS	chorionic villus sampling; cardiovascular			thrombocytopenia
	system		FP	fluorescent polarization
Cx	connexin		FRC	functional residual capacity
CYP450	cytochrome P450		FSH	follicle-stimulating hormone
DA	ductus arteriosus		*FXMR1*	fragile X mental retardation gene
DC	dendritic cells		GABA	gamma-aminobutyric acid
DES	diethylstilbestrol		GBS	group B streptococcus
DHA	docosahexaenoic acid		GC	guanylate cyclase
DHEA-S	dehydroepiandrosterone sulfate		G-CSF	granulocyte colony-stimulating factor
DHT	dihydrotestosterone		GDF9	growth differentiation factor 9
DIC	disseminated intravascular coagulation		GDM	gestational diabetes mellitus
DNA	deoxyribonucleic acid		GERD	gastroesophageal reflux disease
dNK	decidual natural killer cells		GFR	glomerular filtration rate
DOC	deoxycorticosterone		GF	growth factor
DPPC	dipalmitoyl phosphatidylcholine		GGT	serum γ-glutamyl transferase
DRIs	dietary reference intakes		GH-N	pituitary growth hormone
DTaP	diphtheria-tetanus-acellular pertussis		GH-V	human placental growth hormone
DV	ductus venosus		GI	gastrointestinal
DVT	deep vein thrombosis		GIFT	gamete intrafallopian transfer
DZ	dizygotic		GLUT	glucose transporters
E	erythroid		GM	germinal matrix
E_1	estrone		GM-CSF	granulocyte-macrophage colony-stimulating
E_3	estriol			factor
EB	epidermolysis bullosa		GMH	germinal matrix hemorrhage
ECF	extracellular fluid		G6PD	glucose-6-phosphate dehydrogenase
ECG	electrocardiogram		GnRH	gonadotropin-releasing hormone
ECMO	extracorporeal membrane oxygenation		GR	glucocorticoid receptor
EDRF	endothelial-derived releasing factor		GTT	glucose tolerance test
EDV	end-diastolic volume		Hb	hemoglobin
EEG	electroencephalograph		HbA	adult hemoglobin
EFA	essential fatty acids		HbA1c	glycosylated hemoglobin
EGF	epidermal growth factor		HbF	fetal hemoglobin
ELBW	extremely low birth weight		HBIG	hepatitis B immune globulin
ENaC	epithelial sodium channels		HbS	sickle hemoglobin
ENS	enteric nervous system		HBsAg	hepatitis B virus antigen
EONS	early-onset neonatal sepsis		HBV	hepatitis B virus
Eos	eosinophil		HCII	heparin cofactor II
EPCR	endothelial protein C receptor		hCG	human chorionic gonadotropin
EPF	early pregnancy factor		hCG-H	hyperglycosylated hCG
Epo	erythropoietin		HCO_3	bicarbonate
ERPF	effective renal plasma flow		H_2CO_3	carbonic acid
ERV	expiratory reserve volume		hCS	human chorionic somatomammotropin
ESR	erythrocyte sedimentation rate		HDL	high-density lipoprotein
FAS	fetal alcohol syndrome		HDN	hemorrhagic disease of the newborn
FASD	fetal alcohol spectrum disorders		HELLP	hemolysis, elevated liver enzymes, low platelet
FBM	fetal breathing movement			count
FcRn	neonatal FC receptor		HGP	Human Genome Project

HIE	hypoxic-ischemic encephalopathy	LIF	leukemia inhibition factors
HIF	hypoxia-inducible factors	LPS	lipopolysaccharide
HIV	human immunodeficiency virus	L/S	lethicin/sphingomyelin
HLA	human leukocyte antigen	LV	left ventricle
HLHS	hypoplastic left heart syndrome	MA	migraines with aura
HMG	*high mobility group*	MAC1	B-integrin molecule
HMOs	human milk oligosaccharides	MAPK	mitogen-activated protein kinase
HMP	hexose monophosphate	MAS	meconium aspiration syndrome
HOX	homeobox	MCFA	medium-chain fatty acid
HPA	hypothalamic-pituitary-adrenal	MCHV	mean corpuscular hemoglobin volume
HPG	hypothalamic-pituitary-gonadal	M-CSF	macrophage colony-stimulating factor
hPL	human placental lactogen	MCT	medium-chain triglycerides
HPO	hypothalamic-pituitary-ovarian	MCV	mean corpuscular volume
HPT	hypothalamic-pituitary-thyroid	MDI	iodothyronine monodeiodinase
HSV	herpes simplex virus	Mg-ATPase	magnesium-adenosine triphosphatase
I	iodine	MHC	major histocompatibility complex
IBD	inflammatory bowel disease	MIF	macrophage migration-inhibiting factor
IC	inspiratory capacity	miRNA	micro RNA
ICF	intracellular fluid	MIS	müllerian-inhibiting substance
ICSI	intracytoplasmic sperm injection	MK	megakaryocyte
IDM	infant of a diabetic mother	MLCK	myosin light chain kinase
IDO	indolamine 2,3 dehydrogenase	MLPA	multiplex ligation-dependent amplification
IEM	inborn errors of metabolism	MMI	methimazole
IFN-γ	interferon-γ	MMP	matrix metalloproteinase
IgA, IgD, IgE, IgG, IGM	immunoglobulin A, D, E, G, M	MO	migraines without aura
		MoM	multiples of the median
IGFs	insulin-like growth factors	M/P	milk/plasma
IGF-1 or -2	insulin-like growth factor 1 or 2	MPF	maturation promoting factor
IgSCs	immunoglobulin-secreting cells	mRNA	messenger ribonucleic acid
IHs	inhibiting hormones	MRP	multidrug-resistant gene protein
IL	interleukin	MSCI	meiotic sex chromosome inactivation
ILCOR	International Liaison Committee on Resuscitation	MSH	melanocyte-stimulating hormone
		MS/MS	tandem mass spectrometry
iNO	inhaled nitric oxide	MSUC	meiotic silencing of unpaired chromatin
InsP3	1,4,5-triphosphate	mtDNA	mitochondrial DNA
IOM	Institute of Medicine	MVM	microvillous membrane
IOP	intraocular pressure	MVP	maximum vertical pocket; mitral valve prolapse
IRS-1	insulin receptor substrate 1	MW	molecular weight
IRV	inspiratory reserve volume	MZ	monozygotic
ISS	interstitial space	MZT	maternal-to-zygote transition
ITP	immune thrombocytopenia purpura	NADH	nicotinamide-adenine dinucleotide
IUGR	intrauterine growth restriction	NAS	neonatal abstinence syndrome
IVC	inferior vena cava	NEC	necrotizing enterocolitis
IVF	in vitro fertilization	NEFA	nonesterified fatty acid
IVH	intraventricular hemorrhage	NF-κB	nuclear factor-κ-B
IVS	intervillous spaces	NGF	nerve growth factor
IWL	insensible water loss	NICU	neonatal intensive care unit
KISS1R	G-protein coupled receptor	NIDCAP	Neonatal Individualized Developmental Care and Assessment Program
KITL	KIT ligand		
LAM	lactational amenorrhea method	NK	natural killer cell
LBW	low birth weight	NLR	nodlike receptors
LCFA	long-chain fatty acid	NMDA	*N*-methyl-D-aspartate
LCPUFA	long-chain polyunsaturated fatty acids	NMF	natural moisturizing factor
LCR	laryngeal chemoreflex	NNS	nonnutritive sucking
LCT	long-chain triglycerides	NO	nitric oxide
LDL	low-density lipoprotein	NOS	nitric oxide synthetase
LED	light-emitting diode	NPDR	nonproliferative diabetic retinopathy
LES	lower esophageal sphincter	NPO	nothing by mouth
LGA	large for gestational age	NREM	non–rapid eye movement
LGN	lateral geniculate nucleus	nRNA	nuclear RNA
LH	luteinizing hormone	NRP	Neonatal Resuscitation Program

NS	nutritive sucking
NSP	neutrophil storage pool
NST	nonshivering thermogenesis
NT	nuchal translucency
NTD	neural tube defect
NTE	neutral thermal environment
NVP	nausea and vomiting of pregnancy
OAT	organic anion transporter
OCT	oxytocin challenge test
OGTT	oral glucose tolerance test
OSA	obstructive sleep apnea
OTR	oxytocin receptors
P_{50}	PO_2 at which 50% of the hemoglobin is saturated with oxygen
$PaCO_2$	arterial CO_2 pressure
PAF	platelet activity factor
PAH	phenylalanine hydroxylase
PAI	plasminogen activator inhibitor
PAMPs	pathogen-associated molecular patterns
PaO_2	partial pressure of oxygen in arterial blood
PAPP	pregnancy-associated plasma proteins
PBI	protein-bound iodine
PC	protein C; phosphatidylcholine
PCBs	polychlorinated biphenyls
PDA	patent ductus arteriosus
PDE3A	phosphodiesterase 3A
PDGF	platelet-derived growth factor
PEEP	positive end-expiratory pressure
PEP	polymorphic eruption of pregnancy
PEP-CK	phosphoenolpyruvate carboxykinase
PG	prostaglandin
PGC	primordial germ cells
PGDH	hydroxyprostaglandin dehydrogenase
PGI_2	prostacyclin
P-gp	p-glycoprotein
PI	phosphatidylinositol
Pi	inorganic phosphate
PID	pelvic inflammatory disease
PIF	preimplantation factor
PIGF	placental growth factor
PK	pharmacokinetics
PKA	protein kinase A
PKU	phenylketonuria
PMN	polymorphonuclear neutrophils
POMC	proopiomelanocortin
PPHN	persistent pulmonary hypertension of the newborn
PPROM	preterm premature rupture of membranes
PPT	postpartum thyroiditis
PR	progesterone receptors
PRA	plasma renin activity
PRC	pattern recognition receptors
pre-OL	premyelinating oligodendrocytes
PRL	prolactin
PROM	premature rupture of the membranes
PS	protein S
PT	prothrombin time
PTH	parathyroid hormone
PTHrP	parathyroid hormone–related protein
PTL	preterm labor

PTU	propylthiouracil
PUBS	percutaneous umbilical blood sampling
PUD	peptic ulcer disease
PUFA	polyunsaturated fatty acid
PVL	periventricular leukomalacia
PVR	pulmonary vascular resistance
PZ	protein Z
QF-PCR	quantitative fluorescent-polymerase chain reaction
$\dot{Q}p$	capillary perfusion
QS	quiet (deep or NREM) sleep
RAA	renin-angiotensin-aldosterone
RBC	red blood cell
RBF	renal blood flow
RBP	retinal binding protein
RDS	respiratory distress syndrome
REM	rapid eye movement
rEpo	recombinant human erythropoietin
RFLP	restriction fragment length polymorphism
RH	releasing hormone
RLS	restless legs syndrome
RNA	ribonucleic acid
ROP	retinopathy of prematurity
RPF	renal plasma flow
rRNA	ribosomal RNA
rT_3	reverse T_3
RT_3U	resin T_3 uptake
RV	right ventricle; residual volume
RVR	renal vascular resistance
SA	sinoatrial
SaO_2	arterial hemoglobin saturation
Sat PC	saturated phosphatidylcholine
SCT	short-chain triglyceride
S/D	systole versus diastole
SDB	sleep-disordered breathing
sENG	soluble endoglin
SER	smooth endoplasmic reticulum
SF1	steroidogenesis factor 1
s-FLT-1	soluble fms-like tyrosine kinase 1
SGA	small for gestational age
SGOT	serum glutamic-oxaloacetic transaminase
SGPT	serum glutamic-pyruvic transaminase
Shh	sonic hedgehog gene
SIADH	syndrome of inappropriate secretion of antidiuretic hormone
sIgA	secretory immunoglobulin A
SLCO1B1	soluble carrier organic anion transporter polypeptide
SLE	systemic lupus erythematosus
sLE	L-selectin ligands
Sn-MP	tin-mesoporphyrin
Sn-PP	tin-protoporphyrin
SNP	single nucleotide polymorphism
SP	surfactant protein
SpO_2	oxygen saturation
SR	sarcoplasmic reticulum
SRY	sex region on the Y chromosome
SSKI	saturated solution of potassium iodide
SSRI	selective serotonin reuptake inhibitor
StAR	steroidogenic acute regulatory protein